Fifth Canadian Edition

ECOLOGY

CONCEPTS AND APPLICATIONS

Manuel C. Molles Jr.

University of New Mexico

Andrew Laursen

Ryerson University

Mc
Graw
Hill

Ecology: Concepts and Applications
Fifth Canadian Edition

ISBN-13:978-126-0065817
ISBN- 10: 126-0065812

1 2 3 4 5 6 7 8 9 0   M   24 23 22 21 20

Printed and bound in Canada.

Product Director: *Rhondda McNabb*
Portfolio Manager: *Kevin O'Hearn*
Marketing Manager: *Cathie Lefebvre*
Content Developer: *Shalini Khanna*
Portfolio Associate: *Tatiana Sevciuc*
Supervising Editor: *Janie Deneau*
Photo/Permissions Editor: *Indu Arora*
Copy Editor: *Colleen Ste. Marie*
Plant Production Coordinator: *Heitor Moura*
Manufacturing Production Coordinator: *Jason Stubner*
Cover Design: *Katherine Strain*
Cover Image: © *simon2579/Getty Images*
Interior Design: *Liz Harasymczuk*
Page Layout: *MPS Limited*
Printer: *Marquis*

Dedication

To Mary Anne and Misha

M. M.

For Sophia and Norah

A. L.

Manuel C. Molles Jr. is an emeritus Professor of Biology at the University of New Mexico, where he has been a member of the faculty and curator in the Museum of Southwestern Biology since 1975. He teaches ecology and advises graduate students. He received his B.S. from Humboldt State University and his Ph.D. from the Department of Ecology and Evolutionary Biology at the University of Arizona. Seeking to broaden his geographic perspective, he has taught and conducted ecological research in Latin America, the Caribbean, and Europe. He was awarded a Fulbright Research Fellowship to conduct research on river ecology in Portugal and has held visiting professor appointments in the Department of Zoology at the University of Coimbra, Portugal; in the Laboratory of Hydrology at the Polytechnic University of Madrid, Spain; and at the University of Montana's Flathead Lake Biological Station.

Originally trained as a marine ecologist and fisheries biologist, the author has worked mainly on river and riparian ecology at the University of New Mexico. His research has covered a wide range of ecological levels, including behavioural ecology, population biology, community ecology, ecosystem ecology, biogeography of stream insects, and the influence of a large-scale climate system (El Niño) on the dynamics of southwestern river and riparian ecosystems. His current research concerns the influence of climate change and climatic variability on the dynamics of populations and communities along steep gradients of temperature and moisture in the mountains of the Southwest. Throughout his career, Dr. Molles has attempted to combine research, teaching, and service, involving undergraduate as well as graduate students in his ongoing projects. At the University of New Mexico, he has taught a broad range of lower division, upper division, and graduate courses, including Principles of Biology, Evolution and Ecology, Stream Ecology, Limnology and Oceanography, Marine Biology, and Community and Ecosystem Ecology. He has taught courses in Global Change and River Ecology at the University of Coimbra, Portugal; and General Ecology and Groundwater and Riparian Ecology at the Flathead Lake Biological Station. Dr. Manuel Molles was named Teacher of the Year by the University of New Mexico for 1995–96 and Potter Chair in Plant Ecology in 2000.

Andrew Laursen is an Associate Professor in the Department of Chemistry and Biology at Ryerson University in Toronto. He received his B.A. in Biology from Colgate University in 1993 and his Ph.D. in Biology from the University of Notre Dame in 1998, working under the supervision of Dr. Richard Carlton. He held postdoctoral associate positions with Dr. Sybil Seitzinger at Rutgers University's Institute for Marine and Coastal Sciences and with Dr. Charles Kulpa at Notre Dame's Center for Environmental Science and Technology before coming to Ryerson.

Laursen is an ecosystem ecologist, with interests in how systems function, that is, how they process materials, how energy and nutrients flow through these systems, and how they function in the net flux of greenhouse gases. His research draws on elements of microbial ecology, biogeochemistry, community ecology, and ecological modelling. His research has generally focused on the ecology of urban and agricultural systems, systems heavily impacted by human activities. While he suspects that he took a wrong turn somewhere in not studying tropical marine ecosystems or the ecology of cottage country, his research program is driven by the need to understand the ecology of impacted systems and to apply ecological principles to improve their function. His research has included studies of microbial ecology, ecosystem modelling, nitrogen and carbon biogeochemistry, ecology of methanotrophs in hot springs, risks of invasion by aquatic plants, and sustainability of waste management practices.

Ecology, as you will learn, integrates many different traditional subdisciplines of biology. The environmental challenges that professional ecologists need to address cut across other disciplines, including other natural sciences, sociology, psychology, engineering, and law. Laursen is the graduate program director of Ryerson's Environmental Applied Science and Management graduate program. This program trains students to view environmental challenges through a multi-disciplinary lens and to take a broad-based approach to research that addresses these challenges. The nature of this program is reflected in Laursen's collaborations not only with other ecologists, but with geographers, political scientists, chemists, biologists, engineers, urban and regional planners, and faculty in public health. His research often involves collaboration with government agencies and industry that can use the ecological knowledge generated by his research group.

BRIEF CONTENTS

Environmental issues are of pressing concern to Canadians. Discussions of environmental sustainability, increased development, resource extraction, species at risk, and global responsibility are common in the news and among the Canadian public. When faced with choices, it is the science of ecology that provides lawmakers, land managers, and the public the information they need to make informed decisions. However, ecology is a young science, and the rapidly increasing pace of discovery and the ever-increasing list of environmental concerns makes teaching ecology very challenging. As we attempt to educate students to understand and design solutions to environmental problems, every facet of ecology is important. Ideally, an introductory course in ecology would include the foundations of all the major ecological subdisciplines. Including such breadth, and developing it to sufficient depth, is difficult within the time constraints most of us face in the classroom. The fifth Canadian edition of *Ecology: Concepts and Applications* provides careful organization, clear and relevant Canadian and global examples, and a conceptual approach to ease this task. This book is designed with the goal of enhancing student understanding of key ecological principles and concepts, rather than being an encyclopedic source of information.

Introductory Audience

We have written this book for students who are taking their first undergraduate course in ecology. Ecology is an integrative discipline, and thus a foundation in other sciences is important. We have assumed that students in this course have some knowledge of basic chemistry and mathematics and that they have had a course in general biology that included introductions to physiology, biological diversity, and evolution.

Unique Approach

In an address at the 1991 meeting of the Ecological Society of America in San Antonio, Texas, eminent ecologist Paul Risser challenged ecology instructors to focus their attention on the major concepts of the field. If we subdivide a large and dynamic subject such as ecology too finely, we cannot teach it in one or even two academic terms. Risser proposed that by focusing on major concepts, however, we may provide students with a robust framework of the discipline, which they can then build on.

This book attempts to address Risser's challenge. *Each chapter is organized around two to six major concepts, presenting the student with a manageable and meaningful synthesis of the subject.* We have found that while beginning students can often absorb a few central concepts well, they can easily get lost in a sea of details. In this book, each concept is accompanied by case studies and research results that reinforce the central concept being discussed. This approach introduces students to the research methods used in the various areas of ecology, with a strong focus on a scientific approach to understanding ecological principles. Wherever possible, the original research and the scientists who did the research are presented. Allowing the scientists who created this field to emerge from the background and lead students through the discipline breathes life into the subject and helps students retain information. This approach also helps students understand that science is not a list of facts; instead, it consists of active debates, hard work, and real people.

Accessible Writing

Science is fun, and there is no reason that reading about science should be dull. Instead, we believe that textbooks should engage students, helping them learn the material. The opportunity to discover a bit of knowledge that no one has ever before known is a reason many of us became researchers in the first place. However, this sense of enjoyment and excitement is missing from most textbooks, where writing most resembles the terseness of a scientific article. We believe that a textbook that is not read is of little value, no matter how strong the content contained between the covers. Thus, we use a writing style that is accessible to students—one that students are most certain to notice. Brief narratives, attempts at humour, and continued emphasis on the organisms being studied and the people who study them draw the student in to each chapter and concept. Such an approach eases understanding of ecology, increasing the value of this text for students.

Organized Around Key Concepts

Natural history and evolution are the foundations of ecology, and concepts from these disciplines run throughout the entire textbook. The textbook begins with a brief introduction to the nature and history of the discipline of ecology, followed by section 1, which includes three chapters on natural history: life on land, life in water, and a chapter on evolution. Sections 2 through 6 build a hierarchical perspective through the traditional subdisciplines of ecology: section 2 concerns the ecology of individuals; section 3 focuses on population ecology; section 4 presents the ecology of interactions; section 5 summarizes community and ecosystem ecology; and, finally, section 6 discusses large-scale ecology and includes chapters on landscape, macro-, and global ecology. In summary, the book begins with the natural history of the planet, considers portions of the whole in the middle chapters, and ends with another perspective of the entire planet in the concluding chapter.

Within each chapter, key concepts are highlighted, both in the first listing of chapter concepts and at the beginning of each section in which the concepts are discussed. The concept numbers are repeated in the concept review questions that conclude each section. Thus, the beginning and end of each concept is clearly signalled for the student.

Unique Benefits of Molles and Laursen

Teach the foundations of ecology using Canadian examples to help students relate to the material. In this text we focus on the major themes of ecology and include the foundational studies that all students should learn. However, ecology is more than a set of graphs and abstract concepts. At its core is a diversity of species, each with its own unique characteristics and interesting stories. Where possible, we highlight species that students would be familiar with in Canada and research conducted at Canadian universities. By placing complex ideas into a familiar context, students become more engaged and can focus their learning on the ideas the instructor is teaching. Importantly, we do not sacrifice presentation of foundational studies and examples of ecological principles simply to increase the text's "Canadian content." In presenting examples of ecological principles, we try to not only include some Canadian examples but to highlight work from many Canadian institutions, not just the largest research universities. We highlight that ecologists, like Canadians more generally, are a diverse group of people. As well, we include more examples and highlight ecologists that better reflect this diversity than might be found in some past ecology books.

Link the science of ecology to real-world problems. All chapters include an "Ecology in Action" box, in which we highlight how the ecological principles are being used in real-world situations in Canada and around the world. Examples include human-induced evolution in natural populations, fishery management and collapse, using behavioural ecology to reduce human–wildlife conflict, and many others. These boxes emphasize to students that ecology is not an abstract science but, instead, is central to solving real issues of societal concern.

Emphasize the linkage between ecology and evolutionary biology. Evolution results in species that we find on the planet and the diversity of ecological processes that occur. Without ecology, there would be no natural selection. These two disciplines are separated more by time-scales than by concepts, and we emphasize the linkage between them throughout the text. Evolution serves as a thread that helps link the chapters together, facilitating understanding for students of ecology, as well as providing a link to other disciplines of biology.

Enhance students' quantitative understanding. Ecology is a quantitative discipline, and shying away from this would provide a misleading representation of this field of research. However, students often struggle with many aspects of ecology, including interpreting graphs, understanding statistics, and realizing the value of models for addressing ecological questions. We are very aware of the importance of these skills, as well as their difficulty for many students.

To help students learn how to understand graphical information, we have embedded text boxes into some of the figures in the text. These boxes guide the students toward understanding the main points of the graphs, while they read the text on their own.

Within some chapters we also discuss the general statistical approaches that researchers used, while providing the details of different statistical methods in an appendix. The statistical appendix is written in a friendly tone, outlining the most common statistics used in ecology. For those instructors who incorporate statistics into their lectures, this appendix could be an early assigned reading. For those instructors who reduce the quantitative aspects of ecology, the appendix could serve as a resource for students. This approach allows for a focus on key concepts in each chapter while also giving instructors flexibility in how they present statistical information to their students.

Many major concepts in ecology come from the use of models, and we include many of these in the text. To help students understand, rather than simply memorize, these models, we spend significant amounts of text explaining the details of each model. For those instructors who choose to teach these models in their courses, our approach allows the text to reinforce lecture concepts.

Changes in the Fifth Edition

The first edition of Molles and Cahill was the first ecology text specifically for the Canadian market. It was widely adopted throughout Canada at universities and colleges along all three coasts. As a result of real instructors using the previous four editions of this text with real students, we have received helpful feedback as to which aspects of the text worked well and which parts needed to be refined. At the same time, we have actively sought comments from instructors using other texts in their courses, providing unique perspectives and ideas about how this text could be enhanced. Through the incorporation of these comments, along with our ideas that have emerged from our own experiences inside and outside the classroom, we believe this edition will be even more effective at enhancing student learning and teaching ecology.

Perhaps the most common piece of feedback we received was that the previous edition was too long. In some cases, we had included multiple examples to illustrate a single ecological principle. Sometimes the examples overwhelmed students, and the principles were lost. While we had some attachment to the various examples, we tried to streamline the book by removing extra examples where one (or perhaps two) would suffice. We have simplified the narratives in many sections and generally tried to make the overall length of the book shorter and more accessible for students.

In this edition, we have also enhanced the overall flow of information in many chapters, including some rearrangement of figures and section sequences. We have updated content to ensure that the material presented is current and accurate and to include more examples of the ecology of human-dominated systems. In addition to these general changes throughout the text, several chapters have been more substantially altered, warranting particular notice.

In *chapter 1* we have organized the section on ecological research to better reflect some of the tools and approaches commonly used in ecology and also to reflect how various tools may complement each other or be applied to a similar ecological question at different spatial or temporal scales. A new subsection on tools in molecular ecology has been added.

In *chapter 2* and *chapter 3* we have simplified the text by restricting our deep dive into terrestrial biomes and aquatic ecosystems to those that are found in Canada.

In *chapter 7* we rewrote the Introduction and a few other sections to make the text more readable, and we removed equations that appeared in the previous edition that are not necessary to understanding optimal foraging theory. These equations were introduced in previous editions as an expansion on theory but were not applied. To simplify the text and to maintain the focus on the theory, we removed these potential distractions.

In *chapter 9* we have updated the Ecological Tools and Approaches section that explores life history traits as indicators of biological response to climate change. We have included more recent information on climate change and examples of phenological response to climate change.

In *chapter 11* we added a new Ecology in Action section on conservation of sex ratios, including a discussion on the effects of exogenous hormones on fish sex ratios and effects of climate change on sex ratios of reptiles. We discuss implications of climate change on conservation of endangered reptile species.

In *chapter 13* we clarified the Lotka-Volterra modelling section to make this easier for students to follow. We rearranged subsection 13.2 with new headings to make it easier to connect forms of competition, introduced earlier in the chapter, with examples from the literature.

In *chapter 14*, we have rewritten the Ecological Tools and Approaches section to give it a tighter focus on the blending of the tools of molecular ecology and the development of conceptual models to address questions about how exploitative relationships shape evolutionary trajectories. The new section focuses on a differentiation in a parasitoid population experiencing host plant shift.

In *chapter 21* we have rewritten the Introduction to provide a better narrative of and engagement with landscape ecology.

In *chapter 23* we rewrote the Introduction and substantial portions of subsection 23.2, "Human Activity Transforms the World." In particular, this section now places greater weight on evidence of climate change and humans as causative agents thereof. It includes paleoclimate data to complement historic data. There is a new piece on water and air pollution, with a look at hydrofracking. Much of the content has been updated for currency.

The features of this textbook are unique and were carefully planned to enhance students' comprehension of ecology. All chapters beyond the introductory Chapter 1 are based on a distinctive learning system, featuring the following key components:

Introduction

The introduction to each chapter presents students with the flavour of the subject and important background information. Some introductions include historical events related to the subject; others present an example of an ecological process. All attempt to engage students and draw them into the discussion that follows.

Concepts

The goal of this book is to build a foundation of ecological knowledge around key concepts. These key concepts are listed after the chapter introduction to alert students to the major topics to follow and to provide a place where students can find a list of the important points of each chapter. The sections in which concepts are discussed reinforce concepts with a focus on published studies. This case-study approach supports the concepts with evidence and introduces students to the methods and people that have created the discipline of ecology. At the end of each concept is a brief concept review that includes several questions specific to the material the students just read. These

boxes serve as an immediate indicator to students as to whether they understood this section or if they need additional help.

CONCEPT 4.1 REVIEW

1. What is a fundamental evolutionary implication of the large amounts of genetic variation commonly found in natural populations?
2. What would you expect to see in figure 4.3 if alpine, mid-elevation, and lowland populations of *P. glandulosa* were not different genetically?
3. Can V_E be greater than V_G for a trait related to an organism's fitness? Explain.
4. Mutation of a gene in a dermal cell involved in cell cycle control makes the cell cancerous. Will this affect the fitness of offspring? Explain.

Illustrations

A great deal of effort has been put into the development of illustrations, both photographs and line art. The goal has been to create more effective pedagogical tools through skilful design and use of colour and to rearrange the traditional presentation of information in figures and captions. Much explanatory material is located within the illustrations, providing students with key information where they need it most.

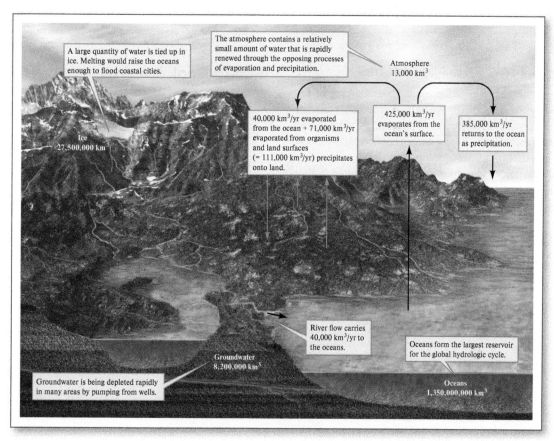

A large quantity of water is tied up in ice. Melting would raise the oceans enough to flood coastal cities.

The atmosphere contains a relatively small amount of water that is rapidly renewed through the opposing processes of evaporation and precipitation.

Atmosphere
13,000 km³

Ice
27,500,000 km³

40,000 km³/yr evaporated from the ocean + 71,000 km³/yr evaporated from organisms and land surfaces (= 111,000 km³/yr) precipitates onto land.

425,000 km³/yr evaporates from the ocean's surface.

385,000 km³/yr returns to the ocean as precipitation.

River flow carries 40,000 km³/yr to the oceans.

Oceans form the largest reservoir for the global hydrologic cycle.

Groundwater
8,200,000 km³

Groundwater is being depleted rapidly in many areas by pumping from wells.

Oceans
1,350,000,000 km³

Ecology in Action

Many undergraduate students want to know how abstract ideas and general relationships can be applied to the ecological problems facing us all. They are concerned with the practical side of ecology and want to know more about the tools of science. Including applications in each chapter motivates students to learn more of the underlying principles of ecology. In addition, it seems that environmental problems are now so numerous and so pressing that they have erased a once easy distinction between general and applied ecology.

ECOLOGY IN ACTION

Diversity of Soil Organisms

Researchers at Redpath Museum at McGill University are cataloguing the biodiversity of Canada. They have developed a user-friendly Web site (The Canadian Biodiversity Web Site) to help people see the diversity of species found in Canada (Bernhardt 2010). They report that, across the world, up to 1.8 million species (approximately 70,000 in Canada) have been described by scientists, with nearly half being insects. These counts include both terrestrial and aquatic species, though it is generally accepted that there is more species diversity on land than in aquatic systems. Does this mean there are approximately 2 million species on the planet? Absolutely not. Estimates of true global biodiversity range from 2 to 100 million, though all of these are simply educated guesses. Scientists are now realizing how little natural history is actually known, even in our own backyards.

A fundamental goal of ecology is to understand the processes that influence the distribution and abundance of organisms. This knowledge can be used to address a variety of environmental issues that people face throughout the world, such as climate change, controlling the spread of **invasive species,** and trying to integrate agriculture, economic development, human housing, and wilderness within a limited amount of land. However, before we are able to explain patterns of abundance, we must first know the organisms we are studying. In many locations (e.g., North America) and for many groups (e.g., birds and mammals), species are so well studied that researchers are unlikely to ever know someone who has identified a new species, let alone find one themselves. However, the natural history of locations with high species diversity, such as tropical forests, is generally poorly documented, and many (non-vertebrate) species remain to be described by scientists.

For those of us with more modest budgets, and for those who want to find a very large number of new species, the answer will be much closer to home. In fact, large amounts of undescribed biodiversity are literally underneath your feet. Soils are the "poor man's tropical rainforest" (Usher et al.

our understanding of exactly how these processes emerge from the complex web of soil interactions is still limited, it is very clear that changes in composition of communities of soil organisms is likely to alter the efficiency of these processes. For example, Dennis Parkinson of the University of Calgary has shown that the introduction of the earthworm, *Dendrobaena octaedra,* to boreal forest soils alters fungal biodiversity and plant growth (Scheu and Parkinson 1994; McLean and Parkinson 2000). Such changes can have significant impacts on a variety of issues of concern to people, including carbon sequestration, primary production, litter buildup, and nutrient leaching. As you will see throughout this book, human activities are changing the composition of species in communities across the planet, with unknown consequences for ecological functioning.

Ecological Tools and Approaches

To understand the results of science, an understanding of the methods of science is required. We believe it is important for students to understand that science is a process, not simply a list of facts. Therefore, in each chapter we highlight a method, or a conceptual approach to understanding, that allows researchers to address questions relevant to the concepts presented in that chapter. These examples are varied, including sampling designs, game theory, stable isotopes, and many others.

End-of-Chapter Material

- **Summary** The chapter summary reviews the main points of the content. The concepts around which each

---

ECOLOGICAL TOOLS AND APPROACHES

Reconstructing Lake Communities

How can we put our knowledge of aquatic life to work? A major question ecologists often face is whether a certain environmental factor will alter an aquatic community. To answer this, we first need a clear understanding of the species composition and abundances of the focal community under current environmental conditions. In chapter 1 we described the experimental approach that David Schindler and colleagues at the Experimental Lakes Area have used to test the impact that fertilization, acidification, and a variety of other factors have had on lake communities. Here we will describe a different approach used by a number of researchers in Canada, including Roland Hall at the University of Waterloo and John Smol and colleagues at PEARL, the Paleoecological Environmental Assessment and Research Laboratory, based at Queen's University. The goal of these researchers is to provide the historical context to environmental change, through detailed study of the paleoenvironmental record on lakes throughout the world. This is the field of paleolimnology, which is broadly defined as the scientific discipline that uses the biological, chemical, and physical information archived in lake sediment profiles to track past environmental changes. By understanding the historical patterns of variation in lake communities, the researchers can generate hypotheses about how

environmental factors have shaped the communities we see now, and possibly predict what we will find in the future.

How to Reconstruct Past Communities

The fundamental research subject in most paleolimnological studies is the sediment core (fig. 3.28a). Suspended in the waters of all lakes are numerous microscopic organisms. When they die, many will sink down to the bottom. Some of these will then decompose, while many will leave behind hard shells and crusts that get covered up by the continuing rain of detritus and dirt that falls from above. Sediments are continually accumulating, and the deeper you dig into them, the further back in time you move. The basic paleolimnological approach is to take a sediment core, divide it into many sections of differing depths, identify the approximate age of each depth, and identify the remains of the organisms and other paleolimnological information found at each depth. By putting this information together, a researcher can infer shifts in lake communities over long periods of time. The validity of this entire process depends upon two critical assumptions: (1) you can accurately determine the age of each depth, and (2) the species you are measuring in the sediment cores are unbiased indicators of past lake conditions.

---

chapter is organized are boldfaced and redefined in the summary to re-emphasize the main points of the chapter.

- **Review Questions** The review questions are designed to help students think more deeply about each concept and reflect on alternative views. These questions supplement the concept review questions located at the end of each concept section. They range from specific to more integrative, and they provide feedback to students about any remaining gaps in the information presented. Our intent is to also use these questions to take students beyond the foundation established in the main body of the chapter and ask them to use their newly found knowledge in novel ways.

End-of-Book Material

- **Appendix** A student-friendly appendix, "Building a Statistical Toolbox," appears at the end of the textbook to give instructors flexibility in terms of how and when to include statistics in their course.

- **Glossary**

- **References** References are an important part of any scientific work, and we give credit to the researchers whose hard work made this book possible.

- **Index**

- **Answers to Concept Review Questions** These answers are available on Connect.

connect

McGraw-Hill Connect® is an award-winning digital teaching and learning solution that empowers students to achieve better outcomes and enables instructors to improve efficiency with course management.

Connect's key features include analytics and reporting; simple assignment management; smart grading; the opportunity to post your own resources; and the Connect Instructor Library, a repository for additional resources to improve student engagement in and out of the classroom.

Instructor Resources for *Ecology: Concepts and Applications,* 5th Canadian Edition

- Instructor's Manual
- Test Bank
- Microsoft® PowerPoint® Presentations
- Answers to Review Questions
- Answers to Concept Reviews

Acknowledgements

In the summer of 2015, I was given a rare and wonderful opportunity by McGraw-Hill Ryerson. I was invited to contribute to a textbook that had been skilfully crafted over the years by Manuel Molles. The earlier Canadian editions, adapted by James Cahill, framed the textbook in a Canadian context and highlighted many examples of contemporary Canadian ecological research. James wove many wonderful narratives into the book that remain. I thank Manuel, James, and McGraw-Hill Ryerson for the opportunity to join this team and to contribute my own vision to this book and to the teaching of young ecologists. Through the efforts of my co-authors, I inherited a strong text, one that provides a good fundamental background in ecology and that was beautifully written. I therefore assumed the risk of making it weaker through well-intended rewriting of key sections and restructuring of some chapters. Apparently, enough of the quality remained after my meddling, and I was invited in 2018 to co-author this current edition. Throughout the publishing process, I have had excellent support from McGraw-Hill Ryerson, including the following: Kevin O'Hearn, senior portfolio manager; Shalini Khanna, product developer; Indu Arora, permissions editor; Denise Foote, group product development manager; Janie Deneau, supervising editor; and Colleen Ste. Marie, copy editor.

Many other people contributed to the development of this fifth Canadian edition, some directly and others indirectly, through their influence on me as an ecologist. Ronald Hoham and Randy Fuller at Colgate University stoked a passion for ecology in a young economics student and set me on a very different career path. Jack Stanford and Ric Hauer at the University of Montana first put the notion of graduate studies into my head. My Ph.D. supervisor, Richard G. Carlton, gave me the support and the freedom to pursue new ideas, and I was fortunate to have the mentorship of Charles Kulpa, Gary Lamberti, and Scott Bridgham while I was a student at the University of Notre Dame. I had the extraordinary good fortune to work as a post-doctoral associate under the supervision of Sybil Seitzinger at Rutgers University (currently at the University of Victoria). My best professional habits I owe to Sybil, whose mentorship, friendship, and patience helped shape me as a scientist. My worst professional habits are entirely my own fault.

I benefit from excellent colleagues at Ryerson University. I am particularly indebted to Lynda McCarthy, Vadim Bostan, and Ronald Pushchak, with whom I have enjoyed many years of friendship and research collaboration and countless hours of good conversation. My students are always an inspiration, and I am deeply grateful for their understanding as deadlines loomed. In particular, I wish to thank my current lab group, including my post-doc Kruti Shukla; and my students Ramesh Lilwah, Jennifer Bello Levieva, Kevin Lucas, Husnah Azmi, Yana Snisarenko, and Kyle Rodger, who have kept the lab moving forward while I have been immersed in this project. I would also like to thank Aslam Hanief, a recent student and post-doc who has had such a strong influence on the direction of my lab.

I wish to thank my wife, Sophia, and my daughter, Norah, for their support throughout this project. Sophia understood from the outset that this would mean long hours and disruption of family time, yet encouraged me to take on this opportunity. I am deeply touched by her support not only on this, but on my other projects. I love you both. Thanks also to my parents, Everett and Jean, and to my in-laws, Mohammed and Margaret, for their interest and support in this project.

We can take well-earned pride in the history and high quality of ecological research in Canada. I wish to acknowledge the community of ecologists, in academia, government, not-for-profit organizations, NGOs, and industry. It is an honour to shine a light on even a fraction of the excellent work they do. I would like to specifically thank David Galbraith at the Royal Botanical Gardens, and Peter Kelly, coordinator of the Cootes to Escarpment Ecopark System, for their help in developing the Chapter 21 Ecology in Action section. Thank you to the many professors who adopted this textbook (and previous editions). Your feedback in the past has been valuable, and I look forward to your thoughts on this edition. And thank you to all of the students who use this book. I understand that you have not chosen the book, but I hope that you will feel a part of its evolution and that you will provide your thoughts. A student at

Memorial University, Abdulkarim, pointed out that one figure depicting terrestrial biomes did not correspond with his local knowledge. We have modified figure 2.7 accordingly, and I would like to thank Abdulkarim Elnaas and his professor, Dr. Yolanda Wiersma, for their comments that helped improve the book. I hope this edition can help you to better understand this field of biology, to grow as a scientist, and perhaps even to consider a career in ecology.

And, finally, I wish to thank all of our reviewers. Reviewers of this edition provided valuable feedback on draft chapters. Along with reviewers of our previous editions, these people have given generously of their time and expertise. Their comments helped strengthen this textbook, improving its value as a learning resource for Canadian students.

Andrew Laursen

Effective. Efficient. Easy-to-Use.

McGraw-Hill Connect is an award-winning digital teaching and learning solution that empowers students to achieve better outcomes and enables instructors to improve course-management efficiency.

Assignments & Automatic Grading

Connect features a question bank that you can select from to create homework, practice tests and quizzes. Dramatically reduce the amount of time you spend reviewing homework and grading quizzes, freeing up your valuable time to spend on teaching.

High-Quality Course Material

Our trusted solutions are designed to help students actively engage in course content and develop critical higher-level thinking skills, while offering you the flexibility to tailor your course to the ways you teach and the ways your students learn.

Analytics & Reporting

Monitor progress and improve focus with Connect's visual and actionable dashboards. Reports are available to empower both instructors and students with real-time performance analytics.

Seamless Integration

Link your Learning Management System with Connect for single sign-on and gradebook synchronization, with all-in-one ease for you and your students.

SUPPORT AT EVERY STEP

McGraw-Hill ensures you are supported every step of the way. From course design and set up, to instructor training, LMS integration and ongoing support, your Digital Success Consultant is there to make your course as effective as possible.

Jenny E. Ross/Getty Images.

CHAPTER 1   INTRODUCTION TO ECOLOGY

CHAPTER CONCEPTS

1.1 Ecologists study environmental relationships ranging from those of individual organisms to factors influencing global-scale processes.

1.2 Ecologists design their studies based on their research questions, the temporal and spatial scale of their studies, and available research tools.

Ecology in Action: Applying the Scientific Method in Conservation

Ecological Tools and Approaches: The Scientific Method

Summary

Review Questions

What is ecology? **Ecology** is from the Greek word for "house," *oĭkos,* and is the branch of science dedicated to the study of relationships among organisms, including how they interact with each other and with the environment. Humans have been students of ecology for as long as we have existed as a species. The earliest hunters and gatherers had to be familiar with the habits of their prey, had to know where to find food plants, and had to know when fruits would ripen. Today, farmers and ranchers are aware of how variations in weather and soils affect their crops and livestock, how yields change depending upon crop rotations, and how pests and pathogens impact their crops. All of this is ecology. A fisher, a hunter, a rancher, or a farmer who does not understand the patterns of nature will not be successful.

From its roots in natural history and its close observation of natural patterns grew the academic discipline of ecology. Natural history serves as a foundation for much ecological research; however, it generally stops at describing observed patterns. Ecology is about understanding the mechanisms causing the patterns that occur in the natural world.

Most people no longer live surrounded by large expanses of natural areas. Instead, the human population is increasingly centred in urban and peri-urban areas. Does this mean that the study of ecology, or the need for it, is disappearing? No. Ecological processes do not end at the boundaries of natural areas. Rather, they occur in all living systems, be they managed farms or fisheries, urban landscapes, engineered systems, or wild areas. Cities, for example, are not sterile areas, devoid of any life other than people. Cities contain a diverse set of flora and fauna, spread in a patchwork of parks, waterways, urban forests, and gardens. These organisms interact with each other and with the physical environment of cities and provide ecological services to people living there. This, too, is ecology.

Taking a step back, we see that cities are just one part of a larger landscape that also includes a mixture of agriculture areas; peri-urban areas; rivers, ravines, and lakes; conservation areas; and wilderness. Organisms move in and out of these patches, corridors, waterways, and islands. Plants spread pollen and seeds across vast distances, with potential movement of genes and seeds across the landscape. No single area on the landscape is in complete isolation; indeed, activities in one area can influence the interactions among organisms and their environment in another. This, too, is ecology.

Taking an even broader view, we see that changes in temperature, varied patterns of precipitation, and altered air and water circulation are occurring across the planet. We see grasslands disappearing in the face of agricultural expansion, fisheries collapsing through over-exploitation, and air and water quality degrading as a consequence of industrial development. These changes influence organisms of all types and compromise the life-sustaining services that ecosystems provide. As a science, ecology is important in identifying patterns and providing solutions that can mitigate some of the problems created by human activities.

Ecologists may study the behaviours of individual organisms; the dynamics of populations; the interactions between different kinds of organisms; or the rates of ecosystem processes, such as photosynthesis. Their theatre of study might be the microscopic gradients within a bacterial biofilm, a patch of forest, a geographic region, or even the whole planet. Ecologists may study phenomena that occur in time scales of seconds or of millennia. Ecology is an interdisciplinary science, and ecologists generally need to know as much about plant biology, animal biology, microbiology, and molecular biology as they do about geography, soil science, chemistry, and physics. While most people tend to think of ecologists as people "out in the field," many ecologists make critical advances through lab experiments and the development of theoretical models and computer simulations. As you can see, the science of ecology covers substantial intellectual terrain. To get a better idea of what ecology is, we will briefly review the scope of the discipline.

1.1 Overview of Ecology

Ecologists study environmental relationships ranging from those of individual organisms to factors influencing global-scale processes. This broad range of subjects can be arranged as levels in a hierarchy of ecological organization, from least complex (autoecology) to most complex (global ecology) with respect to the nature of interactions. Figure 1.1 attempts to display such a hierarchy graphically. This hierarchy is only a conceptual construct, and most ecologists tackle questions that cross these levels. Using figure 1.1 as an example, an ecologist might be interested in how a bison chooses what food to consume (individual level), but the bison's behaviour is influenced by intraspecific competition (a function of population size) and interactions with other species (community of food plants, interspecific competition with other grazers).

Historically, the ecology of individuals has been the domain of **physiological ecology** and **behavioural ecology**. These sub-disciplines have a strong footing in evolutionary theory and rely on a detailed understanding of organismal biology to help understand ecological patterns and processes. Physiological ecologists study the mechanisms that organisms use to gather energy and cope with biotic and abiotic stressors in the environment. Behavioural ecologists focus on the determinants of individual behaviour and how that can influence interactions among individuals and with the environment. Both physiological and behavioural ecologists are commonly working in the realm of **autoecology**, which is the study of how an individual organism—or, more broadly, the species—interacts with its environment.

There is a strong conceptual linkage between studies of individuals and those of populations. For example, natural selection acts upon phenotypic variation among individuals, shaping the genetic structure of populations. **Population ecology** is centred on the factors influencing population structure and dynamics, where a population is a group of individuals of a single species inhabiting a defined area. The processes studied by population ecologists include the distribution and **abundance** of species, population growth and regulation, and many aspects of conservation biology. Population ecologists are particularly interested in how the environment influences these processes, including biotic and abiotic components of the environment.

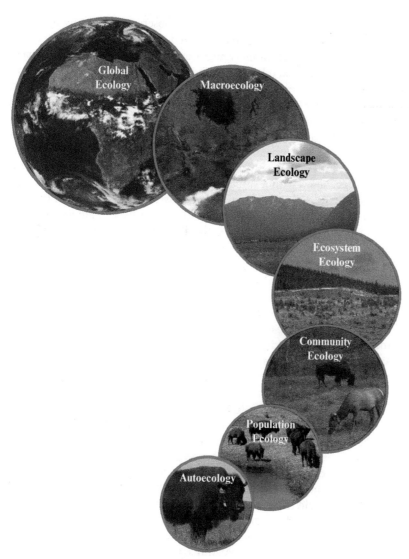

Figure 1.1 Levels of ecological organization. These ecological levels correspond broadly to sections 2 to 6 of this book.

(Global Ecology) Data: AVHRR, NDVI, Seawifs, MODIS, NCEP, DMSP and Sky2000 star catalogue; AVHRR and Sewifs texture: Reto Sockli; Visualization: Marit Jentoft-Nilsen, VAL, NASA GSFC, (Macroecology) Jacques Descloitres, MODIS Rapid Response Team, NASA/GSFC (Autoecology, Population Ecology, Community Ecology, Landscape Ecology, and Ecosystem Ecology), Maria Didkowsky.

Individual members of one species also interact with individual members of other species. These interactions form the basis of the next level of organization within ecology: **community ecology.** Community ecologists study interactions, such as predation, parasitism, mutualism, and competition. Some community ecologists emphasize the evolutionary effects of the interaction on the species involved, while others explore the effect the interaction has on the properties of ecological communities, such as species diversity or the provision of ecological services.

Ecosystem ecology has an even broader scope of study, including the biological, chemical, and physical processes and interactions that occur within a location. One goal of ecosystem ecology is to understand the controls on nutrient cycling and energy flow through ecosystems.

To simplify their studies, ecologists often identify and study isolated communities and ecosystems, such as a pond within a park. However, ecosystems are rarely so discrete, and the definition of the ecosystem often depends on the research question being asked. For example, one might consider the relationship between primary production and limpet communities in the tide pools near Saint John, or one might consider the relationship between primary production and fish communities in the entire Bay of Fundy. The tide pools may be the appropriate spatial scale for the first question, but are not discrete from the Bay.

However, all natural communities and ecosystems are open systems subject to exchanges of materials, energy, and organisms with other communities and ecosystems; the extent of this openness, and the flow of materials and energy, may vary from one ecosystem to another. The study of these exchanges, especially among ecosystems, is the domain of **landscape ecology.** However, landscapes themselves are not isolated but are instead part of regions subject to large-scale and long-term regional processes. These regional processes and patterns are the subjects of **macroecology.** Macroecology in turn leads us to the largest spatial scale and highest level of ecological organization: the **biosphere,** which falls within the realm of **global ecology.**

In our presenting ecology as an organizational hierarchy, the theme for organization was complexity of interactions. You probably also noticed that there is an element of spatial scaling in this hierarchy. From time to time, we will explicitly consider the importance of scale in ecology, but this is implicit throughout. We already discussed that a focus of ecology is identifying patterns and understanding the mechanisms responsible for those patterns. Simon Levin (1992) has argued that scale is a central problem in ecology. An observed pattern may be caused by a number of different mechanisms that do not all operate at the same spatial or temporal scale. Further, when we identify a pattern, we impose our own temporal scale. If you consider the abundance of butterflies in a meadow, for example, the pattern changes if you consider their abundance today versus their abundance over a year, versus their abundance over a decadal scale. The mechanisms that explain your pattern (abundance) may change depending on your temporal lens.

As is likely apparent, before you try to explain a pattern in nature, you have to carefully consider the temporal and spatial scales of your question: Over what time and space does the pattern hold? In addition, you need to consider the scale at which mechanisms explaining your pattern operate. Once defined, you are ready to consider the tools needed to measure your pattern. Different temporal and spatial scales of ecological processes will require different research methods.

1.2 Sampling Ecological Research

Ecologists design their studies based on their research questions, the temporal and spatial scale of their studies, and available research tools. While the overview of ecology presented in the previous section offers a brief preview of material covered in this book, it is a rough sketch and highly abstract. To move beyond the abstraction represented by figure 1.1, we need to connect it to the work of the scientists who have created, or who continue to create, the discipline of ecology. In the last section, we mentioned the importance of scale and of matching the research method to the scale (spatial and temporal) of the question. By considering ecological phenomena at multiple scales (spatial and temporal), ecologists have built a rich body of knowledge, theory, and general understanding of the functioning of the natural world.

In graduate school, a friend once boiled down ecology to this: "You have to be able to build things and count." Because she too is an ecologist, I let it go, and I took away her broader point, which is that ecology can progress through well-designed yet simple experiments that depend on careful and meticulous observation (at least that's what I assume she meant). We will see a great example of this in Robert MacArthur's work (a discussion of which follows). What we "build," how we "count," and what we do with the things we count (i.e., how we process data) depends a great deal on scale. In this section, we will introduce you to some of the different approaches used by ecologists working to describe natural patterns at different scales.

Ecology of Warblers across Spatial Scales: Direct Observation and Stable Isotopes

Robert MacArthur gazed intently through his binoculars. He was watching a small bird, called a warbler, searching for insects in the top of a spruce tree. To the casual observer it might have seemed that MacArthur was a weekend birdwatcher. Yes, he was intensely interested in the birds he was watching, but his scientific observations led to the development of fundamental ecological theory.

The year was 1955, and MacArthur was studying the ecology of five species of warblers that live together in the spruce forests of northeastern North America. All five warbler species—Cape May (*Setophaga tigrina*), yellow-rumped (*S. coronata*), black-throated green (*S. virens*), blackburnian (*S. fusca*), and bay-breasted (*S. castanea*)—are approximately the same size and shape, and all feed upon insects. Existing ecological theory predicted that two species with identical ecological requirements would compete with each other and that, as a consequence, they could not live in the same environment indefinitely. However, MacArthur could see with his own eyes that this theory was incorrect, as the birds were clearly living together. As a scientist, he wanted to understand how species with apparently similar ecological requirements could coexist.

The warblers MacArthur observed fed mainly by gleaning insects from the bark and foliage of trees. He predicted that these warblers might be able to coexist and not compete with each other if they fed on insects living in different zones within trees. To map where the warblers fed, he subdivided trees into vertical and horizontal zones. Using the most basic of field equipment—binoculars and a stopwatch— he then recorded the amount of time warblers spent feeding in each zone. Through careful observation, MacArthur demonstrated that the five warbler species in his study area fed in different zones within spruce trees. As figure 1.2 shows, the Cape May warbler fed mainly among new needles and buds at the tops of trees. The feeding zone of the blackburnian warbler overlapped broadly with that of the Cape May warbler but extended farther down the tree. The black-throated green warbler fed toward the trees' interiors. The bay-breasted warbler concentrated its feeding in the interior of trees. Finally, the yellow-rumped warbler fed mostly on the ground and low in the trees. MacArthur concluded that although these warblers live in the same forest, slight differences in where and when they extract food could reduce competition and permit coexistence of the five species.

MacArthur's study (1958) of foraging by warblers is a true classic in ecology. However, like most studies it raises as many questions as it answers. Among those questions is whether the observations supported the prevailing ecological theory of the time: that competition should not permit the indefinite coexistence of species with nearly identical ecological requirements. To bring back scaling, at the spatial scale of the whole tree, these species did coexist. Yet, at a finer spatial scale (within the tree), the different species were quite segregated, partitioning the space. And what of temporal scale? Would these warbler species coexist within the same tree indefinitely? MacArthur's work stimulated numerous studies of competition by many ecologists. Some of these studies produced results that supported MacArthur's initial theories, and others produced different results. Woven throughout these studies is the concept of scale (e.g., whether competing species overlap at a fine spatial scale or reduce competition by using different parts of the habitat; whether they coexist over a long temporal scale). All of this added to our knowledge of competition and of ecology.

Over half a century later, ecologists are still interested in understanding the movement of birds. The approach and tools that MacArthur used were appropriate at the spatial scale of a tree and spanning a relatively brief period of time. However, addressing questions about larger scale movements, such as migration patterns, requires a different set of tools and approaches. Keith Hobson of Environment Canada has been a leader in developing **stable isotope analysis** for the study of such ecological questions (Hobson 1999). Isotopes of a chemical element have different atomic masses as a result of having different numbers of neutrons. Carbon, for instance, has three isotopes: ^{12}C, ^{13}C, and ^{14}C. Of these three, ^{12}C and ^{13}C are stable isotopes because they do not undergo radioactive decay, whereas ^{14}C decays radioactivity and is therefore unstable. Stable isotopes have proven useful and are now

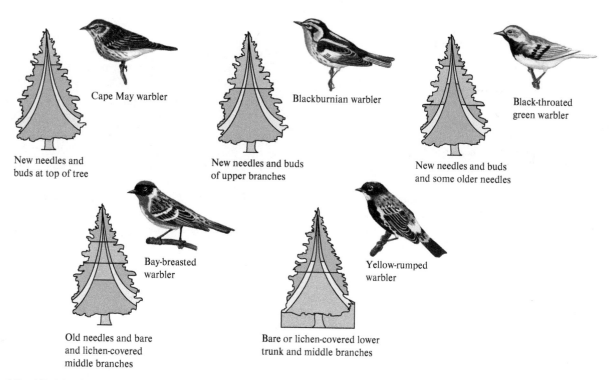

Cape May warbler

Blackburnian warbler

Black-throated green warbler

New needles and buds at top of tree

New needles and buds of upper branches

New needles and buds and some older needles

Bay-breasted warbler

Yellow-rumped warbler

Old needles and bare and lichen-covered middle branches

Bare or lichen-covered lower trunk and middle branches

Figure 1.2　Warbler feeding zones, indicated in beige. The warbler species that coexist in the forests of northeastern North America feed in distinctive zones within spruce trees, thereby reducing the potential for competition.

widely used in the study of ecological processes. For example, organisms that carry out specific processes may preferentially use one isotope versus another, and this discrimination becomes the basis for measuring important ecosystem-level processes (e.g., stable N isotopes allow us to measure processes in the nitrogen cycle) or tracking the source of materials entering ecosystems.

Stable isotopes also can clarify food sources because the proportions of various isotopes differ among food sources or across the environment. Isotopic composition of an animal's body is dynamic, but the pool turns over slowly. The use of stable isotopes, then, allows us to study diet at a longer time scale than other snapshot approaches, such as gut content analysis or observations of feeding.

Ryan Norris of the University of Guelph (Norris et al. 2005) has studied feeding habitats of wide-ranging migratory birds. American redstarts (*Setophaga ruticilla*), another colourful member of the warbler family Parulidae (fig. 1.3), nest in temperate North America during the summer and spend the winters in tropical Central America, northern South America, and the Caribbean islands (fig. 1.4). In Jamaica, older males, along with some females, spend the winter in higher productivity **mangrove forest** habitats, pushing most females and younger males into poorer quality, dry scrub habitat. The dominant plants in these two habitats and the insects that feed on them contain different proportions of the carbon isotopes. Blood samples taken from birds when they return to their summer breeding grounds can reveal whether they spent their winters in the productive mangrove habitat (lower ^{13}C) or in the poor scrub

habitat (higher ^{13}C), which can then be correlated with breeding success in summer habitat.

The studies of MacArthur and Norris show how field studies can be used to address ecological questions concerning interactions among individuals within a species, and concerning different species both within individual trees and across a large geographic extent. But what tools are available to study interactions with the physical environment, particularly at large scales?

Figure 1.3　A male American redstart (*Setophaga ruticilla*).
© Linda Freshwaters Arndt/Alamy.

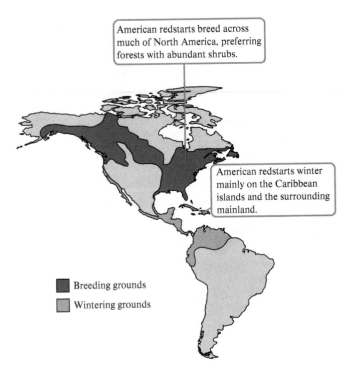

Figure 1.4   The breeding and wintering grounds of the American redstart (*Setophaga ruticilla*).

Figure 1.5   Lake 226 at the Experimental Lakes Area divided in half. The eutrophied half in the background had phosphorus added, while the clear half in the foreground did not.

David Schindler, from D. Schindler. 1974. Eutrophication and recovery in experimental lakes: Implications for lake management of Earth. *Science* 184:897–9.

Understanding Ecosystem Controls through Whole Ecosystem Manipulations

In the early 1960s, scientists and politicians around the world were seeing previously clear lakes turn pea-green, a process called **eutrophication.** Observers quickly realized that some nutrient was likely being added to these lakes, causing rapid algal growth. The question was, which nutrient? In the mid-1960s, the Fisheries Research Board of Canada established the Freshwater Institute to search for the cause of eutrophication. At the time, lab studies were giving conflicting answers, and the leaders of the Freshwater Institute realized that resolution would not be found by adding nutrients to beakers in a lab. Instead, they needed to do their experiments on a much grander scale—adding nutrients to whole lakes. In 1968, the Experimental Lakes Area (ELA) was established in Ontario, and David Schindler was hired as "Leader of Experimental Lake Investigations." Under Schindler's direction, the research team at ELA began to add different nutrients in different combinations to different lakes, measuring the response of each ecosystem.

In landmark papers (e.g., Schindler 1974, 1977), Schindler was able to show that phosphorus (P) was the nutrient responsible for eutrophication. This can be seen clearly in a photograph of Lake 226 (fig. 1.5). For this experiment, the scientists split the lake in half, adding nitrogen and carbon to one side and nitrogen, carbon, and phosphorus to the other. The phosphorus addition caused a dramatic shift in this ecosystem: eutrophication. Schindler travelled throughout North America and the world, explaining his research to many levels of government. Because

of his work, detergents containing phosphorus have been banned from many places, substantially improving the quality of many freshwater ecosystems. Of course, ecology defies the universal answer. As with MacArthur's landmark study, many subsequent experiments and observations confirmed Schindler's hypothesis that phosphorus drives eutrophication of temperate lakes. However, some freshwater systems can shift between P and N limitation spatially, from headwaters to the lake (e.g., McCarthy et al. 2007) or temporally (Elser 1999).

Why did laboratory-scale experiments fail to predict whole ecosystem response to nutrients? The underlying mechanisms driving eutrophication require the ability of the microflora and fauna to shift in species composition as nutrient levels increase, and this could not easily be captured in a small-scale study using beakers. Another aspect that small-scale experiments neglected was the exchange of nitrogen and carbon with the atmosphere. In windswept lakes, more CO_2 from the atmosphere mixes into the water, supporting the increased photosynthesis that occurs during algal blooms. In beaker experiments, there was no such CO_2 exchange between the water and the atmosphere; thus, when phosphorus was added, algal growth often became carbon limited.

Lab-scale experiments in ecology are important, and they do have value. They can give us some guiding principles when we formulate hypotheses about what governs ecosystem behaviour. Schindler would never have manipulated P had lab experiments not commonly (albeit inconsistently) suggested that P was a limiting nutrient. However, lab experiments cannot include all species from natural areas, nor do they allow for interactions with the physical environment—in this example, gas exchange. While laboratory experiments contribute to ecological theory, in order to understand the governing factors of an ecosystem, sometimes you have to manipulate an ecosystem.

Going Big: Tools for Studying Changes over Long Time Periods and Large Spatial Scales

The earth and its life are always changing, and this will be the dominant theme of chapter 23, the final chapter in this book. Climate change is, of course, the defining ecological challenge of our time. You are, also, undoubtedly aware of some other large-scale ecological changes, such as deforestation, eutrophication of coastal oceans, and habitat and biodiversity loss. Changes associated with, for example, epidemics, emerald ash borer beetles, and oil infrastructure development often make the front pages of the newspapers. We are aware of these changes, largely, because of the rate at which they are happening and because we have the tools to map the changes over time. Many other ecological and evolutionary changes occur over such long periods of time and such broad spatial extents that they are difficult to study and even more difficult to distill down to a sound bite to make the news. As is often the case, a critical step in studying large-scale and long-term ecological questions is combining the right research tool with detailed knowledge of the ecological system being studied.

Paleoecology provides us with the tools to study ecological change over a geological time scale. Reconstructing past communities depends on preservation of biological materials or chemical tracers of past biological activity. Margaret Davis is a paleoecologist who has spent much of her professional career studying changes in the distributions of plants during the last 20,000 years. During this period, the earth underwent rapid

climate change, with advancing and retreating glacier fields throughout regions of the Northern Hemisphere.

Davis (1983, 1989) has carefully searched for pollen in sediment from a lake in the Appalachian Mountains. Some of the pollen produced by plants that live near a lake falls on the lake surface, then sinks and becomes trapped in sediments. As sediments build up over the centuries, this pollen is preserved and forms a historical record of the kinds of plants that lived nearby and of how the plant community changes over time. Davis's work demonstrated different rates of migration of tree species following retreat of glaciers, and past histories of species loss, such as the loss of the American chestnut in 1920 (fig. 1.6). Davis's research is being used to predict how tree and other plant species might migrate in response to prolonged climate change.

While Davis's research has developed tools to address ecological change over long time scales, other ecologists have been working to develop tools for large spatial scales. Trevor Platt, for example—as a research scientist in Canada's Department of Fisheries and Oceans, as a professor at Dalhousie University, and now as a professor at Plymouth Marine Laboratory—has spent the past several decades working to understand large-scale patterns in marine productivity. Platt has been particularly interested in determining the factors that control variation in marine primary production and in developing tools to measure it (Platt 1975; Platt and Jassby 1976). Marine ecologists and oceanographers are very interested in understanding the growth of phytoplankton, as these small photosynthetic organisms serve as the base of most marine food webs. Why do people care about changes to such small organisms? Changes in marine productivity can lead to changes in the abundances of other species, including fish and crustaceans harvested by people. A great challenge in Platt's work is that marine systems are enormous, and physically sampling such a large area is not practical. So, Platt

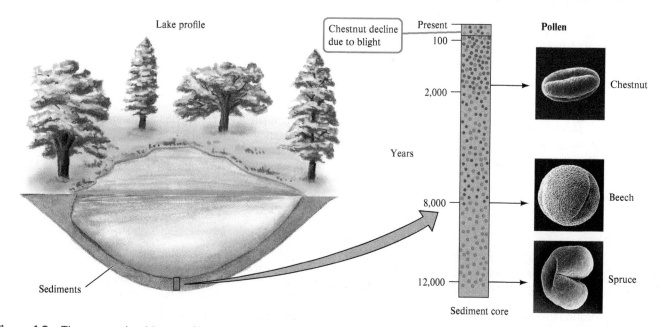

Figure 1.6 The vegetation history of landscapes can be reconstructed using the pollen contained within the sediments of nearby lakes.

Chestnut, beech, and spruce: Courtesy of the Gretchen and Stanley Jones Palynological Collection and the Botanical Research Institute of Texas.

used his knowledge of phytoplankton biology to help develop a number of methods by which these organisms could be sampled remotely, such as spectral reflectance patterns received from satellite imagery. Platt and his colleagues have further enhanced these techniques over time, allowing ecologists to study productivity over large spatial extents. This work is proving critical to understanding how marine systems change in response to shifting climates, and how changes in primary production can influence the success or failure of marine fisheries.

While these new tools provide tremendous geospatial information, extracting meaning from the maps and images requires ingenuity and development of appropriate techniques. This is the domain of spatial and landscape statistics. Marie-Josée Fortin of the University of Toronto and her colleagues have been expanding the statistical tools available to ecologists (Fortin et al. 2000, 2005) and applying these tools to issues of habitat fragmentation, habitat loss, and conservation.

Terrestrial systems tend to be heavily fragmented by natural barriers (e.g., streams) and a diversity of human activities (fig. 1.7). **Ecotones** are transitions from one type of ecosystem to another: for instance, the transition from an agricultural field into the surrounding forest. As landscapes become more and more fragmented through human activities, the amount of transitional area increases. Plant and animal species that occupy transition zones are often at their physiological limits and may be particularly sensitive to any additional environmental change. To understand how core and transitional habitats change and to predict how this may affect plant and animal communities, it is critical to distinguish the boundaries of one community from another and to track changes in these boundaries over time.

Figure 1.7 Boundaries within landscapes created by human activity (background) and natural environmental gradients (foreground).

Alexander Lowry/Science Source.

Tools of Molecular Ecology

The field of molecular biology is booming and generating new tools that migrate into ecology. The polymerase chain reaction (PCR) gave us the ability to detect specific genes in the environment, even when they are present in low copy numbers. This has been useful, particularly in microbial ecology, allowing us to find the needle in the haystack—the microorganism that is rare but present in a sample of soil or water. As the vast majority of bacteria cannot be grown in a lab, this tool has been essential in letting us ask "Who is there?" since it does not require culturing of the bacteria. The use of PCR has opened the door to understanding diversity of the most abundant forms of life and to asking some fundamental ecology questions, such as how the composition of the microbial community relates to its function.

The PCR has become the workhorse of molecular biology, spawning new techniques, such as reverse-transcription PCR (rt-PCR) to identify RNA in the environment. In ecology, this can be useful in answering not "Who is there?" but, rather, "What is it doing?" by amplifying copies of messenger RNA (mRNA) transcripts. Quantitative PCR (qPCR) can be used to quantify, in relative terms, how many copies of a gene are present. This can be useful in knowing the abundance of an organism in the environment when a gene unique to that organism is amplified. Gerard Muyzer and colleagues (1992) introduced a technique called denaturing gradient gel electrophoresis (DGGE) to determine the diversity of microbial communities based on selectively PCR amplifying the 16S ribosomal RNA (rRNA) gene. The gene is common to all bacteria. In principle, all forms of the gene that are present in a sample are amplified in the PCR reaction. DGGE can then separate the different forms of the gene based on differences in nucleotide sequence. On a gel, each band corresponds to a different form of the gene, giving a measure of community diversity. More recently, high throughput sequencing of DNA and the use of other biological markers, such as fatty acids or proteins, offer other tools for creating profiles of community diversity.

The discussion here only scratches the surface of molecular techniques used in ecology. These tools are being used to study many ecological phenomena, such as interactions among organisms, the genetic structure of populations, rates of evolution, relatedness among organisms, migration and dispersal, and feeding relationships. The tools of molecular ecology are often coupled with some of the other tools discussed previously. A good illustration of this is a study by Amanda De La Torre at Northern Arizona University. At the time, De La Torre was a Ph.D. student at the University of British Columbia, under the supervision of Sally Aitken.

De La Torre and colleagues (2014) used ecological niche modelling and paleoclimate data to predict the distributions of two spruce species (*Picea glauca* and *Picea engelmannii*) over the past 21,000 years during postglacial recolonization. These species are commonly found in western North American boreal forests. Niche modelling predicted a long history of range overlap and a long history of potential hybridization. De La Torre and her colleagues extracted DNA from needle samples collected from a number of *P. glauca, P. engelmannii,* and hybrid trees. They performed a genome-wide screen to identify genes that were common in form (DNA sequence) to both species, suggesting interspecific gene flow at these gene loci. The screen also identified gene forms, or alleles, that were species-specific and that might be important for maintaining species boundaries. Although the paleoclimatic and ecological niche modelling suggested a long history (at least 21,000 years) of range overlap, and although most gene loci showed strong evidence of **introgression** of genes, the integrity of species boundaries was maintained by natural selection operating on these species-specific genes (and likely others not assessed).

ECOLOGICAL TOOLS AND APPROACHES

The Scientific Method

Ecologists explore the relationships between organisms and environment using the methods of science. The series of boxes called "Ecological Tools and Approaches" that are found in all the chapters of this book provide various examples of how ecologists address real-world problems. To begin with, we present here not a complex example of the toolkit ecologists employ but, instead, an overview of the scientific method. The best tools available to us cannot be used to answer questions that are poorly framed. The scientific method provides a framework in which science can be productive.

Let us begin this discussion with the most basic question: What is science? The word *science* comes from the Latin word *scientia,* meaning "to know." Broadly speaking, science is a way of obtaining knowledge about the natural world using certain formal procedures. There are a number of different philosophies and approaches to conducting science, but they all share the same goal—understanding the natural world. One approach to science is particularly common and is generally referred to as "the scientific method." The scientific approach is a powerful method for understanding the natural world because it is based on observations about how the world works. The observations must be systematic and objective to be useful. The scientific method consists of five interrelated operations, in this order:

Observation, Question, Hypothesis, Experiment, Conclusions

The scientific method is a way in which a hypothesis (a tentative explanation) is formulated, and it provides a structured approach to gathering information in order to support this hypothesis.

The hypothesis is central to the scientific method. The word *hypothesis* itself can be defined in many ways, and here we use a general definition of "a potential answer to a question." We observe our world. We read published studies; we observe or build models of natural systems. We perform our own preliminary experiments and try new things. All of these activities can be thought of as *observation* or information gathering. These observations may lead us to make guesses about how the world works or to ask *questions*. After observing, we use **inductive reasoning** to formulate a hypothesis that will provide a possible answer to our question and support our observations. Inductive reasoning makes broad generalizations from specific observations. Even if all the premises are true in the statement, inductive reason allows for the conclusion to be false. For example: "John is a grandfather. John is bald. Therefore, all grandfathers are bald." This final statement is not true. Yet, it allows us to formulate a working hypothesis, "All grandfathers are bald," and an opposite or null hypothesis, "Not all grandfathers are bald."

The working (or alternate) hypothesis and the null hypothesis are mutually exclusive and cover all possible outcomes. Formulating a hypothesis provides a mechanism for assessing our study. We will do an experiment, or collect data, and will assess whether these data support our null hypothesis or fail to support the null hypothesis. When making this assessment, we use **deductive reasoning.** We observe a number of grandfathers, determine whether they are bald, and draw a conclusion. It might take this form: "All men observed were grandfathers. Not all men observed were bald. Therefore, not all grandfathers are bald."

You should notice that we are not testing the working hypothesis. We are instead testing whether there is support for any other explanation that may be encompassed in the null hypothesis. This is an important tenet of the scientific method: we do not prove our hypotheses; rather, we determine if there is support for any other explanation (or how probable an explanation is other than our own).

Our data supported the null hypothesis. Now what? In John's case, being bald is not a condition of being a grandfather, and we go back to the observation stage, consider whether there may be any other plausible reason for his being bald, and formulate a new working hypothesis and null hypothesis.

The above example is, of course, a ridiculous one. However, the process applies to other questions that we pursue answers for in science. Questions are the guiding lights of the scientific process. Without them, exploration of nature lacks focus and yields little understanding of the world. Let's consider some questions asked by the ecologists discussed in this chapter. The main question asked by Robert MacArthur in his studies of warblers was "How can several species of insect-eating warblers live in the same forest without one species eventually excluding the others through competition?" David Schindler asked, "What nutrients cause lake eutrophication?" While this focus on questions may seem obvious, one of the most common questions asked of scientists at seminars and professional meetings is "What is your question?"

As with the previous example, the question leads to formulating possible answers (hypotheses) and testing whether they are sound. For MacArthur, one hypothesis was "Several warbler species are able to coexist because each species feeds on insects living in different zones within trees." The central hypothesis of the Schindler study was "Increased phosphorus, not nitrogen or carbon, is responsible for lake eutrophication." A single research question

may generate multiple alternative hypotheses rather than a simple yes/no contrast. For example, an alternative hypothesis for MacArthur's study could have been "Several warbler species are able to coexist because each species feeds on insects at different times within trees." However, we can only accept any given hypothesis once we are satisfied that the data do not support any of the other explanations. In science, there can be more than a single factually correct answer, and researchers who ignore alternative explanations for the patterns they observe do so at their own intellectual peril!

The Scope of Ecology

With this brief review of research approaches and topics, we return to the question asked at the beginning of the chapter: What is ecology? Ecology is indeed the study of relationships between organisms and the environment. However, as you can see from the research we have reviewed, ecologists examine those relationships over a large range of temporal and spatial scales using a wide variety of approaches. Ecology includes Fortin's studies of forests in Quebec and Davis's studies of vegetation movement across North America. Ecology also includes the observational studies of MacArthur, as well as the whole-ecosystem manipulations of Schindler. Some ecological studies, such as Norris's measures of stable isotopes, involve long hours at a bench in a lab. Other studies, such as those of Platt, rely on the use of satellites that orbit Earth. Some ecologists study processes that take place over short periods of time over small spatial scales, while others ask questions that involve millennia and cover large regions of Earth. All this is ecology.

As fun and enjoyable as it is to spend summers conducting field work in beautiful locations throughout the world, one factor that differentiates an ecologist from ecotourists and natural historians is a strict reliance on the scientific method. Ecologists are scientists answering complex questions in natural and managed systems; we are not simply observing the landscape. If you want to predict the impacts of climate change on local species diversity, bring in an ecologist. If you want to understand how predators may alter prey densities, bring in an ecologist. If you want to determine the impact of a new housing

development on a creek's fish community, bring in an ecologist. Critical to our ability to find answers to these questions is our ability to objectively identify and evaluate relationships in complex data sets. Though it may come as a surprise to many, ecology is among the more quantitative disciplines of biology. As a result, a strong understanding of quantitative methods and statistics is critical to the success of students of ecology, and we strongly encourage you read appendix A before diving into the remaining 22 chapters in this book.

As fun and enjoyable as it is to read several pages of statistical methods, we also encourage you to not limit your learning to reading and listening to lectures. Natural history is also a foundation of ecology, and understanding ecology is intimately intertwined with observing nature and doing ecology. Although you will be able to learn the core principles of ecology from this text and your instructors, we encourage you to get out into the field; field data are the ultimate test of the accuracy of theory, predictions, and expectations. We encourage you to explore, to get your hands dirty while learning to "do" ecology.

The brief survey of ecology in this chapter has only hinted at the conceptual and methodological basis for the research described. Throughout this book we emphasize the foundations of ecology. Each chapter focuses on a few ecological concepts, and we explore some of the applications and tools associated with the concepts introduced. We continue our exploration of ecology in section 1 with the natural history of life on land and in water. Natural history is the foundation upon which ecologists built modern ecology.

ECOLOGY IN ACTION

Applying the Scientific Method in Conservation

Ecologists explore the relationships between organisms and environment using the methods of science, as discussed in the Ecological Tools and Approaches box earlier in the chapter. The series of boxes called "Ecology in Action" found in all the chapters of this book will provide a glimpse of some good

follow-up to the discussion on scientific method, and you will be able to recognize the observation that led to questions and the inductive reasoning that yielded a testable hypothesis.

Natural history is the study of patterns, describing how organisms in a particular area respond to factors such as climate, soils, predators, competitors, mutualists. Natural history recapitulates, but does not explain, patterns in the evolutionary history of species. A solid understanding of natural history provides the foundation for modern ecology and conservation biology. Natural history is information and observations that can lead an ecologist to interesting questions. Daniel Janzen is an ecologist, and, like Robert MacArthur (mentioned earlier), he gives us a great example of how a combination of the scientific method, knowledge of natural history, and detailed observation can lead to significant discoveries. Janzen's goal was to restore tropical dry forest to Guanacaste National Park. Guanacaste National Park contains the guanacaste tree (*Enterolobium cyclocarpum*) (fig. 1.8*a*). The tree is a member of the pea family and produces disk-shaped fruit about 10 cm in diameter and 4 to 10 mm thick. The fruit are shaped like an ear, giving name to the fruit (meaning "ear pod"), the tree it grows upon, and the province in which the tree grows.

Each year, a large tree produces up to 5,000 of these fruits, which fall to the ground when ripe. As Janzen studied the guanacaste tree, he asked a simple question: Why does it produce so much fruit? His hypothesis was that the fruit of the tree should promote seed dispersal by animals. As a corollary, Janzen anticipated that the guanacaste tree must have, in its evolutionary history, coexisted with large seed-dispersing animals.

Janzen, however, knew of no native animals of the size and behaviour that would make them dependable dispersers of guanacaste seeds. Dependable dispersers would be necessary to speed restoration of tropical dry forests across Guanacaste National Park. Had the guanacaste tree evolved an elaborate fruit and made thousands of them each year in the absence of native dispersers? On the surface, it appeared so, but this did not seem to make sense. Without some means of dispersing their seeds, the majority of offspring would fall from the tree and remain at the base of the maternal plant. This appears to be a dangerous place for seedlings to grow, as their mother would cast shade over them and draw resources from the soils around them.

Janzen's plans for restoration of tropical dry forests were guided by his knowledge of natural history. As he considered the long-term natural history of Central American dry forest, he found what he was looking for: a whole host of large herbivorous animals, including gomphotheres (elephant-like animals), ground sloths, camels, and horses (fig. 1.8*b*). The dry forest had once supported plenty of potential dispersers of guanacaste seeds, all of which had become extinct about 10,000 years ago. For thousands of years following these extinctions, the guanacaste tree continued its annual production of fruits, but there were few large animals to consume them. Then, about 500 years ago, Europeans introduced horses and cattle, which ate the fruits of the guanacaste tree and dispersed their seeds around the landscape. Janzen recognized the practical value of livestock as seed dispersers and included them in his plan for tropical dry forest restoration.

From this footing in natural history, Janzen then applied a formal scientific method. He first tested, and confirmed, the hypothesis that contemporary horses could act as effective seed dispersers for the guanacaste tree. After this

(a)

(b)

Figure 1.8 (*a*) A guanacaste tree (*Enterolobium cyclocarpum*) growing in Costa Rica. Guanacaste trees, which produce large amounts of edible fruit, require large herbivores to disperse their seeds. (*b*) An artistic rendering of *Phiomia,* a now-extinct gomphothere, in comparison to a modern day African elephant. Gomphotheres are putative consumers of the guanacaste fruit.

test, he applied his knowledge by incorporating horses into the management plan for Guanacaste National Park. The guanacaste tree and other trees in a similar predicament would have their dispersers, and restoration of tropical dry forest would be accelerated. However, he alone could not change the practices of the park. Instead, he realized success would require collaboration and cooperation from people of various sectors of society—those that live around the park as well as those that govern the country.

Janzen's pioneering work (1981a, 1981b) shows how natural history, along with science and community engagement, can be used to address a practical problem. Janzen's work also shows the impact that humans have on ecological interactions, both in their influence on species extinctions as well as through working with governments to effect positive change through restoration. This theme—that people are not separate from ecological processes—will be common throughout the book.

SUMMARY

1.1 Ecologists study environmental relationships ranging from those of individual organisms to factors influencing global-scale processes.

The research focus and questions posed by ecologists differ across the levels of organization studied.

1.2 Ecologists design their studies based on their research questions, the temporal and spatial scale of their studies, and available research tools.

With this brief review of research approaches and topics, we return to the question asked at the beginning of the chapter: What is ecology? Ecology is indeed the study of relationships between organisms and the environment. However, as you can see from the studies we have reviewed, ecologists study those relationships over a large range of temporal and spatial scales using a wide variety of approaches. Ecology includes Davis's studies of vegetation moving across the North American continent over a span of thousands of years. Ecology also includes the observational studies of birds in contemporary forests by MacArthur. Ecology includes Fortin's statistical modelling to define ecological boundaries, and it includes molecular techniques such as those used to answer population genetics and hybridization questions by De La Torre. Ecologists may study processes on plots measured in square centimetres, or, like those studying the ecology of migratory birds, study areas may span thousands of kilometres. Ecology includes all these approaches and many more.

REVIEW QUESTIONS

1. Faced with the complexity of nature, ecologists have divided the field of ecology into subdisciplines, each of which focuses on one of the levels of organization pictured in figure 1.1. What is the advantage of developing such subdisciplines within ecology?

2. What are the pitfalls of subdividing nature in the way it is represented in figure 1.1? In what ways does the figure misrepresent nature?

3. What could you do to verify that the distinct feeding zones used by the warblers studied by MacArthur (see fig. 1.2) are the result of ongoing competition between the different species of warblers? How might you examine the role of competition in keeping some American redstarts out of the most productive feeding areas on their wintering grounds?

4. David Schindler chose to conduct an experiment manipulating an entire ecosystem rather than small areas within the ecosystem. What are the potential costs and benefits of such large-scale approaches to science?

5. How can an understanding of the biology of individual species help ecologists understand long-term population changes?

6. In ecology, there are experimentalists and theorists; some work in the field, some in the lab. Why is there value in using a diversity of philosophical approaches and tools in addressing research questions?

7. How can scientific information be used to inform political decisions? How much evidence is "sufficient" before a scientist advocates for a particular solution?

Stephen J. Krasemann/Photographers Choice/Getty Images.

SECTION 1   NATURAL HISTORY AND EVOLUTION

The science of ecology is built upon a foundation of natural history and evolutionary biology. In this section, we describe some of the common terrestrial and aquatic ecosystems that occur around the world and the dominant environmental factors that influence these systems. We conclude with an overview of evolution, a set of biological processes intimately intertwined with ecological interactions.

Chapter 2   **Life on Land**
Chapter 3   **Life in Water**
Chapter 4   **Evolution and Speciation**

Dean van't Schip/All Canada Photos/Getty Images.

CHAPTER 2   LIFE ON LAND

CHAPTER CONCEPTS

2.1 Uneven heating of the earth's spherical surface by the sun and the tilt of the earth on its axis combine to produce latitudinal variation in climate.

Concept 2.1 Review

2.2 Soil structure results from the long-term interaction of climate, organisms, topography, and parent mineral material.

Concept 2.2 Review

Ecology in Action: Diversity of Soil Organisms

2.3 The geographic distribution of terrestrial biomes corresponds closely to variation in climate, especially prevailing temperature and precipitation.

Concept 2.3 Review

2.4 Human activities (e.g., agriculture and city building) modify climate, biomes' structure, soil, and hydrology, reshaping biological communities.

Concept 2.4 Review

Ecological Tools and Approaches: Biomes of Canada and Winter Ecology

Summary

Review Questions

Life on land can be brutal. Most terrestrial organisms are essentially bags of water surrounded by dry air and are at constant threat of dehydration. Even when organisms can keep their water inside, low temperatures make that water dangerous. When ice crystals form, they puncture and destroy living cells, leading to organ damage and even death. Heat, too, can be a significant challenge for terrestrial organisms. At high temperatures proteins denature, reducing the efficiency of many biological processes. Another basic problem of life on land is the persistent force of gravity. Compared to aquatic organisms, there is no natural buoyancy for organisms that live on land. Elaborate structures are required to simply stand, let alone grow and move. Dealing with all of these stressors requires specific traits, such as woody tissues in plants, the ability to sweat or pant for some mammals, or the ability to lower the freezing point of water as is found among some amphibians. The physiological ecology of dealing with abiotic stressors is discussed in section 2. Here, we describe how common abiotic conditions result in predictable characteristics in species that live under particular temperature and precipitation regimes.

This chapter focuses on major divisions of the terrestrial environment called **biomes.** Biomes are distinguished primarily by the commonly observed plant species, and each is associated with a particular climate. Because each biome will contain different types of plants and animals and occur in regions with very different climates, their natural histories differ a great deal. The main goal of this chapter is to take a large-scale perspective of nature before delving, in later chapters, into finer details of structure and process. We pay particular attention to the geographic distributions of the major biomes within Canada, the climate associated with each, their soils, and the common characteristics of the species able to live under those conditions. At the end of the chapter, we consider the nature of human influences. Now let's move on to the central concepts of this chapter, which concern patterns of climatic variation, soil structure, and ecology, and the global distribution of the major biomes.

2.1 Large-Scale Patterns of Climatic Variation

Uneven heating of the earth's spherical surface by the sun and the tilt of the earth on its axis combine to produce latitudinal variation in climate. In chapter 1, *ecology* was defined as the study of the relationships between organisms and their environment. Consequently, understanding geographic and seasonal variations in temperature and precipitation is fundamental to studying ecology. Several attributes of climate vary predictably over the earth. For instance, average temperatures are lower and more seasonal (varying predictably over the year) at middle and high latitudes than near the equator. Deserts, which are concentrated in a narrow band of latitudes around the globe, receive little precipitation, which generally falls unpredictably in time and space. However, average climatic conditions over a large geographic extent do not necessarily indicate the typical climate for a given location within that broad area. For example, unique geographic features allow wineries to exist in the Niagara Peninsula in southern Ontario, even though the broader region has a climate unsuitable for commercial grape production. In this section, we will discuss the major mechanisms that produce these and other patterns of climatic variation, leaving these local exceptions to later chapters.

Temperature, Precipitation, and Atmospheric Circulation

Much of the earth's climatic variation is caused by uneven heating of its surface by the sun. This uneven heating results from the spherical shape of the earth and the angle at which the earth rotates on its axis as it orbits the sun. Because the earth is a sphere, the sun's rays are most concentrated where the sun is directly overhead. However, the latitude at which the sun is directly overhead changes with the seasons. This seasonal change occurs because the earth's axis of rotation is not perpendicular to its plane of orbit about the sun but is tilted approximately 23.5° away from the perpendicular (fig. 2.1).

Because this tilted angle of rotation is maintained throughout earth's orbit about the sun, the amount of solar energy received by the Northern and Southern Hemispheres changes seasonally. During the northern summer, the Northern Hemisphere is tilted toward the sun and receives more solar energy than the Southern Hemisphere. During the northern summer solstice on approximately June 21, the sun is directly overhead at the tropic of Cancer, at 23.5° N latitude. During the northern winter solstice, on approximately December 21, the sun is directly overhead at the tropic of Capricorn, at 23.5° S latitude. During the northern winter, the Northern Hemisphere is tilted away from the sun and the Southern Hemisphere receives more solar energy. The sun is directly overhead at the equator during the spring and autumnal equinoxes, on approximately March 21 and September 23. On those dates, the Northern and Southern Hemispheres receive approximately equal amounts of solar radiation.

This regular shift in the latitude at which the sun is directly overhead drives the changes we associate with the different seasons of the year. At high latitudes, in both the Northern and Southern Hemispheres, seasonal shifts in input of solar energy produce winters with low average temperatures and shorter day lengths and summers with high average temperatures and longer day lengths. In contrast, between the tropics of Cancer and Capricorn, seasonal variations in temperature and day length are slight, while precipitation may vary greatly. What produces spatial and temporal variation in precipitation?

Heating of the earth's surface and atmosphere drives circulation of the atmosphere and influences patterns of precipitation. As shown in figure 2.2(*a*), the sun constantly heats air at the equator, causing the air to expand and rise. This warm, moist air cools as it rises. Since cool air holds less water vapour than warm air, the water vapour carried by this rising air mass condenses and forms clouds, which produce the heavy rainfall associated with tropical environments.

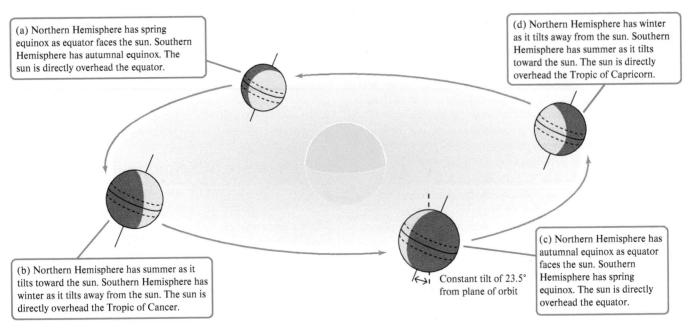

(a) Northern Hemisphere has spring equinox as equator faces the sun. Southern Hemisphere has autumnal equinox. The sun is directly overhead the equator.

(d) Northern Hemisphere has winter as it tilts away from the sun. Southern Hemisphere has summer as it tilts toward the sun. The sun is directly overhead the Tropic of Capricorn.

(b) Northern Hemisphere has summer as it tilts toward the sun. Southern Hemisphere has winter as it tilts away from the sun. The sun is directly overhead the Tropic of Cancer.

Constant tilt of 23.5° from plane of orbit

(c) Northern Hemisphere has autumnal equinox as equator faces the sun. Southern Hemisphere has spring equinox. The sun is directly overhead the equator.

Figure 2.1 The seasons in the Northern and Southern Hemispheres: (*a*) spring equinox in the Northern Hemisphere, (*b*) summer in the Northern Hemisphere, (*c*) autumnal equinox in the Northern Hemisphere, (*d*) winter in the Northern Hemisphere.

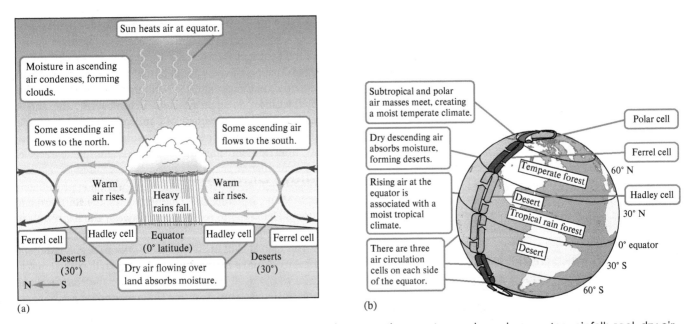

Sun heats air at equator.

Moisture in ascending air condenses, forming clouds.

Some ascending air flows to the north.

Some ascending air flows to the south.

Warm air rises.

Heavy rains fall.

Warm air rises.

Ferrel cell

Hadley cell

Equator (0° latitude)

Hadley cell

Ferrel cell

Deserts (30°)

Dry air flowing over land absorbs moisture.

Deserts (30°)

N ← S

(a)

Subtropical and polar air masses meet, creating a moist temperate climate.

Dry descending air absorbs moisture, forming deserts.

Rising air at the equator is associated with a moist tropical climate.

There are three air circulation cells on each side of the equator.

Polar cell

Ferrel cell

Temperate forest

60° N

Desert

Hadley cell

Tropical rain forest

30° N

Desert

0° equator

30° S

60° S

(b)

Figure 2.2 (*a*) Solar-driven air circulation; warm, moist air rises near the equator, cools, and generates rainfall; cool, dry air descends at ~30° and moves back across the surface toward the equator (Hadley cell) or toward mid-latitudes (Ferrel cell). (*b*) Latitude and atmospheric circulation; rising moist air masses generate rain and moist climates; descending dry air masses (convergence of Ferrel cell and Hadley cell) create dry climates.

Eventually, this equatorial air mass ceases to rise and spreads to the north and south. This high-altitude air is dry, since the moisture it once held fell as tropical rains. As this air mass moves away from the intensity of solar warming found at the equator, it cools, increasing its density. Eventually, this denser air sinks back to the earth's surface at about 30° latitude, where it again spreads both to the north and south. This dry air draws moisture from the lands over which it flows, creating a band of deserts.

Air moving from 30° latitude back to the equator completes a thermal loop, which forms the Hadley cell. As figure 2.2*b* shows, there are three atmospheric cells on either side of the equator, called the Hadley, Ferrel, and Polar cells. The Polar cell functions in a manner similar to the Hadley

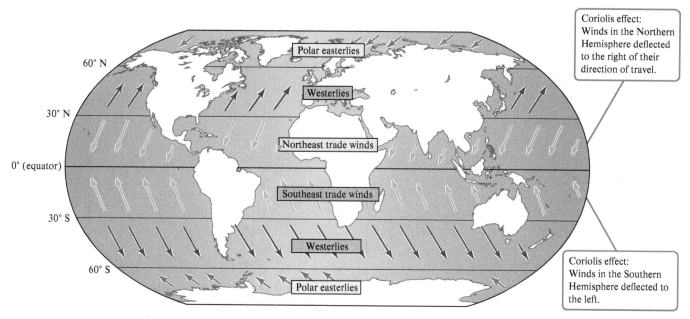

Figure 2.3 The Coriolis effect and wind direction.

cell, driven by air movement associated with warming at 60° latitude and cooling at the poles. The Polar cell is primarily responsible for the weather patterns associated with most northerly and southerly areas, bringing cool weather from the poles. Though displayed as single, narrow arrows in figure 2.2, it is important to recognize that each cell surrounds all longitudes around the earth.

The Ferrel cell occurs at mid-latitudes and is driven in part by the effects of the Hadley and Polar cells. When moist air flowing from the Hadley cell rises as it meets cold air flowing from the Polar cell, moisture picked up from desert regions at lower latitudes condenses to form the clouds that produce the abundant precipitation of temperate regions.

The patterns of atmospheric circulation shown in figure 2.2*b* suggest that air movement is directly north and south. However, this does not reflect what we observe from the earth's surface as the earth rotates from west to east. An observer at tropical latitudes observes winds that blow from the northeast in the Northern Hemisphere and from the southeast in the Southern Hemisphere (fig. 2.3). These are the *northeast* and *southeast trades.* Someone studying winds within the temperate belt between 30° and 60° latitude would observe that winds blow mainly from the west. These are the *westerlies* of temperate latitudes. At high latitudes, our observer would find that the predominant wind direction is from the east. These are the *polar easterlies.*

Why don't winds move directly north to south? The prevailing winds do not move in a straight north–south direction because of the **Coriolis effect.** In the Northern Hemisphere, the Coriolis effect causes an apparent deflection of winds to the right of their direction of travel and to the left in the Southern Hemisphere. We say "apparent" deflection because we see this deflection only if we make our observations from the surface of the earth. To an observer in space, it would appear that winds

move in approximately a straight line, while the earth rotates beneath them.

Geographic variation in temperature and precipitation is very complex but also very important to the science of ecology. The **distribution** of biomes we discuss in this chapter is substantially influenced by geographic variation in temperature and precipitation. How can we study and represent variation in these climatic variables without being overwhelmed by a mass of numbers? This practical problem is addressed by a visual device called a climate diagram.

Climate Diagrams

Climate diagrams were developed by Heinrich Walter (1985) as a tool to explore the relationship between the distribution of terrestrial vegetation and climate. Climate diagrams summarize a great deal of useful climatic information, including seasonal variation in temperature and precipitation, the length and intensity of wet and dry seasons, and the portion of the year during which average minimum temperature is above and below 0°C.

As shown in figure 2.4, climate diagrams summarize climatic information using a standardized structure. The months of the year are plotted on the horizontal axis, beginning with January and ending with December for locations in the Northern Hemisphere, and beginning with July and ending with June in the Southern Hemisphere. Temperature is plotted on the left vertical axis and precipitation on the right vertical axis. Temperature and precipitation are plotted on different scales so that 10°C is equivalent to 20 mm of precipitation.

Because the temperature and precipitation scales are constructed so that 10°C equals 20 mm of precipitation, the relative positions of the temperature and precipitation lines reflect water availability. In general, adequate moisture for

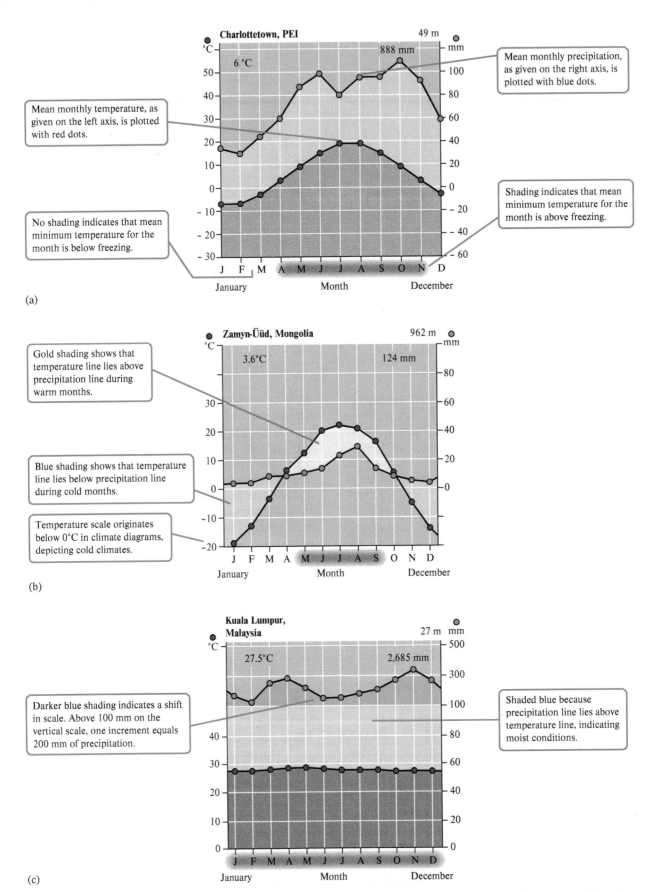

Figure 2.4 (*a*) Climate diagram for Charlottetown, Prince Edward Island, to exemplify the general structure of climate diagrams. (*b*) Climate diagram for a cold desert climate—Zamyn-Üüd, Mongolia. (*c*) Climate diagram for a rain forest climate—Kuala Lumpur, Malaysia.

plant growth exists when the precipitation line lies above the temperature line (fig. 2.4*a*). These moist periods are indicated in the figure by blue shading. When the temperature line lies above the precipitation line, potential evaporation rate exceeds precipitation. These dry periods are indicated by gold shading in the climate diagram. Zamyn-Üüd, Mongolia, is in a cold desert, with mean temperature below freezing from October to April (fig. 2.4*b*). But notice that the gold shading of the climate diagram indicates seasonal drought from April to October, when temperatures are above freezing. The blue shading of the climate diagram for Kuala Lumpur, Malaysia (fig. 2.4*c*), indicates moist conditions year-round. Climate diagrams for wet areas, such as tropical rain forests, compress the precipitation scale for precipitation above 100 mm so that 10°C is equivalent to 200 mm of precipitation. This change in scale is represented by darker shading in the climate diagram for Kuala Lumpur. Notice that the precipitation at Kuala Lumpur exceeds 100 mm during all months of the year.

Climate diagrams also include the mean annual temperature, which is presented in the upper left corner (e.g., 6°C at Charlottetown). The mean annual precipitation (e.g., 2,685 mm at Kuala Lumpur) is presented in the upper right corner of each climate diagram. The elevation of each site, in metres above sea level (e.g., 962 m at Zamyn-Üüd), is also presented in the upper right corner.

As you can see, climate diagrams efficiently summarize important environmental variables. In the following section, we discuss another central aspect of all terrestrial biomes: soil.

CONCEPT 2.1 REVIEW

1. How would seasonality in temperature and precipitation be affected if the earth's rotation on its axis were perpendicular to its plane or orbit about the sun?
2. Why does the annual rainy season in regions near 23° N begin in June?

2.2 Soil: Foundation of Terrestrial Biomes

Soil structure results from the long-term interaction of climate, organisms, topography, and parent mineral material. What is **soil** and why should an ecologist care? It is fair to say that there are few topics that many biology students find less interesting than soils (though decomposition, a topic discussed in chapter 20, is a close second!). An ecologist studies wolves, elk, caribou, and the beauty of the North, right? Yes, some ecologists study those things, and many important questions have been answered. However, none of those things would exist without soil. Soil is a complex mixture of

living and nonliving material upon which most terrestrial life depends. In addition to its importance in sustaining the communities and ecosystems that we can easily see, soils themselves are complex ecological systems. The amount of organic material, living and dead, found in soil is not trivial. In fact, it is estimated that there is more organic carbon stored below ground than above ground (Schimel 1995), leading to the logical conclusion that "the terrestrial world is brown and black, not green" (Wall et al. 2005). Although most students may imagine ecology to be primarily about the study of the charismatic megafauna that you see on nature shows, the reality is that much of what drives the world's systems occurs below our feet. If we want to understand the ecological interactions in communities, or the movement of energy and nutrients within ecosystems, it is critical that ecologists understand what happens below ground at least as well as what happens on the surface. Here we provide an overview of the natural history of soils, including their structure, development, and biodiversity.

From the surface, many soils look quite similar: a dark base covered with a layer of fallen leaves and branches. However, when the soil is broken and a pit is dug, one will typically find differently coloured layers, or horizons, which merge into one another as you dig deeper into the soil (fig. 2.5). At the surface of the soil lies the majority of the organic matter. In Canada, this organic horizon will be called either the O horizon or the LFH horizon. **O (organic) horizons** are found in soils in which the plant material is primarily aquatic (e.g., peat mosses), while **LFH horizons** (litter, fermentation, humus) are generally found in more upland sites. Regardless of the designation, at the surface of the organic horizon you will find freshly fallen organic matter, such as whole leaves, twigs, flowers, and fruits. This organic litter is the food source and home to a wide variety of organisms, and their activity results in the deeper portions of the organic horizon containing highly fragmented and partially decomposed organic matter. Small organic horizons are found in areas with little litter deposition (e.g., deserts and farmland) or high decomposition rates (e.g., tropical rain forests), and deep organic horizons are found in areas with substantial litter inputs and/or low decomposition rates (e.g., bogs and fens).

The **A horizon** contains a mixture of mineral materials, such as clay, silt, and sand, as well as organic material derived from the organic horizon above. The A horizon also supports substantial biological activity, including burrowing animals, such as earthworms, which can mix organic matter from the organic horizon into the A horizon. As a result, the A horizon is generally rich in mineral nutrients, including those essential for plant growth. With rainfall, the A horizon is leached of clays, iron, aluminum, silicates, and **humus** (partially decomposed organic matter), all of which gradually move down through the soil profile into the B horizon.

The **B horizon** contains the materials leached from above, often resulting in a distinctive banding pattern. Below the B horizon is the **C horizon,** consisting of weathered parent material, which has been broken down through the actions of frost, water, microbial activity, and deeply penetrating roots.

LFH Organic horizon. Upper layer contains loose, fragmented plant litter.

LFH or forest floor

A Mineral soil mixed with some organic matter; clay, iron, aluminum, silicates, and soluble organic matter are gradually leached from A horizon.

B Depositional horizon. Materials leached from A horizon are deposited in B horizon. Deposits may form distinctive banding patterns.

C Weathered parent material. The C horizon may include many rock fragments. It often lies on bedrock.

Figure 2.5 Soil profile exposed in a boreal forest site, showing LFH, A, B, and C horizons.
Scott Chang.

This weathering results in the production of the sand, silt, clay, and rock fragments that we generally associate with soils. Under the C horizon, we find unweathered parent material, which is often bedrock.

Although soils appear static, their structure is actually in a constant state of flux due to the interactive actions of climate, organisms, topography, parent material, and time (Jenny 1980). Plants secrete numerous **root exudates,** which, along with the living roots and plant litter, serve as substrates for bacterial, fungal, and animal species. The growth and activity of these organisms provide stability to the mineral components of the soil, allowing the development and maintenance of complex canals of air spaces and cavities within the soil. Climate affects the rates of weathering of parent materials, leaching of organic and inorganic substances, erosion, and decomposition of organic matter through direct weathering effects. Climate can also alter decomposition by directly impacting the activity of soil organisms, as well as indirectly altering soil activity by influencing the type and amount of plant species that can grow in a given area.

Soil is a complex and dynamic entity. It forms the medium in which organisms grow, and the activities of those organisms, in turn, affect soil structure. As with many aspects of ecology, it is often difficult to separate organisms from their environment. The biome discussions that follow provide additional information on soils by including aspects of soil structure and chemistry characteristics of each biome.

CONCEPT 2.2 REVIEW

1. Desert soils and agricultural soils support greatly different amounts of plant growth, but both generally have limited organic layers. Why?
2. Can soils be developed in the absence of plants?

ECOLOGY IN ACTION

Diversity of Soil Organisms

Researchers at Redpath Museum at McGill University are cataloguing the biodiversity of Canada. They have developed a user-friendly Web site (The Canadian Biodiversity Web Site) to help people see the diversity of species found in Canada (Bernhardt 2010). They report that, across the world, up to 1.8 million species (approximately 70,000 in Canada) have been described by scientists, with nearly half being insects. These counts include both terrestrial and aquatic species, though it is generally accepted that there is more species diversity on land than in aquatic systems. Does this mean there are approximately 2 million species on the planet? Absolutely not. Estimates of true global biodiversity range from 2 to 100 million, though all of these are simply educated guesses. Scientists are now realizing how little natural history is actually known, even in our own backyards.

A fundamental goal of ecology is to understand the processes that influence the distribution and abundance of organisms. This knowledge can be used to address a variety of environmental issues that people face throughout the world, such as climate change, controlling the spread of **invasive species,** and trying to integrate agriculture, economic development, human housing, and wilderness within a limited amount of land. However, before we are able to explain patterns of abundance, we must first know the organisms we are studying. In many locations (e.g., North America) and for many groups (e.g., birds and mammals), species are so well studied that researchers are unlikely to ever know someone who has identified a new species, let alone find one themselves. However, the natural history of locations with high species diversity, such as tropical forests, is generally poorly documented, and many (non-vertebrate) species remain to be described by scientists.

For those of us with more modest budgets, and for those who want to find a very large number of new species, the answer will be much closer to home. In fact, large amounts of undescribed biodiversity are literally underneath your feet. Soils are the "poor man's tropical rainforest" (Usher et al. 1979), home to countless numbers of fungi, bacteria, micro- and mesofauna, algae, bryophytes, and other types of organisms. The diversity of these systems is staggering, with many more species unidentified than there are identified (fig. 2.6). The relatively small size and subterranean habitat of these organisms have greatly impeded efforts at identifying and understanding the ecology of soils. Only recently have ecologists appreciated that our lack of knowledge of the most basic natural history of these groups of organisms may be a serious impediment to understanding how natural systems function.

For example, the activity of these soil organisms strongly influences the rates of carbon and nutrient cycling, soil respiration, and the transfer of nutrients to vascular plants. They also provide food and habitat for larger organisms and are key to the development of soil structure. Although our understanding of exactly how these processes emerge from the complex web of soil interactions is still limited, it is very clear that changes in composition of communities of soil organisms is likely to alter the efficiency of these processes. For example, Dennis Parkinson of the University of Calgary has shown that the introduction of the earthworm, *Dendrobaena octaedra,* to boreal forest soils alters fungal biodiversity and plant growth (Scheu and Parkinson 1994; McLean and Parkinson 2000). Such changes can have significant impacts on a variety of issues of concern to people, including carbon sequestration, primary production, litter buildup, and nutrient leaching. As you will see throughout this book, human activities are changing the composition of species in communities across the planet, with unknown consequences for ecological functioning.

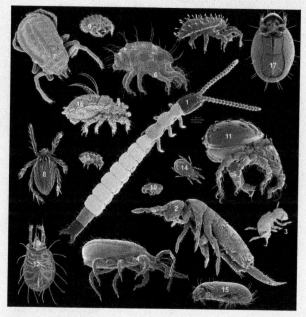

Figure 2.6   A diversity of species live within the soil, the ecology of which remains to be explored. Shown are species of arthropods from the following taxa: 1. Diplura (Japygidae); 2. Collembola (Entomobryidae); 3. Collembola (Neelidae); 4–17 Acari: 4. Mesostigmata (Ologamasidae); 5. Mesostigmata (Zerconidae); 6. Prostigmata (Stigmaeidae); 7. Prostigmata (Labidostomatidae); 8. Prostigmata (Trombiculidae); 9. Endeostigmata (Terpnacaridae); 10. Endeostigmata (Nanorchestidae); 11. Oribatida (Hermanniidae); 12. Oribatida (Phenopelopidae); 13. Oribatida (Brachychthoniidae); 14. Oribatida (Suctobelboideae); 15. Oribatida (Lohmanniidae); 16. Oribatida (Cosmochthoniidae); 17. Oribatida (Phthiracaroidea). These species include predators (1, 4, 5, 6, 7), microbivores/detritivores (2, 3, 10, 13–17), parasites (8), and fungivores (9, 11, 12).
David Walter.

2.3 Terrestrial Biomes

The geographic distribution of terrestrial biomes corresponds closely to variation in climate, especially prevailing temperature and precipitation. In this section, we discuss the climate, soils, and organisms of some of the earth's major biomes and how they have been influenced by humans. However, don't be concerned if you know of some places that do not quite fit any of the biomes discussed. Dividing the world into biomes is a subjective process, and biomes are not truly distinctive entities. Instead they change gradually along environmental gradients, and unique geography can result in disjunct distributions. Even within a large biome, such as the boreal forest, no two locations will be exactly alike. Because of this variability, not all ecologists will agree on whether there are 7, 17, or 27 biomes. In the interest of space (and in the interest of maintaining your interest), we will not cover all terrestrial biomes in detail. Here we present the four major biomes prevalent in Canada: tundra, boreal forest, temperate forest, and temperate grassland. We encourage you to consult other sources to learn more about other biomes not covered herein.

High resolution satellite imagery can be used to map vegetation and to identify biomes (fig. 2.7a). In mapping biomes, as presented in the figure, we are typically considering their

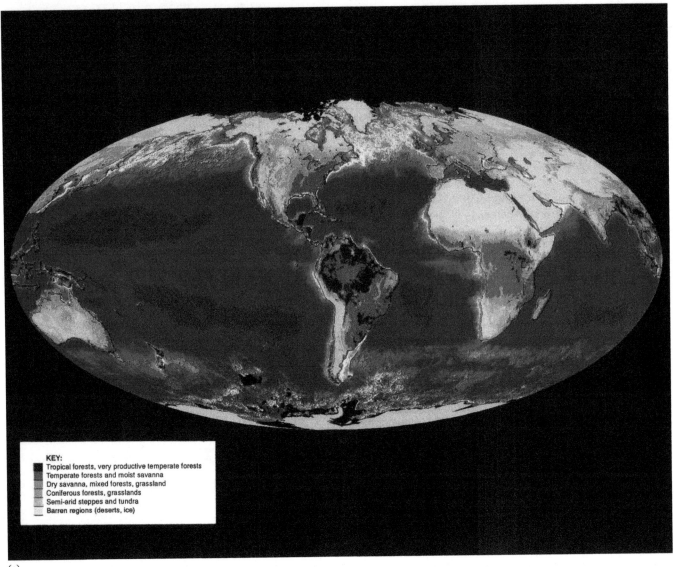

KEY:
Tropical forests, very productive temperate forests
Temperate forests and moist savanna
Dry savanna, mixed forests, grassland
Coniferous forests, grasslands
Semi-arid steppes and tundra
Barren regions (deserts, ice)

(a)

Figure 2.7   (*a*) Variation in climatic conditions results in geographic variation in the distribution of biome types across the planet.

(a) NASA

(Continued)

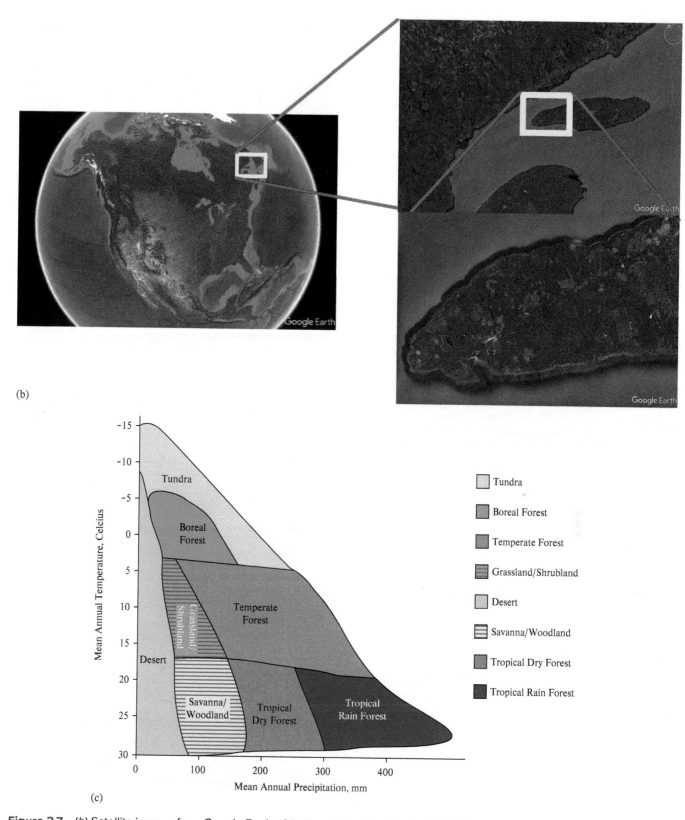

(b)

(c)

Figure 2.7 (*b*) Satellite images from Google Earth of Anticosti Island, QC, in the Gulf of St. Lawrence, at different levels of spatial resolution. (*c*) The distribution of terrestrial biomes can be largely described by differences in precipitation and temperature. You will note that the specific types of biomes described by Whittaker (and presented here) differ slightly from those found in 2.7*a*.

(b) © Google Earth; (c) Modified from Whittaker 1975.

distribution at a regional scale. Of course, at a finer scale, local landscape features and land use can create a patchwork of vegetation types within a larger regional biome type, as illustrated by images of the western end of Anticosti Island, QC, shown at different levels of spatial resolution (fig 2.7b).

What determines where the different biomes are located? The answer to this is simple: "nearly everything," as you will see in subsequent chapters of the book. However, for now we follow the lead of ecologists in the early twentieth century, who often focused on how climate and soils influence the distribution of vegetation. One of the most influential depictions of climate–biome relationships was provided by Robert Whittaker (Whittaker 1975; fig. 2.7c). In viewing Whittaker's diagram in figure 2.7c, it is important to recognize that biome boundaries are fairly subjective; the value of the diagram lies in the presentation of general concepts rather than a precise representation of boundaries defined by precipitation/mean temperature combinations.

Tundra

Beginning in the north, we find an open landscape dotted with small ponds and laced with clear streams (fig. 2.8). This is the **tundra**—covering most of the land north of the Arctic Circle (fig. 2.9). If it is summer and surface soils have thawed, your walk across the tundra might be cushioned by a mat of lichens and mosses, although you might occasionally sink into thick, soggy accumulations of peat. The air will be filled with the cries of nesting birds that visit during the brief summer, feeding upon their plant and animal prey whose populations explode for a very brief time.

The tundra's plant community is shaped by a cold climate with often fierce winds and a short summer, and by soils rich in organic matter, which are frozen much of the year. The cold temperatures mean that even the little precipitation that falls will exceed evaporation, leaving a soggy landscape in summer. The tundra is dominated by a patchwork of herbaceous plants, especially grasses, sedges, and mosses that can take advantage of the short growing season and moist soils. These plants are perennial and slow-growing, with nearly all of the living biomass below ground. They tend to be very short with strong stems, able to withstand the winds of the north. Lichens, associations of fungi and algae, are also abundant, along with some woody vegetation, including dwarf willows and birches and low-growing shrubs.

Figure 2.8   The tundra at the base of the Ogilvie mountains in Tombstone Territorial Park, Yukon, consists primarily of low-growing mosses, lichens, perennial herbaceous plants, and shrubs.
© Cliff LeSergent/Alamy.

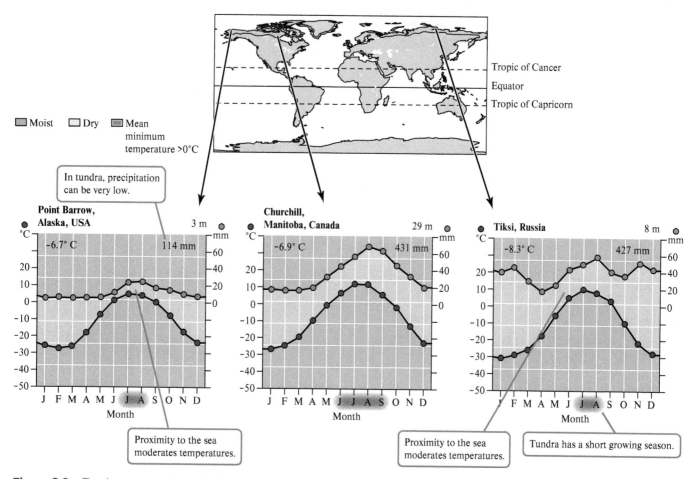

Figure 2.9 Tundra geography and climate.

The tundra is one of the last biomes on Earth that supports substantial numbers of large native mammals, including caribou, reindeer, muskox, bear, and wolves. Small mammals, such as arctic fox, weasel, lemming, and ground squirrel, are also abundant. Resident birds, such as the ptarmigan and snowy owl, are joined each summer by a host of migratory bird species. Insects, although not as diverse as in biomes farther south, are abundant. Each summer, swarms of mosquitoes and other insects emerge from the many tundra ponds and streams.

Soil building is slow in the cold tundra climate. Because rates of decomposition are low, organic matter accumulates in deposits of peat and humus. Surface soils thaw each summer but are often underlain by **permafrost** that may be many metres thick. Permafrost is a layer of soil that remains frozen even during the summer months.

Boreal Forest

The **boreal forest,** or **taiga,** is a world of wood and water that covers over 11% of the earth's land area. This biome stretches from Scandinavia, across Russia, to central Alaska and Canada in a band between 50° and 65° N latitude (fig. 2.10). In places, the trees are so close together you can barely walk through them (fig. 2.11). In other places, the forest is open and you can wander wherever you like on its soft floor of needles and duff. In

sunny patches in the forest, you will find berry bushes of many varieties, where wildlife and people alike pause and snack. A trek through a boreal forest eventually leads to the edge of a lake, river, fen, or bog, where shade and cover give way to light and space. Along the lake margins grow willows and plants that require lots of light for growth and reproduction.

The vegetation of boreal forests is shaped by a climate with winters that are usually longer than six months and summers too short to support temperate forest tree species. Precipitation in the boreal forest is moderate. Yet, because of low temperatures and long winters, evaporation rates are low, and drought is infrequent or brief. When droughts do occur, however, forest fires can burn vast areas of boreal forest.

Generally, the boreal forest is dominated by evergreen conifers, such as spruce, fir, and pines. Larch, a deciduous conifer, dominates in the most extreme Siberian climates. Deciduous aspen and birch trees grow throughout the Canadian boreal forests and may be dominant during the early stages of recovery following fire. Willows grow along the shores of rivers and lakes. Along the base of most trees and on the forest floor lies a lush carpet of mosses and other non-vascular plants. These plants trap much of the rainfall and are home to a large diversity of insects and other organisms. Between the moss and canopy layers, the forest is fairly open with little herbaceous vegetation under the often thick forest canopy.

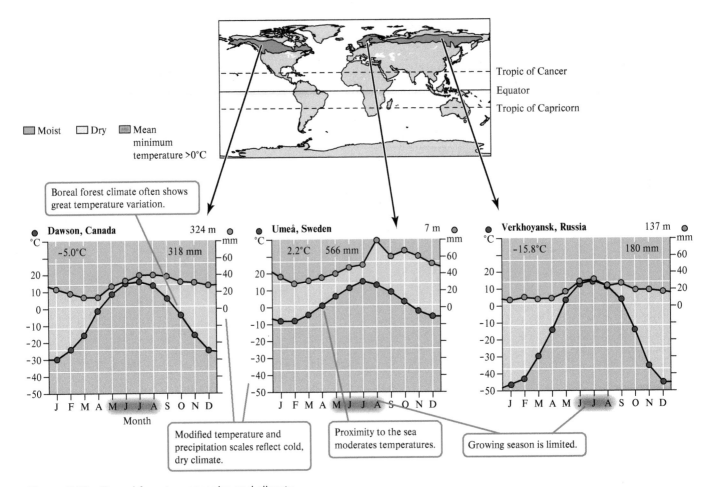

Figure 2.10 Boreal forest geography and climate.

Figure 2.11 Boreal forests, such as this one in Kluane National Park, Yukon, are dominated by a few species of conifer trees.
Stefan Wackerhagen/Getty Images.

Boreal forest soils are highly variable. Decomposition of conifer needles makes soil acidic. In some areas, soils are thin with low fertility; in other areas, they have thick organic layers of high fertility. Low temperatures and low pH typically slow down further decomposition of plant litter. Typically, nutrients are tied up in a thick layer of plant litter that carpets the forest floor, and the plants are adapted to low nutrient availability. Most trees in boreal forests have a dense network of shallow roots that, along with associated mycorrhizal fungi, tap directly into the nutrients bound up in this litter layer.

Scattered throughout much of the boreal forests of the world are large expanses of bogs and fens. These areas have waterlogged "soils," with islands of vascular plants centred around a few trees and shrubs. They are home to countless species, including many plants that feed upon the insects they capture with their leaves. The boreal forest is the winter home of migratory caribou and reindeer and the year-round home of moose and woodland bison. Wolves and bear are major predators of the boreal forest, and many smaller mammals, such as lynx, wolverine, snowshoe hare, porcupines, and red squirrels, also live in boreal forests. Moreover, the boreal forest is the nesting habitat for many birds that migrate from the tropics each spring and is the year-round home of other birds, such as crossbills and spruce grouse.

Temperate Forest

Old-growth **temperate forest** (fig. 2.12) contains the largest living organisms on Earth, perhaps the largest that have ever lived: the sequoias of western North America and the giant

Figure 2.12 Old-growth redwood forest in western North America. Redwoods are the tallest trees in the world, with some individual trees growing to heights of over 100 m.
Pixtal/AGE Fotostock.

Eucalyptus trees of southern Australia. Enter the subdued light of this cool, moist realm, this world of mushrooms and decaying leaves, and feel yourself shrink before the giants of the living world. At dusk in the heart of an old-growth forest, it is easy to understand how cultures around the earth came to make the temperate forest the haunt of diverse mythical creatures, such as the nymphs and elves of European folk tales.

Temperate forest can be found between 30° and 55° latitude (fig. 2.13). In Asia, temperate forest originally covered much of Japan, eastern China, Korea, and eastern Siberia. In western Europe, temperate forests extended from southern Scandinavia to northwestern Iberia and from the British Isles through eastern Europe. North American temperate forests are found from the Atlantic sea coast to the Great Plains and reappear on the West Coast as temperate coniferous forests that extend from northern California through southeastern Alaska. In the Southern Hemisphere, temperate forests are found in southern Chile, New Zealand, and southern Australia.

The plant communities in temperate forests are shaped by moderate to high precipitation, providing moist soils during a relatively long growing season. Temperate forests may be either coniferous or deciduous. Deciduous trees usually dominate where the growing season is moist and at least four months long. Although snowfall may be heavy, winters in deciduous forests are relatively mild. Where winters are more severe or the summers drier, conifers are more abundant. The temperate coniferous forests of the Pacific Coast of North America receive most of their precipitation during fall, winter, and spring and are subject to summer drought. Plant communities are also shaped by soils. Temperate forest soils are usually fertile, particularly in deciduous forests. Soils here are generally neutral or slightly acidic and rich in both organic matter and inorganic nutrients. A rich community of microorganisms is active in the relatively warm and moist soils of deciduous forests, efficiently recycling nutrients from decaying organic matter.

If you ever walk in a mature temperate forest, you will see many different herbaceous plants and trees. The diversity of plants found in temperate forests is high compared with boreal forests and tundra, and although the diversity is lower than that of tropical forests, the forest biomass in temperate forests can be as great or greater. You will be struck by just how thick the plant growth is, with herbs and trees of all different heights completely filling the space. The wide open space between the ground cover and the canopy that you would see in a boreal forest is not evident here. Starting at ground level, you will find the herb layer. Above the herb layer is a layer of shrubs and saplings, then shade-tolerant understorey trees, and finally the canopy, formed by the largest trees. Young saplings of canopy trees have no immediate hope of reaching the canopy high above. Many species will have a "sapling bank," with individual plants staying under 1 m in height for decades. When an opening appears in the canopy, these saplings will grow rapidly to fill the space.

The vertical structure in a temperate forest creates diverse habitat and resources for other forest dwellers. Birds, mammals, and insects make use of all layers of the forest from beneath the forest floor to above the canopy. Small arboreal mammals, such as deer mice, tree squirrels, and flying squirrels, use the tree canopy. Other mammals, such as deer, bear, and fox, live on the forest floor. Bats and other animals find homes inside cavities of large trees; still others burrow into the rich forest soil. But the most important consumers of all are the fungi and bacteria, largely unnoticed members of entirely different kingdoms. They, along with a diversity of microscopic invertebrate animals, consume the large quantities of wood stored on the forest floor. The activities of these organisms recycle nutrients, a process upon which the function of the entire forest depends. Thus, the temperate forest, realm of the giants of the biosphere, emerges as a partnership of the great and the very small.

Temperate Grassland

In their original state, **temperate grasslands** extended unbroken over vast areas (fig. 2.14). Nothing other than the open sea feels quite like standing in the middle of unobstructed prairie, under a dome of blue sky. Early visitors from

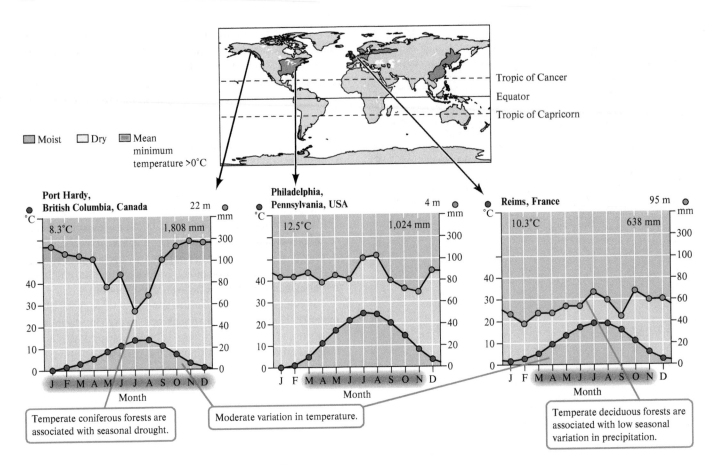

Moist   Dry   Mean minimum temperature >0°C

Port Hardy, British Columbia, Canada   22 m   8.3°C   1,808 mm

Philadelphia, Pennsylvania, USA   4 m   12.5°C   1,024 mm

Reims, France   95 m   10.3°C   638 mm

Temperate coniferous forests are associated with seasonal drought.

Moderate variation in temperature.

Temperate deciduous forests are associated with low seasonal variation in precipitation.

Figure 2.13   Temperate forest geography and climate.

(a)
(b)

Figure 2.14   (*a*) Pronghorn, native grazers of the temperate grasslands of North America. (*b*) Badlands region of southeastern Alberta, Canada.

(a) Rinusbaak/Dreamstime.com/Getstock.com; (b) Darcy C. Henderson.

forested Europe and eastern North America often referred to the prairie in the American Midwest as a "sea of grass." In a spring crossing of this sea on their "prairie schooners" (wagons), these visitors would have seen, among the grasses, showy anemones, sunflowers, prairie smoke, and dozens of other wildflowers (fig. 2.15). They would also have seen great herds of bison and pronghorn that roamed the prairies,

grazing the grasses and, in the process, maintaining the characteristic vegetation.

The temperate grassland is the largest biome in North America and is even more extensive in Eurasia (fig. 2.16). In North America, the prairies of the Great Plains extend from southern Canada to the Gulf of Mexico and from the Rocky Mountains to the deciduous forests of the east. In Eurasia, the

Figure 2.15 Large numbers of plant species can flower at once in this prairie grassland.
© Fallsview|Dreamstime.com.

and annual temperature. However, temperate grasslands are found in regions that are generally drier than those supporting temperate forest, and they experience droughts that may persist for several years. These episodic droughts, along with periodic fires and the pressures of grazing by large herbivores, limit trees and shrubs to the edges of lakes and rivers or to low-lying wet areas. Adaptations to the stresses of drought, grazing, and fire have resulted in herbaceous plant communities that allocate much of their energy and growth to below ground biomass. Temperate grassland plant communities are also shaped by their soils. The most productive soils are deep, basic or neutral, and fertile, and contain large quantities of organic matter. The organic-rich black prairie soils of North America and Eurasia are famous as being among the most fertile soils in the world.

Temperate grasslands once supported huge herds of roving herbivores: bison and pronghorns in North America, and wild horses and saiga antelope in Eurasia. Like fishes in the open sea, the herbivores of the open grassland banded together in social groups; their attendant predators, the steppe and prairie wolves, banded together as well. North American prairies were also the historical home of the grizzly bear. However, human pressures have pushed these animals into the mountains. In many of the grasslands of the world, animals built for speed no longer have great predators from which they need to flee. The smaller animals, such as grasshoppers and mice, inconspicuous among the

temperate grassland biome forms a virtually unbroken band from eastern Europe all the way to eastern China. In the Southern Hemisphere, temperate grassland occurs in Argentina, Uruguay, southern Brazil, New Zealand, and Australia.

Temperate grasslands are found at latitudes similar to temperate forests, so they have comparable growing season length

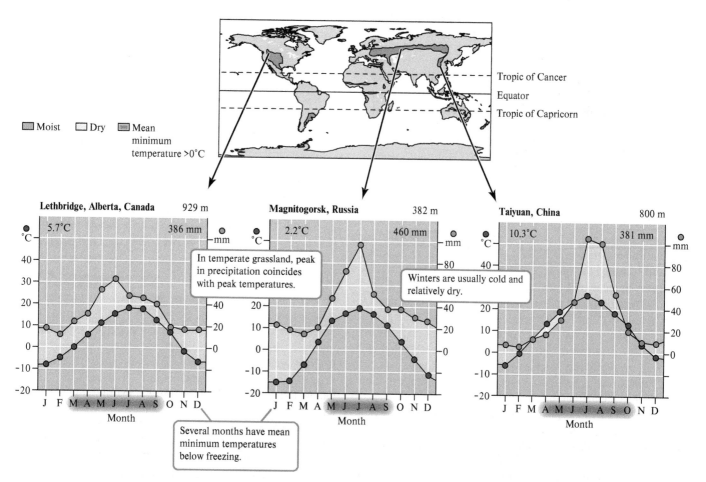

Figure 2.16 Temperate grassland distribution and climate.

herbaceous vegetation, continue to be even more numerous than the large herbivores. Grassland animals of intermediate size generally have one of two lifestyles: there are the burrowing, including the badger and prairie dog, and the fleet, such as the swift fox and prairie falcon.

CONCEPT 2.3 REVIEW

1. Compare the biological diversity of Canada's major terrestrial biomes. What factors account for the relative differences among these biomes?

2. Why are soils in boreal forests generally more depleted of nutrients than soils in temperate forests?

3. Why do biomes differ in the relative amount of plant biomass that is found below ground? Why is most biomass in tundra and grasslands below ground?

2.4 Human-Dominated Systems

Human activities (e.g., agriculture and city building) modify climate and biomes' structure, soil, and hydrology, reshaping biological communities. Patterns of human settlement largely follow resource abundance. People have settled where there is available food, water, and a suitable climate, and—later—access to trade routes. Not surprisingly, the most densely settled areas tend to be those with climates and soils suitable for agriculture (or at least initially suitable). Most often, these areas are located in just a few of the major global biomes. For example, Toronto, Tokyo, Beijing, Moscow, Warsaw, Berlin, Paris, London, New York, Washington (DC), Boston, Chicago, and Vancouver all have in common that they grew in areas that were once temperate forests. Figure 2.17 shows a frequency distribution of the 100 largest global urban centres, based on mean annual rainfall and mean annual temperature. With a few exceptions, these megacities developed in what were woodland (primarily temperate and tropical dry forests) and grasslands biomes. Globally, the impacts of urban and attendant agricultural development are generally greatest in these biomes.

Today, more than 80% of Canadians live in urban areas, with nearly 60% in large cities (100,000 people or more). Globally, more than half of us live in urban areas, and this is expected to reach two out of three of us by 2050. Migration of people from rural areas to urban centres, coupled with overall population growth, may add another 2 to 3 billion people to the global urban population in the next four decades.

Between 35% and 40% of the earth's land surface is used in agriculture, including crops and pasture or range lands. Much of Canada is not suited for agriculture, and only about 7% of the land surface is in agricultural use. Most of this occurs in two ecozones: (1) the Prairies of southern Alberta, Saskatchewan, and Manitoba; and (2) the Mixedwood Plains, a narrow band

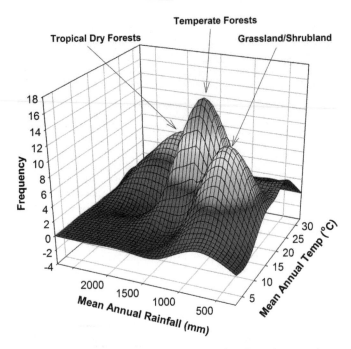

Figure 2.17 Frequency distribution of major urban centres based upon mean annual rainfall and precipitation.

of land along the northern Great Lakes and St. Lawrence River. Not surprisingly, nine of the ten largest urban centres in Canada also lie within these two ecozones.

Urban and agricultural ecosystems are not biomes. However, there are some general characteristics of each type of system in terms of dominant plant communities and productivity, as well as hydrologic cycle, nutrient cycles, and climate (or microclimate). We discuss some of these generalities of urban and agricultural systems here, and how they modify the characteristics ascribed to different biomes in section 2.3. We also introduce these systems here to establish that although human dominated, these are ecological systems, shaped by climate and history (natural and human) and are not apart from ecological theory. Ecology matters, whether we live in city centres or rural areas. Urban and agricultural systems can be better understood when viewed through an ecology lens. Ecological tools can help address many of the challenges we face globally and in our own neighbourhoods.

Urban Ecosystems

Living things are affected by their environments and can, in turn, modify their environments. Humans do this at a scale unlike other animals as a function of both our population size and our ingenuity, modifying land surfaces and waterways. These modifications are not always positive, however. In a dense urban setting, there may be few remnants to remind us of the natural biome from which the city was carved (fig. 2.18). Moreover, the remnants that do remain may be patchy. In clearing land and replacing native plants with built structures, we reduce ecosystem productivity (chapter 19), reduce food and habitat for animals, and simplify community structure (chapter 16). We remove plants and animals and replace them with other, often non-native, plants and animals. These may escape and cause damage

Figure 2.18 Calgary skyline with fragments of urban forest in the foreground.
MaksiMages/Shutterstock.com.

to natural ecosystems (chapter 23). Patchy habitats are poor for many species (chapter 21); however, other native and non-native species may exploit the edges of fragmented habitats. Some will tolerate low-quality habitat provided there is a trade-off, such as less competition or abundant food (chapter 13). Consider herring gulls, which evolved to exploit shoreline habitats and to eat aquatic invertebrates and small fish. These would never be common in a hardwood forest's bird community, but they thrive as dumpster-diving scavengers in cities built within these biomes, trading crustaceans for hot dogs and fries (fig. 2.19).

Urbanization can alter local climate. The loss of dominant trees and grasses can reduce evaporative cooling (chapter 6), while the increase in built structures can result in increased absorption of solar radiation and re-radiation of heat (urban heat island effect). Conversely, cities built in deserts may have more large trees and grasses than would be found in surrounding natural ecosystems, resulting in lower localized temperatures at the urban centre (oasis effect).

Drainage of wetlands and burial, or channelization of streams, simplifies drainage networks and reduces the capacity of these systems to store water and remove pollutants (chapter 3).

Figure 2.19 Gulls scavenging for food in a parking lot. These birds have been able to tolerate the urban environment and exploit new food resources, becoming dominant members of many urban bird communities.
Andrew Laursen.

Increased hardscape, such as asphalt, reduces percolation of rainfall to groundwater. Together, these effects of city building make them prone to flooding; and nearby bodies of water, vulnerable to pollution. Consider the massive floods that struck Calgary and southern Alberta in July 2013 and the Toronto area the following summer. When it rains in the city, streets flood as water quickly finds the lowest spot. Channelized streams may overflow, sewers and other infrastructure may be overwhelmed, and large volumes of water collecting the city's myriad wastes flow quickly to the nearest body of water.

Despite the many common patterns we see in urban development related to plant community structure, climate, and hydrologic cycle, the urban environment cannot be considered a unique biome; the ecology of cities is still largely influenced by the larger scale climatic patterns. Rather, the city is a landscape that overlays and modifies the ecology of its biome.

Agricultural Ecosystems

Development of agriculture runs parallel with urban development. Often the land originally cleared and modified for growing crops or grazing livestock becomes subsumed by the growing population it supports (fig 2.20). A major functional difference is that in a city, vegetation is removed and replaced by built structures, concrete, and asphalt. In agricultural areas, plants are removed and replaced with different plants. Where cities are less productive ecosystems than those they replace, agricultural lands may be more productive (i.e., higher net primary production) since the continual harvesting and replanting keeps the ecosystem in an artificially early development or successional stage (see chapter 18). This production is further enhanced by the use of fertilizer to stimulate crop growth. When natural lands are converted to agriculture, plant communities become less diverse and habitat becomes simplified, supporting a less diverse animal community (chapter 18). This lack of diversity may be reinforced through the use of herbicides to suppress competing plant species and through the use of insecticides to reduce insect populations.

Fertilizers applied to crops to stimulate growth can alter the biogeochemical cycles of agricultural ecosystems (chapter 19), increasing carbon fixation (plant production). Some of the excess nitrogen that is not taken up by crops can be converted to nitrous oxide, a potent greenhouse gas. Some of the unused N and P from fertilizer is lost from agricultural soil with rain or wind-blown dust. These same nutrients that stimulate crop growth can stimulate growth of algae and cyanobacteria in water. With the introduction of commercial fertilizers to North American agriculture, harmful algal and cyanobacterial blooms became a

Figure 2.20   An areal view of farmland in Illinois, with the growing city of Dubuque, Iowa, in the background.
Aaron Roeth Photography.

pervasive problem. The Great Lakes, in particular, experienced severe blooms that were a major trigger for the establishment of the Freshwater Institute in Canada (chapter 1) and the the Environmental Protection Agency in the U.S., through the United States Clean Water Act. In agricultural landscapes, stream channels are often modified to drain wet areas more rapidly. The straightening and shortening of stream channels may contribute to the export of nutrients to lakes and coastal ecosystems since doing so reduces the opportunities for biological processes to trap nutrients in the stream and to remove them through processes such as burial and denitrification (chapter 20).

Hydrological cycles can also be disrupted where the demand for water to irrigate crops outstrips its natural supply through rain, snow, and groundwater recharge. Water for irrigation may be supplied by surface water or groundwater sources, but exploitation of these resources can exacerbate droughts and put agriculture in direct conflict with other interests, such as cities, that also need water. In extreme cases, the redirection of water from rivers for agriculture can leave downstream communities and ecosystems starved of water. The Colorado River provides a stark example. In 1922, Aldo Leopold described "awesome jungles" and "lovely groves" in the Colorado Delta at the Sea of Cortez, Mexico. But the diversion of water to support agriculture in California's dry Central Valley and the growing population in the U.S. Southwest have left a trickle of water in the Colorado River as it enters Mexico (fig. 2.21). In 2014, a water-sharing pact between the United States and Mexico allowed the river to reach its delta for the first time since 1998, but efforts to restore the delta and riparian vegetation are in jeopardy until a political and social will to develop a longer term water-sharing solution emerges. Such a solution will require a reappraisal of the urban and agricultural ecological systems in the U.S. Southwest and of how to better manage those systems for water conservation.

Human Impacts on Biomes

Human settlement has placed a heavy burden on all major biomes, but the footprint has been particularly large in woodlands and grasslands. Ancient temperate forests have largely fallen before axe and saw, clearing the way for fields and cities. Where forest stands remain, they are generally younger and less biologically and structurally complex. Tree plantations, for example, have largely replaced the ancient Black Forest of central Europe. The forests that covered most of the eastern half of North America are largely gone, and fierce conflicts exist among disparate interests over the fate of the remaining 1%–2% of old-growth forests in western North America. An encouraging sign for preservation is that many temperate deciduous forests are

Figure 2.21   Colorado River at its delta in Sonora, Mexico. In 2014, water reached the mouth of the river for the first time in 16 years.

Pete Mcbride/Getty Images.

able to recover following years of logging and agriculture. As well, much of eastern North America has seen an increase in new growth forest cover over the last several decades as old and unproductive agricultural fields have been abandoned.

Intensive settlement and agricultural development over a period of centuries have whittled away at tropical dry forests. Extensive clearing for agriculture has reduced the natural forest in Central America and Mexico to less than 2% of its former area. People have replaced tropical dry forests with cattle ranches, grain farms, and cotton fields. Similarly, a long history of dense human settlements has left a mark on **Mediterranean woodlands and shrublands.** For example, the open oak woodlands of southern Spain and Portugal are the product of an agricultural management system that is thousands of years old, with little trace of the area's natural plant community.

The extent of agricultural development in North America and throughout the world has left grasslands among the most critically endangered biomes. The natural vegetation of grasslands is often a product of fire and grazing by large mammals. The first human populations in grasslands were nomadic hunters. On the savannas, humans first learned to use, make, and control fire. Eventually, they began to deliberately set fires, maintaining and spreading savannas. This use of fire enabled a shift from subsistence by hunting and gathering to pastoralism, a pattern repeated in other grassland ecosystems. Later came the ranchers and the farmers. Ranching exploits the grasslands for grazing by livestock, replacing the natural community of grazing beasts with their domesticated relations. Ranching maintains grasslands, but suppression of fire and different grazing patterns by domesticated animals result in ecosystems with very different plant communities and ecological properties than the native grasslands they replace. Farmers, with their plows, broke the sod and tapped into fertile soils built up over thousands of years. Under the plow, temperate grasslands have produced some of the most fertile farmlands on the earth and fed much of the world. However, continuous agriculture has caused the loss of as much as 35% to 40% of the organic matter in the soils. The more arid grasslands, with their frequent droughts, do not appear capable of supporting farming indefinitely without extensive irrigation. The future of agriculture in temperate grasslands hinges on unanswered questions: Can the losses of organic matter and nutrients be reversed? What level of agricultural production can be sustained over the long term? Unfortunately, development in grasslands is often "invisible" to the average citizen, as many of us grew up viewing grasslands as the place for farms and ranches, rather than as a wild and intact natural region.

The human enterprise creates additional demands and burdens that are borne by other biomes. Sure, we hear about this, but the biomes affected are mostly out of sight and out of mind for urban dwellers in once-upon-a-time forests, so the impacts go largely unnoticed (or unfelt).

Old growth trees in both boreal forests and tropical rain forests are being harvested to meet growing demand for wood products. In many areas, these biomes also have the misfortune of overlying rich mineral and hydrocarbon deposits, placing new pressures on the forest, stemming from tremendous potential economic gain. For example, Alberta currently has allowed oil sand mining in about 3,000 km^2 of boreal forest. However, deeper deposits occur in over 125,000 km^2, raising the potential for extensive deforestation and development. Destruction of these systems is a tragedy for people living within them, who are experiencing the degradation of land and water, as well as the loss of livelihoods and culture. Their destruction is also a serious misfortune for the global human population. Many of the world's staple foods, including maize (called corn in North America and Australia), rice, bananas, and sugar cane, and approximately 25% of all prescription drugs were originally derived from tropical plants. Many more species, directly useful to humans, may await discovery. In addition, the tropics continue to harbour important genetic varieties of domesticated plant species.

In the past, human presence in the tundra was largely limited to small populations of hunters and nomadic herders. Recently, however, human development has increased markedly, with intense exploration and extraction of oil, natural gas, and a variety of minerals, such as diamonds. An equally pressing concern in the North is the impact of rapidly rising temperatures on the permafrost and on rates of decomposition. Because of patterns of global air and ocean circulation, areas of arctic tundra are rapidly warming. Although this is a general global concern, the deep expanses of permafrost in the Arctic raise a unique concern within the tundra biome. As permafrost melts, the rich organic material it contains becomes available to soil microbes for decomposition, potentially releasing enormous amounts of CO_2 into the atmosphere, amplifying the greenhouse effect and global warming. The exact extent to which this will occur is still unclear, in large part because of the difficulties in working in the North and because of our general lack of understanding of the ecology of soils. Such concerns make it clear that human activity can have significant impacts on even the most isolated of regions on the planet. The ecological responses that occur as a result of human activities can in turn have dramatic consequences for humans across the planet. Recent discoveries of large tracts of oil and natural gas in the far North, along with technological developments allowing for more economically viable resource extraction, will ensure increased pressure on the natural environment for generations to come.

Many human cultures have arisen independently in the deserts of North America, Australia, Africa, and Asia. Compared to true desert species, however, humans are profligate water users. Consequently, human populations in desert regions are concentrated around oases and river valleys. Despite natural limitations in water availability, human settlements in deserts frequently display fountains, ancient and modern water diversions, agricultural schemes, and large urban centres complete with artificial lakes and golf courses. When pushed, the desert blooms. Unfortunately, many desert landscapes have been pushed until they now grow little but salt crystals.

CONCEPT 2.4 REVIEW

1. Considering atmospheric circulation patterns and the effects of urbanization on hydrology, why might cities carved out of temperate forest biomes be particularly vulnerable to climate change?

2. Why has agricultural and urban development been more intense in prairies than in boreal forests?

ECOLOGICAL TOOLS AND APPROACHES

Biomes of Canada and Winter Ecology

As we first mentioned in chapter 1, the types of research questions ecologists are able to ask are often limited by the availability of research tools and influenced by different approaches to studying ecology. When new tools are developed, scientists are able to conduct new experiments and once again push back the limits of human understanding. Some of these new tools will involve new laboratory analyses, molecular methods, or remote sensing. Others will be more conceptual, based more upon novel approaches to testing questions. Great advances come when scientists develop new tools and gain new understanding.

Knowledge of natural history is critical to ecology, allowing scientists to have a broader understanding of the system in which they work. Rather than describe the tools needed to learn natural history (time, a notebook, and good binoculars), here we'll discuss how ecologists use knowledge of natural history to describe the ecological landscape of Canada, and how this may influence how ecologists approach their research. We will also discuss an often overlooked aspect of natural history—the winter ecology of species. With changes in global climates, it is becoming more apparent that understanding what species do in winter is going to have important impacts on what happens in the future.

Ecozones of Canada

In this chapter we described how different regions of the planet experience different climates and how this is associated with the development of different biomes. No country contains all of the biomes of the world; instead, each is home to just a few. However, even if a country is home to a single biome, there will still be substantial variation in the distribution of plants and animals across the landscape. No two communities within a single biome will be identical; instead, there is substantial variation in species composition among locations within a single biome. In Canada, this variation has been recognized, and the National Ecological Framework for Canada (Ecological Stratification Working Group 1996) divides Canada not into a small number of biomes but instead into 15 terrestrial (and 5 marine) *ecozones* (fig. 2.22), which are themselves divided into more than 200 *ecoregions*, which can be further divided into *ecodistricts!* The largest level of organization used in Canada, the ecozone, is roughly analogous to the more widely used concept of biomes, with major areas classified based upon dominant vegetation and climate. Ecoregions and ecodistricts allow finer classification, which can be helpful for landscape planning and conservation. Remember, though, that designations of biomes, ecoregions, and ecozones are artificial human constructs that represent tendencies over large geographic regions; they are not accurate information about specific locations. As such, a number of alternative classification systems exist within Canada and around the world (e.g., Biogeoclimatic Ecosystem Classification in British Columbia), with each developed to serve a specific purpose.

In figure 2.22 you can see how the ecozone framework allows for more specificity than the coarse tool of biomes. For example, consider the boreal biome, which would include the boreal shield ecozone, the boreal plain ecozone, and the boreal cordillera ecozone. The boreal shield is the largest ecozone in Canada and is influenced by the underlying bedrock. The boreal plains are considered a different ecozone due to a relative lack of influence by bedrock. These both differ from the boreal cordillera, which has substantial mountainous terrain and is influenced by weather patterns from the Pacific Ocean. These differences have important consequences for the organisms that live within these three zones. An ecologist studying the boreal forest of Canada needs to take into account these differences in topography, soils, and vegetation to understand the ecology of a particular location. These basic differences in natural history can prove to be a critical step to understanding variations in ecological function among communities in a single biome. However, if a single country can have 15 ecozones, you can only imagine how many may be found across the globe, and thus the rough categories of biomes are critical for providing an overview of this variation. For larger scale questions, broad divisions of biomes are helpful; for smaller scale questions, a finer resolution is needed. A critical ecological tool is having the appropriate scale of natural history knowledge necessary to answer your specific ecological question. It is equally critical to recognize that the designations given to an area are generally driven by climatic conditions. As climate changes throughout much of Canada, ecologists expect that there will be shifts in the boundaries of ecoregions throughout the country. For example, the northern limits of the boreal forest are expected to move even further north, and in many places tree and shrub expansion is already occurring. Though these changes are fast relative to historical rates of climatic shifts, they are still slow relative to an individual human lifetime; thus, though ecoregions will eventually need to be redrawn, this is many decades—or centuries—away.

Regardless of whether Canada is divided into a few biomes, more ecozones, or even more ecoregions, one thing is clear: compared to many other areas on the planet, Canada is cold and many areas receive substantial amounts of snow. As a result, one important tool of many Canadian ecologists is an understanding of the natural history of winter. Due to the importance of winter to the organisms that live in Canada, many aspects of winter ecology will be presented throughout the text.

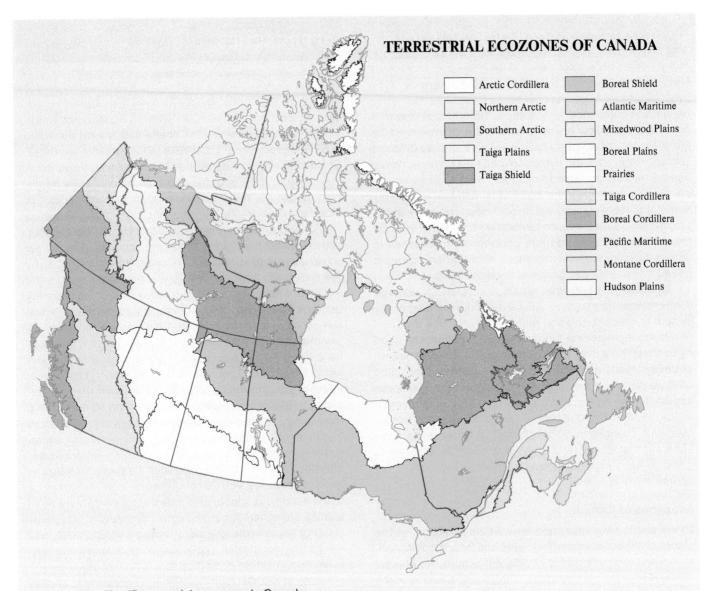

Figure 2.22 The 15 terrestrial ecozones in Canada.

"Ecological Framework," from Atlas of Canada, 6th edition, published by Government of Canada, Natural Resources Canada, 2019. Reproduced with the permission of the Department of Natural Resources, 2019.

SUMMARY

2.1 Uneven heating of the earth's spherical surface by the sun and the tilt of the earth on its axis combine to produce predictable latitudinal variation in climate.

Because the earth is a sphere, the sun's rays are most concentrated at the latitude where the sun is directly overhead. This latitude changes with the seasons because the earth's axis of rotation is not perpendicular to its plane of orbit about the sun but is tilted approximately 23.5° away from the perpendicular. The sun is directly overhead at the Tropic of Cancer, at 23.5° N latitude during the northern summer solstice. During the

northern winter solstice, the sun is directly overhead at the Tropic of Capricorn, at 23.5° S latitude. The sun is directly overhead at the equator during the spring and autumnal equinoxes. During the northern summer, the Northern Hemisphere is tilted toward the sun and receives more solar energy than the Southern Hemisphere. During the northern winter, the Northern Hemisphere is tilted away from the sun and the Southern Hemisphere receives more solar energy.

Heating of the earth's surface and atmosphere drives atmospheric circulation and influences global patterns of precipitation. As the sun heats air at the equator, it expands and rises, spreading northward and southward at high altitudes. This high-altitude air cools as it spreads toward the poles, eventually sinking back to the earth's surface. Rotation of the earth on its axis breaks up atmospheric circulation into six major cells: three in the Northern Hemisphere and three in the Southern Hemisphere. These three circulation cells correspond to the trade winds north and south of the equator, the westerlies between 30° and 60° N or S latitude, and the polar easterlies above 60° latitude. These prevailing winds do not blow directly south because of the Coriolis effect.

As air rises at the tropics it cools, and the water vapour it contains condenses and forms clouds. Precipitation from these clouds produces the abundant rains of the tropics. Dry air blowing across the lands at about 30° latitude produces the great deserts that ring the globe. When warm, moist air flowing toward the poles meets cold polar air, it rises and cools, forming clouds that produce the precipitation associated with temperate environments. Complicated differences in average climate can be summarized using a climate diagram.

Climate affects weathering of parent material, forming the mineral component of soil. Climate also shapes the community of soil organisms, particularly microbes. Collectively, soil organisms, parent mineral material, and climate determine soil structure (fig 2.23).

2.2 Soil structure results from the long-term interaction of climate, organisms, topography, and parent mineral material.

Terrestrial biomes are built upon a foundation of soil, a vertically stratified and complex mixture of living and nonliving material. Most terrestrial life depends on soil, and much life occurs within soil. Soil structure varies continuously in time and space. Soils are generally divided into O (and LFH), A, B, and C horizons. The O and LFH horizons are made up of freshly fallen organic matter, including leaves, twigs, and other plant parts. The A horizon contains a mixture of mineral materials and organic matter derived from the O horizon. The B horizon contains clays, humus, and other materials that have been transported from the A horizon. The C horizon consists of weathered parent material.

2.3 The geographic distribution of terrestrial biomes corresponds closely to variation in climate, especially prevailing temperature and precipitation.

The major terrestrial biomes and climatic regimes found in Canada are as follows: *Tundra:* cold; low precipitation; short, soggy summers; poorly developed soils; permafrost; dominated by low vegetation and a variety of animals adapted to long, cold winters; migratory animals, especially birds, make seasonal use. *Boreal forest:* long, severe winters; climatic extremes; moderate precipitation; infertile soils; permafrost; occasional fire; extensive forest biome, dominated by conifers. *Temperate forest:* moderate, moist winters; warm, moist growing season; fertile soils; high productivity and biomass; dominated by deciduous trees where growing seasons are moist, winters are mild, and soils are fertile; otherwise dominated by conifers. *Temperate grassland:* hot and cold seasons; peak rainfall coincides with growing season; droughts sometimes last several years; fertile soils; fire important to maintaining dominance by grasses; historically inhabited by roving bands of herbivores and predators.

2.4 Human activities (e.g., agriculture and city building) modify climate, biomes' structure, soil, and hydrology, reshaping biological communities.

People have historically settled in areas with agreeable climates and abundant resources. Often, this has meant areas with plenty of rain and lush vegetation to support a diverse biological community. Forests and grasslands have been more extensively modified by conversion to fields and pastures, and by urban

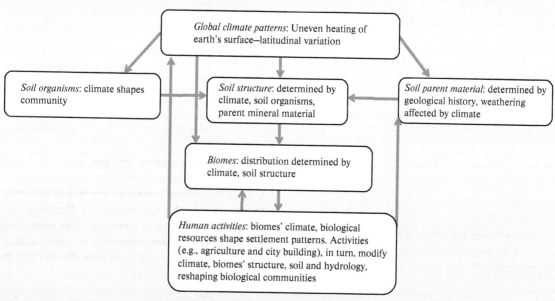

Figure 2.23 Concept map for chapter 2.

development. However, all biomes have been impacted by human development. Tropical rain forests and boreal forests are exploited for timber, and the land beneath is mined for minerals or tapped for oil and gas deposits. Fragile desert and shrubland ecosystems have been used as rangeland for grazing cattle, and the limited water resource has been overtaxed by growing animal and human populations. Arctic tundra is vulnerable to climate change, and carbon stored in frozen soil may be mineralized, releasing CO_2 and methane, creating positive feedback on global warming. The evidence has become more clear that

humans can not only affect the structure of biomes but can also contribute to climate change itself, with feedback on weathering of parent material, community and physical structure of soil, and distribution of the vegetation associated with particular biomes (fig. 2.23). Human-dominated systems, wherever they are located, have some common features: plant communities are simplified, biological diversity is reduced, and hydrology is modified. However, they are still ecological systems, and the lessons drawn from ecology are strongly relevant to the sustainability challenges we face in our cities and on our farms.

REVIEW QUESTIONS

1. Draw a soil profile for the area around your university. Indicate the principal layers, or horizons. Describe the characteristics of each layer.

2. Describe global patterns of atmospheric heating and circulation. What mechanisms produce high precipitation in the tropics? At temperate latitudes? What mechanisms produce low precipitation in the tropics?

3. Use what you know about atmospheric circulation and seasonal changes in the sun's orientation to Earth to explain the highly seasonal precipitation in temperate grasslands. (Hint: Why does most precipitation in this biome come during the summer months?)

4. We focused much of our discussion of biomes on their latitudinal distribution. The reasonably predictable relationship between latitude and temperature and precipitation provides a link between latitude and biomes. Yet temperate grasslands and temperate forests at similar latitudes differ in precipitation and, therefore, vegetation types. What other geographic variable(s), aside from latitude, might affect the distribution of temperature and precipitation and, therefore, of biomes?

5. English and other European languages have terms for four seasons: spring, summer, autumn, and winter. This vocabulary summarizes much of the annual climatic variation at mid-latitudes in temperate regions. Are these four seasons useful for summarizing annual climatic changes across the rest of the globe?

6. Biologists have observed much more similarity in species composition among boreal forests and among areas of tundra in Eurasia and North America than among temperate forests or temperate grasslands around the globe. Can you offer an explanation of this contrast based on the global distributions of these biomes?

7. The use of fire by humans to maintain and extend savanna biomes was our first foray into controlling nature. How was this experiment similar to and different from our foray into agriculture in terms of impacts on natural biomes?

8. Draw a climate diagram for the location of your university. Climate data for Canada can be found at the Environment Canada Web page (http://climate.weather.gc.ca/climate_normals/).

© Norbert Rosing/National Geographic/Getty Images.

CHAPTER 3   LIFE IN WATER

CHAPTER CONCEPTS

The names that people around the world have given to our planet reveal a perspective consistent across cultures. Those names, whether in English (earth), French (*la terre*), Greek (*geos*), or Chinese (*diqiu*), all refer to land or soil, revealing that cultures everywhere hold a land-centred perspective. The Hawaiians, Polynesian inhabitants of the most isolated specks of land on earth, call the planet *ka honua*, an allusion to a level landing place or dirt embankment. The Ojibwe (*aki*) and Mi'kmaq (*Ootsitgamoo*) connote the part of the world on which the people walk.

Yet water lies at the heart of our very identity as Canadians. Canada is surrounded on three sides by oceans and is home to thousands of lakes and streams and vast expanses of wetlands and peatlands. These habitats are a source of beauty and inspiration, of opportunity and utility, of hope and sorrow for the damage done. They permeate our history, from the diverse Indigenous cultures that depended upon fishing or travelled along water routes and built a variety of ingenious water craft; to the French voyageurs; and to later settlers, who built farms and established villages along these same routes. Water and its imagery permeate Canadian culture, from the waterscapes of Group of Seven artists (fig. 3.1) to our music (e.g., Joni Mitchell's "River"). Taking the decidedly long-range view, water also lies in our history as a species. From our perspective as terrestrial organisms, the aquatic realm remains an alien environment governed by unfamiliar rules. Yet life in water is in our very DNA. Or, more accurately, our DNA retains the history of our evolutionary past as denizens of the sea. All major plant and animal phyla (with the exception of Onychophora) evolved in the ocean and later diversified into new flora and fauna, on land and in other aquatic environments. The goal of this chapter is to make this realm more familiar by taking a look at aquatic environments.

Figure 3.1   Lawren S. Harris's *Maligne Lake*.
Maligne Lake, Jasper Park, 1924, Lawren S. Harris, Canadian, 1885–1970, oil on canvas, 122.8 × 152.8 cm, purchased 1928, National Gallery of Canada (no. 3541), © family of Lawren S. Harris.

3.1   The Hydrologic Cycle

The hydrologic cycle exchanges water among reservoirs. Over 70% of the earth's surface is covered by water. The oceans contain over 97% of the water in the biosphere, and the polar ice caps and glaciers contain an additional 2%. Less than 1% is freshwater in rivers, lakes, and actively exchanged groundwater. The situation on Earth is indeed as Samuel Coleridge's ancient mariner saw it: "Water, water, everywhere, nor any drop to drink."

The small amount of freshwater on the planet is not evenly distributed. Nearly 20% is found in Canada, even though Canada contains only 7% of the world's land mass. Across the earth, over 65% of freshwater is found in glaciers and icefields, and nearly 30% is groundwater. This leaves only a very small fraction of the planet's freshwater as surface waters (lakes and streams), upon which we depend. As human populations continue to grow, the demands on existing freshwater reserves also increase, which many places are already beginning to realize. Even in water-rich Canada, freshwater is not unlimited in supply. When we look at the Great Lakes, for example, we might perceive an inexhaustible resource. However, what we are seeing is the stored water; what is not apparent is the relatively slow rate at which this water is replenished.

Water moves among different "reservoirs" (e.g., lakes, rivers, oceans, groundwater, the atmosphere, and even organisms). Water in the different reservoirs is stored for a period of time, and then renewed, or turned over, at different rates. Figure 3.2 summarizes these exchanges of water among reservoirs, which as a whole is called the **hydrologic cycle**. The figure includes volumes of water in each of the reservoirs (km^3) and the rates of exchange of water among reservoirs ($km^3 \, y^{-1}$).

The hydrologic cycle is powered by solar energy, which drives the winds and evaporates water, primarily from the surface of the oceans. Water vapour cools as it rises from the ocean's surface and condenses, forming clouds. These clouds are then blown by solar-driven winds across the planet, eventually yielding rain or snow, the majority of which falls back on the oceans. The water that falls on land may immediately evaporate and re-enter the atmosphere; it may be stored in ice fields and glaciers; it may be consumed by and stored in terrestrial organisms; it may percolate through the soil to become groundwater; or it may end up in lakes and ponds or in streams and rivers and eventually find its way back to the sea.

Reservoirs will be replenished at different rates, and ecologists often measure turnover times: the time required for the entire volume of a particular reservoir to be renewed. Reservoir size and rates of water exchange are two of the main determinants of turnover time; thus, turnover occurs at vastly different rates in the different reservoirs. Water in the atmosphere, for example, turns over about every nine days; a water molecule can expect to remain in the atmosphere only this long before falling as rain, snow, or ice. The renewal time for river water is 12 to 20 days. Lake renewal times are longer, ranging anywhere from days to centuries, depending on the lake's volume and rate of drainage. Renewal time in the Great Lakes, for example, ranges from 2.7 to 173 years (Lakes Erie and Superior, respectively).

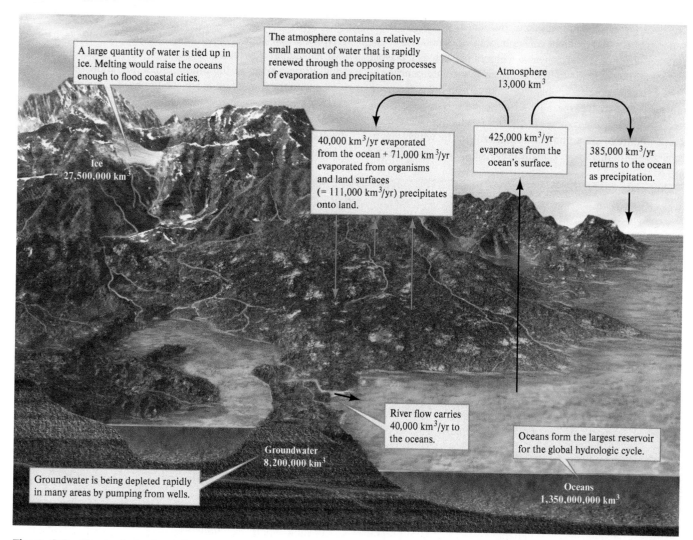

A large quantity of water is tied up in ice. Melting would raise the oceans enough to flood coastal cities.

The atmosphere contains a relatively small amount of water that is rapidly renewed through the opposing processes of evaporation and precipitation.

Atmosphere
13,000 km^3

Ice
27,500,000 km^3

40,000 km^3/yr evaporated from the ocean + 71,000 km^3/yr evaporated from organisms and land surfaces (= 111,000 km^3/yr) precipitates onto land.

425,000 km^3/yr evaporates from the ocean's surface.

385,000 km^3/yr returns to the ocean as precipitation.

River flow carries 40,000 km^3/yr to the oceans.

Oceans form the largest reservoir for the global hydrologic cycle.

Groundwater
8,200,000 km^3

Groundwater is being depleted rapidly in many areas by pumping from wells.

Oceans
1,350,000,000 km^3

Figure 3.2 The hydrologic cycle.

The relatively long renewal rate of water in Lakes Superior, Michigan, and Huron explains why there has been such concern over water diversions. Even though these represent large reservoirs of water, the natural replenishment of this water is low, and extracting water without replacement is not sustainable. The renewal time for the largest reservoir of all, the oceans, is only 3,100 years, perhaps a surprisingly short time given the volume of water involved (over 1.3 billion km^3 of water). The ocean has turned over more than 30 times in the last 100,000 years, since the first *Homo sapiens* gazed out on the deep blue sea.

CONCEPT 3.1 REVIEW

1. How will global warming affect the proportion of the earth's water that resides in the oceans?

2. How can large reservoirs of water be vulnerable to overuse and extraction?

3. How might the construction of dams for storing water—creating reservoirs—affect the turnover time for water in rivers?

3.2 Life in Water and the Aquatic Environments

The biology of aquatic environments corresponds broadly to variations in physical factors, such as light, temperature, and water movements, and to chemical factors, such as salinity and oxygen. In chapter 2 we described a few of the hazards of life on land, including gravity, aridity, and stresses associated with high temperatures. In general, these challenges are reduced for most aquatic organisms. However, a whole other set of environmental stressors faces those who reside in aquatic systems. All organisms carrying out aerobic respiration require a reliable source of oxygen. Organisms need to be able to extract dissolved oxygen from the water (e.g., using gills), store oxygen for prolonged periods (e.g., marine mammals), or transport oxygen from above the water surface to their tissues below (e.g., specialized roots of many aquatic plants). Even when oxygen is accessible, being surrounded by water can itself present problems.

All natural water bodies consist of water, along with a number of dissolved minerals and gases. Similarly, all organisms contain substantial amounts of water, along with a number of dissolved minerals. Think back to introductory biology: What happens when two different concentrations of minerals are separated solely by a semi-permeable membrane (such as a plasma membrane)? Water flows from areas of low solute concentrations to higher concentrations. For an organism living in water, this presents a problem if the internal solute concentrations differ from those of the water outside. This is what we call osmotic stress, and there are a number of mechanisms by which organisms cope with this stress. Aquatic organisms also face challenges associated with temperature regulation, light availability, and access to nutrients and food. In this chapter, we will discuss how various aquatic systems differ in their abiotic stressors, and we will discuss some of the unique traits that allow organisms to cope with the sometimes harsh conditions of life in water.

As with chapter 2, where we could not include all terrestrial biomes, we will not include all of the different types of aquatic systems in this chapter. Rather, we will highlight a few. Figure 3.3 is a summary table that provides information on the

	Physical Conditions			Chemical Conditions		Biology
	Light	Temperature	Water Movement	Salinity	Oxygen	Productivity/ Biodiversity
Open ocean	Limited	Geographically variable but stable within locations; may be thermally stratified	Ocean currents, large amounts of water moved around globe	~34 ppt, some variation	Decreases with depth, generally present throughout water column; some large areas of hypoxia	Low density; low areal productivity; high number of endemic animal phyla; relatively diverse
Kelp forests	High to moderate	Moderate	Washed by currents	Similar to open ocean, kelp tolerate some variation	Well oxygenated	Highly productive and diverse
Coral reefs	High to moderate	Warm, usually in tropics/subtropics	Washed by currents	Similar to open ocean, little range tolerance	Well oxygenated	Highly productive, very diverse
Intertidal zones	High intensity, with wide daily variations	Broad range, geographically and seasonally variable	Wave action and tidal flooding	Highly variable, rain dilutes and evaporation concentrates salt	High but variable	Unique fauna tolerant of prolonged exposure to air; moderate diversity
Estuaries	Relatively low but variable	Variable	Strong movement, usually bidirectional with tide	Variable along length of estuary, and with tidal flushing (0–34 ppt)	Variable	High productivity, biologically diverse
Mangrove forests	High, variable with tidal flooding	Warm, found in tropics	Strong movement, usually bidirectional with tide	Highly variable, freshwater dilutes and evaporation concentrates salt	Highly variable, extreme highs and lows	High productivity, moderate to high diversity
Salt marshes	Highly variable with tidal flooding	Variable, found in high to mid-latitudes	Strong movement, usually bidirectional with tide	Highly variable, freshwater dilutes and evaporation concentrates salt	Highly variable, extreme highs and lows	High productivity, moderate to high diversity
Rivers and streams	Variable with canopy cover and depth	Geographically and seasonally variable	Variable, but generally high relative to some other systems	Low	Generally high	Productivity and diversity variable, often with distance from headwaters
Lakes and ponds	Limiting with depth	Variable with latitude; may be thermally stratified	Low	Low	Variable, may be low at depth	Variable, generally moderate productivity, high diversity
Bogs and fens	Variable, generally high	Variable with season and latitude, often in cold climates	Very low	Low, pH also low in bogs	Very low	Relatively low productivity and diversity

Figure 3.3 Summary table for the physical, chemical, and biological properties of different types of aquatic systems.

physical, chemical, and biological characteristics of various aquatic systems, including some not covered at depth here. We strongly encourage you to consult other sources to learn more about some of the systems omitted for brevity.

Our discussion of aquatic environments begins with the ocean, the largest aquatic environment on the planet. We will include in our tour some of the environments found along the margins of the oceans, including kelp forests and coral reefs. We then venture up rivers and streams, important avenues for exchange between terrestrial and aquatic environments. Finally, we consider the inland aquatic environments of lakes, bogs, and fens. As you will see, all but a few of these freshwater and marine systems are found in and around Canada.

Along the way, we will discuss the variations in light, flow, temperature, and chemistry, the factors that most profoundly shape life in aquatic systems. Light, as we will see, may be attenuated by depth in lakes and the ocean, or affected by shading, such as by trees in the headwaters, or by turbidity in rivers. Temperature is most strongly influenced by climate but may also be affected by depth as cooler, denser water is generally found in the depths of stratified lakes and the ocean. Water chemistry can be affected by weathering of parent material with variation strongly related to local or upstream geology. Salinity increases with evaporation. The ocean is salty because it has a large surface from which water evaporates, distilling water and leaving behind minerals. Salinity decreases as we move up through estuaries into rivers. However, we have made profound changes to the salinity in some freshwater systems though use of salts as de-icers. Oxygen concentrations are largely controlled by flow and depth, and flow is, in turn, controlled by topography and the gravitational movement of water.

The Oceans

The blue solitude of open ocean is something palpable. The only terrestrial biomes that evoke anything close to the feeling of this place are the "big sky" of the open prairies and the "sand sea" of deserts like the Namib. Experience with terrestrial biomes and the organisms that inhabit them cannot prepare you for what you encounter in the deep ocean. While we dream of unknown extraterrestrial beings—some friendly and some monstrous, all with strange and shocking anatomy—and parade them through science fiction literature and films, creatures just as odd and as wonderful live in the deep, dark world beyond the continental shelves. Figure 3.4 shows one of the species found in the deep sea: a female deep-sea anglerfish with her male partner. You'll notice some interesting adaptations to life in the deep ocean, such as a dorsal fin adapted as a lure with symbiotic bacteria that produce bioluminescence, and a male that lives as a sperm-producing parasite attached to the larger female.

The ocean covers over 360 million km^2 of the earth's surface (70%) and consists of one continuous, interconnected mass of water (fig. 3.5). Salinity of the open ocean varies from about 34 g of salt per kilogram of water (34‰ or parts per thousand) to about 36.5‰. The largest of the oceans, the Pacific, has a total area of nearly 180 million km^2 and extends from the Antarctic to the Arctic Ocean. The Atlantic has a total area of over

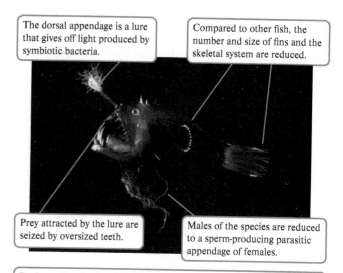

The dorsal appendage is a lure that gives off light produced by symbiotic bacteria.

Compared to other fish, the number and size of fins and the skeletal system are reduced.

Prey attracted by the lure are seized by oversized teeth.

Males of the species are reduced to a sperm-producing parasitic appendage of females.

Darkness, low food availability, and high pressures of the deep-sea environment have selected for organisms quite different from those typical of either shallow seas or the terrestrial environment. Only the females of this deep-sea anglerfish species are active predators.

(a)

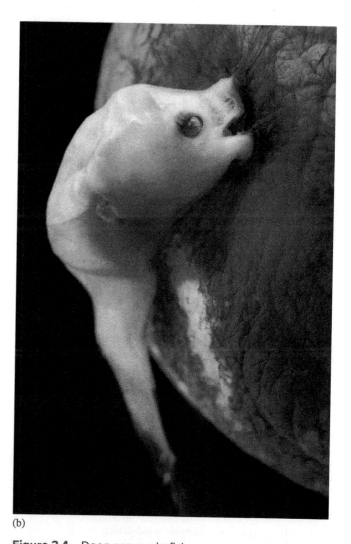

(b)

Figure 3.4   Deep-sea anglerfish.

(a) © Peter David/Getty Images; (b) Solvin Zankl/Alamy Stock Photo.

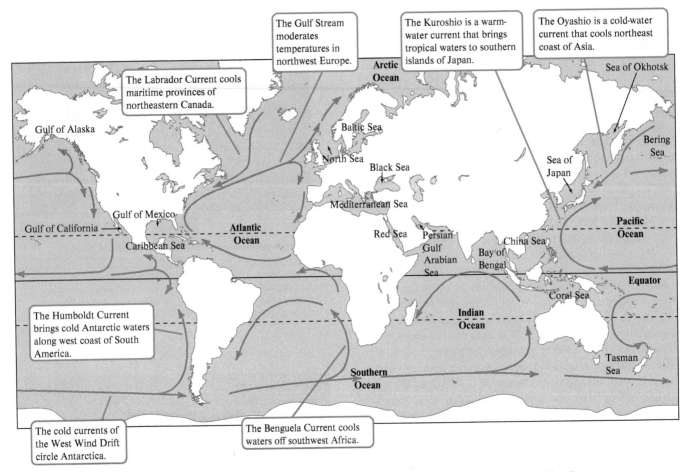

Figure 3.5 Oceanic circulation, which is driven mainly by the prevailing winds, moderates the earth's climate.

106 million km² and extends nearly from pole to pole. The Indian Ocean covers 73 million km² and is bounded by southern Asia to the north, Africa to the west, and southeast Asia and Australia to the south. The Southern Ocean, with an area of 20 million km², extends from Antarctica to 60°S latitude. The smallest of the world's oceans, the Arctic Ocean, covers a total of 14 million km² and is confined to the Northern Hemisphere. The Arctic Ocean is home to the seasonally open Northwest Passage connecting the Atlantic and Pacific oceans through Canada and the United States. A similar Northern Sea Route is seasonally open through Norway and Russia.

The Pacific is also the deepest ocean, with an average depth of over 4,000 m. The average depth of the Atlantic is about 3,500 m, while the average depth of the Arctic Ocean is only 1,000 m. Undersea mountains stud the floor of the deep sea, some isolated and some in long chains that run as ridges for thousands of kilometres. Undersea trenches, some of great depth and volume, rip through the seafloor. One such trench, the Marianas, in the western Pacific Ocean, is over 10,000 m deep—deep enough to engulf Mount Everest with 2 km to spare.

The oceans are never still. Prevailing winds drive currents that transport nutrients, oxygen, and heat, as well as organisms, across the globe. For example, wind-driven surface currents sweep across vast expanses of open ocean to create great circulation systems called **gyres** that move to the right (clockwise)

in the Northern Hemisphere and to the left (counter-clockwise) in the Southern Hemisphere. The great oceanic gyres transport warm water from equatorial regions toward the poles, moderating climates at middle and high latitudes. A segment of one of these gyres, the Gulf Stream, moderates the climate of northwest Europe.

In addition to surface currents, there are deep-water currents, such as those produced as cooled, high-density water sinks at the Antarctic and Arctic and that then move along the ocean floor. When these deep currents reach a land mass, the water may rise, flowing up along the continental slope. This is **upwelling,** and the water will carry nutrients recycled from organic matter decomposing in deep water. Upwelling occurs along the west coasts of continents and around Antarctica, where winds blow surface water offshore, allowing colder water to rise to the surface. The opposite of this is **downwelling,** which occurs when water loses heat, cools, and, becoming more dense, sinks.

The oceans can be divided into several vertical and horizontal zones. The shallow shoreline under the influence of the rise and fall of the tides is called the **littoral zone,** or **intertidal zone.** The **neritic zone** extends from the coast to the margin of the continental shelf, where the ocean is about 200 m deep. Beyond the continental shelf lies the **oceanic zone.** Vertically, the ocean is divided into several depth zones.

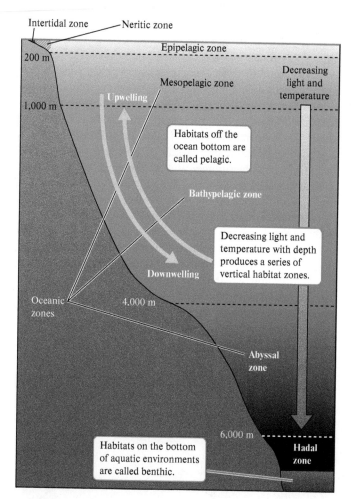

Figure 3.6   Vertical structuring of the oceans is associated with substantial variation in light and temperature with depth.

The **epipelagic zone** is the surface layer of the oceans that extends to a depth of 200 m. The **mesopelagic zone** extends from 200 to 1,000 m, and the **bathypelagic zone** extends from 1,000 to 4,000 m. The layer from 4,000 to 6,000 m is called the **abyssal zone,** and finally the deepest parts of the oceans belong to the **hadal zone.** Habitats on the bottom of the ocean, and other aquatic environments, are referred to as **benthic,** while those off the bottom, regardless of depth, are called **pelagic.** Each of these zones supports a distinctive assemblage of organisms. Figure 3.6 sketches the general structure of the oceans.

In the first 10 m below the surface, the marine environment is bright with all the colours of the rainbow. However, most of the solar energy striking the surface is absorbed in the first few metres, and below 50 or 60 m it is a blue twilight. For most of the ocean's volume, the only light is that produced by bioluminescent fish and invertebrates. As a result, most of the photosynthetic activity and associated biological activity in the ocean is concentrated in the very small, near-surface fraction of the ocean's volume. The most significant photosynthetic inhabitants of this **photic zone** are microscopic organisms called **phytoplankton,** which drift with the currents in the open sea. The small animals that drift with these same currents are called

zooplankton and serve as a food source for other invertebrates and fish.

This biological activity is particularly high in the photic zone near the continental margins, where nutrients are delivered from the land to sea, carried by river water or deposited with dust. The shallow waters near shore support marine communities of great diversity and biomass. The photic zone of the open ocean is often viewed as a biological "desert" with an average rate of photosynthesis that is comparable to a terrestrial desert. In contrast, Robert Whittaker and Gene Likens (1973) estimated that the **rate of primary production** on near-shore algal beds and coral reefs (fig. 3.7) exceeds that of tropical rain forests. This difference in the distribution of primary production shapes the ocean's distribution of fauna. J. H. Ryther (1969) estimated that the open ocean contains less than 1% of the harvestable fish stocks. Most fish are found along the coasts, particularly near highly productive coral reefs and kelp beds. For example, in the western Pacific and eastern Indian Oceans, there are over 600 coral species supporting over 2,000 species of fish. Biotic diversity on reefs is also impressive on a small scale. A single coral head may support over 100 species of polychaete worms (Grassle 1973) and over 75 species of fish (Smith and Tyler 1972).

Although the open ocean (distant from shoreline) has a much lower, desert-like rate of primary production, it is a vast area. Collectively, photosynthesis in the photic zone of the open ocean makes up one-quarter of global primary production; and because some of the biomass produced in the open ocean's photic zone sinks, the deeper ocean is not devoid of life (e.g., see the anglerfish, fig. 3.4). Fish, ranging from small bioluminescent forms to giant sharks, and invertebrates, from tiny crustaceans to giant squid, prowl the entire water column. Even more species are at the bottom; in fact, most species in the ocean live on the ocean floor, many barely visible to the naked eye. So, while we often think of the deep sea as a bottomless desert, it is not; all oceans have a bottom, and to most species, the bottom is home.

It was long assumed that the rain of organic matter from above was the *only* source of food for deep-sea organisms. Then, about two decades ago, the sea surprised everyone. There are entire biological communities on the seafloor that are nourished not by photosynthesis at the surface but by chemosynthesis on the ocean floor (see chapter 7). These oases of life are associated with undersea hot springs and harbour many life forms entirely new to science. Figure 3.8 shows the great density of organisms found on the ocean floors near an undersea hydrothermal vent.

The open ocean is home, the only home, for thousands of organisms with no counterparts on land. The terrestrial environment supports 11 animal phyla, only one of which, Onychophora (velvet worms), is **endemic** to the terrestrial environment—that is, found in no other environments. Fourteen phyla live in freshwater environments, but none are endemic. Meanwhile, the marine environment supports 28 phyla, 13 of which are endemic to the marine environment (fig. 3.9).

So far, we have talked about how absorption of light in the upper few metres can structure the distribution of marine life and

(a)

concentrate biological activity in the photic zone. The absorption of solar energy in surface water has another important effect. It warms this water, and warmer water is less dense than colder water. The surface water then floats on the colder water below, and the layers do not fully mix. These warm and cold layers are separated by a **thermocline**, a layer of water through which temperature changes rapidly with depth. This layering of the water column by temperature, which is called *thermal stratification*, is a permanent feature of tropical seas. Temperate oceans are stratified only during the summer, and the thermocline breaks down as surface waters cool during fall and winter. At high latitudes, thermal stratification is only weakly, if ever, developed.

Estuaries represent a transition from freshwater (rivers) to the ocean. In estuaries, river water may form a lens over the more dense salt water; ultimately, turbulent mixing may break this stratification, resulting in water that has intermediate salinity. Stratification, whether due to temperature or differences in salinity, has an important consequence for ecological function in oceans: the surface layer does not mix with deeper water. As new oxygen enters water through gas exchange with the atmosphere, stratification can affect supply of oxygen to deeper water.

(b)

Figure 3.7   (*a*) A scene from a kelp forest off the west coast of North America. Like terrestrial forests, kelp forests are home to a diversity of organisms. (*b*) Coral reefs, such as this one in the Red Sea, support some of the most diverse assemblages of organisms on earth.

Figure 3.8 Chemosynthesis-based community on the East Pacific Rise.

© James Forte/Getty Images RF.

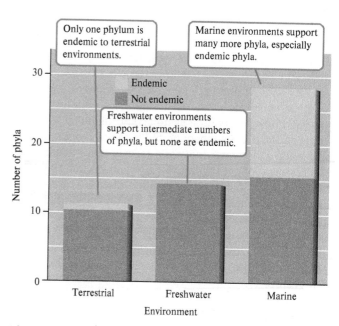

Only one phylum is endemic to terrestrial environments.

Marine environments support many more phyla, especially endemic phyla.

Freshwater environments support intermediate numbers of phyla, but none are endemic.

■ Endemic
■ Not endemic

Figure 3.9 Distribution of animal phyla among terrestrial, freshwater, and marine environments.

Data from Grassle 1991.

Oxygen is present in far lower concentrations and varies much more in the oceans than in air. A litre of air contains about 200 ml of oxygen at sea level, while a litre of seawater contains a maximum of 9 ml of oxygen (but may be much lower). Oxygen concentrations are generally highest near the ocean surface, and decrease progressively with depth down to approximately 1,000 m below the surface. The decrease is driven by aerobic respiration of organic matter that is produced in the photic zone and then sinks. Below 1,000 metres, oxygen concentrations increase with depth due to downwelling of cold, oxygen-rich water near the poles and circulation of this water in deep ocean currents. Oxygen concentrations may also be reduced in the near-shore marine environment, where the production of organic matter is typically highest. When this organic matter sinks and decomposes in deeper water, the water can become depleted in oxygen by respiration. This can be exacerbated if the water column is stratified, whether thermally or due to salinity gradients. Depletion of oxygen in deeper water can pose a threat to the many benthic species of marine animals, particularly those living near shore, where the rain of organic matter—and, therefore, the consumption of oxygen—is greatest.

ECOLOGY IN ACTION

What Lies Below?

Understanding the biodiversity of aquatic systems is just as important for society as is understanding the biodiversity of terrestrial systems (chapter 2). We argued that soils were the biggest frontier for discovery of life on land. What about the world of water? Not too surprisingly, people's tendency to study those things that are more readily observable is not limited to the terrestrial world. We can watch *Shark Week* on TV, but I have yet to see an annual television event focused on microbes and the tiny animals of the world. Nonetheless, as we move from the surface of the ocean toward the sediment below, our understanding of basic natural history becomes as black as the water around us. There are obvious difficulties working in and around sediment and deep oceans, similar to those in soil ecology. The habitat is dark, organisms are difficult and expensive to reach, and many of the most common organisms are small and hard to see. Deep-ocean studies are made even more difficult by extreme pressure differences, where simply bringing organisms up to the surface for study is often fatal to the organism. However, for those willing to take on these challenges, there is a great reward: a chance to explore a truly unknown world (fig. 3.10).

Our lack of understanding of deep waters and sediments is completely counter to their likely importance in the functioning of natural systems and global processes. Because of the expanse of the oceans, coupled with abundant underwater mountain ranges that increase the surface area of the ocean floor, ocean bottoms are the single most common habitat on the planet. The level of biodiversity on the ocean floor is simply staggering. Estimates suggest somewhere between 1 million and 1 billion species live there, with less than 1% of these currently described. Even excluding the practically unknown diversity of bacteria, there could be millions of species yet to be discovered.

One researcher who has dedicated his professional life to understanding the biology of the deep sea is Paul Snelgrove of Memorial University in Newfoundland. He has written extensively on the diversity and importance of ocean sediments as reservoirs of biodiversity and as a key player in global nutrient cycling (Snelgrove 1999, 2000). Snelgrove has been instrumental in the development of the CHONe (Canadian Healthy Oceans Network), a group focused on enabling collaborations among academia and government in an effort to use science to better inform management and protect marine biodiversity (Snelgrove et al. 2012).

Figure 3.10   Some of the diversity found 145 m deep along a fjord wall at Hosie Islands, Barkley Sound, British Columbia. In the photo are glass sponges (*Aphrocallistes vastus*), fish, a variety of invertebrates in the sediment, and the manipulator arm of the remote operated vehicle, ROPOS. The green is fluorescein dye that the researcher squirted onto the sponges to test whether they were actively pumping sea water.

Sally Leys.

Running Waters: Rivers and Streams

As we head from the marine environments up through the brackish waters of the estuaries, we find ourselves in the flowing freshwater of rivers and streams (fig. 3.11). The importance of rivers such as the Nile, Tigris, Euphrates, St. Lawrence, Mekong, Ganges, Rhine, Mississippi, Missouri, Amazon, Seine, Zaire, and Thames to human history, ecology, and economy is

inestimable. However, river ecology has lagged behind the ecological study of lakes and oceans and is one of the youngest branches of aquatic ecology.

When rain falls or snow melts, a portion of it runs off, either over the land's surface or as subsurface flow. Some of this runoff water eventually collects in small channels, which join to become larger and larger water courses until they form a network of channels that drains the landscape. A river basin is that area of a continent or island that is drained by a river drainage network, such as the Mississippi River basin in the United States, the Columbia River basin in Western Canada, or the Congo River basin in Africa. Most rivers eventually flow out to sea or to some interior basin, such as the Aral Sea or the Great Salt Lake. Some rivers, however, do not flow into a lake or ocean but can dry out along their course. The Finke River in central Australia, for example, naturally runs dry in the Simpson Desert. River basins are separated from each other by watersheds, topographic high points. For instance, snowmelt and rainfall on the east side of the Rocky Mountain peaks flow to the Atlantic Ocean, while on the west side, this water flows to the Pacific Ocean. Figure 3.12 shows the distribution of some of the major rivers on earth.

Rivers and streams can be divided along three dimensions: length, width, and depth (fig. 3.13). Along the *length* of a river, we find repeating segments of pools, runs, and riffles. These segments differ mainly in depth. Pools are deeper segments, where water has longer residence time, and flow is slower; riffles are shallower segments where flow is faster. Runs are intermediate

Figure 3.11   The green of the meandering Nicholson River in northern Queensland, Australia, contrasts sharply with the white salt pans in the surrounding landscape.

© Art Wolfe/The Image Bank/Getty Images.

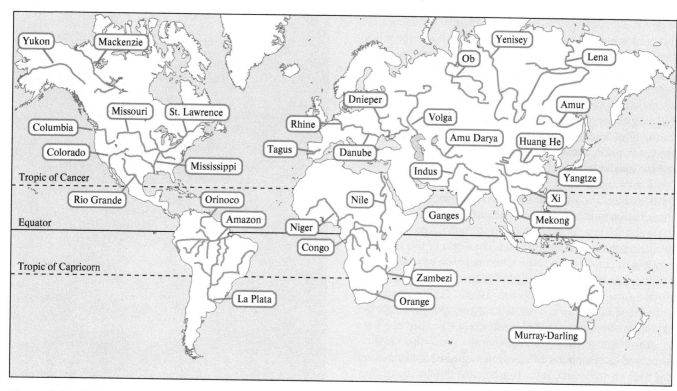

Figure 3.12 Major rivers throughout the world.

Figure 3.13 The three dimensions of stream structure.

in depth, connecting riffle and pool segments. Sometimes the sequence is punctuated by rapids, segments with steep vertical drop and fast flow. Across their *widths*, rivers can be divided into wetted channels and active channels. A wetted channel contains water even during low flow conditions. An active channel, which extends out from one or both sides of a wetted channel, may be dry during part of the year but is flooded annually during high flows. Outside the active channel is the **riparian zone**, a transition between the aquatic environment of the river and the upland terrestrial environment.

Rivers and streams can also be divided *vertically* into the water surface, the water column, and the bottom, or benthic, zone. The benthic zone includes the surface of the bottom substrate and the interior of the substrate through depths at which substantial surface water still flows. The depth of this zone can vary greatly among rivers, depending mainly on how porous the substrate material is. Below the benthic zone is the **hyporheic zone**, a zone of transition between areas of surface water flow and groundwater. The area containing groundwater below the hyporheic zone is called the **phreatic zone**. Each part of a river or stream is a physically and chemically distinctive environment, and each supports different organisms. Unique to stream and river environments is the constant and unidirectional flow of water. As a result, upstream processes generally have a stronger influence on downstream processes than vice versa.

In oceans, we discussed the importance of the photic zone and how biological activity tends to be concentrated in that zone. Photosynthesis is the base for energy flow in the oceans, and the limits of light penetration govern the distribution of biota. Rivers can be a little messier in this regard. Photosynthesis can be important as a source of energy, and algae or plants produce autochthonous organic matter. Or, organic matter might wash in from the landscape, and leaves might fall from trees landing in the water. These represent allochthonous organic matter. Which source of organic matter is most important in the energy budget of a river often depends on light availability, which in turn might depend on the depth and turbidity of the water and the thickness of stream side vegetation and its effect on shading (fig. 3.14). The relative importance of autochthonous and allochthonous organic matter, as we'll see below, is also key in structuring the biological community of rivers.

The amount of water carried by rivers, which is called *river discharge*, differs a lot from one climatic regime to another. River flows are often unpredictable and "flashy" in arid and semiarid regions, where extended droughts may be followed by torrential rains. The flow in tropical rivers varies considerably. Many tropical rivers, which flow very little during the dry season, become torrents during the wet season. Some of the most constant flows are found in forested temperate regions, where, as we saw in chapter 2, precipitation is fairly evenly distributed throughout the year. Forested landscapes can dampen variation in flow by absorbing excessive rain during wet periods and acting as a reservoir for river flow during drier periods. The periodic variation and intensity of this variation is important in shaping the biological community of rivers and streams. High discharge can result in movement of bed material, sometimes to a devastating degree. Even less catastrophic changes can disrupt habitat and send organisms adrift. The life histories of organisms living in

(a)

(b)

Figure 3.14 Headwater streams in: (*a*) forested Tunitas Creek, California; and (*b*) Capitol Reef National Park, Utah. The consumers in headwater streams draining forested lands generally depend on energy from the surrounding forest. Meanwhile, desert streams are open to sunlight and support high levels of photosynthesis by stream algae, the source of most energy for desert-stream consumers.
(a) Design Pics/PunchStock; (b) © William Perry/123RF.

rivers and streams must be compatible with dynamic changes in flow regime.

Disruptions to habitat aside, episodic flooding is part of the ecology of most rivers and streams. It appears that the health and ecological integrity of rivers and streams depend upon keeping the natural flow regime for a region intact. Historical patterns of flooding have particularly important influences on river ecosystem processes, especially on the exchange of nutrients and energy between the river channel and the floodplain and associated wetlands. This idea, which was first proposed as the **flood pulse concept** (Junk et al. 1989), is supported by a growing body of evidence from research conducted on rivers on virtually every continent.

Flow regimes and the nature of food available (quantity, quality, and form) are the most important factors shaping the distribution of animals in rivers and streams. The **river continuum concept** (Vannote et al. 1980; Fig. 3.15) presents a model for how flow regime and food resource change along a temperate river from headwaters to mouth, and how these changes affect distribution patterns of animals. In shady headwaters, the main source of carbon is coarse particulate organic matter

(CPOM) from falling leaves and other plant matter, since the plants block much sunlight reaching the stream. Colonization by fungi and bacteria make the CPOM more nutritious for benthic, or bottom dwelling, invertebrate shredders (such as some caddisflies and amphipods). Shredders break down CPOM into fine particulate organic matter (FPOM), supporting a downstream guild of benthic invertebrate collectors (such as black fly larvae and other caddisflies). As the river becomes larger and the canopy more open, algae become an increasingly important source of carbon, supporting other groups of filter feeding collectors, including bivalves and zooplankton. The distribution of various species of benthic invertebrates within feeding guilds is largely determined by the substrate type (e.g., sandy, silty,

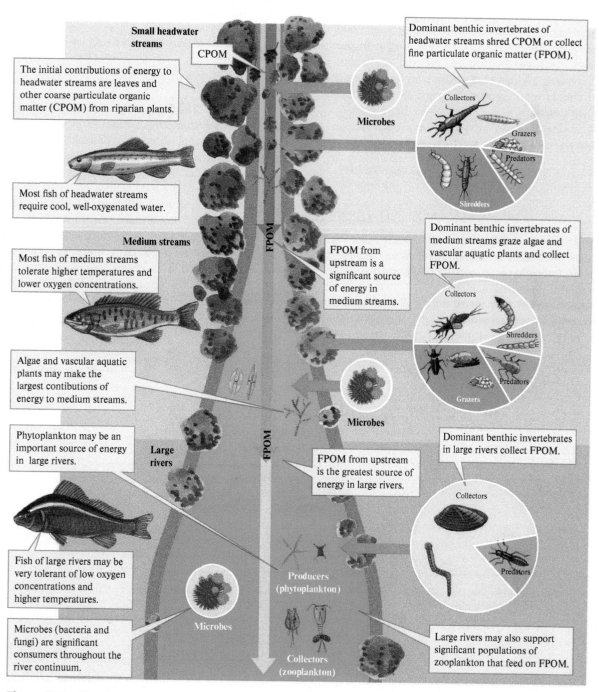

Figure 3.15 The river continuum.

or rocky). Predatory invertebrates and fish are found along the river continuum, with their distributions determined by feeding mode and oxygen tolerance. Fish requiring higher dissolved oxygen concentrations typically are found more in the colder headwater streams; and those tolerating lower concentrations, in the larger, warmer river downstream.

Regional differences also appear important in the structure of riverine communities. As in the terrestrial biomes, large numbers of species inhabit tropical rivers. The number of fish species in tropical rivers is much higher than in temperate rivers. For example, the Mississippi River basin, which supports one of the most diverse temperate fish faunas, is home to about 300 fish species. By contrast, the tropical Congo River basin contains about 669 species of fish, of which over 558 are found nowhere else. The most impressive array of freshwater fish is that of the Amazon River basin, which contains over 2,000 species. The higher species numbers in tropical basins might be caused by differences in flow regime and the extent of floodplain connection with the river. In the rainy season, the floodplains of tropical rivers may offer refuge and diversity of habitat for some fish species.

Still Waters: Lakes and Ponds

A lake is a landscape's most beautiful and expressive feature. It is Earth's eye; looking into which the beholder measures the depth of his own nature.

— Henry David Thoreau, *Walden* (1854)

Lakes are basins in the landscape that collect water like so many rain puddles. Most lakes are found in regions worked over by the geological forces that produce these basins, such as tectonic shifts, volcanism, and glacial activity.

Approximately 4.6 million km² of the planet's surface is covered by over 300,000,000 lakes (Downing et al. 2006). However, most of the water in all of the world's lakes combined is in

Figure 3.16   The five Great Lakes lie between Canada and the United States and contain nearly 20% of the world's fresh surface water.

NASA Geospatial Interoperability Office, Jet Propulsion Laboratory, California Institute of Technology, US Geological Survey, Imaging by Pete Giencke.

a few large lakes. The Great Lakes of North America (fig. 3.16), for example, together cover an area of over 245,000 km² and contain 24,620 km³ of water, approximately 20% of all the freshwater on the surface of the planet (excluding ice). An additional 20% is contained in Lake Baikal, Siberia, the deepest lake on the planet (1,600 m), with a total volume of 23,000 km³. Much of the remainder is within the rift lakes of East Africa; Lake Tanganyika, the second deepest lake (1,470 m), has an additional 20% of global surface water, with a total volume of 23,100 km³. Aside from these few major lakes, there are millions of other lakes, each of which is less than 1 km² in size (Downing et al. 2006). Lakes are often concentrated in "lake districts," such as northern Minnesota, much of Scandinavia, and vast regions across north-central Canada and Siberia. Figure 3.17 shows the locations of some of the larger lakes.

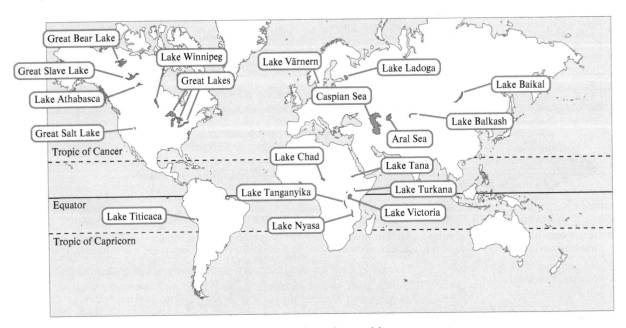

Figure 3.17   Distributions of some major lakes throughout the world.

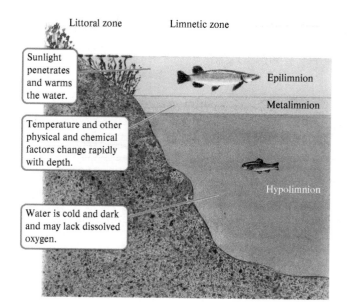

Littoral zone   Limnetic zone

Sunlight penetrates and warms the water.

Temperature and other physical and chemical factors change rapidly with depth.

Water is cold and dark and may lack dissolved oxygen.

Epilimnion

Metalimnion

Hypolimnion

Figure 3.18 Lake structure.

In 1892, F. A. Forel defined the scientific study of lakes as the *oceanography of lakes*, concluding that lakes are much like small seas. Lake structure parallels that of the oceans (fig. 3.18), with differences due, principally, to the smaller size of lakes and their relative isolation. The shallowest waters along the lakeshore, where rooted aquatic plants may grow, is called the littoral zone. Beyond the littoral zone, the open lake is the **limnetic zone.** The principles we discussed about how light and stratification structure the distribution of organisms and their biological activity in oceans apply to deeper lakes as well. In the temperate zone, an **epilimnion** may form in summer as a warm surface layer. Most productivity occurs in this layer, which may limit light penetration to deeper layers. Below the epilimnion is the thermocline, or **metalimnion.** Below the thermocline are the cold, dark waters of the **hypolimnion.** Each of these zones supports a distinctive assemblage of lake organisms. The importance of lake sediments, or benthos, as habitat is another parallel between oceans and lakes.

Penetration of light and the depth of the photic zone depends on the characteristics of the surrounding landscape. The landscape affects water chemistry and, in turn, biological activity. Nutrients enter lakes from the landscape in river water, groundwater influx, runoff, or deposition. Landscapes that contribute high levels of nutrients, such as urbanized or agricultural landscapes, can result in high levels of algae growth. Algae absorb light, limiting its penetration. This causes a shallow, but highly productive, photic zone. Such lakes with high productivity are called **eutrophic.** When lakes receive high levels of dissolved organic compounds, such as humic acids leached from forest soils, they may appear yellow-brown. In these lakes, photosynthesis decreases due to increased absorption of blue light by these compounds. These may be referred to as **dystrophic.** In deep lakes, the landscape may deliver low quantities of either nutrients or dissolved organic compounds relative to the lake's volume of water. Phytoplankton production is generally low in these lakes, and light penetrates to great depths. Lake

Superior, Lake Tahoe in California, and Crater Lake in Oregon, as examples, are nearly as blue as the open ocean. Such lakes are called **oligotrophic.** Many lakes, including Lake Ontario, are mesotrophic and lay along the gradient between oligotrophic and eutrophic.

Many Canadian lakes are thermally stratified during the summer, a condition that limits wind-driven mixing to surface waters above the thermocline. Interestingly, they can sometimes stratify in winter as well. Because water is most dense at 4°C, colder water near the surface will be less dense and resist mixing with deeper water near 4°C. When ice forms, it is a wind barrier that prevents the breakdown of delicate stratification. In the spring and fall, surface water temperatures change and approach temperatures in deeper layers. Stratification then breaks down and winds drive vertical currents that can mix temperate lakes from top to bottom (fig. 3.19). These are the times when a lake renews oxygen in bottom waters and replenishes nutrients in surface waters. This is particularly important in more eutrophic lakes, where the rain of organic matter from the epilimnion to the hypolimnion, and decomposition of this organic matter in the hypolimnion, can create seasonal hypoxia in deeper water.

Aquatic organisms differ widely in their environmental requirements; oligotrophic and eutrophic lakes generally support distinctive biological communities (fig. 3.20). In temperate regions, oligotrophic lakes generally support the highest diversity of phytoplankton. These lakes are usually inhabited by fish requiring high oxygen concentrations and relatively low temperatures, such as trout and whitefish. The benthic faunas of these lakes are rich in species and include the larvae of mayflies and caddisflies, small clams, and, along wave-swept shores, the larvae of stoneflies. Eutrophic temperate lakes tend to be warmer and periodically depleted of oxygen. Fish in these lakes, such as carp and catfish, are generally more tolerant of high temperatures and low oxygen concentrations. Some, such as gars and bowfins, can even breathe air in an emergency. The benthic invertebrate faunas are usually less species rich and tolerant of lower oxygen concentrations. Midge larvae and tubificid worms, common in such lakes, have hemoglobin that helps them extract oxygen from oxygen-poor waters.

Much less is known about the biology of tropical lakes; however, a few generalizations are possible. Tropical lakes can be very productive. Also, their fish faunas may include a great number of species. Three East African lakes—Lake Victoria, Lake Malawi, and Lake Tanganyika—contain over 700 species of fish, approximately the number of freshwater fish species in all of the United States and Canada.

Peatlands: Bogs and Fens

Wetland habitats come in two forms: those that form **peat,** and those that do not. Wetlands are distributed throughout the world but are most extensive at high latitudes of the Northern Hemisphere, including large areas of Canadian boreal forest and the Canadian Arctic (fig. 3.21). Peat consists of partially decomposed plant material that builds up in certain poorly drained wetland habitats. Throughout history, much of northern

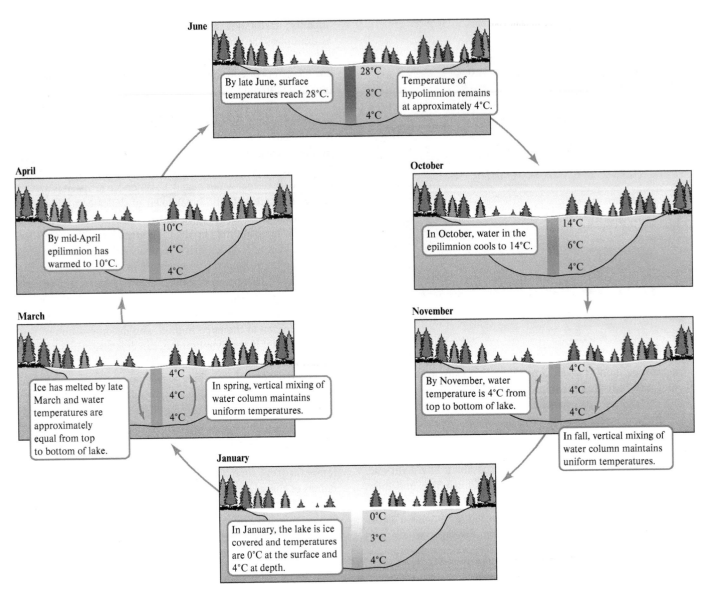

Figure 3.19   Seasonal changes in temperature in a temperate lake.

North America, western Europe, and the Siberian Lowlands have been covered in large expanses of peatlands. Words like *moors, muskegs,* and *mires* continue to be closely identified with the cultures of the British Isles. These areas have been of critical importance to early human populations as a source of fuel (peat bricks and coal) and forage (many berry-producing shrubs). The smell of burning peat is ingrained in the walls and whiskeys of Ireland and Scotland. Here we discuss the two types of peat-forming wetlands: **bogs** and **fens** (fig. 3.22).

The dominant feature of peatlands is a very well-developed layer of mosses and sedges. Peatlands occupy over 5% of the world's land base, with over 80% located in the high latitudes of the boreal and subarctic. Approximately 40% of the world's peatlands are found in North America, and over 15% of Canada's land base is peatland. Peatlands require significant water inputs and, thus, are not found in the drier regions of the world. Although in chapter 2 we discussed the boreal forest as

a terrestrial ecosystem, in a broader view the boreal region is a mixture of forest, bog, fen, and other wetland habitats.

In peatlands, plant growth tends to be slow. However, the decomposition of dead plants is even slower. The result is that dead plant material accumulates. If water tables are stable, this process can continue for millennia, with peat deposits in some areas reaching more than 10 m in depth. The slow decomposition is a result of low oxygen availability, low pH, and cold temperatures. When soil is saturated by water, little oxygen penetrates. Flowing water could introduce oxygen, but peatlands form in areas of stagnant or slow-moving water. Most decomposition is therefore anaerobic, which is much less efficient than aerobic decomposition, made worse by the fact that anaerobic decomposition produces organic acids. The global distribution of peatlands is primarily in boreal forests and tundra, which are below freezing for much of the year. Low oxygen, low pH, and cold temperatures make a terrible combination for decomposition.

Oligotrophic lake   Eutrophic lake

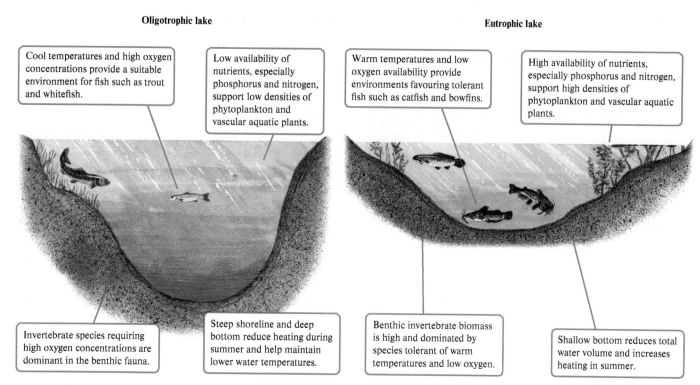

Cool temperatures and high oxygen concentrations provide a suitable environment for fish such as trout and whitefish.

Low availability of nutrients, especially phosphorus and nitrogen, support low densities of phytoplankton and vascular aquatic plants.

Warm temperatures and low oxygen availability provide environments favouring tolerant fish such as catfish and bowfins.

High availability of nutrients, especially phosphorus and nitrogen, support high densities of phytoplankton and vascular aquatic plants.

Invertebrate species requiring high oxygen concentrations are dominant in the benthic fauna.

Steep shoreline and deep bottom reduce heating during summer and help maintain lower water temperatures.

Benthic invertebrate biomass is high and dominated by species tolerant of warm temperatures and low oxygen.

Shallow bottom reduces total water volume and increases heating in summer.

Figure 3.20   Oligotrophic and eutrophic lakes.

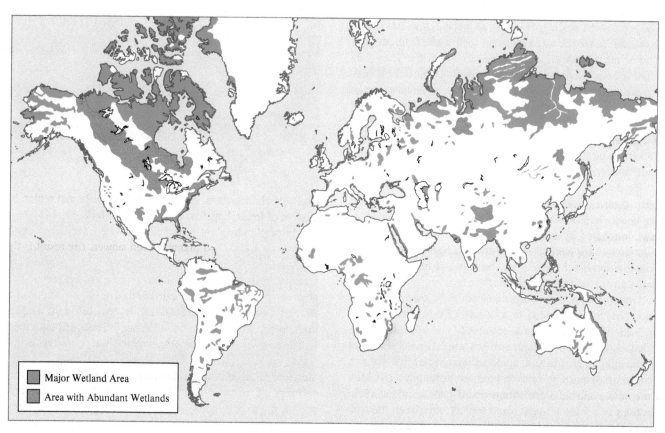

☐ Major Wetland Area
☐ Area with Abundant Wetlands

Figure 3.21   Global distribution of wetlands. Wetlands take different forms in different locations, including marshes, mangrove forests, bogs, and fens.

(a)

(b)

Figure 3.22 Canada is home to substantial expanses of wetland habitats. Shown here are (*a*) a bog on the Labrador Coast, and (*b*) a fen north of Fort McMurray, Alberta.

(a) © Tui De Roy/Minden Pictures/Getty Images; (b) © Peter Essick/Aurora Photos/Alamy Stock Photo.

Bogs and fens differ in the source of water and in topography. Bogs are found in depressions in the landscape, with precipitation being the only source of water into the system. Bogs often exhibit patterns of raised *hummocks* and lower *hollows* (see fig. 3.22*a*). The upper layers of hummocks are above the water table and thus are drier than the rest of the peatlands. As a result, hummocks are aerated, allowing root growth; this means they are home to a diversity of vascular plants. The water in bogs is always acidic (pH < 4.5), as precipitation lacks basic ions to neutralize the acids. Fens get their water from groundwater or surface water, which varies in chemistry. They may therefore be acidic, neutral, or even alkaline. Neutral pH may be more conducive to decomposition. However, fens tend to be flat, with the water level at or near the surface. Because they lack the topographical variation of bogs, they do not have the drier, aerated hummocks where decomposition can occur more efficiently and that permit the growth of vascular plants. As a result, fens may have a relatively low plant diversity.

Despite the harsh regime of many peatlands, they are home to many plants and animals. The types of plants found vary widely across peatlands, with more productive and drier areas dominated by trees and shrubs, and with more acidic, wetter areas having relatively few vascular plants. All peatlands include a dominant moss layer, consisting of many bryophyte species and associated microfauna.

One of the most recognizable features of many bog habitats is that they are home to a variety of carnivorous plants (fig. 3.23). Carnivory is a great example of a novel solution to a difficult situation. For a plant, nitrogen and other soil resources are essential for growth and reproduction (chapter 7). However, because decomposition rates in bogs are extremely slow, little nitrogen is available. Carnivorous plants have a unique adaptation for acquiring nitrogen from sources other than the soil. One of the more common types of carnivorous plants in North American bogs is the pitcher plant. The pitcher is formed from modified leaves. Inside the pitcher, the plants secrete a variety

Figure 3.23 Carnivorous plants, such as this pitcher plant *(Sarracenia purpurea),* are commonly found in bog habitats.

Getty Images/iStockphoto.

of enzymes that accelerate the decomposition of insects that get trapped inside. Further enhancing decomposition is a complex network of fungi and bacteria that live inside the pitchers. These plants are also home to a variety of spiders and other species, creating islands of diversity in a manner similar to epiphytes that are common in tropical and temperate rain forests.

Animal life is not as diverse in peatlands as in other aquatic environments. The low calcium levels tend to reduce abundances of vertebrates and molluscs, though many transient species can be found passing through the area. Insect diversity and numbers are often very high in peatlands, particularly for species with aquatic larval stages.

CONCEPT 3.2 REVIEW

1. If you travelled downriver in a boat, passing through lakes, larger rivers, and an estuary, and finally out to sea, how would biological diversity vary along that journey?

2. Again considering that journey, what factor would you expect to limit productivity in the different ecosystems you pass through along the way?

3. What ecological factors differ between lakes and marine habitats?

3.3 Human Influences on Aquatic Systems

A variety of different human activities affect the physical, chemical, and biological properties of aquatic systems. In chapter 2, we discussed urban areas as being of a kind, the similarities in how urban ecosystems are structured, and how people living at high density affect ecological processes. The result is that a city might have less ecological similarity to the temperate forest from which it was carved than to a city carved from a grassland or tropical forest. People living at high density, and attendant agricultural activity, can also affect aquatic systems. However, the physical characteristics of the aquatic system are paramount, and an urban pond bears more similarity to a rural pond than to an urban river. This aside, there are some common themes to human impact across different kinds of aquatic systems. And because reservoirs of water are connected through the hydrologic cycle (and gravity as water flows from headwaters to the ocean), the things we do in one part of the terrestrial landscape can have impacts on distant, downstream systems.

Think about the first few large global cities that pop into your mind. If you think a bit longer, you will probably be able to name the large body of water on the banks of which the city is built. If not on the coast, most are built on estuaries of large rivers or on the shores of big lakes. London has the Thames; Paris, the Seine; Beijing, the Yangtze; and New York, the Hudson River estuary. Even today, with railroads and highways, global trade is by water, and cities grow on shorelines.

In both the United States and Canada, large populations surround the Great Lakes. The human population around Lake Erie, one of the most altered of the Great Lakes, grew from 2.5 million in the 1880s to over 13 million in the 1980s. The primary ecological impact of these populations has been the dumping of astounding quantities of nutrients and toxic wastes into Lake Erie (fig 3.24). By the mid-1960s, the Detroit River alone was dumping 1.5 billion gallons of waste water into Lake Erie each day. The Cuyahoga River, which flows through Cleveland before reaching the lake, was so fouled with oil in the 1960s that it would catch fire. In the face of such ecological challenges, much of Lake Erie, particularly the eastern end, was transformed from a healthy lake with a rich fish fauna to one that was, for a time, essentially an algal soup in which only the most tolerant fish species could live. The condition of Lake Erie was so poor that Theodor Geisel's (Dr. Seuss) classic *The Lorax* originally contained the verse "I hear things are just as bad up in Lake Erie." With greater controls on waste disposal, the process of degradation began to reverse itself, and Lake Erie recovered much, but not all, of its former health and vitality by the 1980s. And Dr. Seuss deleted the line.

Figure 3.24 Eutrophication in Lake Erie caused by excessive nutrient inputs.
© JK Enright/Alamy.

The preceding example is one simple illustration of how people can impact aquatic environments. We could just as well have picked any of hundreds of global cities to illustrate this. The pressures of high population growth on shorelines has repeatedly led to filling and dredging **salt marshes** and other coastal wetlands, replacing wildlife habitat with human habitat. Increasing discharge of waste—sewage and other—has historically accompanied this growth. The discharge of organic waste depletes oxygen as it decomposes, creating physiological stress for organisms, particularly when the water column is stratified. Heavy metals and organic chemicals discharged into estuaries, wetlands, and lakes can become incorporated into plant and animal tissues, increasing to toxic levels in some species. Wastes discharged into estuaries find their way to the open oceans, which have been used for centuries as a repository for trash of all sorts, with the adage that "the solution to pollution is dilution." But there is a growing realization that dumping garbage does not eliminate the problem, it just moves it downstream or offshore.

An example of moving a problem offshore is found in the northern Pacific Ocean, in the form of the "Great Pacific Garbage Patch," also called the Pacific Trash Vortex. This is a cycling area of enormous size in which small debris (including many plastic fragments) and pollutants are trapped due to ocean currents. Similar garbage patches have been found in the Atlantic and likely occur in other oceans throughout the world. Sometimes, the debris trapped in these patches finds its way back ashore (fig. 3.25).

Figure 3.25 Plastic and other trash washed up on the Hawaiian shoreline.
LCDR Eric Johnson, NOAA Corps, NOAA/Dept. of Commerce.

Images of these garbage patches, and of other disasters, such as 2010's Deepwater Horizon oil spill, which spewed an estimated 780,000 m^3 of crude oil into the Gulf of Mexico, are arresting and command our attention (fig. 3.26). Flying under the radar, however, is something more pervasive and disruptive in lakes and nearshore marine systems: nutrient pollution. The need to feed our growing population has led to extensive fertilization of cropland with nitrogen and phosphorus. These nutrients, as well as N and P from point sources, have been the main culprits in eutrophication of aquatic systems. Nutrient pollution stimulates the growth of algae. On the surface, this does not sound so bad, but when all of the new organic matter sinks and decays, oxygen is depleted in deeper water, resulting in hundreds of large hypoxic zones (often referred to as "dead zones"). The Gulf of Mexico's hypoxic zone forms annually near the mouth of the Mississippi River and covers an area of 14,250 km^2 (about half the size of Vancouver Island). Large seasonal hypoxic zones can also form in Lake Erie; and the St. Lawrence River estuary experiences a large chronic hypoxic area, its depth preventing re-aeration through turnover in fall and winter.

Feeding and supplying a growing human population can also put pressure on the resources of aquatic systems. Shell middens, places where prehistoric people piled the remains of their seafood dinners, from Scandinavia to South Africa, are testimony to the importance of intertidal species to human populations for over 100,000 years. Today, each low tide still finds people all over the world scouring intertidal areas for mussels, oysters, clams, and other species. Relentless exploitation has severely reduced many intertidal populations. Similarly, the fish and shellfish of kelp forests and coral reefs have been heavily exploited. Some coral reefs have been so heavily fished, both for food and for the aquarium trade, that most of the larger fish are rare. Overfishing has led to great declines in commercially important fish stocks, such as the Grand Banks cod population. Recently, the cod fisheries of the Grand Banks have shown signs of recovery, while the same fishery in the Gulf of Maine remains in decline, linked to warmer temperatures and reduced fecundity, demonstrating the complex linkages between aquatic systems and our impacts.

Unwittingly or intentionally, we are often the taxis for fish and other species, moving them around the globe and introducing non-native species to new habitats, such as lakes and rivers. Most introductions lead nowhere, but some species thrive in their new environments, with no natural predators, and become invasive. Invasive aquatic species can devastate ecosystems, changing how they function and changing their communities. We spend hundreds of millions of dollars annually in Canada to control the spread of aquatic invasive species and to rectify the damage done. The sea lamprey provides just one illustration. The canals that were dug to connect the Great Lakes with each other and to bypass Niagara Falls inadvertently introduced the sea lamprey to the upper Great Lakes. Once in the Great Lakes, sea lampreys fed mainly on lake trout, lake herring, and chubs (fig. 3.27). This predation, combined with intense fishing, devastated these commercially important fish populations. These early introductions of fish into the Great Lakes were just a preview of future biological

Figure 3.26   Fire on the drilling platform of Deepwater Horizon, 2010.
U.S. Coast Guard photo.

Figure 3.27   The sea lamprey is one of many Great Lakes invasive species that have created an ecological disaster.
Jacana/Science Source.

challenges, however. The rogues' gallery of introductions to the Great Lakes, which now includes species such as the zebra and quagga mussels, the river ruffe, and the spiny water flea, continues to grow, and there appears to be no end in sight. Attention is now focused on controlling the spread of four species of carp, collectively known as "Asian carp," with a few sterile individuals found in Canadian waters. By 1990, 139 species of fish, invertebrates, plants, and algae had been introduced to the Great Lakes. As a consequence, the Great Lakes have become a laboratory for the study of human-caused biological invasions.

Pollution, overexploitation, and facilitation of biological invasions are long-standing threats stemming from our activities. A more recent and less direct, albeit more widespread, threat is now recognized: that posed by climate change. The declining cod stock populations in the Gulf of Maine, despite catch restrictions, was mentioned previously. Corals provide another example of species that are under stress from warming water. Coral reefs are formed by a close interaction between the coral (phylum Cnidaria) and a variety of zooxanthellae (phylum Dinoflagellata). A number of environmental triggers, including increased temperatures, can cause a breakdown in this relationship, leading to *coral bleaching*, which can devastate large areas of reef. Peatlands are also vulnerable to climate change, both temperature and precipitation; such changes can cause peatlands to contract in areas that become drier and warmer. Moreover, peatlands store 30% of the world's soil carbon, and release of that carbon to the atmosphere through increased decomposition or increased fire frequency may have significant implications for further climate change. Because of the potential for this positive feedback loop in the peatlands, they are currently a hotbed of activity for climate change researchers.

The emissions of CO_2 that fuel climate change have another effect to consider. Much of the CO_2 emitted in recent decades has been absorbed by the ocean. Initially, as we began to understand this, the ocean as a sink seemed to be a good thing. However, the downside is that as CO_2 is dissolved, it generates carbonic acid and decreases the ocean's pH. The effect of acidification, which goes hand in hand with increasing ocean temperatures, has been challenging to pin down since the underlying cause (increased CO_2 in the atmosphere) is the same for both changes. Ivan Nagelkerken and Sean Connell at the Southern Seas Ecology Laboratories at the University of Adelaide in Australia published a meta-analysis of 632 published experiments where ecological effects of pH and temperature change (magnitude and direction) were reported (Nagelkerken and Connell 2015). Acidification appears to result in decreased species abundance in both tropical and temperate waters, with shifts toward a more microbially dominated food web. The effects of acidification appear strongest for calcifying organisms, such as corals, reducing the deposition of calcium phosphate.

As we have seen in the habitats we explored in chapter 2 and this chapter, humans have significant influences on all areas of the planet, no matter how remote they may seem. Because of this, it is important to understand that current ecological processes occur in a world dominated by people. It is up to ecologists to provide robust knowledge on how human activities will alter plant and animal distributions. Generation and dissemination of this information is critical for lawmakers and land managers to make evidence-based policy and decisions that protect the world's biological diversity and ecosystems.

ECOLOGICAL TOOLS AND APPROACHES

Reconstructing Lake Communities

How can we put our knowledge of aquatic life to work? A major question ecologists often face is whether a certain environmental factor will alter an aquatic community. To answer this, we first need a clear understanding of the species composition and abundances of the focal community under current environmental conditions. In chapter 1 we described the experimental approach that David Schindler and colleagues at the Experimental Lakes Area have used to test the impact that fertilization, acidification, and a variety of other factors have had on lake communities. Here we will describe a different approach used by a number of researchers in Canada, including Roland Hall at the University of Waterloo and John Smol and colleagues at PEARL, the Paleoecological Environmental Assessment and Research Laboratory, based at Queen's University. The goal of these researchers is to provide the historical context to environmental change, through detailed study of the paleoenvironmental record on lakes throughout the world. This is the field of paleolimnology, which is broadly defined as the scientific discipline that uses the biological, chemical, and physical information archived in lake sediment profiles to track past environmental changes. By understanding the historical patterns of variation in lake communities, the researchers can generate hypotheses about how environmental factors have shaped the communities we see now, and possibly predict what we will find in the future.

How to Reconstruct Past Communities

The fundamental research subject in most paleolimnological studies is the sediment core (fig. 3.28a). Suspended in the waters of all lakes are numerous microscopic organisms. When they die, many will sink down to the bottom. Some of these will then decompose, while many will leave behind hard shells and crusts that get covered up by the continuing rain of detritus and dirt that falls from above. Sediments are continually accumulating, and the deeper you dig into them, the further back in time you move. The basic paleolimnological approach is to take a sediment core, divide it into many sections of differing depths, identify the approximate age of each depth, and identify the remains of the organisms and other paleolimnological information found at each depth. By putting this information together, a researcher can infer shifts in lake communities over long periods of time. The validity of this entire process depends upon two critical assumptions: (1) you can accurately determine the age of each depth, and (2) the species you are measuring in the sediment cores are unbiased indicators of past lake conditions.

(a)

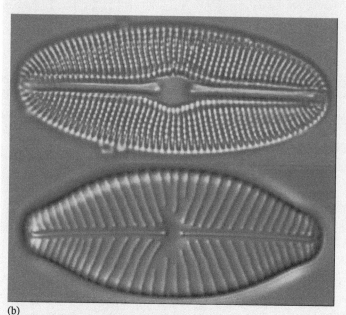

(b)

Figure 3.28 (*a*) A PEARL member collecting a sediment core while resting on the pontoon of a helicopter; (*b*) two species of diatoms showing clearly distinct morphologies.
(a) Kathleen Ruhland; (b) Kathleen Ruhland and Daniel Selbie.

Age

Sediment cores are generally removed from the lake bottom and divided into numerous thin segments. Each segment is then typically subjected to radioisotopic measurement to determine the approximate age of the cores. Accurate measures of age are highly dependent upon the ability of researchers in the field to take reliable and undisturbed

sediment cores. Any significant mixing of sediment during the field sampling will invalidate countless hours of work and cost thousands of dollars. Remember that even studies built upon high-tech analyses and microscopic imagery can fail if the most basic of methods are conducted poorly. Though one often associates the critical point of research as being the "eureka" ideas of the scientist, in fact those breakthroughs can never occur without painstakingly accurate data collection gathered through countless hours of dedicated work in the field and in the lab.

Species Identification

Not all species that live in lakes will be suitable indicator species for paleolimnological studies. Good candidates will be species found in large numbers in the cores that also have hard bodies resistant to decomposition. One commonly used group of algal species are diatoms. Diatoms have hard silicate "shells" and are dominant members of the phytoplankton and periphyton (algae attached to submerged surfaces in shallow waters) in most aquatic communities. The shapes and sculpturing of the silicate structures are species specific, and patterns of abundance for individual species can be followed throughout the depth of the core (fig. 3.28*b*). With over 10,000 species of diatoms, one can observe shifts in the abundance of different species through time, rather than just the presence or absence of diatoms as a group. Additionally, the environmental conditions that are required for the growth of many diatom species are well studied; thus, if paleolimnologists find that a given diatom species was abundant during a particular time period, they are able to infer something about the likely lake conditions, such as climate, pH, and nutrients during that time interval.

It is through linking species identification with basic knowledge about the natural history of these species that paleolimnologists are able to reconstruct lake conditions of times past. We will now explore an example that uses these research tools to address an ecological question.

Climate–Lake Linkages

Due to patterns of global water and air circulation and feedback among ice, snow, and the atmosphere, human-induced climate change is particularly pronounced in polar regions (Moritz et al. 2002). What is less well known is whether this warming is associated with broad ecological changes in arctic lakes (fig. 3.29). There is reason for concern, as primary production and nutrient cycling in arctic lakes are often limited by the short growth season. Increased temperatures could decrease ice cover, alter thermal stratification, and change nutrient cycling. Because all of these factors can influence the species composition of lakes, there is reason to believe that rapid climate change in arctic areas has resulted in rapid ecological shifts.

John Smol and colleagues (Smol et al. 2005) tested the hypothesis that lakes that experienced more climate change will also have experienced greater change in

(a)

(b)

Figure 3.29 Two typical high arctic lakes on Ellesmere Island, Canada. Ice can remain in the centre of some lakes year round.

(a) John Smol; (b) Bronwyn Keatly.

species composition than lakes that have experienced less climate change. They were able to obtain data on temperature changes over the last 50 years in the area of their study lakes, but to determine how ecosystems have changed on longer time frames, before instrumental data were available, they had to use indirect approaches. The team turned to paleolimnology for the tools needed to obtain the biological data. Sediment cores were obtained from lakes that ranged in latitude from 58° N to 82° N, with each core divided by depths, and ages and species composition of diatoms and other hard-bodied organisms were determined. Within each core, they estimated the amount of change in species composition over time, which they report as beta-diversity. The higher the value of beta-diversity, the greater the change in species composition within the lake during the time interval represented in the sediment core. Note that species composition can change over time for reasons other than climate change. To provide a measure of the background

level of change that occurs, Smol and colleagues used a group of 14 non-arctic lakes as a reference area.

Figure 3.30 shows that climate change has been most rapid at more northerly latitudes. Clearly, beta-diversity is higher at more northerly latitudes, suggesting that the rate of ecological change is associated with the rate of warming of a region. In fact, beta-diversity of 81% of the lakes north of the treeline was greater than that found in the reference lakes, while only 58% of the lakes south of the treeline had beta-diversity levels higher than the reference lakes.

These data are a good example of how describing a community in a rigorous scientific framework can lead to great insights into the basic ecology of systems. Although experimental approaches are useful for addressing many ecological questions, we must not forget that in many systems "natural experiments" have already occurred, with the results sitting at the bottom of a lake waiting to be collected.

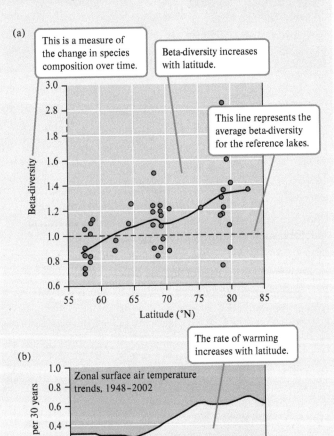

Figure 3.30 Change in (a) beta-diversity; and (b) air temperature as a function of latitude.

Figure 3 from https://www.pnas.org/content/102/12/4397 © J. P. Smol et al. 2005. Climate-driven regime shifts in the biological communities of arctic lakes. *Proceedings of the National Academy of Sciences of the United States of America* 102:4397–402. Copyright (2005) National Academy of Sciences, U.S.A.

CONCEPT 3.3 REVIEW

1. Dilution by discharging waste streams into water is still a commonly used strategy to manage waste. What are the problems in using dilution as a strategy?

2. Why is the prospect of global warming considered to be a serious threat to peatlands?

3. Are the principle threats from human activities the same for lakes and for oceans? How do threats change when we consider different aquatic systems? What ecological factors differ between lakes and marine habitats?

SUMMARY

Humans everywhere hold a land-centred perspective of the planet. However, aquatic life is often most profuse where conditions appear most hostile to people, for example, along cold, wave-swept seacoasts, in torrential mountain streams, and in the murky waters where rivers meet the sea.

3.1 The hydrologic cycle exchanges water among reservoirs.

Of the water in the biosphere, the oceans contain 97% and the polar ice caps and glaciers an additional 2%, leaving less than 1% as freshwater. The turnover of water in the various reservoirs of the hydrologic cycle ranges from only nine days for the atmosphere to 3,100 years for the oceans.

3.2 The biology of aquatic environments corresponds broadly to variations in physical factors, such as light, temperature, and water movements, and to chemical factors, such as salinity and oxygen.

Climate and geology directly and indirectly affect the physical and chemical properties of aquatic systems. In particular, temperature, flow of water, light availability, and water chemistry

shape biological communities (fig. 3.31). Differences in these properties among types of aquatic systems, or spatially and temporally within an aquatic system, help explain the differences in plant and animal diversity and distributions.

The *oceans* form the largest continuous environment on earth. An ocean is generally divided vertically into several depth zones, each with a distinctive assemblage of marine organisms. Limited light penetration restricts photosynthetic organisms to the photic, or epipelagic, zone and leads to thermal stratification. Highest productivity occurs along coastlines, for example in *kelp forests* and *coral reefs*. The open ocean supports large numbers of species and is important to global carbon and oxygen budgets.

Rivers and *streams* are dynamic systems and can be divided several ways into distinctive environments: longitudinally, laterally, and vertically. Periodic flooding has important influences on the structure and functioning of river and stream ecosystems. The flow and chemical characteristics of rivers change with climatic regime. Current speed, distance from headwaters, and the nature of bottom sediments are principal determinants of the distributions of stream organisms.

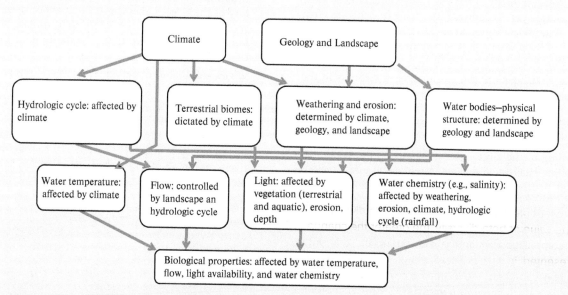

Figure 3.31 Concept map for chapter 3.

Lakes are much like small seas. Most are found in regions worked over by tectonics, volcanism, and glacial activity, the geological forces that produce lake basins. A few lakes contain most of the freshwater in the biosphere. Lake structure parallels that of the oceans but on a much smaller scale.

Peatlands occur primarily in northern latitudes and contain large stores of partially decomposed plant material. Bogs receive water only through precipitation and have very low pH. Fens are fed both through precipitation as well as ground or surface waters, with pH varying among fens. In all peatlands, oxygen levels and microbial activity are low. As a result, decomposition rates are slower than production rates, allowing for the accumulation of peat.

3.3 A variety of human activities affect the physical, chemical, and biological properties of aquatic systems.

Human activities include habitat modification (e.g., channel relocation and conversion of wetlands), which alters the physical structure of aquatic systems, particularly inland or coastal systems (fig. 3.31). Overexploitation of resources such as fish can change the abundance and diversity of aquatic systems. Discharge of wastes and nutrients alter the chemical environment and can result in changes in community composition, loss of biological diversity, and changes in productivity. Associated hypoxia can also change the distribution of benthic species. Our movements around the globe facilitate, accidentally or intentionally, biological invasions of aquatic systems. Our emissions of CO_2 and other greenhouse gases contribute to climate change, which can alter hydrologic cycles in some systems, increase temperatures of other systems, and contribute to the combined effects of warming and acidification on marine ecosystems, with consequent changes to biodiversity, abundance, and productivity of those systems.

REVIEW QUESTIONS

1. Review the distribution of water among the major reservoirs of the hydrologic cycle. What are the major sources of freshwater? Explain why, according to some projections, availability of freshwater may limit human populations and activity.

2. The oceans cover about 360 million km^2 and have an average depth of about 4,000 m. What proportion of this aquatic system receives sufficient light to support photosynthesis? Make the liberal assumption that the photic zone extends to a depth of 200 m.

3. Below about 600 to 1,000 m in the oceans there is no sunlight. However, many of the fish and invertebrates at these depths have eyes. In contrast, fish living in caves are often blind. What selective forces could maintain eyes in populations of deep-sea fish? (Hint: Many species of deep-sea invertebrates are bioluminescent.)

4. Why do you expect to see greater species richness in the near-shore marine environment (e.g., kelp forests or coral reefs) than in the photic zone of the open ocean? Why do we see more species in the benthos than in the water column in marine systems?

5. According to the river continuum model, the organisms inhabiting headwater streams in temperate forest regions depend mainly upon organic material coming into the stream from the surrounding forests. According to the model, photosynthesis within the stream is only important in the downstream reaches of these stream systems. Explain. How would you go about testing the predictions of the river continuum model?

6. How could you test the generalization that lake primary production and the composition of the biota living in lakes are strongly influenced by the availability of nutrients such as nitrogen and phosphorus? Assume that you have unlimited resources and that you have access to several lakes.

7. Biological interactions are important in shaping the distribution of species in a lake. How does the recent history of the Great Lakes (hint: think about recent invasive species) suggest that the interactions among species are important in determining the composition of the biological community?

8. Why are peatlands of particular interest to researchers who study climate change? What factors are likely to influence whether peatlands begin to release their vast stores of carbon into the atmosphere at a much faster rate?

9. What aspects of life in a bog may have favoured selection for carnivory in plants? Why are carnivorous plants relatively rare in all other types of communities, such as temperate forests, salt marshes, and even tropical forests?

CHAPTER 4   EVOLUTION AND SPECIATION

CHAPTER CONCEPTS

4.1 Phenotypic variation among individuals in a population results from the combined effects of genes and environment.

Concept 4.1 Review

4.2 Changes in gene frequency within a population can occur through both natural selection and random processes, such as genetic drift.

Ecology in Action: Human-Induced Evolution

Concept 4.2 Review

4.3 Physical and ecological processes interact with selection and drift to produce new species.

Concept 4.3 Review

Ecological Tools and Approaches: Integrating Population Genetics and Ecology

Summary

Review Questions

The great diversity of organisms that live on the planet, and the even greater diversity of organisms that have gone extinct (chapter 23), are the product of evolution and speciation. These organisms interact in countless ways with each other and their surroundings. The outcome of these ecological interactions influences an individual's survival and reproduction. These variations in survival and reproduction can lead to evolutionary changes, completing the circle. Ecological interactions are the mechanisms that allow for evolution by natural selection. Without these interactions, all individuals in a population would have the same likelihood of passing along genes to the next generation.

Because evolution is central to ecology, it is important that students of ecology have a broad understanding of evolution. Evolutionary biology is integrated into all chapters of this text, not simply in this chapter. However, to help you understand the usage of evolutionary terms and concepts later in the text, we provide a general overview of key aspects of evolutionary biology in this chapter. We begin with a single person who fundamentally changed human understanding of the natural world.

Darwin's theory of evolution by natural selection was crystallized by his observations in the Galápagos Islands. In mid-October of 1835, a small boat moved slowly from the shore of a volcanic island to a waiting ship. The boat carried a young naturalist who had just completed a month of exploring the group of islands known as the Galápagos, which lie on the equator approximately 1,000 km west of the South American mainland. As the seamen rowed into the oncoming waves, the naturalist, Charles Darwin, mused over what he had found on the island. His observations had confirmed expectations built on information gathered earlier on the other islands he had visited in the archipelago. Darwin (fig 4.1) recorded his thoughts in his journal, which he later published (Darwin 1839):

> The distribution of the tenants of this archipelago would not be nearly so wonderful, if, for instance, one island had a mocking-thrush, and a second island some other quite distinct genus—if one island had its genus of lizard and a second island another distinct genus, or none whatever. . . . But it is the circumstance, that several of the islands possess their own species of the tortoise, mocking-thrush, finches, and numerous plants, these species having the same general habits, occupying analogous situations, and obviously filling the same place in the natural economy of this archipelago, that strikes me with wonder.

Darwin wondered at the sources of the differences among clearly related populations and attempted to explain the origin of these differences. He would later conclude that these populations were descended from common ancestors whose descendants had changed after reaching each of the islands. The ship to which the seamen rowed was the HMS *Beagle,* halfway through a voyage around the world. The main objective of the *Beagle*'s mission, charting the coasts of southern South America, would be largely forgotten while the thoughts of the young Charles Darwin would eventually develop into one of the most significant theories in the history of science. Darwin's wondering, carefully organized and supported by a lifetime of

Figure 4.1   The work of Charles Darwin forms the foundation for modern evolutionary theory.
© FPG/Getty Images.

observation, would become the theory of evolution by natural selection, a theory that would transform the prevailing scientific view of life on earth and rebuild the foundations of biology. The theory of natural selection coupled with a strong understanding of natural history is a foundation of the science of ecology.

Darwin left the Galápagos Islands convinced that the various populations on the islands were gradually modified from their ancestral forms. In other words, Darwin concluded that the island populations had undergone a process of **evolution,** which changes populations of organisms over time. Though Darwin left the Galápagos convinced that the island populations had evolved, he had no mechanism to explain the evolutionary changes that he was convinced they had undergone. However, a plausible mechanism to produce evolutionary change in populations came to Darwin almost exactly three years after his taking leave of the Galápagos Islands. In October of 1838, while reading the essay on populations by Thomas Malthus, Darwin was convinced that during competition for limited resources—such as food or space—among individuals within populations, some individuals would have a competitive advantage. He proposed that the characteristics producing that advantage would be "preserved" and that the unfavourable characteristics of other individuals would be "destroyed." As a result of this selection by the environment, those individuals with favourable characteristics would have a greater chance of surviving and producing offspring than individuals without those characteristics. Another way of saying this is that some traits will increase the **fitness** of the individual that possesses that trait, while other traits will decrease the individual's fitness. If the traits can be passed from parent to offspring, the frequency of a trait that enhances fitness should increase in the next generation. Fitness is an individual's relative genetic contribution to all future generations, though Darwin was unaware of genetic mechanisms for his theory. Darwin sketched out the first draft of his theory of natural selection in 1842. It would take him many years and many drafts before he honed the theory to its final form and amassed sufficient supporting information. The theory of **natural selection** can be summarized as follows:

1. More offspring are produced each generation than can be supported by the environment.
2. There is variation in physical, physiological, and behavioural traits among individuals in a population. Some of this variation is heritable (passed on to offspring).
3. Some traits will give some individuals an advantage over the other members of the population. Individuals who possess those traits will have a higher chance of surviving and reproducing than the other members of the population, increasing their fitness.
4. Traits that result in increased fitness will become more common within a population over subsequent generations.

Darwin (1859) proposed that differential survival and reproduction of individuals would produce changes in species populations that increase the fitness of individuals within that environment. Put another way, evolution can lead to **adaptations.** Adaptations are not something that an individual develops out of need or desire; rather, they are traits that have been selected for through natural selection. Darwin now had a mechanism to explain the differences among populations that he had observed on the Galápagos Islands. Still, Darwin was aware of a major insufficiency in his theory. The theory of natural selection depended upon the passage of "advantageous" characteristics from one generation to the next. The problem was that the mechanisms of inheritance were unknown in Darwin's time. In addition, the prevailing idea at the time, blending inheritance, suggested that rare traits, no matter how favourable, would be blended out of a population, preventing change as a consequence.

Of course, it would be unjust not to mention the contributions of Alfred Russel Wallace. Wallace was another British naturalist who spent years travelling and describing the flora and fauna of the Amazon and later the Malay Archipelago and is often heralded as the father of biogeography. He described a divide (the "Wallace Line") between animal species of Asian origin and those of Australian origin that co-occupied the Malay Archipelago. Wallace and Darwin were correspondents who influenced each other's work but who independently proposed the transmutation of species through natural selection. In 1855, Wallace published an influential paper titled "On the Law Which Has Regulated the Introduction of New Species." In 1858, he sent his essay "On the Tendency of Varieties to Depart Indefinitely from the Original Type" to Darwin, asking him to review it and to pass it along to Charles Lyell if he felt it worthy. To establish Darwin's priority, Lyell and Joseph Hooker decided to publish a joint presentation containing Wallace's essay along with a previously unpublished essay of Darwin's, excerpted from a letter to Hooker in 1847. Wallace became one of the strongest defenders of Darwin's *On the Origin of Species* (1859), rebuking Darwin's critics. While many of Wallace's ideas were similar to those of Darwin, Darwin emphasized intraspecific competition for survival and reproduction whereas Wallace emphasized environmental pressures driving selection. Wallace also later proposed that natural selection could foster development of reproductive barriers against hybridization, enforcing reproductive isolation and contributing to speciation (the "Wallace Effect"). As we'll see, these are all key elements of evolutionary theory.

As Darwin explored the Galápagos Islands, halfway around the world in central Europe a schoolboy named Johann Mendel was beginning an education that would eventually lead him to uncover the basic mechanisms of inheritance. Although Darwin and Mendel did not work together, their studies have been combined by later generations to form our modern understanding of evolution by natural selection.

Johann would be renamed Gregor Mendel when he joined the Augustinian order of monks that maintained a monastery near his birthplace. In a garden within the walls of the abbey, Mendel would discover what Darwin's around-the-world voyage would not reveal. Working with the garden pea, *Pisum sativum,* he uncovered what we now call "Mendelian genetics," including the fundamental concept of particulate inheritance. That is the concept that characteristics pass from parent to offspring in the form of discrete packets of information that we now call genes. Mendel also determined that genes come in alternative forms, which we term **alleles.** For instance, Mendel worked with alleles that led to traits such as round versus wrinkled seeds and tall versus short plants. In addition, he found that some alleles prevent the expression of other alleles. We call such alleles *dominant* and the alleles that they suppress *recessive.* Mendel's work also revealed the distinction between genotype and phenotype and the difference between homozygous and heterozygous genotypes. Mendel's work, which disclosed still other aspects of the laws of inheritance, laid a solid foundation for the science of genetics.

In the early part of the twentieth century, the study of biology was largely fragmented, with poor communication among scientists working in different specialized fields. Mendel's work lay largely unnoticed by most of the scientific community until it was rediscovered by Hugo de Vries, a Dutch botanist who built upon Mendel's findings, originating the concept of the gene, introducing the term *mutation,* and developing the concept of evolution by mutation. Mendel's work was brought to a wider audience of botanists by William Bateson in 1900. Early acolytes of Mendel considered discrete inheritance patterns or large jumps in phenotype (resulting from large mutations) to be incompatible with the gradualism and continuous variation in phenotypic traits purported by Darwinians. Put simply, a deep rift separated the protogeneticists and the naturalists.

In the early 1900s, Ronald Fisher, one of the early population geneticists, began to reconcile the ideas of Charles Darwin and Gregor Mendel. He would soon be joined by many other scientists, notably Theodosius Dobzhansky, Ernst Mayr, E. B. Ford, Bernhard Rensch, Sergei Chetverikov, George Gaylord Simpson, and G. Ledyard Stebbins. The "modern synthesis," a term coined by Julian Huxley, would ultimately draw upon genetics, cytology, anatomy and physiology, ecology, and paleontology. It would form a bridge between geneticists and naturalists and would provide the modern framework for the study of biology as a much more integrated discipline with evolution at its core. The synthesis of the theory of natural selection and genetics gave rise to modern evolutionary ecology, a very broad field of study. Here we examine several major concepts within that broad discipline.

4.1 Variation Within Populations

Phenotypic variation among individuals in a population results from the combined effects of genes and environment. In natural selection, phenotypic variation provides the material upon which the environment acts. Determining the extent and sources of variation within populations is fundamental to evolutionary studies. Darwin's theory of natural selection sparked a revolution in thinking among biologists, who responded by studying variation among organisms in all sorts of environments. We have restricted ourselves to three examples below.

Variation in a Widely Distributed Plant

Jens Clausen, David Keck, and William Hiesey, who worked at Stanford University in California, conducted some of the most widely cited studies of plant variation. Their studies provided deep insights into the extent and sources of morphological variation in plant populations, including both the influence of environment and genetics. Though this research group and its successors studied nearly 200 species, they are best known for their work on *Potentilla glandulosa*, or sticky cinquefoil (fig. 4.2) (Clausen, Keck, and Hiesey 1940).

Clausen and his research team worked with clones of several populations of *P. glandulosa*, which they grew in three main experimental gardens: one at Stanford near the coast at an elevation of 30 m, another in a montane environment at an elevation of 1,400 m, and a third in an alpine environment at 3,050 m (fig. 4.3). Clausen and colleagues created clones of a plant from each elevation. They then transplanted clones from each elevation into common experimental gardens located at each elevation. In doing so, they established experimental conditions that could reveal potential genetic differences among populations and that could demonstrate adaptation by *P. glandulosa* populations to local environmental conditions.

The observed growth responses of *P. glandulosa* are summarized in figure 4.3. Plant height differed significantly among sites, indicating an environmental effect on plant morphology. However, plants taken from the lowland, mid-elevation, and alpine plants responded differently to the three environments. While the mid-elevation and alpine plants attained their greatest height in the mid-elevation garden, the lowland plants grew the tallest in the lowland garden.

Differences in response *among* clones (i.e., clones originating from different elevations) and *within* clones (i.e., clones originating from the same plant) provide complementary information. Differences in growth response *among* clones at the three common garden sites indicate genetic differences among

Figure 4.2   *Potentilla glandulosa,* sticky cinquefoil, grows from sea level to over 3,000 m elevation and shows remarkable morphological variation along this elevational gradient.
© A. Scott Earle.

lowland, mid-elevation, and alpine populations of *P. glandulosa.* Meanwhile, differences in growth response *within* clones grown at the three elevations are the result of environmental differences among the common garden sites, not genetic differences. This is an example of **phenotypic plasticity**—variation among individuals in form, function, or physiology as a result of environmental influences.

Other observations by Clausen, Keck, and Hiesey indicate that the genetic variation among the plant populations was associated with adaptation to local environments. For instance, most lowland plants died during their first winter in the alpine garden and those that survived did not produce seeds. Alpine plants showed the opposite trends. They had poor survival in the lowland garden and went dormant in winter, while the lowland plants remained active. Ecologists call such locally adapted and genetically distinctive populations within a species **ecotypes.**

Using transplant and common garden approaches, ecologists have learned a great deal about genetic variation among and within plant populations. These classical approaches, combined with modern molecular techniques, are rapidly increasing our knowledge of genetic variation in natural populations.

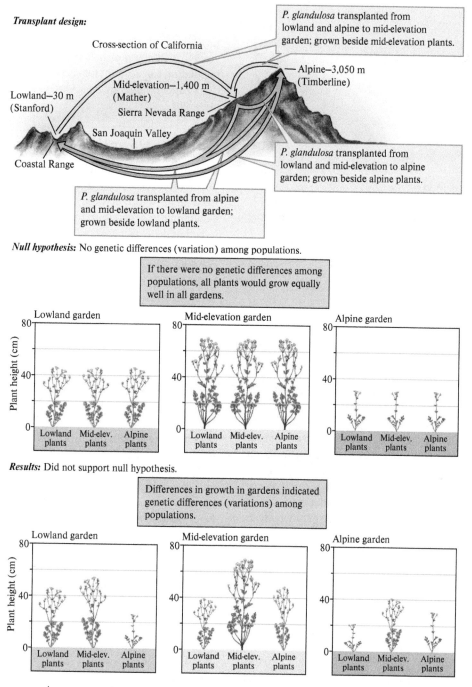

Figure 4.3 A common garden approach to studying genetic variation among populations of *Potentilla glandulosa*. Data from Clausen, Keck, and Hiesey 1940.

Variation in Trinidadian Guppies

If you have even a passing interest in aquariums, you will be familiar with guppies (fig. 4.4). They are a popular tropical fish because of the bright colour patterns in males and because they are easy to maintain. They are hardy and can tolerate a wide range of environmental conditions, which makes them a good choice for the more laissez-faire aquarium owner. They also have relatively high reproductive rates and they tolerate high density. These same traits make them important members of natural freshwater communities; they are common in freshwater pools and streams throughout much of the Caribbean Islands.

We generally learn about evolution as a slow, gradual process—something that operates on a much different time scale than ecological processes. However, in the past two decades it has become clear that trait evolution can occur on short time scales, comparable to those of ecological processes. This creates a strong interplay between evolution and ecology;

Figure 4.4 Trinidadian guppies (*Poecilia reticulata*), a popular aquarium fish and a model organism for evolution and ecology studies.
© Hadot/Dreamstime.com.

changes in the population's genetic and phenotypic variation can modulate expected ecological outcomes, while environmental change affects variation.

The effects of predation on trait evolution of guppies is well studied. David Reznick, Heather Bryga, and John Endler presented a classic paper on life-history evolution of guppies (*Poecilia reticulata*) in response to predation (Reznick et al. 1990). A cichlid predator (*Crenicichla alta*) preys primarily on larger guppies, whereas another natural predator, the killifish (*Rivulus hartii*), preys predominantly on smaller, juvenile stages of guppies. Reznick and colleagues manipulated a natural population of guppies by changing the life stage most vulnerable to predation, removing *C. alta* and replacing them with *R. hartii*. This manipulation led to significant evolutionary change in life history within only 11 years, or 30–60 generations of guppy. When predation pressure shifted from adult guppies to juvenile guppies, they matured later and produced fewer, but larger, offspring. Since this study, predation pressure has been invoked to explain variation in many other traits, including metabolic rates, coloration, and body shape. Evolution of guppy life history traits that diverge in high predation and low predation sites is also layered with differences in population structure (high predation sites have smaller fish with lower density) and environmental factors (low predation sites are typically well-shaded small streams, while high predation sites are typically open canopy and well lit).

As a dominant grazer, guppies play a key role in the recycling of nutrients in these ecosystems. Differences in the rates of nutrient recycling among populations of fish suggest variation in underlying traits related to organism physiology, behaviour, morphology, or tissue composition. If variation in these traits has a genetic basis, differences among populations in nutrient recycling could evolve. Rana El-Sabaawi (University of Victoria) and colleagues found that variation in life history traits of *P. reticulata*, evolving in response to predation pressure, affected

the fishes' rates of nutrient recycling (El-Sabaawi et al. 2015). Fish populations adapted to low predation pressure showed lower rates of ammonium excretion per individual. This suggests that the level or nature of predation pressure on a guppy population can account for variation in nutrient excretion rates, due to underlying trait evolution related to feeding behaviour or physiology.

Genetic Variation and Heritability

Darwin was aware that the only way natural selection can produce evolutionary change in a population is if the phenotypic traits upon which natural selection acts can be passed from generation to generation. In other words, evolution by natural selection depends upon the heritability of traits. We can define **heritability** of a trait—usually symbolized as h^2—in a broad sense as the proportion of total phenotypic variation in a trait, such as body size or eye colour, that is attributable to genetic variance. In equation form, heritability can be expressed as:

$$h^2 = V_G/V_T$$

Here V_G represents phenotypic variance that is based on genotype, and V_T represents total phenotypic variance. (See appendix A for how to calculate variance.) Phenotypic variance is caused by both genetic effects and environmental influences. For instance, the quality of food eaten by an animal can contribute to the growth rate of the animal and to its eventual size. Similarly, the amount of light, nutrients, temperature, and so forth affect the growth form and size of plants. So, when we consider a population of plants or animals, some of the phenotypic variance will be explained by genetics and some will be explained by environmental factors. There are several additional sources that can cause phenotypic variation (e.g., a genotype × environment interaction), though they are beyond the scope of this text. Subdividing V_T in the heritability equation into genetic variance and environmental variance (V_E) produces the following:

$$h^2 = V_G/(V_G + V_E)$$

What our equation says is that the heritability of a particular trait depends on the relative sizes of genetic versus environmental variance. Imagine a situation in which all phenotypic variation is the result of genetic differences between individuals, and none results from environmental effects. In such a situation, V_E is 0 and $h^2 = 1.0$. In this case, since all phenotypic variation is due to genetic effects, the trait is perfectly heritable. We can also imagine the opposite circumstance in which none of the phenotypic variation that we observe in a population is due to genetic variation. In this case, V_G is 0 and so the expression is $h^2 = 0$. Because all of the phenotypic variation we observe in this population is due to environmental effects, natural selection cannot produce evolutionary change in the population. Generally, heritability of traits falls somewhere in between these extremes in the very broad region where both environment and genes contribute to the phenotypic variance shown by a population. For instance, Peter Boag and Peter Grant (1978), the latter formerly a professor at McGill University, estimated bill width in the Galápagos finch (*Geospiza fortis*) to have a heritability of 0.95. By comparison, they estimated that bill length in the species has a heritability of 0.62. We might then expect evolution of bill width phenotype to be more responsive than bill length phenotype to natural selection pressures.

Sources of Genetic Variability

In order for natural selection to operate on any given trait, that trait must be variable within a population, and the variation must have (at least in part) a genetic basis ($h^2 > 0$). So, where does that variation come from? Think back to general biology. When a cell divides by mitosis, it produces two genetically identical daughter cells, right? Well, not exactly identical. When DNA is replicated, the fidelity in replication is astounding—but it is not perfect. The DNA replication machinery does a remarkable job in proofreading a newly synthesized DNA strand and in mismatch repair, but a small number of bases will remain incorrectly paired (the frequency of mistakes varies widely among different organisms, or even among gene loci within an organism's genome). Replication mistakes then introduce a small number of errors (mutations) into the genome with each cell division, and so no two cells are exactly alike. Certain chemicals or sources of energy (e.g., UVB) may damage DNA. Although the cell is very good at repairing damage, occasionally damage goes unrepaired. If mistakes occur within the coding region of a gene, a new allele for that gene is introduced. The allele may affect one or more amino acids in the primary sequence of the peptide coded by the gene. This could result in a new form of the protein and, perhaps, change the function of the protein anywhere along a spectrum from no effect to catastrophic effect. Under certain environmental conditions, the new allele may confer a fitness advantage and be selected for. More commonly, the new allele will have no effect (and selection is neutral) or have a negative effect on fitness and be selected against. It is important to remember that this occurs in all cells, but for sexually reproducing organisms only mutations in germ line cells introduce new alleles to a population. Mutations in somatic (body) cells may affect an individual's fitness but will not be passed on to offspring.

More dramatic genetic variation can be introduced through other processes you may remember from general biology. For example, a breakage in a chromosome is quickly repaired, but a broken fragment may be inverted during the process, reversing the sequence of genes along the fragment and changing their expression. If tetrad alignment is not perfect, exchange between non-sister chromatids during meiosis I may result in one chromatid receiving one or more duplicate genes, and another chromatid losing one or more genes. The offspring inheriting these different chromatids may over-express or under-express certain proteins. The effects on phenotype may result in greater or reduced fitness for the offspring inheriting these chromosomal variants. The phenotypic differences may also result in reproductive isolation between the offspring.

In the next section we will discuss how heritability and ecological interactions combine to cause evolution in natural populations.

CONCEPT 4.1 REVIEW

1. What is a fundamental evolutionary implication of the large amounts of genetic variation commonly found in natural populations?

2. What would you expect to see in figure 4.3 if alpine, mid-elevation, and lowland populations of *P. glandulosa* were not different genetically?

3. Can V_E be greater than V_G for a trait related to an organism's fitness? Explain.

4. Mutation of a gene in a dermal cell involved in cell cycle control makes the cell cancerous. Will this affect the fitness of offspring? Explain.

4.2   Evolution

Changes in gene frequency within a population can occur through both natural selection and random processes, such as genetic drift. These changes are often referred to as "microevolution." Processes that drive these changes can occur independently in isolated populations. These changes may accumulate, resulting in genetic divergence of the isolated populations. This is referred to as "macroevolution" and can lead to speciation.

In the previous sections of this chapter we have shown that phenotypic variation exists in natural populations, due to both environmental and genetic causes. Scientists George H. Hardy and Wilhelm Weinberg have shown independently that under a set of stringent conditions (e.g., infinitely large populations, random mating, no selection), allelic variations in a gene will naturally be maintained within a population. This idea is called the **Hardy-Weinberg principle** and serves as the starting point for a discussion of evolution. The Hardy-Weinberg principle provides a null model for microevolution. If the conditions are met, we should see no changes in gene frequency. If we see divergence from Hardy-Weinberg expectations, this suggests some evolutionary process is acting. In this section, we will link our understanding of variation and heritability to two mechanisms of evolutionary change: natural selection and genetic drift.

The Process of Natural Selection

The basic concept of natural selection is that some heritable traits result in unequal fitness among individuals in a population. As a consequence, over time there is an increase in the frequency of individuals that possess these favourable traits. Although this idea is easy enough to grasp, natural selection does not take the same form everywhere and at all times. Natural selection can act against different forms of a heritable trait under different circumstances. Any two populations will differ in genetic variance with respect to a given trait and will face different selective pressures. This may result in different trajectories in evolution of the trait. We will begin our discussion of natural selection by describing the major forms of selection that occur in a natural population, and then we will discuss the consequences on allelic frequencies.

Stabilizing Selection

One of the conclusions that we might draw from the discussion of genetic variability is that most populations have a high potential for evolutionary change. However, our observations of the natural world suggest that species can remain little changed generation after generation. If the potential for evolutionary change is high in populations, why do we see this phenotypic stability over long periods? One form of natural selection, called **stabilizing selection,** can act to impede directional changes in populations.

Stabilizing selection acts against extreme phenotypes and, as a consequence, favours the average phenotype. Figure 4.5a conceptualizes stabilizing selection, using a normal distribution of body size. Under the influence of stabilizing selection, individuals of average size have higher survival and reproductive rates, while the largest and smallest individuals in the population have lower rates of survival and reproduction. The population tends to sustain the same average phenotype over time while the frequency of extreme phenotypes decreases. If a population is well adapted to a given set of environmental circumstances, stabilizing selection may sustain the match between these prevailing conditions and average phenotype. This comes with a reduction in genetic variance with respect to the trait as the extreme phenotypes, and the associated genotypes, are selected against.

Directional Selection

If we examine the fossil record or trace the history of well-studied populations over time, we can find many examples of how populations have changed in many characteristics. For instance, there have been remarkable changes in body size or body proportions in many evolutionary lineages. Such changes may be the result of **directional selection.**

Directional selection favours an extreme phenotype over other phenotypes in the population. Prevailing conditions may change, and the average phenotype may no longer be well-matched to the environment. Or a new extreme phenotype may be introduced, by migration or mutation, that is better matched. Figure 4.5b presents an example of directional selection, again using a normal distribution of body size. In this hypothetical situation, larger individuals in

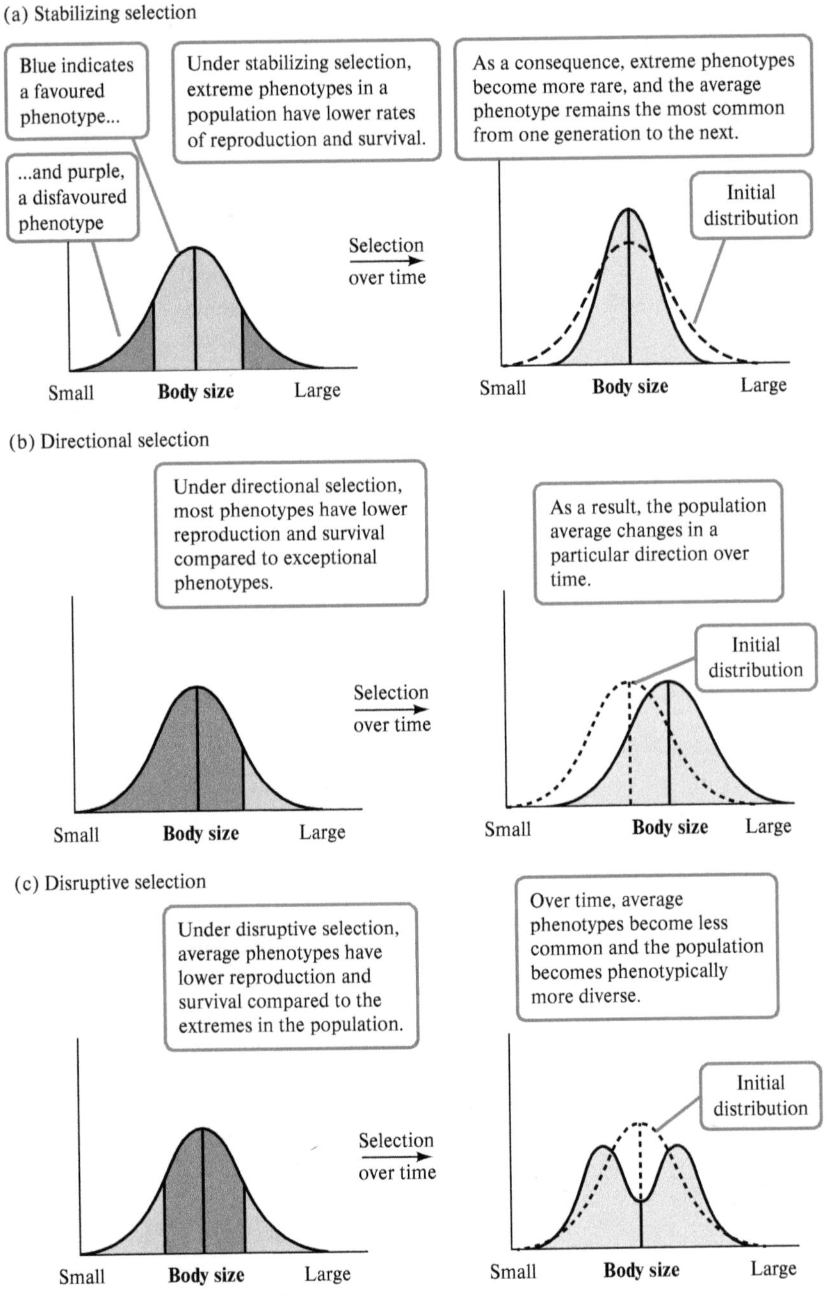

Figure 4.5 Three principle forms of natural selection: (*a*) stabilizing selection, (*b*) directional selection, and (*c*) disruptive selection.

the population realize higher rates of survival and reproduction, while average and small individuals have lower rates of survival and reproduction. As a consequence of these differences, the average body size changes over time.

Disruptive Selection

There are populations that do not show a normal distribution of characteristics such as body size. In some populations, there may be more than one common phenotype. In many animal species, for example, males may be of two discrete sizes. In these species, natural selection seems to favour both extreme phenotypes over the average phenotype; small and large males have higher reproductive success than males of intermediate body size (fig. 4.5c). This is an example of **disruptive selection**. As a consequence, both smaller and larger individuals increase in frequency in the population over time, while individuals with intermediate body size decrease in frequency.

Different types of selection (stabilizing, directional, and disruptive) can operate within a population simultaneously. An average phenotype for a given trait may be stabilized, while an extreme phenotype for a different trait may be selected for or against. One factor that can also vary is the rate of evolution due to natural selection. This is a function of a trait's heritability, as discussed above. It is also a function of the strength of selection. As you can imagine, not all selective pressures are equally strong. Strength of selective pressure can be related to externalities. For example, a rapidly changing set of environmental conditions can impose a strong selective pressure. Strength of selective pressure can also relate to internalities; not all traits are equal contributors to fitness. If, for example, a phenotype that is associated with a given trait is lethal, there is strong selection against that phenotype and evolution is rapid. A phenotype associated with another trait may affect fitness more subtly, requiring thousands of generations before any measurable shift in gene frequency can be found.

Having now introduced the three fundamental modes of natural selection, we provide an example to illustrate each. We will discuss stabilizing selection in egg size for a Ural owl population, directional selection (imposed by hunting) in a population of bighorn sheep (see Ecology in Action), and disruptive selection in a finch population on the Galápagos Islands.

Stabilizing Selection for Egg Size Among Ural Owls

Egg size affects offspring development and survival and thereby affects fitness in many species. Egg size can be highly variable within populations. Pekka Kontiainen and colleagues at the Bird Ecology Unit (University of Helsinki, Finland) studied heritability, phenotypic plasticity, and evolution of egg size in the Ural owl (*Strix uralensis*) (Kontiainen et al. 2008). One of their key questions was how much of the variation in egg size is the result of genetic differences among females (heritability)

and how much is the result of environmental influences (phenotypic plasticity).

Ural owls tend to stay within the pair's territory even when prey populations fluctuate, in contrast with some more nomadic owl species. The main prey species for the owls in the study were field voles (*Microtus agrestis*) and bank voles (*Clethrionomys glareolus*), which undergo regular population cycles in the study area, fluctuating in population density up to 50-fold over time. During the course of their study, the research team made repeated size measurements of eggs laid by 344 female Ural owls in 878 clutches containing a total of nearly 3,000 eggs. The great variation in the owl's prey population combined with its site tenacity provided an opportunity to study the effects of environment versus genetics on egg size. Based on measurements of eggs laid during three phases of a vole population cycle (low, increasing, and decreasing), Kontiainen and colleagues found egg size to be a heritable trait ($h^2 = 0.60$) that could be subject to evolution by natural selection.

In other parts of the study, the research team found that very small and very large eggs hatch at a lower rate compared to intermediate-sized eggs (fig. 4.6). Moreover, females that produced extremely small or large eggs produced fewer fledglings over the course of their lives, mainly because females producing eggs at the extremes of the size distribution had shorter reproductive lives. The result of these combined effects is stabilizing selection for egg size in this population of Ural owls.

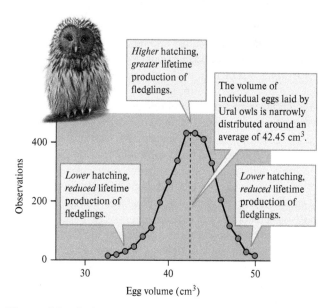

Figure 4.6 Stabilizing selection for egg volume in the Ural owl (*Strix uralensis*). Lower hatching rates by very small and very large eggs combined with reduced lifetime production of fledglings by female owls laying very small or very large eggs sustain stabilizing selection for egg volume in this population of Ural owls.

Data from Kontiainen et al. 2008.

ECOLOGY IN ACTION

Human-Induced Evolution

When we talk about evolution and natural selection, we often think about the Galápagos Islands and Darwin's finches or other species responding to challenges in remote areas of the world. However, this view that evolution is something that happens only in the wilderness is not reflective of reality. Instead, there is reason to believe that humans are the greatest evolutionary force in the world (Palumbi 2001). Humans live, farm, fish, hunt, and build, placing direct selection pressure on populations of many species. Industrial emissions impact even the most remote corners of the globe. These direct and indirect changes impose strong selective pressures on natural populations and can drive observable evolutionary change.

Evidence for evolution by natural selection is everywhere. For example, what does it mean when you hear that some disease-causing bacterium has developed antibiotic resistance? It means that at one point in time a species of bacteria could be killed by the application of some toxin (e.g., an antibiotic). Obviously, this puts an enormous directional selective pressure on the bacterial population, such that any individuals immune to that toxin will have a much higher fitness than those that are killed. As a result, the frequency of the genes that confer resistance increase within the population. This eventually reaches a point where the bacterial population consists primarily of individuals that cannot be killed by that particular antibiotic. This is evolution by natural selection, and it is a serious concern among medical professionals. Development of antibiotic resistance is widespread and rapid. The first evidence of resistance to a new antibiotic generally occurs within 10 years of the drug's first being introduced (Palumbi 2001).

We see similar patterns emerge in plant and insect populations in response to herbicides and insecticides. The introduction of new pesticides imposes a strong selective pressure favouring those individuals with genetic-based resistance. The result is rapid evolution in **weed** populations and populations of common insect pests, rendering the chemicals used to control these populations ineffective.

This pattern extends beyond plants and animals with short generation times. Bighorn sheep live throughout the Rocky Mountains in Western Canada and the United States. Hunters pay thousands of dollars for a licence allowing them to harvest an individual ram. Hunters are especially looking for trophy rams: particularly large rams with big horns (fig. 4.7). David Coltman of the University of Alberta and colleagues from the Université de Sherbrooke, the Alberta Department of Sustainable Development, and the United States decided to explore the evolutionary consequences of trophy hunting in a population of bighorn sheep (Coltman et al. 2003). Coltman explored a data set that contained the measurements of 192 harvested and unharvested rams between 1971 and 2002. This data set also contained information about the parents of all individuals; thus, patterns of paternity could be established.

Figure 4.7   Continued trophy hunting of mountain sheep has caused evolutionary changes in body size and horn length.
Jocelyn Poissant.

Both horn length and body size are heritable traits ($h^2 = 0.69$, 0.41, respectively) that affect fitness. Larger males with bigger horns are likely to sire more offspring than males that are smaller in size or that have smaller horns.

What might happen when hunters begin to kill those males with higher breeding success (i.e., large males with large horns)? Increased risk of mortality means that individual rams are less likely to produce the number of offspring that they would in the absence of harvesting. As a result, the trait that used to confer a fitness advantage (size and horn length) now provides a fitness disadvantage and should become less common in the population through natural selection. This is in fact what Coltman and his colleagues found (fig. 4.8a): longevity decreased with horn-length breeding values, as did the number of paternities. Coltman also found that weight and horn-length breeding values decreased through the course of the study (fig. 4.8b). These results indicate that traits that historically conferred fitness benefits to males, such as enhanced size and larger horns, were becoming liabilities due to human-induced selection. What does this mean over the long term? If these current trends continue, it is reasonable to expect to find this population dominated by smaller males with shorter horns. This may then decrease the attraction of trophy hunting in this population, relaxing this selection pressure. As you can see, evolution by natural selection is continuous.

The example above occurred through the intervention of people; however, the origin of selective pressures (natural or human imposed) is irrelevant to evolutionary processes. What influences gene frequencies is whether there is a shift in the phenotype with the highest fitness, not why that shift has occurred. People can alter the fitness associated with different phenotypes in wild populations, and evolution occurs exactly as is predicted by theory. People cannot be thought of as distinct from the functioning of "natural" populations, for our actions alter the evolutionary trajectories of countless numbers of species. In fact, by understanding the evolutionary responses of different species to our actions, we may be better able to develop sustainable practices that decrease the likelihood of negative changes to natural population.

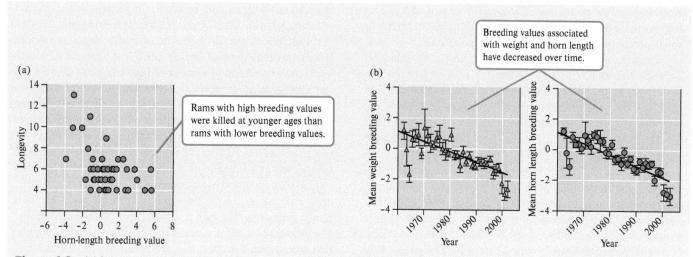

Figure 4.8 (*a*) Longevity decreases with increased horn-length breeding value of harvested rams. (*b*) Mean-weight and horn-length breeding values have decreased over the last 30 years of trophy hunting.

(a), (b) Reprinted by permission from Macmillan Publishers Ltd: NATURE. D. W. Coltman et al. 2003. Undesirable evolutionary consequences of trophy hunting. *Nature* 426:65. Copyright 2003. Used with permission via Rightslink.

Disruptive Selection in a Population of Darwin's Finches

As we have seen, the Galápagos Islands and their inhabitants played a key role in the development of Darwin's theory of evolution by natural selection. Darwin was particularly impressed by the variation in a group of 14 bird species now most commonly known as "Darwin's finches" or, less commonly, as "Galápagos finches." In the second edition of his journal recording his voyage on the *Beagle* (Darwin 1842), Darwin suggests the influence of these birds on his thinking:

> The most curious fact is the perfect gradation in the size of the beaks of the different species of *Geospiza* [a genus of Darwin's finches]—Seeing this gradation and diversity of structure in one small, intimately related group of birds, one might really fancy that, from an original paucity of birds in this archipelago, one species had been taken and modified for different ends. (p. 364)

Darwin's musing anticipated the great contribution made by studies of his finches to our understanding of the evolutionary process. For instance, a recent study led by Andrew Hendry at McGill University provides one of the clearest and most complete examples of disruptive selection in a natural population. Andrew Hendry, Sarah Huber, Luis de León, Anthony Herrel, and Jeffrey Podos (2009) discovered that the *Geospiza fortis* population at El Garrapatero, Santa Cruz Island, Galápagos, is dominated by two distinctive groups of individuals: those with small beaks and those with large beaks (fig. 4.9). Peter Boag and Peter Grant (1978) had previously shown that beak length, depth, and width are highly heritable ($h^2 = 0.62, 0.82$, and 0.95, respectively) and could be subject to natural selection. The study by Hendry and colleagues found that birds with intermediate beak size had higher mortality or possibly higher emigration than birds with small or large beaks. The researchers proposed that this higher mortality/

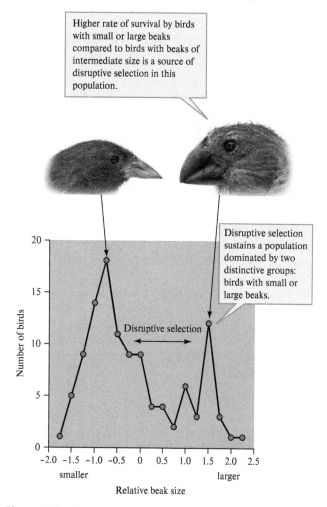

Figure 4.9 Disruptive selection in a population of medium ground finches (*Geospiza fortis*) at El Garrapatero, Santa Cruz Island, Galápagos.

Data from Hendry et al. 2009.

emigration might be the result of either a lack of appropriate food for these birds and/or competition with the more abundant small- and large-beaked individuals in the population.

Ongoing studies have revealed that disruptive selection on beak size at El Garrapatero is reinforced by nonrandom patterns of mate choice in the population. Nonrandom mating itself can be a source of evolutionary change in populations (see also chapter 8) because it violates one of the conditions for Hardy-Weinberg equilibrium. Darwin's finches choose mates at least partly on the basis of beak size and mating song. This is true of the *G. fortis* population as well, and contributes to genetic isolation within the population. Individuals with small beaks mate preferentially with other small-beaked individuals, while large-beaked finches disproportionately choose mates that also have large beaks (de León et al. 2010). Males in the populations having different beak sizes also sing distinctive songs, which may reinforce nonrandom mating (Podos 2010). Disruptive selection reinforced by nonrandom mating has produced genetic differences between small- and large-beaked *G. fortis* at El Garrapatero, further underscoring the evolutionary divergence between the two dominant beak morphs at that site.

Evolution Through Genetic Drift

We often think of evolutionary change as a consequence of natural selection, predictable forces that favour particular genotypes over others. However, allele frequencies also change as a consequence of random processes, such as genetic drift. In fact, genetic drift occurs in all sexually reproducing populations at all times. The strength of drift and the resulting evolutionary change is much greater in small populations than in large ones. Here we will first discuss what genetic drift is and then provide examples of how drift causes evolution in nature.

How Does Genetic Drift Occur?

Consider an individual that is heterozygous at a given gene locus (*Aa*). Following meiosis, one-half of the gametes this individual produces will be *A* and one-half will be *a*. Within the tiny gene pool that is this individual, the allelic ratio (*A:a*) is 1:1. Now suppose this individual mates with another heterozygous individual who also produces *A:a* gametes in a 1:1 ratio. Any offspring produced may be *AA*, *Aa*, or *aa*. If these two individuals produce an infinite number of offspring, this will result in genotypic frequencies of:

$$AA = 0.5(A) \times 0.5(A) = 0.25$$

$$Aa = 0.5(A) \times 0.5(a) + 0.5(a) \times 0.5(A) = 0.50$$

$$aa = 0.5(a) \times 0.5(a) = 0.25$$

The result contributed to the development of the Hardy-Weinberg principle, which states that in an infinitely large population, mating at random and in the absence of evolutionary forces, allele frequencies will remain constant over time. In the absence of selection, gene frequencies in infinitely large populations will remain constant. In other words, without selection, genetic diversity will not be lost within a population.

Populations are not, however, infinitely large. Let us consider an extremely small population. What happens if two *Aa* individuals breed and produce only three offspring? Clearly, it is not possible to produce 25% *AA* offspring, 50% *Aa*, and 25% *aa* (the predictions of Hardy-Weinberg) when only three offspring are produced. Suppose that the three offspring had the following genotypes: *Aa*, *Aa*, and *aa*. The allelic ratio is no longer 1:1 (*A:a*). Instead it is 1:2 (*A:a*). In the absence of any selective pressure, purely as a function of chance and compounded by small sample size, evolution has occurred. This is evolution by genetic drift, and this is just as real a mechanism for evolution as is natural selection. The rate of evolution by genetic drift scales inversely with population size (fig. 4.10). In a very small population, as illustrated in the above example, this rate can be rapid. Yet even in large populations, random chance will change allele frequencies over time.

Genetic drift occurs on all loci within a genome, not only those upon which selection acts. Loss of genetic variation through drift, particularly loss of rare alleles, is a significant concern for small populations, such as those often found in endangered species and on isolated habitats, such as mountain tops and islands.

Genetic Drift in Chihuahua Spruce

One concern associated with human activities on the landscape is that reducing habitat availability will decrease the size of animal and plant populations to the point where genetic drift will reduce the genetic diversity.

Many natural populations have undergone fragmentation as a consequence of changing climates and natural habitat fragmentation. One of those is the Chihuahua spruce (*Picea chihuahuana*), which is now restricted to the peaks of the Sierra Madre Occidental in northern Mexico (fig 4.11). During the Pleistocene glacial period, when the global climate was much cooler, spruce were found much farther south in Mexico and in more extensive populations. Today, all spruce populations in Mexico are restricted to small, highly fragmented areas of subalpine environment in the mountains of Chihuahua and Durango.

The Chihuahua spruce in the state of Chihuahua have been located and counted, with local populations ranging in size from 15 to 2,441 individuals. A joint team of U.S. and Mexican scientists considered whether the Chihuahua spruce has lost genetic diversity as a consequence of reduced population size following climatic warming after the end of the last ice age (Ledig et al. 1997). They were also interested in whether reduced genetic diversity may contribute to continuing decline of the species and its potential for extinction.

Ledig and colleagues found a positive correlation between population size and genetic diversity of their study populations (r = 0.93, n = 7), indicating that the smallest populations of Chihuahua spruce have much lower levels of genetic diversity than the largest populations. It seems clear that drift is causing evolution and reducing genetic diversity in these populations of spruce. Many other researchers have shown similar patterns for

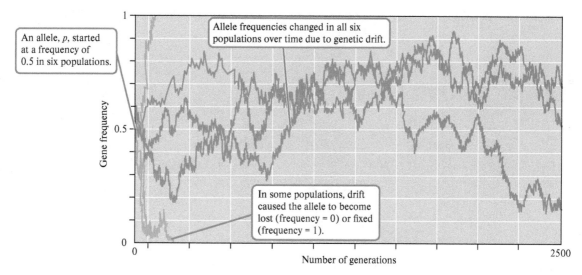

An allele, *p*, started at a frequency of 0.5 in six populations.

Allele frequencies changed in all six populations over time due to genetic drift.

In some populations, drift caused the allele to become lost (frequency = 0) or fixed (frequency = 1).

Figure 4.10 Random events cause allelic frequencies to change over time in a process called genetic drift. Here, three large populations (blue) and three small populations (green) each started with the frequency of an allele = 0.5. Even in the absence of selection, gene frequencies changed over time in all populations. However, the rate of change was much faster in the small populations. Note, too, that in the three small populations, random mating caused the allele to be lost in two populations and fixed in the third.

Figure 4.11 Barrancas Mirador in the Sierra Madre Occidental of Chihuahua. Chihuahua spruce are isolated near peaks of the mountain range.
Steven dosRemedios/Getty Images.

other species of plants, as well as numerous species of animals. As we will see next, populations that colonize new areas are also likely to have low genetic diversity.

Founder Effect in Newfoundland Moose

The geographic range over which a species occurs changes through time. Expansion of a species range into a new area often begins with a small group of colonists. When they arrive in a new habitat, they represent a small sample of the gene pool from which they came. They cannot possibly encompass the full genetic diversity of that pool. If these colonists are followed by a larger tide of immigrants, the resulting population may be genetically similar to, and reflect the genetic diversity of, the parent population. But what if there is no later substantial tide?

The founding group may, by chance, have a higher or lower frequency of rare alleles. Being a very small population, the founding population will be highly susceptible to genetic drift. The population that grows from this initial small founding group may have very different gene frequencies from the parent population, typically characterized by much lower genetic diversity. This is referred to as the **founder effect**. An example of founder effects is provided by Hugh Broders, now at St. Mary's University, who led a team of researchers from Memorial University and the Newfoundland and Labrador Department of Forest Researcher and Agrifoods.

Moose (*Alces alces*) appear throughout the boreal forests of North America. Moose (fig. 4.12) have lived in much of their range for thousands of years, while in other areas they are recent colonists. As of 1999, there were 150,000 moose in Newfoundland, with an additional 400,000 legally harvested since the late nineteenth century (Broders et al. 1999). This is not particularly surprising, until one learns that moose were historically absent from Newfoundland and Labrador and that all of these moose are descendants of just three individuals brought

Figure 4.12   Moose (*Alces alces*), recently introduced to Newfoundland and reintroduced to Cape Breton, are good examples of populations shaped by the founder effect.
Jupiterimages/Getty Images.

over from Nova Scotia in 1878 and three individuals brought from New Brunswick in 1904 (Pimlott 1953). Cape Breton historically had a moose population until humans extirpated them through hunting. In 1947–48, 18 moose were brought in from Alberta to re-establish a Cape Breton population. Broders and his colleagues wanted to know what effects these small initial population sizes had on the genetic diversity of moose.

The rapid development of relatively inexpensive molecular tools has revolutionized the study of population genetics, leading to the development of the field of molecular ecology (see Ecological Tools and Approaches, this chapter). Broders was among the first to use these tools to address an issue of conservation concern, and he turned to **microsatellites** to quantify genetic diversity. The microsatellites used in ecological studies are generally non-coding and, thus, not subject to selection. As a result, mutations will accumulate over time, resulting in different alleles within and between populations. More genetically diverse populations will have more individuals that are *heterozygous* at the microsatellite loci, while low genetic diversity will result in more *homozygosity* within the population.

Broders worked with hunters and wildlife officials in 11 regions in Alberta, Ontario, New Brunswick, Nova Scotia,

and Newfoundland and Labrador to collect muscle samples from 563 moose. The researchers then extracted the DNA from these samples and used five polymorphic (multiple alleles) microsatellite loci to determine the genetic diversity of the different populations. There was strong evidence for a founder effect associated with the introduction of moose to Cape Breton and Newfoundland. Cape Breton moose had 14% less heterozygosity than the Alberta population, and the central Newfoundland population had 23% less heterozygosity than the New Brunswick population. These findings show that colonization by few individuals comes at a cost of low genetic diversity.

Why should ecologist care about the genetic diversity of natural populations and the effects of processes such as genetic drift and founder effects? Genetic diversity can impact the long-term sustainability of natural populations. Changes in climate, new diseases, and other stressors often require specific adaptations to allow individuals to cope. If a population is genetically homogeneous, it is unlikely that novel solutions are lurking within the genomes of individuals; thus, the population is at greater risk of extinction as its environment changes.

CONCEPT 4.2 REVIEW

1. If you observe no changes in gene frequencies in a population over several generations, can you conclude that the population is not subject to natural selection?

2. What factors can lead to low genetic diversity within a population?

3. Can a trait with no heritability ($h^2 = 0$) evolve? Explain.

4. Consider a trait that is heritable and that contributes subtly to increased fitness. Would you expect natural selection or gene drift to have a more profound effect on evolution of that trait? How might the context of population size affect your answer?

4.3 Speciation

Physical and ecological processes interact with selection and drift to produce new species. Natural selection and genetic drift are two mechanisms that can cause dramatic changes in gene frequencies within a population. Such evolutionary changes have obvious implications for interactions among individuals within the larger ecological community. For example, selection toward larger body size in a predator may alter the intensity of predation experienced by the prey. What we have not yet discussed is what happens over even longer time scales, where large changes in gene frequencies can result in the evolution of a new species. Species are the raw material for all ecological interactions; therefore, any process that can alter the rate of speciation has significant ecological consequences. In this section we will discuss a variety of mechanisms that can cause speciation. However, before we can discuss how species evolve, we must first have an understanding of what we mean by *species*.

What Is a Species?

This at first may seem like a trivial question, but in fact this issue is at the heart of substantial disagreement among researchers. Originally, groups of individuals that shared similar morphologies were grouped together as members of a single species. This approach was championed by Carl Linnaeus (later Carolus Linneaus, or Carl von Linné), who is responsible for the Linnaean classification system that is currently used by many biologists. At the essence of this approach lies the concept of Platonic idealism in which there is a single truth that is unchanging. By extension, under the Linnaean system, species were discrete units that were constant through time.

The **morphological species concept** is still widely used. However, the definition of *species* more widely used by ecologists and evolutionary biologists is the **biological species concept,** presented by Ernst Mayr in 1942. Mayr defined *species* as "groups of actually or potentially interbreeding natural populations, which are reproductively isolated from other such groups" (Mayr 1942, p. xxi). This definition of *species* is not based upon arbitrary descriptions of morphology or upon patterns of occurrence. Instead, it is based upon a real (and measurable) ecological concept: reproductive isolation. The morphological species concept is still useful as a construct, particularly when we are considering extinct species with no way to determine whether they could potentially interbreed. Morphological variation may be used to infer levels of gene flow. In paleontology, we may find two fossil specimens with distinct differences in metacarpal length, for example. As metacarpal length is a trait under genetic control, this difference suggests limited gene flow between the populations represented. They likely could not or did not interbreed.

Even with this seemingly precise definition of *species*, we run into some troubles when we look at the population genetics of natural species. Over large geographic areas, an **ecocline** (or **cline**) will exist for some species. An ecocline is a gradual change in genotype and/or phenotype of a species over a large geographic area. Individuals of a species on opposite ends may appear quite different from each other; however, there is no specific location at which individuals "became" different. Other species may consist of a number of distinct ecotypes, a genetically identifiable subclass of a species that has evolved in response to local environmental conditions. If genetically distinct enough, ecotypes can eventually be designated as subspecies or even separate species.

Although the biological species concept is the one most people are familiar with, and one that works well for organisms such as vertebrates and arthropods, it is a poor definition of *species* for many of the organisms that exist on the planet. Many bacteria, fungi, and even plants and animals rarely interbreed, even with individuals from the same "species." Instead, reproduction is often asexual. Additionally, many species readily form viable hybrids with individuals of other species. In these situations, the biological species concept breaks down. If a particular species of fungus consists of many genotypes, none of which ever interbreed, does this mean that each genotype is its own species? If individuals of two seemingly different species are able to produce a viable offspring just once, is that enough to declare them to be of a single species? There are no clear answers, though there are many alternative species concepts that are independent of reproduction. For example, the *phylogenetic species concept* defines *species* based upon evolutionary history and phylogenetic similarity. There is growing support for this concept. Ecologists' increased focus on microbial organisms, coupled with the increased availability of molecular methods, will likely make this species concept more common over the next decade. A more exhaustive discussion of alternative species concepts is beyond the scope of this book. For now, we will simply pretend we never even asked the question and instead try to distract you by talking about sex.

What Is Reproductive Isolation?

As you see from Mayr's definition of *species*, a critical requirement is reproductive isolation between populations. What is not clear, however, is how you go from having a single population of

Essential steps to producing offspring

	Step	Isolating Mechanism
Prezygotic	Find a mate	Ecological
	Both be fertile	Temporal
	Give & receive mating cue	Behavioural
	Mate & form zygote	Mechanical
Postzygotic	Zygote & embryonic development	Hybrid inviability
	Production of grandchildren	Hybrid sterility

Figure 4.13 Reproductive isolation can occur from a diversity of pre- and postzygotic isolating mechanisms.

interbreeding individuals to two populations of reproductively isolated individuals and, thus, two species. To answer this, we need to identify the mechanisms that can cause reproductive isolation.

Isolating mechanisms can be roughly categorized into two groups: pre- and postzygotic isolating mechanisms (fig. 4.13). Prezygotic isolating mechanisms are processes that prevent two individuals from forming a zygote. Postzygotic isolating mechanisms are equally efficient at maintaining species integrity, but they occur after a zygote has been formed.

How do two individuals actually produce a zygote? Though this is the sort of question discussed in grade 4 health class (Ontario's new curriculum notwithstanding), discussion of sex may be equally relevant to university-level ecology students. Two individuals need to find each other, they both need to be sexually receptive at the same time, they need to engage in certain behaviours that allow for mating, their reproductive organs need to be compatible, and the sperm and egg need to be able to fuse. Things can go wrong at any of these steps; therefore, there are a variety of possible prezygotic isolating mechanisms. Ecological isolation occurs when two individuals are physically separated, such that they are unable to encounter each other. This could be as extreme as being isolated on different continents or more subtle, such as being restricted to different heights within a single forest canopy. Temporal isolation occurs when individuals are fertile at different times, such that even if they do encounter each other, they are not both producing viable gametes. Behavioural isolation is found in many animal species that require specific behaviours by one or both partners prior to mating (see chapter 9). Even if both individuals are fertile and appear in the same location, they may not mate if the proper behavioural cues have not been received by one or both individuals. Mechanical isolation can be as obvious as the two individuals having genitalia that simply do not fit together. Mechanical isolation can also be more subtle, such as an inability of one plant's pollen tube to grow through the style of another, or use of different pollinators.

Suppose two individuals have made it through all of these potential isolating mechanisms and formed a zygote. A variety of postzygotic isolating mechanisms exist that can be equally effective at preventing the production of a viable offspring. Hybrid inviability results if zygotic development is abnormal and the developing hybrid dies prior to sexual maturity. Hybrid sterility occurs if the hybrid develops normally but is unable to produce viable gametes.

Figure 4.13 summarizes the steps that must occur for the production of a viable offspring. Evolution can create barriers anywhere along this pathway, and if these changes are of a sufficient magnitude, reproductive isolation can occur and lead to speciation. What factors influence the evolution of the isolating mechanisms?

What Causes Speciation?

The Hardy-Weinberg principle shows that under a certain set of restrictive assumptions, gene frequencies will not change over time. However, in real-world populations, both genetic drift and natural selection can cause significant shifts in gene frequencies. If this occurs for a trait that influences reproduction, reproductive isolation can occur. We generally divide speciation into three forms: allopatric, parapatric, and sympatric.

Allopatric, or *geographic,* **speciation** occurs when a single population becomes spatially subdivided into multiple subpopulations (fig. 4.14). How does a population become spatially subdivided? The most obvious example would be if a mountain range divides a previously contiguous area, and it is impossible for individuals of a species to cross that divide. The appearance of a mountain or river may seem unlikely to occur in ecological timescales, but these events do occur in the deeper scales of geologic and evolutionary time. Faster processes of geographic isolation are also possible, such as the formation of a new river, island, or lake. A second form of speciation, **parapatric speciation,** occurs when a population expands into a new habitat within the pre-existing range of the parent species. For example, individuals of a forest-dwelling species may possess mutations that allow them to live within the grassland areas on the landscape. If these subpopulations do not interbreed, reproduction isolation may evolve, leading to speciation.

In both allopatric and parapatric speciation, the evolution of reproductive isolation could occur through drift or natural selection. Since genetic drift is random, fluctuations in allele frequencies in subpopulations will be independent; thus, loss of genetic diversity through drift could lead to reproductive isolation. Alternatively, many geographic barriers may alter the local environment, or many new habitats within a landscape may contain a new microclimate. In such cases, there could be differential selective pressures on the subpopulations, and genetic differentiation could occur. If this influences a trait related to the production of a viable offspring, reproductive isolation and speciation can occur.

Sympatric speciation has historically been more controversial among ecologists and evolutionary biologists, with many believing that it does not occur. In sympatric speciation, a single parent population forms genetically distinct subpopulations without any geographic barrier or spatial isolation (fig. 4.14). It is unlikely that genetic drift is important in sympatric speciation, and instead it is natural selection that drives this process.

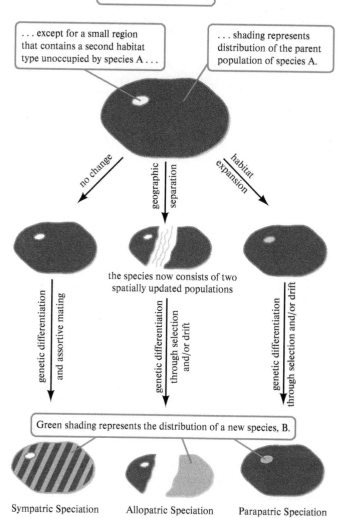

This landscape initially consists primarily of a single habitat type, occupied by species A . . .

. . . except for a small region that contains a second habitat type unoccupied by species A . . .

. . . shading represents distribution of the parent population of species A.

no change

geographic separation

habitat expansion

the species now consists of two spatially updated populations

genetic differentiation and assortive mating

genetic differentiation through selection and/or drift

genetic differentiation through selection and/or drift

Green shading represents the distribution of a new species, B.

Sympatric Speciation   Allopatric Speciation   Parapatric Speciation

Figure 4.14 Speciation can be sympatric, allopatric, or parapatric. In all three cases, reproductive isolation among subpopulations needs to occur; however, the mechanisms that cause this isolation will differ.

The most common model for sympatric speciation is that there exists disruptive selection for some trait (fig. 4.5), resulting in groups of individuals that differ greatly in phenotype even within a single population. If this is coupled with **assortative mating**, genetic differentiation can occur, leading to the evolution of reproductive isolation. What is assortative mating? In assortative mating, individuals may choose as mates individuals that are similar to themselves (positive assortative mating) or individuals that are different (negative assortative mating). It is positive assortative mating that is likely to lead to sympatric speciation. Recall the *Geospiza fortis* population at El Garrapatero, Galápagos (section 4.2). Genetic divergence is occurring between sub-populations with different beak phenotype. Or consider an insect that chooses to mate only with individuals that feed upon the same host plant. There is the potential for

genetic differentiation within the insect population based upon host plant selection.

In recent years, there has been renewed interest among evolutionary ecologists in understanding speciation and testing these models of speciation. This interest has been sparked in part because the development of readily available and inexpensive genetic tools has allowed the collection of data previously unavailable (see Ecological Tools and Approaches in this chapter). In addition, there is widespread interest in the fate of the world's biodiversity, and understanding the causes of speciation is just as important as understanding the causes of extinction. Next we will discuss two studies that are examples of current efforts in understanding whether ecological divergence can lead to reproductive isolation and speciation.

Reproductive Isolation and Ecological Divergence

Allopatric speciation through genetic drift is fairly easy to understand and does not even require any ecology for it to occur! Instead, it simply requires a population to be split, and random events can then cause reproductive isolation. In this section, we discuss issues more relevant to this book: How does ecology influence speciation?

Central to many models of speciation we have discussed is the idea that a diversity of habitats within the range of a species can lead to reproductive isolation. As subpopulations diverge ecologically, reproductive isolation and speciation may occur. This can be reworded into a testable prediction: Increased ecological divergence will be associated with increased reproductive isolation (fig. 4.15a). Dan Funk and colleagues (Funk et al. 2006) decided to conduct a broad test of this prediction. They wanted to examine the widest number of species possible and so dug through a variety of previously published data sets. Each data set contained pairs of closely related species, whose degree of pre- and postzygotic reproductive isolation was identified. Funk and colleagues then went through hundreds of additional studies and gathered information on the habitat that each species was generally found in, such as altitude, vegetation type, and moisture. The research team used a variety of statistical approaches to determine the average difference in habitats (divergence) between two species, and was able to conduct a series of regression analyses (appendix A) to determine whether habitat divergence was associated with reproductive isolation. In total, the data sets used contained over 500 species pairs, including plants, insects, birds, fish, and frogs. They found that the more different the habitats were, the more reproductively isolated the pairs of related species were (fig. 4.15b). This study lends support to a central prediction of several theories that suggest ecological interactions influence speciation by natural selection.

One of the particularly strong examples of natural selection at work is the process of **parallel evolution**, in which species in similar habitats, but geographically isolated, evolve similar traits. Genetic drift is a random process, so it is unlikely to produce similar changes in isolated populations. However, natural selection is nonrandom. Two isolated populations subjected to similar environmental selective pressures may

(a)

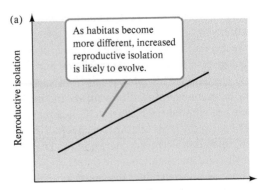

As habitats become more different, increased reproductive isolation is likely to evolve.

Reproductive isolation

Ecological divergence

(b)

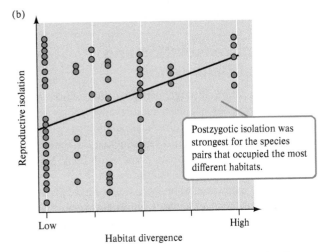

Reproductive isolation

Postzygotic isolation was strongest for the species pairs that occupied the most different habitats.

Low   High

Habitat divergence

Figure 4.15 (*a*) Theory predicts that the strength of reproductive isolation should increase with increasing habitat divergence between closely related species. (*b*) This pattern was found for most groups of organisms by Funk et al. (2006), with the results from angiosperm plants presented here.

D. J. Funk et al. 2006. Ecological divergence exhibits consistently positive associations with reproductive isolation across disparate taxa. *Proceedings of the National Academy of Sciences of the United States of America* 103:3210, Figure 1b–c. Copyright 2006 National Academy of Sciences, U.S.A.

Figure 4.16 The threespine stickleback (*Gasterosteus aculeatus*) has been used as a model organism for the study of evolutionary ecology.
Dave Pressland/FLPA/Science Source.

independently evolve similar innovations. Parallel speciation is a logical extension of this concept, in which the traits that result in reproductive isolation evolve similarly in species subjected to similar conditions and selective pressures. Dolph Schluter and his lab at the University of British Columbia have conducted extensive research on this issue, focusing their efforts on small fish called sticklebacks (fig. 4.16; *Gasterosteus* spp.). Currently, there is a diversity of *Gasterosteus* species, which occupy marine and freshwater habitats, with the freshwater species derived from the anadromous threespine stickleback (*Gasterosteus aculeatus*). Anadromous fish are those that migrate from the ocean into rivers, breeding in freshwater. This stickleback species is particularly interesting for study as it has marine and stream populations throughout the world, often co-occurring. Schluter's research team wanted to know what role ecological divergence plays in the early stages of speciation (McKinnon et al. 2004). To do this, they collected fish from marine (anadromous) and

stream (resident) populations in Alaska, British Columbia, Iceland, Scotland, Norway, and Japan. They brought these fish back to the lab and placed them in experimental aquaria. They were particularly interested in knowing which combinations of individuals would or would not mate. Their experimental factors included ecotype (anadromous or resident) and location (same or different region). McKinnon and colleagues found a much greater level of mating compatibility between individuals of the same ecotype, regardless of whether they were from the same area or from areas separated by thousands of kilometres. In other words, reproductive isolation occurred based upon ecological differentiation, not primarily geographic isolation.

What trait likely caused this result? It appears there has been divergent selection between habitats, resulting in the stream ecotypes being much smaller than the anadromous ecotypes. Additionally, there was strong evidence for size-assortative mating in which females were less likely to mate with males of very different sizes. As we discussed previously, divergent selection coupled with assortative mating are expected to be preconditions for sympatric speciation. Overall, this study provides strong evidence that changes in the ecology of an organism can lead to reproductive isolation of sympatric populations. Additionally, because stream (resident) ecotypes were smaller than the anadromous ecotypes in numerous geographic regions, it suggests that similar habitats can apply similar evolutionary pressures, allowing for parallel evolution to occur.

These studies by Funk and McKinnon show that many of the assumptions and predictions made by current models of speciation through natural selection are supported by ecological data. We are a long way from understanding all of the conditions necessary for speciation to occur, leaving much opportunity for the next generation of ecologists. At the core of understanding speciation is the need to understand and identify genotypic and phenotypic variations within and across species. In the Ecological Tools and Approaches section, we discuss many of the ecological tools that allow scientists to explore the genetic basis of variation.

CONCEPT 4.3 REVIEW

1. Reproductive isolation effectively eliminates many individuals as possible mates for each other. Is this likely to influence the fitness of the isolated individuals? Explain.

2. Allopatric, sympatric, and parapatric speciation can all occur in the same location at the same time. How?

3. What ecological processes are likely to speed up or slow down the rate of speciation?

ECOLOGICAL TOOLS AND APPROACHES

Integrating Population Genetics and Ecology

The molecular revolution has hit ecology, and it is now common for ecologists to use traditional field methods, advanced quantitative analyses, as well as molecular techniques to help them answer their research questions. The blending of molecular biology and ecology is most pronounced among evolutionary ecologists. These approaches have become so popular, and the answers to questions so important, that new subdisciplines have been formed, including *molecular ecology* and *conservation genetics*.

We have already discussed Broder's studies of moose population genetics, which used molecular methods to answer ecological questions. Broder and colleagues used one tool, *microsatellites*, to measure genetic diversity within a population. It is possible for researchers to measure dozens of microsatellites or even thousands of base pairs if they are using gene sequences, both of which allow for enhanced detection of genetic variability. DNA studies are becoming predominant in population genetics, as they are a more direct measure of genetic variation than the techniques based on protein variation that used to predominate. DNA studies have an added advantage in that they require very small amounts of tissue, while protein studies require relatively large samples. DNA-based molecular methods allow ecologists to use samples from smaller organisms or even just tufts of hair from larger organisms. For example, DNA in hair that grizzly bears leave behind when rubbing on trees is being used to estimate the growth rate of the grizzly bear population of Glacier National Park and the Northern Continental Divide Ecosystem of northwestern Montana (Kendall 2010).

To obtain sufficient quantities of DNA for analysis, such as that contained within a hair follicle, biologists most commonly use a procedure called polymerase chain reaction, or PCR (Hillis et al. 1996). During the PCR process, short, single-stranded DNA are used as primers for DNA synthesis. Each primer is highly specific for a given nucleotide sequence and can be used to amplify a specific locus or gene.

Once a sufficient quantity of DNA has been obtained, the sample may be analyzed in several ways. One commonly applied method uses **restriction enzymes:** enzymes produced naturally by bacteria to cut up foreign DNA.

Restriction enzymes cut DNA molecules at particular places called **restriction sites.** Because restriction sites are determined by a specific sequence of base pairs on the DNA molecule, differences in number and location of restriction sites reflect differences in DNA structure.

Although restriction fragments are still used by ecologists, they are losing popularity as newer, more powerful tools become available (and affordable). We have already discussed one such tool: microsatellites. As we mentioned, these are short, repeating sequences of DNA. All species will have a large number of microsatellite loci, but not all will be useful to the ecologist. To measure genetic variability within a population, the ecologist needs to find microsatellite loci that are variable within the population, rather than loci that are fixed for all individuals. The publication of microsatellites for a number of species provides a valuable research tool for ecologists around the world.

An even more sensitive, though not yet as widely used, tool for measures of genetic variability are single nucleotide polymorphisms, or SNPs (pronounced "snips"). SNPs are a powerful tool as they represent single base pair changes within a region of DNA rather than the presence/absence of an entire microsatellite allele. The ability to detect single base pair differences is relatively new to ecologists and has not yet been widely used. However, like all other aspects of molecular biology, the costs are rapidly decreasing and the power of SNPs will likely let them be more useful to ecologists in the near future.

The approach that gives the highest resolution picture of the genetic makeup of individuals and populations is **DNA sequencing.** This process reveals the sequence of nucleic acids along DNA molecules. Therefore, this tool gives the ultimate genetic information. The number of DNA sequences described is increasing rapidly, and our ability to interpret and compare DNA sequence data is also increasing at an impressive rate (Hillis et al. 1996). While the human genome project has assumed centre stage (NIH 2016), the genomes of hundreds of other species are also completely described, and many more will be soon. As we will show next, DNA sequencing is a valuable tool for ecologists, even when single genes, rather than the entire genome, are analyzed.

Species Identification

One area where molecular methods are strongly influencing ecological research is the ability to quickly and reliably identify species. In 2003, Paul Hebert of the University of Guelph suggested it would be possible to create a unique DNA "barcode" for species (Hebert et al. 2003). Just as actual barcodes allow anyone to rapidly determine information (e.g., price and identity) of any item in a grocery store, a DNA barcode could provide information about species. The basic idea is that each species contains sequences of DNA that are unique to it and to no other species on the planet. Hebert's idea has inspired scientists to make his vision a reality. The Biodiversity Institute of Ontario, located at the University of Guelph, is home to the Canadian Centre for DNA Barcoding, where basic research is conducted to develop accurate barcodes. This centre works closely with others around the world through initiatives such as the Barcode of Life Initiative and the International Barcode of Life Project.

There are a variety of reasons why such efforts are urgently needed. First, accurate ecological studies often require species identification, and it is impractical to think each ecologist will also be an expert in species identification. This is particularly an issue for researchers of diverse groups, such as insects, bacteria, and fungi. In theory, the DNA barcode system would allow an ecologist to extract a DNA sequence for a specimen collected in the field, compare it to sequences in a large database, and identify the species. Such a database would be a significant help to ecological field studies. A second need for DNA barcodes comes as the result of one of the great tragedies of modern scientific funding: a nearly worldwide decline in taxonomic expertise in universities and museums. Because of this, fewer and fewer people are able to accurately identify specimens collected in the field. If DNA barcodes existed for many taxonomic groups, there would be reduced demand for taxonomic experts. However, DNA barcodes are likely to be most effective when combined with continued support for taxonomy. For example, the barcode database is only as good as the data it contains. Taxonomists are needed to add new species, to verify existing records, and to provide guidance when molecular methods provide ambiguous results. Hebert's DNA barcodes are a great example of how continually developing molecular methods may fundamentally alter ecological research.

When Species Boundaries Are "Fuzzy"

One complication of natural systems is that species boundaries are not always as discrete as we might imagine. Instead, species may hybridize with other species, resulting in fertile offspring. Here, molecular tools are also critical for ecologists, allowing them to understand the frequency and potential conservation concerns of gene flow among species.

Molecular methods have shone a light on a reality of nature—species boundaries are not always distinct, as individuals of different species can sometimes hybridize, producing viable offspring. If hybridizations are rare, one can typically ignore them as one-off events. However, if they are common in the wild, they present a significant challenge to the biological species concept. A related conservation concern is the introgression of genes from one species into another. Introgression is the movement of genes from one distinct gene pool into another. Over time, introgression can result in movement of specific traits from one group to another, or even a homogenization of the two gene pools. Ecologists are particularly concerned about introgression when the genes of domesticated species enter the gene pools of wild species, as has been documented in some instances. For example, a gene for herbicide tolerance has moved from a crop species, *Brassica napus* (canola), into its wild relative, *Brassica rapa* (Warwick et al. 2008). As you may realize, the best way to know whether hybridization and/or introgression has occurred is to study the DNA and directly determine whether there has been a mixture of DNA among species.

James Mallet has published a review of studies that have documented hybridization among wild species (Mallet 2008). Though comprehensive lists of hybridization are not yet available for most taxonomic groups, Mallet was able to show that hybridization in the wild can be quite common (fig. 4.17). For example, up to 25% of the vascular plant species of Great Britain are documented to hybridize, and even 6% of the mammals of Europe have been shown to form viable hybrids. Mallet points out that hybridization can lead to speciation and may be responsible for over 50% of the known diversity of vascular plants. At a minimum, these rates of hybridization suggest that boundaries between species are more exact in most introductory biology textbooks than they are for wild populations. Ecologists need to be aware of the "fuzziness" of species boundaries and be prepared for specimens that cannot be identified by barcode or taxonomic key.

Hybrids can be found even among iconic species, such as polar bears. In 2006, a polar bear × grizzly hybrid was shot and killed in the Northwest Territories. Another putative

Taxon	Location	Fraction of Species with Hybrids (%)
Vascular plants	Great Britain	25
Butterflies	Europe	16
Birds	Worldwide	9
Mammals	Europe	6

Figure 4.17 A survey of published reports suggest hybridization is common in the wild.

hybrid was shot as recently as spring 2010. As climate change continues, grizzly bears are expected to become more common in the Arctic, and hybridization may increase. Species that cannot be clearly delineated pose obvious challenges to species conservation efforts. Bears are not the only well-known group of species to form hybrids. Coywolves, hybrids of coyotes and wolves, appear to be quite common throughout eastern North America. More generally, sympatric ranges between species that can interbreed is likely to lead to increased rates of hybridization. Whether this will become frequent enough to lead to speciation or to cause a breakdown of existing species designations is not yet known. However, the field of molecular ecology will provide the tools to answer these questions.

SUMMARY

Although they did not work together, the twin visions of Darwin and Mendel revolutionized biology. The synthesis of the theory of natural selection and genetics gave rise to modern evolutionary ecology. Here we examine four major concepts within the area of population genetics and natural selection.

4.1 Phenotypic variation among individuals in a population results from the combined effects of genes and environment.

The first biologists to conduct thorough studies of phenotypic and genotypic variation and to incorporate experiments in their studies focused on plants. Clausen, Keck, and Hiesey explored the extent and sources of morphological variation in plant populations, including both the influences of environment and genetics. Reznick, Bryga, and Endler described phenotypic variation in life history characteristics of Trinidadian guppies and demonstrated that some of this variation could be explained by the nature and intensity of predation risk. Molecular genetic studies offer a powerful way of assessing the genetic variation in populations.

4.2 Changes in gene frequency within a population can occur through both natural selection and random processes, such as genetic drift.

Natural selection can lead to changes in gene frequencies within populations (directional and disruptive selection) or can be a conservative force impeding change (stabilizing selection). These three forms of selection differ as a function of which phenotypes are favoured. In directional selection one extreme is favoured, in stabilizing selection the average phenotype is favoured, and in disruptive selection both extremes are favoured. In all types of selection, the rate of evolution increases with the strength of the selective force. There is abundant evidence from a variety of species showing that natural selection is a continuous process, occurring in extant species. Evolution also occurs by the random process of genetic drift. Although drift occurs continuously in all populations, it is a greater evolutionary force in small populations, where chance events can impact a greater proportion of the individuals of the population. In populations of Chihuahua spruce, small populations were associated with lower levels of genetic diversity, attributed to loss through drift.

A lack of genetic diversity can be associated with increased risk of local extinctions.

4.3 Physical and ecological processes interact with selection and drift to produce new species.

Both natural selection and genetic drift can cause reproductive isolation to occur between populations of a single species. Reproductive isolation can occur at both prezygotic and postzygotic stages through changes in location, timing, behaviour, morphology and physiology, and development pathways. Reproductive isolation is a necessary condition for speciation. Speciation can occur within a single location (sympatric speciation), when a population is geographically separated (allopatric speciation), or when a species extends into a new habitat (parapatric speciation). Increased habitat divergence is positively correlated with increased reproductive isolation, suggesting that the current ecology of organisms can influence the likelihood of speciation. Ecological similarity can cause parallel evolution in geographically distinct populations, and assortative mating can lead to sympatric speciation.

The molecular revolution has allowed ecologists to ask more detailed questions about the nature of species and the movement of genes from one group to another. A number of tools are available, including restriction fragments, microsatellites, and gene sequencing. These tools are being used to develop DNA barcodes, potentially leading to an easily accessible catalogue of biological diversity. The use of molecular methods has also revealed that species boundaries are not as discrete as commonly assumed. Hybridization rates can be very high, and many species show introgression of genes from captive to wild species.

To assist you in synthesizing the materials from this chapter, figure 4.18 presents a concept map that incorporates the four tenets of Darwin's theory of evolution by natural selection (labelled as 1–4) and that builds upon the concepts of ecological "levels" introduced in chapter 1. Interactions between individuals and conspecifics (population level), other species (community level), and their physical environment (ecosystem level) impose pressures, and can determine which of the individuals born in a given generation survive and reproduce. The concept map extends Darwin's tenets to consider what happens when two isolated populations each follows their own unique microevolutionary path.

Population 1

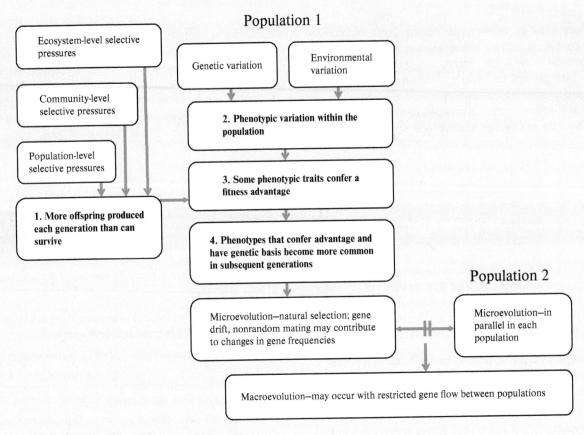

Figure 4.18 Concept map for chapter 4.

REVIEW QUESTIONS

1. Contrast the approaches of Charles Darwin and Gregor Mendel to the study of populations. What were Darwin's main discoveries? What were Mendel's main discoveries? How did the studies of Darwin and Mendel prepare the way for the later studies reviewed in this chapter?

2. How did the studies of phenotypic plasticity conducted by Reznick, Bryga, and Endler complement the earlier studies of Clausen, Keck, and Hiesey?

3. What is genetic drift? Under what circumstances do you expect genetic drift to occur? Under what circumstances is genetic drift unlikely to be important? Does genetic drift increase or decrease genetic variation in populations?

4. Suppose you are a director of a captive breeding program for a rare species of animal, such as Siberian tigers, that are found in many zoos around the world but are increasingly rare in the wild. Design a breeding program that will reduce the possibility of genetic drift in captive populations.

5. Colonization of new habitat brings with it certain genetic risks. How can these risks be reduced if a large population rather than a small population establishes in a new area?

6. How might the distribution of beak sizes in the medium ground finch population differ from that shown in figure 4.9 if mate choice in the population was random with respect to beak size?

7. Phenotypic variation has both a genetic and an environmental component. Do each of these contributions to an individual's phenotype affect its fitness? Do each of these contributions affect the evolutionary trajectory of the population?

8. DNA barcoding will not be effective if traditional taxonomists no longer exist. Why?

9. Some biologists are skeptical of sympatric speciation. What ecological conditions would make sympatric speciation more likely to occur? What evidence could an ecologist collect that would support, or refute, a claim that a particular species is the result of sympatric speciation?

SECTION 2   INDIVIDUALS

In this section we discuss how individual organisms interact with their local surroundings. As a foundation for these discussions, we present the concepts of allocation and ecological trade-offs. Three dominant factors that influence individuals are temperature, water, and the need for energy and nutrients. An organism's physiology (chapters 5, 6, and 7) and behaviour (chapter 8) influence its ability to cope with its environment and neighbours. The total set of strategies, abilities, and limitations of an individual species is described as its life history and will determine the shape of its niche (chapter 9).

CHAPTER 5   TEMPERATURE RELATIONS

CHAPTER CONCEPTS

Many organisms regulate the temperature of part of, if not their entire, body. For example, at least one plant of the arctic tundra regulates the temperature of its reproductive structures. Peter Kevan, of the University of Guelph, went to Ellesmere Island to study sun-tracking behaviour by arctic flowers. It was summer, there was little wind, and at 82° N latitude, the sun stayed above the horizon 24 hours each day. As the sun's position in the arctic sky changed, one of the common tundra flowers, *Dryas integrifolia* (fig. 5.1), tracked its movement across the sky.

Kevan found that by following the sun, *Dryas* increased the temperature of its flowers. Though the air temperature hovered around 15°C, the temperature of the *Dryas* flowers was nearly 25°C. Kevan discovered that the flowers act like small solar reflectors, concentrating solar energy on the reproductive structures. He also observed that many species of small insects, attracted by their warmth, basked in the sun-tracking *Dryas* flowers, elevating their body temperatures as a consequence (fig. 5.1). *Dryas* depends on these insects to pollinate its flowers.

How do *Dryas* and its insect visitors benefit from their basking behaviours? How does cloud cover affect the temperature and sun-tracking behaviour of *Dryas* flowers? These are the kinds of questions addressed by Kevan (1975) and other ecologists who study the ecology of temperature relations, a fundamental aspect of ecology. Temperature is a major factor influencing the growth of individuals and the distributions of species.

Why are ecologists so concerned about how temperatures influence ecological interactions? Small differences in temperature can be associated with greatly altered performances of enzymes and organisms. Extreme temperatures can cause discomfort, reduced fitness, and even death. Long-term changes in temperature have set entire floras and faunas marching across continents, with some species thriving, some holding on in small refuges, and others becoming extinct. Areas now supporting temperate species were at times tropical and at other times the frigid homes of reindeer and woolly mammoths. The dynamic environmental history of the earth has become more significant as we face the reality of rapidly rising global temperatures.

We defined *ecology* as the study of the relationships between organisms and their environments. In this chapter, we examine the relationship between organisms and temperature, particularly relevant in the face of today's rapidly changing climate.

5.1 Microclimates

Macroclimate interacts with the local landscape to produce microclimatic variation in temperature. As we saw in chapter 2, temperatures are extremely variable across the planet in both space and time. For instance, which is warmer: Regina, Saskatchewan; or Tofino, British Columbia? The answer depends on "When?" Tofino is generally warmer than Regina in the winter but is cooler in the summer. But the answer is also going to depend on "Where?" Is someone standing on the open coastline of Tofino while another is under an aspen stand in Regina? As you will see in this section, the actual temperatures that an individual encounters will be strongly influenced by the fine details of the local environment and by the behaviour of the individual.

Microclimate is a fundamental aspect of environmental variation. What do we mean by *macroclimate* and *microclimate*? **Macroclimate** is not the weather today but, rather, the prevailing, typical weather for an area. Your weather report may say that today is 2° below normal. "Normal" is based on years of data that tell you what the typical weather conditions are in your area at this time of year. That is your macroclimate. Macroclimate is determined by the global patterns of air and water circulation and other forces, also described in chapters 2 and 3. **Microclimate**, on the other hand, is climatic variation on a scale of a few kilometres, metres, or even centimetres, usually measured over short periods of time. If you live in a city, your weather might be recorded at a nearby airport. But at your home, it may be generally warmer or cooler. Maybe you live near water or catch more wind, or have more shade in your yard. At my house, for example, in the summer the front yard may be a full 3° warmer than the backyard. The front of the house and the back of the house have different microclimates. Microclimate is influenced by landscape features, such as elevation (altitude), aspect, vegetation, colour of the ground, and presence of boulders and burrows. Macroclimate and microclimate can be substantially different, and for organisms that live out their lives in very small areas, macroclimate may be less important than microclimate.

Elevation and Aspect

Temperatures are generally lower at high elevations. Atmospheric pressure decreases with elevation, and air rising up the side of a mountain expands. The energy of motion (kinetic energy) required to sustain the greater movement of air molecules in the

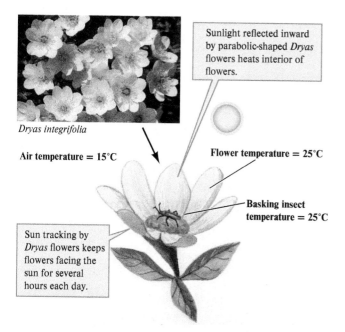

Figure 5.1 Sun-tracking behaviour of the arctic plant *Dryas integrifolia* heats the reproductive parts of its flowers, making them attractive to pollinating insects. This species is found in many Canadian arctic and alpine habitats.

Dryas integrifolia

Air temperature = 15°C

Sunlight reflected inward by parabolic-shaped *Dryas* flowers heats interior of flowers.

Flower temperature = 25°C

Basking insect temperature = 25°C

Sun tracking by *Dryas* flowers keeps flowers facing the sun for several hours each day.

Figure 5.2 The north-facing slope at this site supports a Mediterranean woodland while the vegetation on the south-facing slope is mainly grassland.

© muha04/Getty Images RF.

expanding air mass is drawn from the surroundings, which cool as a result. There is also less atmosphere to trap and radiate heat back to the ground at the top of a mountain than at its base.

Even small changes in elevation can affect microclimate. Topographic features, such as hills and valleys, create microclimates that would not occur in a flat landscape. Hillsides do so by shading parts of the land. In the Northern Hemisphere, the shaded areas are on the north-facing sides, or *northern aspects,* of hills, mountains, and valleys, which face away from the equator. The *southern aspect,* in contrast, will receive more direct sun and will be generally warmer and drier. The microclimates of north- and south-facing aspects of hillsides may support very different types of vegetation (fig. 5.2).

Similar microclimates can occur on the northern versus southern aspects within the built environment, affecting urban forest and plant distributions. Vegetation plays many important roles in the ecology of cities, including the moderation of climate. Andrew Millward and colleagues at Ryerson University studied the effects of trees and vines on solar gain received by buildings, installing pairs of temperature loggers on the surfaces of buildings in downtown Toronto and measuring building surface temperatures over six months. One logger in each pair was shaded while the other was in full sunlight. During high solar intensity, the average temperature differential was 11.7°C, with 10–12 hours of sustained cooling benefit per day for the portion of the building surface in the shade (Millward et al. 2014). Vegetation shading the west aspect of buildings provided the greatest benefit in microclimate moderation, followed by shading on the south aspect. Interestingly, perennial vines were as effective as trees in moderating built surface temperature.

Vegetation and Ground Colour

Because they also shade the landscape, trees, shrubs, and *plant litter* (fallen leaves, twigs, and branches) can produce ecologically important microclimates. For example, the desert landscape often consists of a mosaic of vegetation and bare ground. It is also a patchwork of sharply contrasting thermal environments. Such a patchwork is apparent near Kemmerer, Wyoming. On one summer's day, Robert Parmenter and his colleagues (1989) measured the temperatures in various parts of the landscape. They found that while the temperature on bare soil soared to 48°C, a few metres away in plant litter under a tall shrub the temperature was only 21°C (fig. 5.3). A small organism in this landscape could choose microclimates differing in temperature by 27°C!

Soil surface in full sun heats to high temperatures.

Shading of soil surface by low shrubs lowers maximum temperatures.

A layer of leaf litter lowers maximum temperatures even more.

Greater leaf area and numerous twigs of tall shrubs intercept more light, creating the coolest temperatures.

48°C in bare soil away from shrubs

29°C in litter under low shrub

27°C in soil under low shrub

21°C in litter under tall shrub

23°C in soil under tall shrub

Figure 5.3 Desert shrubs create distinctive thermal microclimates in the desert landscape.

Data from Parmenter, Parmenter, and Cheney 1989.

(a)   (b)   (c)

Figure 5.4 Ground cover and colour such as shown here in (*a*) white sand, (*b*) black sand, and (*c*) snow in Nunavut alter the local albedo, causing altered microclimates. High albedos are found in white snow and white sand, with low albedos found in dark sand and other dark soils.
(a) © Corbis RF; (b) © Medioimages/PunchStock RF; (c) Max Forgues/Shutterstock.com.

Two additional factors that can affect temperature are the colour of the ground and the presence of any covering, such as vegetation or snow (fig. 5.4). Cover and colour influence microclimates through their effects on the local **albedo,** the reflectivity of the landscape. Objects that appear white reflect all visible colours and have a high albedo. Objects that appear black absorb all visible colours and have a low albedo. Vegetation is generally green, which means it absorbs some colours and reflects others, resulting in moderate albedo.

Albedos are not fixed properties of landscapes and instead will change as local conditions change. Snow cover reflects large amounts of light, resulting in a cooling effect. When snow melts, the underlying soil will generally have a lower albedo and absorb more light energy, causing local warming. As a result, any change in snow cover can have cascading effects on local temperatures. Over larger areas, decreased snow and ice cover across much of the landscape, potentially associated with global climate change, has the potential to further enhance the warming that is currently occurring. More locally, small-scale human-induced changes, such as deforestation and transition from peatlands to forests, also alter albedo, with potentially cascading impacts on temperatures.

Boulders and Burrows

Many children soon discover that the undersides of stones harbour a host of organisms seldom seen in the open. This is partly because the stones create distinctive microclimates. E. B. Edney's classic studies (1953) of the seashore isopod *Ligia oceanica* documented the effect of stones on microclimate. Edney found that over the space of a few centimetres, *Ligia* could choose air temperatures ranging from 20°C in the open to 30°C in the air spaces under stones, which heated to between 34°C and 38°C.

Animal burrows also have their own microclimates, in which temperatures are usually more moderate than outside ambient conditions. For example, the Eurasian badger (*Meles meles*) constructs extensive burrows, called *setts*. In a study of temperatures inside and outside several setts on farmland, Moore and Roper (2003) found that setts generally had average temperature fluctuations of less than 1°C each day while surface temperatures generally varied by 9°C daily. Over an entire year, there was only a 10°C variation within setts but more than a 20°C variation outside. Moore and Roper also found that setts occupied by a badger were on average 2.5°C warmer than unoccupied setts, highlighting the fact that organisms themselves can alter their own microclimates.

Aquatic Temperatures

Water temperature generally fluctuates less than air temperature. The aquatic environments with greatest thermal stability are generally large ones, such as the open sea. These environments store large quantities of heat energy, and daily fluctuations are often less than 1°C. Even the temperatures of small streams, however, usually fluctuate less than the temperatures of nearby terrestrial habitats (fig. 5.5). The thermal stability of the aquatic environment derives partly from the high capacity of water to absorb heat energy without changing temperature (a capacity called *specific heat*), partly from the large amount of heat absorbed by water as it evaporates (which is called the *latent heat of vaporization*), and partly from the heat energy that water gives up to its environment as it freezes (the *latent heat of fusion*). The evaporation of even small amounts of water can result in significant cooling; thus, the water in a desert stream can be a cool relief to the hot temperature of the air. On the other end of the temperature spectrum, heat energy that must be lost for water to freeze can forestall freezing during periods when air temperatures fluctuate around 0°C.

Riparian vegetation, vegetation that grows along rivers and streams, can also influence the temperature in streams in the same way that vegetation modifies the temperature of desert soils—by providing shade. Shading by riparian vegetation reduces temperature fluctuations by insulating the stream environment, with important consequences for the many animals that live within the stream (see Ecology in Action, this chapter).

There are, of course, limits to the thermal stability of aquatic systems, and changes in temperature in aquatic environments will have two major consequences. First, there will be the direct effects of altered temperatures on the organisms living in the water (described later in the chapter). Second, and often of greater importance in aquatic systems, is the effect that

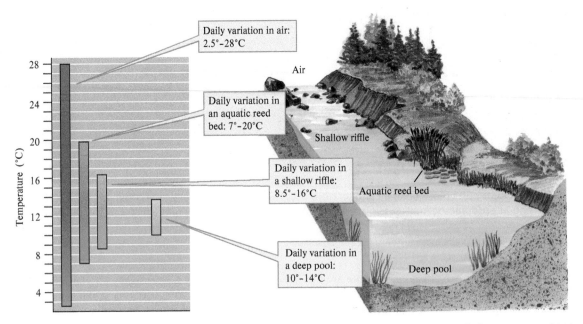

Figure 5.5 Aquatic microclimates: aquatic environments generally show less temperature variation compared to terrestrial environments.
Data from Ward 1985.

changes in temperature have on the amount of dissolved oxygen in the water. Recall that, in chapter 3, we emphasized that low oxygen levels were a hazard for organisms living in the water. Cold water holds more dissolved oxygen than warm water; thus, increases in water temperature can pose a direct thermal stress and can induce oxygen-limiting conditions for some aquatic species.

At this point, we hope you will forgive a minor digression, but one that speaks to the interplay of temperature, dissolved oxygen, and trade-offs in fitness that can occur in aquatic systems. If you ever dive deep into a lake during the summer, you will notice that the water gets cooler. If you go deep enough, you will hit a zone where this temperature transition is rapid. This is the thermocline, described in chapter 3: the transition zone from warm surface water to the colder, denser bottom water. As discussed in chapter 3, a consequence of stratification is that deep water can become depleted of oxygen during the summer, despite the cooler temperature, because of respiration by bacteria using organic matter (such as algae) raining down from shallower water. In the process, the bacteria recycle nutrients such as N and P, making the deep water relatively rich in nutrients. We often see a peak density of algae near the thermocline, accessing the nutrients from deeper water yet near enough to the surface to access sunlight (fig. 5.6). The algae absorb light, which, along with attenuation by water, makes the deep water a dark zone.

Zooplankton are a diverse group of invertebrate animals living in the water column. Where, within a stratified lake or marine system, should zooplankton live? Sharp transitions in light, temperature, and dissolved oxygen create unique, vertically adjacent microhabitats. There are trade-offs associated with occupying the different microhabitats. Warm water would

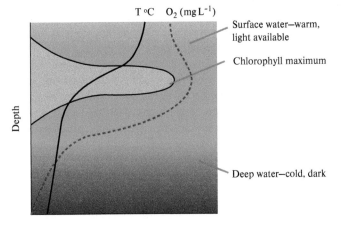

Figure 5.6 Stratified water column showing thermocline, oxygen gradient, and light gradient (indicated by shading). Deep water is cold and dark; algae grow most densely near the thermocline, where light is available from above and nutrients are available from below. Stratification creates diversity of vertically distributed micro-niches through which zooplankton may daily migrate.

permit greater growth and reproductive rates, so shouldn't zooplankton live near the surface? But the food for the zooplankton, algae, are concentrated near the thermocline so perhaps they should live there. Of course, zooplankton get eaten, and often their main predators are fish. Fish are visual feeders so perhaps zooplankton should hide in deep, dark water.

As it turns out, many species of zooplankton, across phyla, exhibit diel vertical migration (DVM) behaviour, exploiting different parts of the water column at different times of the day. Zooplankton face a trade-off in their ability to exploit resources (warm water and availability of food) and their vulnerability to fish predation (Leibold 1991). This trade-off results in what has been termed "normal" DVM patterns, where zooplankton remain in the cool, dark waters during the day, migrating up through the thermocline at night to feed (Lampert et al. 2003). Zooplankton exhibiting this type of behaviour experience suboptimal growth temperatures during much of the day but may still optimize fitness by avoiding fish.

CONCEPT 5.1 REVIEW

1. What advantages might the warm microenvironments of *Dryas* flowers offer to the insects attracted to them?

2. Contrast the microclimates of the leaves and roots of a tree in the boreal forest in summer.

3. Why is thermal stability greater in large, rather than small, bodies of water?

5.2 Evolutionary Trade-Offs

Adapting to one set of environmental conditions generally reduces fitness in other environments. Imagine an organism that is not only capable of living in any environment but thrives in all environments. In the language of evolution, such an organism would have high fitness across all environmental conditions. In everyday language, we might refer to such a life form as a "super" organism. Whatever we might call them, however, such life forms do not, as far as we know, exist. All known organisms are adapted to a limited range of environmental conditions, at least partially as a consequence of energy limitation.

The Principle of Allocation

All organisms have access to limited energy supplies. This simple idea has significant implications for our understanding of the ecology of individuals. We introduce the concept of energy limitation here and will examine it again in chapter 7. One consequence of energy limitation is that energy allocated to one of life's functions—such as reproduction, defence against disease, or growth—reduces the amount of energy available for other functions. Darwin appreciated the implications of energy limitation and included it in his writings. However, Richard Levins was the first to use a mathematical approach to analyze the evolutionary consequences of such trade-offs, which he referred to as the principle of allocation (Levins 1968). In his book *Evolution in Changing Environments,* Levins concluded that as a population adapts to a particular set of environmental conditions, its fitness (see chapter 4) in other environments is reduced.

Testing the Principle of Allocation

Demonstrating the evolutionary trade-offs proposed by the principle of allocation has been challenging. In fact, a direct test of the principle has been nearly 40 years in coming. The

major difficulty with all such evolutionary questions is the time required for performing evolutionary experiments with living organisms. Albert Bennett and Richard Lenski solved this time problem by studying the evolution of microbial populations (Bennett and Lenski 2007), which can go through hundreds of generations in a week. The central question of their work was whether adaptation to a low temperature (20°C) would be accompanied by a loss of fitness at a high temperature (40°C). Their working hypothesis was that they would observe just such a trade-off in fitness, a prediction that follows directly from Levins's principle of allocation.

Bennett and Lenski's experiments focused on 24 different lineages of the bacterium *Escherichia coli*. These lineages were derived from a single ancestral strain of *E. coli* that had been grown at 37°C (human body temperature) for 2,000 generations. Bennett and Lenski used this ancestral strain to establish six replicate populations at four temperature regimes: constant 32°C, 37°C, and 42°C, and daily alternation between 32°C and 42°C. They maintained these 24 populations at these temperature regimes for 2,000 generations, sufficient time for each population to adapt. Bennett and Lenski next used bacterial cells from each of their 24 populations to establish 24 new populations, which were all grown at 20°C for 2,000 generations, theoretically adapting to this relatively low temperature in the process.

To address their original question—"Will adaptation to a low temperature (20°C) be accompanied by a loss of fitness at a high temperature (40°C)?"—Bennett and Lenski compared the fitness of the low-temperature-selected line with the fitness of the ancestral line at 20°C and at 40°C. Their measure of fitness was the rate of population doubling of a selected line of *E. coli* compared to that of its ancestral line. Two major results stand out. First, the lines grown at 20°C had *higher* (positive) *fitness* at 20°C temperature compared to their immediate ancestors. However, the lines that had adapted to 20°C had, on average, *lower* (negative) *fitness* compared to their immediate ancestor when grown at 40°C. Therefore, as predicted by the principle of allocation, selection for higher fitness at 20°C had been accompanied by an average loss in fitness at higher temperatures (fig. 5.7).

Later work from Bennett and colleagues considered whether adaptation to high temperature (42°) would be accompanied by a loss of fitness at a lower temperature. The team adapted 114 clones of *E. coli* to high temperature for 2,000 generations (Rodríguez-Verdugo et al. 2014). All of the populations showed an increase in the upper thermal limit for growth. However, the fitness trade-off at low temperature (20°C) was observed in only about half of the populations. Interestingly, whether there were fitness trade-offs depended, in part, on different genetically based pathways for adaptation to thermal stress. In other words, variance in the genetic basis by which each population adapted to high temperature contributed to whether the population exhibited a fitness trade-off at low temperature.

Bennett and Lenski's results provide the first direct experimental evidence in support of Levins's principle of allocation. Rodríguez-Verdugo's results provide direct evidence that there

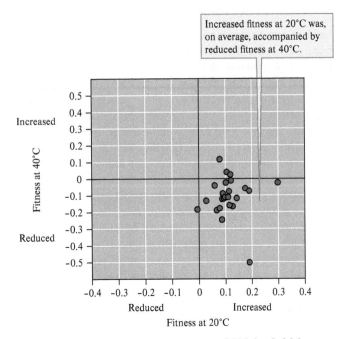

Increased fitness at 20°C was, on average, accompanied by reduced fitness at 40°C.

Figure 5.7   *Escherichia coli* grown at 20°C for 2,000 generations showed increased fitness at that temperature compared to ancestral lines, which were adapted to higher temperatures. However, they had reduced fitness at 40°C compared to ancestral lines.

Data from Bennett and Lenski 2007.

is a genetic basis for whether a population conforms to Levin's principle of allocation. Where there is a genetic basis, then conforming to this principle can, itself, be adaptive. This principle, in turn, offers an explanation for the observation that most organisms perform best under a limited range of environmental conditions, including thermal conditions.

CONCEPT 5.2 REVIEW

1. If growing lines of *Escherichia coli* at 20°C for 2,000 generations increased their fitness at 20°C without reducing their fitness at 40°C, how would the distribution of points in figure 5.7 change?

2. If your research team obtained the hypothetical results described in question 1, what could you conclude about the principle of allocation?

5.3   Temperature and Performance of Organisms

Most species perform best in a fairly narrow range of temperatures. In the previous section, we saw this with Albert Bennett and Richard Lenski's experiments with *E. coli*. Although we can find bacteria or archaea growing and active at temperatures below freezing and others growing at temperatures well

above 70°C, any given species has a fairly narrow range of temperatures in which it will grow.

Ecologists concerned with the ecology of individual organisms study how environmental factors, such as temperature, water, and light, affect the physiology and behaviour of organisms: how fast they grow; how many offspring they produce; how fast they run, fly, or swim; how well they avoid predators; and so on. We can group these phenomena and say that ecologists study how environment affects the "performance" of organisms. Victor Shelford was an influential ecologist active in the early 1900s who studied the link between species distributions and their physiology. His studies led him to propose the **law of toleration** (Shelford 1911): the abundance and distribution of an animal can be determined by the deviation between the local conditions (e.g., temperature) and the optimum set of conditions for a species. Shelford was among the first to explicitly link the ability of a species to tolerate local environmental conditions with its range and abundance.

What led Shelford to this conclusion? He was able to recognize from his own research, and from that of others, that the performance of organisms generally varies as a function of differences in temperature, moisture, light, nutrient availability, and other environmental conditions. At extreme levels of any of these factors, many species are unable to survive. At severe levels, species may survive but not thrive. At more moderate levels, growth and reproduction may be highest. In other words, the performance of most species is greatest in a fairly narrow range of environmental conditions (fig. 5.8). The entire range of conditions (e.g., temperature) over which a species is able to survive is called its **range of tolerance**. What do you

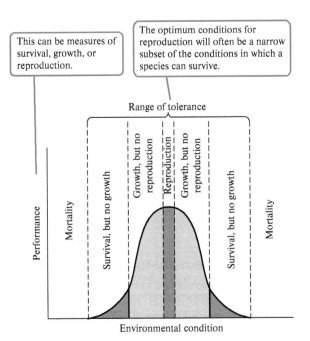

Figure 5.8   An individual's performance can be limited by environmental conditions, such as temperature. According to the law of toleration, species abundances will tend to be largest in areas with environmental conditions most similar to the performance optima for a species.

imagine will be the consequences for individuals living just on the edge of their range of tolerance?

Temperature and Animal Performance

Let's begin our discussion of temperature and an organism's overall performance by considering basic biochemistry. You will recall that enzymes work most efficiently over a limited range of temperatures. We would predict that an organism that lives outside this range of temperatures, or that is unable to maintain its body temperature within this range, will not thrive. We might also predict that, through adaptation, the range of temperatures over which an enzyme functions effectively will match the range of temperatures in which its organism lives (or the range of internal body temperatures the organism maintains).

 **ECOLOGY IN ACTION**

Impacts of Stream Temperature on Salmon Recruitment

The family *Salmonidae* consists of both trout and salmon. Canada is home to many species of wild salmon. Most species and populations of wild salmon are anadromous, meaning the adults live primarily in the ocean and then move into fresh waters to spawn. After the eggs hatch, the developing fry initially feed and grow in the streams, eventually migrating to the ocean. Adults typically return to their own birthing grounds to spawn. Changes to the vegetation surrounding the spawning grounds of salmon can alter the thermal environment of the streams, reducing the reproductive success of returning salmon. These temperature changes, then, have significant impacts on the health of individual salmon species.

Given the importance of salmon in Canada, economically and culturally, extensive research has been conducted on the factors that influence the health of wild salmon populations. Like all organisms, salmon have upper lethal temperatures, above which mortality occurs (fig. 5.8). These lethal upper temperatures vary among species and life-stage. The adult fish is at limited risk of death due to changes in temperature as it migrates upstream. However, as we saw earlier in the chapter, there is generally a unimodal relationship between temperature and performance. Reproduction happens only in a narrow range of temperatures even though survival can occur in a larger range. Increases in temperature, then, do not have to kill a fish to put its population at risk. Even minor changes to stream temperatures can reduce, or prevent, reproduction. However, not all streams are equal, and they can vary greatly in size. Spawning grounds located in the smallest streams in the headwaters will be most sensitive to change. Why?

One factor that can influence stream temperature is logging activity. In small streams, trees often overhang the water, reducing light penetration to the water surface (fig. 5.9). If the vegetation is completely removed, there is a clear and immediate increase in stream temperature. For example, Steve MacDonald of Fisheries and Oceans Canada and his colleagues at Simon Fraser University found that stream temperatures can be raised by 4°C–6°C, even five years after logging (MacDonald et al. 2003). The

Figure 5.9 Many salmon spawning grounds, such as the Little Qualicum River in British Columbia, consist of water surrounded by forest.
© Steve Ford/Dreamstime.com.

temperature changes can be mitigated in part by logging management practices, such as maintaining an unharvested buffer zone along the stream edge. However, MacDonald shows that trees in these buffers are susceptible to wind damage, reducing their effectiveness over time.

Humans influence stream temperatures in a variety of other ways, including by constructing dams. Dams used to generate electrical power generally cause variations in stream flow, depending upon the electrical needs at any point in time. As a result, there will be substantial variation in stream depths and temperatures, as a function of how much water is being released through a dam.

In Newfoundland, salmon rivers are closed to anglers on days when river flow is low and river temperatures are high, out of concern that angling will further decrease the sustainability of Atlantic salmon populations. Brian Dempson and his colleagues at Fisheries and Oceans Canada found that the frequency of stream closures due to these "environmental" reasons has increased (Dempson et al. 2001), suggesting an increase in the frequency of warm waters that could put these fish populations at risk. Interestingly, the increase in frequency of these events is not due to dams but may instead reflect changes in climate. Changes in patterns of precipitation and rising temperatures could further stress salmon fisheries.

Erika Eliason and colleagues at the University of British Columbia and Fisheries and Oceans Canada have found evidence for physiological adaptation to temperature in sockeye salmon (Eliason et al. 2011). Optimal temperatures for a number of cardiac and aerobic measures vary as a function of the historical temperatures of migratory rivers. Interestingly, populations appear to differ in their abilities to adapt to higher temperatures, suggesting that while some

populations may be able to adapt to rising temperatures, other populations could be vulnerable to thermal stress.

Salmon are but one example of a group of species whose abundance can be influenced by changes in temperature. The ideas of upper and lower lethal temperatures are not abstract ecological concepts but, rather, are critical pieces of information needed to understand how species will respond to continued human-mediated changes. Indirect effects of human activity have significant consequences for a diverse set of species, and it is a role of ecologists to understand why and to work with government and industry to develop solutions to reduce the risk to natural populations.

Peter Hochachka, formerly of the University of British Columbia, was one of Canada's leading zoologists. He had a diverse research program, with a particular emphasis on adaptational biochemistry. One line of his research program involved the influence of temperature on the activity of acetylcholinesterase, an enzyme produced at the synapse between neurons. In one study, Baldwin and Hochachka (1970) found that rainbow trout (*Oncorhynchus mykiss*) produce two forms of acetylcholinesterase. One form has highest affinity for acetylcholine at 2°C, that is, at winter temperatures. However, the affinity of this enzyme for acetylcholine declines rapidly above 10°C. The second form of acetylcholinesterase shows highest affinity at 17°C, at summer temperatures. However, the affinity of this second form of acetylcholinesterase falls off rapidly at both higher and lower temperatures (fig. 5.10).

This influence of temperature on the performance of acetylcholinesterase makes sense if you consider the temperatures of the rainbow trout's native environment. Rainbow trout are

native to the cool, clear streams and rivers of western North America. During winter, the temperatures of these streams hover between 0°C and 4°C, while summer temperatures approach 20°C. These environmental temperatures are similar to the temperatures at which the acetylcholinesterase of rainbow trout performs optimally. The two forms of the enzymes are adaptations to the habitat of the rainbow trout.

Temperature and Plant Performance

One of the most fundamental characteristics of plants is their ability to photosynthesize. It will probably come as no surprise that **photosynthesisis** is temperature sensitive, and, within a species of plant, there is a narrow range of temperatures over which photosynthesis is optimal (fig. 5.11). A species of moss from the boreal forest, *Pleurozium schreberi*, and a desert shrub,

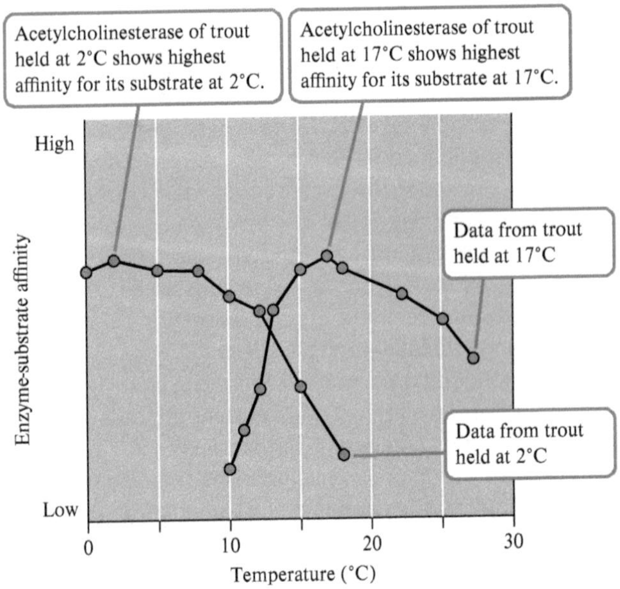

Figure 5.10 Enzyme activity is affected substantially by temperature.
Data from Baldwin and Hochachka 1970.

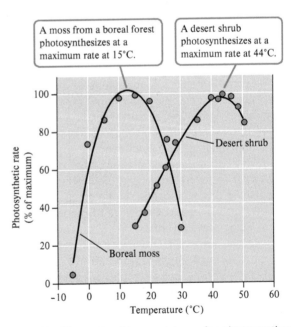

Figure 5.11 The optimal temperatures for photosynthesis by a boreal forest moss and a desert shrub differ substantially.
Data from Kallio and Kärenlampi 1975, Pearcy and Harrison 1974.

Atriplex lentiformis, provide a good demonstration of this. The moss and the shrub have substantially different optimal temperatures for photosynthesis. These differences clearly reflect differences in the thermal environments where these species live and seem to say something about their evolutionary histories.

Plant responses to temperature, as well as those of animals, can also reflect the short-term physiological adjustments called **acclimation.** The term *adaptation* is often misused when *acclimation* is meant. Remember from chapter 4 that a population adapts through differential reproductive success of individuals within the population. Adaptation involves a change in the gene pool of the population. Acclimation involves physiological, not genetic, changes in response to temperature; acclimation is generally reversible with changes in environmental conditions. An individual can acclimate to changing conditions but cannot adapt (although the capacity to acclimate is, itself, an adaptation shared by members of the population, and the degree to which individuals can acclimate will vary within a population).

Studies of *A. lentiformis* by Robert Pearcy (1977) demonstrate the effect of acclimation on photosynthesis. Pearcy located a population of this desert shrub in Death Valley and grew plants from cuttings for his experiments. By propagating plants from cuttings, he was able to conduct his experiments on genetically identical clones. The clones from the Death Valley plants were grown under two temperature regimes: one set in hot conditions of 43°C during the day and 30°C at night; the other set under cool conditions of 23°C during the day and 18°C at night.

Pearcy then measured the photosynthetic rates of the two sets of plants. The plants grown in a cool environment photosynthesized at a maximum rate at about 32°C. Those grown in a hot environment photosynthesized at a maximum rate at 40°C, a difference in the optimum temperature for photosynthesis of 8°C (fig. 5.12). Remember that the experimental plants were clones grown from cuttings and exhibited no genetic diversity upon which selection could act. Pearcy used clones to eliminate potential for adaptation and to uncover the effects of physiological adjustment through acclimation.

The physiological adjustments made by *A. lentiformis* correspond to what these plants do during an annual cycle. The plant is evergreen and photosynthesizes throughout the year, in the cool of winter and in the heat of summer. The physiological adjustments suggest that acclimation by *A. lentiformis* may shift its optimal temperature for photosynthesis to match seasonal changes in environmental temperature. Plants from cooler areas also acclimate in response to changing temperatures. These changes allow many boreal species to photosynthesize later into fall than could occur without acclimation.

Temperature and Microbial Activity

Although often overlooked, microbes control the flow of energy and nutrients in terrestrial and aquatic ecosystems. Changes in microbial activity have significant consequences for the other organisms that live alongside these organisms. It may come as

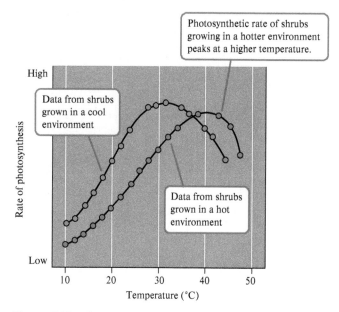

Figure 5.12 Growing the same species of shrub in cool versus hot environments altered the shrubs' optimal temperature for photosynthesis. This change was a short-term physiological adjustment due to acclimation.
Data from Berry and Björkman 1980, after Pearcy 1977.

no surprise that microbes can be extremely sensitive to changes in temperature.

Microbes appear to have adapted to all temperatures at which there is liquid water, from the frigid waters around the Antarctic to boiling hot springs. However, while each of these environments harbours one or more species of microbes, no known species thrives across all these conditions. All microbes that have been studied perform best over a fairly narrow range of temperatures. Let's look at one example of microbes growing in hot springs to illustrate.

Microbes have been found living in all of the hot springs that have been studied. Some of these heat-loving, or **thermophilic,** microbes grow at temperatures above 40°C in a variety of environments. The most heat-loving microbes are the hyperthermophiles, which have temperature optima above 80°C. Some hyperthermophiles grow best at 110°C! Some of the most intensive studies of thermophilic and hyperthermophilic microbes have been carried out in Yellowstone National Park by Thomas Brock (1978) and his students and colleagues. One of the genera they have studied is *Sulfolobus,* a member of the microbial domain Archaea, which obtains energy by oxidizing elemental sulfur. Jerry Mosser and colleagues (1974) used the rate at which *Sulfolobus* oxidizes sulfur as an index of its metabolic activity. The temperature optimum for the *Sulfolobus* populations ranged from 63°C to 80°C and for each population was related to the temperature of the particular spring from which the microbes came. For instance, one strain isolated from a 59°C spring oxidizes sulfur at a maximum rate at 63°C. This *Sulfolobus* population oxidizes sulfur at a high rate within a temperature range of about 10°C (fig. 5.13). Outside this temperature range, its rate of sulfur oxidation is much lower.

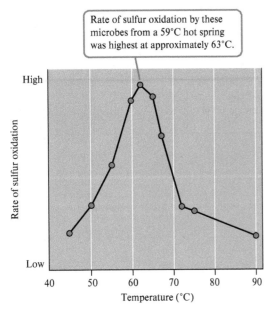

Rate of sulfur oxidation by these microbes from a 59°C hot spring was highest at approximately 63°C.

Figure 5.13 Hot spring microbes have a very high optimal temperature for population growth.
Data from Mosser, Mosser, and Brock 1974.

We have reviewed how temperature can affect animal performance, plant photosynthesis, and microbial activity. These examples demonstrate that most organisms perform best over a fairly narrow range of temperatures. Consider the effects of temperature on the performance of organisms relative to our discussion of how temperatures can vary greatly over small distances. In addition, the climate diagrams presented in chapter 2 showed us that temporal variation in temperature can also be substantial. Taken together, an ecosystem may have a mosaic of thermal niches, each favouring different plant, microbial, or even animal species, compressed into a relatively small area. This contributes to the species diversity. Organisms can partition the temperature gradient in a manner analogous to MacArthur's warbler species' partitioning of food resources (see chapter 1), allowing coexistence rather than competitive exclusion (an idea revisited in chapter 13). In the next section, we review how some organisms respond to variation in environmental temperatures.

CONCEPT 5.3 REVIEW

1. Signs of thermal stress in fish include swimming on their sides and swimming in spirals. Using what you know about temperature and acetylcholinesterase, explain.

2. How can we be sure that the distinctive response to temperature shown by *Atriplex lentiformis* was due to acclimation and not the result of genetic differences?

3. Will all species within a single habitat have similar temperature optima for a given ecological process, such as photosynthesis? Explain.

5.4 Regulating Body Temperature

Many organisms have evolved ways to compensate for variations in environmental temperature by regulating body temperature. So how do organisms respond to the juxtaposition of thermal heterogeneity in the environment and their own fairly narrow thermal requirements? Do they sit passively and let environmental temperatures affect them as they will, or do they take a more active approach? Many organisms have evolved ways to regulate body temperatures.

Balancing Heat Gain Against Heat Loss

Organisms regulate body temperature by manipulating heat gain and loss. An equation, used by K. Schmidt-Nielsen (1983), can help us understand the components of heat that may be manipulated:

$$H_s = H_m \pm H_{cd} \pm H_{cv} \pm H_r - H_e$$

Here, H_s, the total heat stored in the body of an organism, is made up of H_m, heat gained from metabolism; H_{cd}, heat gained or lost through conduction; H_{cv}, heat lost or gained by convection; H_r, heat gained or lost through electromagnetic radiation; and H_e, heat lost through **evaporation** (fig 5.14). These heat components represent ways that heat is transferred between an organism and its environment. **Metabolic heat, H_m**, is the energy released within an organism during the process of cellular respiration. **Conduction** is the movement of heat between objects in physical contact, as occurs when you sit on a stone bench on a cold winter's day; **convection** is the process of heat flow between a solid body and a moving fluid, such as wind or flowing water. During the process of conduction or

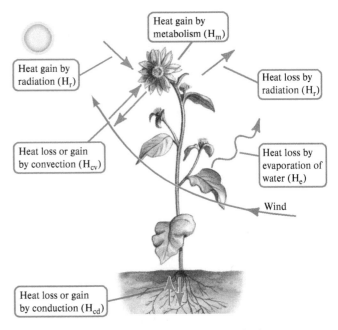

Heat gain by metabolism (H_m)

Heat gain by radiation (H_r)

Heat loss by radiation (H_r)

Heat loss or gain by convection (H_{cv})

Heat loss by evaporation of water (H_e)

Wind

Heat loss or gain by conduction (H_{cd})

Figure 5.14 There are multiple pathways for heat exchange between organisms and the environment.

convection, H_{cd} and H_{cv}, the direction of heat flow is always from the warmer region to the colder. Most of the **radiation** is in the infrared part of the spectrum. Infrared light is responsible for most of the warmth you feel when standing in front of a fire or that you feel radiating from the sunny side of a building on a winter's day. Radiative heat flux, from you to the atmosphere, is responsible for the chilling effect you feel standing outdoors on a cold, windless day. An organism may lose heat, H_e, as water evaporates from its surface. The ability of water to absorb a large amount of heat as it evaporates makes cooling systems based on the evaporation of water very effective.

So how do these factors interact to determine body temperature, and how can organisms maintain a constant internal temperature? Not all species have constant body temperatures. **Poikilotherms** have body temperatures that vary in response to changes in the external environment. In contrast, **homeotherms** maintain relatively constant internal temperatures even in the face of changing external temperatures. A variety of physiological challenges are unique to each of these conditions. For homeotherms, stabilizing selection will favour enzymes with temperature optima generally near the constant internal environment of the organism (and selection will favour a body temperature near enzyme optima!). For poikilotherms, internal temperatures are variable. Many poikilotherms have redundant enzyme systems for critical functions, each with a different temperature optimum (recall the two forms of acetylcholinesterase in trout from section 5.3). Can you imagine any energetic cost associated with maintaining redundant systems? If so, why aren't all species homeotherms?

The answer is that homeothermy also has costs associated with the mechanisms that organisms use to maintain constant body temperatures. Some organisms, such as humans, are **endotherms**. Most endotherms that will spring to mind are also homeotherms, although we will see later in the chapter that some endotherms are poikilotherms. Endotherms rely heavily on internally derived metabolic heat energy, H_m, to elevate internal temperatures over external temperatures. Endothermic birds and mammals use metabolic energy to heat most of their bodies, while some endothermic fish and insects selectively heat critical organs. For endotherms, lowering the body temperature is generally more difficult than raising the body temperature. As a result, most endotherms are able to survive at ambient temperatures well below their set body temperatures while at only a limited range of temperatures above their set body temperature.

Ectotherms are able to control their body temperatures through the use of external sources of energy, manipulating predominantly H_{cd}, H_{cv}, H_r, and H_e. Ectotherms will often use behaviour to control their internal temperatures. In doing so, some will maintain a relatively constant internal temperature (homeothermy), while others will allow internal temperature to vary. For example, many reptiles can be found laying still on roads, rocks, and other exposed objects early in the morning. Why? This behaviour exposes their body to the sun, resulting in an elevated temperature. Later in the day, these same animals will often be found in crevices, cracks, or underground, preventing their body temperature from reaching a lethal point.

Clearly, being an ectotherm will "cost" less energy than being an endotherm since they have lower metabolic rates. Why then are not all species ectotherms? One answer may come to you if you consider how rarely you actually see snakes, lizards, and other terrestrial ectotherms being active.

There is a great natural diversity in temperature relations between organisms and their environments. It is because of this diversity of nature that the old terms *cold-blooded* and *warm-blooded* are frustratingly inaccurate. For example, the behavioural changes of many ectotherms are so effective that they are actually homeotherms, at least for part of the day. Ectotherms of the deep ocean are also homeotherms, as the lack of change in the external temperatures results in a lack of change in body temperatures. Some endotherms, such as many hummingbirds, maintain constant body temperatures during the day and then are poikilothermic during the night.

Every organism is adapted to its thermal environment. In most cases, this means adaptations that allow the organism to cope with a dynamic thermal environment. We see some common themes emerge that relate to the heat budget equation. For example, a variety of plants and animals in cold temperatures may have dark pigment to increase radiative heating, and body forms that minimize conductive heat loss. Plants and animals in high temperature regimes often lack pigmentation or have structures that increase reflectance, limiting radiative heating. We commonly see adaptations that increase radiative or evaporative cooling at night. Evaporative cooling lies at an intersection between maintaining heat balance and water balance (chapter 6), and adaptations often represent fitness trade-offs between thermal regulation and water balance. Life in water comes with its own unique challenges for temperature regulation, and we see common theses for minimizing convective heat loss to surrounding water.

There are many fascinating examples of unique adaptations in plants and animals that relate to temperature regulation. However, we will look at only a few examples that illustrate the more general patterns described above.

Temperature Regulation by Plants: Tundra and Desert Plants

Cold or hot environments present a variety of unique challenges to plants. Freezing can destroy a plant's vascular systems, and enzymatic reactions are slower under cold conditions. Similarly, enzymatic reactions can slow down above their thermal optima. High temperatures can also change membrane fluidity, making it more challenging to maintain cellular homeostasis. Allowing temperature to drop too low or climb too high for prolonged periods has significant consequences for plant fitness. How do plants thermoregulate in very cold or very hot climates? They use morphology, physiology, and behaviour to alter heat exchange with the environment.

To stay warm, arctic and alpine plants have three main options: (1) increase their rate of radiative heating, H_r; (2) increase their rate of conductive heating, H_{cd}; and/or (3) decrease their rate of convective cooling, H_{cv}. It appears that many have evolved to do both and, as a result, can heat up to temperatures far above

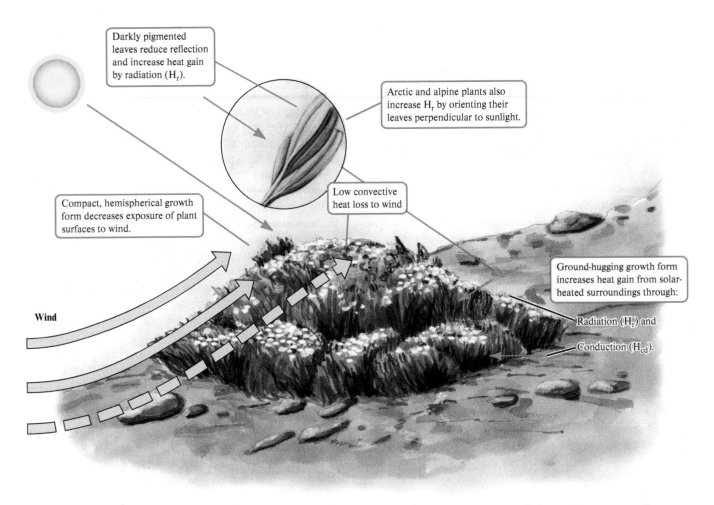

Darkly pigmented leaves reduce reflection and increase heat gain by radiation (H_r).

Arctic and alpine plants also increase H_r by orienting their leaves perpendicular to sunlight.

Compact, hemispherical growth form decreases exposure of plant surfaces to wind.

Low convective heat loss to wind

Ground-hugging growth form increases heat gain from solar-heated surroundings through:

Radiation (H_r) and

Conduction (H_{cd}).

Wind

Figure 5.15 Arctic and alpine cushion plant form and orientation increase heat gain from sunlight and the surrounding landscape and conserve any heat gained.

air temperature. Natural selection has favoured arctic and alpine plants with dark pigments that absorb light. These dark pigments increase radiative heat gain, H_r. Arctic and alpine plants, such as the *Dryas integrifolia* (see fig. 5.1), also increase their H_r gain by orienting their leaves and flowers perpendicular to the sun's rays. In addition, many plants increase their H_r gain from the surroundings by assuming a "cushion" growth form that "hugs" the ground (fig. 5.15). The ground often warms to temperatures exceeding that of the overlying air and radiates infrared light, which can be absorbed by cushion plants. Cushion plants can also gain heat from warm substrate through conduction, H_{cd}. The cushion growth form reduces convective heat loss, H_{cv}, because growing close to the ground gives cushion plants some shelter from the wind. The compact, hemispherical growth form of cushion plants also reduces the ratio of surface area to volume, which slows the movement of air through the interior of the plant.

Plants growing in hot deserts have three main options to avoid overheating: decreasing heating by conduction, H_{cd}; increasing rates of convective cooling, H_{cv}; and reducing rates of radiative heating, H_r. In contrast to tundra and alpine plants, many desert plants place their foliage far enough above the ground to reduce heat gain by conduction. Many desert plants have also evolved very small leaves and an open growth form,

adaptations that give high rates of convective cooling because they increase the ratio of leaf surface area to volume and the movement of air around the plant's stems and foliage. Where many tundra and alpine plants have evolved dark pigmentation, many desert plants have evolved reflective surfaces and light-coloured leaves (chapter 2) to reduce radiative heat gain, H_r. This lighter colouring is often obtained by covering their leaves with a dense coating of white plant hairs, reflecting visible light. Plants can also modify radiative heat gain, H_r, by changing the orientation of leaves and stems. Many desert plants reduce heating by orienting their leaves parallel to the rays of the sun or by folding them at midday, when sunlight is most intense. Figure 5.16 portrays the main processes involved in heat balance in desert plants.

Temperature Regulation by Ectothermic Animals: Lizards and Grasshoppers

Like plants, the vast majority of animals, including fish, amphibians, reptiles, and invertebrates, use external sources of energy to regulate body temperature. These ectothermic animals use means analogous to those of plants, including variations in body

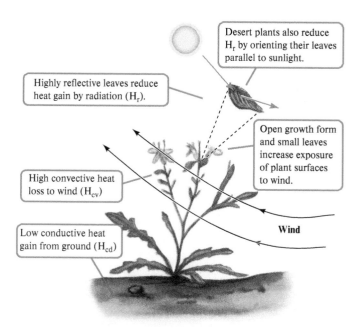

Desert plants also reduce H$_r$ by orienting their leaves parallel to sunlight.

Highly reflective leaves reduce heat gain by radiation (H$_r$).

Open growth form and small leaves increase exposure of plant surfaces to wind.

High convective heat loss to wind (H$_{cv}$)

Low conductive heat gain from ground (H$_{cd}$)

Wind

Figure 5.16 The form and orientation of desert plants reduces heat gain from the environment and facilitates cooling.

size, shape, pigmentation, and behaviour. The obvious difference between plants and ectothermic animals is that the animals have more options for using behaviour to thermoregulate. Yet, as we shall see, the difference between the behaviour of these animals and that of plants is more a matter of degree than of kind.

Behavioral adaptations can impact radiative heating/cooling, H$_r$. The eastern fence lizard (*Sceloporus undulatus*) is an ectotherm that regulates its body temperature by behaviours such as basking in the sun to warm its body or seeking shade to cool it (fig 5.17). Many grasshoppers also bask in the sun. The clear-winged grasshopper (*Camnula pellucida*) is found in grasslands throughout North America, including those of the southwest United States, southern Canada, and even up into the Yukon. Needless to say, this species experiences a great diversity of climates. During early morning, *Camnula* orients its body perpendicular to the sun's rays and quickly heats to between 30°C and 40°C. Later in the day, it may orient its body parallel to the sun's rays to reduce radiative gain. Given the opportunity, young *Camnula* will maintain a body temperature around 38°C to 40°C, very close to its optimal temperature for development.

In addition to their behavioural repertoire, animals may thermoregulate by altering morphology. R. I. Carruthers and

Figure 5.17 The eastern fence lizard (*Sceloporus undulates*).
Rob Hainer/Shutterstock.com.

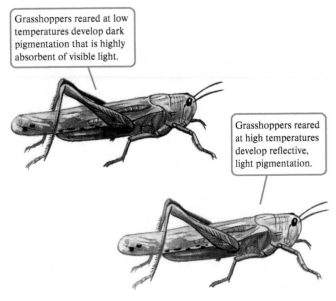

Grasshoppers reared at low temperatures develop dark pigmentation that is highly absorbent of visible light.

Grasshoppers reared at high temperatures develop reflective, light pigmentation.

Figure 5.18   Rearing temperatures influence the pigmentation of the clear-winged grasshopper.

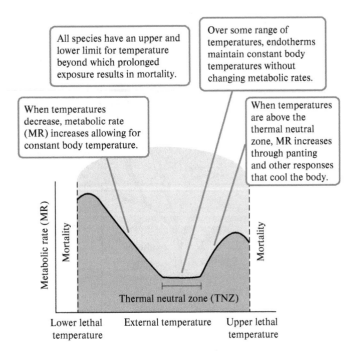

All species have an upper and lower limit for temperature beyond which prolonged exposure results in mortality.

When temperatures decrease, metabolic rate (MR) increases allowing for constant body temperature.

Over some range of temperatures, endotherms maintain constant body temperatures without changing metabolic rates.

When temperatures are above the thermal neutral zone, MR increases through panting and other responses that cool the body.

Figure 5.19   In response to changing external temperatures, endotherms vary metabolic rates to maintain a constant body temperature.

his colleagues (1992) described how some species of grasshoppers vary the intensity of their pigmentation during development. When reared at low temperatures, these species appear to compensate by developing dark pigmentation (fig. 5.18). This plasticity in pigmentation allows a grasshopper to increase (by producing darker pigment) or decrease (by producing less pigment) potential H_r gain.

Temperature Regulation by Endothermic Animals

Do endothermic animals thermoregulate differently than the other organisms we have discussed? Endotherms use all the anatomical and behavioural tricks used by other organisms to manipulate heat exchange with the environment. However, the relative importance of terms in the heat budget equation differs. Endotherms rely a great deal more on metabolic heat, H_m, to maintain constant body temperature.

Environmental Temperature and Metabolic Rates

P. F. Scholander and his colleagues (1950) studied thermoregulation in several endothermic species by monitoring metabolic rate while exposing them to a range of temperatures. The range of environmental temperatures over which the metabolic rate of a homeothermic animal does not change is called its **thermal neutral zone** (fig. 5.19). When environmental temperatures are within the thermal neutral zone of an endothermic animal, its metabolic rate stays steady at resting metabolism. An endotherm's metabolic rate will rapidly increase to two or even three times resting metabolism if the environmental temperature falls below or rises above the thermal neutral zone.

What causes metabolic rates to rise when environmental temperatures are outside the thermal neutral zone? We can use

humans as a model for the responses of endotherms generally. At low temperatures, we start shivering, which generates heat by muscle contractions. We also release hormones that increase our metabolic rate, the rate at which we metabolize our energy stores, which are mainly fats. Increasing metabolic rate increases the rate at which we generate metabolic heat, H_m. At high temperatures, heart rate and blood flow to the skin increase. This increased blood flow transports heat from the body core to the skin, where an evaporative cooling system based on sweating accelerates unloading of heat to the external environment. Many large endotherms, such as horses and camels, also cool by sweating. Other endotherms do not sweat but evaporatively cool by other means: dogs and birds pant, and marsupials and rodents moisten their body surfaces by salivating and licking.

The breadth of the thermal neutral zone varies a great deal among endothermic species. Tropical species have narrow thermal neutral zones, as environmental temperatures in the tropics do not vary greatly during the year. In contrast, arctic species that experience a large change in environmental temperatures across seasons have broad thermal neutral zones.

From evolutionary and ecological perspectives, the important point of this discussion is that thermoregulation outside the thermal neutral zone costs energy that could be otherwise directed toward reproduction. How might such energetic costs affect the distribution and abundance of organisms in nature? This is one of the central questions of ecology.

Aquatic Animals

Now let's turn to thermoregulation by aquatic endotherms, where the aquatic environment limits the possible ways by which organisms can regulate their body temperatures. Why is that? First, the capacity of water to absorb heat energy without changing temperature is about 3,000 times that of air. Second, conductive and convective heat losses to water are much more rapid than to air: over 20 times faster in still water and up to 100 times faster in moving water. Thus, the aquatic organism is surrounded by a vast heat sink. The potential for heat loss to this heat sink is great, particularly for gill-breathing species that must expose a large respiratory surface directly to the environment to extract sufficient oxygen from water. In the face of these environmental difficulties, only a few aquatic species are truly endothermic.

Aquatic birds and mammals, such as penguins, seals, and whales, can be endothermic in an aquatic environment for two major reasons. First, they are all air breathers and do not expose a large respiratory surface to the surrounding water. Second, many endothermic aquatic animals, including penguins, seals, and whales, are well-insulated from the heat-sapping external environment by a thick layer of fat, while others, such as the sea otter, are insulated by a layer of fur that traps air. The parts of these animals that are not well insulated, principally appendages, are outfitted with *countercurrent heat exchangers,* vascular structures that reduce the rate of heat loss to the surrounding aquatic environment. Figure 5.20 diagrams the structure and functioning of a countercurrent heat exchanger in the flipper of a dolphin.

Until recently, whole body endothermy was thought to be the province of mammals and birds, setting them apart from other animals. A small number of highly active fish (fewer than 0.1% of species) have adapted to retain some metabolic heat. These are referred to as regional endotherms, and, unlike birds or mammals, they maintain elevated temperatures only of specific organs or tissues. Tunas and lamnid sharks, for example, warm their aerobic swimming muscles, while billfish warm only their

eyes and brain regions. The lateral swimming muscles of tuna and lamnid sharks are well supplied with blood vessels that function as countercurrent heat exchangers, allowing them to maintain efficient movement in the open ocean. The opah (*Lampris guttatus*) is the only fish currently known to exhibit whole body endothermy (Wegner et al. 2015). It generates heat through the constant flapping of its pectoral fins and minimizes heat loss in the water with countercurrent heat exchange in the gills.

In this section, we have considered how various organisms regulate their body temperatures by using external sources of energy, internal sources of energy, or both. Thermoregulation is possible where organisms face temperatures within their range of tolerance. However, organisms do not always respond to variation in environmental temperatures by thermoregulating. In many circumstances, they use various means to survive extreme environmental temperatures, as we shall discuss next.

CONCEPT 5.4 REVIEW

1. Why would selection likely act against the production of light pigmentation and white hairs on the leaf surface of arctic plants?
2. Can behavioural thermoregulation be precise? What evidence supports your answer?
3. Why are all endothermic fish relatively large?

5.5 Surviving Extreme Temperatures

Organisms exhibit a diversity of mechanisms to cope with extreme temperatures. Think of an environment that is either very cold or very hot: perhaps a −40°C winter day in the boreal forest. For certain, you are likely to notice less obvious biological activity on that day than you would in the same location in the middle of the summer. However, even that cold winter day is not devoid of life. In this section we will discuss strategies that have evolved that allow species (if not always individuals) to survive extreme temperatures.

When we use the term *extreme,* keep in mind that this is a relative term: what is extreme to one species may, in fact, be quite comfortable to another. We use the term to indicate temperatures well beyond the range of tolerance for most species (fig. 5.8). For example, although many species of spruce trees are able to survive at temperatures as low as −80°C, most scientists would agree that this is an extreme temperature. Or, put another way, few ecologists would themselves choose to work outside under such conditions! Extreme conditions can last for a day, a week, or months, with different strategies existing for each of these scenarios. One thing that is common in response to extreme temperatures is that relatively simple solutions, such as panting, increasing hair cover, or other minor behavioural and physiological changes, can help an organism cope for short periods of time. However, individually these options are likely

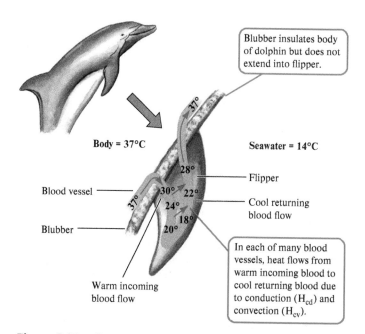

Figure 5.20 Countercurrent heat exchange in dolphin flippers promotes conservation of body heat.

Figure 5.21 Plants and animals exhibit a variety of adaptations to surviving extreme winter conditions.
(Clockwise from top left): A. E. Derocher, University of Alberta; Dmitry Deshevykh/Getty Images; Brian Dust; Outdoorsman/Dreamstime.com/
GetStock.com; David Hik.

not quite enough to allow for survival over longer time periods. Instead, dramatic environmental conditions have resulted in the evolution of equally dramatic ecological responses. Here we examine some of the more common responses to extreme temperatures, particularly responses to extreme cold (fig. 5.21).

Death

You may not consider death to be a particularly adaptive response to extreme conditions, but in fact it is a common strategy used by many organisms. Although death is a terrible survival strategy for the individual, it may be an effective strategy for the individual's genes, improving the chances of passing

them on to the next generation. Why? To answer this we must consider energy budgets. All organisms have a certain amount of energy based upon what they eat (or produce by photosynthesis). This can be represented in a pie diagram, with the size of the pie representing the total amount of energy available to the organism (fig. 5.22). For a given organism at a given point in time, the size of the pie is fixed, and energy spent on one biological process cannot also be spent on another process. The main types of energy expenditure for all organisms (plants, animals, microbes, etc.) can be broken down into four general groups: growth, maintenance, activity, and reproduction (fig. 5.22). Growth consumes all the energy needed to build new tissues and organs; maintenance represents the basal metabolic

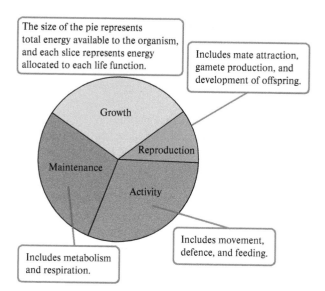

The size of the pie represents total energy available to the organism, and each slice represents energy allocated to each life function.

Includes mate attraction, gamete production, and development of offspring.

Growth

Reproduction

Maintenance

Activity

Includes metabolism and respiration.

Includes movement, defence, and feeding.

Figure 5.22 Pie diagrams can be used to represent energy budgets for organisms.

costs of simply staying alive; reproduction costs include the production of reproductive organs (e.g., flowers), mechanisms of mate attraction (e.g., nectar, showy plumage), and the development of offspring; and activity costs include the extra energy required to move, eat, defend territories, and most anything else that organisms do when they are not asleep or dormant. The relative size of each of these slices of pie will differ among species. For example, endotherms will have much larger maintenance costs than will ectotherms.

How does this relate to extreme environments? One strategy for surviving harsh conditions can be increased energy expenditures for maintenance (e.g., increasing metabolic rate, construction of freeze-resistant tissues, etc.), resulting in less energy available for other activities, such as reproduction. For many other organisms, natural selection has favoured a solution that involves minimal investment in maintenance and maximal investment in reproduction. What types of organisms do this? "Annual" plants and many insects are among the more common examples. What does being "annual" actually mean for plants? It means that an individual completes its life cycle within a single year. As it turns out, the adult life-stage generally dies just prior to the more extreme temperatures, which would be winter for most parts of Canada.

A reasonable question to ask is this: If extreme conditions kill the adults of a particular species, how is it possible to find that same species in the same location the following year? The solution to this problem lies in the realization that many species or organisms have different life-stages that have inherently different morphologies and ranges of tolerance. For example, each seed of a flowering plant is a living, breathing organism (with its own very small energy pie); it is not an inert piece of the soil. Pause to consider this for a minute. How many lives are you killing when you grind wheat to make a loaf of bread? How about when you eat a single strawberry, with all of those seeds exposed on the outer surface of the fruit? Although most

seeds are unable to withstand the grinding abilities of grain mills or your teeth, many seeds do have seed coats and other protective tissues that allow them to withstand environmental conditions that would kill them as adults. As a result, when spring arrives, these seeds are able to germinate, grow, and reproduce, until the arrival of winter causes their death as well. Protective structures and coatings are also found in the eggs and early instars of many insects, the spores of many fungi, and the cell walls of many bacteria (organisms you also regularly consume—intentionally or not).

Migration

The boreal forest comes alive in the spring and summer with the arrival of countless bird species that winter in warmer climates. There are over 300 bird species in the boreal forest, and over 90% of these migrate south as winter approaches. These species result in an estimated 3 billion breeding adults and 5 billion migrating individuals (adults and offspring) each year. Needless to say, migration is a common method of coping with extreme temperatures! Small animals, with large surface area:volume ratios are at particular risk from extreme temperatures; thus, it is not surprising that many small songbirds fly south each winter.

Extreme shifts in temperature drive the migration of many other species as well, including the monarch butterfly, which summers in southern Canada and throughout the United States, wintering in the mountains of Mexico. Actually, the monarch has a summer generation that develops in southern Canada and the U.S., then migrates to Mexico, spawning a winter generation. The winter generation then migrates back to Canada, spawning the next summer generation. For a small bird or butterfly, the energy needed to migrate is very high. So why don't these birds and butterflies stay in their "winter" homes all year long? How can it be worthwhile to migrate? The answer will lie in the specific costs and ability to withstand extreme temperatures for each species. In general, we would expect species to migrate when the fitness costs of staying through the extreme conditions are greater than the costs of migration.

Resistance

The third general strategy for coping with extreme weather conditions is possession of traits that allow the individual to tolerate extreme temperatures. Individuals that find themselves in harsh temperatures and that do not possess specialized traits (or either of the two strategies described above) are destined to become evolutionary losers—producing fewer and lower quality offspring than their neighbours that are adapted to life under extreme conditions. Across plant and animal species, we find substantial variation in an organism's ability to survive and thrive under low temperature conditions. Many tropical plant species die when temperatures reach a relatively warm 5°C, while white spruce is able to survive temperatures as low as −80°C! Because of this variation, the minimum temperature that is reached during the winter months (chapter 2) sets the northern limit of the range of many species (chapter 10). What do you think might happen to the ranges of such temperature-limited species under global warming? Books can (and have!) been written about the specialized traits that allow some species to thrive where others die. Here are a few of the more common adaptations to extreme temperatures.

Fur, Fat, and Feathers

Here is the problem. Imagine you are a homeothermic endotherm living in the Arctic, and you will stay active during the winter. As the air temperature decreases below the lower limit of the thermal neutral zone (fig. 5.19), you will need to increase your basal metabolic rate to maintain your body temperature. However, this process uses substantial energy reserves, leaving less energy available for other activities. What do you do? One effective strategy is to increase the insulative properties of your body, which has the result of decreasing your heat energy lost by radiation or convection. Many mammals do this by depositing a subcutaneous layer of fat at the onset of winter, as well as by increasing production of body hair (fur). The fat often serves two roles. First, it provides increased stored energy that can be used to pay for the increased metabolic rates often associated with winter. Second, increased fat decreases heat loss through radiation while also decreasing the rate at which the body cools down. Fur, and feathers in birds, also enhance the thermal properties of the organism by trapping warm air near the body.

Acclimation

Early in the chapter, we described the idea of acclimation and explained that exposure to mild cold (or heat) causes physiological changes in many species. Acclimation is a critical adaptation for many species that live in extreme environments. This may best be shown by the numerous studies conducted by C. J. Weiser and the laboratory of cold hardiness at the University of Minnesota. Weiser found that for many species, the lower lethal temperature (i.e., killing temperature) decreases as winter approaches (Weiser 1970). For example, *Cornus stolonifera* (red-osier dogwood) will die if exposed to temperatures near freezing in July or August. However, that same species can withstand temperatures below $-30°C$ in November (Weiser 1970). Clearly, acclimation to cold plays an important role in allowing species to live in extreme environments.

Inactivity, Tolerance, and Avoidance

A simple way to avoid extreme environmental temperatures is to seek shelter during the hottest or coldest times of the day. During the cold nights of the tropical alpine zone, *Liolaemus* lizards take shelter in burrows, where temperatures are several degrees warmer than on the surface. This form of behavioural response is common among many organisms, including reptiles, amphibians, and many insects, and it is equally effective in avoiding extreme heat.

Going underground is not always an option in cold climates, where the ground itself is frozen solid. Instead, many species take relief from the cold air by forming burrows within the snow. Fresh snow is an extremely good insulator—even better than the glass wool used in the walls of many modern homes (Marchand 1996)! With a deep enough snow pack, ground temperatures can hover near zero, even if air temperatures are well below that value. This warm refuge serves as a critical way that many small mammals, unable to add substantial fat or fur, are able to survive in the north. The insulative properties of snow are also of great importance to people who live and travel in extreme temperatures.

Not all species will, or can, move to warmer microclimates, and instead their bodies will be exposed to subzero temperatures for at least some part of the winter. Having ice inside one's body is dangerous; ice crystals can rip apart cells and tissues, destroying critical organs in the process. However, freezing is not inevitable, even when temperatures are below zero. Why? You may recall from introductory chemistry that water freezes at $0°C$ only under very stringent conditions. The freezing point of water is actually quite variable and is modified by changes in pressure and solute concentration. Organisms have little control over atmospheric pressure, but they can exert significant control over the solute concentration of the intra- and extracellular fluids, in effect manipulating them to become anti-freeze agents. As a result, many plants, insects, and polar marine fish are able to avoid having critical tissues destroyed by ice formation, even when temperatures are below zero.

A more extreme solution is found in a variety of ectotherms of northern areas: freeze tolerance. A number of species of turtles, snakes, and frogs are able to survive extreme temperatures because they allow their bodies to freeze, rather than spending substantial amounts of energy on the avoidance-of-freezing strategy dominant among endotherms. One of the best known examples is the wood frog (*Rana sylvatica*). The wood frog is found in forests over a broad geographic range, from above the Arctic Circle down into the Appalachian Mountains. It is found as far east as the Maritime provinces and west into Alaska. In a review of freezing tolerance in ectothermic vertebrates, Kenneth and Janet Storey of Carleton University describe many of the freezing features of this remarkable animal (1992). Wood frogs can survive more than 10 days frozen, with body temperatures of $-6°C$. During this time, over 60% of the body fluids can be frozen solid (fig. 5.23). There is evidence of acclimation for freezing, with frogs in the fall having higher freezing-survival than do frogs of the spring. During the freezing, heartbeat slows to around 4 beats/min, and then stops once the frog has frozen. The heart starts again within an hour of the body temperature reaching more than $3°C$.

How can these frogs do this? Freeze tolerance requires several critical adaptations. One of the most important is the presence of ice-nucleating compounds. These can be proteins, minerals, or microbes that initiate and control extracellular ice formation, the opposite effect to the one we found for the anti-freeze agents with the freeze-avoidance strategy, above. Without these nucleating compounds, ice formation would either be nonexistent or, worse, would occur in a haphazard manner within the body, causing serious tissue damage. A second critical adaptation is the presence of high levels of cryoprotectants, such as glucose. Rapid synthesis of glucose in the liver by wood frogs occurs immediately following ice crystallization on the body surface. The glucose is distributed to cells throughout the body, where it reduces cell damage. The exact mechanisms

Figure 5.23   Wood frogs can survive freezing during cold winter months.
J.M. Storey.

there is little available food. As a result, their maintenance costs (e.g., metabolism) will be greater than their entire energy budget; thus, substantial weight loss and/or mortality may ensue. There is nothing an animal can do about whether its food items are available or not; however, the maintenance cost of the organism can be controlled. Many organisms enter periods in which they reduce their metabolic rates, thereby reducing their energy demands.

Hummingbirds depend upon a diet of nectar and insects to maintain a high metabolic rate and a body temperature of about 39°C. When food is abundant, they maintain these high rates throughout the day and night. However, when food is scarce and night temperatures are cold, they may enter a state of torpor (fig. 5.24). **Torpor** is a state of self-induced hypothermia that generally lasts for only a few hours. In torpor, metabolic rates are reduced and core body temperatures are lowered, saving energy. F. L. Carpenter and colleagues (1993) estimated that rufous hummingbirds that maintain full body temperature all night metabolized 0.24g of fat. In torpor, these birds used only 0.02g of fat, an energy savings of over 90%. Torpor can also be found in other bird species and in some mammals, including various species of bats.

More prolonged states of reduced metabolic activity are common in many other species. If this occurs mainly in winter, it is called **hibernation;** in summer, it is called **estivation.** During hibernation, the body temperature of arctic ground squirrels may drop to 2°C. The metabolic rates of hibernating marmots may fall to 3% of their levels seen during active periods. During estivation, the metabolic rates of long-neck turtles may fall to 28% of their normal metabolic rate. Such reductions in metabolism allow individuals to survive long arctic and alpine winters or hot and dry periods in the desert, during which they must rely entirely on stored energy reserves. Without this reduction in metabolism, metabolic costs would be too great for their energy budget, and mortality would occur.

involved remain unclear. A third critical adaptation in wood frogs is that prior to freezing, much of the extracellular fluids are removed from critical organs and stored in the lymphatic system and coelom. A few jagged ice crystals in these locations are less likely to cause significant damage.

Reduction of Metabolic Rate

The last group of physiological adaptations to extreme temperatures are likely the most familiar to you, and all involve reducing an organism's metabolic rate. One of the great difficulties for many organisms that live in areas of extreme temperatures is that even if they are able to survive exposure to the conditions,

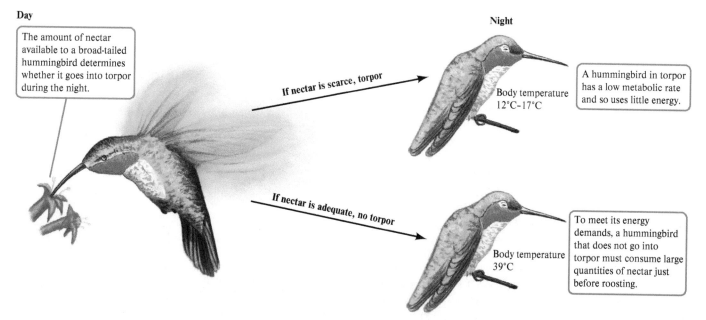

Figure 5.24   The availability of nectar affects whether broad-tailed hummingbirds enter torpor at night.

Temperature relations are a significant factor influencing the ecology of a diversity of species across the globe. This branch of ecology is attracting increased attention within the scientific community, fuelled by concerns about the ecological consequences of global warming, a topic we discuss in depth in chapter 23. In the Ecological Tools and Approaches section, we look at how studies of temperature relations and climatic warming are helping to explain the local extinction of a species.

ECOLOGICAL TOOLS AND APPROACHES

Climatic Warming and the Local Extinction of a Land Snail

Between 1906 and 1908, a graduate student named G. Bollinger (1909) studied land snails in the vicinity of Basel, Switzerland. Eighty-five years later, Bruno Baur and Anette Baur (1993) carefully resurveyed Bollinger's study sites near Basel for the presence of land snails. In the process, they found that at least one snail species, *Arianta arbustorum*, had disappeared from several of the sites. This discovery led the Baurs to explore the mechanisms that may have caused localized extinctions of *A. arbustorum*.

A. arbustorum is a common land snail in meadows, forests, and other moist, vegetated habitats in northwestern and central Europe. The species lives at elevations up to 2,700 m in the Alps. The adults, which are hermaphroditic, deposit their eggs in moss, under plant litter, or in the soil. Eggs generally hatch in two to four weeks, depending upon temperature. The egg is an especially sensitive stage in the life cycle of land snails. *A. arbustorum* often lives alongside *Cepaea nemoralis*, a land snail with a broader geographic distribution that extends from southern Scandinavia to the Iberian peninsula.

The Baurs found *A. arbustorum* still living at 13 of the 29 sites surveyed by Bollinger near Basel. Eleven of these remaining populations lived in deciduous forests and the other two lived on grassy riverbanks. However, the Baurs could not find the snail at 16 sites. Eight of these sites had been urbanized, which made the habitat unsuitable for any land snails because natural vegetation had been removed. Between 1900 and 1990, the urbanized area of Basel had increased by 500%. However, the eight other sites where *A. arbustorum* had disappeared were still covered by vegetation that appeared suitable. These sites still supported populations of five other land snail species, including *C. nemoralis*.

What caused the extinction of *A. arbustorum* at sites that supported other snails? The Baurs compared the characteristics of these sites with those of the sites where *A. arbustorum* had persisted. They found no difference between these two groups of sites in regard to slope, percent plant cover, height of vegetation, distance from water, or number of other land snail species present. The first major difference the Baurs uncovered was in elevation. The sites where *A. arbustorum* was extinct have an average elevation of 274 m. The places where it survived have an average elevation of 420 m. The places where the snail had survived were also cooler.

A thermal image of the landscape taken from a satellite showed that surface temperatures in summer around Basel ranged from about 17°C to 32.5°C. Surface temperatures where *A. arbustorum* had survived averaged approximately 22°C, while the sites where the species had gone extinct had surface temperatures that averaged approximately 25°C. The sites where the snail was extinct were also much closer to very hot areas with temperatures greater than 29°C. Figure 5.25 is based on the Baurs' thermal image of the area around Basel and shows where the snail was extinct and where it persisted.

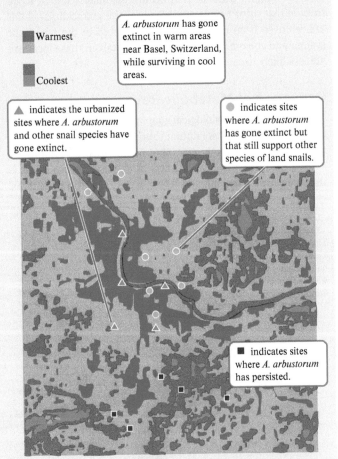

Figure 5.25 Relative surface temperatures and patterns of extinction and persistence by the snail *Arianta arbustorum* around Basel, Switzerland.

Data from Baur and Baur 1993.

The Baurs attributed the higher temperatures at the eight sites where the snail is extinct, but vegetation is still suitable, to heating by thermal radiation from the urbanized areas of the city. Buildings and pavement store more heat than vegetation. In addition, the cooling effect of evaporation from vegetation is lost when an area is built over. Increased heat storage and reduced cooling make urbanized landscapes thermal islands. Heat energy stored in urban centres is transferred to the surrounding landscape through thermal radiation, H_r.

Are the temperature differences the Baurs observed sufficient to exclude *A. arbustorum* from the warmer sites? The researchers compared the temperature relations of *A. arbustorum* and *C. nemoralis* to find some clues. They concentrated their studies on the influence of temperature on reproduction by these two snail species.

The eggs of each species were incubated at four temperatures: 19°C, 22°C, 25°C, and 29°C. These temperatures fall within the range measured by the satellite image (fig. 5.25). The eggs of both species hatched at a high rate at 19°C. However, at higher temperatures, their eggs hatched at significantly different rates. At 22°C, less than 50% of *A. arbustorum* eggs hatched, while the eggs of *C. nemoralis* continued to hatch at a high rate. At 25°C, no *A. arbustorum* eggs hatched, while approximately 50% of the *C. nemoralis* eggs hatched. At 29°C, the hatching of *C. nemoralis* eggs was also greatly reduced (fig. 5.26).

The results of this study show that the eggs of *A. arbustorum* are more sensitive to higher temperatures than are the eggs of *C. nemoralis*. This greater thermal sensitivity can explain why *A. arbustorum* is extinct at some

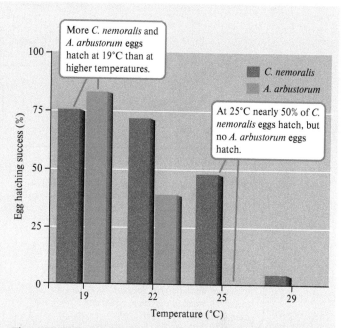

Figure 5.26 Temperature and hatching success of two snail species; the eggs of *Arianta arbustorum* are sensitive to high temperatures.
Data from Baur and Baur 1993.

sites, while *C. nemoralis* survived. These results also suggest that climatic warming can lead to the local extinction of species. As we face the prospect of warming on a global scale, studies of temperature relations will assume greater importance. In chapter 6, we look at a related topic, water relations.

CONCEPT 5.5 REVIEW

1. How can death be considered an evolutionarily successful strategy for coping with extreme temperatures?

2. Do plants and animals have similar or completely different mechanisms for dealing with extreme temperatures? Explain.

3. Why don't hummingbirds save energy by going into torpor at night even when food supplies are abundant? In other words, what would be a possible disadvantage of routine, nightly torpor?

SUMMARY

5.1 Macroclimate interacts with the local landscape to produce microclimatic variation in temperature.

The sun's uneven heating of the earth's surface and Earth's permanent tilt on its axis produce macroclimate. Macroclimate interacts with the local landscape—mainly albedo, elevation, aspect, vegetation, colour of the ground, and small-scale structural features, such as boulders and burrows—to produce microclimates (fig. 5.27). For the individual organism, macroclimate may be less significant than microclimate. The physical nature of water limits temperature variation in aquatic environments, although thermal stratification can create a compressed temperature gradient through which some organisms migrate daily.

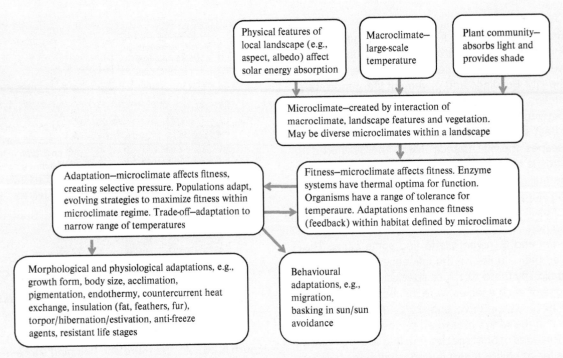

Figure 5.27 Concept map for chapter 5.

5.2 Adapting to one set of environmental conditions generally reduces fitness in other environments.

The principle of allocation, which is supported by research on bacterial populations, proposes that evolutionary trade-offs are inevitable since organisms have access to limited amounts of energy. Adaptations enhance fitness within the microclimate, but generally this makes the organism poorly adapted across a broad temperature range.

5.3 Most species perform best in a fairly narrow range of temperatures.

The influence of temperature on the performance of organisms begins at the molecular level, where extreme temperatures impair the functioning of enzymes. Rates of photosynthesis and microbial activity generally peak in a narrow range of temperatures and are much lower outside this optimal temperature range. How temperature affects the performance of organisms often corresponds to the current distributions of species and their evolutionary histories.

5.4 Many organisms have evolved ways to compensate for variations in environmental temperature by regulating body temperature.

Temperature regulation balances heat gain against heat loss. Plants and ectothermic animals use morphology and behaviour to modify rates of heat exchange with the environment (fig. 5.27). Birds and mammals rely heavily on metabolic energy to regulate body temperature. The physical nature of the aquatic environment reduces the possibilities for temperature regulation by aquatic organisms. Most endothermic aquatic species are air breathers. Some organisms improve performance by selectively heating parts of their anatomy. The

energetic requirements of thermoregulation may influence the distribution of species.

5.5 Organisms exhibit a diversity of mechanisms to cope with extreme temperatures.

Many species are unable to live in extreme temperatures, restricting their range. For some species, the adult stages of many organisms will die during extreme events, while an alternative life-stage, such as seeds, persists during these periods. Other species avoid extreme temperatures through regular migrations to more moderate climates. For species that stay year-round in extreme environments, maintaining a positive energy budget is difficult. Energy budgets can be described by pie diagrams, with trade-offs in allocation between growth, maintenance, reproduction, and activity. Increasing insulative properties of the organism through fur, fat, and feathers reduces heat loss through radiation. Moderate microclimates can often be found underground or beneath deep snow pack, reducing the need for elevated metabolic rates. Many animals enter a state of torpor, reducing metabolic rates during periods of inactivity. Periods of reduced metabolic rates can also persist for several months. If this occurs mainly in winter, it is called hibernation. In summer, it is called estivation. Energy savings from reducing metabolic rates allow organisms to live in environments even when resources are periodically scarce and temperatures are extreme.

Long-term studies of populations of land snails around Basel, Switzerland, have documented local extinctions of these land snails. These extinctions are attributable to habitat destruction and climatic warming. The results of these studies suggest that climatic warming can lead to the local extinction of species. As we face the prospect of climatic warming at a global scale, studies of temperature relations will assume greater importance.

REVIEW QUESTIONS

1. Many species of plants and animals that are associated with boreal forests also occur on mountains far to the south of the boreal forests. Using what you have learned about microclimates, predict how aspect and elevation would influence their distributions on these southern mountains.

2. Consider a mammalian species that has a range extending from Virginia to central Quebec. In Quebec, the population is near its lower limit of tolerance (see fig. 5.8), where individuals may survive but are not likely to be successful in reproduction. How might this species persist in this portion of its range?

3. Imagine a desert beetle that uses behaviour to regulate its body temperature above 35°C. How might this beetle's use of microclimates created by shrubs, burrows, and bare ground change with the season?

4. Figure 5.10 shows how temperature influences the activity of acetylcholinesterase in rainbow trout. Assuming that the other enzymes of rainbow trout show similar responses to temperature, how would trout swimming speed change as environmental temperature increases above 20°C?

5. The Ecological Tools and Approaches section reviews how the studies of Bruno Baur and Anette Baur (1993) have documented the local extinction of the land snail *Arianta arbustorum*. Their research also shows that these extinctions may be due to reduced egg hatching at higher temperatures. Do these results show conclusively that the direct effect of higher temperatures on hatching success is responsible for the local extinctions of *A. arbustorum*? Propose and justify alternative hypotheses. Be sure you take into account all of the Baurs' observations.

6. Butterflies, which are ectothermic and diurnal, are found from the tropical rain forest to the Arctic. They can elevate their body temperatures by basking in sunlight. How would the percentage of time butterflies spend basking versus flying change with latitude? Would the amount of time butterflies spend basking change with daily changes in temperature?

7. Some plants and grasshoppers in hot environments have reflective body surfaces, which make their radiative heat gain less than it would be otherwise. If you were to design a beetle that could best cope with thermal challenges associated with living on snow, what colour would it be? If these beetles were white, what would that tell us about the relative roles of thermoregulation and predation pressure in determining beetle colour?

8. Why do species exhibit different strategies for coping with extreme temperatures? Why hasn't evolution resulted in all species doing a single "right" thing under these conditions?

9. Draw energy budgets using pie diagrams for a typical endotherm and ectotherm. What aspects of these budgets likely represent the largest energy expenditure? Which type of organism likely has more food intake and a larger overall energy budget?

10. Many animals huddle together in extreme cold. What is the possible energetic benefit of this behaviour? Under what climatic conditions is huddling likely to be disadvantageous?

Paul Nicklen/National Geographic/Getty Images.

CHAPTER 6   WATER RELATIONS

CHAPTER CONCEPTS

hapter 5 introduced the relationship between organisms and temperature. Most of the time, warm temperatures do not directly cause significant harm to organisms. They generally remain in their microclimates, and tissue temperatures do not climb to dangerous heights. However, increased temperatures can lead to high rates of water loss, which can be lethal. This is the more salient threat caused by high temperatures. Water plays a central role in the lives of all organisms in all habitats, though water acquisition and conservation are particularly critical for desert organisms. As a consequence, many ecologists studying the water relations of organisms have focused their attention on desert species. An example is found in the Sonoran Desert cicada (*Diceroprocta apache*). Even when air temperature in the shade hovers around 46°C and the ground surface temperature is over 70°C, the buzz of cicada can be heard. All other animals take refuge from the desert heat as these temperatures cause rapid water loss and dehydration. Aside from the cicada, the desert can be quiet, with the exception of an ecologist trying to understand how the cicada copes with these extreme conditions.

Eric Toolson knows a lot about cicadas, and he has learned to associate the call of *Diceroprocta* with the hottest hours of the day, when air temperatures often exceed the lethal limit for the species (Toolson 1987, Toolson and Hadley 1987). Toolson wanted to understand how this species could be active in temperatures that would cause dehydration for most others. We might ask the same question of Toolson himself. How did he maintain a body temperature of approximately 37°C in this desert heat? Humans cool by sweating, so to keep from becoming dehydrated, Toolson drank a lot of water. This enabled him to maintain sufficient internal water and continue to evaporatively cool by sweating. But what about the cicada, which did not have a bottle of water?

Did the cicada conserve water and keep cool by using small, shady microclimates in the mesquite tree from which it called? Did the cicada somehow manage to evaporatively cool? As it turns out, cicada do both. The latter came as a surprise as biologists have long assumed that insects are too small and too vulnerable to water loss to evaporatively cool, but *Diceroprocta* are able to acquire water indirectly from deep underground, drinking water transported in the tree's xylem. A reliable water source, evaporative cooling, and behaviour (exploiting cooler microclimates) are the critical pieces to an ecological puzzle: "How can the cicada remain active when air temperature would appear lethal for the species?" (fig. 6.1).

Water and life on earth are closely linked, with most organisms consisting of between 50% and 90% water. To survive and reproduce, organisms must maintain appropriate internal concentrations of water and dissolved substances. To maintain these internal concentrations, organisms must

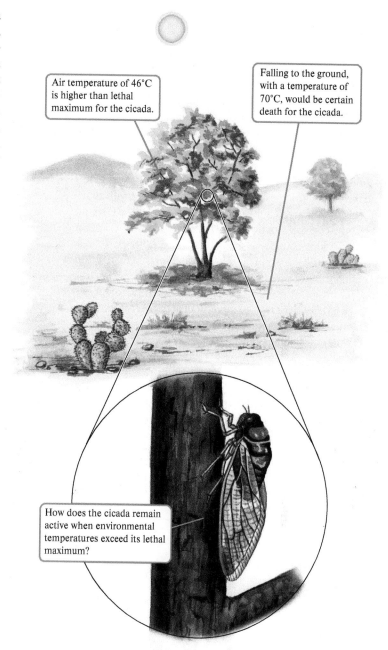

Air temperature of 46°C is higher than lethal maximum for the cicada.

Falling to the ground, with a temperature of 70°C, would be certain death for the cicada.

How does the cicada remain active when environmental temperatures exceed its lethal maximum?

Figure 6.1 An ecological puzzle: the cicada (*Diceroprocta apache*) is active when air temperatures would appear to be lethal for the species.

balance water losses to the environment with water intake. How organisms maintain this water balance is called their *water relations*, which is the subject of this chapter, and it will be intimately intertwined with temperature relations, the subject of chapter 5.

The problem of maintaining proper water balance is especially strong for those organisms, such as *Diceroprocta*, that live in arid terrestrial environments. A parallel challenge faces organisms that live in aquatic environments with a high salinity. Most organisms, in nearly all habitats, must expend some energy to maintain their internal pool of water.

6.1 Water Availability

Concentration gradients influence the movement of water between an organism and its environment. The tendency of water to move down concentration gradients and the magnitude of those gradients between an organism and its environment determine whether an organism tends to lose or gain water from the environment. To understand the water relations of organisms, we must understand the basic physical behaviour of water in terrestrial and aquatic environments.

In chapter 2, we saw that water availability on land varies tremendously among biomes, from the tropical rain forest with abundant moisture throughout the year to hot deserts with year-round drought. In chapter 3, we reviewed the considerable variation in salinity among aquatic environments. These range from near 0 ppt (parts per thousand) in the diluted waters of tropical rivers to greater than 300 ppt in hypersaline lakes). The majority of aquatic environments fall somewhere between these extremes. Salinity, as we shall see, reflects the relative "aridity" of aquatic environments.

In snow-covered areas, such as the arctic tundra and boreal forests, water availability can be particularly variable within a single year. As we saw in chapter 2, tundra habitats can be dry, with less than 200 mm precipitation a year, or relatively moist, with over 500 mm per year. Such variability also occurs in the boreal forest. One dominant feature of these colder habitats is that whatever precipitation falls can remain frozen for much of the year, making it unusable by most resident organisms until snowmelt. Even within Canada there is substantial geographic variation in both the average duration and average maximum snow depth (fig. 6.2). Notice that in the far north there are relatively few days without snow cover each year. As a consequence, liquid water is available to support growth and activity for only short periods of each year. Throughout most of Canada, however, snowmelt generally results in moist soils in the spring, and water is not generally limiting to spring and early summer plant growth. Water may become more limiting during the summer, depending upon the amount of rainfall that is received.

These broad comparisons across biomes ignore the substantial variation faced by individual organisms within their microclimates—such as those experienced by a desert animal that lives at an oasis, where it has access to abundant moisture; or a rain forest plant that lives in the forest canopy, where it is exposed to full tropical sun and drying winds. As with temperature, to understand the water relations of an organism we must consider its microclimate. We begin by considering a simple question that will affect how much water is available to an organism within its microclimate: How does water move?

Water Potential and Movement in Organisms

There is no plant more emblematic of country than the maple tree. Canada has 10 native species of maple tree, and perhaps the most majestic is the sugar maple (*Acer saccharum*). These

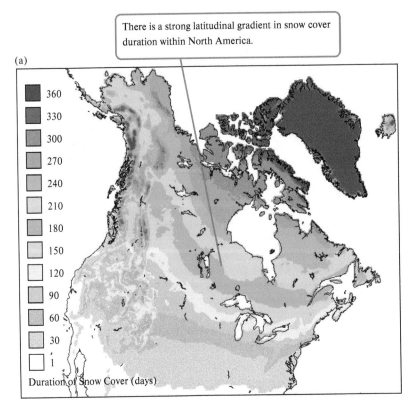

(a)

There is a strong latitudinal gradient in snow cover duration within North America.

Duration of Snow Cover (days)

360
330
300
270
240
210
180
150
120
90
60
30
1

Figure 6.2   (*a*) Mean duration (days).

(a) From Ross D. Brown, Environment Canada, Atmospheric Science and Technology Directorate, Climate Research Division, Climate Processes Section, Toronto.

(Continued)

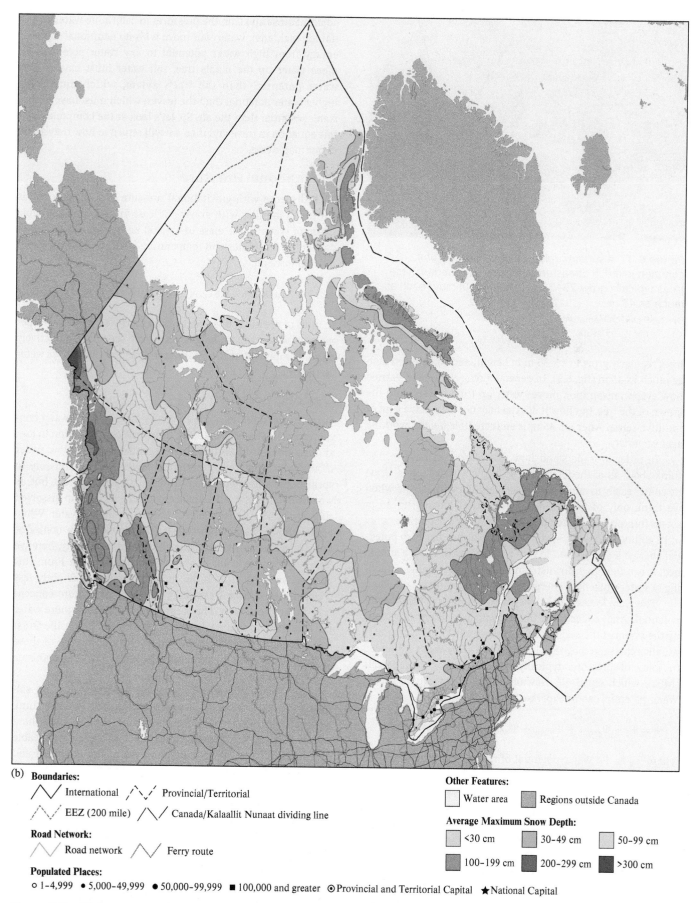

(b) Boundaries:

⋀⋁ International ⋰⋱⋰ Provincial/Territorial

⋰⋱⋰ EEZ (200 mile) ⋀⋁ Canada/Kalaallit Nunaat dividing line

Road Network:

⋀⋁ Road network ⋰⋱⋰ Ferry route

Populated Places:

○ 1–4,999   • 5,000–49,999   ● 50,000–99,999   ■ 100,000 and greater   ⊙ Provincial and Territorial Capital   ★ National Capital

Other Features:

☐ Water area   ▨ Regions outside Canada

Average Maximum Snow Depth:

▨ <30 cm   ▨ 30–49 cm   ▨ 50–99 cm

▨ 100–199 cm   ▨ 200–299 cm   ▨ >300 cm

Figure 6.2 (*b*) Average maximum depth (mm) of snow cover throughout northern latitudes.

(b) Map: Average Maximum Snow Depth, Atlas of Canada, 6th edition, Natural Resources Canada, 2019. Reproduced with the permission of the Department of Natural Resources, 2019.

Figure 6.3 A sugar maple tree (*Acer saccharum*), common in much of eastern and central Canada. These trees typically grow 25–35 m in height but may reach as much as 45 m.

Design Pics/Don Hammond.

trees regularly grow to 25–35 m in height, and some may reach as much as 45 m (fig. 6.3). In general biology you have learned how evapotranspiration moves water up from the soil into the crown of the tree, but how it does so may not have made a lot of intuitive sense. After all, 45 m is an incredible height, working against gravity.

In order to understand how this works, we have to first think about all of the forces that collectively move water. Gravity comes easily to mind; we are very familiar with it. And when we think only of gravitational force, water moving up 35 m seems improbable. **Water potential** is water's potential energy or its ability to do work. Water flowing in a river has high potential energy: it can be used to turn a wheel; it can erode a stream bed; it can float logs downstream. But, again, this understanding of water's potential energy reflects a gravity bias.

There are forces other than gravity that contribute to water potential. And, collectively, they explain why water can move up the xylem of the maple tree to the very top. Water potential is usually represented by the Greek letter Ψ (Psi) and is expressed in units of pressure, typically pascals (Pa) or megapascals (MPa), which equal 10^6 Newtons of force per square metre. Water potential can be expressed as:

$$\Psi = \Psi_0 + \Psi_{gravity} + \Psi_{solute} + \Psi_{humidity} + \Psi_{matric} + \Psi_{pressure}$$

where Ψ_0 is the water potential of a reference solution (typically pure water at 1 atmosphere, and set to a reference value of 0 MPa), $\Psi_{gravity}$ is the force of gravity acting over a unit of area, Ψ_{solute} is osmotic pressure, $\Psi_{humidity}$ is **water vapour pressure,** Ψ_{matric} is **matric pressure** caused by interactions with surfaces, and $\Psi_{pressure}$ is the sum of extraneous pressures imposed on a system. (We'll return to these later.)

You have learned in the past that a favourable chemical reaction involves a decrease in potential energy. Similarly, water will move in a direction of high potential energy to low (high water potential to low water potential). If we compare two

adjacent areas and sum the pressures to determine water potential for each area, water will move with no additional input of energy from high water potential to low water potential. To move water up the maple tree, soil water must have higher water potential than the tree's xylem, which must have higher water potential than the leaves, which must have higher water potential than the air. So, let's look at the components of this equation in turn, and then we will return to how they apply to our maple tree.

Gravitational Pressure

We'll dispense with gravitational pressure ($\Psi_{gravity}$) quickly, as we are all familiar with gravity, at least in concept. One cubic metre of water has a mass of ~1,000 kg (with some variation depending on solutes and temperature). This will have a gravitational force of

$$1{,}000 \text{ kg} \times 9.81 \text{ ms}^{-2} = 9{,}810 \text{ N (kg} \cdot \text{ms}^{-2})$$

In units of pressure, this water would exert 9.81×10^{-6} MPa per metre of water column height. As we will see, this is a relatively minor component of the total water potential that moves water up the tree.

Osmotic Pressure

Osmotic pressure (Ψ_{solute}) is driven by differences in water concentration. Just as solutes move from high concentration to low, and reactions progress from high potential energy to low, water moves from high concentration to low. It may sound silly to speak of the amount of water in an aquatic environment, but, as we saw in chapter 2, all aquatic environments contain dissolved substances. These dissolved substances dilute the water. While oceanographers and limnologists (those who study bodies of freshwater) generally focus on salt content, or salinity, here we take the opposite point of view—a focus on water. From this perspective, pure H_2O is the most concentrated. Slightly less concentrated will be freshwater, which is itself more concentrated than the oceans. The oceans, in turn, contain more water per litre than do saline lakes, such as the Dead Sea or the Great Salt Lake. The relative concentration of water in each of these environments strongly influences the biology of the organisms that live in them.

The body fluids of all organisms contain water and solutes, including inorganic ions and amino acids. We can think of aquatic organisms and the environment that surrounds them as two aqueous solutions separated by a selectively permeable membrane. If the internal environment of the organism and the external environment differ in concentrations of water and salts, these substances will tend to move down their concentration gradients. This movement of solutes is called **diffusion.** We give the movement of water across a semipermeable membrane a special name, **osmosis,** where water moves from areas of high water concentration to low water concentration. As a point of clarification, if you were hoping you could learn ecology through "osmosis" by placing this text under your pillow at night and having all the nuggets of knowledge move into your brain, you are woefully incorrect. Osmosis refers specifically to the movement of water. As long as knowledge moves in the form of particles, then the "under pillow" method is an example of diffusion (particles of ecological knowledge moving from high concentration in the text to low concentration in the brain of the student needing to sleep on a textbook). Either way, *please* do not let this be your approach.

In the aquatic environment, water moving down its concentration gradient produces osmotic pressure. Osmotic pressure, like other component pressures, can be expressed in Pa or MPa. The strength of the osmotic pressure across a semipermeable membrane, such as the gills of a fish or a red blood cell, depends upon the difference in water concentration across the membrane. Larger differences, between organism and environment, generate higher osmotic pressures.

As a brief but important aside from our discussion of water movement up the maple tree, aquatic organisms generally live in one of three environmental circumstances: (1) Organisms with body fluids containing the same concentration of water as the external environment are **isosmotic**. You may also be familiar with the term **isotonic**, which emphasizes the solute concentration of the external environment. In an isotonic solution, the organism is isosmotic. (2) Organisms with body fluids with a higher concentration of water (lower solute concentration) than the external medium are **hypoosmotic** and tend to lose water to the environment (and the external medium is **hypertonic** relative to the organism). (3) Organisms with body fluids with a lower concentration of water (higher solute concentration) than the external medium are **hyperosmotic** and are subject to water flooding inward from the environment (and the environment or external medium is **hypotonic** relative to the organism).

In the face of these osmotic pressures, aquatic organisms must expend energy to maintain a proper internal environment. How much energy the organism must expend depends upon the magnitude of the osmotic pressure between them and the environment and the permeability of their body surfaces. Figure 6.4 summarizes the movement of water and salts into and out of isosmotic, hyperosmotic, and hypoosmotic organisms.

To frame how important osmotic pressure might be in the context of our maple tree, let's consider a relatively small concentration difference. Suppose you had a volume of pure water and a volume of water containing 1% solute. Let's use the osmotic pressure equation ($\pi = MRT$) where π is pressure (atm), M is molarity (mol L^{-1}), R is the ideal gas constant (0.08206 L•atm mol^{-1}K^{-1}), and T is temperature (K). Given the molarity of pure water (55.5 mol L^{-1}), the difference in molarity across the membrane would be 0.55. The osmotic pressure across the membrane at 25°C would be 13.58 atm, or 1.37 MPa. This is not enormous pressure, but as you can see a relatively small difference in solute concentration across a membrane can create osmotic pressure that is orders of magnitude greater than gravitational pressure described above.

Vapour Pressure

Osmotic pressure is relevant to fluid-filled spaces, where there are two aqueous solutions separated by a membrane permeable to water. In air, or in air-filled spaces, water will not move by

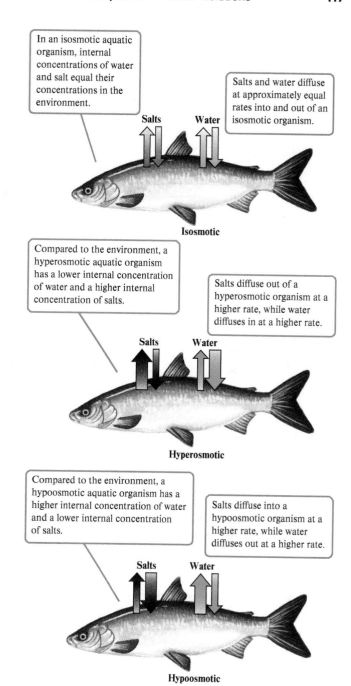

In an isosmotic aquatic organism, internal concentrations of water and salt equal their concentrations in the environment.

Salts and water diffuse at approximately equal rates into and out of an isosmotic organism.

Isosmotic

Compared to the environment, a hyperosmotic aquatic organism has a lower internal concentration of water and a higher internal concentration of salts.

Salts diffuse out of a hyperosmotic organism at a higher rate, while water diffuses in at a higher rate.

Hyperosmotic

Compared to the environment, a hypoosmotic aquatic organism has a higher internal concentration of water and a lower internal concentration of salts.

Salts diffuse into a hypoosmotic organism at a higher rate, while water diffuses out at a higher rate.

Hypoosmotic

Figure 6.4 Water and salt regulation by isosmotic, hyperosmotic, and hypoosmotic aquatic organisms.

osmosis. Here, it is more relevant to consider vapour pressure ($\Psi_{humidity}$). It is rare that air is entirely dry. Generally, there is some quantity of water vapour as a component gas of air (just like there is some N_2, some O_2, etc.). Vapour pressure is related to the quantity of water in air. The actual amount of water in air is measured directly as the mass of water vapour per unit volume of air, given as mg H_2O/L (or g H_2O/m^3). The quantity of water vapour that air can potentially hold is its *saturation water vapour density*. Saturation water vapour density changes with temperature, and, as a result, warm air can hold more water vapour than cold air.

A visual demonstration of this difference in water holding capacity of air as a function of temperature is seen each winter. Why exactly can you see your breath on a cool winter morning? As an endotherm, your breath will be a fairly consistent temperature of approximately 37°C. Additionally, the function of gas exchange in our lungs is dependent upon the alveoli being saturated with water. As a result, our breath is generally at 100% **relative humidity,** which at body temperature results in over 40 g water/m³ air leaving our bodies upon exhalation. What happens when that wet, hot air leaves your body? If the air is dry, some of the water in your breath will be absorbed by the surrounding air. However, if the air temperature is low, such as 0°C, it will hold substantially less water (5 g/m³ at 0°C). This means the remaining 35 g/m³ cannot enter the air and, instead, condenses into a cloud, and you see your breath.

One of the most useful ways of expressing the quantity of water in air is in terms of the pressure it exerts. We usually think about *total atmospheric pressure,* the collective pressure exerted by all the gases in air, but you can also calculate the partial pressures due to individual atmospheric gases, such as N_2, O_2, or H_2O (water vapour). We call this last quantity *water vapour pressure* (described earlier). At sea level, one atmosphere of pressure equals approximately 101.3 kPa. The pressure exerted by the water vapour is a fraction of this total pressure. In air that is saturated with water, this fraction is called **saturation water vapour pressure.** As the curve in figure 6.5 shows, this pressure increases with temperature.

We can also consider the *relative* saturation of air with water. We can express this relative saturation by calculating a **vapour pressure deficit (VPD),** the difference between the actual water vapour pressure and the saturation water vapour pressure at a particular temperature. In warm, moist environments, air is near saturation, and VPD is low. In warm, dry environments, relative humidity is lower, and VPD is higher. In terrestrial environments, water flows from organisms to the atmosphere at a rate influenced by the vapour pressure deficit of the air surrounding the organism. Figure 6.6 shows the relative rates of water loss by an organism exposed to air with a low versus high VPD. In the context of our maple tree, VPD may be important in moving water from leaves to the atmosphere. At 25°C, the VPD between leaf tissue and dry air may be as much as 3 kPa (or 0.003 MPa)—again, not strong pressure, but orders of magnitude greater than the countervailing pressure exerted by gravity.

Matric Pressure

If you stick a straw into a glass of water, you may notice that the water forms a meniscus inside the straw that is slightly higher than the surface of water in the glass. If you replace this with a straw of smaller diameter, you'll notice the meniscus is even higher above the water surface. What explains this? You have probably heard this explained as capillary action, but it is driven by matric (or matrix) pressure (Ψ_{matric}). A matrix is defined as a surrounding medium or structure. In the straw example, the matrix is the inner wall of the straw. When we are talking about water moving from soil, into a plant, and up through the vascular tissues of the plant, the matrix will include first soil and clay particles, and then the inner walls of xylem cells.

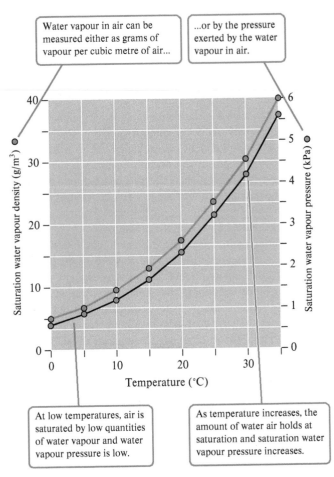

Water vapour in air can be measured either as grams of vapour per cubic metre of air...

...or by the pressure exerted by the water vapour in air.

At low temperatures, air is saturated by low quantities of water vapour and water vapour pressure is low.

As temperature increases, the amount of water air holds at saturation and saturation water vapour pressure increases.

Figure 6.5 The relationship between air temperature and two measures of water vapour saturation of air.

Water is a polar molecule, giving it a tendency to adhere to surfaces of particles that make up the matrix, such as clay and sand within the soil, walls of plasmolysed xylem cells, or the wall of your straw. Water will also adhere to other water molecules through hydrogen bonding. These molecular interactions promote surface tension and the formation of films and menisci within the pore spaces of particles. The water attracted by and adhering to particle surfaces has a lower free energy state than bulk water. So, the interactions of water molecules with particles reduce water potential as it moves through the pore space. The strength of matric pressure depends on the distances between particles: as the distance increases, matric pressure decreases. In soils, matric pressure is greater for clays than for sandy soils. Matric pressure is often a greater contributor to water potential than the other component pressures.

Additional Pressures

Beyond those discussed above, there may be additional pressures exerted on an organism or on a system that affect water potential. The most common, and the most relevant to our maple tree, is the pressure related to evapotranspiration. Water molecules adhere to each other. As one molecule leaves the leaf tissue due to evapotranspiration, it tugs on the

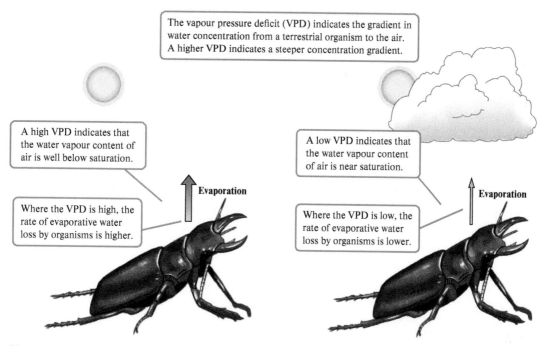

Figure 6.6   The potential for evaporative water loss by terrestrial organisms increases with increased vapour pressure deficit.

neighbouring water molecules, pulling them closer to the pores. This negative pressure can contribute to the upward movement of water through the tree. The strength of this pressure depends on the moisture content of the air, specifically the vapour pressure difference between the leaf tissue and the air.

Gravity-Defying Movement of Water in the Maple Tree

Finally, if we consider the various components of water potential collectively, we can understand how water flows upward, counter to our intuition. In water-saturated soil, water potential is near 0 MPa. The air-filled spaces of the vadose zone will have lower (more negative) water potential than the saturated zone, and some water will move into these pores due to a combination of vapour pressure differential and matric pressure (fig. 6.7).

The plant roots will have a lower water potential than the surrounding pore water. Ions that are required as nutrients for the plant are actively pumped into the plant roots and become concentrated in the vascular tissue (xylem). As a result, osmotic pressure favours the movement of water across the membrane of the root epithelium and into the xylem. The plasmolysed cells of the xylem provide large surface area and small pores, increasing matric effects and further decreasing water potential. The combined effects of these pressures (osmotic and matric), plus the evapotranspirational pull of water into leaf tissue, move water into the tree and push it toward the crown. The movement follows a gradient of decreasing water potential and is energetically favourable, easily overcoming gravitational pressure.

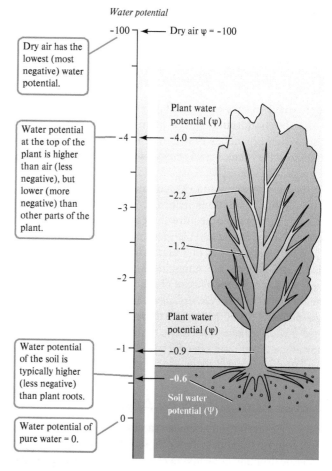

Figure 6.7   Water potential (MPa) decreases (becomes more negative) as you move from saturated soil to the vadose zone, to the tree, and finally to the atmosphere.
Data from Wiebe et al. 1970.

This section has given us a basis for considering the availability of water to organisms living in terrestrial and aquatic environments. Let's use the foundation we have built here to explore the water relations of organisms on land and in water. To survive and reproduce, organisms must maintain appropriate internal concentrations of water and dissolved substances. As a consequence, in the face of variation in water availability, organisms have been selected to regulate their internal water.

CONCEPT 6.1 REVIEW

1. Why is water potential in nature generally negative?

2. Why does the active transport of dissolved nutrients into roots allow water to move against the pull of gravity?

3. Imagine you have sand in an aquarium. The lower half of the sand is saturated and the upper half has air-filled pore spaces. You blow dry air across the surface to dry out the sand. What components of water potential are relevant to the movement of water from sand to air?

6.2   Water Regulation on Land

Terrestrial plants and animals regulate their internal water by balancing water acquisition against water loss. When organisms first moved into the terrestrial environment, they faced two major water-related challenges: (1) potentially massive losses of water to the environment through evaporation and (2) reduced access to replacement water. Many adaptations helped terrestrial organisms meet these challenges and acquire the capacity to regulate their internal water content.

The main avenues of water gain and loss by terrestrial plants and animals are summarized in figure 6.8. The figure presents a generalized picture of the water relations of terrestrial organisms. However, organisms in different environments face different environmental challenges, and they have developed a wide variety of solutions to those problems. Let's now look at the diverse ways in which terrestrial plants and animals regulate their internal water.

Water Acquisition by Animals

Many small terrestrial animals can absorb water from the air. Most terrestrial animals, however, satisfy their need for water either by drinking or by taking in water with food. In moist climates there is generally plenty of water, and, if water becomes locally scarce, the mobility of most animals allows them to move to a water source. In deserts, animals that need abundant water must live near oases. Those that live out in the desert itself, away from oases, have evolved adaptations for living in arid environments.

Some desert animals acquire water in unusual ways. Coastal deserts, such as the Namib Desert of southwest Africa, receive very little rain but are bathed in fog. This aerial moisture is the water source for some animals in the Namib. One of these, a beetle in the genus *Lepidochora* of the family Tenebrionidae, digs trenches on the face of sand dunes to condense and concentrate fog. The moisture collected by these trenches runs down to the lower end, where the beetle waits for a drink. Another Tenebrionid beetle, *Onymacris unguicularis,* collects moisture by orienting its abdomen upward. Fog condensing on this beetle's body flows to its mouth (fig. 6.9). *Onymacris* also takes in water with its food. Some of this water is absorbed within the tissues of the food. The remaining water is produced when the beetle metabolizes the carbohydrates, proteins, and fats contained in its food. We can see the source of this **metabolic water** if we look at an equation for oxidation of glucose:

$$C_6H_{12}O_6 + 6\,O_2 \rightarrow 6\,CO_2 + 6\,H_2O$$

Paul Cooper (1982) estimated the water budget for free ranging *Onymacris* from the Namib Desert near Gobabeb. He estimated the rate of water intake by this beetle at 49.9 mg of H_2O per gram of body weight per day. Of this total, 39.8 mg came from fog, 1.7 mg came from moisture contained within food, and 8.4 mg came from metabolic water. The rate of water loss by these beetles, 41.3 mg of H_2O per gram per day, was slightly less than water intake. Of this total, 2.3 mg were lost with feces and urine, and 39 mg by evaporation (fig. 6.10).

While *Onymacris* gets most of its water from fog, other small desert animals get most of their water from their food. Kangaroo rats of the genus *Dipodomys* are found throughout the arid regions of Canada, the United States, and Mexico. These rodents possess traits that allow them to avoid needing to drink at all. Knut Schmidt-Nielsen (1964) showed that the approximately 60 ml of water gained from 100 g of barley makes up for the water a Merriam's kangaroo rat (*D. merriami*) loses in feces, urine, and evaporation. The 100 g of barley contains only 6 ml of absorbed water, that is, water that can be driven off by drying. The remaining 54 ml of water is released as the animal metabolizes the carbohydrates, fats, and proteins in the grain. The importance of metabolic water in the water budget of Merriam's kangaroo rat is pictured in figure 6.11.

While animals generally obtain most of their water by drinking or with their food, these options are not available to plants. Though many plants can absorb some water from the air, most get the bulk of their water from the soil through their roots.

Water Acquisition by Plants

Plants in dry climates generally grow more, and deeper, roots than do plants in moist climates. Roots may account for up to

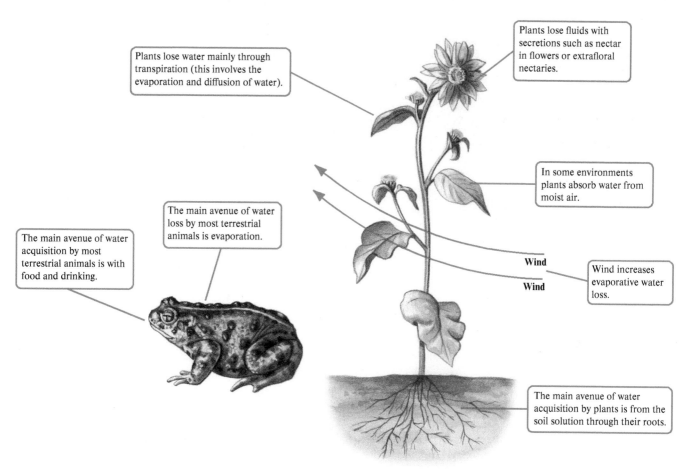

Plants lose water mainly through transpiration (this involves the evaporation and diffusion of water).

Plants lose fluids with secretions such as nectar in flowers or extrafloral nectaries.

The main avenue of water loss by most terrestrial animals is evaporation.

In some environments plants absorb water from moist air.

The main avenue of water acquisition by most terrestrial animals is with food and drinking.

Wind

Wind

Wind increases evaporative water loss.

The main avenue of water acquisition by plants is from the soil solution through their roots.

Figure 6.8 Terrestrial plants and animals can be characterized by analogous pathways for water gain and loss.

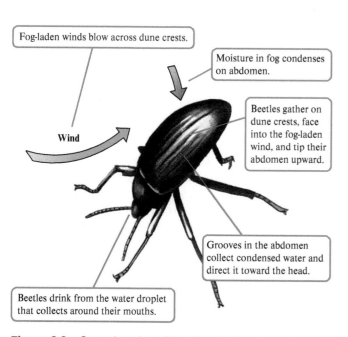

Fog-laden winds blow across dune crests.

Moisture in fog condenses on abdomen.

Wind

Beetles gather on dune crests, face into the fog-laden wind, and tip their abdomen upward.

Grooves in the abdomen collect condensed water and direct it toward the head.

Beetles drink from the water droplet that collects around their mouths.

Figure 6.9 Some beetles of the Namib Desert can harvest sufficient moisture from fog to meet their needs for water.

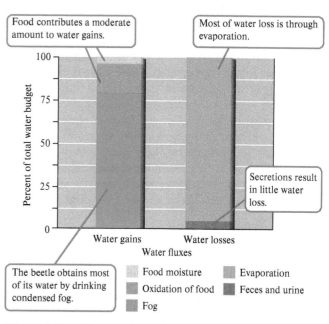

Food contributes a moderate amount to water gains.

Most of water loss is through evaporation.

Secretions result in little water loss.

The beetle obtains most of its water by drinking condensed fog.

Percent of total water budget

Water gains   Water losses
Water fluxes

Food moisture   Evaporation
Oxidation of food   Feces and urine
Fog

Figure 6.10 Water budget of the desert beetle (*Onymacris unguicularis*).
Data from Cooper 1982.

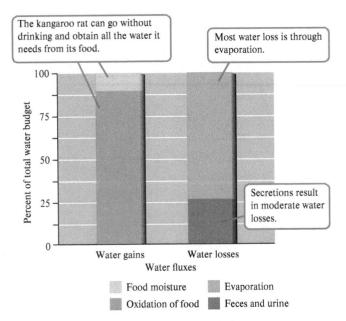

The kangaroo rat can go without drinking and obtain all the water it needs from its food.

Most water loss is through evaporation.

Secretions result in moderate water losses.

Food moisture

Oxidation of food

Evaporation

Feces and urine

Figure 6.11 Water budget of Merriam's kangaroo rat (*Dipodomys merriami*).

Data from Schmidt-Nielsen 1964.

On dry sites, the plant grows a dense network of deeply penetrating roots.

On moist sites, the plant grows a sparse network of shallow roots.

Figure 6.12 Soil moisture influences the extent of root development by *Artemisia frigida*, a desert forb.

Data from Coupland and Johnson 1965.

90% of total plant biomass in deserts, grasslands, and tundra. In contrast, roots in coniferous forests typically constitute only about 25% of total plant biomass. The tap roots of some desert shrubs can extend 30 m down into the soil, giving them access to deep groundwater.

Even within a species, the depth of rooting and percent of below-ground biomass can vary with microclimate. For example, Stewart Rood, Sarah Bigelow, and Alexis Hall at the University of Lethbridge found that the median rooting depth of riparian cottonwood tree species (genus *Populus*) was strongly related to the local moisture regime. Cottonwoods in wetter areas tend to rely on water from precipitation while those in drier regions extend their roots to the capillary fringe above the groundwater feeding stream flow (Rood et al. 2011). R. Coupland and R. Johnson (1965) compared the rooting characteristics of plants growing in the dry mixed grasslands of western Canada. By carefully excavating the roots of over 850 individual plants, they found that many species have lower root biomass and higher above-ground biomass in moist microclimates than in the drier areas (fig. 6.12). These deeper roots often help plants from dry environments extract water from deep within the soil profile.

Water Conservation by Plants and Animals

Another way to balance a water budget is by reducing water losses. For example, animals adapted to dry conditions may produce concentrated urine or feces with low water content, may condense and reabsorb the water vapour in breath, and may restrict activity to times and places that decrease water loss or exploit microclimates that are cooler than the surrounding environs. Plants may cut down on water loss by restricting stomatal opening during the hottest, driest parts of the day and by limiting the surface area of leaves, across which water can be lost. One of the most obvious ways that both animals and plants cut down on water losses is by waterproofing to reduce evaporation. Many terrestrial plants and animals cover themselves with a fairly waterproof "hide" impregnated with a variety of waxes. However, some organisms are more waterproof than others, and rates of evaporative water loss vary greatly from one animal or plant species to another.

Why do the water loss rates of organisms differ? One reason is that species have evolved in environments that differ greatly in water availability. As a consequence, selection for water conservation has been more intense in some environments than others. Species that evolved in warm deserts are generally much more resistant to desiccation than relatives that evolved in moist tropical or temperate habitats. In general, populations that evolved in drier environments lose water at a slower rate.

Neil Hadley and Thomas Schultz (1987) studied two species of tiger beetles in Arizona that occupy different microclimates. *Cicindela oregona* lives along the moist shoreline of streams and is active in fall and spring. In contrast, *Cicindela obsoleta* lives in the semiarid grasslands of central and southeastern Arizona and is active in summer. The researchers suspected that these differences in microclimate select for differences in waterproofing of the two tiger beetles.

Hadley and Schultz studied the waterproofing of the tiger beetles by comparing the amount of water each species lost while held in an experimental chamber. They pumped dry air through the chamber at a constant rate and maintained its temperature at 30°C. They weighed each beetle at the beginning of an experiment and then again after three hours in the chamber. The difference between initial and final weights

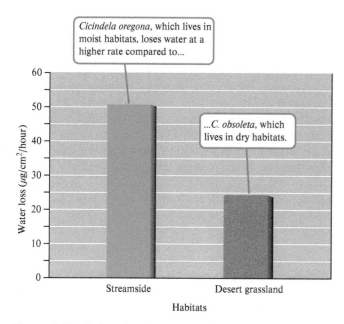

Figure 6.13 A tiger beetle species from a moist habitat lost water at a higher rate than one from a dry habitat.
Data from Schultz and Hadley 1987.

gave them an estimate of the water loss rate of each beetle. By determining water loss for several individuals of each species, they estimated the average water loss rates for *C. oregona* and *C. obsoleta*. Hadley and Schultz found that *C. oregona* loses water two times as fast as *C. obsoleta* (fig. 6.13). In other words, the species from the drier microclimate, *C. obsoleta*, appears to be more waterproofed. This difference was likely due to the higher concentration of waterproofing hydrocarbons in the cuticle of *C. obsoleta*.

The tiger beetles example above demonstrates differences in water conservation between species adapted to different climates. We might also expect to see variations in water conservation within a species when we compare populations adapted to different local conditions. Over long periods of time, as the American Southwest became increasingly arid, the ancestors of today's Merriam's kangaroo rats were subject to natural selection that favoured a range of adaptations to dry environments, including water conservation. We previously described that Merriam's kangaroo rats conserve water so well that they can live entirely on the moisture contained within their food and on "metabolic water" (see fig. 6.11). However, not all populations of Merriam's kangaroo rats are subject to the same intensity of selection for water conservation. This is a widespread species that lives from 21° N latitude in Mexico to 42° N latitude in northern Nevada. Over this large geographic range, Merriam's kangaroo rat populations are exposed to a very broad range of environmental conditions.

Richard Tracy and Glenn Walsberg studied three populations of Merriam's kangaroo rats across a climatic gradient. Their main objective was to determine if different populations of Merriam's kangaroo rat vary in their degree of adaptation to living in dry environments (Tracy and Walsberg 2000, 2001, 2002). The three populations that were studied live in southwest

Arizona near Yuma, in central Arizona, and in north-central Arizona, at elevations of 150 m, 400 m, and 1200 m, respectively. Mean annual maximum temperatures at the study sites are 31.5°C, 29.1°C, and 23.5°C, and mean annual precipitation at the three sites is 10.6 cm, 33.6 cm, and 43.6 cm.

Tracy and Walsberg tested whether rates of evaporative water loss differed among the Merriam's kangaroo rats from dry, intermediate, and moist sites. The results of this study show clear differences among the study populations. The mean rate of evaporative water loss at the dry site was 0.69 mg of water per g per hour, compared to 1 mg H_2O/g/h and 1.08 mg H_2O/g/h at the intermediate and moist sites, respectively (fig. 6.14). In additional studies, Tracy and Walsberg found that acclimating animals to laboratory conditions did not eliminate the differences in water conservation among populations. In other words, even after being kept in the laboratory under controlled conditions, Merriam's kangaroo rats from the driest study site continued to lose water at a lower rate. The evidence from these studies supports the conclusion that these three populations differ in their degree of adaptation to desert living.

Plants have also evolved a wide variety of means for conserving water, which result in different water-use efficiencies (WUE). WUE is defined as the biomass of plant tissue produced per gram of water used, and this value will vary among species. The WUE of a plant depends in part on its leaf area relative to its root area or length. Plants with more leaf surface per length of root tend to lose more water. Compared to plants from moist climates, arid land plants generally have lower leaf area:root area ratios and correspondingly higher water-use efficiencies.

Many plants reduce leaf area over the short term by wilting during dry periods or by dropping leaves in response to drought. Some desert plants, such as the ocotillo of the Sonoran Desert,

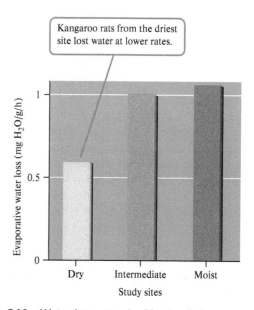

Figure 6.14 Water loss rates by Merriam's kangaroo rats from across a moisture gradient suggest adaptation to local climate by each of the populations.
Data from Tracy and Walsberg 2001.

produce leaves only in response to soaking rains and then shed them when the desert dries out again.

Nona Chiariello and her colleagues (1987) discovered an intriguing example of adjusting leaf area in the moist tropics. *Piper auritum,* a large-leafed, umbrella-shaped plant, grows in clearings of the rain forest. Because it grows in clearings, the plant often faces drying conditions during midday. However, it reduces the leaf area it exposes to the midday sun by wilting. Wilting at midday reduces leaf area exposed to direct solar radiation by about 55%; and leaf temperature, by up to 4°C to 5°C. These reductions decrease the rate of transpiration by 30% to 50%, which is a substantial water savings. The behaviour of this tropical rain forest plant reminds us that even the rain forest has its relatively dry microclimates.

Other plant adaptations that conserve water include thick leaves, which have less transpiring leaf surface area per unit volume of photosynthesizing tissue than thin leaves do. They also have few stomata on leaves rather than many; structures on the stomata that impede the movement of water; dormancy during times when moisture is unavailable; and alternative,

water-conserving pathways for photosynthesis. (We discuss these alternative pathways for photosynthesis in chapter 7.)

Plants have developed adaptations to cope with periodic water stress; however, these adaptations are often at odds with human needs. For example, although closing stomata reduces water loss and is likely to be a favoured strategy over evolutionary time, closing stomata also ceases photosynthesis (for most plants; see chapter 7), which is bad news for a farmer trying to grow a crop. Because of this evolutionary solution to short-term water stress, many agricultural fields are irrigated through the dry summer months, particularly in the southern prairies. As we will see from Steward Rood's work in the Ecology in Action that follows, changes in stream flow—for whatever purpose—will influence other habitats within the broader prairie landscape. How plants deal with water stress and how humans rely on plants for survival have changed the face of the prairies over the last century. This struggle continues as human consumption of water continues to rise, and climate change increases rates of evaporation and alters precipitation patterns.

ECOLOGY IN ACTION

Dams, Flows, and Cottonwoods

The western prairies of North America are often viewed as flat and dry expanses of unending fields of grasses. However, cutting through these areas are rivers and streams, often flowing out from the Rocky Mountains. Along these rivers we find a completely different type of habitat, a wetter riparian area dominated by trees (fig. 6.15). Standing on the bank of a river in the prairies, you will find yourself in floodplain forests, underneath the shade provided by the cottonwoods (*Populus* spp.). When you walk just a few hundred metres away, these species are nowhere to be found. Floodplain forests are oases in the prairie for many native animals as well as livestock. They are home to species of plants, insects, fungi, and other organisms not found in the drier regions of the prairie landscape; thus, these forests are critical both to maintenance of biodiversity and the economic health of the dry prairies of western North America. However, over the last several decades there has been a severe decline in cottonwood abundances throughout the west, raising great concerns. To try to understand why this decline has occurred, and to see if the pattern can be reversed, we turn to the work of Stewart Rood of the University of Lethbridge.

We begin by trying to understand why cottonwoods are restricted to riparian habitats rather than distributed broadly throughout the prairie itself. Cottonwoods tend to be early colonizers of bare riparian areas, providing a critical service of stream-bank stabilization (Rood et al. 2003). Isotopic

analyses (see the Ecological Tools and Approaches section later in this chapter) indicate that cottonwoods predominantly use **alluvial groundwater** (water that comes from a surface stream) rather than deeper groundwater, at least during dry periods of the summer (Rood et al. 2003).

As a result of this reliance on surface waters, these plants are very sensitive to drought. The trees respond quickly to reduced water availability through altered hormonal levels, stomatal closures (to reduce evaporation), and decreased photosynthesis (Rood et al. 2003). Over longer periods, drought leads to reduced growth and increased plant mortality. One of the unique aspects of cottonwood water relations is that they are particularly prone to **cavitation.** In cavitation, air bubbles form in the xylem, effectively breaking the chain of water from roots to leaves. Once cavitation occurs in the xylem, those cells no longer have the ability to move water; thus, cavitation can render large parts of the vascular tissue useless for these trees. In summary, cottonwoods colonize bare riparian soil, use predominately shallow waters, and are uniquely sensitive to drought. These factors can explain why we do not find cottonwoods in the driest parts of the prairies. However, what would explain why they are declining from areas that are traditionally the wettest parts of the landscape?

To answer this, we begin with a look at long-term trends in river flows heading east and west from the Rocky Mountains (Rood et al. 2005). Rood and his colleagues collected

(a)

(b)

(c)

Figure 6.15 (*a*) Cottonwood forests along the Old Man River in southern Alberta; (*b*) a flood on the Old Man River; (*c*) bands of cottonwood trees of different ages, each established during different river floods.

(a)–(c) Stewart Rood.

data from a variety of existing long-term data sets of flows through 31 river reaches, with data collected upstream of any dams (we will get to dams shortly!). After adjusting for global climatic cycles (chapter 23), they found significant flow declines in 15 of the 31 river reaches. On average, rivers had a 0.22%/year flow reduction, with some Albertan rivers showing a recent decline as high at 0.5%/year. As we discussed in chapter 5, decreased water levels result in increased stream temperatures, with a variety of potential consequences for fish and other animals that live within the streams. Based upon what we know about cottonwoods, their reliance on surface waters means reduced stream flows also put them at increased risk of mortality and

reduced growth. These changes in stream flows occurred upstream of dams and, thus, are likely caused by large-scale climatic changes (e.g., global warming). However, direct human activity is putting additional pressures on these forest floodplain habitats.

Some activities, such as clearing forests for housing or agricultural development or harvesting trees for fuel and money, cause obvious negative consequences for riparian habitats that do not take any scientific knowledge to understand. Instead, we will discuss a subtler and widespread challenge to these systems: dams. By design, dams modify stream flows, often with the intent of reducing flooding events and protecting property and infrastructure. Interestingly, even if dams provide a constant rate of river flow, cottonwood forests seem to decline. In other words, there is more than just water relations driving the loss of these forests. Rood and colleagues have explored the impacts of dams on riparian forests and have found ways to work with dam operators to help restore these challenged riparian areas (Rood et al. 2005).

As you may recall, cottonwoods colonize bare and wet ground. Where is that bare ground found on the landscape? It is found along rivers after floods. Floods can rip out existing trees, cause severe erosion to stream beds, and leave large deposits of organic material on large expanses of the prairie. Over timescales of decades and centuries, floods are common to the rivers of the west and are most frequent during the early summer months. Cottonwood reproduction is suited to this fairly regular occurrence, with seed dispersal and seedling establishment following the summer floods. If a dam prevents flooding, it can also prevent successful establishment of cottonwoods. But how can you reconcile flood prevention with cottonwood preservation? Rood has been part of many restoration projects where he works with dam operators to help allow for flood events without putting human infrastructure at risk. These projects have resulted in dramatic recruitment of cottonwoods along both the Old Man and St. Mary rivers in Alberta (fig. 6.15).

The work of Rood and his colleagues is a wonderful example of how knowledge about the ecology of an organism, coupled with an understanding of the abiotic environment, can be used to address issues of societal concern. Without understanding how extreme water events influence cottonwood regeneration, understanding how to prevent further population declines would be difficult. Rood has shown that ecologists can directly impact environmental decisions, in this case by helping to develop a new method of flow management from dams. However, floodplain forests still face the challenge of reduced flows even upstream of the dams, likely due to changes in global climate. It will be up to the next generation of ecologists to help solve this issue.

Dissimilar Organisms with Similar Approaches to Desert Life

There are many novel adaptations we could chronicle here to describe strategies for balancing water budgets. Instead, let's look at one pair of species, camels and saguaro cacti, that on the surface appear entirely different (fig. 6.16). The comparison illustrates some important common themes in how organisms under water stress maintain water balance. Both the camel and the saguaro cactus acquire massive amounts of water when water is available, store water, and conserve water.

The camel can go for long periods in intense desert heat without drinking, up to six to eight days in conditions that would kill a person within a day. During this time, the animal survives on the water stored in its tissues and can withstand water losses of up to 20% of its body weight without harm. For humans, a loss of about 10% to 12% is near the fatal limit. One important adaptation that makes this possible is ovoid red blood cells, which are less likely to clump when blood volume decreases and which can withstand a broader range of osmotic pressure. When the camel has the opportunity, it can drink and store prodigious quantities of water, up to one-third of its body weight at a time. Such consumption of water by humans is generally fatal because it changes blood and interstitial fluid volume and solute concentrations too rapidly. The camel, however, can store the water in its digestive tract, allowing it to be slowly absorbed, restoring blood and interstitial volume.

Between opportunities to drink, the camel is a master of water conservation. One way it conserves body water is by reducing its rate of heat gain. To prevent overheating, the camel faces into the sun, reducing the body surface it exposes to direct sunlight. In addition, its thick hair insulates it from the intense desert sun, and rather than sweating sufficiently to keep its body temperature down, the camel allows its body temperature to rise by up to 7°C. This reduces the temperature difference between the camel and the environment and so decreases the rate of additional heating. Reducing the temperature differential with the atmosphere also reduces water loss by evaporation. The camel instead stores the heat during the day and will dissipate the heat at night when it can do so with less evaporative loss.

The saguaro cactus takes a similar approach. The trunk and arms of the plant act as organs in which the cactus can store large quantities of water. During droughts, the saguaro draws on these stored reserves and so can endure long periods without water. When it rains, the saguaro, like a camel at an oasis, can ingest great quantities of water, but instead of drinking, the saguaro gets its water through its dense network of shallow roots. These roots extend out in a roughly circular pattern to a distance approximately equal to the height of the cactus. For a 15 m tall saguaro, this means a root coverage of over 700 m² of soil.

The saguaro also reduces its rate of evaporative water loss in several ways. First, like other cacti, it keeps its stomata closed during the day when transpiration losses would be highest. In the absence of transpiration, in full sun, the internal temperature of the saguaro rises to over 50°C, which is among the highest temperatures recorded in plants. However, as we noted for the camel, higher body temperature can be an advantage because it reduces the rate of additional heating. The saguaro's rate of heating is also reduced by the shape and orientation of its trunk and arms. At midday, when the potential for heating is greatest, the saguaro exposes mainly the tips of its arms and trunk to direct sunlight. However, the tips of the saguaro's arms and trunk are insulated by a layer of plant hairs and a thick tangle of spines, which reflect sunlight and shade the growing tips of the cactus.

The parallel approaches to desert living seen in saguaro cacti and camels are outlined in figure 6.17. As the figure illustrates, sometimes organisms of very different evolutionary

(a)

(b)

Figure 6.16   Two desert dwellers: (*a*) saguaro cactus, and (*b*) camel; as different as they are, they seem to show parallel adaptations to desert environments.

(a) Kristy-Anne Glubish/Getty Images; (b) © Lukasz Kasperek/Dreamstime.com.

The saguaro reduces heat gain by exposing only tops of its trunk and branches to the midday sun.

The trunk and branch tips are shaded and insulated with a high density of spines, which reduces heat gain.

The camel does not store water in its hump but fat, which is a source of metabolic water.

The camel reduces heat gain by facing into the sun.

The camel is covered with dense hair, which reduces heat gain.

Water is stored in the massive trunk and arms.

The saguaro reduces water loss by transpiration by keeping stomates closed and allowing its temperature to rise.

When water is available, both the saguaro and camel take in massive quantities.

The camel reduces evaporative water loss by not sweating and allowing body temperature to rise.

Figure 6.17   Dissimilar organisms with similar approaches to desert living.

lineages employ functionally similar approaches. And it will probably not surprise you that sometimes similar organisms employ radically different approaches to balancing their water budgets. In short, the means by which terrestrial organisms balance water acquisition against water loss are almost as varied as the organisms themselves. Similar variation occurs among aquatic organisms.

CONCEPT 6.2 REVIEW

1. The tiger beetle *Cicindela oregona* has a distribution that extends from Arizona through the temperate rain forests of Alaska. Why should the amounts of cuticular hydrocarbons vary geographically among populations of *C. oregona*?

2. During severe droughts, some of the branches of shrubs and trees die, while others survive. How might losing some branches increase the probability that an individual plant will survive a drought?

3. How are water and temperature regulation related in many terrestrial organisms?

6.3 Water and Salt Balance in Aquatic Environments

Marine and freshwater organisms use complementary mechanisms for water and salt regulation. As we mentioned before, we continue here our discussion on water relations from the perspective of "water" rather than "solutes." Aquatic organisms, like their terrestrial kin, regulate internal water by balancing water gain (e.g., by drinking) against water loss (e.g., by secretion). By osmosis, an aquatic organism may either gain or lose water, depending on the organism and the environment in which it is found.

Marine Fish and Invertebrates

Most marine invertebrates maintain an internal concentration of solutes equivalent to that in the seawater around them. What does the animal gain by remaining isosmotic with the external environment? The isosmotic animal does not have to expend energy overcoming an osmotic gradient in order to maintain water balance.

Although the total concentration of solutes is the same inside and outside the isosmotic animal, there are still differences in the concentrations of some individual solutes. In sharks, skates, and rays, inorganic ions constitute only about one-third of the solute

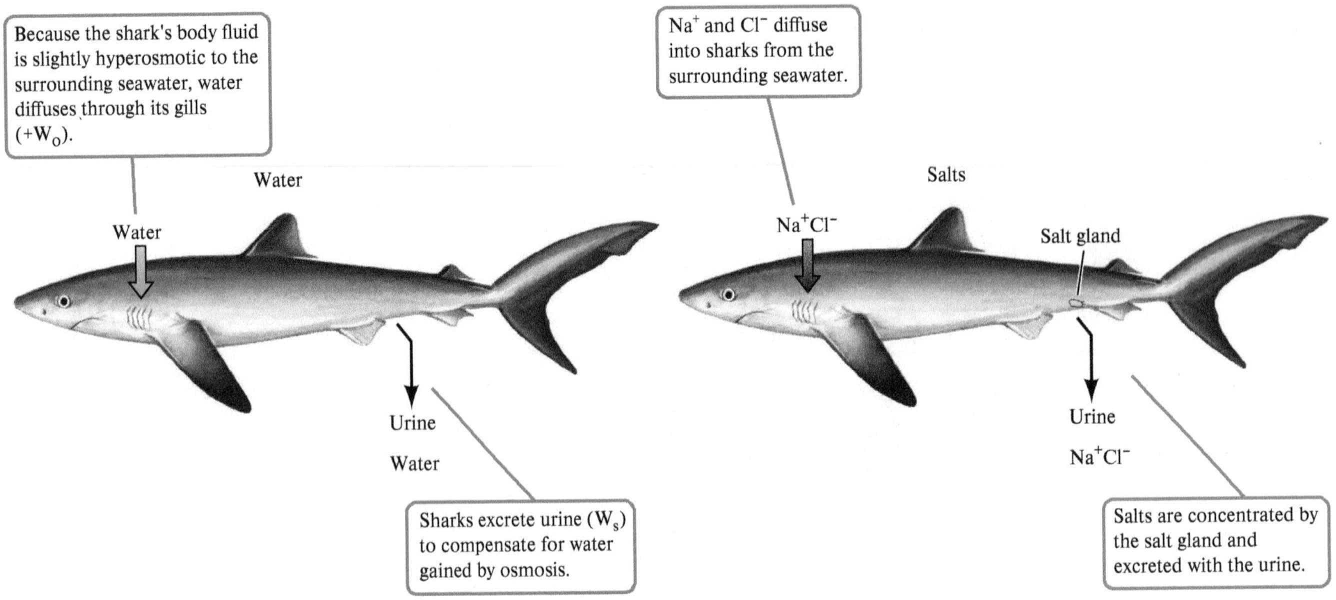

Because the shark's body fluid is slightly hyperosmotic to the surrounding seawater, water diffuses through its gills ($+W_o$).

Water

Water

Urine

Water

Sharks excrete urine (W_s) to compensate for water gained by osmosis.

Na^+ and Cl^- diffuse into sharks from the surrounding seawater.

Salts

Na^+Cl^-

Salt gland

Urine

Na^+Cl^-

Salts are concentrated by the salt gland and excreted with the urine.

Figure 6.18 Osmoregulation by sharks.

in shark's blood; the remainder consists of the organic molecules urea and trimethylamine N-oxide (TMAO). These animals actually maintain high enough levels of urea and TMAO that their bodies are slightly hyperosmotic to seawater, but they achieve this while maintaining a disequilibrium in concentrations of inorganic ions. Sodium, because it is maintained at approximately two-thirds its concentration in seawater, diffuses into sharks from seawater across the gill membranes; some sodium enters with food. Sharks excrete excess sodium mainly through a specialized gland associated with the rectum called the salt gland. The main point here is that sharks and their relatives reduce the costs of osmoregulation by decreasing the osmotic gradient between themselves and the external environment (fig. 6.18).

In contrast to most marine invertebrates and sharks, marine bony fish have body fluids that are strongly hypoosmotic to the surrounding medium. As a consequence, they lose water to the surrounding seawater, mostly across their gills. Marine bony fish make up these water losses by drinking seawater. However, drinking adds to salt influxes through their gills. The fish rid themselves of excess salts in two ways. Specialized "chloride" cells at the base of their gills secrete sodium and chloride directly to the surrounding seawater, while the kidneys excrete magnesium and sulfate. These ions exit with the urine. The urine represents a loss of water. However, this loss of water through the kidneys is low because the quantity of urine is small.

The larvae of some mosquitoes in the genus *Aedes* live in saltwater. These larvae meet the challenge of a high-salinity environment in ways analogous to those used by marine bony fish. Like marine bony fish, saltwater mosquitoes are hypoosmotic to the surrounding environment, to which they lose water. They also make up this water loss by drinking large amounts of seawater, up to 130% to 240% of body volume per day. This would impress even a camel! While this prodigious drinking solves the problem of water loss, it creates another: large quantities of salts that must be eliminated. Saltwater mosquitoes secrete these salts into the urine using specialized cells that line

the posterior rectum. Here, saltwater mosquitoes do something that marine bony fish cannot: they excrete a urine that is hyperosmotic to their body fluids, which reduces water loss through the urine. The parallels in water and salt regulation by marine bony fish and saltwater mosquitoes are outlined in figure 6.19.

Freshwater Fish and Invertebrates

Freshwater bony fish face the opposite water balance problem faced by marine bony fish. Freshwater fish are hyperosmotic: they have body fluids that contain more salt and less water than the surrounding medium. As a consequence, water floods inward and salts diffuse outward across their gills. Freshwater fish excrete excess internal water as large quantities of dilute urine. They replace the salts they lose to the external environment in two ways. First, chloride cells at the base of the gill filaments absorb sodium and chloride from the water. Remember this same adaptation in marine bony fish moved chloride in the opposite direction, out of the body. Second, some ions lost in urine or diffusion across the gills are replaced by salts ingested with food.

Like freshwater fish, freshwater invertebrates are hyperosmotic to the surrounding environment. Freshwater invertebrates must expend energy to pump out the water that floods their tissues. They also expend energy by actively absorbing salts from the external environment. However, the concentration of solutes in the body fluids of freshwater invertebrates ranges from between about one-half to one-tenth that of their marine relatives. This lower internal concentration of solutes reduces the osmotic gradient between freshwater and the outside environment and so reduces the energy that freshwater invertebrates must expend to osmoregulate.

Mosquito larvae again provide a good illustration of how aquatic invertebrates maintain water balance; this time they are used to illustrate osmoregulation in freshwater. Saltwater mosquitoes notwithstanding, the larvae of approximately 95% of mosquito species live in freshwater. Here they face osmotic

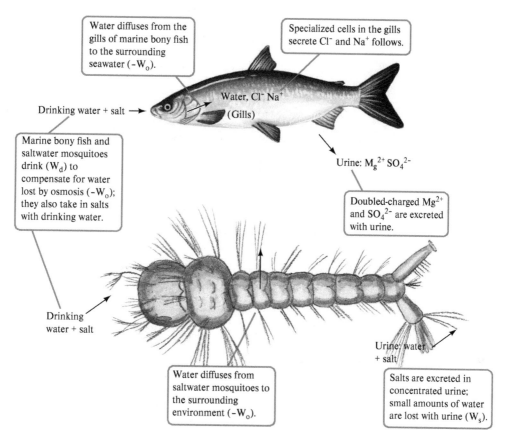

Water diffuses from the gills of marine bony fish to the surrounding seawater ($-W_o$).

Specialized cells in the gills secrete Cl^- and Na^+ follows.

Drinking water + salt →

Water, Cl^- Na^+ (Gills)

Marine bony fish and saltwater mosquitoes drink (W_d) to compensate for water lost by osmosis ($-W_o$); they also take in salts with drinking water.

Urine: M_g^{2+} SO_4^{2-}

Doubled-charged Mg^{2+} and SO_4^{2-} are excreted with urine.

Drinking water + salt

Urine; water + salt

Water diffuses from saltwater mosquitoes to the surrounding environment ($-W_o$).

Salts are excreted in concentrated urine; small amounts of water are lost with urine (W_s).

Figure 6.19   Osmoregulation by marine fish and saltwater mosquitoes.

challenges very similar to those faced by freshwater fish. Like freshwater fish, mosquito larvae must solve the twin problems of water gain and ion loss. They drink very little water, they conserve ions taken with the diet by absorbing them with cells that line the midgut and rectum, and they secrete a dilute urine. Freshwater mosquito larvae replace the ions lost with urine by actively absorbing Na^+ and Cl^- from the water with cells in their anal papillae. Freshwater mosquitoes and fish use totally different structures, but at a cellular level they use the same motifs (active transporter proteins for ions) to meet nearly identical environmental challenges. Figure 6.20 compares water and salt regulation by freshwater fish and mosquitoes.

Living with Variable Salinity Levels

Above, we have described the challenges that many animals face in marine water or freshwater. Many organisms experience great variability in salinity over the course of their lifetime. In one life stage, an animal may face the challenges of being hyperosmotic relative to its environment; and, in a later life stage, of being hypoosmotic to its environment. As we described in chapters 2 and 3, unique abiotic conditions are found where the ocean meets the land. The organisms that live within estuaries, salt marshes, and intertidal zones experience periods of high and low salinity, temperature, and water levels depending upon the lunar cycle and local climatic conditions. These organisms typically have a high tolerance (chapter 5) to high salt levels and may be able to acclimatize (chapter 5) to changing conditions.

Anadromous fish—including many species of salmon (fig. 6.21), the sea lamprey (*Petromyzon marinus*), Atlantic sturgeon (*Acipenser oxyrinchos*), and steelhead trout (*Oncorhynchus mykiss*)—hatch and spend some of their juvenile developmental stages in freshwater. They then migrate to the ocean, where they will spend most of their lives, before returning to freshwater to spawn. Catadromous fish, including many species of freshwater eels, do the opposite, spawning in saltwater and spending most of their lives in freshwater.

Migration from saltwater to freshwater over an animal's life history requires a number of fairly complicated traits, including the ability to remember and navigate, the ability to tolerate variable temperature regimes and food items, and the ability to cope with both hypo- and hypersaline conditions.

It may come as no surprise that understanding the detailed physiology of salmon is of great interest to researchers throughout the world, as salmon fisheries are highly valuable. Changing salinity levels triggers a number of hormonal responses in anadromous (and catadromous) fish, resulting in changes in the gill proteins that regulate internal osmolarity (McCormick 2001). Continued exposure to new salinity levels results in a degree of acclimation, allowing the fish to live in its new environment. A more detailed explanation of how these fish are able to cope with such variable salinities is beyond the scope of this book. However, the pattern of the environment presenting a number of abiotic stressors, and some species' possessing specific traits allowing them to mitigate the effects of these stressors, is a common theme in the study of physiological ecology.

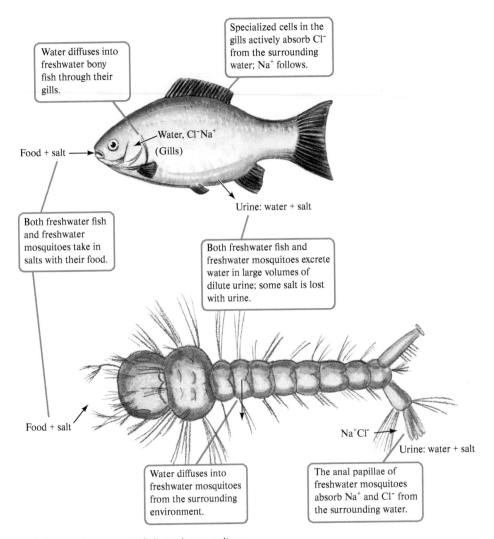

Water diffuses into freshwater bony fish through their gills.

Specialized cells in the gills actively absorb Cl⁻ from the surrounding water; Na⁺ follows.

Water, Cl⁻Na⁺ (Gills)

Food + salt →

Urine: water + salt

Both freshwater fish and freshwater mosquitoes take in salts with their food.

Both freshwater fish and freshwater mosquitoes excrete water in large volumes of dilute urine; some salt is lost with urine.

Food + salt

Na⁺Cl⁻ →

Urine: water + salt

Water diffuses into freshwater mosquitoes from the surrounding environment.

The anal papillae of freshwater mosquitoes absorb Na⁺ and Cl⁻ from the surrounding water.

Figure 6.20   Osmoregulation by freshwater fish and mosquitoes.

Figure 6.21   A diverse array of fish spend part of their lives in the ocean and other parts in freshwater, including many salmon species, such as sockeye salmon (*Oncorhynchus nerka*).

© Steven J. Kazlowski/Alamy Stock Photo.

In this chapter, we have reviewed the water relations of individual organisms. The relationship between individual organisms and the environment is a fundamental aspect of ecology. However, ecologists are also concerned with levels of organization above the individual, such as the ecology of populations or of entire biomes. The following example in the Ecological Tools and Approaches section shows how an understanding of the water relations of individual organisms is helping ecologists study the distribution of biomes across a continent.

CONCEPT 6.3 REVIEW

1. Why do isosmotic marine invertebrates expend less energy for osmoregulation compared to hypoosmotic marine fish?

2. The body fluids of many freshwater invertebrate species have very low internal salt concentrations. What is the benefit of such diluted internal fluids?

ECOLOGICAL TOOLS AND APPROACHES

Using Stable Isotopes to Study Water Uptake by Plants

To fully understand the ecology of an individual plant or the dynamics of an entire landscape, ecologists need information about what happens below the earth's surface as well as about surface structure and processes. However, ecologists have produced much more information about the surface realm than about the subsurface, the domain of soil microbes, burrowing animals, and roots. As we discussed in chapter 2, many ecologists have worked very hard to fill this gap in our knowledge, and once again a major contributor to progress in ecology has been the development of new tools. One of the most important of those is stable isotope analysis, which involves the analysis of the relative concentrations of stable isotopes, such as the stable isotopes of carbon ^{13}C and ^{12}C, in materials. Stable isotope analysis is increasingly used in ecology to study the flow of energy and materials through ecosystems (Dawson et al. 2002). For instance, stable isotope analysis has proven to be a powerful tool in studies of water uptake by plants. To understand the applications of this analytical tool, we need to know a little about the isotopes themselves and about their behaviour in ecosystems.

Stable Isotope Analysis

Most chemical elements include several stable isotopes, which occur in different concentrations in different environments or differ in concentration from one organism to another. Stable isotopes of hydrogen include ^1H and ^2H, which is generally designated as D, an abbreviation of *deuterium*. Stable isotopes of carbon, for example, include ^{13}C and ^{12}C; stable isotopes of nitrogen include ^{15}N and ^{14}N; and stable isotopes of sulfur include ^{34}S and ^{32}S. The relative concentrations of these stable isotopes can be used to study the flow of energy and materials through ecosystems because different parts of the ecosystem often contain different concentrations of the light and heavy isotopes of these elements.

Different organisms contain different ratios of light and heavy stable isotopes because they use different sources of these elements, or because they preferentially use (fractionate) different stable isotopes, or because they use different sources *and* fractionate. For instance, the lighter isotope of nitrogen, ^{14}N, is more likely to be excreted than is ^{15}N by organisms during protein synthesis. As a consequence of this preferential excretion of ^{14}N, an organism becomes relatively enriched in ^{15}N compared to its food. Therefore, as materials pass from one trophic level to the next, tissues become richer in ^{15}N. The highest trophic levels within an ecosystem contain the highest relative concentrations of ^{15}N, while the

lowest trophic levels contain the lowest concentrations. Stable isotope analysis can also measure the relative contribution of C_3 and C_4 plants to a species' diet. This is possible because C_4 plants are richer in ^{13}C than are C_3 plants. Other processes affect the relative concentrations of stable isotopes of sulfur. Because different sources of water often have different ratios of D to ^1H—for example, shallow soil moisture versus deep soil moisture—hydrogen isotope analyses have been valuable aids to identifying where plants acquire their water.

The concentrations of stable isotopes are generally expressed as differences in the concentration of the heavier isotope relative to some standard. The units of measurement are differences ($\pm$) in parts per thousand ($\pm$ ‰). These differences are calculated as:

$$\delta X = \left(\frac{R_{sample}}{R_{standard}} - 1 \right) \times 10$$

where:

$\delta = \pm$

$X =$ the relative concentration of the heavier isotope, for example, D, ^{13}C, ^{15}N, or ^{34}S in ‰

$R_{sample} =$ the isotopic ratio in the sample, for example, D:^1H, ^{13}C:^{12}C, or ^{15}N:^{14}N

$R_{standard} =$ the isotopic ratio in the standard, for example, D:^1H, ^{13}C:^{12}C, or ^{15}N:^{14}N

The reference materials used as standards in the isotopic analyses of hydrogen, nitrogen, carbon, and sulfur are the D:^1H ratio in Standard Mean Ocean Water, the ^{15}N:^{14}N ratio in atmospheric nitrogen, the ^{13}C:^{12}C ratio in PeeDee limestone, and the ^{34}S:^{32}S in the Canyon Diablo meteorites.

The ecologist measures the ratio of stable isotopes in a sample and then expresses that ratio as a difference relative to some standard. If $\delta X = 0$, then the ratios of the isotopes in the sample and the standard are the same; if $\delta X = - X$ ‰, the concentration of the heavier isotope is lower (e.g.,^{15}N) in the sample compared to the standard; and if $\delta X = +X$ ‰, the concentration of the heavier isotope is higher in the sample compared to the standard. The important point here is that these isotopic ratios are generally different in different parts of ecosystems. Therefore, ecologists can use isotopic ratios to study the structure and processes in ecosystems. Here is an example of how hydrogen isotope ratios have been used to study the uptake of water by plants in a natural ecosystem. We will discuss other uses of stable isotopic analyses in later chapters.

Using Stable Isotopes to Identify Plant Water Sources

The laboratory of James Ehleringer, director of the Stable Isotope Ratio Facility for Environmental Research at the University of Utah, was a pioneer in the development of stable isotope analysis as a tool for assessing water relations among plants and within ecosystems (e.g., Ehleringer et al. 2000). In an early study, Ehleringer and several colleagues (Ehleringer et al. 1991) used deuterium:hydrogen (D:^{1}H) ratios, or δD, to explore the use of summer versus winter rainfall by various plant growth forms in the deserts of southern Utah. They could use δD to determine the relative utilization of these two water sources since summer rains are relatively enriched with D and winter rains are relatively depleted of D. The δD of summer and winter rains in southern Utah at the time of Ehleringer's study were -25 ‰ and -90 ‰, respectively (fig. 6.22).

Ehleringer measured δD in the xylem fluid of several plant growth forms during spring, when soil moisture at all rooting depths would be predominantly from winter precipitation, and summer, when summer precipitation would be present as moisture in surface soils and winter precipitation would predominate at deeper soil layers. Ehleringer and his research team found that a succulent, several herbaceous perennials, and several woody perennials used winter moisture in the spring (fig. 6.22). However, when summer rains fell, the succulent species shifted entirely to using soil moisture from summer rains that were stored mainly at shallow soil depths. Meanwhile herbaceous and woody perennials continued to use significant amounts of deeper soil moisture that fell the previous winter. So, stable isotope analysis opens a window to the water relations of plants that would not be accessible without this innovative tool.

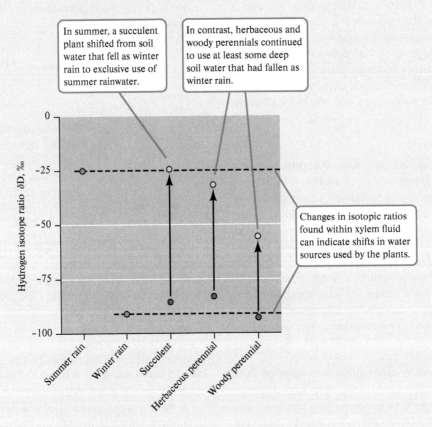

Figure 6.22 Stable isotope analysis identified the water sources used by three groups of desert plants during the spring and summer. In the figure, the lower dashed line corresponds to the isotopic ratio found in winter rain, while the upper dashed line corresponds to the isotopic ratio found in summer rain.

Data from Ehleringer et al. 1991.

SUMMARY

6.1 Concentration gradients influence the movement of water between an organism and its environment.

Macroclimatic variation affects large-scale patterns of water availability. At a finer scale, factors such as topography, soil type, and, in water, solute concentration affect microclimatic variations in water availability (fig. 6.23). Within a microclimate, water moves from areas of greater quantity to lesser quantity. Quantity can be understood in units of pressure, and water moves from higher pressure to lower pressure. We refer to this pressure as water potential, which is the sum of several component pressures, including vapour pressure, osmotic pressure, and matric pressure.

On land, the tendency of water to move from organisms to the atmosphere can be approximated by the difference in vapour pressure deficit between the organism and the air. Vapour pressure deficit is calculated as the difference between the actual water vapour pressure and the saturation water vapour pressure.

In the aquatic environment, water moves down its concentration gradient from solutions of higher water concentration and lower salt content (hypoosmotic) to solutions of lower water concentration and higher salt content (hyperosmotic). This movement of water creates osmotic pressure. Larger osmotic differences, between organism and environment, generate higher osmotic pressures.

6.2 Terrestrial plants and animals regulate their internal water by balancing water acquisition against water loss.

The availability of water in a microclimate, and the loss of water to the environment due to osmotic pressure or VPD, affect fitness of organisms (fig. 6.23). Organisms have a variety of behavioural and morpho-physiological adaptions to water stress and to regulation of water. Some very different terrestrial plants and animals, such as the camel and saguaro cactus, use similar mechanisms to survive in arid climates. Some organisms, such as cicadas, use radically different mechanisms. Comparisons such as these suggest that natural selection is opportunistic.

6.3 Marine and freshwater organisms use complementary mechanisms for water and salt regulation.

Marine and freshwater organisms face exactly opposite osmotic challenges. An aquatic organism may either gain or lose water through osmosis, depending on the organism and the environment. Many marine invertebrates reduce their water regulation problems by being isosmotic with seawater. Some freshwater invertebrates also reduce the osmotic gradient between themselves and their environment. Sharks, skates, and rays elevate the urea and TMAO content of their body fluids to the point where they are slightly hyperosmotic to seawater. Marine bony fish and saltwater mosquito larvae are hypoosmotic relative to their environments, while freshwater bony fish and freshwater mosquito larvae are hyperosmotic.

While the strength of environmental challenge varies from one environment to another, and the details of water regulation vary from one organism to another, all organisms in all environments expend energy to maintain their internal pool of water and dissolved substances.

Stable isotope analysis, an important new tool in ecology, involves the analysis of the relative concentrations of stable isotopes in materials. Examples of stable isotopes include the stable isotopes of hydrogen ^2H (which is usually symbolized by D, referring to deuterium) and ^1H, and the stable isotopes of carbon, ^{13}C and ^{12}C. Stable isotope analysis has proven to be a powerful tool in studies of water uptake by plants. For example, deuterium:hydrogen (D:^1H) ratios, or δD, have been used to quantify the relative use of summer versus winter rainfall by various plant growth forms in the deserts of southern Utah.

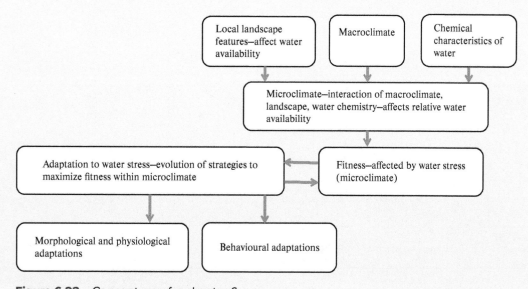

Figure 6.23 Concept map for chapter 6.

REVIEW QUESTIONS

1. Cottonwood regeneration is dependent upon periodic flooding. How can land managers use this information to maintain stable cottonwood populations?

2. Distinguish between vapour pressure deficit, osmotic pressure, and water potential. How can all three phenomena be expressed in the same units of measure: pascals?

3. Leaf water potential is typically highest just before dawn and then decreases progressively through midday. Should lower leaf water potentials at midday increase or decrease the rate of water movement from soil to a plant? Assume soil water potential is approximately the same in early morning and midday. Are the water needs of the plant greater in early morning or at midday?

4. Compare the water budgets of the tenebrionid beetle (*Onymacris*) and the kangaroo rat (*Dipodomys*), shown in figures 6.10 and 6.11. Which of these two species obtains most of its water from metabolic water? Which relies most on condensation of fog as a water source? In which species do you see greater losses of water through the urine?

5. In the Sonoran Desert, the only insects known to evaporatively cool are cicadas. Explain how cicadas can employ evaporative cooling while hundreds of other insect species in the same environment cannot.

6. Many desert species are well waterproofed. Evolution cannot, however, eliminate all evaporative water loss. Why not? (Hint: Think of the kinds of exchanges that an organism must maintain with its environment.)

7. While we have concentrated in this chapter on regulation of water and salts, most marine invertebrates are isosmotic with their external environment. What is a potential benefit of being isosmotic?

8. Review water and salt regulation by marine and freshwater bony fish. Which of the two is hypoosmotic relative to its environment? Which of the two is hyperosmotic relative to its environment? Some sharks live in freshwater. How should the kidneys of marine and freshwater sharks function?

9. Some plants in the tropics use wilting as a mechanism to decrease internal water potentials and thus increase water uptake. However, many plants in temperate and boreal regions also wilt on hot summer days. Does wilting have a similar physiological effect on these plants from different regions, or are different mechanisms of water uptake operating in different parts of the world?

10. Stable isotopes can be used to distinguish the source of water used by plants and how this shifts over seasons. Suppose you have a tree growing on the bank of a river that might use water from the river or from deeper groundwater. How might you determine which source of water it uses?

© Don Johnstolt All Canada Photos/Getty Images.

CHAPTER 7   ENERGY AND NUTRIENT RELATIONS

CHAPTER CONCEPTS

7.1 Organisms use one of three main sources of energy: solar radiation, organic molecules, or inorganic molecules.
Concept 7.1 Review

7.2 The rates at which organisms can take in energy and nutrients are limited.
Concept 7.2 Review

7.3 Natural selection will influence how organisms feed, and this process can be understood through the use of optimal foraging theory.
Concept 7.3 Review

Ecology in Action: Using Ecological Knowledge to Predict C$_4$ Plant Distributions in a Changing World

Ecological Tools and Approaches: Bioremediation—Using the Trophic Diversity of Bacteria to Solve Environmental Problems

Summary

Review Questions

Ascorpion fish lies half-buried in the sand near the edge of a coral reef; the only clues to its presence are movements of its gill covers. Its head looks so much like an algae-covered stone that several tiny shrimp gather over it and swim lazily in the current. A small fish on the nearby reef sees the shrimp and darts over to feed on them. The scorpion fish opens its mouth and swallows the small fish in a lightning-quick movement. However, before the scorpion fish can settle back into the sand, a green moray eel, nearly 2 m long, darts from the reef, grabs the scorpion fish with its razor-sharp teeth, and swallows it (fig. 7.1). Small parasitic isopods growing in the gills of the moray indirectly get their share of the scorpion fish by way of the moray's tissues. Eventually the moray will die, perhaps sped along by the damage inflicted by the isopods; and the bacteria, fungi, and a host of detritivorous invertebrates get their turn. As they do, some of the nutrients are released from the decaying moray. These nutrients, along with energy from the sun, allow growth of algae, which are attractive to the shrimp that started the whole cycle. And, somewhere, Elton John sings "The Circle of Life."

To read this chapter, you're going to need some energy; to get through the whole course, you'll need even more. Not to suggest you aren't enjoying every minute of ecology (we sincerely hope you are), but, as living beings, everything you do requires some energy. So grab a snack if you need to, and then read on.

You, like all living things, need to capture and consume nutrients and elements. For most of you, the "capture" has become pretty mundane. But for many people, and for most other living things, the challenges are greater. Countless unique solutions have emerged through natural selection for capturing energy and nutrients, although for the most part these can be placed into a few general strategy bins, such as autotrophy, herbivory, predation, parasitism, and detritivory, each of which we saw in the coral reef.

For many of the organisms described above, the energy and nutrients captured came in the form of organic molecules. However, for the algae, the energy came in the form of light while the nutrients came from the water column released from the decomposing moray. Still other organisms capture energy from inorganic molecules—often, from the oxidation of these molecules. Because different organisms acquire energy and nutrients in diverse ways, we organize our discussion under the umbrella of three major concepts: (1) energy sources, (2) energy and nutrient limitation, and (3) energy and nutrient capture.

Figure 7.1 The moray eel meets its energy and nutrient needs by being an effective predator.
© Corbis RF.

7.1 Energy Sources

Organisms use one of three main sources of energy: solar radiation, organic molecules, or inorganic molecules. Biological diversity is often taught to students phylogenetically, lumping groups of organisms together on the basis of shared evolutionary histories. This approach can be useful as it helps students understand evolutionary innovations in a context of relatedness. However, it is not a particularly helpful way to understand ecological interactions. An alternative way of grouping organisms is based upon functional similarities among species, such as the means by which organisms obtain energy, or their **trophic (feeding) biology.**

Organisms that use inorganic sources of both carbon and energy are called **autotrophs** ("self-feeders") and are of two types: **photosynthetic** and **chemosynthetic.** Photosynthetic autotrophs use carbon dioxide (CO_2) as a source of carbon and solar radiation in the form of light as a source of energy. This group includes the plants, photosynthetic protists, and photosynthetic bacteria. These taxa have independent evolutionary histories but share a key aspect of their ecology: the means by which they acquire energy. Chemosynthetic autotrophs also use CO_2 as a source of carbon and use other inorganic molecules as a source of energy. More specifically, they couple the oxidation of inorganic molecules (and the associated decrease in free energy) with reactions that require energy (endergonic reactions). This group contains a large diversity of chemosynthetic bacteria.

Heterotrophs ("other-feeders") are organisms that use organic molecules as a source of carbon and, for most, as a source of energy. Humans are good examples of this. The food we eat provides both the carbon we need to grow and the energy we need to do it (and to do all the other things we do). There are some photoheterotrophs that use organic carbon to grow

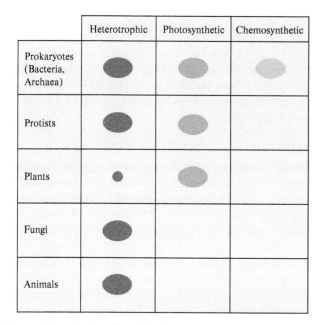

	Heterotrophic	Photosynthetic	Chemosynthetic
Prokaryotes (Bacteria, Archaea)	●	●	●
Protists	●	●	
Plants	·	●	
Fungi	●		
Animals	●		

Figure 7.2 A plot of trophic diversity across the major groups of organisms. The highest trophic diversity is found among the prokaryotic bacteria and archaea, while the least trophic diversity is found among fungi and animals.

but use light energy to produce ATP, as is discussed below. The heterotrophs include bacteria, fungi, protists, animals, and parasitic plants.

Prokaryotes show more trophic diversity than the major eukaryotic biological groupings (fig. 7.2). Of course, the prokaryotes (bacteria and **archaea**) have had a nearly 2-billion-year head start on diversification. Prokaryotes, you will recall, have cells with no membrane-bound nucleus or organelles. This is, admittedly, a grouping of convenience and tradition. The archaea are chemically and genetically more similar to eukaryotes than to bacteria and are structurally and physiologically distinct from bacteria. Though first discovered in association with extreme environments, the archaea are now known to be widely spread in the biosphere, particularly in the oceans. We are quickly learning more about archaeal genetic and physiological diversity, including their trophic biology. We now recognize that both bacteria and archaea include photosynthetic, chemosynthetic, and heterotrophic species. Eukarotes, in contrast, have lower trophic diversity. The protists are mostly single-celled organisms and are the most diverse of the eukaryotic groupings. Protists include both photosynthetic or heterotrophic members. Most plants are photosynthetic, and all fungi and animals are heterotrophic.

Photosynthesis

The Solar-Powered Biosphere

As we saw in chapters 2 and 3, solar energy powers the winds and ocean currents, and annual variation in sunlight intensity drives the seasons. In chapter 5, we also discussed how organisms use sunlight to regulate body temperature. Here, building on those discussions, we look at light from the sun as a source of energy for photosynthesis.

Light propagates through space as a wave, with all the properties of waves, such as frequency and wavelength. When light interacts with matter, however, it acts not as a wave but as a particle. Particles of light, called *photons*, bear a finite quantity of energy. Longer wavelengths, such as *infrared light*, carry less energy than shorter wavelengths, such as *visible* and *ultraviolet light*.

Infrared radiation is very important for temperature regulation by organisms. As we saw in chapter 5, many organisms alter their behaviour to either increase or decrease the absorption and retention of this heat energy, allowing them to modify their body temperatures. The main effect of infrared light on matter is to increase the motion of whole molecules, which we measure as increased temperature. However, infrared light does not carry enough energy to drive photosynthesis. At the other end of the solar spectrum, ultraviolet light carries so much energy that it breaks the covalent bonds of many organic molecules and can destroy the complex biochemical machinery of photosynthesis. Between these extremes of solar radiation wavelengths is the light we can see—so-called visible light. Visible light is better referred to as **photosynthetically active radiation (PAR)** and contains wavelengths of solar radiation between about 400 and 700 nm. These wavelengths carry sufficient energy to drive the light-dependent reactions of photosynthesis (see below) but not so much as to destroy organic molecules. PAR makes up about 45% of the total energy content of the solar spectrum at sea level; infrared light, approximately 53%; and ultraviolet light, most of the remainder.

Measuring PAR

Ecologists quantify PAR as **photon flux density (PFD),** the number of photons striking a square metre surface each second. Measuring light as photon flux density makes sense ecologically because chlorophyll absorbs light as photons. The number of photons is expressed as micromoles (μmol), so PFD is expressed as μmol photons (or quanta) $m^{-2}\ s^{-1}$. PFD in Edmonton on a clear summer day can reach 1,800–2,000 μmol $m^{-2}\ s^{-1}$, while the values can exceed 2,400 μmol $m^{-2}\ s^{-1}$ near the equator. In your classroom, PAR is likely <100 μmol $m^{-2}\ s^{-1}$, even with all the lights turned on. This may give you some idea of why it can be hard to grow plants even in what you think of as a well-lit room.

Light changes in quantity and quality with latitude, with the seasons, with the weather, and with the time of day. In addition, landscapes, water, and even organisms themselves change the amount and quality of light. For example, in aquatic environments (see chapter 3), only the superficial **euphotic zone** receives sufficient light to support photosynthetic organisms. The amount of light penetrating the depths of aquatic systems is influenced by many factors, including the amount of particles suspended in the water or the amount of dissolved substances that absorb light. Depending upon water clarity, the euphotic zone (the part able to support photosynthesis) can range in depth from a few metres to about 100 m. In addition to changes in the quantity of light that penetrates through the water column, there are shifts in the spectral composition of light due to selective absorption of certain wavelengths of light by plant pigments and also due to physical influences of the water itself.

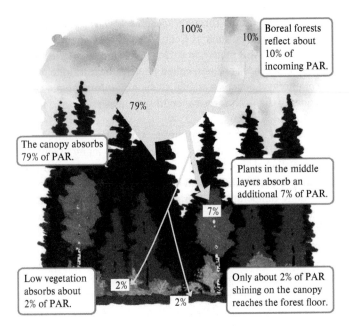

Boreal forests reflect about 10% of incoming PAR.

100%   10%

79%

The canopy absorbs 79% of PAR.

Plants in the middle layers absorb an additional 7% of PAR.

7%

Low vegetation absorbs about 2% of PAR.

2%

2%

Only about 2% of PAR shining on the canopy reaches the forest floor.

Figure 7.3 Photosynthetically active radiation (PAR) diminishes substantially with passage through the canopy of a boreal forest.
Data from Larcher 1995, after Kairiukstis 1967.

For example, if you dive you may have noticed that in the ocean, below a certain depth, everything appears blue. This is because the longer wavelengths of light are absorbed nearer the surface. Photosynthetic pigments absorb light most efficiently over limited ranges of the PAR spectrum. Chlorophyll has absorption maxima in both the blue and the red portion of the spectrum. The ability of algae to use blue light for photosynthesis extends the depth of the euphotic zone.

As in the sea, sunlight changes as it shines through vegetation on land. A mature temperate or boreal forest can reduce the total *quantity* of light reaching the forest floor to about 1% to 2% of the amount shining on the forest canopy (fig. 7.3).

This filtering of light through the canopy also changes the *quality* of light. Leaves absorb mainly blue and red light and transmit mostly green light with a wavelength of about 550 nm. As in the deep sea, the organisms on the forest floor live in a kind of twilight. Only here, the twilight is green. We will discuss how plants respond to altered light quality in chapter 13, when we discuss competition.

Alternative Photosynthetic Pathways

During photosynthesis, the photosynthetic pigments of plants, algae, or bacteria absorb light and transfer their energy to electrons. Subsequently, the energy carried by these electrons is used to synthesize ATP and NADPH (the reduced form of nicotinamide adenine dinucleotide phosphate, or $NADP^+$). This process generally requires complex photosystems and occurs only in the light. Perhaps it comes as no surprise that these reactions are commonly referred to as "light reactions." These molecules, in turn, serve as donors of electrons and energy for the synthesis of sugars. This second stage also generally occurs in the light, although it is not directly dependent upon light, so these reactions are often called "dark reactions"; you may recall these reactions as the Calvin cycle. Through these two sets of reactions, photosynthetic organisms convert the electromagnetic energy of sunlight into energy-rich organic molecules.

Biologists often speak of photosynthesis as "carbon fixation," which refers to the reactions in which CO_2 becomes incorporated into a carbon-containing acid. In the photosynthetic pathway used by most plants and all algae, the CO_2 first combines with a five-carbon compound called *ribulose 1,5-bisphosphate*, or *RuBP*. The product of this initial reaction, which is catalyzed by the enzyme RuBP carboxylase (RUBISCO), is two *phosphoglyceric acid,* or *PGA*, molecules, each a three-carbon acid. This photosynthetic pathway is usually called **C₃ photosynthesis** and the plants that employ it are called C₃ plants (fig. 7.4).

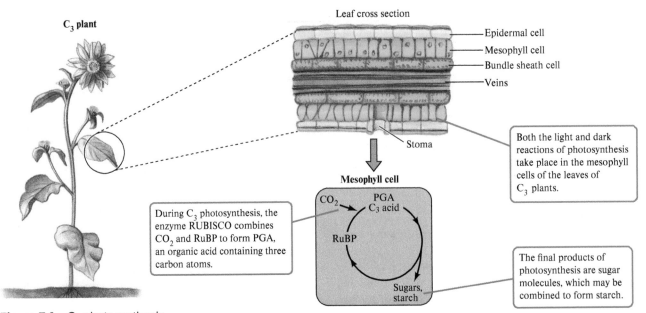

C₃ plant

Leaf cross section

Epidermal cell
Mesophyll cell
Bundle sheath cell
Veins

Stoma

Both the light and dark reactions of photosynthesis take place in the mesophyll cells of the leaves of C₃ plants.

During C₃ photosynthesis, the enzyme RUBISCO combines CO_2 and RuBP to form PGA, an organic acid containing three carbon atoms.

Mesophyll cell

CO_2 PGA
C₃ acid

RuBP

Sugars, starch

The final products of photosynthesis are sugar molecules, which may be combined to form starch.

Figure 7.4 C₃ photosynthesis.

To fix carbon, plants must open their stomata to let CO_2 into their leaves, but as CO_2 enters, water exits. Water vapour flows out faster than CO_2 flows in. The movement of water is more rapid because the gradient in water concentration from the leaf to the atmosphere is much steeper than the gradient in CO_2 concentration from the atmosphere to the leaf. In C_3 plants, there is another factor that contributes to a low rate of CO_2 uptake: RUBISCO has a low affinity for CO_2. Relatively high rates of water loss are generally not a problem for plants that live in cool, moist conditions, but in hot, dry climates, high rates of water loss can close the stomata and shut down photosynthesis by C_3 plants (see chapter 6).

In arid environments, two alternative photosynthetic pathways have repeatedly evolved, both of which separate (in space or time) the initial fixation of carbon from the light-dependent reactions. In **C_4 photosynthesis**, carbon fixation and the light-dependent reactions of photosynthesis occur in separate cells (fig. 7.5). C_4 plants fix CO_2 in mesophyll cells by combining it with a three-carbon molecule called *phosphoenolpyruvate*, or *PEP*, to produce a four-carbon acid. This initial reaction, which is catalyzed by PEP carboxylase, concentrates CO_2. Because PEP carboxylase has a high affinity for CO_2, C_4 plants can reduce their internal CO_2 concentrations to very low levels. Low internal concentration of CO_2 increases the gradient of CO_2 from

atmosphere to leaf, which in turn increases the rate of diffusion of CO_2 inward. Consequently, compared to C_3 plants, C_4 plants need to open fewer stomata to deliver sufficient CO_2 to photosynthesizing cells. By having fewer stomata open, C_4 plants conserve water.

In C_4 plants, the acids produced during carbon fixation diffuse to specialized cells surrounding a structure called the **bundle sheath**. There, deeper in the leaf, the four-carbon acids are broken down to a three-carbon acid and CO_2. C_4 photosynthesis also benefits plants by reducing **photorespiration**. Although RUBISCO is a carboxylase (it binds CO_2 to RuBP), it can also serve as an oxygenase, binding O_2 to RuBP. When this happens, RuBP is partly broken down and a CO_2 molecule is released from the plant, a process known as photorespiration. Needless to say, release of CO_2 from a plant is counter to the needs of photosynthesis. One of the major factors influencing photorespiration is the concentration of O_2 relative to CO_2, with increased photorespiration in a relatively oxygen-rich and carbon dioxide-poor atmosphere. C_4 plants reduce photorespiration by segregating RUBISCO into the bundle sheath cells. By doing this, plants put this enzyme in an area of high CO_2 concentration (remember, it is transported out of the mesophyll cells) and low O_2 concentrations (O_2 generated by the light reactions of photosynthesis occurs in the mesophyll, not the bundle

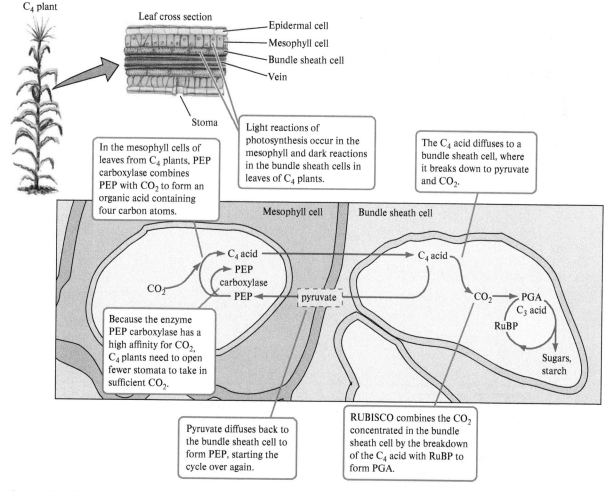

Figure 7.5 C_4 photosynthesis.

sheath cells). Note that C_4 plants appear to have evolved primarily during periods of low atmospheric CO_2 (Sage 2004). The impacts of atmospheric oxygen and carbon dioxide levels will have strong selective forces on plant photosynthesis and evolution, something we will discuss more in the Ecology in Action section of this chapter.

CAM (crassulacean acid metabolism) photosynthesis is largely limited to succulent plants in arid and semiarid environments. In both C_3 and C_4 plants, the light-dependent and Calvin cycle reactions all occur during the day. In CAM photosynthesis, carbon fixation typically takes place at night, when lower temperatures reduce the rate of water loss during CO_2 uptake. CAM plants fix carbon by combining CO_2 with PEP to form four-carbon acids. These acids are stored until daylight, when they are broken down into pyruvate and CO_2, which then enter the C_3 photosynthetic pathway (fig. 7.6). In CAM plants, all

these reactions take place in the same cells. While CAM plants do not normally show very high rates of photosynthesis, their water use efficiency, as estimated by the mass of CO_2 fixed per kilogram of water used, is higher than that of either C_3 or C_4 plants.

Separating initial carbon fixation from the other reactions reduces water losses during photosynthesis: C_3 plants lose about 380 to 900 g of water for every gram (dry weight) of tissue produced. C_4 plants lose about 250 to 350 g of water per gram of tissue produced, while CAM plants lose approximately 50 g of water per gram of new tissue. The differences in these numbers give us one of the reasons C_4 and CAM plants do well in hot, dry environments.

Given what you have learned above, are you surprised to know that most plant species (~95%) are C_3 plants? You have just read that CAM plants are the masters of water conservation,

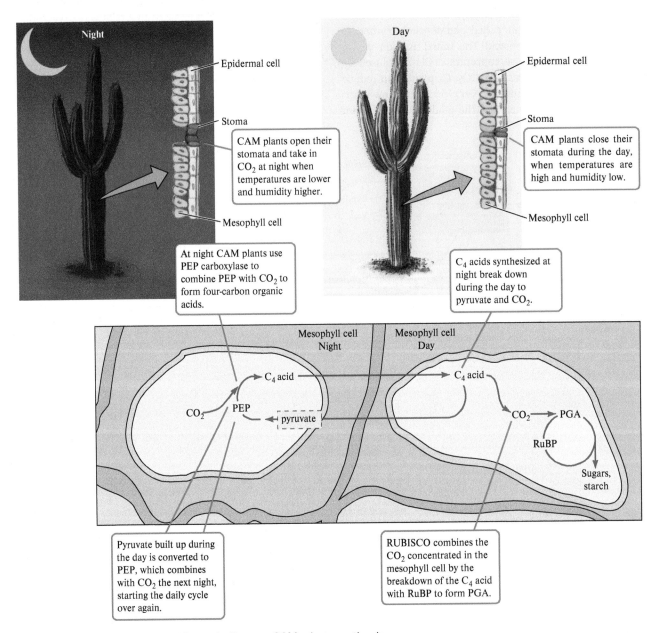

Figure 7.6   Crassulacean acid metabolism, or CAM, photosynthesis.

although it was mentioned that they generally have lower photosynthetic rates. But why isn't it a C_4 world?

The C_4 pathway requires more energy, an additional 2 ATP per molecule of CO_2 fixed. This energy is required for the translocation of pyruvate, and the regeneration of PEP. In chapter 5, we discussed allocation of resources. Cellular energy is allocated to many processes beyond growth. When energy is finite, an investment of 2 ATP per carbon can translate to less efficient growth. Further, Rowan Sage and colleagues at the University of Toronto have suggested that the nature of the C_4 plant leaf (i.e., the physical separation of light and dark reactions) may limit RUBISCO activity. This could be exacerbated at low temperatures, limiting C_4 plant growth in cooler climates (Kubien et al. 2003) (see Ecology in Action at the end of this chapter). James Ehleringer and Olle Björkman (1977) studied the effects of temperature and O_2 concentrations on **quantum yield** (molecules of carbon fixed per photon absorbed) in C_3 and C_4 plants. At atmospheric oxygen concentrations (21%) and at 30°C, C_3 and C_4 plants had the same quantum yield and should compete on equal footing. However, at low oxygen concentrations (2%), C_3 plants had ~35% higher quantum yield. Under low light conditions, cellular respiration within the leaf tissue may depress oxygen concentrations and provide some advantage to C_3 plants. When quantum yield was measured at different temperatures, Ehleringer and Björkman showed that C_3 plants had higher quantum yield at temperatures below 30°C, while C_4 plants had higher quantum yields above 30°C (fig 7.7). At most latitudes, prevailing climate would give C_3 plants a competitive advantage, despite the inefficiencies described earlier.

Whether the pathway of carbon fixation is CAM, C_3, or C_4, plants and photosynthetic algae and bacteria capture energy from sunlight and carbon from CO_2. These photosynthesizers package this energy and carbon in organic molecules. The photosynthesizers and other autotrophs opened the way for the evolution of organisms that could get their energy and carbon from organic molecules.

Chemical Composition and Nutrient Requirements

So far, we've been talking about carbon. Plants and other photosynthetic organisms fix carbon and use it to grow. But if you think about all the different types of macromolecules in a cell, you'll realize that plants need more than just carbon to grow; they need nitrogen for proteins and nucleotide bases, phosphorus for cell membranes and nucleic acids, and carbon and hydrogen for virtually all biomolecules. Because nearly all organisms produce the same kinds of macromolecules, the chemical composition of organisms is quite similar, with just five elements—(carbon [C], oxygen [O], hydrogen [H], nitrogen [N], and phosphorus [P])—making up 93% to 97% of the biomass of plants, animals, fungi, and bacteria. However, there are some important differences in chemical composition, and these differences shape ecological interactions.

Plants are most chemically distinct from animals, fungi, and bacteria, containing lower concentrations of phosphorus and nitrogen relative to carbon (fig. 7.8). The nitrogen content of plant tissues averages about 2%, while it is typically 5%–10% in fungi, animals, and bacteria. **Ecological stoichiometry** concerns the balance of multiple chemical elements in ecological interactions. If you think about an animal that eats plants (a herbivore), its food is relatively poor in N compared with carbon. How does the herbivore eat a diet with a C:N of 24 and maintain its own stoichiometry of C:N at 5.5? It needs to retain the plant's N while expelling (by respiration or excretion) much of the plant's carbon. The herbivore will have to find and consume more of the plant biomass than it needs to meet its carbon requirement because the plant's nutritional value is limited by its nitrogen content. In this way, differences in stoichiometry between the plant and animal shape feeding behaviour and intensify interactions between plants and animals.

Differences in C:N ratios among tissues or among organisms significantly influence what organisms eat, how rapidly consumers reproduce, and how rapidly organisms decompose.

We see some other important stoichiometric differences among groups of animals based on the kinds of structures they build and maintain. For example, vertebrate animals typically have a high demand for calcium and phosphorus to support a mineral-rich internal skeleton, while demand for these elements is typically reduced among invertebrate species. That said, bivalve mollusks may be limited in where they can grow by the availability of calcium. Plants have relatively high demand for essential nutrients (e.g., potassium, zinc, and iron), while animals have higher demand for sodium (Na) and iodine (I); diatoms require more silica (Si) for building their outer cases (frustules). Fast-growing organisms require relatively more nutrient-rich resources to support their higher allocation to tissue building compared to those with slower growth rates that can accumulate elements like N and P more slowly. Thus, how an organism allocates elements has consequences for its

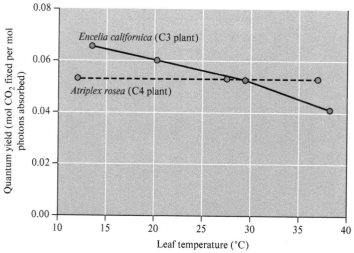

Figure 7.7 Photosynthetic efficiency, measured as quantum yield, varies in C_3 plants as a function of temperature. C_3 plants are more efficient than C_4 plants at lower temperatures and less efficient at higher temperatures.

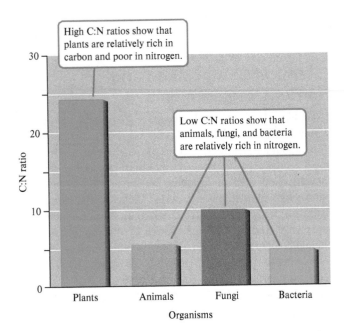

Figure 7.8 On average, the ratio of carbon to nitrogen is much higher in terrestrial plants than in other major groups of organisms.

elemental requirements and how it meets those requirements (e.g., what and how much an animal eats).

Plant leaves capture the energy found in sunlight with pigments and obtain carbon from the air through stomata. The other essential nutrients are captured mainly from the soil through plant roots. As a result, plants obtain different essential resources through different organs (leaves versus roots), which results in potential energetic conflicts associated with foraging for these different resources. In contrast, most consumers obtain both the energy they require and essential nutrients with the food they consume with their mouth (or similar organ), resulting in comparatively simpler foraging strategies. We will discuss these differences in plant and animal foraging later in this chapter, but now turn to the energy and nutrient relations of heterotrophs.

Heterotrophs

Heterotrophic organisms use organic molecules both as a source of carbon and as an energy source. They depend, ultimately, on the carbon and energy fixed by autotrophs. Heterotrophs have evolved numerous ways of feeding. Here, we will concentrate on three major categories of consumers: **detritivores**, organisms that feed on nonliving organic matter; **herbivores**, organisms that eat living plants; and **carnivores**, organisms that mainly eat living animals. Detritivores, herbivores, and carnivores must solve fundamentally different problems to obtain adequate supplies of energy and nutrients.

Detritivores

Globally, most of the biomass produced by photosynthesis is consumed after that biomass is dead, not while it is alive. It is not the charismatic organisms typically featured in nature

documentaries that are feeding upon these dead tissues, however. Instead, the consumers are primarily small-bodied insects and worms, fungi, and bacteria. These consumers are referred to as detritivores, and they control the movement of energy and nutrients in most ecosystems.

The vast majority of biomass contained in living organisms is found in plants, bacteria, and fungi, not in animals. As a result, the most dominant food sources for detritivores will be dead plants and plant parts, and the dominant detritivores will be bacteria and fungi. A central problem faced by detritivores is that dead plants are rich in carbon and energy but poor in nitrogen. In other words, dead logs are great for the campfire but not for dinner. Dead plant litter is of lower quality (where quality refers to N content) than living plants (fig. 7.9), and we have already seen that live plants are low in N relative to the organisms that feed upon them (fig. 7.8). Why might dead leaves contain less N than living leaves? Nitrogen, unlike light energy, can be recycled within a plant. It is often the most limiting nutrient for plant growth in natural systems. As a result, there has been strong selection acting on plants to increase their **nitrogen use efficiency (NUE)**. NUE represents how much plants are able to grow per unit of nitrogen. One mechanism to improve NUE is to reabsorb nitrogen contained in plant organs, such as leaves, before the leaves are dropped from the plant, leaving a nitrogen-poor substrate for the detritivores.

Detritivores have preferred food sources, which, not surprisingly, will tend to be fruits, dead animals, and other organic matter with relatively high concentrations of nitrogen. Recycling of nitrogen by plants, in contrast, creates a poor food source and slows down the recycling rate of leaf litter by detritivores. However, as a leaf begins to decompose and is converted to bacterial and fungal biomass, the C:N decreases, and it becomes a relatively better food source for detritivorous animals, accelerating final decomposition.

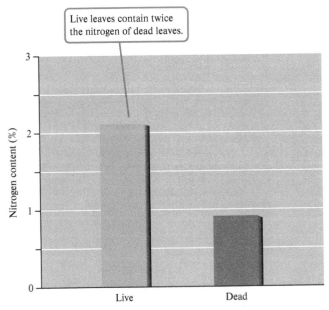

Figure 7.9 Nitrogen content of live and dead leaves.
Data from Killingbeck and Whitford 1996.

Because of the importance that size plays in influencing the feeding ecology of these species, terrestrial detritivores are often classified by their size, rather than solely by their taxonomic affiliation. Across species, detritivore body sizes range from less than one micrometre for some bacteria to over two metres for some giant earthworms. Most detritivorous animals are small. The smallest (microfauna) live primarily within films of water that adhere to soil or detrital particles. The slightly larger mesofauna tend to be found in larger pore spaces within the soil, while the macrofauna, such as earthworms, are able to create habitat through their movement. In addition to creating pore spaces in the soil, these larger classes of detritivores are also active in converting large fragments of litter (e.g., dead leaves) into small fragments, facilitating the feeding of the smaller detritivores.

Due to the relatively high abundance of plants in most communities, the abundance of food is not usually limiting to the growth of detritivorous species. Instead, the abiotic environment and chemical composition of the dead material have more direct impacts. In particular, limited soil moisture greatly reduces the activity and growth of the smaller detritivores, particularly the microfauna that live within water films. As for most ectotherms (chapter 5), increased soil temperatures will increase body temperatures and enzymatic activity of detritivores; however, if this is coupled with reduced soil moisture, many species will become dormant or will move to cooler and moister areas within the soil (i.e., shaded, deeper, etc.).

Herbivores

While a herd of elk grazing in the foothills of Alberta (fig. 7.10) or a sea turtle munching on sea grass in a tropical lagoon may suggest a life of ease, this image does not accurately represent the life of a herbivore. To only a slightly less severe extent than detritivores, herbivores face substantial problems related to nutritional chemistry; again, most plant tissues contain a great deal of carbon but low concentrations of nitrogen (fig. 7.8). A hint of the difficulties faced by herbivores comes when we realize that cattle have multiple stomachs, the gut lengths of vertebrate herbivores are generally longer than the gut lengths of vertebrate carnivores, and many insects have specific enzymes that detoxify their food.

As with detritivores, herbivores come in a variety of shapes and sizes. The size of food (e.g., litter fragment) that a detritivore eats is often strongly related to its size. This relationship does not hold up for herbivores, where individuals of greatly different sizes may all eat the same parts of the same plant. For example, when you commit the herbivorous act of biting into an apple, you are likely aware of the chance that a smaller herbivore, the larvae of the codling moth (*Carpocapsa* spp.), may itself already be consuming that fruit. You may be less aware that on the surface of that fruit a variety of mites, aphids, and other insects may have been, or still are, consuming the same apple. In other words, a single part of a plant can be a food for animals of dramatically different sizes. If you were instead to consume a different part of a plant, such as plant leaves in a

Figure 7.10 Herbivores of greatly different sizes can feed upon the same plant tissues. Although here we can see an elk feeding upon the plants beneath it, not seen are multiple smaller organisms likely feeding in and upon the same tissues.
Brent Moores/Getty Images.

salad, you would, once again, likely be consuming a diversity of animals and fungi along with the plant tissue. Many of these animals were likely themselves busily eating away before you ruthlessly put them and their host plant into your salad bowl. These herbivores include other species of aphids, leafhoppers, caterpillars, beetles, mites, and ants. Aside from the small herbivores that were hoping to share your lunch, there may also have been deer and rabbits snacking in your garden before you arrived. We can learn many things from these examples. First, the idea that a person could ever create a diet completely devoid of the consumption of living animals is, well, not biologically plausible. Second, the differences in the species composition of the herbivores found on different plant tissues are not just random events. Instead, different plant tissues are structurally and chemically dissimilar, even within a single plant. Because of these differences, you will find adaptations among herbivores as a function of what they eat, even if they differ greatly in size.

Herbivores must overcome a variety of chemical and physical defences presented by plants before they are able to derive nutrition from their vegetarian diet. For example, the use of cellulose and lignin to strengthen plant tissues increases the C:N ratios of these tissues (fig. 7.11), decreasing their value to herbivores as a food source—or even preventing small mouthparts of many insects from penetrating the plant tissue. Even if the lignin and cellulose are ingested, most animal species do not possess the enzymes needed to fully digest these compounds. As a result, the time and energy spent feeding on these plant tissues returns little energetic gain due to the relative unsuitability of the food source, even for herbivores. This has likely contributed to rarity of species that specialize feeding on the least nutritious of plant parts—bark, roots, and stem tissues—at least in comparison to the diversity of species that feed on

leaves, fruits, and seeds. This pattern is roughly analogous to the relatively low diversity of species we find in environments with harsh conditions (chapter 22). Nonetheless, many species do survive eating only (well, at least primarily!) plant tissues. How do animals overcome the problem of consuming food that contains such high C:N ratios?

One way of looking at a vegetarian diet is as a search for rare essential nutrients hidden within a sea of carbon. For animals that eat whole tissues (as opposed to fluid feeders, such as aphids), an essential first step will be the physical disintegration of the ingested food. This can be the crushing of a seed by a bird in its beak, or repeated bouts of chewing by large ungulates. This process increases the surface area exposed to digestive enzymes and liberates nutrients. The gut of many herbivores is home to a diverse collection of microbial **symbionts**. These bacteria, fungi, and protists are able to digest cellulose and other complex plant compounds, converting them into new microbes. Essentially, they are a community of detritivores living in the gut of the herbivore. The physical processing by the herbivore makes it easier for these endosymbionts to use the plant material. The herbivore host, in turn, digests the dead microbes, which can be the source of over 50% of the available N absorbed by ungulates. Despite the actions of endosymbionts, and the adaptations associated with increasing surface area for digestion and absorption, plants remain a relatively poor food for most animals. As a result, individual animals generally need to consume large amounts of material, with only a small proportion of the ingested food being fully digested. For example, the feces and urine of domestic cattle generally represent over 80% of the weight of their ingested food. In other words, most of what a large herbivore puts into its mouth simply comes out the other end. Ah, the magic of a high-fibre diet!

We should also think about herbivory as an ecological interaction from the plant's perspective. The day it is eaten is a bad day for almost any organism. Herbivory should then act as a strong selective force in the evolution of plant defences. In fact, chemists have identified thousands of toxins from a diversity of plant species understood to deter herbivory. These toxins, in turn, act as a strong selective force on herbivores. Herbivores possess different physiological mechanisms to detoxify these chemicals. This could be as simple as having an alkaline pH to neutralize some compounds, to more elaborate adaptations, such as mixed function oxidases (MFOs), which detoxify a variety of compounds. Moreover, many herbivores make behavioural choices that allow them to eat better food, both in terms of nutrient content and of reduced toxicity. Some of these examples will be discussed in chapter 8 (Behavioural Ecology) and chapter 14 (Herbivory and Predation). In chapter 14 we will also consider some outcomes of the evolutionary arms race between plants and herbivores.

Carnivores

In contrast to detritivores and herbivores, carnivores consume prey that are nutritionally rich and with a chemical composition similar to themselves. However, just as selection has favoured plant defences against herbivory, so too has selection favoured prey defences against predators. In chapter 14 we will

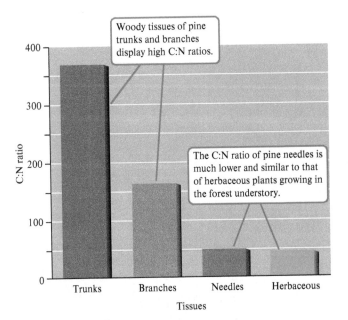

Figure 7.11   C:N ratios differ a great deal among the tissues of pines and between the woody tissues of pines and those of herbaceous plants on the forest floor.
Data from Klemmedson 1975.

discuss a variety of specific adaptations that are common to prey species and that help reduce predation. Here we focus on the predator. Just like detritivores and herbivores, carnivores vary greatly in size and include predatory nematodes, mites, beetles, birds, and mammals (fig. 7.12).

In contrast to the wildly variable C:N ratios within the tissues of an individual plant (fig. 7.11), there is very little variation in C:N ratios across different animal species. As a result, different prey species available to a single carnivore are fairly similar in nutrient content, meaning that changes in diet composition have relatively minor nutritional impacts on carnivores. Consequently, there can be substantial variation in the diets of individuals within a single population of carnivores, as well as variation among populations across the entire range that a particular species occupies.

Because predators must catch and subdue their prey, they often select prey by size, a behaviour that ecologists call **size-selective predation**. Because of this, prey size is often correlated with predator size, especially among solitary predators. Why should prey and predator size be correlated? Large prey may be difficult to subdue and may even injure the predator, while small prey may be difficult to find or catch, and the return is small if the prey is only snack sized. Larger predators may be able to capture larger prey with less risk of injury, while for a smaller predator the risk of injury may outweigh the benefit of a larger meal. As an example, the puma (*Felis concolor*) ranges from the Canadian Yukon to the tip of South America. Puma size changes substantially along this latitudinal gradient. Large mammals, especially deer, are its main prey in the northern part of its range in North America. However, Augustin

Figure 7.12 Predators come in a diversity of shapes and sizes.

Fish: Bob Semple; wolverine: Visceralimage/Dreamstime.com/GetStock.com; mountain lion: Brand X Pictures/PunchStock; malachite kingfisher: Digital Vision/PunchStock; praying mantis: IT Stock/PunchStock; crab: Bonfire007/Dreamstime.com/Getstock.com.

Iriarte and his colleagues (1990) found that as pumas decrease in size southward, the average size of their prey also decreases (fig. 7.13). Habitat characteristics can modulate size-selective predation. Luke Anderson and John Reynolds at Simon Fraser University studied size-selective predation by bears (*Ursus arctos* and *U. americanus*) on chum (*Oncorhynchus keta*) and pink (*O. gorbuscha*) salmon in streams along the central coast of British Columbia (fig 7.14). Bears selectively captured larger than average fish, but this bias was less pronounced in streams that offered salmon refuge (e.g., streams with more pools, undercut banks, and woody debris) (Andersson and Reynolds, 2017). Size-selective predation shaped the size distribution of salmon in the stream populations, but the study demonstrated that habitat characteristics can alleviate this selective pressure on the prey population.

Now let's turn from typical heterotrophs, such as wolves and pumas, to organisms that obtain their energy from inorganic molecules. These are the chemosynthetic autotrophs. Though less familiar to most of us, chemosynthesis may be one of the world's oldest professions.

Chemosynthetic Autotrophs

In the late 1960s, in the wake of the space race and on the heels of the first moon landing, the international community turned also toward further exploration of our own planet—specifically, the deep ocean. The Intergovernmental Oceanographic Commission, under the auspices of the United Nations Educational, Scientific, and Cultural Organization (UNESCO) declared an International Decade of Ocean Exploration (1971–1980). The program was intended to increase knowledge of the ocean and its resources, enhance their use for peaceful purposes, and allow rational planning and management of increased use. An unusual confluence of interests led to some of the most audacious research in earth science to date. The U.S. National Academy of Science agreed to co-fund a high-risk joint program with the French government for deep-sea exploration, exploring the floor for seismic activity and evidence of plate tectonics. The U.S. Navy was still grappling with the tragic loss of the nuclear submarine the *Thresher* in 1963, sinking in 2,500 metres of water and taking the lives of 127 crew members. The Navy was investing heavily in rapid deployment deep-sea search-and-rescue equipment, including a deep-sea sonar and camera system called Deep Tow. Deep Tow led to many important scientific discoveries, including a surprise find during the Southtow expedition in 1972, in which cameras found circular mounds and detected seismic activity (mini-quakes) suggestive of hydrothermal activity.

Returning to the area in 1977, an expedition towing a deep sea sled captured some 3,000 colour photos, including 13 that would change our understanding of the ocean and, indeed, the nature of life in profound ways. These photos included a lava flow covered with hundreds of clam and mussel shells, taken as the sled passed through a thermal anomaly on the sea floor. The submersible *Alvin* was deployed to further explore this area, and the biological diversity discovered was staggering. Ecologists had long assumed that photosynthesis provides the energy for nearly all life in the sea. However, these scientists aboard the *Alvin* entered a world based upon an entirely different energy source: energy captured by chemosynthesis. The world they discovered is inhabited by giant worms up to 4 m long with no digestive tracts, by filter-feeding clams, and by carnivorous crabs tumbling over each other in tangled abundance (chapter 3). These organisms live on nutrients discharged by deep-sea volcanic activity through an oceanic rift, a crack in the sea floor. Interconnected systems of rifts extend tens of thousands of kilometres along the sea floor. Subsequent explorations have confirmed that chemosynthetic communities exist at many points of volcanic discharge along the sea floor.

The autotrophs upon which these submarine oases depend are chemosynthetic bacteria. Some of the most common are

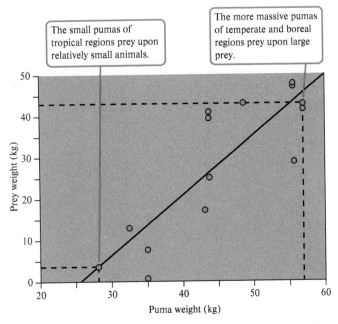

Figure 7.13   The size of pumas and their prey change with latitude.

Data from Iriarte et al. 1990.

Figure 7.14   Brown bears (*Ursus arctos*) exhibit size-selective predation.

moodboard/Glow Images.

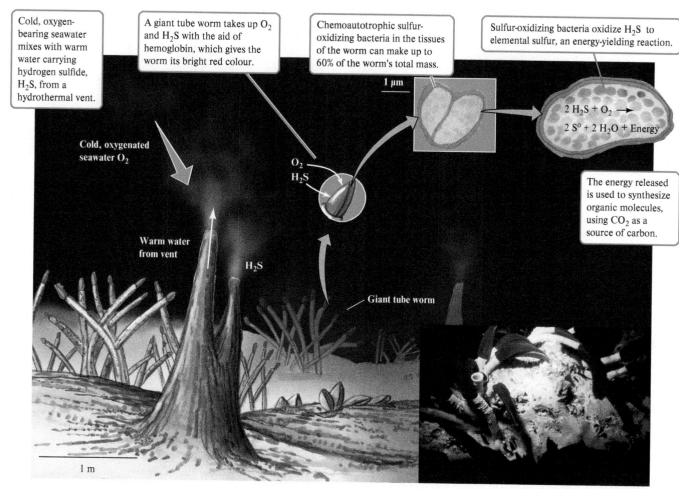

Figure 7.15   Hydrogen sulfide as an energy source for chemoautotrophic bacteria in the deep sea. Inlay is photo of giant tube worms at a deep sea thermal vent in the Pacific Ocean

Inlay: OAR/National Undersea Research Program (NURP)/College of William & Mary/NOAA.

sulfur oxidizers, bacteria that use CO_2 as a source of carbon and get their energy by oxidizing elemental sulfur, hydrogen sulfide, or thiosulfite. The submarine volcanic vents with which these organisms are associated discharge large quantities of sulfide-rich warm water. The sulfur-oxidizing bacteria that exploit this resource around the vents are of two types: free-living forms and those that live within the tissues of a variety of invertebrate animals, including the giant tube worms (fig. 7.15). Other communities dependent upon sulfur-oxidizing bacteria have been discovered in thermal vents in deep freshwater lakes, in surface hot springs, and in caves.

Other chemosynthetic bacteria oxidize ammonium, nitrite, iron (Fe^{2+}), manganese (Mn^{2+}), methane (CH_4), hydrogen (H_2), or carbon monoxide (CO). Of these, the nitrifying bacteria, which oxidize ammonium to nitrite and nitrite to nitrate, are undoubtedly among the most ecologically important organisms in the biosphere, given their role in cycling nitrogen. As we saw earlier in this chapter, nitrogen is a key element in the chemical makeup of individual organisms. It also plays a central role in the economy of the entire biosphere. In the Ecological Tools and Approaches section of this chapter, we will see how bacteria can be used to remediate polluted areas.

Mixotrophy and Omnivory

In this chapter we have presented species as if each has only a single way of capturing energy. Though this will be true for many species, others are able to exploit more than one source of carbon. One group of organisms that you are likely familiar with are the **omnivores**. These species are able to gain energy from, and regularly consume, both plant and animal matter. Humans, of course, are a good example of omnivores, with teeth suited both for biting (incisors) and grinding (molars). Grizzly bears are another example and are able to include berries, roots, small mammals, and fish in their diets.

A similar group of organisms, though less well known and studied, are the **mixotrophs**. Mixotrophic species are able to gain energy both from photosynthesis and from consuming organic or inorganic compounds. A variety of algae, bacteria, and protist species are mixotrophs. One of the best examples of mixotrophy in the wild comes from Quebec. David Bird and Jacob Kalff, both from McGill University, determined that four common species of the lake alga *Dinobryon* (fig. 7.16) consumed substantial amounts of bacteria (Bird and Kalff 1986). In a detailed study testing the feeding rates of different planktonic species, they

Figure 7.16 Algal species of the genus *Dinobryon* not only photosynthesize but are also efficient predators of bacteria.
blickwinkel/Alamy Stock Photo.

found *Dinobryon* could consume bacteria at a rate similar to non-photosynthetic predators, such as rotifers. Further, they estimate that, under low light conditions, up to 50% of the carbon obtained by the alga comes from feeding upon bacteria, rather than from photosynthesis! There is likely a very large number of tiny organisms that are mixotrophs, although, like the small species found in the soil, this remains a black hole of ecological research.

Another group of organisms that occupy an unusual trophic position are the carnivorous plants. Less than 1,000 species of vascular plants fall into this group, with fewer than 50 occurring in North America. Canada is home to several species of carnivorous plants, including bladderworts, sundews, and pitcher plants (fig. 7.17). These species tend to be restricted to aquatic (bladderworts) or low nitrogen environments, such as bogs and fens. For these plants, predation is not about the carbon but, rather, about the nitrogen. Digestion of insects results in significant increases in the nitrogen that these plants are able to capture.

As you can see, the trophic diversity among organisms is great. However, at least one ecological characteristic is shared by all organisms, regardless of the trophic group to which they belong—all organisms take in energy at a limited rate.

Figure 7.17 Pitcher plants are carnivorous, typically capturing insects for their nitrogen. The plant shown here is a member of the family Nepenthaceae, found in Southeast Asia, but members of the family Sarracenia are found in North America, including in Canada.
Getty Images/iStockphoto.

7.2 Energy and Nutrient Limitation

The rates at which organisms can take in energy and nutrients are limited. Imagine that when you are at your hungriest, you go with your friends and family to an all-you-can-eat buffet. The food is amazing, and not just because you are hungry. How much might you eat? At some point, the quantity of food is no longer the limitation. There are limits to what you will eat. You only have so much time and stomach capacity, and of course those plates are little. Physical and physiological limitations on consumption are common to all species, even in the presence of an unlimited supply of resources (light, prey, etc.). Limits on rates of energy intake by plants have been demonstrated by studying how photosynthetic rate responds to photon flux density. Limits on the potential rate of energy and nutrient intake by animals have been demonstrated by studying how feeding rate increases as the availability of food increases.

CONCEPT 7.1 REVIEW

1. What are the principle similarities between how photosynthetic, chemoautotrophic, and heterotrophic organisms capture energy from their "food" sources?

2. Why can many different sizes of herbivores consume a single leaf when it is alive, while there is strong size bias in which detritivores can consume that same leaf when it dies?

3. How can a diverse community of animals be supported around hydrothermal vents deep in the ocean where photosynthesis cannot provide the base of the food web?

Photon Flux and Photosynthetic Response Curves

Plant physiologists generally test the photosynthetic potential of plants in environments that are ideal for the particular species being studied. These environments have abundant nutrients and water, normal concentrations of oxygen and carbon dioxide, ideal temperatures, and high humidity. If you gradually increase the intensity of light shining on plants growing under these conditions, that is, if you increase the photon flux density, the plants' rates of photosynthesis gradually increase and then level off. Organisms that show this type of photosynthetic response curve include terrestrial plants, lichens, planktonic algae, and benthic algae.

The photosynthetic response curves of different plant species generally level off at different maximum rates of photosynthesis. This rate in figure 7.18 is indicated as P_{max}. The **irradiance**, or PFD, required to reach P_{max} will also differ among species. The irradiance required to saturate photosynthesis is shown as I_{sat}. The **light compensation point**, or LCP, is the amount of light necessary for a plant to have a zero net oxygen production. This can be seen as the x-intercept in the photosynthetic response curve. Remember that plants, like all eukaryotic organisms, undergo oxidative respiration and, thus, are continually consuming oxygen. The LCP represents the amount of light necessary for the rate of photosynthesis to equal the rate of respiration. If more light is available, the plant is producing more sugars than it consumes. If less light is available, the plant is in trouble as it is spending more sugars than it is producing. The LCP will also vary from species to species. Plants adapted to low light will have a lower LCP than species typically found in high light environments.

Differences in photosynthetic response curves have been used to divide plants into "sun" and "shade" species. The response curves of plants from shady habitats suggest selection for efficiency at low light intensities. The photosynthetic rate of shade plants levels off at lower light intensities, and they are often damaged by intense light. However, at very low light

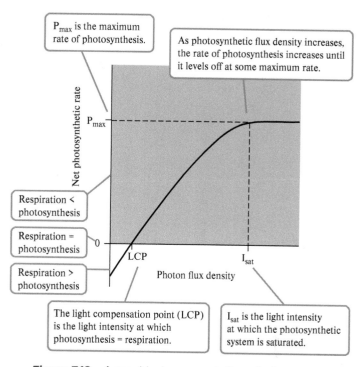

Figure 7.18 A graphical representation of a "typical" photosynthetic response curve.

intensities, shade plants usually have higher photosynthetic rates than sun plants.

The ability of seedlings to tolerate shade has important consequences for regenerating forests following the death of canopy trees. Victor Lieffers and Simon Landhausser, of the University of Alberta, have conducted extensive research into the physiological ecology of the trees of the boreal forest. In one study (Landhausser and Lieffers 2001), they grew seedlings of six species of common boreal forest trees in either the natural forest understory (shade) or in an adjacent sunny site (open). They then measured the light response curves of all the plants over two years (fig. 7.19). For nearly all species, the plants grown

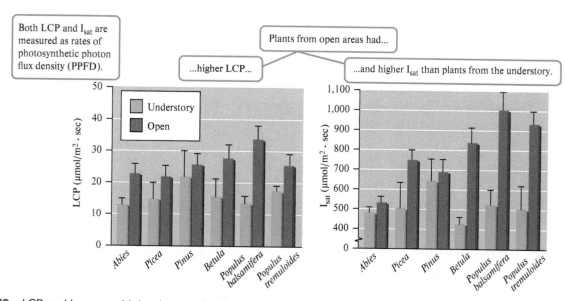

Figure 7.19 LCP and I_{max} were higher in open habitats than in understory habitats for six boreal tree species.

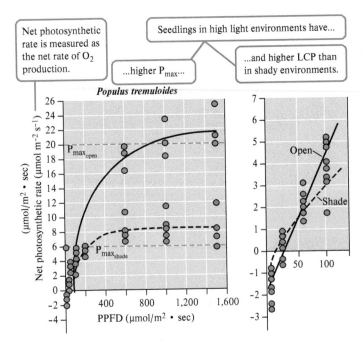

Figure 7.20 Light response curve for one tree of the boreal forest. Orange dots correspond to shade plants; and blue dots, to plants in the open. The figure on the right is an enlargement of the lower left part of the figure on the left, allowing improved visualization of the LCP differences among sun and shade plants.

under open conditions had higher rates of maximum photosynthesis (P_{max}), saturated photosynthesis at higher levels of irradiance (I_{max}), and higher light compensation points than the same species grown in the shade (fig. 7.20). This result should indicate a few things. First, this is a clear example of acclimation, as discussed in chapter 5. For most species, continued growth under high light conditions allowed them to more efficiently exploit that resource than did growth under low light conditions. Second, this is also an example of phenotypic plasticity, where a single individual has the potential to express a variety of alternative phenotypes (e.g., high or low LCP) depending upon its local environment. Finally, you may also notice that there is a physiological trade-off occurring. Increasing P_{max} is generally associated with an increase in the plant's LCP. In other words, plants that adapted to use high light levels are poorly suited to growing under low light levels. Landhausser and Lieffers have shown that such trade-offs can exist among species from a single habitat. Even more extreme differences can occur from species from different habitats.

Whether a shade or sun plant, photosynthetic response curves eventually level off. In other words, the rate at which photosynthetic organisms can take in energy is limited. As we shall now see, animals also take in energy and nutrients at a limited rate.

Food Density and Animal Functional Response

If you gradually increase the amount of food available to a hungry animal, its rate of feeding increases and then levels off. This

relationship between food availability and feeding rate is called the **functional response**. Ecologists use graphs to describe functional responses. C. S. Holling, a former professor of zoology at the University of British Columbia (1959), described three types of functional responses. Though all three forms level off at a maximum feeding rate at high prey densities, they differ in the shape of the curve at low and intermediate prey densities (fig. 7.21).

Type 1 functional responses are those in which feeding rate increases linearly (as a straight line) as food density increases and then levels off abruptly at some maximum feeding rate. The only animals that are known to have type 1 functional responses are consumers that require little or no time to process their food: for example, some filter-feeding aquatic animals that feed on small prey.

In a type 2 functional response, feeding rate at first rises linearly at low food densities, rises more slowly at intermediate food densities, and then levels off at high densities. At low food densities, feeding rate appears limited by how long it takes the animal to find food. At intermediate food densities, the animal's feeding rate is partly limited by the time spent searching for food and partly by the time spent handling food. "Handling" refers to such activities as cracking the shells of nuts or snails, removing distasteful scent glands from prey, and chasing down elusive prey. At high food density, an animal does not have to

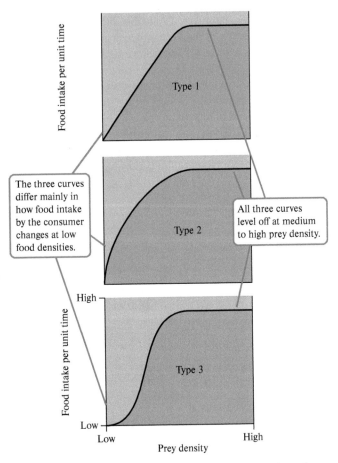

Figure 7.21 Three theoretical response curves describe the relationship between prey density and feeding rate.

search for food at all and the feeding rate is determined almost entirely by how fast the animal can handle its food. At these very high densities, the animal, in effect, has "all the food it can handle."

The type 3 functional response is S-shaped. At low food densities, type 3 functional response curves increase slowly. Food intake then rises steeply at intermediate food densities, eventually levelling off at higher densities. What mechanisms may be responsible for the more complicated shape of the type 3 functional response? At low densities, food organisms may be better protected from predators because they occupy relatively protected habitats, or "safe sites." In addition, animals often ignore uncommon foods, focusing most of their attention on more abundant foods. Animals may also require some learning to exploit food at a maximum rate. At low food densities, the animals may not have sufficient exposure to a particular food item to fully develop their searching and handling skills. Holling's research provided a theoretical basis for later empirical studies of animal functional response.

Of the hundreds, perhaps thousands, of functional response curves described by ecologists, the most common is the type 2 functional response. For example, John Gross and colleagues (1993) conducted a study of the functional responses of 13 mammalian herbivore species. The researchers manipulated food density by offering each herbivore various densities of fresh alfalfa (*Medicago sativa*). The rate of food intake was measured as the difference between the amount of alfalfa offered to an animal at the beginning of a trial and how much was left over at the end. Gross and his colleagues ran 36 to 125 feeding trials for each herbivore species for a total of over 900 trials. Every species of herbivore examined, from lemmings to prairie dogs to moose (fig. 7.22), showed a type 2 functional response.

Type 2 functional responses are remarkably similar to the photosynthetic response curves shown by plants (see fig. 7.20) and have the same implications. Even if you provide an animal with unlimited food, its energy intake eventually levels off at some maximum rate. This is the rate at which energy intake is limited by internal rather than external constraints. What conclusions can we draw from this parallel between plants and animals? We can conclude that, even under ideal conditions, organisms as different as moose and the plants eaten by moose take in energy at a limited rate. As we shall now see, limited energy intake is a fundamental assumption of optimal foraging theory.

CONCEPT 7.2 REVIEW

1. In type 3 functional response, what mechanisms may be responsible for low rates of food intake—compared to type 1 and type 2 functional response—at low food densities?

2. Why are plants such as mosses living in the understory of a dense forest, which show higher rates of photosynthesis at low irradiance, unable to live in environments where they are exposed to full sun for long periods of time? Think not only about what you learned in this section but also about what you learned in chapter 6.

3. What conclusion can we draw from the parallel between photosynthetic response curves in plants and functional response curves of animals?

7.3 Energy and Nutrient Capture

Natural selection will influence how organisms feed, and this process can be understood through the use of optimal foraging theory. Evolutionary ecologists predict that if organisms have limited access to resources (e.g., nutrients, energy), and if these resources limit fitness, then natural selection is likely to favour individuals within a population that are more effective at acquiring the limiting resources. This prediction spawned an area of ecological inquiry called **optimal foraging theory**. Optimal foraging theory assumes that if energy supplies are limited, organisms cannot simultaneously maximize all of life's functions. Allocation of energy to growth or reproduction, for example, reduces the amount of energy available to defence. Similarly, there will be a trade-off of time allocation for most organisms. For example, a prairie dog that is feeding upon grasses cannot simultaneously stand guard, on the look-out for hawks high above. As a consequence, there must be compromises between competing demands. This inevitable conflict

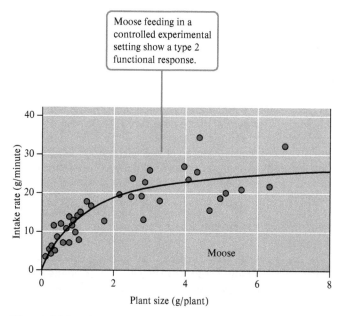

Moose feeding in a controlled experimental setting show a type 2 functional response.

Figure 7.22 An observed type 2 functional response by moose (*Alces alces*).

Data from Gross et al. 1993.

between energy allocations has been called the principle of allocation, and this is the basis for the energy budgets presented in figure 5.22. These budgets can be expanded to include "time" as a resource, resulting in "time-energy budgets." Here, however, we focus on energy, nutrients, and foraging.

Optimal foraging theory attempts to model how organisms feed as an optimizing process. In some situations, the environment may favour individuals that assimilate energy or nutrients at a high rate (e.g., some filter-feeding zooplankton and short-lived weedy annual plants growing in disturbed habitats). In other situations, selection for minimum water loss appears much stronger (e.g., cactus and scorpions in the desert). Optimal foraging theory attempts to predict what consumers will eat and when and where they will feed. Early work in this area concentrated on animal behaviour. More recently, the acquisition of energy and nutrients by plants has also been investigated as forms of foraging behaviour. It is important to recognize that optimal foraging theory is not a single "grand" idea but instead is a general approach to understanding behaviour. We will discuss two aspects: movement among patches and diet selection.

Movement Among Patches

One of the initial ideas of optimal foraging theory that drew the attention of many researchers was the **marginal value theorem**, proposed by Eric Charnov (1976). This study has been cited in over 2,800 papers, making it one of the most frequently cited papers in ecology—ever. The value of Charnov's contribution can be seen in the simplicity of the question he asked and in the elegance of the answer he provided.

Charnov was interested in understanding how long an individual organism should forage in a single location before moving to a new location. He imagined a world in which food items were organized into patches, such as Saskatoon berries on a bush or flowers on a plant. Some patches will have lots of food; others, little. The question that Charnov wanted to answer was this: When should an animal abandon the patch where it is currently feeding and move to a new one? He recognized that when an individual first reaches a patch, consumption rates will be at their maximum, as there will be lots of food remaining in the patch. However, as the individual consumes the food, the rate of intake will slow, as it will take longer to find the remaining food items. Using a series of equations, Charnov was able to predict that the optimal time to leave a patch was dependent on the time it would take to move to a new patch, on the qualities of a patch, and on aspects of the foraging environment. In general, one should stay in a patch longer if transit time to a new patch is high (fig. 7.23), if the environment is

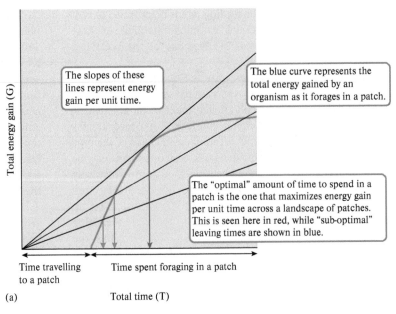

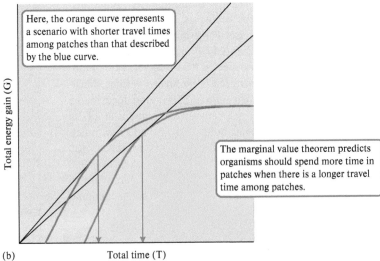

Figure 7.23 A graphical representation of the marginal value theorem. The x-axis represents the total time spent foraging, which includes both travel to a patch and time spent in a patch. The y-axis represents the total amount of energy gained by the organism as a function of time spent foraging. (*a*) The rate of energy gain can be calculated as the slope of G/T. This value is maximized at the point where a line drawn from the origin is tangential to the gain curve. The optimal time to spend in the patch is determined by the value of the x-axis directly below the point of intersection. (*b*) Here we see two possible scenarios: short travel time (orange) and longer travel time (blue). The optimal foraging strategy is to spend less time in a single patch when travel times are shorter.

generally low in food items, or if a selected patch is particularly high value.

The marginal value theorem has been tested hundreds of times in a diversity of species. Though its predictions do not hold for all organisms under all conditions, it remains a central concept in understanding how animals move among food patches in a heterogeneous world. Another productive avenue of research has been to use optimal foraging theory to predict the composition of animal diets.

Diet Composition

When ecologists determine what prey a consumer might eat, they try to identify the prey attributes that may affect the rate of energy intake by the predator. One of the most important factors is the abundance of a potential food item. All things being equal, a more abundant prey item yields a larger energy return than an uncommon prey. In optimal foraging studies, prey abundance is generally expressed as the number of the prey encountered by the predator per unit of time, N_e. Another prey attribute is the amount of energy, or costs, expended by the predator while searching for prey, C_s. A third characteristic of potential prey that could affect the energy return to the predator is the time spent processing prey in activities such as cracking shells, fighting, removing noxious scent glands, and so forth. Time spent in activities such as these are summarized as handling time, H. Ecologists ask, given the searching and handling capabilities of an animal and a certain array of available prey, do animals select their diet in a way that yields the maximum rate of energy intake? We can rephrase this question mathematically by incorporating the terms for prey encounter rate, N_e, searching costs, C_s, and handling time, H, into a model.

One of the most basic questions that we might ask about feeding by a predator concerns the number of prey items that should be included in its diet. Put another way, what mix of prey can a predator consume that will maximize its energy intake, while minimizing the time it spends feeding? Should it feed upon the common but low nutritive value prey items? How about the rare but high-quality items? Maybe the predator should simply be a **generalist**, eating everything it can find. As you may recognize, the answer to this question is going to depend on the specific costs and benefits of consuming each prey type.

Early work on this question was published by MacArthur and Pianka (1966) and Charnov (1973) and several others. We can represent the rate of energy intake of a predator as E/T, where E is energy and T is time. Earl Werner and Gary Mittelbach (1981) modelled the rate of energy intake for a predator feeding on a single prey species as follows:

$$\frac{E}{T} = \frac{N_{e1}E_1 - C_s}{1 + N_{e1}H_1}$$

In this equation, N_{e1} is the number of prey (1) encountered per unit of time. E_1 is the energy gained by feeding on an individual of prey 1 minus the costs of handling. C_s is the cost of searching for the prey. H_1 is the time required for "handling" an individual prey (1). Once again, this equation expresses the net rate at which a predator takes in energy when it feeds on a particular prey species.

What would be the rate of energy intake if the predator fed on two types of prey? The rate is calculated as follows:

$$\frac{E}{T} = \frac{(N_{e1}E_1 - C_s) + (N_{e2}E_2 - C_s)}{1 - N_{e1}H_1 + N_{e2}H_2}$$

This is an extension of the first equation. Here, we have added encounter rates for prey 2 (N_{e2}), the energetic return from feeding on prey 2 (E_2), and the handling time for prey 2 (H_2).

The searching costs, C_s, are assumed to be the same for prey 1 and prey 2.

Optimal foraging theory predicts that a predator will feed exclusively on prey 1, ignoring other available prey, when:

$$\frac{N_{e1}E_1 - C_s}{1 + N_{e1}H_1} > \frac{(N_{e1}E_1 - C_s) + (N_{e2}E_2 - C_s)}{1 + N_{e1}H_1 + N_{e2}H_2}$$

This expression says that the rate of energy intake is greater if the predator feeds only on prey 1. If the predator feeds on both prey species, the rate will be lower. If feeding on two prey species gives the predator a higher rate of energy intake than feeding on just one (i.e., if the term on the right of the equation is greater than the term on the left), optimal foraging theory predicts that predators will include the second prey species in their diet. The term on the right of the equation could readily be expanded to include any number of prey species, but to illustrate the predictions of optimal foraging theory in a simple way, we consider here just the first two species. The general prediction is that predators will continue to add different types of prey to their diet until the rate of energy intake reaches a maximum. This is called **optimization**.

Now let's get back to our basic question: Do animals select food in a way that maximizes their rate of energy intake? Testing such a prediction requires a great deal of information. Fortunately, mathematical models such as this one help focus experiments and observations on a few key variables.

Foraging by Bluegill Sunfish

Some of the most thorough tests of optimal foraging theory have been conducted on the bluegill sunfish (*Lepomis macrochirus*). The bluegill is a medium-sized fish native to eastern and central North America, where it inhabits a wide range of freshwater habitats, from small streams to the shorelines of small and large lakes. Bluegills feed mainly on benthic and planktonic crustaceans and aquatic insects, prey that differ in size and habitat and in ease of capture and handling. Bluegills often choose prey by size, feeding on organisms of certain sizes and ignoring others. This behaviour is convenient because it gives the ecologist a relatively simple measure to describe the composition of the available prey and the composition of the theoretically optimal diet.

Werner and Mittelbach used published studies to estimate the amount of energy expended by bluegills while they search for (C_s) and handle prey. They used laboratory experiments to estimate handling times (H) and encounter rates (N_e) for various prey. For these laboratory experiments, they constructed approximations of the places where bluegills forage in nature: open water, sediments, and vegetation. These model habitats were constructed in large aquaria and stocked with some of the important prey of bluegills: damselfly larvae, midge larvae, and *Daphnia*. These experiments showed that encounter rates increase as fish size, prey size, and prey density increase, and that handling time depends on the relative sizes of predator and prey. Small bluegills require a relatively long time to handle large prey, while large bluegills expend little time handling small prey.

The energy content of prey was calculated by measuring the lengths of prey available in lakes and ponds; prey length was converted to mass, and then mass was converted to energy content using published values. With this information, Werner and Mittelbach characterized the prey available in Lawrence Lake, Michigan, and then estimated the diet that would maximize the rate of energy intake. They then sampled the bluegills of Lawrence Lake and examined their stomach contents to see how closely their diet approximated the diet predicted by optimal foraging theory.

The upper graph in figure 7.24 shows the size distribution of potential prey in vegetation in Lawrence Lake. The middle graph shows the composition of the optimal diet as predicted by the optimal foraging model just presented. Finally, the bottom graph shows the actual composition of the diets of bluegills from Lawrence Lake. Bluegills feeding in vegetation selected prey that were uncommon and larger than average. The match between the optimal diet and the prey that bluegills in Lawrence Lake actually ate seems uncanny. A similar match was obtained for bluegills feeding on zooplankton in open water.

Werner and Mittelbach found that optimal foraging theory provides reasonable predictions of prey selection by natural populations of bluegills. Ecologists studying plants have developed an analogous predictive framework for foraging by plants.

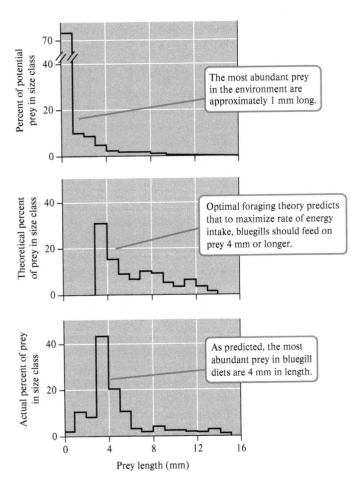

Figure 7.24 Optimal foraging theory predicts composition of bluegill sunfish diets.

Data from Werner and Mittelbach 1981.

Optimal Foraging by Plants

Do plants forage? When we think of foraging, fish, elk, wolves, and squirrels often come to mind. But in its most basic sense, foraging is simply the search for and acquisition of resources, something that all organisms do, including plants. The more interesting question, then, is not whether plants forage (they do), but instead whether plants are able to exhibit some form of optimality, similar to what we saw with the sunfish.

How do plants forage? Quite simply, they put their resource-capturing organs (leaves and roots) in the locations that have the resources. Selection should favour plants that put those organs in areas of high resource availability and not in areas of low resource availability.

As we consider resource-capturing organs in plants, we can simplify plants by dividing them into two parts: (1) shoots, which acquire light; and (2) roots, which acquire mineral resources and water. Using economic theory, Arnold Bloom and colleagues (Bloom et al. 1985) suggested that plants will adjust their allocation of energy to growth in such a way that all resources are equally limited. This idea is itself related to Liebig's law of the minimum, in which Justus von Liebig postulated that plant growth will be limited by the scarcest essential resource rather than the total amount of resources available to a plant. Therefore, Bloom reasoned that if light limits plant growth, plants would invest more energy in growth of shoots and less in roots. If instead soil resources are more limiting than light, plants would be expected to increase root growth relative to shoot growth. There have been numerous experimental tests of these predictions. Most experiments generally consist of growing a certain species of plant under high and low nutrient conditions. After a given period of time, the plant is harvested, and root and shoot biomass are weighed. In one **meta-analysis**, Heather Reynolds and Carla D'Antonio (1996) found that in 75% of the 206 cases they surveyed, plants had relatively less root growth under high nitrogen conditions than under low nitrogen conditions. This result was further supported by Nichole Levang-Brilz and Mario Biondini (2002), who found that root:shoot ratios of 62% of the 55 species they tested decreased when nitrogen was added to the soil. These studies show that across a large number of species, plants do alter their relative production of roots and shoots in response to the relative abundance of mineral resources, in a manner consistent with optimal foraging theory. Although altering root:shoot ratios themselves are one means by which plants can adjust their foraging strategy to match the local conditions, it is not a particularly precise one. Instead, you could imagine that within the soil surrounding an individual plant, there will be some patches of soil that are enriched in nutrients relative to the rest of the area, perhaps due to urination by a local herbivore. These enriched patches are likely short-lived, either washed away in the rain or exploited by the surrounding plants. If these patches are common in natural systems, selection may have favoured mechanisms for their exploitation—something more elegant than the blunt hammer approach of altered root:shoot ratio.

M.C. Drew, of Letcombe Laboratory in England, conducted the first of what would lead to many studies on the ability of plants to alter their root growth in response to small-scale variation in nutrient distributions (Drew 1975). Drew grew barley plants in pots filled with sand, through which he continuously irrigated a nutrient solution. In a very clever experimental design, Drew divided the pots into three vertical compartments and was able to give different parts of the root system different levels of nutrients. What he found was striking. Plants grew roots relatively uniformly in response to a uniform distribution of nutrients, while they proliferated roots in zones of high nutrients compared to zones of low nutrients. In other words, plants were able to alter the distribution of their foraging organs in response to differences in the distribution of resources! This is a form of optimal foraging.

Since Drew's study, ecologists have been working furiously to determine how widespread this phenomenon is and whether it has any general ecological consequences. A critical step in this process has been the documentation that most natural communities are inherently heterogeneous in soil nutrient distributions, a finding summarized by Martin Lechowicz and Graham Bell of McGill University (Lechowicz and Bell 1991). They show that in many natural communities, nutrient levels can vary by orders of magnitude within the rooting zone of an individual plant. This indicates that the potential for evolution of foraging in plants exists, as the selective environment favouring precise root placement is likely widespread. At the same time, there have been countless experiments using a large number of plant species replicating Drew's basic design, though generally varying nutrients horizontally rather than vertically. In a recent paper by one of this book's authors and a former graduate student, Steve Kembel, we attempted to summarize this literature (Kembel and Cahill 2005). We compiled data for over 125 plant species and subjected them to a meta-analysis. On average, plants placed approximately twice as many roots in areas of high nutrient availability than in areas of low nutrient availability. Additionally, most species were significantly larger when grown in heterogeneous soil than when grown under uniform conditions. In short, most plants can forage, and when given the opportunity to do so, they perform better than under uniform conditions.

CONCEPT 7.3 REVIEW

1. According to optimal foraging theory, under what conditions should a predator add a new prey species to its diet?

2. Do patterns of feeding by bluegills include any evidence that these consumers ignore certain potential prey?

3. What ecological conditions likely favour the evolution of optimal foraging in plants?

ECOLOGY IN ACTION

Using Ecological Knowledge to Predict C₄ Plant Distributions in a Changing World

C_3 and C_4 plants possess different photosynthetic pathways (figs. 7.4 and 7.5) and, as a result, perform differently under different temperature and moisture conditions. This interaction between plant physiology and abiotic conditions has profound implications for population growth and the geographic distribution of plants. For example, a clear latitudinal gradient currently exists in the distribution of C_4 plants, with C_4 plants representing an increasing proportion of the local flora as we move away from the poles and toward the equator (fig. 7.25). But the world is changing. Local and global climates are being rapidly modified through a variety of human activities, causing changes to temperatures, precipitation, and evapotranspiration in the soil. (See chapter 23 for further discussion about climate change.) A shift in local climate can exert selective pressures on the species that reside within the local community. For a plant, a debate over the causes of climate change is irrelevant to the potential selective forces associated with increased atmospheric temperatures and altered precipitation. Here we will show how a strong understanding of physiological ecology can provide insights into questions of global concern. Specifically, we will address how increased temperatures may impact global distributions of C_4 plants.

Rowan Sage at the University of Toronto is a world leader in understanding the ecology of C_4 plants. Sage has blended a variety of disciplines in his work, including evolution, physiology, chemistry, ecology, and atmospheric sciences. By having such a diverse set of tools, Sage is able to address the question of how climate change may impact C_3 and C_4 plants from a more holistic perspective than specialists in any of these individual disciplines. C_4 plants represent a relatively small fraction of the world's diversity—only 7,500 of the estimated 250,000 species of land plants (Sage 1999), with the vast majority being grasses and sedges. However, in many warm climates, C_4 plants are dominant, while decreasing in abundance as

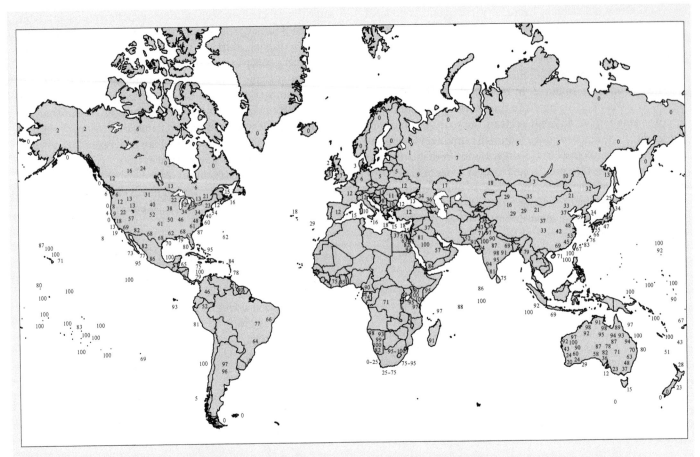

Figure 7.25   Percentage representation of C_4 grasses in grass flora from different regions of the world.
Reprinted from R. F. Sage and R. K. Monson. 1999. The biogeography of C_4. *Plant Biology* 1:316–17. With permission from Elsevier.

we move toward the poles or up in elevation. C_4 plants are responsible for approximately 25% of all plant growth on the planet (Sage and Kubien 2003) and include species of critical agronomic importance, such as corn. We have already discussed explanations for why C_4 plants can outperform C_3 plants in bright, warm conditions, but what is less clear is why they get outperformed in cooler environments. In other words, what is the cost of C_4 photosynthesis?

Recent work by Sage and colleagues (Kubien et al. 2003) suggests that the architecture of C_4 leaves has resulted in reduced RUBISCO concentrations. Under hot conditions, this is not an issue, as high levels of RUBISCO in C_3 plants also result in high levels of photorespiration, reducing C_3 efficiency. However, photorespiration is reduced under cooler conditions, and the reduced levels of RUBISCO appear to limit rates of photosynthesis in C_4 plants. In other words, there appears to be a fundamental trade-off, where the photosynthetic machinery is either optimized for warm or for cool conditions. What happens, then, when the world becomes hotter?

In analyzing current C_4 distributions, midsummer temperature is a strong correlate of C_4 plant abundance in North America, where C_4 plants are unlikely to occur if midsummer temperatures go below 10°C (fig. 7.26), or if average midsummer temperatures are below 13°C (Sage and Kubien 2003). From all of this information, it is obvious, then, that an increase in temperatures will result in a range expansion of C_4 plants, right? Not necessarily. It is here that we must step back and realize that an increase in global temperature is relatively meaningless to an individual plant or even to a particular species. What matters much more is what degree of change is found in a given locality and during what time of year this change occurs. Sage and Kubien (2003) summarize current warming trends and point out that many of the predictions regarding climate change suggest that the greatest changes will occur in the winter, rather than in the summer. This would actually result in an extended cool-growing season, favouring C_3, not C_4, plants! Even if warming does occur in the summer, if this is coupled with increased aridity, that could effectively shut down summer growth, leaving only spring and fall (the cooler seasons) for growth, again favouring C_3 plants. However, if precipitation also increases during the warmer summers, then this should increase C_4 growth at the expense of C_3 plants. In short,

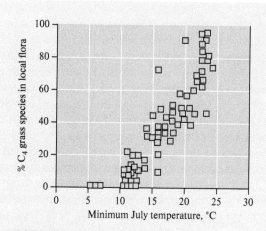

Figure 7.26   Relationship between midsummer temperature and the relative abundance of C_4 plants in North America.

Adapted from Wan and Sage (2001). *Canadian Journal of Botany*, Figure 3b, vol. 79:474–486. © Canadian Science Publishing or its licensors.

without detailed information about the exact climatic conditions a particular location is likely to experience, it will be difficult to predict the likely impact on plant distributions. This is even without considering that there are other factors at play, including fire frequency, light, CO_2 levels, and many more.

It is clear that Sage and others are not yet able to conclusively say what will happen to plants with climate change, but you should be able to see that scientists are actively working on these questions. Questions of global patterns are particularly difficult to answer, as they require integrating many disciplines as well as numerous interacting variables (e.g., temperature, water, etc.). Work by Sage, and others, provides examples that the most effective ecologists will possess a deep understanding of the basic biology of the organisms they study. Global questions are not answered solely by describing patterns, but instead they require an understanding of the functional mechanisms that generate the patterns.

ECOLOGICAL TOOLS AND APPROACHES

Bioremediation—Using the Trophic Diversity of Bacteria to Solve Environmental Problems

Imagine yourself in the centre of a densely populated region with thousands of leaky gasoline tanks or complex mine wastes contaminating the groundwater. How would you solve these environmental problems? Where would you turn for help? Increasingly, we are turning to nature's own cleanup crew: bacteria. Here, we describe how an understanding of nutritional and energetic ecology can itself serve as a research tool. Environmental managers are taking advantage of the exceptional trophic diversity of bacteria to perform a host of environmental chores.

Leaking Underground Storage Tanks

Gasoline and other petroleum derivatives are stored in underground storage tanks all over the planet. Those that leak are a serious source of pollution. Maribeth Watwood and Cliff Dahm (1992) explored the possibility of using bacteria to clean up soils and aquifers contaminated by leaking storage tanks. The first step in their work was to determine if there are naturally occurring populations of bacteria that can break down complex petroleum derivatives, such as benzene.

Watwood and Dahm collected sediments from a shallow aquifer that contained approximately 8.5×10^8 bacterial cells per gram of wet sediment. Of these, 6.55×10^4 bacterial cells per millilitre were capable of living on benzene as their only source of carbon and energy. By exposing

sediments from the aquifer to benzene for six months, the researchers increased the populations of benzene-degrading bacteria approximately 100 times.

How rapidly can these bacteria break down benzene? Watwood and Dahm found that with no prior exposure, bacterial populations could break down 90% of the benzene in their test flasks within 40 days (fig. 7.27). Exposing sediments to benzene prior to their tests increased the rate of breakdown.

Briefly, this study demonstrated that naturally occurring populations of bacteria can rapidly break down benzene leaking from underground storage tanks. This study suggests that these bacteria will eventually clean up the organic contaminants from leaking gasoline storage tanks without manipulation of the environment. However, in the next example, environmental managers found that they had to manipulate the environment to stimulate the desired bacterial cleanup of a contaminant.

Cyanide and Nitrates in Mine Spoils

Many gold mines were abandoned when they could not be mined profitably with the mining technology of the nineteenth and early twentieth centuries. Then, in the 1970s, techniques were developed to economically extract gold from low-grade ores. One of the main extraction techniques was to leach ore with cyanide (CN). Dissolved CN forms

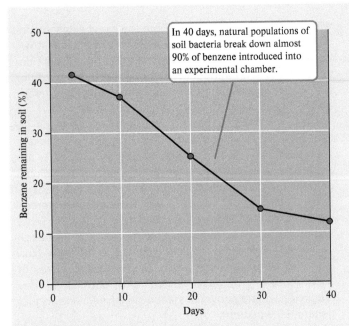

Figure 7.27 Benzene breakdown by soil bacteria.
Data from Watwood and Dahm 1992.

In 40 days, natural populations of soil bacteria break down almost 90% of benzene introduced into an experimental chamber.

chemical complexes with gold and other metals. The solution containing gold-bearing CN can be collected and the gold and CN removed by filtering the solution with activated charcoal.

This new method of mining solved a technical problem but contaminated soils and groundwater. When the leaching process is finished, the leached ore is stored in piles; however, much CN remains. Several kinds of bacteria can break down CN and produce NH_3. This NH_3 can, in turn, be used by nitrifying bacteria as an energy source, producing NO_3. Thus, leaching gold-bearing ores and subsequent microbial activity can contaminate soil and groundwater with CN, a deadly poison, and with nitrate, another contaminant.

Carleton White and James Markwiese (1994) studied a gold mine that had been worked with the CN leaching process. The leached ores from the mine were gradually releasing CN and NO_3 into the environment. The researchers looked to bacteria to solve this environmental problem. They first documented the presence of CN degraders by looking for bacterial growth in a diagnostic medium. This medium contained CN as the only source of carbon and nitrogen. Using this growth medium, White and Markwiese estimated that each gram of ore contained approximately 10^3 to 10^5 cells of organisms capable of growing on, and breaking down, CN.

The leached ores presented bacteria with a rich source of nitrogen in the form of CN and NO_3, but the ores contained little organic carbon. White and Markwiese predicted that adding a source of carbon to the residual ores would increase the rate at which bacteria break down CN and reduce the concentration of NO_3 in the environment. Why should adding organic molecules rich in carbon increase

bacterial use of nitrogen in the environment? Look back at figure 7.8, which shows that bacteria have a carbon:nitrogen ratio of about 5:1. In other words, growth and reproduction by bacteria require about five carbon atoms for each nitrogen atom.

White and Markwiese tested their ideas in the laboratory. In one experiment, they added enough sucrose to produce a C:N ratio of 10:1 within leached ores. This experiment included two controls, both of which contained leached ores without sucrose. One of the controls was sterilized to kill any bacteria. The other control was left unsterilized.

Bacteria in the treatments containing sucrose broke down all the CN within the leached ore in 13 days. Meanwhile, only a small amount of CN was broken down in the unsterilized control and no CN was broken down in the sterilized control (fig. 7.28). Why did the researchers include a sterilized control? The sterilized control demonstrated that nonbiological processes were not responsible for the observed breakdown of CN.

Figure 7.28 shows that adding sucrose to the residual ore, reducing C:N to 10:1, stimulates the breakdown of CN. However, remember that this process ultimately leads to the production of NO_3. Does adding sucrose to eliminate CN lead to the buildup of NO_3, trading one pollution problem for another? No, it does not. In another experiment, White and Markwiese (1994) showed that adding sucrose also stimulates uptake of NO_3 by heterotrophic bacteria and fungi. These organisms use organic molecules, in this case sucrose, as a source of energy and carbon, and NO_3 as a source of nitrogen. The nitrogen taken up by bacteria and fungi becomes incorporated in biomass as complex

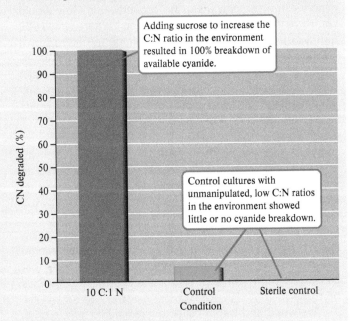

Adding sucrose to increase the C:N ratio in the environment resulted in 100% breakdown of available cyanide.

Control cultures with unmanipulated, low C:N ratios in the environment showed little or no cyanide breakdown.

Figure 7.28 Manipulating C:N ratios to stimulate breakdown of cyanide (CN).
Data from White and Markwiese 1994.

organic molecules. Nitrogen in this form is recycled within the microbial community and is not a source of environmental pollution.

White and Markwiese recommended that sucrose be added to leached gold-mining ores to stimulate breakdown of CN and uptake of NO_3 by bacteria. This environmental cleanup project was successful because the researchers were thoroughly familiar with the energy and nutrient relations of bacteria and fungi. Another key to the project's success was the great trophic diversity of bacteria. Bacteria will likely continue to play a great role as we address some of our most vexing environmental problems.

SUMMARY

7.1 Organisms use one of three main sources of energy: solar radiation, organic molecules, or inorganic molecules.

Organisms use a variety of sources of energy to support ATP production and growth, can use different sources of carbon for building biomass (CO_2 versus organic C), and must acquire nutrients from the environment. This has led to the evolution of various feeding strategies (fig. 7.29). Photosynthetic plants and algae use CO_2 as a source of carbon, and light—of wavelengths between 400 and 700 nm—as a source of energy. Light within this band, which is called photosynthetically active radiation, or PAR, accounts for about 45% of the total energy content of the solar spectrum at sea level. PAR can be quantified as photosynthetic photon flux density, generally reported as μmol m^{-2} s^{-1}. Among plants, there are three major alternative photosynthetic pathways: C_3, C_4, and CAM. C_4 and CAM plants are more efficient in their use of water than are C_3 plants, and they have reduced rates of photorespiration. However, C_3 plants may have greater photosynthetic efficiency in lower lighting or reduced oxygen concentrations.

Heterotrophs use organic molecules both as a source of carbon and as a source of energy. Herbivores, carnivores, and detritivores face fundamentally different trophic problems. Herbivores feed on plant tissues, which often contain a great deal of carbon but little nitrogen. Herbivores must also overcome the physical and chemical defences of plants. Detritivores feed on dead plant material, which is even lower in nitrogen than living plant tissues. Carnivores consume prey that are nutritionally rich but may be hard to capture. Chemosynthetic autotrophs, which consist of a highly diverse group of bacteria, use inorganic molecules as a source of energy. Bacteria are the most trophically diverse organisms in the biosphere.

7.2 The rates at which organisms can take in energy and nutrients are limited.

The relationship between photon flux density and plant photosynthetic rate is called photosynthetic response. Plants from sunny habitats have high maximum photosynthetic rates that level off at high irradiance and high light compensation points. The lowest maximum rates of photosynthesis and LCP occur among plants from shady environments. The relationship between food density and animal feeding rate is called the functional response. The shape of the functional response is generally one of three types. The forms of photosynthetic response curves and type 2 animal functional responses are remarkably similar. Energy limitation is a fundamental assumption of optimal foraging theory.

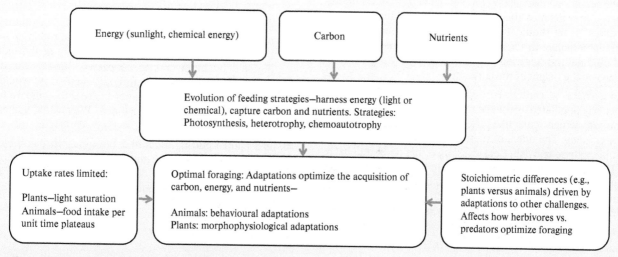

Figure 7.29 Concept map for chapter 7.

7.3 Natural selection will influence how organisms feed, and this process can be understood through the use of optimal foraging theory.

Evolutionary ecologists predict that if organisms have limited access to energy, natural selection is likely to favour individuals that are more effective at acquiring energy and nutrients. Many animals select where they feed and what they eat in a way that appears to maximize the rate at which they capture energy. Plants allocate energy to roots versus shoots in a way that increases their rate of intake of the resources that limit their growth. In environments rich in light but poor in nutrients, plants tend to invest more energy in the growth of roots.

Within a root system, root distributions will vary vertically and horizontally as a function of resource distributions.

The trophic diversity of bacteria, which is critical to the health of the biosphere, can also be used as a tool to address some of our most challenging waste disposal problems. Bacteria can be used to clean up soils and aquifers polluted by petroleum products, such as benzene, and eliminate the pollution caused by some kinds of mine waste. The success of these projects requires that ecologists understand the energy and nutrient relations of bacteria. Bacteria will likely continue to play a great role as we address some of our most vexing environmental problems.

REVIEW QUESTIONS

1. Why don't plants use highly energetic ultraviolet light for photosynthesis? Would it be impossible to evolve a photosynthetic system that uses ultraviolet light? Does the fact that many insects see ultraviolet light change your mind? Would it be possible to use infrared light for photosynthesis? (Photosynthetic bacteria tap into the near-infrared range.)

2. In what kinds of environments would you expect to find the greatest predominance of C_3, C_4, or CAM plants? How can you explain the co-occurrence of two, or even all three, of these types of plants in one area? (Think about the variations in microclimate that we considered in chapters 5 and 6.)

3. What are the relative advantages and disadvantages of being a detritivore, a herbivore, or a carnivore? What kinds of organisms were left out of our discussions of detritivores, herbivores, and carnivores? Where do parasites fit?

4. Design a planetary ecosystem based entirely on chemosynthesis. You might choose an undiscovered planet of some distant star or one of the planets in our own solar system, either today or at some distant time in the past or future.

5. What kinds of animals would you expect to have type 1, 2, or 3 functional responses? How should natural selection for better prey defence affect the height of functional response curves? How should natural selection for more effective predators affect the height of the curves? What net effect should natural selection on predator and prey populations have on the height of the curves?

6. The rivers of central Portugal have been invaded, and densely populated, by the Louisiana crayfish (*Procambarus clarkii*), which looks like a freshwater lobster about 12 to 14 cm long. The otters of these rivers can easily catch and subdue these crayfish. Consider the Werner and Mittlebach (1981) model for prey choice. Explain why the diets of the otters of central Portugal would shift from a highly diverse menu, which includes fish, frogs, water snakes, birds, and insects, to a diet dominated by crayfish. For the crayfish,

assume low handling time, very high encounter rates, and high energy content.

7. The data of Iriarte and colleagues (1990) suggest that prey size may favour a particular body size among pumas. However, this variation in body size also correlates well with latitude: the larger pumas live at high latitudes. Consequently, this variation in body size has been interpreted as the result of selection for efficient temperature regulation. Homeothermic animals are often larger at high latitudes, a pattern called Bergmann's rule. Larger animals, with lower surface area relative to their mass, would be theoretically better at conserving heat. Smaller animals, with higher surface area relative to their mass, would be theoretically better at keeping cool. So what determines predator size? Is predator size determined by climate, predator–prey interactions, or both? Design a study of the influence of the environment on the size of homeothermic predators.

8. How is plant allocation to roots versus shoots similar to plant regulation of temperature and water? (We discussed these topics in chapters 5 and 6.) Consider discussing these processes under the more general heading of homeostasis. (Homeostasis is the maintenance of a relatively constant internal environment.)

9. If herbivores are able to optimally forage, why do they not more efficiently extract resources from their food? Why has natural selection allowed for the majority of the biomass ingested by herbivores to be passed through the digestive system without being fully digested? How would you expect the C:N of plant matter in feces to compare to the C:N of the plant matter consumed? Why would you expect the change?

10. Is a plant's putting roots in a resource-rich patch but not in a low-resource patch the same as a predator's foraging in an area of high prey density but not in an area of low prey density? Is intelligence necessary for behaviour? Why or why not?

Eastcott Momatiuk/Stone/Getty Images.

CHAPTER 8   BEHAVIOURAL ECOLOGY

CHAPTER CONCEPTS

8.1 Natural selection favours those behaviours that increase the inclusive fitness of individuals.

Concept 8.1 Review

8.2 The evolution of sociality is generally accompanied by cooperative feeding, defence of the social group, and restricted reproductive opportunities.

Ecology in Action: Human–Wildlife Conflict

Concept 8.2 Review

8.3 Mate choice by one sex and/or competition for mates among individuals of the same sex can result in selection for particular traits, a process called sexual selection.

Concept 8.3 Review

Ecological Tools and Approaches: Using Game Theory to Understand Behaviour

Summary

Review Questions

During a short swim over a coral reef, you can observe a diversity of interactions among individuals of many species. At dusk, you may see a school of fish move steadily toward an opening in the reef, heading into the open sea for a night of feeding. Approached underwater, the edge of the school looks like a giant translucent curtain stamped with the silhouettes of thousands of seemingly identical fish. Their coloration—counter-shaded dark above and silvery below—their highly coordinated movements, and their great numbers give the fish within the school some protection from predators. Though seabirds and fish attack the school as it makes its way, only a small proportion of the schooling fish are eaten.

Meanwhile, along the reef, damselfish are distributed singly on territories. The damselfish retain possession of their patches of coral rubble, living coral, and sand by patrolling the boundaries and driving off any fish attempting to intrude. At certain times, some territory-holding males are joined by females, where they court and deposit eggs and sperm on the nest site prepared by the male. Where the distribution of the schooling fish was shaped by behaviour that reduces predation risk, the distribution of these male damselfish is shaped by mating behaviour.

Higher along the reef face a male bluehead wrasse mates with one of the females that live within his territory (fig. 8.1). In contrast to the male with his blue head, black bars, and green body, the female is mostly yellow with a large black spot on her dorsal fin. As the blueheaded male extrudes sperm to fertilize the eggs laid by the female, small males similar in colour to the female streak by the mating pair, discharging a cloud of sperm along the way. Some of the female's eggs will be fertilized by the large territorial blueheaded male, while others will be fertilized by the sperm discharged by the smaller yellow streakers. We thus see two types of

reproductive behaviour, even within this single species: dominance and sneakiness. We also see two distinct male morphologies that allow each of these behaviours to be successful mating strategies. Moreover, we see elaborate colours in the dominant males, driven by female reproductive behaviour, exercising mate selection. Close observation of natural history guides behavioural ecologists in their studies of how such behaviours evolve, and the relative cost and benefits of such different strategies.

Such intriguing behaviours occur all around us. In coral reefs, forests, soils, lakes, and streams, we find interactions among members of the same species that are as significant to the long-term success of the individual organism as are its interactions with temperature, food, or the quantity and quality of available water. We will see that elaborate behaviours occur not only in the large vertebrates with which we are most familiar, but also in invertebrates, plants, and even microbes. Cognition is critical for us to discuss and recognize behaviour, but cognition is not required for an organism to exhibit behaviour. Even plants exhibit behaviour, foraging nonrandomly for food (chapter 7).

Behavioural ecology is a broad field, with origins in the close observations of animals both in the wild and in captivity: natural history and animal husbandry. The scientific study of behaviour is typically called *ethology*, a subdiscipline of zoology heavily influenced by the pioneering work of Konrad Lorenz on imprinting by geese. When aspects of behaviour are integrated into ecological questions, we enter the domain of behavioural ecologists. Although ethology lies at its origin, behavioural ecology has grown to include questions related to behaviour of non-sentient organisms, including prokaryotes, protists, fungi, and plants.

In general, behavioural ecologists study the relationships between organisms and environment that are mediated by behaviour (fig. 8.2). We have already discussed many aspects of behavioural ecology in the preceding chapters, such as optimal foraging and movements associated with temperature and water regulation. Some of these behaviours are relatively easy to study, as they can be quantified. Other behaviours may be far more difficult to quantify, making behavioural ecology both an exciting and a challenging field of study. In this chapter we will explore the theoretical underpinning of behavioural ecology. We will also study issues associated with group living, and how natural selection can favour cooperation rather than competition. We will then discuss sex and mating systems, combining evolutionary, ecological, and behavioural information to study a process Charles Darwin called sexual selection. Behavioural ecology consists of many more topics than can be presented here, and issues of behaviour will be woven throughout our later chapters on species interactions, such as competition, predation, and disease. Here we present three central concepts to this fascinating field of ecology, which in combination form the framework of this chapter: (1) evolution and behaviour, (2) sociality, and (3) mating systems and mate choice.

Figure 8.1 Bluehead wrasse males with yellow females of the species. If the blueheaded male is removed from a territory, the largest female in the territory can change to a fully functional blueheaded male within days.
© Gregory G. Dimijian/Science Source.

Figure 8.2 Organisms exhibit a diversity of behaviours, which include (clockwise from upper left), foraging and vigilance, mate selection, heat regulation, and herding.

Clockwise from upper left: Courtesy of David Hik; © Timpollack–Dreamstime.com; Wu Swee Ong/Getty Images; Design Pics/Natural Selection David Ponton.

8.1 Evolution and Behaviour

Natural selection favours those behaviours that increase the inclusive fitness of individuals. In chapter 4 we presented the central aspects of Darwin's theory of natural selection, including the idea that if a given trait had a heritable component and if alternative expressions of that trait resulted in differential fitness among individuals then the frequency of that trait would increase within the population. A critical aspect of this theory is that selection acts upon *individuals*, which can cause evolution within *populations*.

When we think of natural selection, we often imagine traits such as beak size, seed number, and body size being associated with fitness and serving as the raw materials upon which selection can act. We don't usually think of behaviour. However, a variety of commonly observed behaviours have genetic bases. One of the clearest examples of this comes from collaboration by researchers at the University of Toronto, University of Illinois

at Urbana-Champaign, and the Université de Bourgogne (Ben-Shahar et al. 2002). The team of researchers was interested in the genetic control of foraging in honey bees. In honey bee colonies, worker bees work in the hive when they are young (e.g., brood care), and forage when they are older (two to three weeks later). This represents a fundamental shift in behaviour of individuals over the course of their life. The timing of this switch is not fixed but can be influenced by needs within and external to the hive. How does this switch occur? The researchers focused on a single gene, *for* (short for *foraging*), which codes for a specific protein kinase, PKG. They found that mRNA expression was significantly higher in foraging bees than in bees that remained at work in the hive. When the researchers experimentally increased PKG levels, the bees switched to foraging behaviour sooner than untreated bees. In other words, simply increasing the abundance of a single protein, coded for by a single gene, can cause a dramatic change in bee behaviour. There are numerous other examples of genetic control of behaviour, including foraging decisions of zebra finches (Lemon 1993), anti-predator movement patterns in *Daphnia* (DeMeester 1993), and even anti-competitor growth in tobacco plants (Schmitt et al. 1995). In total, these studies provide examples that complex behaviours can have a genetic basis and that cognitive "choice" is not the sole determinant of how an organism behaves.

What is the evolutionary basis for this variation in behaviour as a function of bee age? It is unknown; however, there is reason to believe that certain behaviours are more *adaptive* under some circumstances than others. For example, bees that are active foragers before the hive is constructed, or before plants are producing nectar, are likely less fit than bees that do not forage until later. Thus foraging and hive building behaviours are both adaptive behaviours; however, their value is dependent upon local conditions (the presence or absence of nectar and a suitable hive), which may correlate with animal age or developmental stage. One of the great findings in behavioural ecology over the past 50 years has been that the adaptive value of a given trait is often contingent upon the specific environmental conditions that an organism faces. The idea that *either* nature *or* nurture causes individuals to act a certain way is great for sales in the media but is sadly out of date among biologists. In other words, a squirrel exposing itself to predation risk by a hawk for a food reward makes more sense as (1) the value of the reward increases, (2) the hunger level of the squirrel increases, and (3) the probability of predation decreases. So, if we see a squirrel run after some nuts when hawks are visible, it is not fair to say that the "nature" of the squirrel is to be inherently risky; instead, the squirrel possesses the ability to *either* run after the food *or* not. Evolution may fine-tune this process by setting the threshold for risk-taking higher or lower depending upon local conditions, provided there is *intraspecific* variation in behaviours. You may recall from chapter 4 that if variations in behaviour are related to mating, they could even serve as effective isolating mechanisms leading to speciation.

At a larger level, we can see *interspecific* differences in behaviour. For example, Laurence Packer, of York University, has studied the evolution of sociality and nest architecture among several species of closely related bees (Halictidae) (Packer 1991). These species are known to vary greatly in behaviour, with social bee species forming large colonies each year, some species being completely solitary, and others forming a perennial colony. What was unknown was whether these interspecific differences were the result of multiple (and random) evolutionary events, or if instead there was a general pattern to the evolution of the behaviours. After constructing a phylogeny for his eight study species, Packer mapped the known behaviours against it. The results were striking: in this group, social behaviour was an ancestral trait, with solitary behaviour recently derived. It has been suggested that in animals with an annual life cycle, the length of active season might explain these interspecific differences in sociality. Selection may operate against sociality when the season is too short to produce successive broods. Paul Davison and Jeremy Field recently tested this hypothesis by transplanting foundresses of the eusocial sweat bee (*Lasioglossum malachurum*) from the south to the far north of the United Kingdom, far beyond its natural range (Davison

and Field, 2018). In doing so, they found that the short season and harsher environmental conditions could preclude expression of eusocial behaviour.

Packer's work was among the first to show that some interspecific variation in behaviour is likely the result of evolution, and, like the more commonly studied physical traits such as beak size, behaviour can be passed on to daughter species. Davison and Field demonstrated that environmental factors may impose a selective pressure on social behaviour and contribute to evolution of interspecific differences in sociality.

There is certainly evidence that species and individuals vary in behaviour. We also know that individuals will alter their behaviour depending upon local conditions (do you always order the same food from every restaurant?). Such variation can rapidly overwhelm us, and it is helpful to have a broader theoretical framework on which we can base our discussion of behavioural ecology.

Inclusive Fitness and Types of Behaviour

Before we go any further in our discussion of behaviour, it is necessary for us to have a broader understanding of fitness, called **inclusive fitness**. The concept of inclusive fitness was developed by William D. Hamilton (1964). He proposed that an individual's inclusive, or overall, fitness is determined by its own survival and reproduction, plus the survival and reproduction of individuals with whom the individual shares genes. Under some conditions, individuals can increase their inclusive fitness by helping increase the survival and reproduction of genetic relatives that are not offspring. Because this help is given to relatives, or kin, the evolutionary force favouring such behaviour is called **kin selection**.

Using the concept of inclusive fitness, Hamilton explored the potential evolutionary consequences of different forms of social interactions. He classified all social interactions into four main classes and argued that natural selection will favour certain types of behaviour and select against others (fig. 8.3). Specifically, Hamilton views social relations as an interaction between a "donor" and a "recipient." A donor performs a given action, such as singing a song, removing parasites from another, or displaying a threat. The recipient is the individual

		Fitness Consequences to Recipient	
		+	−
Fitness Consequences to Donor	+	Cooperation	Selfishness
	−	Altruism	Spite

Figure 8.3 Hamilton (1964) proposed that social interactions can be classified into four groups based upon the potential fitness consequences for the donor and recipient of any given interaction.

who recognizes the given behaviour. Hamilton classified all behaviours as having a potential negative or positive effect on the fitness of the two participants. Using this model, we see that two sets of behaviours, *altruism* and *spitefulness,* have negative fitness consequences for the donor, and, as a result, natural selection should select against these behaviours. In contrast, *cooperation* and *selfishness* have positive fitness consequences for the donor and should be favoured by natural selection.

Although it may be tempting to argue that all observed behaviours are inherently adaptive and the result of natural selection, this approach is negatively referred to as *adaptationist.* Adaptationist stories in ecology are similar to Kipling's *Just So Stories,* such as "How the Camel Got His Hump." In these stories, Kipling provided fanciful "mechanisms" that generated the patterns we observe in nature, such as hump-backed camels. Modern behavioural ecologists are well aware of the adaptationist trap, and they recognize that many behaviours are evolutionarily neutral, neither selected for nor against. As a result, behavioural ecologists are not content to simply suggest an evolutionary consequence of a behaviour but instead actively work to test whether selection actually occurs. A related issue is that for natural selection to occur, there needs to be a large heritable component to a given behaviour. This in no way suggests that all behaviours need to have a genetic component; instead, only those behaviours that have a genetic component could be influenced by natural selection.

An additional concern is that, according to Hamilton's classification, some behaviours, such as altruism, should not persist as they would be selected against. However, we can look a a variety of systems and see animals exhibiting behaviours that put them in immediate bodily harm, yet appear to prevent harm in others. This behaviour can be shown repeatedly within a species, strongly suggesting a genetic basis. In other words, we can see altruism, and we believe it can have a genetic basis. How can this be reconciled with Hamilton's ideas that altruism should be selected against?

Altruism and Natural Selection

Since 1989, a team of researchers from the University of Alberta, McGill University, and Guelph University have been making detailed studies of a red squirrel population in the Yukon as part of the Kluane Red Squirrel Project. The three principle investigators, Stan Boutin, Murray Humphries, and Andrew McAdam, along with a legion of graduate and undergraduate students, have kept meticulous notes of every squirrel birth and death in the population (fig. 8.4). The research team employs both observational and molecular methods to determine the relatedness of different individuals in the population, providing a detailed pedigree of the population. One day in the field, Jamie Gorrell, a graduate student at the University of Alberta, was up in a tree checking on the squirrel nests. He noticed that one nest had an extra baby—one female squirrel had adopted the offspring of another squirrel. Needless to say, Jamie wanted to figure out what was going on. Jamie and his colleagues (Gorrell et al. 2010) soon realized that .their larger data set contained five different instances of adoption. Using Hamilton's classifications, an altruistic act is one that benefits the recipient but harms the donor, and these should not be common in nature. What conditions would allow a squirrel to adopt the offspring of another? It

Figure 8.4 Some red squirrels adopt the offspring of related individuals, a likely example of kin selection promoting the evolution of an altruistic act. Jamie Gorrell.

turns out that behavioural ecologists have a number of explanations for the puzzle posed by altruism in nature.

One of the earliest sets of explanations for altruism came from V. C. Wynne-Edwards (1962), who argued in favour of group selection as a means to explain many observed phenomenon. In his presentation of **group selection**, Wynne-Edwards argued that individuals may act counter to their own personal interests for the betterment of the group. For instance, an organism may reduce its reproductive rate to prevent a population from exhausting its resources. This line of thinking, however, was rapidly attacked by many scientists (Williams 1966, Smith 1964) as being inherently adaptationist without any consistency with current evolutionary understanding. These scientists were very effective in moving discussions of altruism toward a gene-centred, rather than group-centred, level. However, over the past 40 years, the evidence has accumulated that group selection can occur in some special circumstances (Wade 1977). It has been rebranded under the term "multilevel selection," and its role in the evolution of altruism is still debated. Perhaps more importantly than whether group selection can exist is that ecologists have uncovered a number of other causes of altruism: kin selection, manipulation, and reciprocal altruism.

We now turn our attention to the more widely accepted idea that kin selection can promote altruism. We know that we each receive 50% of our genes from each of our two biological parents. From a parental point of view, this means that each offspring is equivalent to approximately 50% of a parent's own genetic material. The **coefficient of relationship** can be determined for any two individuals. It will be 25% between grandparent and grandchild, 12.5% between great-grandparent and great-grandchild, 50% between full siblings, and 25% between half-siblings. Have you figured out the pattern? There is a reduction of 50% in the coefficient in relationship for every additional connection between any two related individuals. So what? From an inclusive fitness point of view, if a sister had the choice to save the lives of her two siblings at the expense of her own life, her inclusive fitness would be equal regardless of what behaviour she chose. However, selection would favour her heroic act of self-sacrifice if she were able to save three siblings, or two siblings and a cousin, or any other combination of relatives whose coefficients of relationship sum to more than 1.

Consider another hypothetical example: a familial group with five sisters. Suppose resources are limited and the group can collectively only support and rear three offspring. Should each sister have one offspring and let them compete for resources? Suppose instead only one individual had all three of the offspring, and the other sisters helped protect and provide for them. From the mother's standpoint (the recipient's), the benefit is obvious. But for each nonreproductive sister (each donor), there is also individual benefit. The coefficient of relationship between a nonreproductive individual and her sister's offspring is 25%. The coefficient of relationship with her own offspring would be 50%. If she helps provide for and ensure the survival of three of her sister's offspring, each with a 25% coefficient of relationship, this is a better payoff in terms of transmitting her genes to the next generation than if she produced her own single offspring with 50% coefficient of similarity but only a 60% chance of surviving. Of course, for this "helper" phenotype to evolve, (1) it must have a genetic basis that can be transmitted to the next generation, and (2) the expression of the trait must be flexible and situational. If the offspring in the next generation express the trait and forgo direct reproduction, that's the end of the line for the population.

Of course, most behaviours do not result in certain death or reduced fitness for the donor. Nor do they result in certain survival or increased fitness for the recipient. So the costs and benefits of an action to one's fitness is generally less than 1. Hamilton (1964) formalized the situation under which a particular behaviour would be advantageous as:

$$\frac{\text{Cost}}{\text{Benefit}} < \text{Coefficient of Relationship}$$

In this model, selection would favour a given behaviour only if the inclusive fitness gains exceed the inclusive fitness costs. The obvious question is whether this really happens. Jamie Gorrell was aware of the importance of kin selection as he investigated the phenomenon of squirrel adoption high in the trees of a Yukon forest. Using microsatellites (chapter 4), the research team was able to confirm that the adopted squirrels were related to the females that adopted them. Further, because they had detailed information on the costs associated with having more babies in a nest (e.g., less food available for the other babies and thus reduced survival of natal litter), as well as the potential gains through inclusive fitness, Gorrell and his colleagues were able to determine that Hamilton's rule was satisfied; in all cases, adoption resulted in increased fitness for the adoptive mother, providing a possible solution to his puzzle. However, in some cases altruism can also occur even without benefits to the donor. As we show next, sometimes an individual can be tricked into being altruistic.

The brown-headed cowbird (*Molothrus ater*) has a rather interesting mechanism for incubating its eggs and rearing its young. It is an obligate **brood parasite**, meaning that a female must lay her eggs in the nests of birds of other species. The host birds then keep the parasitic bird's eggs warm and feed the hatchling until it can fledge from the nest. Based on the principle of allocation we discussed in chapters 5 and 7, you can see an obvious problem. If the host bird gives food and thermal energy to this parasitic bird, less will be available for its own offspring, reducing its own fitness. In other words, why would these host birds perform this altruistic act? The short answer to this question is that this is an example of *manipulation,* where the song sparrow does not appear to possess any obvious means of preventing this from occurring or where the cost of prevention would be too great. (If the host bird could not discriminate between its eggs and cowbird eggs, it could roll them all out of the nest. But that would be a steep price to pay.) In a study at Delta Marsh, the field station associated with the University of Manitoba, Todd Underwood and Spencer Sealy added artificial objects of different shapes to nests of American robins and gray catbirds (Underwood and Sealy 2006), two species that are commonly parasitized by brown-headed cowbirds. The researchers found that robins and catbirds were able to discriminate "odd-shaped" items, such as cubes or cylinders, as being different from their eggs and eject them from the nest. However, they could not discriminate spherical items as different and retained them more frequently in the nest. Although cowbird and host eggs are distinctly different to a researcher, the host birds apparently could not tell the difference; thus, cowbirds induce altruism through manipulation of the reproductive biology of their hosts.

James Smith and Peter Arcese (1994), from the University of British Columbia, have measured the potential fitness consequences of cowbird parasitism on a song-sparrow population on an island off the coast of British Columbia. In a 16-year study, they found the presence of a cowbird egg in a sparrow nest reduced the number of sparrows that fledged from the nest by 79%, although this was reduced to 27% when food was experimentally added. Sparrows were also more likely to fledge no sparrows from nests when they were parasitized than when they were not parasitized. In short, having a cowbird egg in your nest is bad news to your fitness, although obviously you are doing the cowbird a nice favour. This form of altruism persists in nature because the host cannot do anything about it. Such an example highlights the need to avoid attributing fitness benefits to all observed behaviours.

We will provide one final explanation for altruism, which is **reciprocal altruism**. Under this model, individuals do not have to be related to each other for altruism to be evolutionarily stable. Instead, this model is based upon recognition and experience and is also called "tit-for-tat." We will discuss this idea in depth in the Ecological Tools and Approaches section at the end of this chapter. In brief, this idea says that natural selection will favour altruistic behaviours to unrelated individuals if that individual will repay in kind at some point in the future. The reciprocal act does not need to be immediate (that would be cooperation, not altruism), but it does need to occur with a high degree of certainty.

In this section we have provided a general background into how natural selection can influence behaviour. We find that initially counterintuitive actions, such as altruism, can also be the result of natural selection, as long as we allow ourselves to think more broadly about who benefits, why, when, and whether there is even any choice. We will now continue with more examples of how selection can influence behaviour, with a focus on group living.

CONCEPT 8.1 REVIEW

1. If a researcher is interested in understanding the evolution of a behaviour, why does it matter if that behaviour has a genetic basis? Does a genetic basis of a behaviour necessarily mean the behaviour will always be expressed?

2. What is the difference between inclusive fitness, as discussed in this chapter, and fitness as defined in chapter 4?

3. What conditions are likely necessary for the evolution of altruistic behaviours in a species?

8.2   Sociality

The evolution of sociality is generally accompanied by cooperative feeding, defence of the social group, and restricted reproductive opportunities. A fundamental change in relationships among individuals within a population takes place when individuals begin living in groups, such as colonies, herds, or schools. Cooperation generally involves exchanges of resources between individuals or various forms of assistance, such as defence of the group against predators. Group living and cooperation signal the beginnings of **sociality**. The degree of sociality in a species ranges from acts as simple as mutual grooming or group protection of young, to highly complex, stratified societies, such as those found in colonies of ants or termites. This more complex level of social behaviour is called **eusociality**. Eusociality is generally thought to include three major characteristics: (1) individuals of more than one generation living together, (2) cooperative care of young, and (3) division of individuals into sterile, or nonreproductive, and reproductive castes.

Because individuals in social species often appear to have fewer opportunities to reproduce compared to individuals in nonsocial species, the evolution of sociality has drawn a great deal of attention from ecologists. The apparent restriction of reproductive opportunities that comes with sociality appears to challenge the idea that the fitness of an individual is determined by the number of offspring it produces. We began to address this paradox in the previous section. Evolution of sociality is intimately connected with the previous discussion on evolution of altruism in an inclusive fitness context. Arguably, within any social species' behavioural repertoire, some altruism that furthers inclusive fitness is evident. We'll begin by illustrating this in co-operative breeders.

Cooperative Breeders

Approximately 100 species of birds and several species of mammals, such as wolves and African lions, engage in **cooperative breeding**. Cooperative breeders live in groups, with many adults cooperating during the process of producing and/or rearing offspring. Such cooperation extends to offspring that are not their own. Help may include defending the territory or the young, preparing and maintaining a nest or den, or feeding the young. Since the young that receive the care are not the offspring of the helpers, we might ask what benefits do helpers gain from their cooperation? As we saw in the example of adoption of red squirrels, one potential gain could be an increase in the helper's own inclusive fitness. Although the young being helped are not the helper's own young, this does not necessarily mean that they are completely unrelated.

African Lions

Craig Packer and Anne E. Pusey have studied cooperation among African lions in the Serengeti (Packer and Pusey 1982, 1983, 1997; Packer et al. 1991). Their studies have revealed a great deal of complexity in lion societies. Female lions live in groups of related individuals called prides (fig. 8.5). Prides of female lions generally include three to six adults but may contain as many as eighteen or as few as one. In addition to adult females, prides also include their dependent offspring and a coalition of adult males. Male coalitions may be made up of closely related individuals or of unrelated individuals.

Within lion societies, one can observe many forms of cooperation. Female lions nurse each other's cubs; cooperate when hunting large, difficult-to-kill game, such as zebra and buffalo; and cooperatively defend their pride's territory against encroaching females. However, the most critical form of cooperation among females is their group defence of the young against infanticidal males. These attacks on the young generally take place as a male coalition is displaced by another invading coalition. While a single female lion has little chance in a fight against a much larger male lion, cooperating females are often successful at repelling attacking males. Males, in turn,

Figure 8.5 African lions are highly social predators.
© pjmalsbury/iStockPhoto.

cooperate in defending the territory against invading males that threaten the young they have sired and against threats from other predators, such as hyenas. The challenge for the ecologist has been to determine whether these various forms of cooperation can be reconciled with evolutionary theory.

Since the females in lion prides are always close relatives, their cooperative behaviour can be readily explained within the conceptual framework of kin selection. As females cooperate in nursing, hunting, or defending young against males, they contribute to the growth and survival of their own offspring or to those of close kin, adding to the inclusive fitness of individual females.

In contrast, male coalitions are sometimes made up of close relatives and sometimes not. Cooperation among closely related males in a coalition can contribute to inclusive fitness of individual males, just as cooperation among related females can contribute to inclusive fitness of individual females. However, cooperation among unrelated or distantly related males in a coalition represents a greater challenge to evolutionary theory. However, Packer and colleagues (Packer et al. 1991) discovered that the rules associated with the formation and behaviour of coalitions are also consistent with predictions of evolutionary theory. Because single males have virtually no chance of claiming and defending a pride of female lions, they must form coalitions with other males. This represents a type of ecological constraint on viable choices open to males. If males form a coalition with brothers and cousins, cooperative behaviour that increases the production and survival of offspring of the coalition will increase an individual male's inclusive fitness. However, a male within a coalition with unrelated males must produce some offspring of his own or he is merely increasing the fitness of others at the expense of his own fitness.

ECOLOGY IN ACTION

Human–Wildlife Conflict

It is easy to understand how one could be drawn into the world of behavioural ecology. The blend of ecology, evolution, and physiology presents a continuous intellectual challenge. Even more, many of the behaviours one observes in the wild are mirrored by members of our own species. But there is another more practical benefit of this line of research: helping develop strategies to reduce human–wildlife conflict.

Each year, tens of thousands of conflicts occur between people and wildlife throughout Canada. The "problem wildlife" involved in these interactions are often killed, resulting in large numbers of potentially preventable animal deaths. A number of these conflicts also kill or injure people—again, potentially preventable casualties associated with animal behaviour. Sources of human–wildlife conflict are manifest in traffic collisions, crop damage, home invasions by polar bears, and birds flying into jet engines. The frequency of such encounters are increasing as we expand into formerly remote areas, and as transportation networks become even more heavily used. Some conflicts concern hyper-abundant and human-habituated animals in urban areas, such as geese in parks and coyotes in suburban areas. Habituated animals have little fear of people and congregate in densely populated areas because they can avoid wary predators and feed on the rich resources provided by human garbage and horticultural practices. Everyone is familiar with the pirating gulls (*Larus* species) of the fast-food restaurant parking lot, but most do not consider this behaviour to be a problem. However, your perception may change if it is your job to clean up their mess every day.

Can behavioural ecologists use their knowledge to reduce human–wildlife conflict, finding solutions that both maintain the physical safety of people while also allowing animals to be wild? Elk (*Cervus elaphus*) are prone to habituation in mountainous urban areas. Their large size and aggressive behaviour create opportunity for injury, and Banff reported an average of seven contact charges between elk and humans each year in the 1990s (G. Peers, Warden, Banff National Park, pers. comm.). Most of these occurred in or near the townsite of Banff, which is situated in the highly productive Bow Valley in the heart of the spectacular rocks and ice that make up most of the park. Solving the problem of habituated elk in Banff and elsewhere is difficult. Translocated animals typically return to their capture sites or die in their new locations. Killing habituated animals is unpalatable to many people and disrupts the social structure of the animal populations. Approaching the problem by focusing on the habituated behaviour appears to offer some promise for a lasting solution. Working in conjunction with Banff Park biologists and wardens, Colleen St. Clair and her MSc student Elsabé Kloppers, from the University of Alberta, sought to reduce conflict by teaching habituated elk to be more wary of people (Kloppers et al. 2005).

To achieve this, they designed an experiment that used 24 radio-collared elk, which allowed daily monitoring of movement and behaviour (fig. 8.6). Sixteen elk were assigned to one of two "predator-resembling chase treatments." The remaining eight animals were designated as controls: captured, handled, and monitored but not chased. In both chase treatments, the researchers used repeated (up to 10 times) chase sequences during the winter, each of which lasted 15 minutes. One chase treatment used researchers and wardens wielding guns with cracker and screamer shells to chase elk away from the town core

(a)

(b)

(c)

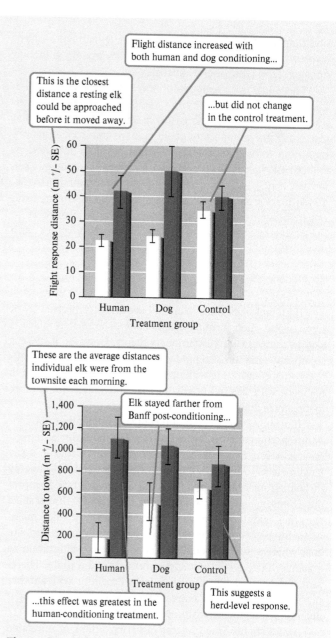

Figure 8.6 (*a*) Elk in Banff; (*b*) human-based conditioning treatment; (*c*) dog-based conditioning treatment.
(a)–(c): Kloppers et al. 2005.

Flight distance increased with both human and dog conditioning...

This is the closest distance a resting elk could be approached before it moved away.

...but did not change in the control treatment.

These are the average distances individual elk were from the townsite each morning.

Elk stayed farther from Banff post-conditioning...

...this effect was greatest in the human-conditioning treatment.

This suggests a herd-level response.

Figure 8.7 Flight response distance and elk location were influenced by avoidance conditioning in Banff townsite. Flight response distance is the nearest a resting elk could be approached before it moved away. White bars correspond to measures taken before treatments were imposed and purple bars are measures post-treatment.
Data from Kloppers et al. 2005.

(ecologists have the coolest jobs!). The second chase treatment included hiring a professional dog handler to get border collies to emulate wolf hunting behaviour as they herded the elk out of town. Realistic predator simulation appeared to be important; a pilot study indicated that the silent hunting style of the collies initiated a flight response by the elk, while hunting associated with barking by New Zealand Huntaways resulted in charges by the elk! Both types of chases provided what psychologists would term *aversive conditioning,* a form of operant learning. Operant learning may be positive or negative and occurs whenever an animal learns to associate an unconditioned stimulus (e.g., noisy cracker shells and chasing) with a conditioned stimulus (e.g., the appearance of a human on foot). The principle of allocation (chapter 7) should favour learning that minimizes energetic costs and maximizes foraging gains. We will discuss more of the "ecology of fear" in chapter 14.

After conditioning, the treated elk fled from approaching humans when they were at greater distances, tended to spend more time being vigilant, and foraged farther from the town perimeter relative to the control elk (fig. 8.7) (Kloppers et al. 2005). Interestingly, some aspects of the strength of the conditioning effects were strongest when wolves were not very active and less effective when they were present.

Overall, aversive conditioning appears to work as a means of reducing elk–human conflict; elk are much less common now in the townsite and there has been only one contact charge in the initial four years since it was implemented, while the treatments were maintained. Both dogs and humans are still used, but the guns (which were offensive to tourists) have been replaced with equally effective hockey sticks (yes, hockey sticks).

This study is an example of how the concepts of behavioural ecology have clear and direct conservation and management implications. The research team demonstrated that these animals can learn to avoid humans through conditioning, even without receiving an actual physical deterrent or without being captured and translocated. St. Clair and her lab are using aversive conditioning and other methods to dissuade black bears from consuming garbage in Whistler and grizzly bears from being hit by trains in Banff, to encourage habituated elk to reinstate traditional migratory routes, and

to understand the movement patterns of coyote in an urban landscape. St. Clair also leads the large "Research on Avian Protection Project" (RAPP), whose focus is to increase bird protection associated with the large tailings ponds created in the process of tar sand development. The scale of the "ponds" is significant, covering 176 square kilometres in 2010 (Alberta Environment and Parks 2015). St. Clair's RAPP project began through a court-ordered creative sentence applied to Syncrude for ineffectively preventing the landing and thus increasing the mortality of migratory birds in 2008. The ongoing work integrates toxicology, bird physiology, behaviour, and ecology. Though not as exciting as cracker guns, the outcome of the work has important implications for Canada.

If all males within a coalition have an equal probability of reproducing, then forming coalitions with unrelated males is easy to reconcile with evolutionary theory. However, if there is significant variation in reproductive opportunities within coalitions, then cooperating with unrelated males is more difficult to reconcile with theories predicting that individuals will attempt to maximize their inclusive fitness.

It turns out that in a coalition of two, both males sire a similar proportion of cubs, while in larger coalitions, lower ranked males sire very few cubs. An implication of this is that an unrelated male in a larger coalition risks investing time and energy in helping maintain a pride without an opportunity to reproduce himself, and without improving his inclusive fitness since the other coalition members are not relatives. Unrelated males in coalitions of two, however, each have opportunities to sire cubs whereas neither would have opportunities acting alone, as a solitary male would not successfully defend a pride. Therefore, if the only viable option is to form a coalition with another unrelated male, there is a direct fitness advantage over going it alone, albeit no inclusive fitness advantage.

Males should avoid joining larger coalitions of unrelated males, and this is just what Packer and his colleagues found. Figure 8.8 shows the percentage of males with unrelated partners in coalitions of different sizes. These patterns show clearly that males that team up with unrelated individuals mostly do so in coalitions of two or three. Larger coalitions of four to nine individuals are almost entirely made up of relatives.

In summary, evolution of cooperative breeding in African lions appears to be a response to environmental conditions. To survive, reproduce, and successfully raise offspring to maturity, African lions must work in cooperative groups, as the lone lion has no chance of meeting the ecological challenges presented by living on the Serengeti in lion society with its aggressive prides and invasive and infanticidal male coalitions.

While the complexities of African lion societies have taken decades to uncover, they pale beside the intricacies of life among eusocial species, such as bees, termites, and ants. Let's explore eusociality in some animal populations to get some insights into the evolution of these complex social systems.

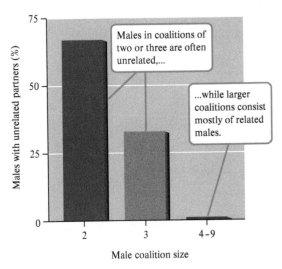

Figure 8.8   Relatedness and size of male coalitions among African lions.

Data from Packer et al. 1991.

Eusocial Species

Probably the most thoroughly studied of eusocial species is the ant species. Ants and their complex behaviours have attracted the attention of people from the earliest times and appear in the oldest writings, such as the Bible and the classical writings of ancient Greece. One of the most socially complex groups of ants is the leafcutter (fig. 8.9). The 39 described species of leafcutter ants, which belong to two genera, are found only in the Americas, from the southern United States to Argentina. Leafcutter ants make their living by cutting and transporting leaf fragments to their nest, where the leaf material is fragmented and used as a substrate upon which to grow fungi. The fungi provide the primary food source for leafcutter ants.

Leafcutter ants live in social groups in which individuals are divided among **castes** that engage in very different activities. We can define a caste as a group of physically distinctive individuals that engage in specialized behaviour within the colony.

Figure 8.9 Leafcutter ants carrying leaf fragments back to the nest, where they will be processed to create a substrate for growing the fungi that the ants eat. Smaller ants riding on leaf fragments offer protection from aerial attack by parasitoid flies.
© Nature Picture Library/Alamy.

Figure 8.10 Naked mole rats live in a large social group in a shared burrow complex that may stretch several kilometres. Only one female and a one to three males in the group reproduce.
© Aughty Venable–Dreamstime.com.

E. O. Wilson (1980) studied how labour is divided among castes of ants in a laboratory colony of *A. sexdens* that he established and studied over a period of eight years. When Wilson compared *A. sexdens* with three non–leafcutter ant species, he found that *A. sexdens* included a larger number of castes (seven versus the average of three) and engaged in a wider variety of behaviours. Wilson identified a total of 29 distinctive tasks performed by the leafcutter ants compared to an average of 17.7 tasks performed by the three other species. He found that the division of labour within the *A. sexdens* colony was mainly based on size. Possibly because of the large number of specialized tasks that need to be performed by leafcutter ants, they have one of the most complex social structures and one of the greatest size ranges found among ants. Within *A. sexdens* colonies, the head width of the largest individuals (5.2 mm) is nearly nine times the head width of the smallest individuals (0.6 mm).

As a consequence of this great variation, someone watching a trail of leafcutter ants bring freshly cut leaf fragments back to their nest is treated to a rich display of size and behavioural diversity. While medium-sized ants carry the leaf fragments above their heads, the largest ants line the trail like sentries, guarding against ground attacks on the column of ants carrying leaf fragments. Very small ants ride on many of the leaf fragments, protecting the ant carrying a leaf fragment from aerial attacks by parasitic flies. Meanwhile, other size classes of leafcutters—performing behaviours associated with processing leaves, tending larvae, and maintaining fungal gardens—remain hidden in the nest.

Aside from leafcutter ant, there are many other eusocial animals, including the only eusocial mammal, the naked mole rat (fig 8.10). Careful study has revealed some remarkable parallels in the structures of naked mole rat and leafcutter ant societies. The social behaviour of naked mole rats was first reported by Jennifer Jarvis (Jarvis 1981). Her study was based on more than six years of observation and experimentation with colonies of naked mole rats.

The social organization of the colony appeared more similar to an ant colony than to any other mammal population known. Within a colony of naked mole rats, one female (the queen) and only a few males breed. Behavioural ecologists have found that life in a naked mole rat colony centres on the queen and her offspring, and the queen's behaviour appears to maintain this focus. She is the most active member of the colony and literally pushes her way around the colony. By physically pushing individuals, she appears to call them to action when there is work to be done or when the colony is threatened and needs defending. The aggressiveness of the queen also appears to maintain her dominance over other females in the colony and prevent them from coming into breeding condition. If the queen dies or is removed from the colony, one of the other females in the colony will assume the role of queen. If two or more females compete for the position of queen, they may fight to the death during the process of establishing the new social hierarchy.

In contrast to leafcutter ant colonies, where all workers are females, both males and females work in naked mole rat colonies. Jarvis found that work is divided among colony members, as in leafcutter ant colonies, according to size. However, in contrast to leafcutter ants, colonies of naked mole rats include only two worker size classes, small and large. Small workers are the most active. Small workers excavate tunnels, build the nest, which is deeper than most of the passageways, and line the nest with plant materials for bedding. In addition, small workers also harvest food, mainly roots and tubers, and deliver it to other colony members, including the queen, for feeding. Since they spend most of their time sleeping, the role of large non-breeders was unclear for some time. However, eventually researchers working in the field were able to observe these large non-breeders in action. It turns out that the large workers, as in ant colonies, are a caste specializing in defence. If the tunnel system is breached by members of another colony, the large non-breeders move out quickly from their resting places to defend the colony from the invaders, literally throwing themselves into the breach. Eventually the large non-breeders push up enough soil to wall off the intruders. However, they may be most important in defending against snakes, the most dangerous predators of naked mole rats. When confronted with a snake, the large non-breeders will try to kill the snake or spray it with soil until it is driven off or buried.

Evolution of Eusociality

Despite their distinctive evolutionary histories and other biological differences, the studies of Wilson and Jarvis suggest interesting parallels in the organizations of leafcutter ant and naked mole rat colonies (fig. 8.11). Similarities include division of labour within colonies based on size, with smaller workers specializing in foraging, nest maintenance, and excavation of extensive burrow systems. Meanwhile, larger workers in both species specialize in defence. In addition, reproduction in both species is limited to a single queen and her mates. These areas of convergence in social organization between such different organisms may help shed light on the forces responsible for the evolution of eusociality.

What factors may have been important in the evolution and maintenance of naked mole rat and leafcutter ant sociality? Kin selection may play a role. Leafcutter ants, along with other Hymenoptera, such as bees and wasps, have an inheritance system called **haplodiploidy**. The term *haplodiploid* refers to the number of chromosome sets possessed by males and females. In haplodiploid systems, males develop from unfertilized eggs and are haploid while females develop from fertilized eggs and so are diploid. One of the consequences of haplodiploidy is that worker ants within a colony can be very similar genetically. In an ant colony where there is a single queen that mated with a single male, the workers will be more related to each other than they would be to their own offspring. W. D. Hamilton (1964) was the first to point out that under these conditions, the average genetic similarity among workers would be 75%, while their relationship with any offspring they might produce would be 50%.

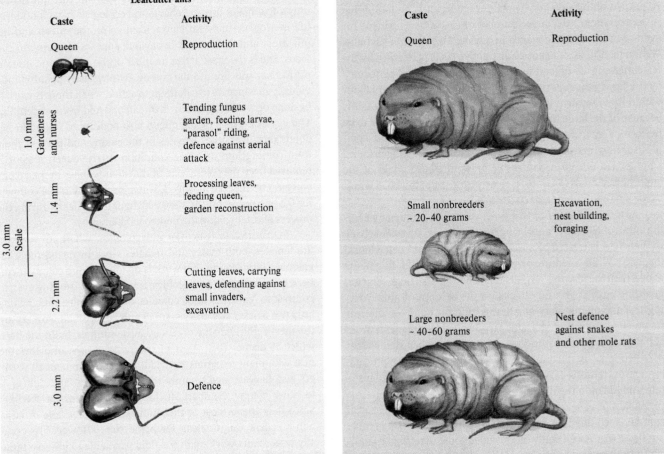

| Division of labour in both leafcutter ant colonies and naked mole rat colonies is based on size. |

Figure 8.11 Division of labour among castes of leafcutter ants (*Atta sexdens*) and naked mole rats (*Heterocephalus glaber*). Ant sizes are head widths of workers typically engaged in each activity.
Data from Wilson 1980; Jarvis 1981; and Sherman, Jarvis, and Braude 1992.

Under these conditions, it makes sense for a worker to invest more in the survival of her siblings (one of whom will one day be a queen) than to invest in her own offspring, from an inclusive fitness perspective.

What is the source of this high degree of relatedness? Remember that in a diploid species, the mother and father each contribute 50% of the genetic material to offspring. Of the 50% coming from the father, the chromosomal assortment into gametes is random. So, two siblings will each have 50% of their genetic material from the father, but half of this (or 25% of each sibling's total genetic material) will be the same. Similarly, each will inherit 25% of the same genetic material from their mother. Adding these together, the siblings will have 50% identical genetic information to each other (on average). Now consider the haplodiploid ant. The queen mates only during her mating flight and stores the sperm she receives to fertilize all the eggs she lays to produce daughters. If she mates with a single male, since he is haploid, all her daughters (the workers) will receive the same genetic information from the father. As a consequence, the 50% of the genetic makeup that workers receive from their male parent will be identical. In addition, workers will share an average of 25% of their genes received from the queen, yielding an average genetic relatedness of 50% + 25% = 75%. The important point here is that the activity of workers promotes the production of their sisters rather than their own offspring. Because an individual's sisters are more genetically similar than her own direct offspring, the activities of workers increase their own inclusive fitness via kin selection. Provided the behaviour has a genetic basis, it can thus evolve.

Because naked mole rat colonies are relatively closed to outsiders, the individuals within each colony, like the workers within leafcutter ant colonies, are also very similar genetically. Paul Sherman, Jennifer Jarvis, and Stanton Braude (1992) reported that approximately 85% of matings within a colony of naked mole rats are between parents and offspring or between siblings. As a consequence of these matings between close relatives, the relatedness between individuals within a colony is about 81%, suggesting that kin selection may be involved in the maintenance of non-reproductive helpers in colonies of naked mole rats.

What factors other than kin selection may have contributed to the evolution of eusociality? Many factors have been implicated. While researchers working on ants and other social Hymenoptera have emphasized the potential importance of kin selection, studies of cooperative-breeding vertebrate species have emphasized ecological constraints. What sorts of ecological common constraints are faced by leafcutter ants and naked mole rats? One of the most obvious is the work associated with the creation, maintenance, and defence of extensive burrow systems. The more social organisms are studied, the less likely it has become that one or a few simple mechanisms will be adequate to explain their evolution. However, the results of studies such as those of Wilson and Jarvis should encourage continued careful comparative studies as a means for eventual understanding of the evolution of sociality.

CONCEPT 8.2 REVIEW

1. What are the evolutionary implications of the fact that larger coalitions of male lions consist almost entirely of close relatives?

2. Among the ants and other eusocial Hymenoptera, why would kin selection favour workers that helped rear sister workers rather than their own offspring?

3. What are the two major ecological challenges favouring colony living shared by leafcutter ants and naked mole rats?

8.3 Mating Systems and Mate Choice

Mate choice by one sex and/or competition for mates among individuals of the same sex can result in selection for particular traits, a process called sexual selection. From a human perspective, sexual reproduction appears to be the norm. However, asexual reproduction is common among many groups of organisms, such as bacteria, fungi, protozoans, plants, invertebrates, and even some vertebrates. Questions about the evolutionary costs and benefits of sexual and asexual reproduction are fascinating—but are also beyond the scope of this text. In this section, we focus on the behaviour of sexually reproducing species.

Most described species of plants and animals have male and female functions, even in species that are able to reproduce asexually. The male and female functions can be distributed among individuals in a variety of ways, or **sex types**. The most obvious to us may be the condition of being a single sex (male or female). The **females** are the sex that produces larger and typically more energetically expensive gametes (ova), while the **males** produce smaller and typically less costly gametes (sperm). Other species have more complicated sex types, which can include **hermaphrodites**, in which an individual is able to perform both male and female reproductive functions. Hermaphroditism is found in over 75% of all flowering plant species and even occurs in a variety of fish species. Individuals can be instantaneous hermaphrodites, in which they perform male and female function at the same time, or sequential hermaphrodites, in which the individual changes sex over the course of its life. In plants, individual flowers on a single plant can perform both male and female functions, or these functions may occur in separate flowers on the same plant. In short, nature produces a diversity of sex types, much richer than simple male and female forms.

The complexity of nature was the basis for research into the evolution of different reproductive strategies. Once again, we visit the work of Eric Charnov, here in collaboration with

J. Maynard Smith and James Bull (1976). These scientists addressed several fundamental questions related to the evolution of sex in a classic paper, "Why Be a Hermaphrodite?" The authors identified three conditions that should favour a hermaphroditic population over one with separate sexes: (1) low mobility, which limits the opportunities for male-to-male competition; (2) low overlap in resource demands by female and male structures and functions, such as in plants where pollen production often occurs much earlier than seed and fruit maturation; and (3) sharing of costs for male and female function, for instance in insect-pollinated plants where attractive flowers promote both male and female reproductive success. In this section we will explore several evolutionary and behavioural patterns associated with sex in a diversity of species. We begin by describing the overall social interactions that commonly are found in groups of reproductive individuals, and then end with discussing the evolutionary implications of mate selection.

Mating Systems

The first step in understanding the social interactions of individuals related to sexual reproduction is to be able to describe the sex types that naturally occur and that are fertile within a population. This task is relatively straightforward for most species and can be accomplished through basic skills in natural history (chapters 2 and 3). The next step, however, is more difficult and requires more expertise in behavioural ecology— understanding the social structure of populations in relation to sex. Do individuals mate with multiple individuals, or do they appear to mate with just one? Do all individuals in a population have equal access to mates, or are fertile mates a guarded resource? Are putative fathers actually genetically related to the young they help rear? These are questions answered by understanding **mating systems**: the social, sexual structure of a population. Though both plants and animals have a diversity of interesting mating systems, we focus here on those of animals.

We are likely most familiar with **monogamy**, at least in concept. In monogamous mating systems, one male and one female have an exclusive relationship, at least for some duration of time. However, just because two individuals have a *pair-bond* does not necessarily mean that all offspring from the female of the pair were sired by the male. Instead, nature is full of examples of males who are engaged in seemingly monogamous relationships but who are being *cuckolded*.

To help separate paternity from investment, animal behavioural ecologists often refer to two types of monogamy: *social monogamy* and *genetic monogamy*. Songbirds are frequently seen in socially monogamous relationships during the nesting season, where one male and one female will share a nest and rear any offspring produced by that female. It was traditionally assumed that such provision of resources from the male was due to his being the father of these offspring. In fact, the influential avian ecologist David Lack estimated that 93% of passerines are monogamous in their mating (Lack 1968). However, a recent review of rates of nonpaternity in passerines suggests that despite the appearance of fidelity based upon social monogamy, over 90% of species actually show evidence of a lack

of genetic monogamy (Griffith et al. 2002)! Needless to say, one never quite knows what is going on up in those nests.

If many mating systems are not truly monogamous, then what are they? Many species exhibit different types of **promiscuity**, in which individuals may have multiple sexual partners. Promiscuous mating systems can be further defined as **polygyny**, **polyandry**, and **polygynandry**, which describe, respectively, systems in which one male mates with multiple females while each female mates (putatively) with just one male; one female mates with multiple males while each male mates (putatively) with just one female; and groups of multiple males and multiple females mate with each other. Of these, polygyny appears most common among vertebrates; polyandry occurs among species of diverse taxa, including insects, frogs, birds, fish, and mammals; and polygynandry is quite rare, apparently restricted to a few species of primates. Regardless of the exact mating system of a species, males and females will end up choosing specific individuals as their mates. If the complex behaviours related to mating systems have genetic bases, the social interactions involved and the divergence in these interactions among closely related species may be the result of evolutionary change. Different behavioural patterns may be selected for within isolated populations. The divergent behaviours may also be the engine of further evolutionary changes, reinforcing genetic isolation among species as a prezygotic isolation mechanism (chapter 4).

Pioneering work by Thomas Insel and Lawrence Shapiro provided some fascinating insights into the neurophysiological basis of mating systems. Different vole species (genus *Microtus*) display a variety of social and mating systems. For example, prairie voles (*Microtus ochrogaster*) and montane voles (*Microtus montanus*) display many similar physical characteristics and nonsocial behaviours but have strong differences in social behaviour. For example, the prairie vole typically forms long-term monogamous pairs while the montane vole lives in solitary burrows and shows no evidence of monogamy.

Insel and Shapiro studied the distribution of oxytocin receptor expression in the brains of these vole species (Insel and Shapiro 1992). This research was triggered as the neuropeptide oxytocin (and later vasopressin) were being implicated in various types of bonding behaviours. Insel and Shapiro used a radioactive analogue of oxytocin to bind to putative oxytocin receptors, collected coronal sections of vole brains, and visualized the locations and intensities of binding through autoradiography. They found that receptor density in prairie voles was highest in specific loci, including the prelimbic cortex and lateral amygdala. In montane voles, receptor density was low or not measured in these loci but was highest in other brain centres, including the hypothalamus and cortical nucleus of the amygdala. The oxytocin analogue used in the study was a derived vasotocin, structurally related to both oxytocin and vasopressin, and might not fully distinguish between receptors for these neuropeptides. This is relevant to later research by Miranda Lim and colleagues, who used a viral vector to insert a constitutively active prairie vole vasopressin receptor gene (V1aR) into the forebrain of male meadow voles (*Microtus pennsylvanicus*) (Lim et al. 2004). The meadow vole, like the montane vole, does not normally display monogamous pair bonding behaviour. This treatment targeted the brain centres identified by Insel and Shapiro as having high receptor density in prairie voles. Manipulating the expression level of the single vasopressin receptor gene resulted in the normally promiscuous male meadow vole spending substantially more time with his partner, demonstrating similar pair bonding to the reference prairie voles. This study is interesting in demonstrating that a complex mating system behaviour may be under relatively simple gene regulation, and that the location and perhaps timing of the gene's expression may be important in mating system phenotype. This could then provide a basis for natural selection to act upon mating system.

Sexual Selection

Charles Darwin (1871) proposed that the social environment, particularly the mating environment, could exert significant influence on the characteristics of organisms. He was particularly intrigued by the existence of what he called "secondary sexual characteristics," the origins of which he could not explain except by the advantages they gave to individuals during competition for mates. Darwin used the term *secondary sexual characteristics* to mean characteristics of males or females not directly involved in the process of reproduction. Some of the traits that Darwin had in mind were "gaudy colors and various ornaments . . . the power of song and other such characters." How do we explain the existence of characteristics such as the antlers of male deer, the bright peacock's tail, or the gigantic size and large nose of the male elephant seal? To explain the existence of such secondary sexual characteristics, Darwin proposed a process that he called **sexual selection**. Sexual selection results from differences in reproductive rates among individuals as a result of differences in their mating success.

Sexual selection is thought to be important under two circumstances. The first is where individuals of one sex compete among themselves for mates, which results in a process called **intrasexual selection**. For instance, when male mountain sheep or elephant seals fight among themselves for dominance or mating territories, the largest and strongest generally win such contests. In such situations, the result is often selection for larger body size and more effective weapons, such as horns or teeth. Since this selection is the result of contests within one sex, it is called intrasexual selection.

Sexual selection can also occur when members of one sex consistently choose mates from among members of the opposite sex on the basis of some particular trait. Because two sexes are involved, this form is called **intersexual selection**. Examples of traits used for mate selection include female birds choosing among potential male mates based on the brightness of their plumage or on the quality of their songs. Darwin proposed that once individuals of one sex begin to choose mates on the basis of some anatomical or behavioural trait, sexual selection would favour elaboration of the trait. For instance, male birds' plumage might become brighter over time, their songs might become more elaborate, or both.

There are limits to how much sexual selection can elaborate a trait. Elaboration may be limited by genetic variability within the population; if there is no variation among males' plumage, female preference cannot drive selection for ever brighter colours. Elaboration may also be limited when males begin to suffer higher mortality due to other sources of natural selection, such as that exerted by predators. Darwin proposed that sexual selection will continue to elaborate a trait until balanced by other sources of natural selection, such as predation. Since Darwin's early work on the subject, research has revealed a great deal about how organisms choose mates and about the basis of sexual selection. An excellent model for such studies is the guppy (*Poecilia reticulata*).

Mate Choice and Sexual Selection in Guppies

It would be difficult for experimental ecologists interested in mate choice and sexual selection to design a better experimental subject than the guppy (fig. 8.12). Guppies are native to the streams and rivers of Trinidad and Tobago, to islands in the southeastern Caribbean, and to the rivers draining nearby parts of the South American mainland. The waters inhabited by guppies range from small, clear mountain streams to murky lowland rivers. Along this gradient of physical conditions, guppies also encounter a broad range of biological situations. In the headwaters of streams above waterfalls, guppies live in the absence of predaceous fish or with the killifish (*Rivulus hartii*), which preys mainly on juveniles and is not a very effective predator of adult guppies. In contrast, guppies in lowland rivers live with a wide variety of predaceous fish, including the pike cichlid (*Crenicichla alta*), an effective visual predator of adult guppies (see chapter 4).

Male guppies show a broad range of coloration both within and among populations. What factors may produce this range of variation? Well, genetic variation that determines phenotypic variation is one component. Beyond this, fitness trade-offs are important in maintaining diversity in coloration. It turns out that female guppies, if given a choice, will mate with more brightly coloured males. Anne Houde (1997) summarized

Figure 8.12 A colourful male guppy courting a female guppy: What are the influences of mate selection by female guppies and natural selection by predators?
© Dr. Paul A. Zahl/Science Source.

findings of many studies on mate selection among guppies and concluded that bright coloration and a high number of coloured spots were attractive to females. All else being equal, bright coloration increases fitness for male guppies.

However, brightly coloured males are attacked more frequently by visual predators. This trade-off between higher mating success by bright males but greater vulnerability to predators provides a mechanistic explanation for variation in male coloration among different habitats. The most brightly coloured male guppies are found in populations exposed to few predators, while those exposed to predators, such as the pike cichlid, are much less brightly coloured (Endler 1995). Thus the coloration of male guppies in local populations may be determined by a dynamic interplay between natural selection exerted by predators and by female mate choice.

John Endler (1980) performed a classical study of natural selection for colour pattern in guppies, showing evolutionary shifts over short periods of time. The study included two separate, complementary experiments, one in artificial ponds in a greenhouse at Princeton University (fig. 8.13) and one at field sites (fig. 8.14). For the greenhouse experiments, Endler constructed 10 ponds. All ponds were lined with dyed gravel of mixed colours (black, white, green, blue, red, and yellow). This was standardized since the influence of prey colour on

vulnerability to predators depends on the background against which the prey is viewed by visual predators. Endler stocked each experimental pond with 200 guppies, drawn from 18 different populations, to include a substantial amount of colour variation. After allowing the guppies time to acclimate, he placed a single pike cichlid in each of four ponds, placed six *Rivulus* in each of four ponds, and maintained the other two ponds with no predators as controls. These three groups of ponds represented three levels of predation: high predation (pike cichlid), low predation (*Rivulus*), and no predation.

Endler's second experiment was conducted in the field within the drainage network of the Aripo River (fig. 8.14), where he encountered three distinctive situations within a few kilometres. Within the mainstream of the Aripo River, guppies coexisted with a wide variety of predators, including pike cichlids, which provided a "high predation" site. Upstream from the high predation site, Endler discovered a small tributary that flowed over a series of waterfalls. Because the waterfalls prevented most fish from swimming upstream, this tributary was entirely free of guppies but supported a population of the ineffective predator *Rivulus*. This potential "low predation" site provided an ideal situation for following the evolution of male colour. The third site, which was a bit farther upstream, was a small tributary that supported

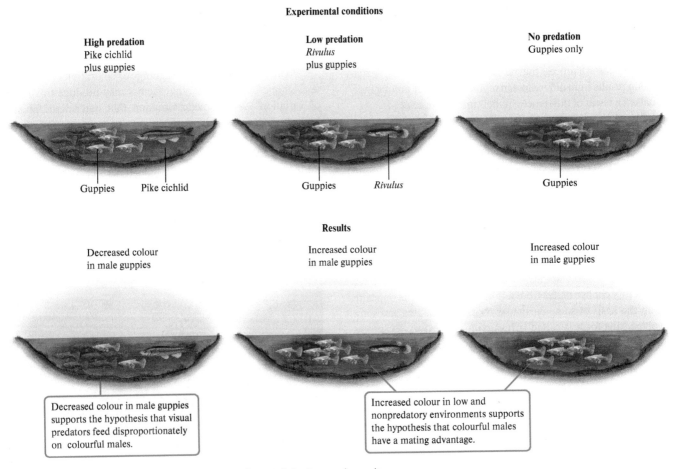

Figure 8.13 Summary of greenhouse experimental design and results.
Information from Endler 1980.

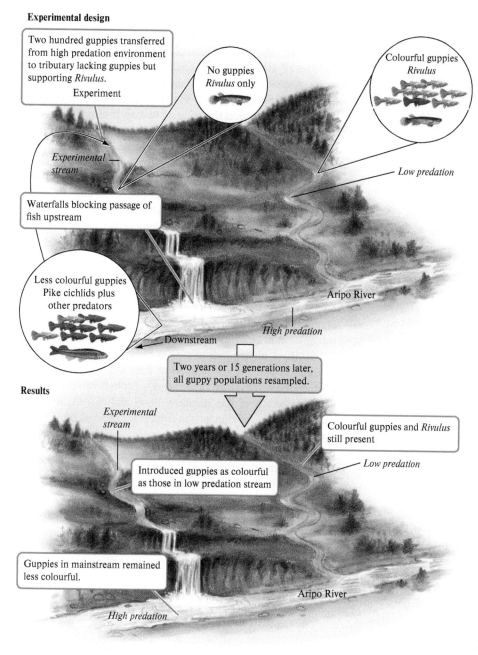

Figure 8.14 Field experiment on effects of predation on male guppy coloration. Information from Endler 1980.

predators and with *Rivulus*, but decreased in the high predation ponds containing pike cichlids. Figure 8.16, which summarizes the results of Endler's field experiment, compares the number of spots on males in high predation and low predation stream environments with guppies transferred from the high predation environment to a low predation environment. Notice that the transplanted population converged with the males at the low predation reference site during the experiment. In other words, when freed from predation, the average number of spots on male guppies increased. This result, along with the results of the greenhouse experiment, supports the hypothesis that predation reduces male showiness in guppy populations, and that evolution of male coloration reflects a trade-off between this predation pressure and female preference for bright coloration.

Sexual Conflict Among Water Striders

When we discussed characteristics that affect the fitness of male guppies, we did so in a bit of a vacuum. While reading, you might have thought to yourself, "That's all well and good for the males, but what does this all mean for the females' fitness?" If so, good for you! While it is not clear that selection of colourful males is a net positive or negative for the female's fitness, there are other examples where traits (behavioural and physical) that enhance the fitness of one sex actually come at a fitness cost to the other sex. In other cases, there is *sexual conflict*, an asymmetry between the sexes in the potential evolutionary costs and benefits of any particular mating event, or more broadly, mating system.

To begin to understand the conflict, sex isn't free. Although one can immediately recognize the potential reproductive benefits of sex, there are a variety of potential costs. One of the most obvious is the risk of sexually transmitted diseases, which can cause significant damage to the genitalia and reproductive machinery of plant and animal species. Needless to say, being castrated by a fungus that was acquired through sex is not good for one's fitness (well, except for the fitness of the parasite!). There are, however, much more subtle costs of sex, most of which return us to the principle of allocation we discussed in chapters 5 and 7. Mating takes time, and depending upon the details of the species involved, it can also require expenditure of significant amounts of energy. During mating, an individual

guppies along with *Rivulus*. This third site gave Endler a low predation reference site for his study. Endler captured 200 guppies in the high predation environment, measured the coloration of these guppies, and then introduced them to the site lacking guppies. Six months later the introduced guppies and their offspring had spread throughout the previously guppy-free tributary. Finally, two years later, or about 15 guppy generations after the introduction, Endler returned and sampled the guppies at all three study sites.

The results of the greenhouse and field experiments supported each other. As shown in figure 8.15, the number of coloured spots on male guppies increased in the greenhouse ponds with no

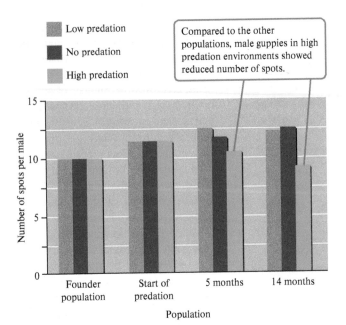

Figure 8.15 Results of greenhouse experiment, which exposed populations of guppies to no predation, low predation (killifish), and high predation (pike cichlid) environments.
Data from Endler 1980.

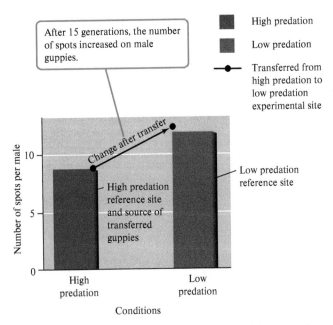

Figure 8.16 Results of field experiment involving transfer of guppies from high predation site to site with killifish, a fairly ineffective predator, with number of spots per male measured 15 generations after the transfer.
Data from Endler 1980.

is unable to perform other tasks, such as foraging, defending, or even finding an alternative (more suitable) mate. In some cases, these costs are shared equally by both males and females. In other cases, there is sexual conflict. Locke Rowe, of the University of Toronto, along with a diverse group of colleagues, has

conducted extensive theoretical and empirical studies of sexual conflict, with particular emphasis on water striders.

Water striders (Heteroptera) are commonly found on the surfaces of slowly flowing bodies of fresh water throughout North America (fig. 8.17). Their graceful appearance moving across the water surface is in sharp contrast to their mating system. Conflict between the sexes at mating is visually apparent, with males chasing and grasping females in an attempt to mate. More often than not, the female escapes from the male, and mating does not occur. However, if the male grabs hold, there is a vicious struggle in which significant energy is spent and both sexes are at a greatly increased risk of predation. Only occasionally does the male maintain hold, and mating occurs (Rowe et al. 1994). The classic explanation for such conflict has been that in water striders, females are able to retain viable sperm for about 10 days, and thus repeated mating is unnecessary to achieve full fertilization for the female. In contrast, males are likely to sire more offspring if they are the last male to mate with a female rather than the first, and thus selection should favour male promiscuity. However, Rowe and colleagues have pointed out that this classic explanation is lacking an explanation for the female behaviour, in that these mating events are not neutral for the females but instead are actually detrimental to their fitness. This physical conflict also results in evolutionary conflict between the sexes.

In a review of the literature, Rowe and colleagues suggest two key costs of mating for the female: (1) reduced female skating speed while carrying a male reduces foraging efficiency; and (2) mating females are at increased predation risk due to slower speed. As might be expected, sexual selection appears to have resulted in the evolution of a variety of physical and behavioural adaptations that mitigate the level of resistance in females. At the heart of this is the realization that both resisting and submitting to mating pose energetic and fitness costs to the female. As a result, evolution should favour strategies in females that minimize the costs of these two detrimental options. As you might expect, the "solution" to this problem will be dependent upon the local environmental conditions around a particular female and her population. For example, females of some species tend to spend more time hiding in vegetation when males are present than when they are absent. Though this decreases her ability to forage, this cost is likely less than what she would incur during a mating struggle.

Over longer periods, sexual conflict can have significant evolutionary consequences. In a study combining comparative and experimental approaches, Goran Arnqvist and Locke Rowe (2002) have found evidence that sexual conflict has caused the **co-evolution** of male and female armaments (clasping and anti-clasping appendages) in water striders. Female armaments increase the efficacy of resistance, and male armaments increase the ability of males to overcome this resistance. *Co-evolution* can be defined as a reciprocal evolutionary interaction between two or more species (or evolving groups, such as males and females). In co-evolution, genetic change in one group results in genetic change in another, with this process repeating over time. In water striders, this plays out with the evolution of unique morphologies in males that increase their ability to clasp, and in females that allow them to prevent clasping. Arnqvist and Rowe predicted that the relative difference in possession

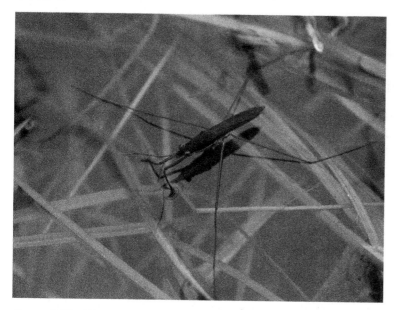

Figure 8.17 Water striders serve as a model organism for the study of sexual conflict between males and females.
Chris MacQuarrie.

probability of fertilizing the available ovules? Or is mating nonrandom? What mechanisms might produce nonrandom mating among wild radish? Nonrandom mating could result from competition among pollen (analogous to male elk competing for access to a female), maternal control over the fertilization process (analogous to a female guppy choosing a suitable mate), or a combination of the two processes. If nonrandom mating does occur in plants, it establishes the conditions necessary for sexual selection (i.e., maternal control) in plants. However, as Marshall and Michael Folsom (1991) pointed out, though sexual selection is well documented in animals, its occurrence among plants is a controversial and open question.

In greenhouse experiments, Marshall tested the hypothesis that plants mate nonrandomly (1990). In this experiment, Marshall mated three seed parents or maternal plants with six pollen donors. Marshall used the six pollen donors to make 63 kinds of crosses: 6 single donor crosses plus 57 mixed donor crosses, on each maternal plant. Her crosses included all possible mixtures of pollen from one to six donors. Plants were pollinated in the greenhouse by hand. To assess

of such "armaments" between males and females would drive mating (or escape) success. They found that when females were more heavily armed, mating was rarer and when males were more heavily armed, the number of copulations was higher. It is not difficult to see, then, how sexual selection will favour the evolution of increased armaments in the sex that is at a relative disadvantage in this conflict.

We now turn our attention to plants. Though many undergraduates are surprised even to learn that plants have sex, the behavioural ecology of mating by plants is even more complex than that found among animals.

Nonrandom Mating Among Wild Radish

Wild radish grows as an annual weed in California, where it can be commonly seen along roadways and in abandoned fields (fig. 8.18). The seeds of wild radish germinate in response to the first winter rains of California's Mediterranean climate (chapter 2), and the plants flower by January. Flowering may continue to late spring or early summer, depending on the length of the wet season. During their flowering season, wild radishes are pollinated by a wide variety of insects, including honeybees, syrphid flies, and butterflies. Wild radish flowers have both male (**stamens**) and female (**pistils**) parts and produce both pollen and ovules. However, a wild radish plant cannot pollinate itself, a condition called **self-incompatibility**. Because they must mate with other plants, a researcher working on wild radishes can more easily control matings between plants.

The insects that pollinate wild radishes generally arrive at flowers carrying pollen from several different plants, and as a consequence a wild radish plant typically has about seven mates. Under these circumstances of multiple mates, Diane Marshall asked whether siring offspring is a random process. In other words, do the seven mates of a typical wild radish plant have an equal

Figure 8.18 The wild radish (*Raphanus sativus*) has become a model for studying the mating behaviour of plants.
© Richard Parker/Science Source.

the possibility of nonrandom mating, Marshall compared the performance of different pollen donors. She estimated pollen donor performance in three ways: (1) number of seeds sired in mixed pollinations, (2) positions of seeds sired, and (3) weight of seeds sired. Some of the results from the mixed donor experiments indicated that pollen donors varied widely in their performance (fig. 8.19). Donor 1, for example, fared well siring a high percentage of seeds. Donor 3, in contrast, fared poorly in mixed donor experiments, siring a relatively low percentage of

seeds and seeds of low weight. In other words, mating in this experiment was nonrandom.

Marshall's study, and a subsequent study by Marshall and Ollar Fuller (1994) where maternal plants were grown under field conditions, demonstrated unequal mating success among pollen donors. So, does this nonrandom mating mean that plants exhibit sexual selection, with the maternal plant somehow selecting the mate (pollen donor)? Or is pollen competition occurring, with the winner having greater success in siring seeds? Or are both occurring? The answer is unclear regarding sexual selection. However, additional work by Marshall and her colleagues (Marshall et al. 1996) suggests that competition between pollen grains may contribute to the nonrandom mating. In this study, they used three maternal plants, crossed with seven pollen donors (A, B, C, D, E, F, Z). The maternal plants were pollinated from single donors and from pairs of donors. The paired pollinations (A + B, C + D, etc.) were done in two ways. In one set of experiments, the pollen from the two donors was mixed as in the previous experiments, described earlier. Because the two pollen types were in physical contact with each other in these "mixed" pollinations, the opportunity for interaction between pollen types was high. In the second set of experiments, the pollen of the two donors used was not mixed. Each was applied to adjacent halves of the stigma, the tip of the pistil that acts as a pollen-receptive area. Since the two pollen types did not contact each other in these adjacent areas, there was a reduced chance that they would interact. Pollen response to these conditions was measured as the percentage of pollen that germinated within 90 minutes of pollination. Reduced percentage of germination would indicate lower pollen responsiveness, and the possibility of inhibition through pollen-to-pollen interactions.

Some of the results of this experiment are shown in figure 8.20. The percentage of pollen that germinated after 90 minutes was essentially the same in the single donor and adjacent

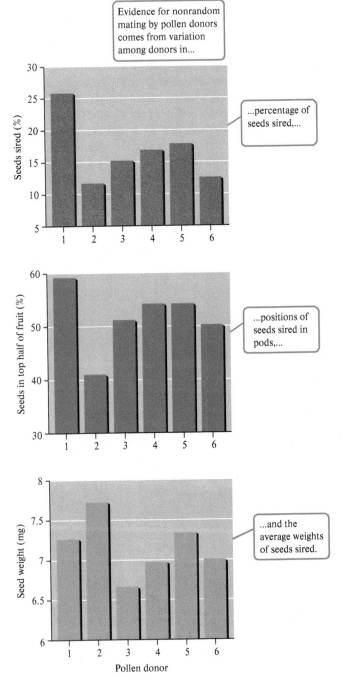

Figure 8.19   Evidence for unequal mating success among wild radish pollen donors in a mixed pollen donor experiment in a greenhouse environment.
Data from Marshall 1990.

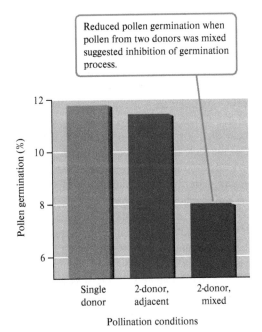

Figure 8.20   Competition between pollen from different donors.

pollinations. Meanwhile, the rate of germination when pollen from the two donors was mixed was much reduced. This reduced germination indicates that interactions between pollen inhibited pollen germination. These results suggest **interference competition** among pollen grains, which usually involves some form of aggressive or inhibitory interactions between individuals.

While ecological interactions between plants are often much less obvious than those between animals, careful and ingenious experiments such as those of Marshall and her colleagues are proving that they are every bit as rich and fascinating. Additionally, because sexual reproduction is the foundation of agriculture, understanding these basic ecological issues is of critical economic and societal importance.

CONCEPT 8.3 REVIEW

1. Why do behavioural ecologists differentiate between social and genetic monogamy?

2. In Endler's field experiment, why did male colourfulness increase in the absence of effective predators and not just remain static?

3. What would you expect to see in figure 8.20 if nonrandom mating in wild radish was driven by sexual selection only, and not by pollen competition?

ECOLOGICAL TOOLS AND APPROACHES

Using Game Theory to Understand Behaviour

Behavioural ecologists can take a variety of approaches in their research. They can use observation to document behaviours, trying to discern whether some behaviours are more frequently exhibited under some conditions than under others. They can conduct manipulative experiments in which they modify the environment, testing whether certain factors directly influence behaviour. They can also measure the fitness costs and benefits of a variety of behavioural choices, such as movement, breeding, and predator alarm calls.

Linking all of these branches of behavioural ecology is theory. It is in theory that ecologists are able to imagine alternative worlds and behaviours, testing what responses are optimum under which set of conditions. From theory can come focused experiments to test the resulting hypotheses. Behavioural ecology, however, poses a particular challenge. Individuals are able to exhibit alternative behaviours based upon the *choices* that other individuals make. For example, ground squirrels are less likely to make alarm calls in response to seeing a predator if another individual has already made a call. This makes evolutionary sense, as there is likely little benefit of alerting a predator to your presence if your kin are already aware that a predator is in the area.

Understanding the relative fitness of different behaviours gets very complicated when their value is contingent upon the choices of others. This sounds an awful lot like a game. Behavioural ecologists have adapted the methods of game theory, a branch of mathematics devoted to the study of strategy in which the players seek to maximize their individual returns.

Game theory was initially developed for use in economics, where it still forms the basis for much economic theory. Many aspects of economics, sociology, and ecology overlap (organizations = populations and communities; returns =

fitness; etc.), and there is substantial overlap in the theoretical tools used by researchers in these seemingly distinct disciplines. It was John Maynard Smith (1982) who emphasized the potential benefits of game theory to understanding behavioural ecology, and its use has grown since then. Here we will discuss one form of a classic "game" from game theory, and show how it has been used to provide a theoretical foundation for behavioural ecology.

Evolutionary Stable Strategies

In most ecological "games," the theorist uses changes in fitness as a measure of the potential costs and benefits of different strategic decisions. Under some combinations of behaviours, fitness may increase, while under other combinations, fitness may decrease. Using game theory, researchers are able to explore if one behaviour is resistant to invasion by another behaviour. In other words, if one behaviour results in a fitness of "X," but a new behaviour results in a fitness of "X + 1," natural selection will favour the second behaviour, displacing the first. One goal of game theory is to determine which behaviour (or sets of behaviours) is (are) the **evolutionary stable strategy**, often abbreviated ESS. ESS represents the behavioural decision that is resistant to invasion and most likely to be maintained by natural selection. ESS is a critical aspect of game theory as applied to ecology and will be discussed throughout the following examples.

Hawk–Dove

John Maynard Smith introduced many behavioural ecologists to game theory in his book titled *Evolution and the Theory of Games* (Maynard Smith 1982). One of the games described in the book is the Hawk–Dove game. There are many variations of the game, and we

		Behaviour of Opponent	
		Hawk	Dove
Behaviour of Attacker	Hawk	Each Hawk wins ½ the time and gets hurt ½ the time Hawk (attacker) = 0.5·R − 0.5·C	Hawk always wins and never gets hurt Hawk = R
	Dove	Dove always retreats and never gets hurt Dove = 0	Each Dove wins ½ the time and never gets hurt Dove (attacker) = 0.5·R

will discuss one possible form. Imagine a scenario in which two individuals interact over a contested resource. Individuals within a population can exhibit one of two behaviours: (1) they can always attack the other individual, taking the resource (R) when they win (Hawk). However, if a Hawk encounters another Hawk, it will win only one-half of the time, and when it loses, will suffer an injury cost (C). The alternative strategy in our game is to (2) present a threat display but never actually engage in a fight (Dove). Doves will take the resource one-half of the time against another Dove (the other one backs down first) but will always lose the resource to a Hawk. However, because the Doves are not engaging in a fight, they suffer no injury costs. An important rule to the game is that individuals cannot switch behaviours over time; once a Dove, always a Dove. These behaviours are roughly similar to the selfishness (Hawk) and cooperation (Dove) classifications of Hamilton that we discussed earlier in this chapter. The basic question to the game is whether the Hawk or Dove strategy is evolutionarily stable. To answer this question, we can devise a payoff matrix that describes the four possible situations that could occur. In our matrix, R represents the value of the resource and C represents the cost of injury.

The next step is to determine which strategy is an ESS. Because the payoffs to an attacker are dependent upon the behaviour of its opponent, we need to introduce another term, p, which represents the proportion of individuals that are Hawks in the population (and thus $1 - p$ represents the proportion of Doves in the population). Using these proportions, we can now calculate the average payoff (= fitness) for Hawks and Doves.

Hawks will encounter other Hawks with a frequency of p, and thus the return for this scenario is $p \cdot (0.5 \cdot R - 0.5 \cdot C)$. Hawks will encounter Doves at a frequency of $1 - p$, and their return will be $(1 - p) \cdot R$. Putting these together, the payoff for the Hawk strategy is:

$$\text{Hawk} = p \cdot (0.5 \cdot R - 0.5 \cdot C) + (1 - p) \cdot R$$

Doves will encounter Hawks at a frequency of p with a payoff of $p = 0$, and they will encounter other Doves with a

frequency of $(1 - p)$ and a payoff of $(1 - p) \cdot (0.5 \cdot R)$. Putting these together, the payoff for the Dove strategy is:

$$\text{Dove} = p \cdot 0 + (1 - p) \cdot (0.5 \cdot R)$$

So which strategy is an ESS for this game? Well, we can start by imagining a population that consists solely of Doves ($p = 0$). In this world, the fitness of a Dove would be 0.5·R. Now we can imagine a world of only Hawks ($p = 1$). The fitness of the Hawk would be 0.5·R − 0.5·C. Clearly, the fitness of Doves in a Dove world is higher than the fitness of Hawks in a Hawk world (0.5·R must be greater than 0.5[R − C]), and thus the Dove strategy is the ESS, right? No. Let's imagine we live in the world of Doves, and a single Hawk enters the population. What would its fitness be? Because it is so rare, we can still let $p = 0$, and it will only encounter other Doves. In such a scenario, the Hawk's fitness will be R, exactly twice as high as that Dove's fitness (0.5·R)! This will result in strong selection for the Hawk behaviour, and the Doves will quickly be displaced. That means, then, that the Hawk is the ESS, right? Not necessarily.

What happens if we live in a Hawk world, and a single Dove enters? That Dove will always encounter Hawks, resulting in a Dove fitness of 0. Whether or not Hawk is an ESS depends on whether 0.5·R − 0.5·C is greater or less than 0, the fitness of the Dove. Rearranging this equation, we see that the Hawk strategy in our game will be an ESS if R > C. In other words, a Hawk-only population will be stable if, and only if, the value of the resource is greater than the potential cost of injury. If instead injury is more costly than the resource, then neither the Hawk nor Dove population is an ESS! Instead, the ESS population will consist of individuals of both behaviours. Game theory can actually predict the frequency of Hawks and Doves that will occur in a stable population.

What does it mean for Hawks and Doves to both persist? It simply means that the fitness of the Hawk strategy is equal to the fitness of the Dove strategy, and thus selection would not favour one over the other. But how is this possible, given that the rewards and costs are fixed (at least within a population)? The variable that can change is p, the frequency of Hawks. We can thus use the two equations:

$$\text{Hawk} = p \cdot (0.5 \cdot R - 0.5 \cdot C) + (1 - p) \cdot R$$

$$\text{Dove} = p \cdot 0 + (1 - p) \cdot (0.5 \cdot R)$$

We can then set Hawk = Dove:

$$p \cdot (0.5 \cdot R - 0.5 \cdot C) + (1 - p) \cdot R = p \cdot 0 + (1 - p) \cdot (0.5 \cdot R)$$

And solve for p:

$$p = R/C$$

What does this mean? We already know that if rewards are greater than costs (R > C), the ESS will be a Hawk-only world, and $p = 1$. If instead rewards are less than costs, then p will be less than one. For example, if R = 50 and C = 100, then the mixed ESS solution will be Hawks at a frequency of 50/100 = 0.5. In other words, in this game, with those values for R and C, the ESS is a population that consists of equal numbers of Hawks and Doves. If R and C were 50 and 75, respectively, then the mixed ESS solution would be 50/75, Hawks = p = 2/3.

Our Hawk–Dove example shows that determining the relative fitness of individual actions will be dependent upon the frequency of other behaviours in the population, as well as upon the costs and rewards of a given action. A population consisting of only Doves results in the highest average fitness of individuals, but it is the least stable in this game—susceptible to invasion by Hawks regardless of the values of the reward and costs of fighting. Remember from chapter 4 that selection does not act on the absolute fitness of individuals but instead on the relative differences in fitness among individuals within a population. Natural selection does not work toward a goal of maximizing fitness in a population; instead, it simply favours those with the highest relative fitness.

These games can be expanded in a variety of ways, including adding costs of display for the Doves or costs of fighting for Hawks (independent of injury), and can include additional behaviours. Next we discuss a few examples of how researchers are using game theory to address real ecological questions.

Game Theory in Modern Ecology

In a collaboration between researchers at the University of Otago and the Université du Québec à Montréal (Poulin and Vickery 1995), game theory was used to explore cleaning symbioses. Many organisms engage in cooperative behaviours regarding the removal of dead tissue and parasites. These interactions include birds removing ticks from the backs of large ungulates, and wrasses removing parasites from other fish on coral reefs. Many of these interactions are spectacular to watch, such as wrasses that move in and out of the jaws of much larger fish, without any apparent risk of predation. However, there is ample opportunity for cheating by both parties. The cleaners could easily feed upon living tissue and blood of the host, while the host itself could feed upon the cleaners. Poulin and Vickery explored the conditions under which cheating may become favoured. A major influence for both cleaners and clients was the relative fitness value of being cleaned (or eating parasites) versus eating the cleaner (or the client). In other words, if the value of R is high, relative to the alternative food source, honesty is an ESS. You may recognize this has some similarities to our discussion of optimal foraging in chapter 7.

Dubois and Giraldeau (2005), also from the Université du Québec à Montréal, discuss the strengths and weaknesses of using the Hawk–Dove game to model the defence of resources by animals. They explain that the classic game theory model says that when the cost of defence is low, there should be increased aggression and defence of resources. However, they are able to expand this original model and show that aggression is itself going to be dependent upon the spatial distribution of resources, predation risk, the density of individuals in a population, and the value of the resources themselves. They demonstrate that animal behaviour extends well beyond simple interactions between two individuals and that to truly understand how individuals will interact it is essential to also understand the landscape in which they will compete. In other words, behaviour is displayed by individuals, but is done in response to a diversity of simultaneously interacting factors. These ideas will be more fully explored in chapter 21, Landscape Ecology.

It may surprise you that the conditional behavioural strategies that can be modelled by game theory can also apply to plants. Recall from chapter 7 that plants are very flexible in where they put their roots in response to varied nutrient levels in the soil. Not surprisingly, one of the determinants of root placement is the *choices* made by other plants, as we will explore in chapter 13. Mordechi Gersani and his colleagues (2001) explored the ESS of the "choice" faced by plants: Do you put your roots near other plants to try and take all of their resources, or do you put your roots away from plants, "sharing" resources among all? Their model produced an outcome similar to the traditional Hawk–Dove model, where the ESS appears to be increased root allocation when neighbours are present, causing an increase in competition and a reduction in the absolute number of seeds (fitness) produced. Although there is currently much controversy surrounding experimental work testing these ideas (Schenk 2006), the study by Gersani and colleagues shows that the usefulness of game theory extends well beyond the realm of animals.

SUMMARY

The behaviour of organisms and their social relations can frequently directly impact the reproductive contribution of individuals to future generations, a key component of fitness. The field of behavioural ecology blends understanding of physiology, evolution, and ecology. Many patterns observed in nature are difficult to understand without a firm grounding in behavioural ecology.

8.1 Natural selection favours those behaviours that increase the inclusive fitness of individuals.

Many behaviours have a genetic basis and are, thus, at least partially heritable. As a result, there is the potential for natural selection to influence not only phenotype, but also social relations (fig. 8.21). Critical to understanding the adaptive value of different behaviours is the concept of inclusive fitness, which accounts for the similarity in genetic composition of closely related individuals. By using this broader view of fitness, seemingly maladaptive behaviours, such as altruism, can be favoured through natural selection, through a process called kin selection. In kin selection, individuals are more likely to perform a given behaviour if the potential benefit to their inclusive fitness is greater than the cost. Not all behaviours among individuals are altruistic, and instead selection can also favour selfishness. For example, brood parasites such as the cowbird are often successful in inducing altruistic acts from their host by manipulating pre-existing behaviours and limitations. Natural selection does not necessarily favour the "nicest" behaviours, only the most effective. Cooperation can occur among individuals when there is a tit-for-tat arrangement in which each individual is assured of cooperation from the other. In this scenario, altruism can occur even among unrelated individuals and without manipulation.

8.2 The evolution of sociality is generally accompanied by cooperative feeding, defence of the social group, and restricted reproductive opportunities.

The degree of sociality in a social species ranges from acts as simple as mutual grooming or group protection of young, to highly complex, stratified societies, such as those found in colonies of ants or termites. This more complex level of social behaviour, which is considered to be the pinnacle of social evolution, is called eusociality. Eusociality is generally thought to include three major characteristics: (1) individuals of more than one generation living together, (2) cooperative care of young, and (3) division of individuals into sterile, or nonreproductive, and reproductive castes. Cooperation among African lions appears to be a response to environmental conditions that require cooperation for success. To survive, reproduce, and successfully raise offspring to maturity, African lions must work in cooperative groups of females, which are called prides, and of males, which are called coalitions.

8.3 Mate choice by one sex and/or competition for mates among individuals of the same sex can result in selection for particular traits, a process called sexual selection.

Species vary greatly in the combination of sex types that they contain, ranging from hermaphrodites to single sexes, with

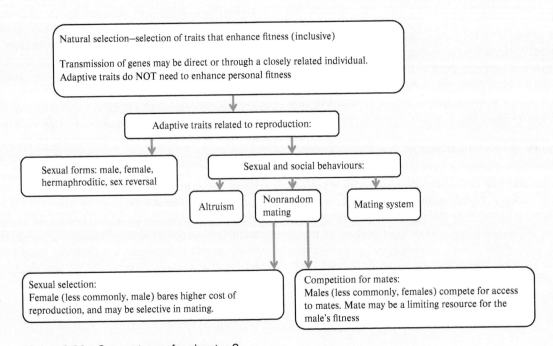

Figure 8.21 Concept map for chapter 8.

nearly all possible alternatives found somewhere in nature. Sex types are arranged into different mating systems, depending upon the social interactions among individuals. Sexual selection results from differences in reproductive rates among individuals as a result of differences in their mating success. Sexual selection is thought to work either through intrasexual selection, where individuals of one sex compete with each other for mates, or through intersexual selection, when members of one sex consistently choose mates from among members of the opposite sex on the basis of some particular trait.

In some species, such as water striders, the immediate fitness consequences of mating will differ between males and females, resulting in sexual conflict. Repeated mating is not inherently beneficial for female striders, as it can increase predation risk and reduce foraging time, and it is redundant if they already contain enough sperm for fertilization of their eggs. However, male striders benefit from being the last to mate with a given female. As a result, natural selection has resulted in an escalating arms race in morphologies that allow the male to clasp the females and allow the females to escape. The relative difference in armaments between the sexes greatly influences the outcome of mating attempts.

Experimental evidence supports the hypothesis that the coloration of male guppies in local populations is determined by a dynamic interplay between natural selection exerted by predators, under which less colourful males have higher survival, and by female mate choice, which results in higher mating success by more colourful males. Studies of mating in the wild radish indicate nonrandom mating and suggest interference competition among pollen from different pollen donors.

Game theory is an essential theoretical tool for behavioural ecologists. Understanding the relative fitness of behaviours is often difficult because their values are dependent upon the actions of others. By imagining behavioural interactions as a game, it is possible to determine which behaviour is evolutionarily stable and resistant to invasion by alternative behaviours. In the Hawk–Dove game, a world of Doves results in the highest absolute fitness, but it is easily invaded by a Hawk. The ESS will be a mixture of Hawks and Doves, with the frequency of each being a function of the costs and benefits of each strategy. Game theory has been applied to a variety of situations in behavioural ecology, including defence of resources among both plants and animals, as well as cleaner–client relationships.

REVIEW QUESTIONS

1. The introduction to this chapter included sketches of the behaviour and social systems of several fish species. Using the concepts that you have learned in the chapter, revisit those examples, consider the forms of sexual selection occurring in each species, and think about how these forms of selection explain the phenotypes (behavioural or physical) of the species.

2. One of the basic assumptions of the material presented in this chapter is that the form of reproduction will exert substantial influence on social interactions within a species. How might interactions differ in populations that reproduce asexually versus ones that engage in sexual reproduction? How might having separate sexes versus hermaphrodites affect the types of social interactions within a population? How should having several forms of one sex, for example, large and small males, influence the diversity of behavioural interactions within the population?

3. Is altruism likely to become a common trait within a species if there is no fitness benefit (in either the short or long term) to the individual performing the altruistic act? Why?

4. Endler (1980) pointed out that though field observations are consistent with the hypothesis that predators may exert natural selection on guppy coloration, some other factors in the environment could be affecting variation in male colour patterns among guppy populations. What other factors, especially physical and chemical factors, might affect male colours, and should each influence male colour?

5. A study by Astrid Kodric-Brown considered the mating success of male guppies based on two different traits: attractiveness to females and aggression toward other males. A male guppy might be attractive to a female and dominant (aggressive toward other males); attractive but subordinate; unattractive to females but dominant; or unattractive and subordinate. While most of the male guppies that successfully mated were dominant, a substantial proportion of attractive males that sired broods were subordinate. How might we interpret this reproductive success by attractive but subordinate males? What might these results indicate about the potential influence of female choice on mating success among male guppies?

6. Locke Rowe and colleagues have explored sexual conflict between male and female water striders. What ecological and environmental conditions are likely to result in sexual conflict in other species?

7. The results of numerous studies indicate nonrandom mating among plants, at least under some conditions. These results lead to questions concerning the biological mechanisms that produce these nonrandom matings. How might the maternal plant control or at least influence the paternity of her seeds? What role might competition between pollen determine in the nonrandom patterns observed?

8. The details of experimental design are critical for determining the success or failure of both field and laboratory experiments. Results often depend on some small details. For instance, Jennifer Jarvis waited one year after establishing

her laboratory colony of naked mole rats before attempting to quantify the behaviour of the laboratory population. Why? What might have been the consequence of beginning to quantify the behaviour of the colony soon after it was established?

9. Behavioural interactions are often difficult to study because an individual's behaviour can be dependent upon the behavioural responses of other individuals of the same and different species. How does this differ from the physiological responses of organisms to their abiotic environment? How does game theory allow behavioural ecologists to develop theory to understand these social interactions?

10. Choose a problem in the behavioural ecology of social relations, formulate a hypothesis, and design a study to test your hypothesis. Take two approaches. In one approach use field and laboratory experiments to test your ideas. In the second design, develop a study that uses the comparative method.

© John White Photos/Getty Images.

CHAPTER 9   LIFE HISTORIES AND THE NICHE

CHAPTER CONCEPTS

9.1 Because all organisms have access to limited energy and resources, there are fundamental trade-offs in how these can be allocated between survival, offspring number, and offspring size.

Ecology in Action: How Life Histories Influence Extinction Risk

Concept 9.1 Review

9.2 The great diversity of life histories observed in nature can be classified on the basis of a few common characteristics.

Concept 9.2 Review

9.3 The fundamental niche reflects the environmental requirements of species, while the realized niche also includes interactions with other species.

Concept 9.3 Review

Ecological Tools and Approaches: Using Life-History Information as Indicators of Biological Effects of Climate Change

Summary

Review Questions

ifferent species living side-by-side differ in a number of important ways. They may reproduce at vastly different rates, have lifetimes that differ by several orders of magnitude, and produce offspring of substantially different sizes. Some may reproduce asexually; others, sexually. For some, offspring may disperse and live independently, while others may grow as an interconnected network of genetically identical "individuals." Despite these fundamental differences in aspects of their biology, co-occurring species have something in common: the ability to live and reproduce under similar environmental conditions.

Imagine sitting by a stream on a sunny day in the Great Bear Rainforest along British Columbia's central coast (fig. 9.1). You are cooled by the deep shade cast by the giant western red cedar tree (*Thuja plicata*), which has lived for centuries.

On this summer morning, you see a female mayfly along with thousands of others of her species shedding their larval exoskeletons as they transform from their aquatic stage to their flying stage. As a larva, the mayfly had lived in the stream for a year. Her adult stage lasts just this one day, during which she mates, deposits her eggs in the stream, and then dies. As the mayflies swarm, some will be eaten by birds nesting in trees that grow along the stream, some will be caught by bats that roost among the giant cedars, and some, as they linger too long on the surface, will be eaten by the trout that they had successfully eluded for a year of larval life. And, if you are quiet, you may even see a bear come down to catch a trout as it rises to the surface.

The cedars, mayflies, birds, fish, and bear all have lives that are intertwined but that differ greatly in scale and timing. They reproduce at different rates, have lifetimes that differ by several orders of magnitude, produce offspring of substantially different sizes, and differ in how they invest in these offspring. While the cedar produces seeds numbering in the millions over a lifetime that will stretch for centuries, the mayfly will spend a year in the stream and then emerge to lay eggs that will number in the hundreds. The trout's spawn will number in the thousands, deposited over the several years of her life. The bear will produce just a few cubs. And you may have even fewer offspring, but each will require a significant investment of time and energy for decades. (Speaking for parents, it's not that we necessarily want you leave, we're just wondering how long you'll be staying!) Yet, despite the differences in how these species live, they all are able to live and reproduce under similar environmental conditions in this part of British Columbia.

In previous chapters of this section, we focused on how organisms deal with isolated environmental and social conditions. However, individuals never encounter these factors in isolation, and instead natural selection acts upon all of these factors simultaneously. Because of limited amounts of energy, resources, and genetic variation, not all organisms are able to cope with all potential combinations of environmental conditions. Instead, for each species there will be a limited set of conditions suitable for growth and reproduction. That combination of suitable conditions is a species' **niche**, and we might expect to find a species occupying areas of the landscape in which environmental conditions match the species' niche requirements. However, even species that overlap in niche requirements may differ greatly in important factors, such as the number and size of offspring they produce, the timing of first reproduction, and patterns of survival. These sorts of questions fall within the domain of those who study **life histories**. This chapter presents several concepts from these two central aspects of ecology.

Figure 9.1   The Great Bear Rainforest is a lush region of coastal British Columbia.

9.1 Trade-Offs

Because all organisms have access to limited energy and resources, there are fundamental trade-offs in how these can be allocated between survival, offspring number, and offspring size. In 1976, while still a graduate student at the University of British Columbia, Stephen Stearns wrote a seminal paper on life history traits (Stearns 1976). The paper provided a synthesis of what was understood regarding patterns of reproductive output (size of brood and size of young), age distribution of reproductive output, relationships between reproductive output and mortality (parental and juvenile), and the variation in these traits among offspring. Moreover, it launched a new field in ecology; it led to the development of specific, testable hypotheses regarding which combinations of life history traits should evolve in organisms living under specific conditions. Much of what we will discuss in this chapter stems from the work of ecologists who responded to and tested the hypotheses presented in Stearns's seminal paper.

In chapters 5 to 7, we discussed how trade-offs in energy allocation influence an organism's ability to cope with abiotic stressors, such as low water availability or extreme temperatures. However, the principle of allocation is just as important in influencing how an organism allocates energy within a given segment of its energy budget, such as reproduction. For example, producing five large offspring costs more energy than producing five small offspring. If the amount of energy an organism has available to allocate to reproduction is limited, there is an inevitable trade-off between offspring number and offspring size. Perhaps an individual increases its energetic allocation to reproduction, allowing it to produce many large offspring. Has this individual avoided a trade-off? No. That increased allocation to reproduction must come at the cost of reduced allocation to some other life function, such as growth rate or "maintenance." As a result, though this organism may breed, it is likely to either have reduced growth or increased risk of mortality—remember the annual plants we discussed in chapter 5 that reproduce and die rather than allocating resources to surviving winter. So, without reallocating energy from other functions to reproduction, an individual might produce one large offspring or five small offspring at equal cost. Which should it produce? Well, it depends. The five small offspring would seem to increase fitness, unless the single large offspring has a much greater chance of survival, and this may come down to the environmental conditions this organism experiences. Understanding trade-offs serves as the foundation of the study of life histories. In this section, we explore a few of the many trade-offs that structure life histories.

Allometry

In this chapter we will discuss various trade-offs, particularly as they relate to reproductive output. Before we do, we should introduce you to the principle of allometric scaling, or **allometry**. Allometry is a study of scaling between body size and various biological functions, including shape, anatomy, physiology, and behaviour. Many biological attributes do not scale linearly with body size. A common example of this is body mass among mammals. A doubling in the length of a mammal results in more than a doubling in mass. Mass increases exponentially with body length, and the relationship between length and mass shows positive allometry. In contrast, mammalian basal metabolic rates decrease with mass, not linearly but, rather, as a power function. An elephant has a much lower mass-specific basal metabolic rate than a cat. This is an example of negative allometry. Germane to our discussion on trade-offs, body size will constrain how organisms behave (chapter 8); how they acquire water, nutrients, and energy (chapters 6 and 7); their relationships with temperature and heat or cold tolerance (chapter 5);

their reproductive strategies and longevity (this chapter); dispersal of populations and colonization (chapter 10); and how they interact with other species (chapters 13–15). While we may not always discuss allometry in these other chapters, keep in mind that much of an organism's niche is related to body size over its life stages and to the limitations that body size imposes.

Size and Number of Offspring

Fish Egg Size and Number

Because of their great diversity (more than 20,000 existing species), the wide variety of environments in which they live, and the relative isolation of populations, fish show more variation in many life-history traits than any other group of animals (Winemiller 1995). For instance, the number of offspring that fish produce per brood ranges from the one or two large, live young produced by Mako sharks, to the 600,000,000 eggs per clutch laid by the ocean sunfish.

Tom Turner and Joel Trexler investigated life-history variation among populations of darters (Turner and Trexler 1998). Darters are small, streamlined benthic fish that live in rivers and streams throughout eastern and central North America, including Canada (fig. 9.2). Darters consist of 174 species in three genera within the family Percidae, making them one of the most species-rich groups of vertebrates in North America. Despite the fact that the darters as a whole live in similar habitats and have similar anatomy, they vary widely in their life histories. Turner and Trexler were particularly interested in the relationship between egg size and egg number, also known as **fecundity**. Fecundity is simply the number of offspring produced by an organism.

Turner and Trexler sampled 64 locations on streams and rivers in the Ohio, Ozark, and Ouachita Highlands regions of Ohio, Arkansas, and Missouri, the heart of freshwater fish diversity in North America. Of the darters they collected at these locations, they chose 20 species for detailed study. Overall, the species ranged in length from 44 to 127 mm; the number of

Figure 9.2   Darters such as this male greenside darter form a diverse and distinctive subfamily of fish within the perch family, native only to North America.
blickwinkel/Alamy Stock Photo.

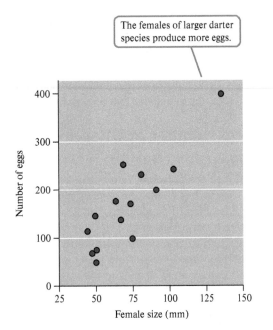

The females of larger darter species produce more eggs.

Figure 9.3 Relationship between female darter size and number of eggs.

Data from Turner and Trexler 1998.

differences in life histories relate to other ecological processes, such as gene flow? Turner and Trexler proposed that gene flow would be higher among populations producing more numerous smaller eggs, that is, among populations with higher fecundity.

Turner and Trexler found a negative relationship between egg size and gene flow, but a strong positive relationship of gene flow with the number of eggs produced by females (fig. 9.5). That is, populations of darter species that produce many small eggs showed less variation in genetic diversity across the study region than did populations that produce fewer larger eggs.

How do differences in egg size and number translate into differences in gene flow among populations? It turns out that the larvae of darters that hatch from larger eggs are larger when they hatch. These larger larvae begin feeding at an earlier age on prey that live on the stream bed and spend less time drifting with the water current. Consequently, larvae hatching from larger eggs disperse shorter distances and therefore carry their genes shorter distances. As a result, populations of species producing fewer larger eggs will be more isolated genetically from other populations. Because of their greater isolation,

mature eggs that they produced ranged from 49 to 397; and the size of eggs produced varied from 0.9 to 2.3 mm in diameter. Turner and Trexler found that these variables were interrelated. For example, larger darter species produce larger numbers of eggs (fig. 9.3). Further, darters that produce larger eggs produce fewer eggs (fig. 9.4), suggesting a trade-off between offspring size and number.

Similar relationships have been found among other vertebrates, leading ecologists to view the negative relationship between offspring size and number as a general rule structuring animal life histories. That by itself is interesting, but the pattern also leads to new questions. For example, how do these

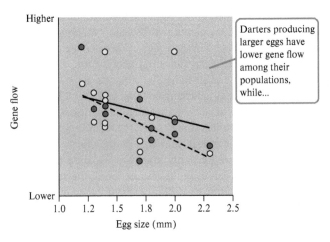

Darters producing larger eggs have lower gene flow among their populations, while...

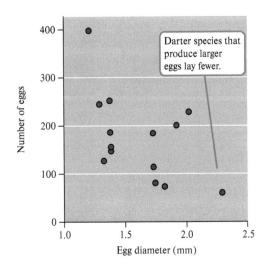

Darter species that produce larger eggs lay fewer.

Figure 9.4 Relationship between the size of eggs laid by darters and the number of eggs laid.

Data from Turner and Trexler 1998.

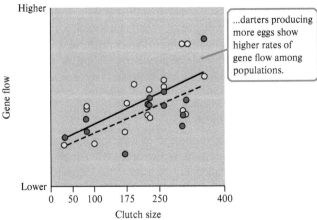

...darters producing more eggs show higher rates of gene flow among populations.

Figure 9.5 Relationship between egg size and egg number and gene flow in darter species. Solid lines and yellow dots represent estimates by one genetic method, and dashed lines and red dots by a second method.

Data from Turner and Trexler 1998.

such populations will differentiate genetically more rapidly compared to populations of species that produce many smaller larvae that disperse longer distances.

Turner and Trexler's study not only provides a case history consistent with the generalization that there is a trade-off between offspring size and number, it also reveals some of the consequences of that trade-off. For example, because larger offspring will travel shorter distances before feeding than smaller offspring will, populations of species that produce large offspring will be more genetically distinct than the species with small offspring. This is because gene flow acts to reduce the genetic diversity between populations, making them more similar. In a species that produces large offspring, there will be limited flow of alleles between populations, and these populations can differentiate genetically. Genetic differentiation is a necessary precursor to speciation events (chapter 4); thus, this most basic of life-history trade-offs, offspring size vs. number, has the potential to influence macro evolutionary processes, such as variation in speciation rates.

Ecologists have found parallel relationships among terrestrial plants, involving seed size and number.

Seed Size and Number in Plants

Like fish, plants vary widely in the number and size of offspring they produce (fig. 9.6). Botanists have long recognized a negative relationship between seed size and seed number (Stevens 1932), reflecting a trade-off in reproductive investment. The sizes of seeds produced by plants range over 10 orders of magnitude, from the tiny seeds of orchids, which weigh 0.000002 g, to the giant double coconut palm with seeds that weigh up to 27,000 g. While some orchids are known to produce billions of seeds, coconut palms produce small numbers of huge seeds. Figure 9.7 shows the relationship between average seed mass and the number of seeds per plant among species in four families of plants: daisies (Asteraceae), grasses (Poaceae), mustards (Brassicaceae), and beans (Fabaceae). In all four families,

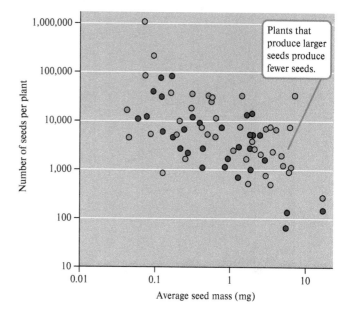

Figure 9.7 Relationship between seed mass and seed number.

Data from Stevens 1932.

species producing larger numbers of seeds on average produce fewer seeds.

In the darter example, we saw that dispersal and offspring size were related. Is that also the case for plants? Mark Westoby, Michelle Leishman, and Janice Lord (1996) conducted a study to determine if the mechanisms of seed dispersal related to seed size. The study included the seeds of hundreds of plant species from five different regions: three in Australia (New South Wales, central Australia, and Sydney), one in Europe (Sheffield, United Kingdom), and one in North America (Indiana Dunes National Lakeshore).

Westoby and his coauthors sorted seeds from each species into one of six dispersal strategies based on morphology: unassisted (no specialized structures for dispersal), **adhesion-adapted**, wind-dispersed, ant-dispersed, vertebrate-dispersed (primarily birds), and scatterhoarded (seeds typically gathered and cached by mammals). Their study found that plants that disperse their seeds in different ways tend to produce seeds of different sizes (fig. 9.8). Plants that they had classified as unassisted dispersers produced the smallest seeds while wind-dispersed seeds were slightly larger. Animal-dispersed seeds were the largest, particularly those that are scatterhoarded. Westoby et al. (1996) concluded that between 21% and 47% of the variation in seed size within their study was accounted for by a combination of mode of dispersal and **plant growth forms** (e.g., climbing plants tended to have very heavy seeds while grasses tended to have small seeds).

Although dispersal mode and growth form explained much variation in seed size within Westoby's study, there remained

Figure 9.6 A small sample of the great diversity of seed sizes and shapes.

© Sabrina E. Russo/Harvard University Herbarium.

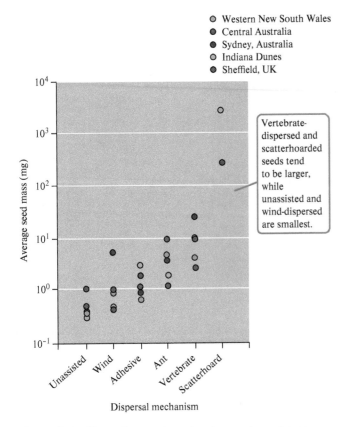

Figure 9.8   Plant dispersal mechanism and seed mass.
Data from Westoby, Leishman, and Loard 1996.

plots, although the relative advantage in recruitment for larger seeds was less pronounced in disturbed plots.

It appears that by investing more energy into a seed, the maternal plant increases the probability that her offspring will successfully establish itself. This advantage associated with large seed size is probably very important in environments such as the grasslands studied by Jakobsson and Eriksson, where competition with established plants is likely to be high. Such maternal investment is likely not necessary, or is even wasteful, in areas with low competition, such as in disturbed soils. Thus both small and large seeds can provide fitness benefits under different ecological conditions; as a result, one expects to find substantial variation in this life-history trait among species.

As we can see from these examples in fish and plants, there is broad evidence for an offspring size vs. offspring number trade-off. But more important than simply quantifying that pattern is the realization that this trade-off has significant implications for other aspects of the ecology and evolution of these species.

In addition to showing variation in the number and sizes of offspring produced, organisms also show a great deal of variation in the age at which they begin reproducing, and in the relative amount of energy they allocate to reproduction versus growth and maintenance. We discuss some general patterns in age of reproductive maturity and relative investment in reproduction next.

Adult Survival and Reproductive Allocation

Reproductive effort is the allocation of energy, time, and other resources to the production and care of offspring. Within an individual, reproductive effort involves trade-offs with the organism's other needs, including allocation to growth and maintenance. Because of these trade-offs, allocating energy to

substantial unexplained variation. So, what are some other factors that maintain variation in seed size? To maintain such variation, there must be advantages and disadvantages of producing either large or small seeds. What are those advantages and disadvantages?

Jakobsson and Eriksson (2000) investigated the relationship between seed size and **recruitment** among 50 plant species living in meadows. Recruitment in the context of plants is where a new plant grows to a size it can be counted. This means that it has not only successfully germinated but has also produced a viable shoot. At their field sites, Jakobsson and Eriksson planted the seeds of each species in small plots; some were sown into undisturbed plots and some into separate plots that were disturbed before planting by scratching the soil surface and removing any accumulated litter. Jakobsson and Eriksson found that recruitment success (total number of individual shoots divided by the total number of seeds planted) varied widely among species, from approximately 5% to nearly 90%. Differences in seed size explained much of the observed differences in recruitment success among species (fig. 9.9). On average, larger seeds, which produced larger seedlings, were associated with a higher rate of recruitment. This was true in both disturbed and undisturbed

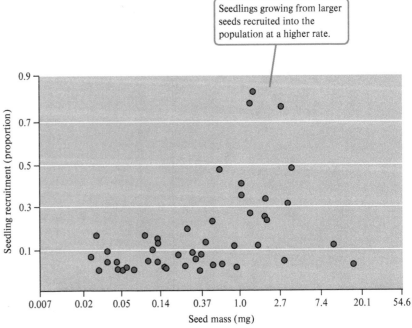

Figure 9.9   Seed mass and recruitment rates in grassland plants.
Data from Jakobsson and Eriksson 2000.

reproduction early in life may reduce the probability that an organism will survive or reduce its lifespan. However, delaying reproduction also involves risk. An individual that delays reproduction runs the risk of dying before it can reproduce. Consequently, evolutionary ecologists have predicted that variation in mortality rates among adults will be in association with variation in the age of first reproduction or age of reproductive maturity. Specifically, they have predicted that where adult mortality is higher, natural selection will favour early reproductive maturity; and where adult mortality is low, natural selection is expected to favour delaying reproductive maturity.

Variation Among Species

The relationship between mortality, growth, and age at first reproduction or reproductive maturity has been examined in a large number of organisms. Early work, which concentrated on fish, shrimp, and sea urchins, suggested linkages between mortality or survival, growth, and reproduction. Richard Shine and Eric Charnov (1992) explored life-history variation among snakes and lizards to determine whether generalizations developed through studies of fish and marine invertebrates could be extended to another group of animals living in very different environments (fig. 9.10).

Shine and Charnov (yes, the same Charnov from Chapter 8) began their presentation with a reminder that, in contrast to most terrestrial arthropods, birds, and mammals (including humans), many animals continue growing after they reach sexual maturity. In addition, most vertebrate species begin reproducing before they reach their maximum body size. As a result, the energy budgets of these other vertebrate species, such as fish and reptiles, are different before and after sexual maturity. Before these organisms reach sexual maturity, energy acquired by an individual is allocated to one of two competing demands: maintenance and growth. However, after reaching sexual maturity, limited energy supplies are allocated to three functions: maintenance, growth, and reproduction. Because they have fewer demands on their limited energy supplies, individuals delaying reproduction until they are older will grow faster, reaching a larger size. Because of the increase in reproductive rate associated with larger body size (see fig. 9.3), deferring reproduction would lead to a higher reproductive rate but beginning later in life. However, where mortality rates are high, deferring reproduction increases the probability that an individual will die before reproducing. These relationships suggest that mortality rates will play a pivotal role in determining the age at first reproduction.

Shine and Charnov gathered information from published summaries on annual adult survival and age at which females mature for several species of snakes and lizards. The annual rate of adult survival among snakes in their data set ranged from approximately 35% to 85% of the population, while age at reproductive maturity ranged from 2 to 7 years. Meanwhile, the annual rate of lizard survival ranged from approximately 8% to 67% of the population, and their age at first reproduction ranged from a little less than 8 months to 6.5 years. The results of Shine and Charnov's study showed clearly that as survival of adult lizards and snakes increases, their age at maturity also increases (fig. 9.10a).

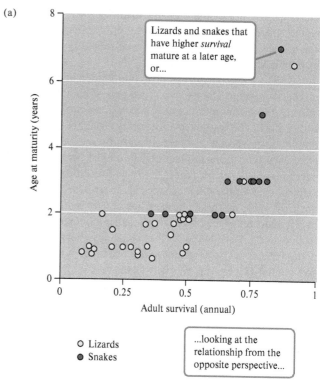

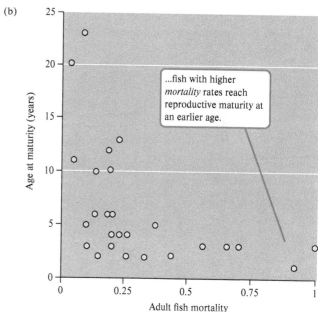

Figure 9.10   Relationship between (*a*) adult survival among lizards (yellow dots) and snakes (red dots) and (*b*) adult fish mortality and age of reproductive maturity. Data from (*a*) Shine and Charnov 1992 and (*b*) Gunderson 1997.

More recent analyses of the relationship between adult mortality rate and age at maturity among fish species provide additional support for the prediction that high adult survival leads to delayed maturity. Donald Gunderson (1997) explored patterns in adult survival and reproductive effort among several populations of marine fish. Like Shine and Charnov, Gunderson's results show a clear relationship between adult mortality and age of reproductive maturity (fig. 9.10*b*). These results support the idea that natural selection has acted to adjust age at reproductive maturity to rates of mortality experienced by populations.

Gunderson's analysis also gives information on variation in reproductive effort among species. As part of his study, he estimated reproductive effort as each population's **gonadosomatic index (GSI)**. GSI was taken as the ovary weight of each species divided by the species' body weight and adjusted for the number of batches of offspring produced by the species per year. His calculations of GSI spanned more than a 30-fold difference, from a value of 0.02 for the rougheye rockfish to 0.65 for the northern anchovy. What do these numbers mean? The yearly allocation to reproduction by the rougheye rockfish is approximately 2% of its body weight, while the northern anchovy allocates approximately 65% of its body weight to reproduction! When Gunderson plotted GSI against mortality rates (fig. 9.11), the results supported the prediction from life-history theory that species with higher mortality would show higher relative reproductive effort.

Variation Within Species

To this point in our discussion we have emphasized life-history differences between species. However, even within a species one can find variation in critical aspects of life history. Once again, some of the best examples come from ecologists studying fish.

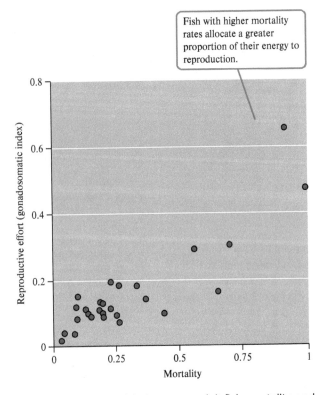

Fish with higher mortality rates allocate a greater proportion of their energy to reproduction.

Figure 9.11 Relationship between adult fish mortality and reproductive effort as measured by the gonadosomatic index, or GSI.

Data from Gunderson 1997.

Mart Gross, of the University of Toronto, has conducted a number of studies that provide understanding of how intraspecific variation in life histories can lead to alternative behaviours among salmonoid fish, particularly the coho salmon (*Oncorhynchus kisutch*) (e.g., Gross 1985, 1991). We have discussed salmon many times in this book, particularly in the context of their moving between fresh and saltwater habitats (chapter 6). However, these organisms also exhibit substantial plasticity in their life histories, resulting in important consequences for mating behaviour.

Female coho salmon typically reach sexual maturity after 18 months in the ocean, at which time they return to their birth stream, spawn, and die. Males are more variable. Some mature after 18 months in the ocean, while others mature at smaller body sizes after only 6 months at sea. These alternative life histories are commonly referred to as the "jack" (6 month) and "hooknose" (18 month) forms of male coho salmon. The developmental "decision" to mature at an early or late stage is irreversible and appears dependent upon a number of environmental, genetic, and size-related factors. In general, fry that grow rapidly are larger as juveniles and are more likely to become jacks, while the slower growing individuals tend to become hooknose. In addition to differences in size at sexual maturity, individual salmon have options when it comes to mating strategies.

There are two alternative mating behaviours available to males: "fighting" and "sneaking." Fighters will typically fight for proximity to a desired female who is about to spawn while sneakers will try to fertilize the female's eggs while other males are engaged in fighting.

One of the key questions Gross was interested in understanding is why both hooknose and jack forms coexist within a population. The answer to this question appears to be that hooknose and jack forms have roughly equivalent lifetime fitness, such that both can be evolutionary stable strategies (chapter 8). How is this possible? By observing males of different sizes, Gross (1985) was able to determine that both very small males and very large males had roughly equal success in getting close to females, while intermediate sized males were rarely able to get near a female. As you likely imagined, large fish were very good at fighting and, generally, were successful in fights. Small fish were poor fighters but good at hiding and, thus, were successful in sneaking. Intermediate sized fish were too large to sneak, yet too small to successfully fight, and thus they rarely were able to get near females. As a result of these effects of size on behavioural outcomes, coho salmon are experiencing disruptive selection (chapter 4) on the key life-history trait of age of sexual maturity. As long as conditions remain constant, these two alternative forms should coexist within the population. However, Gross (1991) points out that conditions are not constant, and commercial and recreational anglers disproportionally harvest the larger hooknose fish, imposing directional selection. Removing the largest fish from the population should decrease the size at which fighting is a successful strategy. This in turn could lead to changes in the frequencies of jacks in subsequent populations (Gross 1991), or may simply reduce the mean size of hooknose males.

Figure 9.12 Male pumpkinseed sunfish (*Lepomis gibbosus*) build their nests in the shallows of lakes and ponds. They guard their nests against intrusions by other males and attempt to attract females of their species to deposit eggs within them.

©MattiaATH/Shutterstock RF.

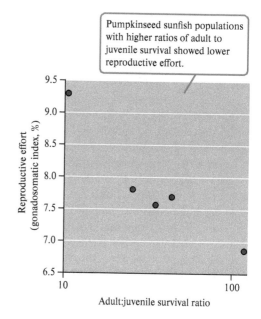

Pumpkinseed sunfish populations with higher ratios of adult to juvenile survival showed lower reproductive effort.

Figure 9.13 Adult:juvenile survival ratio and reproductive effort as measured by the gonadosomatic index, or GSI. Data from Bertschy and Fox 1999.

Gross's work demonstrates that alternative life histories can coexist within a population and that behavioural strategies are intimately tied to the fitness of individuals. If the costs or benefits of alternative aspects of a life-history change (e.g., increased mortality from anglers at larger size), this could result in natural selection toward alternative life-history traits. Additional support for the idea of viewing life histories not as an end point that characterizes a species but instead as a delicate evolutionary balance among costs and benefits associated with multiple traits comes from a comparative study of several populations of the pumpkinseed sunfish (*Lepomis gibbosus*) (fig. 9.12).

Kirk Bertschy and Michael Fox of Trent University (1999) studied the influence of adult survival on pumpkinseed sunfish life histories. One of the major objectives of their study was to test the prediction of life-history theory that increased adult survival, relative to juvenile mortality, favours delayed maturity and reduced reproductive effort. They selected populations of pumpkinseed sunfish living in five lakes in southern Ontario, similar in area and depth and small enough that Bertschy and Fox had a reasonable chance of estimating mortality rates and variation in other life-history characteristics.

Bertschy and Fox estimated life-history characteristics from annual samples of approximately 100 pumpkinseed sunfish taken from each lake. They measured age (by counting annual rings

in scales), weight, length (in mm), sex, and reproductive status of females. Female reproductive effort was measured using the gonadosomatic index (GSI), as described previously. Bertschy and Fox used mark and recapture surveys to estimate the number of adult pumpkinseed sunfish and the age structure of pumpkinseed populations in each lake. These surveys gave a basis for estimating rates of adult survival for each age class in each lake's population.

Bertschy and Fox found significant variation in most life-history characteristics across their study lakes. Pumpkinseed sunfish matured at ages ranging from 2.4 to 3.4 years in the different study lakes, and they showed reproductive investments (gonadosomatic indexes, or GSI) ranging from 6.9% to 9.3%. The comparison of survival rate and age at maturity across the five populations suggests that populations with higher adult survival mature at a greater age. Further, where females pumpkinseeds survived to greater age, their reproductive effort decreased (fig. 9.13). The patterns described by Bertschy and Fox are consistent with those of Gunderson. Collectively, these studies suggest that higher rates of adult mortality can favour greater allocation of resources to reproduction, whether we are comparing life-history traits among species (Gunderson) or among populations of the same species (Bertschy and Fox).

ECOLOGY IN ACTION

How Life Histories Influence Extinction Risk

The extinction of species is an issue of concern in Canada and around the world. Ecologists are at the forefront of research into understanding the causes and consequences

of extinction, and are providing ideas for how to protect the species that remain. The immediate causes of species loss are, in a broad sense, well known and often referred to as the "evil quartet": overexploitation, habitat loss, competition with introduced species, and trophic dependency leading to cascading chains of extinction (Diamond 1984). All of these topics will be discussed in later chapters of the book.

Although we often hear about a global biodiversity crisis, not all species are equally likely to go extinct, even when faced with the same environmental challenges (fig. 9.14). In later chapters we will discuss aspects of how human activities impact population dynamics and viability of a diversity of species. We will also discuss how the Species at Risk Act may be used to help protect some species in Canada. Here, we ask a different question: What aspects of a species' life history increase its susceptibility to extinction? There are a few motives for asking this question. On a practical level, John Reynolds (2003), of Simon Fraser University, has pointed out that because the money available for conservation programs is very limited, having some easily measurable life-history trait, or set of traits, would help managers determine which species should become priorities for recovery. On a more fundamental level, understanding functional linkages between life history and population growth and extinction is a worthy scientific goal, one likely to result in a variety of unintended benefits.

Andy Purvis of Imperial College and his colleagues have been leaders in research to understand how the biology of different species interacts with human-mediated changes to cause increased extinction risks. Purvis and colleagues (2000) summarized and tested eight hypotheses gathered from the literature. Here we will focus on one of these, the hypothesis that species with "slow" life histories will be more at risk than those with "fast" life histories. What do we mean by a slow life history? We mean species that have slow growth rates, reach sexual maturity only late in life, breed infrequently and in small numbers, and have similar life-history traits. Purvis and colleagues tested this hypothesis by collecting these life-history traits from previously published studies for Carnivora and Primate mammals. Measures of extinction risk were also collected from the literature, specifically the International Union for the Conservation of Nature and Natural Resources Red List.

For the carnivores, extinction risk increased with gestation length and age of sexual maturity, supporting the "slow life history" hypothesis. However, these traits were not related to extinction risk in primates. For primates, increased size rather than species-specific life-history traits influenced extinction risk. Purvis and colleagues suggest that primates actually do not exhibit substantial variation in life history independent of size, and thus they question the meaning of that particular result. Their study highlights that life history characteristics matter when it comes to extinction (although other ecological characteristics—such as geographic range, population density, and trophic position—are also important). While the results of their study may not seem particularly surprising, never before have

Pterotrogus principalis

Picalgoides picimajoris

Figure 9.14 These species are all at risk of extinction. Species with "slow" life histories, and species that live in or on endangered species, are at increased risk of extinction.

Gorilla: Elliothurwitt/Dreamstime.com/GetStock.com; snow leopard: Mrolands/Dreamstime.com/Getstock.com; peregrine falcon: Klikk /Dreamstime.com/Getstock.com; great white shark: Shutterstock/ Thomas Duerrenberger; swift fox: Colette6/Dreastime.com/Getstock. com; woodpecker: Image by R. Ehrnsberger, J. Dabert, and H. Proctor.

these ideas been so rigorously tested and explored. Having a degree of certainty in the validity of scientific ideas and conclusions is critical to the ability of ecologists to provide useful information and guidance to policy makers.

Purvis and colleagues (Cardillo et al. 2004) built upon their previous model to predict extinction risk for Carnivora in Africa under pressure from human populations. They found that biological factors (including life-history traits) are better predictors of extinction risk than is human population density alone. This finding is most pronounced in areas of high population density, where the biology of the species explains over 80% of the variation in extinction risks! In other words, to predict which species are at risk for extinction in areas of high human densities, you need to understand the basic biology of the local species.

Using demographic projections extending to 2030, Cardillo and colleagues predicted which species will become at risk or will increase their level of risk, based on the disruptive pressures of human population density and the biological traits of local species. Such a predictive approach to conservation biology has great potential to help managers respond to conservation needs before they happen, rather than continue in a state of repair. The work by Purvis and his colleagues is a great example of how ecology can be used to address real problems of local and global concern.

The link between life history and extinction risk is not limited to life on land but also holds for the chondrichthyans (sharks, rays, chimaeras) of the oceans. Nicholas Dulvy, of Simon Fraser University, is a leader in understanding the linkages among population dynamics, life histories, and conservation biology of these always interesting groups of organisms. In a recent review, Dulvy and Forrest (2010) found there was a significant negative relationship between the body length of a shark species and its population growth. Underlying this are a number of familiar life-history trade-offs: smaller species reproduce earlier and die younger than larger species. These life-history characteristics make smaller sharks generally more resilient to fishing pressures than larger species (Dulvy and Forrest 2010). It may thus be of little surprise that the large pelagic sharks of the open ocean are the most threatened (Dulvy and Forrest 2010).

Although the public generally sees images of these large carnivores and primates in the media, they represent just a small fraction of the species on the planet and only a segment of the species at risk of extinction. Many species are dependent upon others for survival, such as butterfly larvae that feed on only a few plant species, and host-specific parasites. What happens to the butterfly or parasite if its only host species goes extinct? Unless it is immediately able to expand the breadth of its niche to include other hosts, it, too, is doomed. As a result, species that have very specific niche requirements, dependent upon other species, are exposed to increased extinction risk. An international team of researchers, including Heather Proctor of the University of Alberta, explored whether the potential for these "species coextinctions" were of sufficient magnitude to warrant concern (Koh et al. 2004). To address this question, the research team developed a model that calculated the probability of a species' going extinct if its host went extinct. They compiled information from the literature describing the host-specificity of these "affiliate" species. The model then weighted both the probability of the host's going extinct (as some species are more at risk than others) and whether the affiliate had multiple possible hosts. For the nearly 8,500 host species that are currently endangered, their model estimates that there are another 6,000 affiliate species at risk! In short, their research clearly indicates that aspects of a species' niche, in this case host-specificity, can contribute to a species' risk of extinction.

Although this talk of extinction is often disheartening, particularly when we realize how many species are overlooked by scientists and the media, it is also very important. Extinctions are real and are happening at an extremely high rate. If we wish to reduce these rates, at least in cases where humans are contributing to the risk, it is essential that we understand how human disturbances and species' biology interact. Work by ecologists studying life histories and niches can augment governmental protections and recovery programs, providing our society with the greatest hope of reducing the permanent ecological and evolutionary changes associated with extinctions.

Genetic Control of Life History

Variation in life-history traits, such as the relationship between adult and juvenile survival, can be due to differences in both the ecological and the environmental conditions faced by individuals and populations. However, this environmentally induced variation can only influence evolution if there is also a genetic, and heritable, component to life-history variation among individuals within and between populations (chapter 4). David Innes, of Memorial University

of Newfoundland, has published extensively on one of the most fundamental aspects of life history: sexual versus asexual reproduction. As you will see, his work has clearly shown that aspects of life history can be influenced by both environmental and genetic factors.

Daphnia pulex (Crustacea: Cladocera), commonly referred to as a water flea, is a small crustacean that is common in lakes, ponds, and temporary water bodies throughout the world (fig. 9.15). The reproductive cycle of *D. pulex* is a bit more

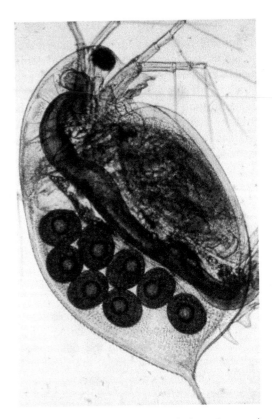

Figure 9.15 Different forms of *Daphnia pulex* can be either sexually reproducing or obligately parthenogenetic. This female is developing a brood of parthenogenetic eggs.

David Innes.

complicated than what we find in most vertebrate species. Two forms of *D. pulex* exist: the first is similar to most species of *Daphnia* and reproduces by *cyclical* **parthenogenesis**. In this form of reproduction, individuals create *diploid* eggs through *mitosis*, rather than producing *haploid* eggs through *meiosis*, as is the norm for vertebrates. The diploid eggs develop into offspring, resulting in genetic clones of the mother water flea. Since these offspring are clones of their mom, they must all be females, right? No. *D. pulex* has environmental sex determination, with the eggs developing into females at low population density and into males at high population density. As a result, a single female is able to produce genetically identical males and females! Occasionally, these females will undergo meiosis, producing haploid diapausing (resting) eggs that require fertilization by the males to develop. However, a second form of *D. pulex* also exists in which individuals reproduce only through *obligate* parthenogenesis. These clones produce diapausing eggs through mitosis, not meiosis, and thus have no haploid aspect to their life cycle. In a very elegant study, David Innes and his former postdoctoral supervisor Paul Hebert (chapter 4) (formerly at the University of Windsor) exploited this variation in life history to explore the genetic basis of obligate parthenogenesis in *D. pulex* (Innes and Hebert 1988).

Innes and Hebert grew cultures of several clones collected from natural populations throughout Ontario, Illinois,

Michigan, and Iowa. They then took males from an obligately parthenogenetic clone and mated them with females from a cyclically parthenogenetic clone. In total, they conducted 19 such crosses, resulting in 102 hybrid clones. Innes and Hebert collected the diapausing eggs that were produced by 10 of these hybrids. Why the focus on the diapausing eggs? If you recall, the diapausing eggs are produced through mitosis for the clones that use obligate parthenogenesis and through meiosis for the clones that use cyclical parthenogenesis. By looking at protein variations of the individuals that emerged from the diapausing eggs, Innes and Hebert were able to infer the mode of reproduction. Those eggs derived from mitosis would have uniform protein patterns, indicating obligate parthenogenesis, while those derived from meiosis would show variation, indicating cyclical parthenogenesis. What they found was quite striking: four hybrids reproduced by obligate parthenogenesis like their father, while six hybrids reproduced by cyclical parthenogenesis like their mother. In other words, although all of the mothers reproduced by cyclical parthenogenesis at the start of the experiment, mating with the males derived from obligate parthenogenesis causes a switch in reproductive behaviour in approximately one-half of the hybrids! Clearly, the males contained genes that suppressed meiosis, indicating that this extremely fundamental aspect of life history may be under relatively simple genetic control, at least in this species. There are numerous examples of other animal species, as well as plants and bacteria, that show genetic influences on life history. Ecology and evolution are linked, and this is rarely made more clear than in the study of life histories.

As we explored the relationship between offspring size and number and the influence of mortality on the timing of maturation and reproductive effort, we have accumulated a large body of information on life histories. We have also seen that aspects of life history within a species are under genetic control. Where there is genetic variability, these life history traits are subject to selection and evolution. This can alter the basic parameters of how a species lives, grows, and reproduces. Let's step back now and try to organize that information to make it easier to think about life-history variation in nature.

CONCEPT 9.1 REVIEW

1. Imagine two species of mice that are about the same size but have different basal metabolic rates. What differences might you see in age and size at sexual maturity between the two species? Why?

2. What is a main difference between the study by Bertschy and Fox (1999) and that of Gunderson (1997)?

3. What are the evolutionary implications of life-history traits that are, or are not, influenced by an individual's genotype?

9.2 Life-History Classification

The great diversity of life histories observed in nature can be classified on the basis of a few common characteristics. Classification systems never capture the full diversity of nature. They are an abstraction from nature, and most species fall somewhere in between extreme types. However, they provide a way to make sense of the often bewildering variety in nature. Thus, these classification schemes should be used as a framework to consider life history strategies broadly, not to assign a classification to every species.

r and K Selection

One of the earliest attempts to organize information on the great variety of life histories that occur among species was under the heading of *r* and K selection (MacArthur and Wilson 1967). The terms *r* and K selection refer to parameters of population growth models that will be described in depth in chapter 12, and only briefly here. The *r* represents a measure of population growth rate, with larger values corresponding to populations that are growing rapidly. The K represents the maximum sustainable size of a population, such that habitats with larger K values could contain larger populations than areas with smaller K values. Robert MacArthur and E. O. Wilson adopted these population growth parameters as ways of describing variation in life histories among species. They suggest that for some species, selection will favour those life-history traits that cause increases in growth rates, so called "*r*-selected" species. MacArthur and Wilson suggested that *r* selection would be strongest in species often colonizing new or disturbed habitats, with high levels of disturbance leading to ongoing *r* selection. In contrast, they proposed that in other species, selection will act upon life-history traits important for when habitats are "full" of a population. These "K-selected" species are likely to have life-history traits that favour efficient utilization of resources such as food and nutrients, rather than maximizing growth rates. They envisioned that K selection would be most prominent in those situations where species populations are near the "carrying capacity" of the habitat much of the time.

Eric Pianka (1970, 1972) developed the concept of *r* and K selection further in two important papers. Pianka pointed out that *r* selection and K selection are the endpoints on a continuous distribution and that most organisms are subject to forms of selection somewhere in between these extremes. His analysis clarified the contrast in biological characteristics between the two selective extremes (fig. 9.16). The most fundamental contrasts are, of course, between potential growth rates, *r*, which should be highest in *r*-selected species, and competitive ability, which should be highest among K-selected species. According to Pianka, development should be rapid under *r* selection and relatively slow under K selection. Meanwhile, early reproduction and smaller body size will be favoured by *r* selection, while K selection favours later reproduction and larger body size. Pianka predicted that reproduction under *r* selection will tend toward a single reproductive event in which many small offspring are produced. This type of reproduction, which is called

Characteristics Favoured by *r* versus K Selection		
Population Attribute	***r* Selection**	**K Selection**
Potential of population rate, *r*	High	Low
Competitive ability	Not strongly favoured	Highly favoured
Development	Rapid	Slow
Reproduction	Early	Late
Body size	Small	Large
Reproduction	Single, semelparity	Repeated, iteroparity
Offspring	Many, small	Few, large

Figure 9.16 Life history characteristics commonly associated with *r* and K selection.
After Pianka 1970.

semelparity, occurs in organisms such as annual weeds and salmon. In contrast, K selection should favour repeated reproduction, or **iteroparity**, of fewer, larger offspring. Iteroparity, which spaces out reproduction over several reproductive periods during an organism's lifetime, is the type of reproduction seen in most perennial plants and most vertebrate animals. Pianka's contrast puts a name on and fleshes out the comparison we developed in the Ecology in Action example in this chapter, where organisms with "fast" life histories, analogous to *r*-selected species, were less likely to be at an extinction risk than organisms with "slow" life histories, analogous to K-selected species (fig. 9.17).

The ideas of *r* and K selection helped greatly as ecologists and evolutionary biologists attempted to think more systematically about life-history variation and its evolution. However, ecologists who found that the dichotomy of *r* versus K did not include a great deal of known variation in life histories have proposed alternative classifications.

Plant Life Histories

r and K strategies are a useful shorthand for talking about groups of correlated life-history traits for all taxa. However, some organisms, such as plants, may be better described using a different shorthand. Phil Grime (1977, 1979) proposed that variation in environmental conditions has led to the development of distinctive strategies or life histories among plants. The two variables that he selected as most important in exerting selective pressure on plants were the intensity of disturbance and abiotic stress. Grime also argues that competition can exert strong pressures on plants and that competition should be relatively more important when stress and disturbances are low. Grime contrasted four extreme environmental types, which he characterized by combinations of disturbance intensity and stress intensity. Four environmental extremes envisioned by

(a)

(b)

Figure 9.17   (*a*) The deer mouse and (*b*) the African elephant represent extremes among mammals of *r* versus K selection.

(a) James Gathany/CDC; (b) © Corbis RF.

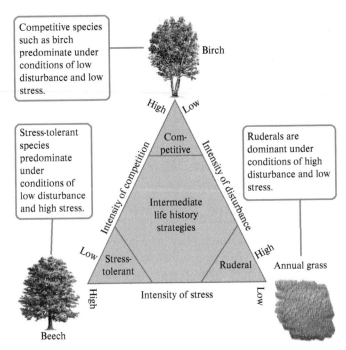

Figure 9.18   Grime's classification of plant life-history strategies.

After Grime 1979.

Grime were (1) low disturbance–low stress, (2) low disturbance–high stress, (3) high disturbance–low stress, and (4) high disturbance–high stress. Drawing on his extensive knowledge of plant biology, Grime suggested that plants occupy three of his theoretical environments but that there is no viable strategy among plants for the fourth environmental combination, high disturbance–high stress.

Grime next described plant strategies, or life histories, that match the requirements of the remaining three environments. His strategies were ruderal, stress-tolerant, and competitive (fig. 9.18). **Ruderals** are plants that live in highly disturbed habitats and that may depend on disturbance to persist in the face of potential competition from other plants. Grime summarized several characteristics of ruderals that allow them to persist in habitats experiencing frequent and intense **disturbance**, which he defined as any mechanisms or processes that limit plants by destroying plant biomass. One of the characteristics of ruderals is their capacity to grow rapidly and produce seeds during relatively short periods between successive disturbances. This capacity alone would favour persistence of ruderals in the face of frequent disturbance. However, ruderals also invest a large proportion of their biomass in reproduction, producing large numbers of seeds that are capable of dispersing to new habitats made available by disturbance. The term *ruderal* is sometimes used synonymously with the term *weed*. Animals that are associated with disturbance, that have high reproductive rates, and that are good colonists are also sometimes referred to as ruderals.

Grime (1977) began his discussion of the second type of plant life history, stress-tolerant, with a definition of **stress** as "... external constraints which limit the rate of dry matter production of all or part of the vegetation." What environmental conditions might create such constraints? Our discussions in chapters 5, 6, and 7, where we considered temperature, water, and energy and nutrient relations, respectively, provide several suggestions. Stress is the result of extreme temperatures, high or low; extreme hydrologic conditions, too little or too much water; or too much or too little light or nutrients. Because different species are adapted to different environmental conditions, the absolute levels of light, water, temperature, and so forth that constitute stress will vary from species to species. In addition, conditions that induce stress will vary from biome to biome. For instance, the amount of precipitation leading to drought stress is different in rain forest and desert, or the minimum temperatures inducing thermal stress are different in tropical forest compared to boreal forest.

The important point that Grime made, however, was that in every biome, some species are more tolerant than other species to the environmental extremes that occur. These are the species that he referred to as "stress-tolerant." Stress-tolerant plants are those that live under conditions of high stress but low disturbance. Grime proposed that, in general, stress-tolerant plants grow slowly; are evergreen; conserve fixed carbon, nutrients, and water; and are adept at exploiting temporary favourable conditions. In addition, stress-tolerant plants are often unpalatable to most herbivores. Because stress-tolerant species endure some of the most difficult conditions a particular environment has to offer, they are there to take advantage of infrequent favourable periods for growth and reproduction.

The third plant strategy proposed by Grime is a competitive life history. In Grime's classification, competitive plants occupy environments where disturbance intensity is low and the intensity of stress is also low. Under conditions of low stress and low disturbance, plants have the potential to grow well. As they do so, however, they eventually compete with each other for resources, such as light, water, nutrients, and space. Grime's model predicts that the plants living under such circumstances will be selected for strong competitive abilities.

In presenting the initial model, we have emphasized the extreme strategies that represent each of the corners of "Grime's triangle." However, Grime recognized that life histories in nature will fall along a continuum of these axes, and thus the middle of the triangle represents intermediate plant strategies.

How does Grime's system of classification compare with the *r* and K selection contrast proposed by MacArthur and Wilson and Pianka? Grime proposed that *r* selection corresponds to his ruderal strategy of life history, while K selection corresponds to the stress-tolerant end of his classification. Meanwhile, he placed the competitive life-history category in a position intermediate between the extremes represented by *r* selection and K selection. However, while attempting this reconciliation of the two classifications, Grime suggested that a linear arrangement of life histories with *r* selection and K selection occupying the extremes fails to capture the full variation shown by organisms. He suggested that more dimensions are needed and, of course, Grime's triangular arrangement (fig. 9.18) adds another dimension. The factors varying along the edges of Grime's triangle are intensity of disturbance, stress, and competition. Other ecologists have also recognized the need for more dimensions in representing life-history diversity.

Opportunistic, Equilibrium, and Periodic Life Histories

In a review of life-history patterns among fish, Kirk Winemiller and Kenneth Rose (1992) proposed a classification of life histories based on some of the aspects of population dynamics. They drew particular attention to survivorship, especially

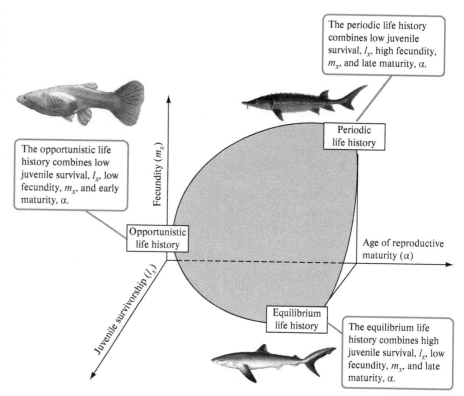

Figure 9.19   Classification of life histories based on juvenile survival, fecundity, and age at reproductive maturity.
After Winemiller and Rose 1992.

among juveniles; fecundity, or number of offspring produced; and generation time, or age at maturity.

Winemiller and Rose start with the concept of trade-offs. Their trade-offs are among fecundity, survivorship, and age at reproductive maturity. Using variation in fish life histories as a model, Winemiller and Rose proposed that life histories should lie on a semi-triangular surface, as shown in figure 9.19. The three-dimensional space depicted represents the adaptive space that accommodates various life-history trait combinations of age to reproductive maturity, juvenile survivorship, and fecundity. The curved lines bounding this adaptive space represent diminishing returns in the bivariate relationships among these traits. Winemiller and Rose called the three endpoints on their surface "opportunistic," "equilibrium," and "periodic" life histories. The opportunistic strategy, by combining low juvenile survival, low numbers of offspring, and early reproductive maturity, maximizes colonizing ability across environments that vary unpredictably in time or space. It is important to keep in mind, however, that while the absolute reproductive output of opportunistic species may be low, the percentage of their energy budget allocated to reproduction is high. Winemiller and Rose's equilibrium strategy combines high juvenile survival, low numbers of offspring, and late reproductive maturity. Finally, the periodic strategy combines low juvenile survival, high numbers of offspring, and late maturity. Among fish, periodic species tend to be large and produce numerous small offspring. By producing large numbers of offspring over a long lifespan, periodic species can take advantage of infrequent periods when conditions are favourable for reproduction.

It is difficult to map the exact correspondence of Winemiller and Rose's classification of life-history strategies to either the *r*–K continuum of MacArthur and Wilson and Pianka or the triangular classification of plant life histories developed by Grime. For instance, opportunistic species share characteristics with *r*-selected and ruderal species. However, opportunistic species differ from the typical *r*-selected species because they tend to produce small clutches of offspring. The equilibrium strategy, which combines production of high juvenile survival, low numbers of offspring, and late reproductive maturity, approaches the characteristics of typical K-selected species. Winemiller and Rose point out, however, that many fish classified as "equilibrium" are small, while typically K-selected species tend toward large body size (see fig. 9.17). Periodic species are not captured by the linear *r* to K selection gradient. Meanwhile, the periodic and equilibrium species in Winemiller and Rose's classification share some characteristics with Grime's stress-tolerant and competitive species but differ in other characteristics.

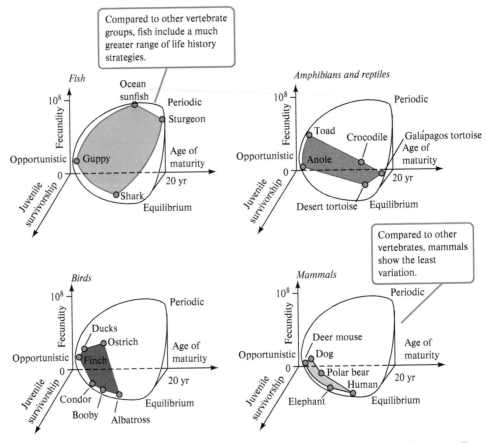

Figure 9.20 Variation in life histories within vertebrate animals. The curvilinear outline represents the potential adaptive space considering trade-offs among these three life-history traits. Individual vertebrate groups represent a portion of this total potential adaptive space.

After Winemiller and Rose 1992.

Thus far in this review of systems for life-history classification, we have focused on just three of the many that have been proposed. Even with just these three, however, translation from one classification to another is difficult. What are the sources of these differences in perspective? One of the sources is that different ecologists have worked with different groups of organisms. While MacArthur and Wilson's system was built after years of work on birds and insects, respectively, Pianka had worked mainly with lizards. Grime's classification was built on, and intended for, plants. Finally, the perspective of Winemiller and Rose was influenced substantially by their work with fish. Because these ecologists worked with such different groups of organisms, it is not surprising that their classifications of life histories do not overlay precisely.

However, it may be that the analysis by Winemiller and Rose has laid the foundation for a more general theory of life histories. By basing their classification system on some of the most basic aspects of population ecology, Winemiller and Rose (1992) established a common currency for representing and analyzing life-history information for any organism. Variation in life-history traits of other groups could be plotted using the same model to describe how much of this potential adaptive space is occupied. Figure 9.20 demonstrates differences in the amount of life-history variation found within different vertebrate groups. Notice that fish show the greatest variation and mammals the least, while birds and reptiles and amphibians include intermediate levels of variation.

The knowledge of species' life histories revealed by the studies of life-history ecologists has produced a subdiscipline of ecology rich in both theory and biological detail. In the challenges that lie ahead as we work to conserve endangered species, both theory and detailed knowledge of the life histories of individual species will be important. For instance, life-history information is playing a key role in the conservation of riparian forests across western North America.

In this chapter we have seen how simple energetic trade-offs can produce life-history strategies. We have also seen how some ecological factors tend to be associated with certain life-history strategies, while other conditions will favour alternative strategies. In chapters 5–7 we learned that species vary greatly in their ability to cope with diverse energetic and environmental challenges, and that this too was governed by the theory of allocation. In the next section we will begin to put the puzzle together, and describe one of the most important concepts in ecology: the *niche*.

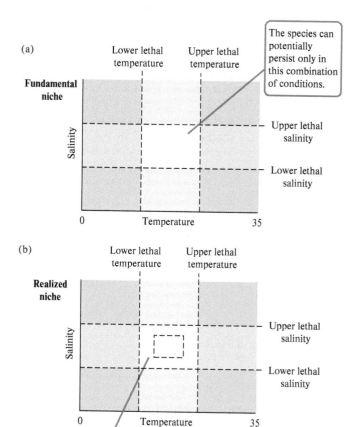

Figure 9.21 Two dimensions of (*a*) fundamental niche and (*b*) realized niche of a hypothetical species. The niches of most species will be defined by a larger number of dimensions.

9.3 Fundamental and Realized Niches

The fundamental niche reflects the environmental requirements of species, while the realized niche also includes interactions with other species. In chapters 5 to 8, we discussed how individual factors such as temperature, water availability, and food resources can have significant implications for the evolution and ecology of organisms. Although species vary greatly in their adaptations to these environmental factors, one commonality is that most adaptations require energy. A common theme through the chapters of section 2 has been the *principle of allocation*, in which allocation of energy to one aspect of the energy budget means there is less energy to allocate for other uses. This idea is a unifying concept in ecology and is never more apparent than in discussions of life histories and the niche.

The niche concept was developed independently by Joseph Grinnell (1917, 1924) and Charles Elton (1927), who use the term *niche* in slightly different ways. In his early writings, Grinnell's idea of the niche focused on the influences of the physical environment, while Elton's earliest concept included both biological interactions and abiotic factors. However their thinking and emphasis may have differed, it is clear that the views of these two researchers had much in common and that our present concept of the niche rests squarely on their pioneering work.

G. Evelyn Hutchinson (1957) crystallized the niche concept, defining the niche as an *n-dimensional hypervolume*, where *n* equals the number of environmental factors important to the survival and reproduction of a species. Hutchinson called this hypervolume, which specifies the values of the *n* environmental factors permitting a species to survive and reproduce, the **fundamental niche** of the species (fig. 9.21). The fundamental niche defines the physical conditions under which a species might live, in the absence of interactions with other species. This should sound vaguely familiar, as a multidimensional extension of the range of tolerance discussed in chapter 5. In that chapter, we discussed how all organisms will have a range of environmental conditions (e.g., temperature) in which they perform well, poorly, or not at all. Each axis of the *Hutchinsonian* niche is made of different environmental parameters,

each with its own range of tolerance. The niche itself consists of the space defined by the overlapping tolerance zones for each environmental parameter. In figure 9.21, the fundamental niche of a species is defined by the overlapping zones of tolerance for temperature and salinity.

As a grossly oversimplified example, and an extension of figure 9.21, imagine a fish species. The fish cannot tolerate summer mean water temperatures above 22°C or mean winter temperatures below 2°C. It cannot tolerate stagnant water but would be swept away in water moving faster than 2 m s⁻¹. It requires well oxygenated water, above 5 mg L⁻¹. It can tolerate salinities only up to 1 part per thousand. The fundamental niche of this fish is any slowly moving, well aerated body of freshwater in a temperate climate with mild winters. Of course, there may be additional environmental factors that further limit this fish's fundamental niche, but this is a good starting point.

Importantly, the niche is *not* a physical location, but instead it is an abstract representation of the environmental conditions necessary for a species to survive. The fish's niche, for example, is not North Carolina. It may be found there, but any abstract body of water meeting the tolerance criteria might be suitable.

Hutchinson's contribution to the niche concept extends beyond the fundamental (i.e., Hutchinsonian) niche. Hutchinson recognized that interactions among species, such as competition, may restrict the environments in which a species actually persists. As a result, a species may use only a portion of its fundamental niche. Hutchinson referred to these more restricted conditions as the **realized niche**. This too makes sense given our discussion of the range-of-tolerance concept in chapter 5. Although a species may be able to survive across a broad range of temperatures (or another environmental factor), its performance is likely greatest only in a narrow subset of this range. It is here where it can compete most effectively. When it is at the edge of its thermal range it is more likely to be displaced. As a result, the fundamental niche represents the maximal niche size of an organism, while the realized niche will be smaller.

Again, consider the fish species. While a fish may be able to tolerate any body of water meeting the criteria we described, if we were to look into any candidate stream, the fish may not be there. Why? Maybe the stream does not support the fish's preferred prey. Or maybe another species is already in the stream and it outcompetes our fish or preys upon it. This particular body of water may be suitable in the abstract but may fall outside the fish's realized niche.

Species may change which portion of the fundamental niche they use based on environmental conditions, including the presence of other species. In the face of competition, a species might concentrate on a part of the fundamental niche in which it has a competitive advantage, even if this part of the niche would have marginal utility in the absence of competitors. Niche partitioning often means narrowing, allowing more competing species to occupy overlapping fundamental niche space. Partitioning may also involve a niche shift. A population may begin to use a marginal portion of its fundamental niche in response to a change in local conditions. For example, a predator may force a species to use a portion of its fundamental niche that it might otherwise not use.

It is probably not possible to measure Hutchinson's $n-$dimensional hypervolume niche for any species. However, it appears that niches are determined mostly by a few environmental factors, so ecologists are able to apply a simplified version of Hutchinson's comprehensive concept. Below we discuss two examples illustrating realized niche and how realized niche may narrow in face of competition or shift in response to local environmental conditions.

The Feeding Niches of Galápagos Finches

As we saw in chapter 7, availability of suitable food significantly affects the evolution, survival, and reproduction of many animals. Among the most well-studied animals are the Galápagos finches. Because the kinds of food used by birds is largely reflected by the form of their beaks, Peter Grant (1986) and his colleagues were able to represent the feeding niches of Galápagos finches by measuring their beak morphology. For instance, differences in beak size among small, medium, and large ground finches translate directly into differences in diet. The large ground finch, *Geospiza magnirostris*, eats larger seeds; the medium ground finch, *G. fortis*, eats medium-sized seeds; while the small ground finch, *G. fuliginosa*, eats small seeds (fig. 9.22).

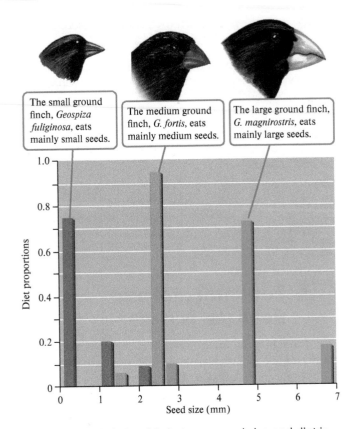

The small ground finch, *Geospiza fuliginosa*, eats mainly small seeds.

The medium ground finch, *G. fortis*, eats mainly medium seeds.

The large ground finch, *G. magnirostris*, eats mainly large seeds.

Figure 9.22   Relationship between seed size and diet in three Galápagos finch species differing in beak depth. Data from Grant 1986.

The size of seeds that can be eaten by Galápagos finches can be estimated by simply measuring the depths of their beaks. Studies of seed use by *G. fortis* on Daphne Major Island showed clearly that even within species, beak size affects the composition of the diet. Within this population, individuals with the deepest beaks fed on the hardest seeds, while individuals with the smallest beaks fed on the softest seeds.

The realized feeding niche occupied by each of the finch species (fig. 9.22) represents a portion of total fundamental niche. For example, *G. magnirostris* could likely use seeds below 3 mm in diameter. However, it may not handle them as efficiently as *G. fortis*. When seed size is 2.5 mm, *G. fortis* may have a competitive advantage in exploiting the food resource, limiting the use of these seeds by *G. magnirostris*. Competition may, then, be important in defining realized niche. Species occupying the same habitat, and having highly overlapping fundamental niche, may reduce competition by partitioning the niche, with each species using that portion in which it has a relative competitive advantage. Figure 9.23 provides a hypothetical example building on the feeding niches observed in the Galápagos finches. The top panel shows realized niche widths in absence of competition, while the bottom panel shows how each species may narrow its realized niche width in the face of competition, reducing overlap in seed use. Please understand that this is meant to illustrate the point and does not represent data from Peter Grant's work. Here we consider this partitioning in one dimensional space (seed size), but we can imagine this partitioning of fundamental niche to occur in *n*-dimensional space. We will return to resource niche partitioning in chapter 13.

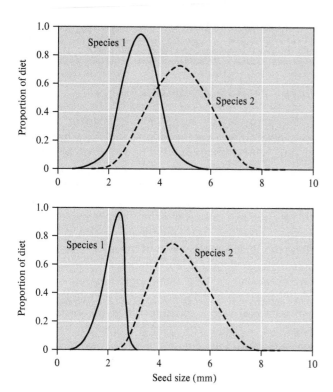

Figure 9.23 Hypothetical shift in the feeding niche for two species when they are subject to competition for seeds. The top panel is realized niche in absence of competition. The bottom panel demonstrates how each species may narrow its niche and exploit that portion of the food resource where it has a competitive advantage.

The Behavioural Niche of European Blackbirds

Ana Catarina Miranda and colleagues have studied behavioural differences between urban bird populations and their rural counterparts (2013). Animal personalities may play a role in their success when colonizing urban areas—not just any beast can cut it in the big city! Previous studies have demonstrated a genetic component for some personality traits in birds (Van Oers et al. 2004, Schielzeth et al. 2011), suggesting that certain personality differences between populations can be shaped by natural selection. Miranda and colleagues studied hand-raised European blackbirds (*Turdus merula*) from a rural area and a nearby urban area. The birds were raised under the same conditions so that if the two populations behaved differently, it might reflect a genetic difference between the populations rather than a difference in learned response.

Miranda observed how birds responded to a new object in their garden. When a new object is installed in a familiar environment (a bird feeder's perch), it can be discomforting, and a bird might be a little more hesitant to visit the feeder. After installing new objects, Miranda and colleagues videotaped bird feeders and determined how long it took birds to alight on the perch and begin feeding. When birds saw a new object, they took longer to alight on the perch. This was true of birds from both urban and rural populations. However, the birds from the city were generally more cautious than the rural birds, taking

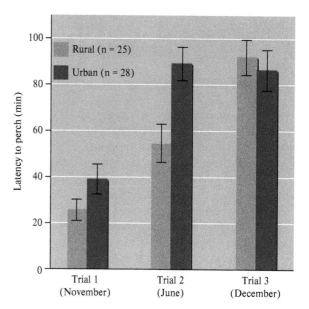

Figure 9.24 Time delay (latency) for birds to alight, relative to birds in control group.

A. C. Miranda et al. 2013, September. Urbanization and its effects on personality traits: A result of microevolution or phenotypic plasticity? *Global Change Biology* 19(9):2634–44. © 2013 John Wiley & Sons Ltd.

longer to perch near a new object (fig. 9.24). Are the rural birds more naive or the city birds more worldly and jaded? More likely the intrinsic personality differences resulted from natural selection in these different environments. Birds that were inherently more cautious may have had greater survival in the city, passing on this behavioural trait to subsequent generations. In any case, the differences in personality demonstrate that the rural and urban populations are using different portions of a behavioural niche. Local conditions in the city may account for a niche shift in the urban population.

The knowledge of species life histories and the concept of the niche have created subdisciplines of ecology rich in both theory and biological detail. In the challenges that lie ahead as we work to conserve endangered species, both theory and detailed knowledge of the life histories and the limits of a species' fundamental niche will be important. For instance, changes in life-history parameters are signalling biological impacts of climate change.

CONCEPT 9.3 REVIEW

1. How do trade-offs influence both the shape of a niche and the form of a species' life-history strategy?
2. Why can't the realized niche be larger than a species' fundamental niche?
3. If niches do not represent actual locations on a map, and instead represent a set of conditions necessary for survival, how could an ecologist measure the niche of a species?

ECOLOGICAL TOOLS AND APPROACHES

Using Life-History Information as Indicators of Biological Effects of Climate Change

Throughout the text we have discussed a variety of aspects of climate change, and we will continue to do so in many of the remaining chapters. One of the reasons for this attention should be pretty clear to you by now: interactions with the environment influence nearly every aspect of an organism's life, and thus climate change has the potential to fundamentally alter evolution, populations, and communities. Understanding the ecological consequences of climate change is one of the great challenges faced by ecologists in the twenty-first century. There is an awful lot we just do not know. Here we will show how life-history parameters themselves are being used by ecologists as a way to measure the ecological consequences of climate change. As you will see, understanding one aspect of an organism can allow the scientist to use that information to answer other questions.

Climate change is a vague term for a complex topic, one that we will explore in more detail in chapter 23. Climate change can include anything from altered temperature, rainfall, snowfall, humidity, and so on, with these factors changing at different rates and intensities in different places across the planet. Here we will focus on one of the more common aspects, temperature. The average global temperature has been increasing by ~0.2°C per decade, and the global average temperature in 2017 was ~1°C higher than during the period of 1850–1900 (IPCC 2018). This change in temperature is not spread evenly across the planet; instead, there can be 3°C–5°C changes in northwestern Canada, and even slight cooling in other locations. It is difficult to understand what exactly this level of warming means for biological systems, although the consensus expressed in the IPCC's 2018 report is that an increase of 1.5°C (only half a degree warmer than 2017) will pose severe risks to unique and threatened ecosystems, particularly Arctic ecosystems and warm water corals. Yes, this rate of change is melting ice caps, contributing to severe storms and flooding, and could even alter some fundamental aspects of global circulation. All of these things will clearly alter a variety of biological processes, not to mention cause an unprecedented level of destruction to human populations throughout the planet. But how do we actually know when climate change is of a magnitude sufficient to cause ecological change? Is this already occurring, or are we just in a phase where we can predict, but not show, how climate change can alter life on the planet? These questions are being asked by ecologists across the planet, and researchers have found that one of the clearest ways of showing evidence of a biological effect of altered temperatures is by showing changes to one particular aspect of life histories: phenology.

Phenology is the study of the timing of events in an organism's life. Some examples include when leaves flush out, when offspring are born, when hibernation begins and ends, and when migrations occur. These are all examples of critical aspects of an organism's life history, and these are generally closely tuned to the environment. This link between timing and life cycle makes a good deal of sense. You could imagine strong selection against producing a new flush of leaves in the middle of winter or for initiating a large migration just when food becomes available. This same logic has led ecologists to recognize that phenology is likely one aspect of an organism's life history most sensitive to environmental change. As a result, changes in phenology may serve as an early sign that climate change is having biological consequences. In this section, we will present a variety of examples of research into this branch of ecology, showing how researchers are able to link life-history changes to changes in local environmental temperatures. We start by presenting some general patterns.

Patterns

How do you actually establish that there is a connection between climate change and phenology? How much evidence is necessary to say that this is a global phenomenon and not just specific to individual locations? When are the effects one observes "important"? These questions were addressed in recent papers by Carmille Parmesan and Gary Yohe (2003) and Terry Root and his colleagues (2003).

Parmesan and Yohe suggest that finding such a fingerprint will be achieved not by focusing solely on detailed studies of individual taxa and single locations but, instead, by finding consistent patterns across taxa and throughout the planet. They argue that for most any biological process, the immediate local processes will nearly always be more important than global change over the short term. For example, even if it is getting warmer on average across the planet, an unusually cold summer can greatly alter plant and animal growth in one location. As a result, they argue that finding a climate fingerprint does not require identifying which particular species are unquestionably responding to climate change but, instead, requires finding a recurring pattern across a large spatial scale.

It would be impossible for any pair of researchers to do the field work themselves to try to detect such a fingerprint at such a large spatial scale. Instead, Parmesan and Yohe (2003) conducted a meta-analysis in an attempt to find recurring results. We have discussed such analyses throughout this book, and the importance of meta-analyses in ecology is continuing to grow. The first step of their study was to compile a large database of existing studies of phenological changes. They found data for 677 species, including plants, birds, insects, amphibians, and fish. The studies measured various phenological events, such as bud break, migration, and so forth over a period that varied from 16 to 132 years. Overall, 27% of the species showed no shift in phenology, 9% showed that spring-timed events were delayed, and 62% showed evidence that spring was approaching earlier, a finding consistent with a causal effect of climate change on biology.

Terry Root and his colleagues (2003) also used a meta-analytic approach to try to find a climate fingerprint based on phenological shifts. They had different criteria for determining which studies would be included in the analysis than that used by Parmesan and Yohe, resulting in a total of 694 species and species groups in their database. They found that when averaged across all species, spring-timed events are arriving earlier by 5.1 days each decade! This date varies among taxonomic groups. Particularly slow-growing groups, such as trees, have a slower rate of change than faster growing species, such as insects. When they further divided their data, they found that the rate of phenological change is greater near the poles than farther from the poles. This, too, supports climate data showing that rates of warming increase as we approach the poles.

These two studies are critical in establishing that, yes, climate change has had significant effects on important aspects of life histories for species distributed across the planet. There is little debate among ecologists about whether climate change will alter natural systems, and these studies are just some of the reasons why many view this as a question to which the answer is known. The more difficult questions that remain are in understanding how climate change will impact specific species in specific locations, and the even harder question is, what can we do about it? In the remaining parts of this section we will describe a few specific examples of how climate change has influenced phenology, and we will discuss some potential evolutionary and ecological consequences. We begin in Manitoba.

Earlier Greening

One of the first signs of spring is the breaking of buds and the greening of the landscape. Satellite imagery provides a great tool for looking at changes in vegetation at large spatial scales, regional to global. Lanhui Wang and colleagues have used 34 years of satellite images to calculate leaf area index and to study the spatio-temporal patterns of vegetation (Wang et al. 2018). Specifically, they have studied the dynamics of spring greening. Wang and colleagues correlated spatio-temporal leaf area index data with climate data and land use data to tease apart their relationships to the

rate of greening. The team analyzed the temporal patterns of increased leaf area index for each of 1,175,453 pixels (1/12° spatial resolution each). They found that in ~20% of their pixels, the rate of greening increased over time (from 1982 to 2015), while 8.6% of the pixels showed a decreasing rate of greening. On a global scale, warming has accelerated greening most in high latitude forest ecosystems and Arctic regions. Their findings suggest changes in plant growth patterns at a global scale that could affect the availability and timing of food resources for animals.

Bird Migration

Since 1939, researchers at the Delta Waterfowl and Wetlands Research Station, located in south-central Manitoba, have been recording the dates of the first spring sightings for 231 species of birds. Delta Marsh is among the largest of freshwater marshes in the Canadian prairies, and the research station run by the University of Manitoba is of national importance. Spencer Sealy and a group of students and colleagues at the University of Manitoba decided it was time to explore this long-term database and find out whether there was an effect of temperature on spring arrivals (Murphy-Klassen et al. 2005).

Species varied greatly in their arrival dates, with the Horned Lark arriving (on average) on February 24, and the Common Nighthawk not arriving until May 19. Over the 63 years, mean temperatures for February–May increased. The greatest changes were seen for February, which increased 3.8°C, and for March, which increased 3.1°C, compared to 0.6°C and 1.4°C for April and May, respectively. In total, 27 of the 96 species showed altered arrivals, with 25 arriving earlier and 2 later. This, too, supports the idea of a climate fingerprint. It is important to note that of the 69 species that did not show a *statistically significant* shift in arrival, 50 of them had a trend toward earlier arrival!

Supporting the idea that these shifts are due to warming is the strong relationship the researchers found between arrival date and the actual temperature of the month in which the bird arrived (fig. 9.25). In fact, they found a trend for such a relationship for 84 of their 96 species, strongly supporting the idea that spring arrival is influenced by local climatic conditions.

It is important to remember that all species are connected to other species through a network of ecological interactions. All cylinders need to be firing in sync for an organism to meet its niche requirements, and, as climate changes, the certainty of this synchronization for some species is less clear.

A recent study by Stephen Mayor at Memorial University in Newfoundland, working with a large and diverse team, speaks to this synchronization or, more correctly, to asynchrony (Mayor et al. 2017). The team used satellite imagery to determine green-up date based on an "onset of greenness increase" for the years 2001–2012. These data

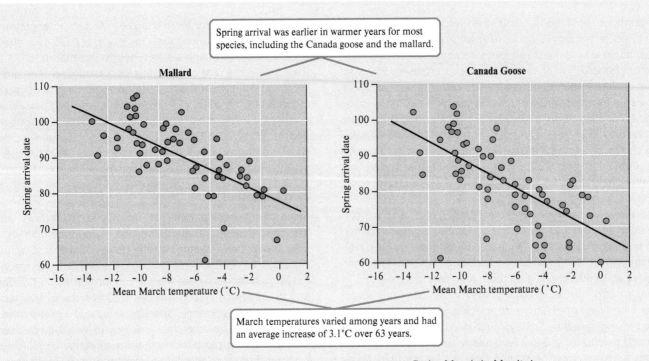

> Spring arrival was earlier in warmer years for most species, including the Canada goose and the mallard.

> March temperatures varied among years and had an average increase of 3.1°C over 63 years.

Figure 9.25   Arrival dates of migratory birds is related to temperature at Delta Marsh in Manitoba.
H. M. Murphy-Klassen et al. 2005. Long-term trends in spring arrival dates of migrant birds at Delta Marsh, Manitoba, in relation to climate change. *Auk* 122:1120–48, Figure 4.

were used to determine the rate of change in green-up dates using linear regression. Consistent with accelerating greening reported by Wang and colleagues, Mayor's team found that the onset of greening was earlier for much of Canada and the rest of North America, although it tended to come later along the Pacific coast and western prairies. Bird arrival dates for 48 passerine species were collected from eBird, a citizen science database. Consistent with patterns of greening, birds in the east are shifting the timing of their arrivals. However, the change in arrival dates of many bird species are not keeping pace with the change in green-up dates. The lag in the interval between bird arrival and green-up has been increasing by half a day per year, on average. The result is that the arrival of eastern bird species is lagging further behind green-up, while birds in the west have begun arriving earlier relative to green-up. If this trend continues, birds will be out of sync with available food resources in both the east (where they may arrive too late) and in the west (where they may arrive too early).

Reproduction

Can climate change cause evolutionary changes in populations, which then influence their life history? Or does climate change happen at a speed much greater than natural selection, meaning that only those species that are phenotypically plastic are able to cope with the changing environment? A team of researchers from McGill University, University of Alberta, and the Université du Québec à Rimouski decided to test these questions, studying the life-history traits of squirrels (Réale et al. 2003; Berteaux et al. 2004).

The North American red squirrel is found in much of the forested areas of North America. The research team decided to focus on one phenological measure: the parturition date (timing of birth). Prior work indicated that parturition dates are in part heritable, with an $h^2 = 0.16$ (chapter 4). Additionally, parturition dates generally coincide with food abundance and shifts in spring weather. These factors make it a good candidate for the study of the evolutionary consequences of climate change. The focal population they used was located near Kluane Lake, in the Yukon. The entire population has been studied for years, with all individuals tagged and reproductive activity monitored from 1989–2001. Because the researchers had tracked the maternity of all squirrels, they were able to estimate how much of the observed phenotype (parturition dates) was heritable and how much was phenotypic plasticity (see chapter 4 for a review of these terms). During this period, spring temperatures increased by nearly 2°C, and the number of spruce cones available for feeding by the squirrels increased by 35%. Parturition dates also changed, becoming earlier by two weeks in just 10 years (fig. 9.26). Through their understanding of the maternity of the squirrels in their population, they were able to show that nearly 15% of the shift in parturition dates

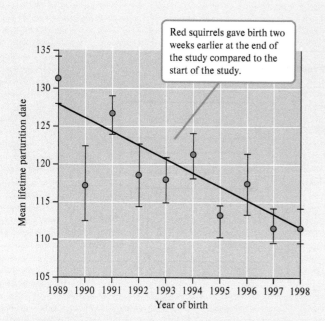

Figure 9.26 Parturition dates became earlier during the course of the study for red squirrels.

D. Reale et al. 2003. Genetic and plastic responses of a northern mammal to climate change. *Proceeding of the Royal Society of London Series B-Biological Sciences* 270(1515):591–6.

was due to selection on this trait. The rest of the variation was due to phenotypic plasticity and other unidentified factors. This study is important in showing that, yes, natural selection can result in phenological shifts of critical life-history parameters over very short periods of time. In other words, although most species have some phenotypic plasticity to climate, prolonged climate change is likely to cause evolutionary shifts in natural populations. In fact, as the researchers have shown, for some species, it already has.

As you can see from the studies we have presented here, there is substantial evidence that climate change is impacting natural populations in biologically significant ways. Shifts in phenology are being used as a climatic fingerprint, providing some of the first biological evidence that change not only might occur but has in fact already occurred. As ecologists continue to develop the methods needed to detect the importance of climate change, it is certain we will learn much more about how biology and the abiotic environment interact to influence life histories and niches. Only through continued research will society be able to mitigate some of the negative consequences of these changes, helping protect species that otherwise may be in peril due to human activities.

SUMMARY

A niche represents the set of conditions in which a species could survive. Life history consists of the adaptations of an organism that influence aspects of its biology, such as the number of offspring it produces, its survival, and its size and age at reproductive maturity (fig. 9.27). This chapter presents discussions bearing on some of the central concepts of niches and life history.

9.1 Because all organisms have access to limited energy and resources, there are fundamental trade-offs in how these can be allocated among survival, offspring number, and offspring size.

Turner and Trexler found that larger darter species produce larger numbers of eggs. Their results also support the generalization that there is a trade-off between offspring size and number. On average, darters that produce larger eggs produce few eggs. They found a strong positive relationship between gene flow among darter populations and the number of eggs produced by females, and a negative relationship between egg size and gene flow. Plant ecologists have also found a negative relationship between sizes of seeds produced by plants and the number of seeds they produce. Westoby, Leishman, and Lord

found that plants of different growth form and different seed dispersal mechanisms tend to produce seeds of different sizes. Larger seeds, on average, produce larger seedlings, which have a higher probability of successfully recruiting, particularly in the face of environmental challenges, such as shade and competition.

Where adult survival is lower, organisms begin reproducing at an earlier age and invest a greater proportion of their energy budget into reproduction. Where adult survival is higher, organisms defer reproduction to a later age and allocate a smaller proportion of their resources to reproduction. Shine and Charnov found that as survival of adult lizards and snakes increases, their age at maturity also increases. Gunderson found analogous patterns among fish. In addition, fish with higher rates of mortality allocate a greater proportion of their biomass to reproduction. In other words, they show higher reproductive effort. These generalizations are supported by comparisons both between and within species. Male coho salmon display jack and hooknose life-history strategies, each of which is typically associated with a particular mating strategy. Pumpkinseed sunfish allocate greater energy, or biomass, to reproductive effort where adult pumpkinseed survival is

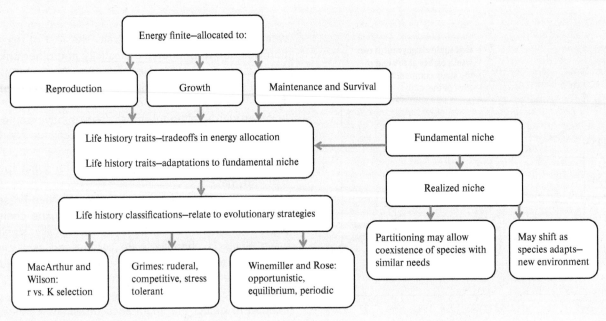

Figure 9.27   Concept map for chapter 9.

lower. Many life-history traits, such as sexual reproduction in *Daphnia pulex*, can be inherited traits subject to evolutionary pressures.

9.2 The great diversity of life histories observed in nature can be classified on the basis of a few common characteristics.

One of the earliest attempts to organize information on the great variety of life histories that occur among species was under the heading of *r* selection and K selection. *r* selection refers to the per capita rate of increase, *r*, and is thought to favour higher population growth rate. *r* selection is predicted to be strongest in disturbed habitats. K selection refers to the carrying capacity in the logistic growth equation and is envisioned as a form of natural selection favouring more efficient utilization of resources, such as food and nutrients. Grime described plant strategies, or life histories, that match the requirements of three environments: (1) low disturbance–low stress, (2) low disturbance–high stress, (3) high disturbance–low stress. His plant strategies matching these environmental conditions were competitive, stress-tolerant, and ruderal. Based on life-history patterns among fish, Kirk Winemiller and Kenneth Rose proposed a classification of life histories based on survivorship, especially among juveniles; fecundity, or number of offspring produced; and generation time, or age at maturity. By basing their classification system on some of the most basic aspects of population ecology, Winemiller and Rose established a common currency for representing and analyzing life-history information for any organism.

9.3 The fundamental niche reflects the environmental requirements of a species while the realized niche also includes interactions with other species.

The niche concept was developed early in the history of ecology and has had a prominent place ever since. Hutchinson developed the concepts of the *fundamental niche*, the physical conditions under which a species might live in the absence of other species, and the *realized niche*, the more restricted conditions under which a species actually lives as the result of interactions with other species. While a species' niche is theoretically defined by a very large number of biotic and abiotic factors, Hutchinson's *n*-dimensional hypervolume, the most important attributes of the niche of most species can often be summarized by a few variables. For instance, the niches of Galápagos finches are largely determined by their feeding requirements, while the niche of a salt marsh grass can be defined by tidal levels. A species' realized niche may become narrower when a competitor is present. This reduction in realized niche of competing species may allow the coexistence of competing species. A species may also experience a shift in its realized niche as it adapts to the newest of environmental conditions (fig. 9.27).

Life-history information is being used to find evidence that climate change is having effects on natural populations. The search for a climate fingerprint has centred on shifts in phenology, the timing of life events. There is substantial evidence that spring events, such as bud break and mating, are occurring earlier in areas of increased temperature. These changes occur in a diversity of taxa and are the result of phenotypic plasticity, behavioural responses, and natural selection.

REVIEW QUESTIONS

1. Researchers have characterized the niches of some species not as a multi-dimensional hypervolume, but on the basis of a small number of environmental variables. For example, the niches of Galápagos finches have been described by beak size (which correlates with diet), and the niches of salt marsh grasses by position in the intertidal zone. How would you characterize the niches of sympatric canid species, such as red fox, coyote, and wolf in North America? What characteristics or environmental features do you think would be useful for representing the niches of arctic plants?

2. The discussion of seed size and number focused mainly on the advantages associated with large seeds. However, research by Westoby, Leishman, and Lord has revealed that the plants from widely separated geographic regions produce a wide variety of seed sizes. If this variation is to be maintained, there must be some advantages to producing small seeds. What are some of these advantages?

3. Under what conditions should natural selection favour production of many small offspring versus the production of a few well-provisioned offspring?

4. The studies by Shine and Charnov (1992) and Gunderson (1997) addressed important questions of concern to life-history ecologists, and their work provided robust answers to those questions. However, the methods they employed differed substantially from those used in most of the studies discussed in this and other chapters. The chief difference is that both relied heavily on data of life histories published previously by other authors. What was it about the nature of the problems addressed by these authors that constrained them to use this approach? In what types of studies would it be most appropriate to perform a synthesis of previously published information?

5. Much of our discussion of life-history variation involved variation among species within groups broadly defined as "fish," "plants," or "reptiles." However, the work of Bertschy and Fox revealed significant variation in life history within a species. In general, what should be the relative amount of variation within a species compared to that among many species? Develop your discussion using relative amounts of genetic variation upon which natural selection might act. You might review the sections discussing the evolutionary significance of genetic variation in chapter 4.

6. David Innes demonstrated that sexual vs. asexual reproduction in *Daphnia pulex* could be altered depending upon the life-history traits possessed by the parents. Pick another species or organism and a different life-history trait. Design a study that will allow you to determine whether this aspect of life history is heritable. Why does this issue of heritability matter?

7. Grime's classification does not consider the fourth identified environmental extreme, high disturbance/high stress. Consider the characteristics necessary to cope with high disturbance and those necessary to cope with high stress. Why does Grime conclude that no plants would have the combination of traits needed to persist in these conditions?

8. Where would you place the following plant species in Grime's and in Winemiller and Rose's classifications of life histories? The plant species lives in an environment where it has access to plenty of water and nutrients but is subject to disturbance by flooding and wind. An average individual produces several million seeds per year and may live several centuries. However, ideal conditions for reproduction by the species occur only once or twice per decade.

9. Climate change consists of variation in many factors other than temperature. How might shifts in precipitation patterns impact phenology for the plants and animals of the prairies? How about for the wetter temperate forest?

10. Will species be able to adjust to climate changes, resulting in no altered risks of extinctions? What factors influence these abilities?

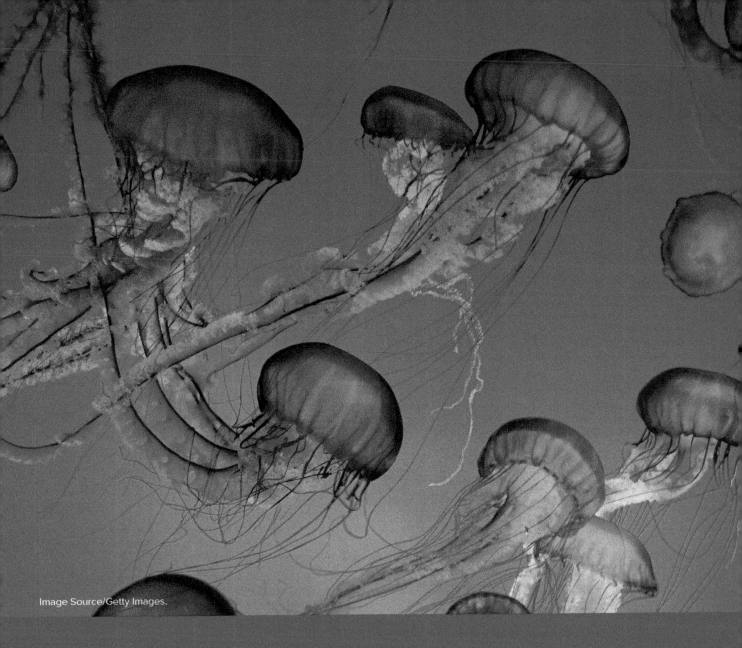

Image Source/Getty Images.

SECTION 3 POPULATION ECOLOGY

In this section, we discuss the properties and dynamics of populations. Population ecology is at the interface between physiological ecology (section 2), and community and landscape level processes (sections 4 and 5). We begin by describing the geographic distribution of populations and species (chapter 10). We then discuss different ways of quantifying population structure (chapter 11), and conclude this section by exploring major factors that influence population growth and the models ecologists use to describe these changes (chapter 12).

Kevin van der Leek Photography/Flickr/Getty Images

CHAPTER 10

DISTRIBUTION AND ABUNDANCE OF POPULATIONS AND SPECIES

CHAPTER CONCEPTS

10.1 The physical environment limits the geographic distribution of species.
Concept 10.1 Review

10.2 Dispersal can alter species distributions and local population densities.
Concept 10.2 Review

10.3 Some populations, called metapopulations, consist of interconnected subpopulations.
Concept 10.3 Review

10.4 On small scales, individuals within populations are distributed in patterns that may be random, regular, or clumped; on larger scales, individuals within a population are clumped.
Concept 10.4 Review

Ecology in Action: Using Ecology to Protect Threatened Species

10.5 Population density declines with increasing organism size.
Concept 10.5 Review

10.6 Commonness and rarity of species are influenced by population size, geographic range, and habitat tolerance.
Concept 10.6 Review

Ecological Tools and Approaches: Estimating Abundance

Summary

Review Questions

The distributions and dynamics of populations vary widely among species. While some populations contain only dozens of individuals within a highly restricted distribution, other populations number in the billions of individuals, ranging over vast areas of the planet.

Standing on a headland in Nunavut overlooking the Arctic Ocean, you might see a breeding colony of Arctic terns (*Sterna paradisaea*) (fig. 10.1*a*), with both males and females defending the nest site from potential threats. These birds are particularly aggressive, as you'll find out if you get a bit too close to them. Ecologists surveying these colonies might carry sticks, not to hit birds but as decoys. The terns may then fly at their stick "heads" and leave their actual heads alone. When winter comes in the north, this entire population will fly to feeding grounds in the south, reaching the coast of Antarctica. Each bird, even the young fledglings, makes this round trip of over 18,000 km each year. In the process, these birds see more daylight and have the longest regular migration of any species on the planet.

(a)

(b)

Figure 10.1   (*a*) During their annual migration, the entire population of Arctic terns moves from the Arctic Ocean in the northern summer to as far south as Antarctica in the southern summer. (*b*) Muskox populations remain in the Arctic all year, though they migrate to higher elevations in the winter to avoid deep snow.

While several students are watching the birds, others observe a small herd of muskox (*Ovibos moschatus*) grazing on a variety of plants in a nearby river valley (fig. 10.1*b*). Even a casual observer recognizes that these animals have traits that allow them to withstand extremely cold temperatures. Most obvious is their fur coat, with numerous thick guard hairs nearly reaching the ground. These guard hairs are water repellent and help protect the insulative properties of the finer undercoat. On closer inspection, this herd appears to consist of only males, many of whom are engaged in competition, trying to achieve a dominant position within the herd. In winter, these animals do not leave the Arctic. Instead, they form herds consisting of both sexes and move to higher elevations. In these winter grounds, they find less snow, allowing them to more easily find suitable forage for grazing.

Arctic terns and muskox, as different as they may appear, lead parallel lives. As climatic conditions change and food becomes more scarce or harder to find, the entire population moves to a new area. Although the distance travelled differs between the species, the causes of migration are similar. However, as the students continue to look at the landscape, well after these animals have moved on, they realize that the more abundant organisms on the landscape, numerous plant and lichen species, do not migrate at all. The students are able to find hundreds of species of clubmosses, lichens, ferns, mosses, and flowering plants within just a short distance of their base camp. And although the colony of terns appears large, with tens of thousands of birds present, that is just a pittance compared to the millions of individual plants that are present around the students on the tundra.

With these examples, we begin to consider the ecology of populations. Ecologists usually define a **population** as a group of potentially interbreeding individuals of a single species inhabiting a specific area. A population of plants or animals might occupy a mountaintop, a river basin, a coastal marsh, or an island, all areas defined by natural boundaries. Just as often, the populations studied by biologists occupy artificially defined but societally important areas, such as a particular country or park. The areas inhabited by populations range in size from the few cubic centimetres occupied by the bacteria in a rotting apple to the millions of square kilometres occupied by a population of migratory terns. A population studied by ecologists may consist of a highly localized group of individuals representing a fraction of the total individuals of a species, or it may consist of all the individuals of a species across its entire range.

Many attributes of populations are determined by interactions between the physiological ecology of a species and the biotic and abiotic conditions that individuals in a population encounter. These interactions act as ecological filters that determine where different species may become established and where they may thrive. Ecological filters will include attributes of the physical environment, such as soil type and microclimate, and biological interactions, such as competition, predator–prey interactions, and mutualism, which will be subjects of later chapters. These filters define the niche. Population ecology serves as a bridge between physiological and community ecology, topics discussed in other sections of this book. Ecologists study populations for a number of reasons. First, like all levels of ecological organization, detailed understanding of natural populations can provide insight into the general processes that drive ecological interactions. However, population-level interactions serve as the foundation for many resource-based economies, and thus there are often strong societal pressures to understand population dynamics. Just hearing the words *cod fishery, zebra mussel,* or *mountain pine beetle* sends shudders down the spines of many Canadians. At the core of the economic crises involving these species have been issues related to population ecology. Population ecologists provide valuable insight into the understanding and possible control of numerous species that cause economic, aesthetic, and functional harm to Canada's natural resources. Population ecology is also at the centre of many studies of species at risk, with recovery plans often constructed to allow for the recovery of threatened populations. Finally, one of the greatest pressures faced by many plant and animal species around the planet has at its heart a shift in the population of a single species—the exponential growth of human populations.

All populations share several characteristics. The first is distribution. The distribution of a population includes the size, shape, and location of the area (or volume) it occupies. A population is also characterized by the number of individuals within it and their **density**: the number of individuals per unit area. Population density can be further refined as either **absolute density** or **ecological density**. Absolute density is what most scientists refer to when they simply say "density" (as we will do in this chapter), and it is the number of individuals of a population per unit area (e.g., number of muskox per square kilometre). Ecological density incorporates the concept of the niche (chapter 9), in that not all of the conditions found within a given area will contain the niche requirements of a particular species. For example, within a large tract of land in the tundra, there will be areas suitable for muskox grazing and rocky areas that do not support suitable plant growth. The ecological density of the muskox would be the number of individuals per unit of suitable habitat.

Additional characteristics of populations—their age distributions, sex ratios, birth and death rates, immigration and emigration rates, and rates of growth—are the subject of chapters 11 and 12. In this chapter, we focus on three population characteristics: distribution, abundance, and dispersal.

10.1 Distribution Limits

The physical environment limits the geographic distribution of species. A major theme in chapters 4 to 8 is that natural selection has resulted in the evolution of physiological, morphological, and behavioural characteristics that enable individuals to compensate for environmental variation. In chapter 9 we saw how these characteristics were driven in part by a series of trade-offs, resulting in a diversity of life histories and niches. Here we move from our understanding of the conditions that organisms need to persist and thrive, to understanding the locations in which those conditions are found. You may recall from chapter 9 that the niche represents the multidimensional set of conditions necessary for a species to persist. The niche is an abstract concept, not a tangible trait or specific location on the landscape.

However, across a landscape there will be variability in environmental conditions, prey distributions, and other critical axes of the niche. This means that the conditions defined by a species' niche will be found only in specific locations; therefore, species should be found on the landscape only in locations where conditions fall within those required by that species' niche. One determining factor of a species' geographic distribution, then, will be the underlying distribution of biotic and abiotic conditions in combination with that species' niche requirements.

When a species occupies habitat that contains conditions on the edge of those found within the species' niche, the metabolic costs of compensating for environmental stressors will take up a greater part of the organism's energy budget (e.g., thermoregulation). Partly because of these energy constraints, the physical environment places limits on the distributions of populations. Let's now turn to some actual species and explore the factors that limit their distributions.

Kangaroo Distributions and Climate

The Macropodidae include the kangaroos and wallabies, which are some of the best known of the Australian animals. However, this group of large-footed mammals includes many less familiar species, including rat kangaroos and tree kangaroos. While some species of macropods can be found in nearly every part of Australia, no single species ranges across the entire continent.

G. Caughley and his colleagues (1987) found a close relationship between climate and the distributions of the three largest kangaroos in Australia (fig. 10.2). The eastern grey kangaroo (*Macropus giganteus*) is confined to the eastern third of the continent, a portion of Australia that includes several biomes (see chapter 2). Temperate forest grows in the southeast; and tropical forests, in the north. Mountains, with their varied climates, occupy the central part of the eastern grey kangaroo's range. The climatic factor that distinguishes these varied biomes is little seasonal variation in precipitation or dominance by summer precipitation. The western grey kangaroo (*M. fuliginosus*), on the other hand, lives mainly in the southern and western regions of Australia. Most of the western grey kangaroo's range coincides with temperate woodland and shrubland biomes in Australia. The climatically distinctive feature is a predominance of winter rainfall. Meanwhile, the red kangaroo (*M. rufus*) wanders the arid and semiarid interior of Australia. The biomes that cover most of the red kangaroo's range are savanna and desert (chapter 2). Of the three species of large kangaroos, the red kangaroo occupies the hottest and driest areas.

As a group, the distributions of these three large kangaroo species cover most of Australia. However, none of these species lives in the northernmost region of Australia, where tropical forests are common. Caughley and his colleagues explain that these northern areas are probably too hot for the eastern grey kangaroo, too wet for the red kangaroo, and too hot in summer and too dry in winter for the western grey kangaroo. However, they are also careful to point out that these limited distributions may not be determined by climate directly. Instead, the kangaroo may possess the physiological traits needed to survive under

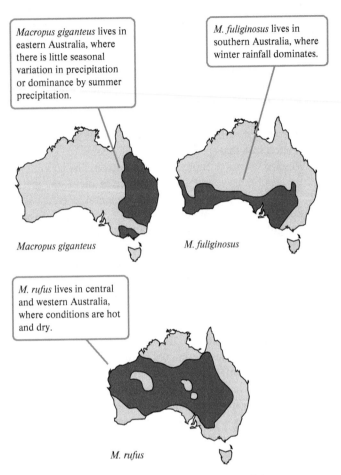

Macropus giganteus lives in eastern Australia, where there is little seasonal variation in precipitation or dominance by summer precipitation.

M. fuliginosus lives in southern Australia, where winter rainfall dominates.

Macropus giganteus

M. fuliginosus

M. rufus lives in central and western Australia, where conditions are hot and dry.

M. rufus

Figure 10.2 Climate and the distributions of three kangaroo species.
Data from Caughley et al. 1987.

(a)

(b)

Figure 10.3 (*a*) *Chthamalus stellatus* and (*b*) *Balanus balanoides* occur in different zones within intertidal regions. Ecologists have studied these species extensively, leading to insights into the processes that govern species distributions.
(a) A. J. Southward; *(b)* © Diane Nelson.

those conditions, but may yet be limited due to lack of food production or suitable habitat. Climate also affects the incidence of parasites, pathogens, and competitors that can further restrict the realized niche of species.

Regardless of how the influences of climate are played out, the relationship between climate and the distributions of species can be stable over long periods of time. The distributions of the eastern grey, western grey, and red kangaroos have been stable for at least a century. In the next example, we discuss distributions of two species in a much smaller spatial scale: the intertidal pool, where we will find that species that occur close together may have very different physiological limits.

Distributions of Barnacles Along an Intertidal Exposure Gradient

The marine intertidal zone presents a steep gradient of physical conditions from the shore seaward. Organisms high in the intertidal zone are exposed by virtually every tide, while the organisms that live at lower levels in the intertidal zone are exposed by the lowest tides only. Exposure to air differs at different levels within the intertidal zone. Organisms that live in the intertidal zone have evolved different degrees of resistance to drying, a major factor contributing to zonation among intertidal organisms.

Barnacles, one of the most common intertidal organisms (fig. 10.3), show distinctive patterns of zonation within the intertidal zone. For example, Joseph Connell (1961a, 1961b) described how, along the coast of Scotland, adult *Chthamalus stellatus* are restricted to the upper levels of the intertidal zone, while adult *Balanus balanoides* are limited to the middle and lower levels (fig. 10.4). What role does resistance to drying play in the intertidal zonation of these two species? Unusually calm and warm weather, combined with very low tides, gave Connell some insights into this question. In the spring of 1955, warm weather coincided with calm seas and very low tides. As a consequence, no water reached the upper intertidal zone occupied by both species of barnacles. During this period, *Balanus* in the upper intertidal zone suffered much higher mortality than *Chthamalus* (fig. 10.5). Meanwhile, *Balanus* in the lower intertidal zone showed normal rates of mortality. Of the two species, *Balanus* appears to be more vulnerable to desiccation. Higher rates of desiccation may exclude this species of barnacle from the upper intertidal zone.

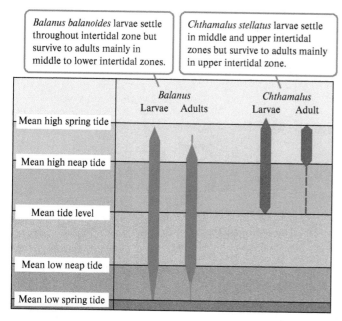

Figure 10.4 Distributions of two barnacle species within the intertidal zone.
Data from Connell 1961b.

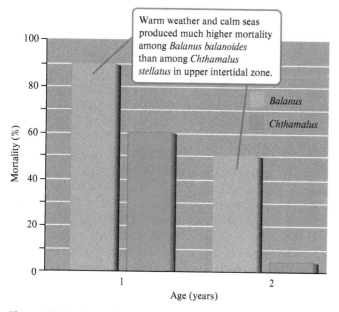

Figure 10.5 Barnacle mortality in the upper intertidal zone.
Data from Connell 1961b.

Vulnerability to desiccation, however, does not completely explain the pattern of intertidal zonation shown by *Balanus* and *Chthamalus*. What excludes *Chthamalus* from the lower intertidal zone? Though the larvae of this barnacle settle in the lower intertidal zone, the adults rarely survive there. Connell explored this question by transplanting adult *Chthamalus* to the lower intertidal zone and found that transplanted adults survive very well in the lower intertidal zone. If the physical environment does not exclude *Chthamalus* from the lower intertidal zone, what does? It turns out that this species is excluded from the

lower intertidal zone by competitive interactions with *Balanus*. We discuss the mechanisms by which this competitive exclusion is accomplished in chapter 13.

These barnacles remind us that the environment consists of more than just physical and chemical factors. An organism's environment also includes biological factors. In many situations, biological factors may be even more important than physical factors in determining the distribution and abundance of some species. Often, the influences of biological factors remain hidden, however, because of the difficulty of demonstrating them. In ecology, we must usually probe deeper to see beyond outward appearances, as Connell did when he transplanted *Chthamalus* from the upper to the lower intertidal zone. The influence of biological factors, such as competition, predation, and disease, on the distribution and abundance of organisms is a theme that enters our discussions frequently in the remainder of this book, especially in chapters 13, 14, and 15.

Now that we have considered factors limiting the distributions of individuals, let's consider the dispersal of organisms, which will change species distributions and affect local population densities.

10.2 Dispersal

Dispersal can alter species distributions and local population densities. The seeds of plants disperse with wind or water or may be transported by a variety of mammals, insects, or birds. Adult barnacles may spend their lives attached to rocks, but their larvae travel the high seas on far-ranging ocean currents. A host of other sessile marine invertebrates, algae, and many highly sedentary reef fish also disperse widely as larvae. Some young spiders spin a small net that catches winds and carries them for distances up to hundreds of kilometres. Young mammals and birds often disperse from the area where they were born and may join other local populations. As a consequence of movements such as these (fig. 10.6), the population ecologist trying to understand local population structure must consider dispersal *into* (**immigration**) and *out of* (**emigration**) the local population. As we will discuss later in this chapter, dispersal of individuals allows for the persistence of metapopulations and has important consequences for natural communities. It is important to recognize that dispersal is different from migration. Migration is the seasonal movement of individuals

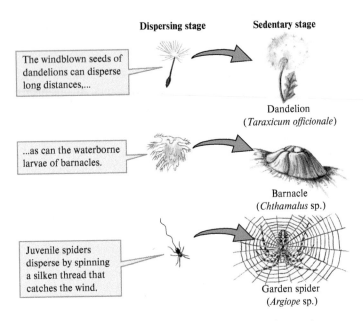

Figure 10.6   Dispersing and sedentary stages of organisms.

from one location to another, while dispersal is (typically) a permanent exodus from one population into another. The causes and consequences of these differences are significant, though beyond the scope of this text.

Despite its importance, dispersal is one of the least-studied aspects of population ecology. Its study is clearly a difficult undertaking. One of the richest sources of information on dispersal and some of the clearest examples come from studies of expanding populations.

Dispersal of Expanding Populations

Expanding populations are those that are in the process of increasing their geographic range. Why should this type of population provide us with some of the best records of species dispersal? The appearance of a new species in an area is quickly noted and recorded, especially if the species impacts the local economy or human health or safety. For instance, the expansion of Africanized bees through South and North America is well documented (fig. 10.7). The legendary aggressiveness of these bees ensures that their dispersal into an area does not escape notice for long.

Honeybees (*Apis mellifera*) evolved in Africa and Europe, where their native range extends from tropical to cold, temperate environments. Across this extensive environmental range, this species has differentiated into a number of locally adapted subspecies. In an attempt to improve the adaptability of managed honeybees to their tropical climate, Brazilian scientists imported queens of the subspecies *Apis mellifera scutellata* from Tanzania in 1956. These queens mated with the European honeybees used by Brazilian beekeepers, producing what we now call Africanized bees.

Africanized honeybees differ in several ways from European honeybees. Temperate and tropical environments have apparently selected for markedly different behaviour and population dynamics. For example, natural selection by a high

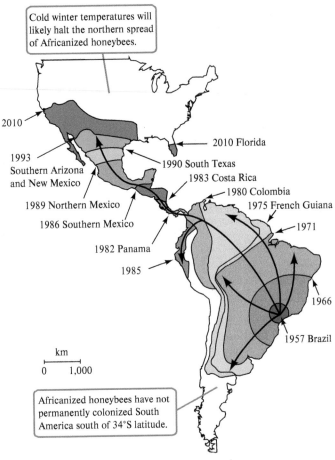

Figure 10.7   The expansion of Africanized bees from South America through Central and North America, 1956 to 2008. Data from Winston 1992, USDA Agricultural Research Service 2011.

diversity and abundance of nest predators has probably produced the greater aggressiveness shown by Africanized bees. Most important to this discussion of dispersal, Africanized honeybees produce swarms that disperse to form new colonies at a much higher rate than do European honeybees.

High rates of colony formation and dispersal have caused a rapid expansion of Africanized honeybees through South and North America. Their rate of dispersal has ranged from 300 to 500 km per year. Within 30 years, Africanized honeybees occupied most of South America, all of Central America, and most of Mexico. Africanized bees reached southern Texas in 1990, and southern Arizona and New Mexico in 1993. The honeybees stopped spreading southward through South America by about 1983, stopping at about 34° S latitude. However, they continue to spread northward through North America, particularly along the Pacific coast with its mild winters. As of 2018, their distribution included most of southern and central California. Population ecologists predict that Africanized honeybees are reaching the northern limit of their distribution within North America. Cold winter temperatures outside their range of tolerance are likely to halt their northward dispersal (chapter 5). Environmental conditions in northern North America generally do not overlap with the niche requirements of this species (chapter 9).

How does this rate of expansion by African honeybees compare to rates of expansion by other populations? Figure 10.8, which summarizes rates of dispersal for a variety of mammals and birds, shows that rates of dispersal differ by three orders of magnitude. While some species, such as Africanized bees, spread at rates of tens or hundreds of kilometres per year, others disperse only a few hundred metres per year. This is about the same rate at which North American trees expanded their distributions following the retreat of the glaciers.

Range Changes in Response to Climate Change

In response to climate change following retreat of the glaciers northward in North America beginning about 16,000 years ago, organisms of all sorts began to move northward from their ice age refuges. Temperate forest trees have left one of the best preserved records of this northward dispersal. In chapter 1 we saw how Margaret Davis was able to show the migration of tree species through well-preserved pollen records in lake sediment. For example, the northward advance of maple and hemlock is shown in figure 10.9.

The pollen preserved in lake sediments indicates that forest trees in eastern North America spread northward following the retreat of the glaciers at the rate of 100 to 400 m (0.1–0.4 km) per year. This rate of dispersal is similar to that of some large mammals, such as the North American elk. However, it is 1/1,000 the dispersal rate of Africanized bees across South, Central, and North America.

The work of Davis has shown us that trees are able to disperse large distances over relatively short periods of time

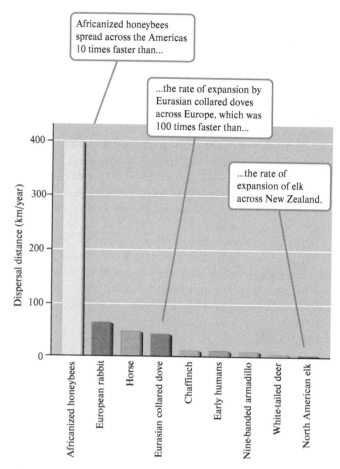

Figure 10.8 Rates of expansion by animal populations.
Data from Caughley 1977, Hengeveld 1988, and Winston 1992.

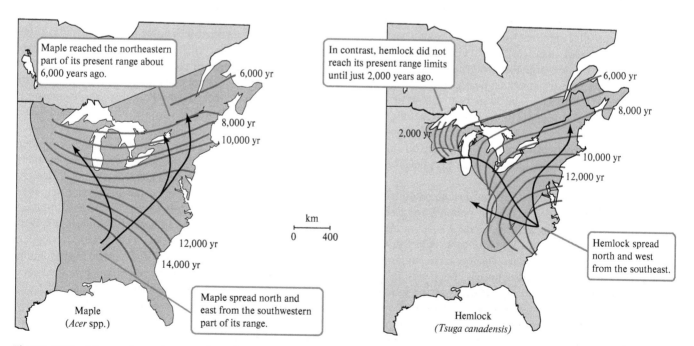

Figure 10.9 The northward expansion of two tree species in North America following glacial retreat.
Data from Davis 1981.

in response to climate change. The period of rapid climatic change in which we now find ourselves will push many populations to their limits of tolerance (or beyond) over some portion of their current range. Climate change will also open new areas to colonization that previously fell outside a species' fundamental niche. In theory, dispersal could allow species' ranges to move, readjusting to changing climate. However, the rate of climate change will outpace the rate of dispersal for some populations, making these populations vulnerable. Moreover, since the last ice age there has been substantial human alteration of the landscape. It remains unclear to what extent these alterations will prevent, slow, or facilitate the dispersal of plant and animal species in response to the current climate change.

The previous examples concern dispersal by populations in the process of expanding their ranges. Significant dispersal also takes place within established populations whose ranges are not changing. Movements within established ranges can be an important aspect of local population dynamics, as we'll see below.

Dispersal in Response to Changing Food Supply

In some years, northern landscapes are alive with small rodents called voles, of the genus *Microtus*. Go to the same place during other years and it may be difficult to find any. In northern latitudes, vole populations usually reach high densities (> 1,000/km²) every three to four years. Between these peak times, population densities crash. Population cycles in different areas are not synchronized, however. In other words, while vole population density is very low in one area, it is high elsewhere.

Erkki Korpimäki and Kai Norrdahl (1991) conducted a 10-year study of voles and their predators. The study began in 1977 during a peak in vole densities, and continued through two more peaks in 1982 and 1985–86. The researchers estimated that between these population peaks, vole densities per square kilometre fell to as low as 70 in 1980 and 40 in 1984. During this period, the densities of the European kestrel (*Falco tinnunculus*), short-eared owl (*Asio flammeus*), and long-eared owl (*Asio otus*) closely tracked vole densities (fig. 10.10). How do kestrel and owl populations track these variations in vole densities?

C.S. Holling (1959) described **numerical responses** as changes in the density of predators in response to increased prey density. What mechanisms produce the numerical responses by kestrels and owls to changing vole densities? Look at figure 10.10 for a clue. The peaks in raptor densities in 1977, 1982, and 1986 match the peaks in vole densities almost perfectly. If reproduction was the source of numerical response by kestrels and owls, there would have been more of a delay, or time lag, in kestrel and owl numerical response, as they have much slower reproductive rates than voles. From this close match in numbers, Korpimäki and Norrdahl proposed that kestrels and owls must move from place to place in response to local increases in vole populations.

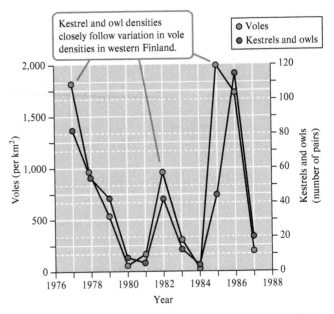

Figure 10.10   Dispersal and numerical response by predators. Data from Korpimäki and Norrdahl 1991.

This conclusion was supported by mark and recapture data of raptors, which strongly suggested that the hawks and owls in western Finland are nomadic, moving from place to place in response to changing vole densities. Dispersal contributed strongly to local populations of kestrels and owls. Many other local populations are strongly influenced by dispersal. One of the environments in which dispersal has a major influence on local populations is in streams and rivers.

Dispersal in Rivers and Streams

One of the most distinctive features of the stream and river environment is *current*, the downstream flow of water. As you may recall from chapter 3, the effects of current are substantial and influence everything from the amount of oxygen in the water to the size, shape, and behaviour of stream organisms. In this section, we stop and consider how stream populations are affected by current.

Let's begin with a question. Why doesn't the flowing water of streams eventually wash all stream organisms, including fish, insects, snails, bacteria, algae, and fungi, out to sea? All stream dwellers have a variety of characteristics that help them maintain their position in streams. Some fish, such as trout, are streamlined and can easily swim against swift currents, while other fish, like sculpins and loaches, avoid the full strength of currents by living on the bottom and seeking shelter among or under stones. Microorganisms resist being washed away by adhering to the surfaces of stones, wood, and other substrates. Many stream insects are flattened and so stay out of the main force of the current, while others are streamlined and fast-swimming.

Despite these means of staying in place, stream organisms do get washed downstream in large numbers, particularly during flash floods, or **spates**. Stream ecologists refer to this

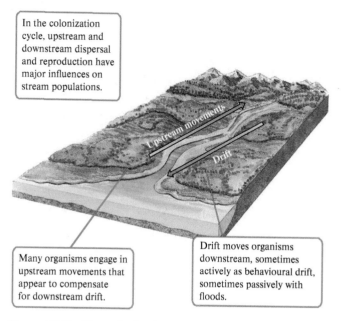

In the colonization cycle, upstream and downstream dispersal and reproduction have major influences on stream populations.

Many organisms engage in upstream movements that appear to compensate for downstream drift.

Drift moves organisms downstream, sometimes actively as behavioural drift, sometimes passively with floods.

Figure 10.11 The colonization cycle of stream invertebrates.

downstream movement of stream organisms as **drift**. Some drift is due to displacement of organisms during flash floods. However, some is due to the active movement of organisms downstream.

Whatever the cause, stream organisms drift downstream in large numbers. Karl Müller (1954, 1974) hypothesized that drift would eventually wash entire populations out of streams unless organisms actively moved upstream to compensate. He proposed that stream populations are maintained through a dynamic interplay between downstream and upstream dispersal that he called the **colonization cycle** (fig. 10.11).

Many studies support Müller's hypothesized colonization cycle. In the adult stages, most aquatic insects fly, and females can disperse upstream before laying eggs. As larvae, aquatic insects disperse upstream as well as downstream by swimming, crawling, and drifting. However, it is not only insects that exhibit colonization cycles. A snail that lives in a tropical stream in Costa Rica provides a well-documented example.

The Rio Claro flows approximately 30 km through tropical forest on the Osa Peninsula of Costa Rica before flowing into the Pacific Ocean. One of the most easily observed inhabitants of the Rio Claro is the snail *Neritina latissima*, which occupies the lower 5 km of the river. The eggs of *Neritina* hatch to produce free-living planktonic larvae that drift down to the Pacific Ocean. After the larvae metamorphose into small snails they re-enter the Rio Claro and begin moving upstream in huge migratory aggregations of up to 500,000 individuals (fig. 10.12). These aggregations move slowly and may take up to one year to reach the upstream limit of the population. Because an organism that is visible to the naked eye does all of this in a clear stream, and does so at a snail's pace, we are provided with a unique opportunity to observe how dispersal— here, the colonization cycle—can strongly influence local populations.

(a)

(b)

Figure 10.12 *(a)* A close-up *Neritina latissima. (b)* A wave of migrating *Neritina* snails in the Rio Claro, Costa Rica.
(a) Collection Natural History Museum Rotterdam, NMR 53717;
(b) © Daniel W. Schneider and John Lyons.

CONCEPT 10.2 REVIEW

1. Why might a species like Africanized honeybees be less threatened by climate change than maple trees are?

2. Some ecologists who have hung clear plastic sheets (coated with adhesive capable of trapping flying insects) from river bridges have found that the side of the sheets facing downstream traps more adult aquatic insects than the upstream-facing side. Explain how this relates to the colonization cycle.

10.3 Metapopulations

Some populations, called metapopulations, consist of interconnected subpopulations. Populations of many species occur not as a single, continuously distributed population but in spatially isolated patches, with significant exchange of individuals among patches. A group of subpopulations living on such patches connected by exchange of individuals among patches make up a **metapopulation**. Why are some populations divided into subpopulations and other populations able to persist as a single integrated population?

Metapopulations develop due to interactions between the biology of the species of interest and the landscape upon which it lives. For example, some species have very specific habitat requirements, such as a butterfly that can only oviposit on certain meadow plants. If meadows exist as large and continuous areas, then you would also expect the butterfly population to be large and continuous. However, if the meadows are only found as small patches of land surrounded by forest, agricultural fields, or other habitat unsuitable for this butterfly, then you would expect this species to form small populations in these meadows. If the biology of the organism allows for dispersal of individuals from one meadow to another, this then forms a metapopulation. Other species may have historically existed as a large, connected population, with changes to the landscape causing fragmentation (chapter 21) and the development of metapopulations. Such changes can include carving out agricultural fields from forests, expanding oil and gas exploration into boreal forests, and building housing developments in meadows. As human development of formerly intact areas continues, more species are potentially facing the fragmentation of their habitat and populations (chapter 21).

Regardless of the mechanism that is causing small populations to exist within proximity to each other, the question is whether individuals are able to disperse from one population to another. If dispersal does not occur, then several small and unconnected populations occur on the landscape. If dispersal is common, these small populations can be viewed as subpopulations of a larger metapopulation. More information about the characteristics of metapopulations can be found in figure 10.13.

A Metapopulation of an Alpine Butterfly

Butterflies have been well represented in studies of metapopulations. One of these butterflies is the Rocky Mountain Parnassian butterfly (*Parnassius smintheus*). The range of *P. smintheus*

Metapopulations are complex networks of movement and residency that have important consequences for species abundances, extinctions, and gene flow. Here are a few essential points about metapopulations:

1. Metapopulations are a population of subpopulations.
2. The subpopulations are connected by movement of individuals from one subpopulation to another.
3. Any subpopulation can go extinct and be re-colonized repeatedly over time.
4. The risk of subpopulation extinction is generally greatest for small subpopulations, which usually occur in small patches on the landscape.
5. Density-dependent and density-independent population dynamics (chapters 11, 12) occur within each subpopulation.

Figure 10.13   Metapopulations share several characteristics.

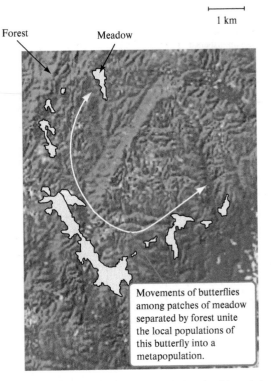

Movements of butterflies among patches of meadow separated by forest unite the local populations of this butterfly into a metapopulation.

Figure 10.14   A metapopulation of the Rocky Mountain Parnassian butterfly (*Parnassius smintheus*).

extends from northern New Mexico along the Rocky Mountains to southwest Alaska (figure 10.14). Along this range, *P. smintheus* caterpillars feed mainly on the leaves and flowers of stonecrop (*Sedum* sp.) in areas of open forest and meadows. Because of their tie to a narrow range of host plants, *P. smintheus* populations are often distributed among the habitat patches occupied by their host plant, appearing to form metapopulations.

One such metapopulation was studied by Jens Roland, Nusha Keyghobadi, and Sherri Fownes of the University of Alberta in Edmonton (Roland et al. 2000). Roland, Keyghobadi, and Fownes focused their attention on a series of 20 alpine meadows on ridges in the Kananaskis region of the Canadian Rocky Mountains. The study meadows ranged in area from about 0.8 ha to 20 ha. While some meadows were adjacent to each other, others were separated by up to 200 m of coniferous forest. The host plant of *P. smintheus* in the study meadows was the lanceleaf stonecrop (*Sedum lanceolatum*).

A combination of fire suppression and global warming appears to be decreasing the size of alpine meadows and increasing their isolation from each other by intervening forest. In 1952, the study meadows averaged approximately 36 ha in area. By 1993, the average area of these meadows had declined to approximately 8 ha. These changes motivated the research team of Roland, Keyghobadi, and Fownes to study the influences of meadow size and isolation on movements of *P. smintheus*.

The research team used mark and recapture techniques (see Ecological Tools and Approaches) to estimate population size in each meadow and to follow their movements. Butterflies were hand-netted and marked on the hind wing with a three-letter identification code, using a fine-tipped permanent marker. The team recorded the sex of the captured *P. smintheus* and its location within

20 m. Upon recapture, dispersal distance of an individual was estimated as the straight line distance from its last point of capture.

Over the course of the study, the size of *P. smintheus* populations in the 20 study meadows ranged from 0 to 230. Dispersal distances were fairly small: the average distance was < 150 m in both years of study (1995 and 1996), with maximum dispersal distances of 1,729 m in 1995 and 1,636 m in 1996. Most of the butterflies recaptured had remained within their meadow patches, although some had dispersed to other patches (5.8% in 1995 and 15.2% in 1996).

One of the questions posed by Roland and colleagues was how meadow size and population size might affect dispersal by *P. smintheus*. Average butterfly population size increased with meadow area (fig. 10.15). It turned out that butterflies were more likely to leave small patches with small populations. They generally immigrated to larger patches with larger populations. The results of this study indicate that as alpine meadows in the Rocky Mountains decline in area, due in part to climatic warming, populations of *P. smintheus* will become progressively more compressed into fewer and fewer shrinking meadows, perhaps disappearing entirely in parts of their range.

In the last two sections we have discussed patterns of dispersal, including mechanisms by which species are dispersed, environmental factors that influence dispersal, and dispersal among interconnected subpopulations. We next turn to patterns of distribution in subsection 10.4. Distribution patterns relate to population densities and the localized spatial variation in these densities. We will see that those patterns vary from one population to another and may depend upon the scale at which ecologists make their observations. Is there any way to predict the average population density of populations? While it is not possible to make precise predictions, the examples in subsection 10.5 will show that population densities are very much influenced by organism size.

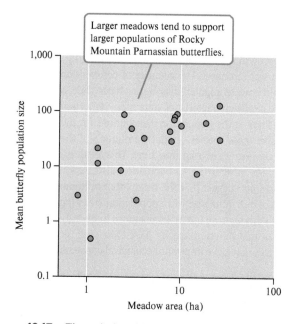

Figure 10.15 The relationship between meadow area and the size of Rocky Mountain Parnassian butterfly (*Parnassius smintheus*) populations. With forest encroachment into alpine meadows in the Rocky Mountains, populations of *P. smintheus* will likely decline.

Caption within figure: Larger meadows tend to support larger populations of Rocky Mountain Parnassian butterflies.

Axis labels: Mean butterfly population size (y-axis); Meadow area (ha) (x-axis)

10.4 Distribution Patterns

On small scales, individuals within populations are distributed in patterns that may be random, regular, or clumped; on larger scales, individuals within a population are clumped. In chapter 9 we considered how environmental factors define the niche, resulting in geographic limits to the distribution of species. When you map the distribution of a species, you are highlighting the range of the species (e.g., fig. 10.2). Your map shows where individuals of the species live and where they are absent, but it says nothing about how the individuals that make up the population are distributed in the areas where they are present. Are individuals randomly distributed across the range? Are they regularly distributed? As we shall see, the distribution pattern observed by an ecologist is strongly influenced by the scale at which a population is studied.

Ecologists refer frequently to **large-scale phenomena** and **small-scale phenomena**. What is "large" or "small" depends on the context. For this discussion, *small scale* refers to distances of no more than a few hundred metres, over which there is little environmental change significant to the organism under study. *Large scale* refers to areas over which there is substantial environmental change. In this sense, large scale may refer to patterns over an entire continent or patterns along a mountain slope, where environmental gradients are steep. Let's begin our discussion with patterns of distribution observed at small spatial scales.

Distributions of Individuals on Small Scales

Three basic patterns of distribution are observed on small scales: random, regular, or clumped. A **random distribution** is one in which individuals within a population have an equal chance of living anywhere within an area. A **regular distribution** is one in which individuals are uniformly spaced. In a **clumped distribution**, individuals have a much higher probability of being found in some areas than in others (fig. 10.16).

These basic patterns of distribution are produced by the kinds of interactions between individuals within a population, by the structure of the physical environment, or both. Individuals within a population may *attract* each other, *repel* each other, or *ignore* each other. Mutual attraction creates clumped, or aggregated, patterns of distribution. Clumped distributions can also occur if individuals produce offspring that fail to disperse far from the parents. Regular patterns of distribution are produced when

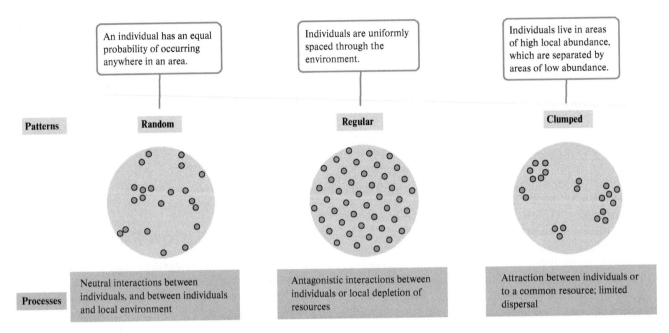

An individual has an equal probability of occurring anywhere in an area.

Individuals are uniformly spaced through the environment.

Individuals live in areas of high local abundance, which are separated by areas of low abundance.

Patterns   **Random**   **Regular**   **Clumped**

Neutral interactions between individuals, and between individuals and local environment

Antagonistic interactions between individuals or local depletion of resources

Attraction between individuals or to a common resource; limited dispersal

Processes

Figure 10.16   Random, regular, and clumped distributions.

individuals avoid each other or claim exclusive use of a patch of landscape. Neutral responses contribute to random distributions.

The patterns created by social interactions may be reinforced or reduced by the structure of the environment. An environment with patchy distributions of nutrients, nesting sites, water, and so forth also fosters clumped distribution patterns. An environment with a uniform distribution of resources and frequent, random patterns of disturbance (or mixing) tends to reinforce random or regular distributions. Let's now consider factors that influence the distributions of some species in nature.

Distributions of Tree Species on Vancouver Island

Both competition among individuals (chapter 13) and local environmental conditions can influence the spatial distribution of individuals within a population. These factors may also interact, such that competition may be more, or less, important under some environmental conditions than other levels. As a result, discerning the mechanisms that cause spatial patterns in natural populations can be a challenge. A team of researchers from Canada and Germany decided to tackle this issue and try to understand what factors influenced the small-scale distribution of trees in a Douglas-fir forest (fig. 10.17) on Vancouver Island, British Columbia (Getzin et al. 2006).

They chose as a study site a set of forest stands on southeastern Vancouver Island. These stands differed in age, ranging from old-growth (254 years old) to relatively young (39 years old). The research team mapped the locations and species identity of all the dead and living trees in several plots within each stand. They were primarily interested in three species: Douglas-fir (*Pseudotsuga menziesii*), western hemlock (*Tsuga heterophylla*), and western red cedar (*Thuja plicata*). If competition was important in structuring these populations, they predicted that trees in clumps were more likely to suffer greater mortality than more widely dispersed trees; therefore, the distribution of trees should become more

regular over time (moving from the young stand to the old stand). Strong influences of local site characteristics would likely be seen as clumped distributions being maintained through time. Why? Trees of a given species would be found only in areas that have the necessary site conditions for their survival and growth, and these conditions are not expected to move over time.

At the smallest spatial scales, trees tended to be clumped together, suggesting influence of the local habitat. For the Douglas fir and the red cedar, the clumped patterns persisted over time, suggesting strong influences of small-scale, highly localized site characteristics that did not change over time. Interestingly, Getzin and colleagues did find a positive correlation between spatial aggregation and competition. Intensity of competition was measured as the relationship between the distance of a tree to its nearest neighbour and its growth rate. Where trees were most highly clumped, competition was strongest. Yet intensity of competition did not result in a shift toward regular distribution over time, suggesting that small-scale site characteristics were more important than competition in shaping the population distributions for these two species. But unlike these species, spatial distribution of the western hemlock became more regular over time. This result is consistent with competition structuring its population distribution. The research team's results suggest that the factors that influence spatial distributions of individuals within a population are going to vary among species. Although we use generalizations frequently, it is important to realize that different species have their own niches, and these differences may have important ecological consequences.

Distributions of Individuals on Large Scales

We have considered how individuals within a population are distributed on a small scale. Now let's step back and ask how individuals within a population are distributed on a larger scale over which there is significant environmental variation.

Figure 10.17 The small-scale distribution of different tree species in a Douglas-fir forest is determined by both biotic and abiotic interactions.

Photo 27746972 © Brandon Smith–Dreamstime.com.

Bird Populations Across North America

Terry Root (1988) mapped patterns of bird abundance across North America using the "Christmas Bird Counts." These bird counts provide one of the few data sets extensive enough to study distribution patterns across an entire continent. Christmas Bird Counts, which began in 1900, involve annual counts of birds during the Christmas season. The first Christmas Bird Count was attended by 27 observers, who counted birds in 26 localities—two in Canada and the remainder in 13 states of the United States. In the 1985–86 season (which provided the data used by Root), 38,346 people participated in 1,504 localities throughout the United States and much of Canada. In the 2018–2019 season, observers in 23 countries counted 46,978,083 birds in 2,482 localities, including 429 in Canada! Even one brave soul in Rankin Island, Nunavut, braved the cold to count 202 ravens and one song sparrow. This annual count continues to produce a unique record of the distribution and population densities of wintering birds across most of North America and, increasingly, Central and South America and the Caribbean.

Root's analysis centres around a series of maps that show patterns of distribution and population density for 346 species of birds that winter in the United States and Canada. Although species as different as swans and sparrows are included, the maps show a consistent pattern. At the continental scale, bird populations have clumped distributions. Clumped patterns occur in species with widespread distributions, such as the American crow (*Corvus brachyrhynchos*), as well as in species with restricted distributions, such as the fish crow (*C. ossifragus*). Though the winter distribution of the American crow includes most of the continent, the bulk of individuals in this population are concentrated in a few areas. These areas of high density, or "hot spots," appear as orange dots in figure 10.18*a*.

The fish crow population, although much more restricted than that of the American crow, is also concentrated in a few areas near open water along the Gulf of Mexico and the southern half of the United States Atlantic coast (fig. 10.18*b*). Like the more widely distributed American crow, the abundance of fish crows diminishes rapidly away from these centres of high density.

Why do these bird species, and many others, demonstrate such clumped distributions? There can be many explanations, including predation, disease, and dispersal; however, a common explanation again returns us to the niche concept (chapter 9). Because environmental conditions vary across geographic areas, only certain locations will have the combination of necessary environmental conditions for a given species. When the environmental conditions of a specific location match the optimum growth conditions described by a species' niche, that species has potential to thrive. When conditions are near the survival thresholds for some niche axes, we might more reasonably expect reduced growth and population sizes of the species.

CONCEPT 10.4 REVIEW

1. At a large scale, we see clumped distributions for bird species, such as fish crows, while at a small scale, we might expect the distributions to be regular. Why might we see such differences at different scales?

2. Why do population densities generally decline as you move from the centre to the edge of a species' range?

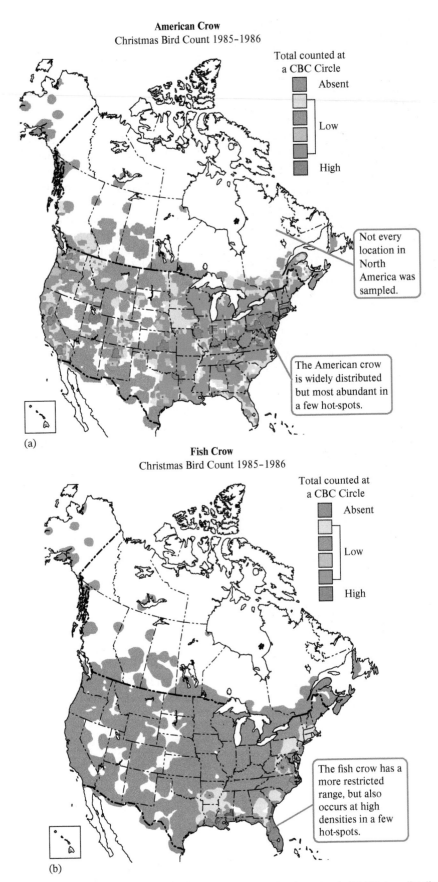

Figure 10.18 (*a*) Winter distribution of the American crow (*Corvus brachyrhynchos*). (*b*) Winter distribution of the fish crow (*C. ossifragus*).

Data from National Audubon Society.

ECOLOGY IN ACTION

Using Ecology to Protect Threatened Species

In the media we often hear reports of species on the verge of extinction and of government efforts underway to protect remaining populations. The laws protecting these species vary widely among countries; in Canada, we have the Species at Risk Act (SARA, 2002). By November 2018, there were 789 species formally listed and given legal protection in Canada under SARA (Canada, Environment Canada 2019; fig. 10.19). But what exactly does this mean? Who actually makes this determination, what happens after such a designation is made, and what role does ecology play in this process?

As stated in the summary of SARA itself,

The purposes of this enactment are to prevent Canadian indigenous species, subspecies and distinct populations of wildlife from becoming extirpated or extinct, to provide for the recovery of endangered or threatened species, to encourage the management of other species to prevent them from becoming at risk. (Canada, Species at Risk Act Public Registry 2007)

To achieve these goals there are two important steps: (1) the identification of species at risk, and (2) the development and implementation of a recovery and/or protection plan. Both of these steps require substantial research into understanding issues such as species distributions and the causes of changes to population size.

Decisions about at-risk designations involve substantial deliberation among an independent body of experts, the Committee on the Status of Endangered Wildlife in Canada (COSEWIC). In 2019, COSEWIC consisted of 30 members, including governmental members from the wildlife agencies of each of the 13 territories or provinces; members from four federal agencies (Canadian Wildlife Service, Parks Canada, Department of Fisheries and Oceans, and the Federal Biodiversity Partnership); and nongovernmental representatives, including three science members, nine members from the Species Specialist Subcommittees, and one co-chair from the Aboriginal Traditional Knowledge Subcommittee. COSEWIC makes decisions about whether the best science and traditional knowledge support a case for listing a particular species as endangered. It is then up to the Minister of the Environment to act upon that recommendation. However, listing many species can present significant economic and political challenges; thus, despite recommendations based upon sound ecological science, not all species recommended for listing by COSEWIC are listed by the Minister of the Environment. In other words, science

Figure 10.19 Species currently endangered in Canada include (*a*) the burrowing owl (*Athene cunicularia*); (*b*) Taylor's checkerspot (*Euphydryas editha taylori*); (*c*) Aurora trout (*Salvelinus fontinalis timagamiensis*); and (*d*) the Western spiderwort (*Tradescantia occidentalis*).
(a) Shutterstock/Don Mammoser; *(b)* Andrew Fyson; *(c)* Ed Snucins; *(d)* Joyce Gould.

and politics both influence the legal status of species in Canada.

The first step in giving a species an at-risk designation is for COSEWIC to become aware of a potential threatened species. This is not a trivial undertaking, considering that there are over 70,000 known wild species in Canada. These efforts are assisted by biologists at the provincial, territorial, and federal governmental levels who regularly assess a number of species, forwarding species of concern to COSEWIC. Additional inputs on species for consideration can come from nongovernmental organizations and private citizens. Assessments are based mainly on changes in abundance and distribution of the species in Canada using quantitative benchmarks based upon those elaborated by the International Union for Conservation of Nature (IUCN). Factors that get considered include species range, population size, rates of population decline, habitat fragmentation, and the existence of current or expected threats to the species (e.g., introduced species, disease, habitat destruction, etc.).

Although only species thought to be at risk are brought to COSEWIC, upon further study of the data the committee often finds that not all of these species are actually at risk. For example, as of April 2006, COSEWIC had evaluated 727 species (COSEWIC 2006). Of these, 157 (22%) were found to be not at risk, meaning the best science to date suggests that these species will continue to persist without special protection. An additional 41 species (5%) were deemed "data-deficient," which means there were not enough data available to make a sound scientific recommendation for or against protection. The remaining 529 species (73%) were recommended for listing by COSEWIC. However, only 389 were actually listed by November 2006 under SARA. Some of the 140 remaining have since been listed, and some were intentionally not listed by the Minister of the Environment. More recently, during 2018, COSEWIC looked at 361 species and considered 83 as high priority candidates for listing. Of these, 17 have been listed for protection under SARA.

The Minister of the Environment has the ability to make non-science-based discretionary decisions that reflect concerns about potential economic or political implications of a listing. In contrast to the Endangered Species Act in the United States, Canada's SARA does not provide the opportunity for private citizens to appeal such discretionary decisions. Although SARA does provide some protections, it is a substantially weaker act than is in place in the United States, and history has demonstrated that it can be exercised based on political considerations. For example, among fish species recommended for listing by COSEWIC, those that are commercially harvested are much less likely to receive protection under SARA. Another historical bias has been a reluctance to list northern species recommended by COSEWIC, while southern species are much more likely to be listed.

Despite evidence of politics influencing the decision to protect some species, other species do end up with legal protection. Being at risk can take several forms, from the most extreme being already extinct (no longer found anywhere) or extirpated (no longer found in Canada but found in other countries), to less extreme forms of risk, such as endangered (facing imminent extirpation or extinction), threatened (likely to become extinct or extirpated unless actions are taken), and of special concern (may become threatened without actions being taken). Once a species has been listed, a recovery plan is developed that is designed to meet the unique needs of that species. Actions can include harvest moratoriums, captive breeding programs, control of competing or predating species, translocation of individuals to enhance existing or establish new populations, and education programs that promote changes in land use. These efforts are made through the cooperation of government agencies, a variety of nongovernmental organizations, scores of local volunteers, and with the help of landowners and industrial stakeholders. Although not every species will be able to be successfully recovered, several populations of several protected species have improved.

For example, the swift fox (*Vulpes velox*) is a small fox found in southern Alberta and Saskatchewan. It was listed as extirpated in 1978. Between 1983 and 1997, foxes were reintroduced, resulting in a population of 279 foxes in the wild in Canada in 1999, and the species was thus downgraded to endangered. The populations appear to be continuing to grow, and though this species is still endangered, there has been improvement over the past several decades. There are other successes, such as the downlisting of the red-shouldered hawk from special concern to not-at-risk as populations increase; as well, populations of peregrine falcon continue to grow. For all listed species, continued monitoring to assess the effectiveness of recovery efforts is critical, with the eventual hope to be able to de-list recovered species.

Although being listed as "at risk" provides legal protection to many species, it is important to recognize that we do not have good data on all species in Canada. For example, it is widely acknowledged that there is currently a bias in data collection toward vertebrates. In fact, over 60% of the species brought forward to COSEWIC have been vertebrates, with only 2% being insects, even though vertebrates make up only a small fraction of Canada's biodiversity. These biases mean that many inconspicuous species likely at risk are unprotected. Yet these species can be extremely important to ecosystem function and have equal ethical rights for consideration under COSEWIC guidelines. It is also important to recognize that species do not recognize political boundaries. Many of the species of concern in Canada are abundant and have healthy populations in the United States. Thus Canada represents the northern edge-of-range for many otherwise common species. One argument suggests that edge populations are particularly valuable as they may hold unique genotype. An alternative argument suggests that approaches to conservation should transcend national borders, taking into consideration the full spatial extent of a species' distribution.

It is the job of future generations of ecologists to learn more about the biodiversity of Canada and other locations in the world and to decide the best path forward. One thing is clear—without dedicated intervention by ecologists, species extinction rates would be higher than they currently are. Only through continued ecological research is there any hope to preserve a diverse world for future generations.

10.5 Organism Size and Population Density

Population density declines with increasing organism size. If you estimate the densities of organisms in their natural environments, you will find great ranges. Bacterial populations in soils or water can exceed 10^9 individuals per cubic centimetre. Phytoplankton densities often exceed 10^6 individuals per cubic metre. Populations of large mammals and birds can average considerably less than one individual per square kilometre. What factors produce this variation in population density? One factor appears to be body size. In general, population densities decrease with increasing body size of individuals.

While it makes sense that small organisms generally live at higher population densities than larger ones, quantifying the relationship between body size and population density provides valuable information. Measuring the relationship between body size and population density for a wide variety of species reveals different relationships for different groups of organisms. Differences in the relationship between size and population density can be seen among major groups of animals.

Animal Size and Population Density

John Damuth (1981) produced one of the first clear demonstrations of the relationship between body size and population density. He focused his analysis on herbivorous mammals, ranging from small rodents, with a mass of about 10 g, to rhinoceros, with a mass well over 10^6 g. Meanwhile, average population density ranged from about 0.1 individuals per 1 km^2 to about 10,000 per 1 km^2. As figure 10.20 shows, the population density of 307 species of herbivorous mammals decreases with increased body size.

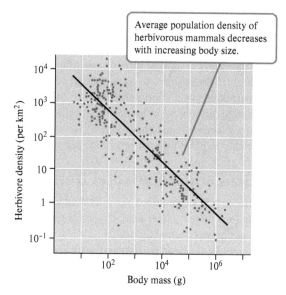

Figure 10.20 Body size and population density of herbivorous mammals.
Data from Damuth 1981.

Building on Damuth's analysis, Robert Peters and Karen Wassenberg (1983), of McGill University, explored the relationship between body size and average population density for a wider variety of animals, including terrestrial invertebrates, aquatic invertebrates, mammals, birds, and poikilothermic vertebrates. In their study they included animals that ranged in mass from 10^{-8} g to nearly 10^6 g. For these same species, population density ranged from nearly 10^{12} individuals per square kilometre to fewer than 1 individual per square kilometre. Peters and Wassenberg, like Damuth, found that population density decreased with increased body size.

If you look closely at the data in figure 10.21, however, it is clear that there are differences among the animal groups.

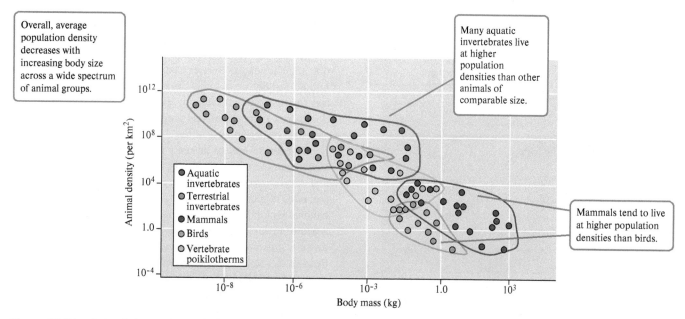

Figure 10.21 Animal size and population density.
Data from Peters and Wassenberg 1983.

First, aquatic invertebrates of a given body size tend to have higher population densities than terrestrial invertebrates of similar size. Second, mammals tend to have higher population densities than birds of similar size. These differences suggest that although there appears to be a general ecological principle of decreasing population densities with increasing body size, taxonomic differences influence the specific shape of this relationship. Plant ecologists have found a qualitatively similar relationship in plant populations, as we see next.

Plant Size and Population Density

James White (1985) summarized the relationship between size and density for a large number of plant species spanning a wide range of plant growth forms (fig. 10.22).

Plant population density decreases with increasing plant size (fig. 10.22), similar to the pattern observed for animals. However, the biological details underlying the size–density relationship shown by plants are quite different from those underlying the size–density patterns shown by animals. The different points in figures 10.20 and 10.21 represent different species of animals. A single species of tree, however, can span a very large range of sizes and densities during its life cycle. Even the largest trees, such as the giant sequoia (*Sequoia gigantea*), start life as small seedlings. These tiny seedlings can live at very high densities. As the trees grow, density declines progressively until the mature trees live at low densities. We discuss this process, which is called *self-thinning*, in chapter 13. Thus, the size–density relationship changes dynamically within plant populations and also differs significantly between populations of plants that reach different sizes at maturity.

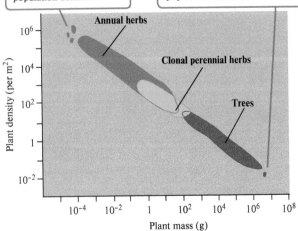

As in animals, plant population density decreases with increasing plant size across a wide range of plant growth forms.

Duckweed, *Lemna*, one of the smallest flowering plants, lives at very high population densities.

The coastal redwood, *Sequoia sempervirens*, one of the largest trees, lives at one of the lowest population densities.

Figure 10.22   Plant size and population density.
Data from White 1985.

The value of such an empirical relationship, whether for plants or animals, is that it provides a standard against which we can compare measured densities and gives an idea of expected population densities in nature. For example, suppose you go out into the field and measure the population density of some species of animal. How would you know if the densities you encounter are unusually high, low, or about average for an animal of the particular size and taxon? Without an empirical relationship such as that shown in figures 10.21 and 10.22 or a list of species densities, it would be impossible to make such an assessment. One question that we might attempt to answer with a population study is whether a species is rare. As we shall see next, rarity is a more complex consideration than it might seem at face value.

CONCEPT 10.5 REVIEW

1. What are some advantages of Damuth's strict focus on herbivorous mammals in his analysis of the relationship between body size and population density?

2. How might energy and nutrient relations explain the lower population densities of birds compared to comparable sized mammals?

10.6   Commonness and Rarity

Commonness and rarity of species are influenced by population size, geographic range, and habitat tolerance. Viewed on a long-term, geological timescale, populations come and go, and extinction seems to be the inevitable punctuation mark at the end of a species' history. However, some populations seem to be more vulnerable to extinction than others. What makes some populations likely to disappear, while others persist? At the heart of the matter are patterns of distribution and abundance. Species that are rare even in the absence of human activity seem to be more vulnerable to extinction. Species for whom human activity causes loss of habitat, introduction of new competitors and predators, or harvest for economic gain may be particularly at risk.

The loss of species diversity is a global issue and has generated a number of global responses. One of the most important first steps in reducing species extinction rates is a scientifically grounded catalogue of species at risk across the planet. The International Union for the Conservation of Nature (IUCN) is a large group of researchers from across the world, including over 1,300 member organizations in 165 countries. The IUCN produces the Red List of Threatened Species, which, as of 2019, estimates that a minimum of 27,000 known species are threatened with extinction, which is nearly 28% of all species assessed. For amphibians, this climbs to 40% of all assessed species. Although vertebrates tend to be well studied, little information is available for organisms that live in aquatic systems, those that live in particularly species-rich locations (e.g., tropical rain forests), and those from particularly species-rich taxonomic groups (e.g., fungi, invertebrates, plants). Thus, although ecologists can identify many species at risk, we also recognize that there are many more for whom sufficient data are just not available. Complicating efforts is a realization that rarity by itself is not a cause for concern, as many species can persist indefinitely at low population sizes. To help prioritize species for conservation efforts, and to better understand extinction, we need to first understand the seven forms of rarity.

Seven Forms of Rarity and One of Abundance

Deborah Rabinowitz (1981) devised a classification of *commonness* and *rarity*, based on combinations of three factors: (1) the geographic range of a species (*extensive* versus *restricted*),

(2) habitat tolerance (*broad* versus *narrow*), and (3) local population size (*large* versus *small*). Habitat tolerance is related to the range of conditions in which a species can live. For instance, some plant species can tolerate a broad range of soil texture, pH, and organic matter content, while other plant species are confined to a single soil type. As we shall see, tigers have broad habitat tolerance; however, within the tiger's historical range in Asia lives the snow leopard, which is confined to a narrow range of conditions in the high mountains of the Tibetan Plateau. Small geographic range, narrow habitat tolerance, and low population density are all attributes of rarity.

As shown in figure 10.23, there are eight possible combinations of these factors, seven of which include at least one attribute of rarity. The most abundant species and those least threatened by extinction typically have extensive geographic ranges, broad habitat tolerances, and large local populations

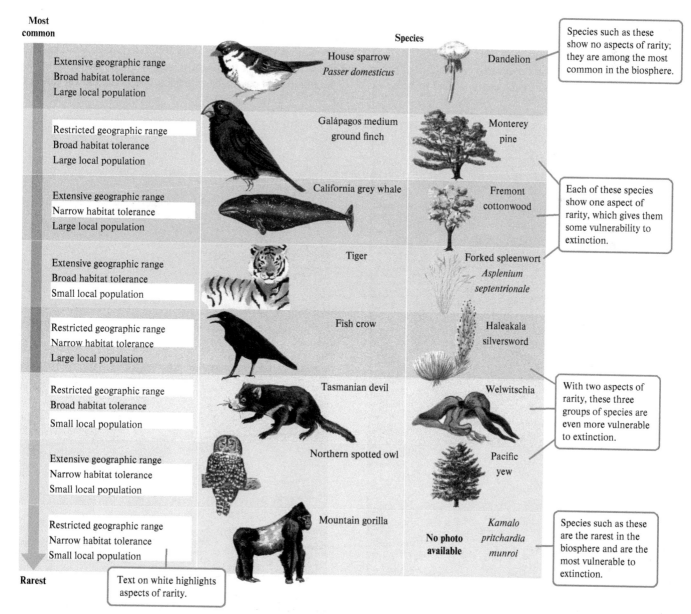

Figure 10.23 Commonness, rarity, and vulnerability to extinction.

at least somewhere within their range. Some of these species, such as starlings, Norway rats, and house sparrows, are associated with humans and are considered pests. However, many species of small mammals, birds, and invertebrates not associated with humans, such as the deer mouse (*Peromyscus maniculatus*) or the marine zooplankton (*Calanus finmarchicus*), also fall into this most common category.

Ecologists exploring the relationship between size of geographic range and population size have found that they are not independent. Instead, there is a strong positive correlation between the two variables for most groups of organisms. In other words, species abundant in the places where they occur are generally widely distributed within a region, continent, or ocean, while species living at low population densities generally have small, restricted distributions. However, these factors are considered independently in Rabinowitz's model of rarity, and with reason. Species such as the Galápagos medium ground finch have large local populations but very small geographic range, while species such as tigers may have broad geographic range but small local populations (fig. 10.23).

Most species are uncommon; seven combinations of range, tolerance, and population size each create a kind of rarity. As a consequence, Rabinowitz referred to "seven forms of rarity." Species that combine small geographic ranges with narrow habitat tolerances and low population densities are the rarest of the rare. This group includes species such as the mountain gorilla, the giant panda, and the California condor (fig. 10.24). Species showing this extreme form of rarity are clearly the most vulnerable to extinction. Many island species have these attributes, so it is not surprising that island species are especially vulnerable. Of the 171 bird species and subspecies known to have become extinct since 1600, 155 species were restricted to islands. Of the 70 species and subspecies of birds known to have lived on the Hawaiian Islands, 24 are now extinct and 30 are considered in danger of extinction.

Organisms that are restricted to small areas on continents have narrow habitat tolerance and small population sizes, making them vulnerable to extinction. Examples of populations in such circumstances are common. For example, the Ash Meadows blazingstar (*Mentzelia leucophylla*) inhabits a unique desert wetland ecosystem in Amargosa Desert in southwestern Nevada. Its entire range is about 2.5 km^2 and the population may be fewer than 100 individuals. Until recently the total habitat of the Socorro isopod (*Thermosphaeroma thermophilum*) of Socorro, New Mexico, was limited to a spring pool

(a)

(b)

(c)

Figure 10.24 *(a)* The mountain gorilla, *(b)* the California condor, and *(c)* the giant panda represent a high degree of rarity.
(a) Getty Images/Flickr RF; *(b)* © Rinus Baak–Dreamstime.com; *(c)* Ingram Publishing/age Fotostock.

and outflow with a surface area of a few square metres. Meanwhile, a palm species, *Pritchardia munroi*, which is found only on the island of Maui in the Hawaiian Islands, has a total population in nature of exactly one individual!

Examples such as these fill books listing endangered species. In nearly all cases, the key to a species' survival is increased distribution and abundance. One of the most fundamental needs for managing species, endangered or not, is making accurate estimates of population size. Some of the conceptual and practical issues that population ecologists must consider when censusing a population are the subject of the Ecological Tools and Approaches section.

ECOLOGICAL TOOLS AND APPROACHES

Estimating Abundance

The abundance of organisms and how abundance changes in time and space are among the most fundamental concerns of ecology. These factors are so basic that some authors define *ecology* as the study of distribution and abundance of organisms. Because abundance is so important, ecologists should understand how to estimate it for a wide variety of organisms. Accurate estimates of abundance are critical for the management of many species, such as those at risk or those of economic value. Accurate measures are also a critical tool for ecologists to use in understanding the underlying biology of populations. Knowing how abundant an organism is can tell us whether its population is growing, declining, or

stable. However, to estimate the abundance of species, the ecologist must contend with a variety of practical challenges and conceptual subtleties. Some of these are discussed here.

One of the first challenges that an ecologist wanting to estimate population sizes will face is the diverse array of methods available (fig. 10.25). Sessile organisms, such as plants and many intertidal invertebrates, are among the simplest groups to sample, as they do not have the nasty habit of walking away. For these groups, ecologists will often lay down a quadrat of a known size, and simply count the number of individuals that occur in that space. By using many quadrats, ecologists are able to estimate population densities. Flying organisms can

Figure 10.25   Shown here are students conducting ecological research in a diversity of field sites in Alberta. Different focal taxa and geographic locations require diverse methodologies.

(clockwise from top left) © Heather Proctor; Photo 33436259 © Vkarafill–Dreamstime.com; Rolf Vinebrook; Gordon G. McNickle; Anthony Bertrand; Jeffery Newton.

be a bit trickier and generally require a lure, such as a phero-mone trap for moths or coloured traps for bees, or they can be caught mid-flight using a mist net (for small birds) or a sweep net (for insects). Mammals are generally trapped, although larger, more dangerous mammals often need to be chemically immobilized. Though we may be most familiar with using traps and mist-nets to catch animals in the summer months (chap-ter 11), the winter can be an effective time of year to measure the population sizes of many animals. Any ecologist with even a basic understanding of natural history will understand that measures of populations based only on summer numbers are likely less informative than those that include winter data, at least for species that are active and resident year round. How, though, does an ecologist measure populations in winter?

In much of Canada, the ground is snow covered and much of the vegetation has died back during winter (chapter 5). As a result, large animals have relatively few places to hide and can be easily identified and counted from the air. Ecolo-gists regularly use surveys in helicopters and fixed-wing air-craft to estimate population sizes of large mammals, such as elk, over large expanses of land. Small animals, such as insects, can still be caught directly during winter. Subnivean traps can be placed below the snow to trap small animals that are active in the warm space between the ground and the surface of the snow (chapter 5).

Population sizes can also be estimated using a number of indirect measures based upon evidence of animal activity, rather than direct capture or observation. By counting tracks in snow of animals such as wolves, accurate estimates of local activity and population size can be constructed. These meas-ures can be made even more accurate by including pellet/dung counts and using molecular methods to identify indi-viduals within the population (chapter 4). Other animals, such as hare, leave tell-tale signs of their presence through unique damage left on the stems of the browse they leave behind. A much more thorough discussion of population sampling is beyond the scope of this textbook but may be found in ecol-ogy labs and advanced ecology courses at your university.

A number of other factors complicate sampling, includ-ing spatial heterogeneity in species distributions, the physical size of the organisms, and rarity. Aquatic organisms present a whole set of additional complications, given that they are much better at surviving under water than is the student attempting to sample them. Below we provide a more detailed description of some sampling methods used on some aquatic species.

Estimating Whale Population Size

In 1989, the journal *Oceanus* published a table that listed the estimated sizes of whale populations. The table included the following note: "All estimates . . . are highly speculative." Why is it difficult to provide firm estimates of whale popula-tion size? Briefly, whales live at low population densities and may be distributed across vast expanses of ocean. They also spend much time submerged and move around a great deal. As large as they are, you cannot count all the whales in the ocean. Instead, marine ecologists rely on population

estimation. Each method of estimation has its own limita-tions and uncertainties.

One method used to estimate population sizes of elu-sive animals involves marking or tagging some known num-ber of individuals in the population, releasing the marked individuals so they will mix with the remainder of the popu-lation, and then sampling the population at some later time. The ratio of marked to unmarked individuals in the sample gives an estimate of population size. The simplest formula expressing this relationship is the Lincoln-Peterson index:

$$M/N = m/n$$

where:

M = the number of individuals marked and released

N = the actual size of the study population

m = the number of marked individuals in a sample of the population

n = the total number of individuals in the sample

The major assumption of the Lincoln-Peterson index is that the ratio of marked to unmarked individuals in the popula-tion as a whole equals the ratio of marked to unmarked indi-viduals in a sample of the population. If this is approximately so, then the population size is estimated as:

$$N = Mn/m$$

However, on average, the Lincoln-Peterson index overesti-mates population size. To reduce this tendency to over-estimate, N. Bailey (1951, 1952) proposed a corrected formula:

$$N = \frac{M(n+1)}{m+1}$$

Some of the assumptions of mark and recapture studies are as follows:

- All individuals in the population have an equal probabil-ity of being captured.
- The population is not increased by births or immigration between marking and recapture.
- Marked and unmarked individuals die and emigrate at the same rates.
- No marks are lost.

Although real populations rarely meet all these assump-tions, mark and recapture estimates of population size are often the best estimates available.

Whale populations have been studied using mark and recapture techniques for some time. In the early days of whale population studies, population biologists marked whales by shooting a numbered metal dart into their blub-ber. Refined mark and recapture methods do not require artificially marking or capturing whales. In the "marking" phase of newer procedures, a whale is photographed and its distinguishing marks are identified. These photo-graphs, along with information such as where the photograph was taken and whether the whale was accom-panied by an offspring, are catalogued for future reference.

Figure 10.26 Unique markings identify individual humpback whales. A humpback whale called "Siphon," #700, photographed in Frenchman Bay, Maine, in 1995 (top panel) and in 1993 (bottom panel).

© Tom Fernald, College of the Atlantic, Bar Harbor, Maine.

In the "recapture" phase the whale is photographed at a later date and identified from previous photos. This method is called *photoidentification*.

Since the early 1970s Steven Katona (1989) has used photoidentification to study the humpback whales (*Megaptera novaeangliae*) of the North Atlantic. Humpback whales are particularly rich in individual marks, especially on the tail, or flukes. This is convenient for photographic studies because humpback whales generally raise their flukes above the water before they dive. This behaviour, called "fluking," exposes the flukes to the photographer and reveals potentially unique markings (fig. 10.26).

Using photographs of these marks, Katona and his colleagues have produced the North Atlantic Humpback Catalog. In 2014, the catalogue listed its 8,000th individual whale. There are now more than 32,000 individual photos included in the catalogue, along with information on where each photograph was taken, whether the whale was accompanied by an offspring, and other available observations. More than 650 individuals. researchers, and organizations have contributed to this growing database. This photographic record is an invaluable source of information for determining

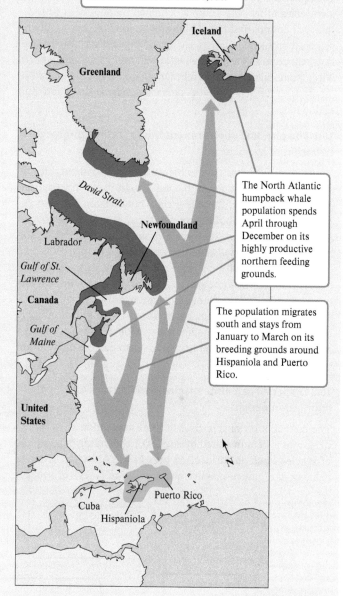

Figure 10.27 Photoidentification and the North Atlantic humpback whale population.

the migration routes, feeding grounds, breeding grounds, calving intervals and survival of individuals, and the size of the North Atlantic humpback whale population (fig. 10.27).

Though it may be more challenging physically, the process of counting whales is much like counting many other kinds of animals, such as humans, lynxes, trout, or lady beetles. However, ecologists must use different methods to estimate the abundance of organisms that have a more variable growth form or differ greatly in size. The best way to learn the different ways to study natural populations is to get some experience in the field. Chasing whales, counting butterflies, and walking through forests is not a horrible way to spend a summer.

SUMMARY

Ecologists define a population as a group of individuals of a single species inhabiting an area delimited by natural or human-imposed boundaries. Population studies hold the key to solving practical problems, such as saving endangered species, controlling pest populations, or managing fish and game populations. All populations share a number of characteristics. Chapter 10 focused on two population characteristics: distribution and abundance.

10.1 The physical environment limits the geographic distribution of species.

While there are few environments on earth without life, no single species can tolerate the full range of earth's environments. For instance, there is a close relationship between climate and the distributions of the three largest kangaroos in Australia. Large- and small-scale variation in temperature and moisture limits the distributions of certain plants. However, differences in the physical environment only partially explain the distributions of some species, a reminder that biological factors constitute an important part of an organism's environment. The physical environment determines availability of suitable habitat, and dispersal, whether it is outside of a species' current range or within the current range, determines the distribution of the species (fig. 10.28).

10.2 Dispersal can alter species distributions and local population densities.

The contribution of dispersal to local population density and dynamics is demonstrated by studies of expanding populations of species, such as Africanized bees in the Americas. Climate changes can induce massive changes in the ranges of species.

As availability of prey changes, predators may disperse, which increases and decreases their local population densities. Stream organisms actively migrating upstream or drifting downstream contribute to the dynamics of local populations.

10.3 Some populations, called metapopulations, consist of interconnected subpopulations.

Populations of many species occur not as a single continuously distributed population but in spatially isolated patches with significant exchange of individuals among patches. These patches may be natural, or human activities may contribute to the patchy nature of a species distribution (fig. 10.28). A group of subpopulations living on such patches connected by exchange of individuals among patches make up a metapopulation, such as is found for the Rocky Mountain Parnassian butterfly (*Parnassius smintheus*) in Alberta, Canada.

10.4 On small scales, individuals within populations are distributed in patterns that may be random, regular, or clumped.

Patterns of distribution can be produced by the social interactions within populations, by the structure of the physical environment, or by a combination of the two. Social organisms tend to be clumped; territorial organisms tend to be regularly spaced. An environment in which resources are patchy also fosters clumped distributions. On larger scales, individuals within a population are clumped. In North America, populations of birds are concentrated in a few hot spots of high population density. Clumped distributions are also shown by plant populations living along steep environmental gradients on mountainsides.

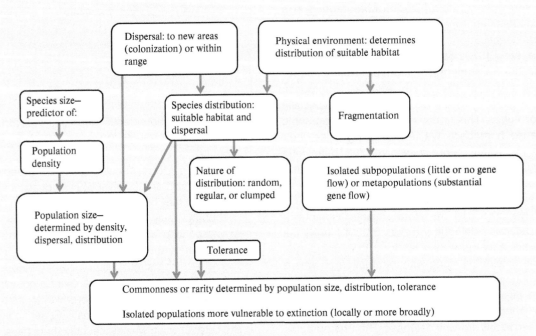

Figure 10.28   Concept map for chapter 10.

10.5 Population density declines with increasing organism size.

In general, animal population density declines with increasing body size. This negative relationship holds for animals as varied as terrestrial invertebrates, aquatic invertebrates, birds, poikilothermic vertebrates, and herbivorous mammals. Plant population density also decreases with increasing plant size. However, the biological details underlying the size–density relationship shown by plants are quite different from those underlying the size–density patterns shown by animals. A single species of tree can span a very large range of sizes and densities during its life cycle. The largest trees start life as small seedlings that can live at very high population densities. As trees grow, their population density declines progressively until the mature trees live at low densities. Locally, a decrease in population density will result in a smaller population size.

10.6 Commonness and rarity of species are influenced by population size, geographic range, and habitat tolerance.

Rarity of species can be expressed as a combination of extensive versus restricted geographic range, broad versus narrow habitat tolerance, and large versus small population size (fig. 10.28). The most abundant species and those least threatened by extinction combine large geographic ranges, wide habitat tolerance, and high local population density. All other combinations of geographic range, habitat tolerance, and population size include one or more attributes of rarity. Rare species are vulnerable to extinction. Populations that combine restricted geographic range with narrow habitat tolerance and small population size are the rarest of the rare, and are usually the organisms most vulnerable to extinction.

The abundance of organisms and how abundance changes in time and space are among the most fundamental concerns of ecology. To estimate the abundance of species, the ecologist must contend with a variety of practical challenges. Mark and recapture methods are useful in the study of populations of active, elusive, or secretive animals. Mark and recapture techniques, which use natural distinguishing marks, are making an important contribution to the study of populations of whales. Patterns of distribution and abundance are ultimately determined by underlying population dynamics.

REVIEW QUESTIONS

1. What kinds of interactions within an animal population lead to clumped distributions? What kinds of interactions foster a regular distribution? What kinds of interactions would you expect to find within an animal population distributed in a random pattern?

2. How might the structure of the environment, for example, the distributions of different soil types and soil moisture, affect the patterns of distribution in plant populations? How should interactions among plants affect their distributions?

3. Suppose one plant reproduces almost entirely from seeds and its seeds are dispersed by wind, and a second plant reproduces asexually, mainly by budding from runners. How should these two different reproductive modes affect local patterns of distribution seen in populations of the two species?

4. Suppose that in the near future, the fish crow population in North America declines because of habitat destruction. Now that you have reviewed the large-scale distribution and abundance of the fish crow, devise a conservation plan for the species that includes establishing protected refuges for the species. Where would you locate the refuges? How many refuges would you recommend?

5. Use the empirical relationship between size and population density observed in the studies by Damuth (1981) (see fig. 10.20) and Peters and Wassenberg (1983) (see fig. 10.21) to answer the following: For a given body size, which generally has the higher population density, birds or mammals? On average, which lives at lower population densities, terrestrial or aquatic invertebrates? Does a herbivorous mammal twice the size of another have on average one-half the population density of the smaller species? Less than half? More than half?

6. Outline Rabinowitz's classification (1981) of rarity, which she based on size of geographic range, breadth of habitat tolerance, and population size. In her scheme, which combination of attributes makes a species least vulnerable to extinction? Which combination makes a species the most vulnerable?

7. Can the analyses by Damuth (1981) and by Peters and Wassenberg (1983) be combined with that of Rabinowitz (1981) to make predictions about the relationship of animal size to its relative rarity? What two attributes of rarity, as defined by Rabinowitz, are not included in the analyses by Damuth and by Peters and Wassenberg?

8. Suppose you have photoidentified 30 humpback whales around the island of Oahu in one cruise around the island. Two weeks later you return to the same area and photograph all the whales you encounter. On the second trip you photograph a total of 50 whales, of which 10 were photographed previously. Use the Lincoln-Peterson index with the Bailey correction to estimate the number of humpback whales around Oahu during your study.

9. Outline Müller's (1954, 1974) colonization cycle. If you were studying the colonization cycle of the freshwater snail *N. latissima*, how would you follow colonization waves upstream? How would you verify that these colonization waves gain individuals from local populations and also contribute individuals to those same local populations?

10. Historically, when species are recommended by COSEWIC for protection under the Species at Risk Act (SARA), southern species have been far more likely to receive this protection than northern Canadian species; species that are commercially harvested; and species with cultural significance to, and that are traditionally hunted by, First Nations and Inuit peoples. Why do you think this is so?

CHAPTER 11   POPULATION STRUCTURE

CHAPTER CONCEPTS

11.1 A survivorship curve summarizes the pattern of survival in a population.
Concept 11.1 Review
Ecology in Action: Conservation of Sex Ratios

11.2 The age distribution of a population reflects its history of survival, reproduction, and potential for future growth.
Concept 11.2 Review

11.3 Population sex ratios can change depending upon the relative fitness of different sexes within a population.
Concept 11.3 Review
Ecological Tools and Approaches: Using Population Structure to Assess the Impact of Human-Mediated Change
Summary
Review Questions

In chapter 10, we discussed how populations were distributed on the landscape. In this chapter, we will look at the underlying **population structure** found within individual populations. Population structure can be defined by a number of factors, including patterns of mortality, age distributions, sex ratios, and dispersal. Uncovering these patterns within natural populations requires extended field studies, and population ecology has a tradition of combining understanding gained through natural history with the rigour central to scientific study. One example of this approach comes from a family living in remote regions of Alaska over 50 years ago.

Adolph Murie is a foundational figure in population ecology, and one of the first wildlife biologists in North America. As a young man, Adolph travelled through northern Alaska with his brother Olaus, who was investigating caribou populations (fig. 11.1). After several years in the backcountry, Adolph returned to finish his undergraduate degree and then earned a Ph.D. from the University of Michigan. Adolph's largest contributions to science came when he returned to Alaska with his wife, Louise; daughter, Gail; and son, Jan. Adolph published many books and papers during his career, including *The Wolves of Mount McKinley* [Denali] (Murie 1944) and *A Naturalist in Alaska* (Murie 1961).

One of Adolph's greatest works was in his detailed study and observations of interactions among wolves and sheep. As Adolph Murie watched, a grey wolf (*Canis lupus*) ran downhill toward a herd of 20 Dall sheep (*Ovis dalli*). As the wolf approached, the herd of white sheep split into two bands. One band circled the wolf and ran up the slope, while the other ran downhill. In response, the wolf stopped. The two bands of sheep also stopped, only 30 to 40 m away from the wolf. Suddenly the wolf sprinted after the lower band, but they easily outran him on the steep terrain. Again, the sheep and the wolf stopped and rested. After an hour, the wolf broke the stalemate and again charged the lower band. The sheep avoided him, circling the wolf and rejoining the other half of their herd. A few minutes

Figure 11.2   The Dall sheep (*Ovis dalli*), a mountain sheep of far northern North America, was the subject of one of Murie's classic studies of survivorship within natural populations.
©Chase Swift/Getty Images RF.

later the wolf abandoned the hunt, trotting away as the herd of Dall sheep watched from the ridge above (fig. 11.2).

Despite this particular wolf's failure, wolves are often successful. Murie was hired by the U.S. National Park Service to study the interactions of wolves and Dall sheep in what is now Denali National Park, Alaska. The main purpose was to determine whether wolves kill enough sheep to justify the call for reducing the wolf population (Murie 1944). This was a controversial issue at the time, as hunters, naturalists, scientists, and politicians were all interested in wolves and sheep (Rawson 2001). It is also a distant echo of the arguments of today about the impacts of wolves on threatened populations of woodland caribou (*Rangifer tarandus caribou*) in Alberta, and a number of other species throughout Canada. What was needed in 1944, as is needed today, was sound science to help direct a management strategy.

Murie adopted several methods for his studies. As we described above, he directly observed wolves and sheep. He also indirectly studied their interactions by tracking wolves through

Figure 11.1   Olaus and Adolph Murie were influential in the development of the field of wildlife ecology.
Photo by Alfred Eisenstaedt/The LIFE Picture Collection via Getty Images.

winter snow to find their kills. The tracks left a record of wolf interactions with their prey. Where wolves had killed Dall sheep, they often left the skulls, which provided a record as rich as the telltale tracks. Murie could age and sex the sheep based upon the skulls by the size of the horns. The teeth provided an indication of the sheep's general condition: worn teeth were a sign of poor nutrition and weakness. A careful search of Mount McKinley National Park yielded a sample of 608 sheep skulls, which Murie used to explore the causes and age of death. The skulls showed Murie that death within the Dall sheep population fell mainly on the very young and the very old. Most sheep in the population could, as his direct observations had shown, avoid attack by wolves. Today, studies of mortality and predation risk would also include GPS-collared individuals, allowing researchers to study movement patterns and unique information not available just a few decades ago.

Adolph Murie's studies of wolves and Dall sheep represent one aspect of population structure, the description of the patterns of mortality among individuals within a population. However, population structure includes many more topics, and these too have been studied by a Murie out in the field. However, now we see Jan Murie, son of Adolph Murie and Professor Emeritus at the University of Alberta, studying ground squirrels in southern Alberta. From his experiences living with his family in remote Alaska, Jan recognized the scientific value of detailed observations of individuals over time. Through live-trapping and detailed observation, Murie and his colleagues were better able to understand the structure of Columbian ground squirrel populations *Spermophilus columbianus* (Boag and Murie 1981; Murie 1985). In one study, Murie and his colleague Dave Boag found that populations of adult ground squirrels consistently contained more females than males, even though populations of juveniles were balanced between sexes (Boag and Murie 1981). This bias could be explained by observing the dynamics of the juvenile males. Males dispersed more often and farther from the natal population than females, with some moving over 6 km away. Mortality of males, both juvenile and adult, was also higher than females (Boag and Murie 1981), resulting in adult populations with unbalanced sex ratios.

Although separated by 40 years, thousands of kilometres, and studying different species, both Jan Murie and his father focused on critical aspects of population structure. For all populations, the patterns of distribution and abundance we studied in chapter 10 result from a dynamic balance between rates of birth, death, immigration, and emigration. In this chapter we will explore these topics in more depth, providing the foundation for understanding how populations will change over time, the topic of chapter 12.

11.1   Patterns of Survival

A survivorship curve summarizes the pattern of survival in a population. One of the most fundamental descriptions of a population is the pattern of mortality and survival among individuals. Patterns of survival vary a great deal from one species to another and, depending on environmental

circumstances, can vary within a single species. Some species produce young by the millions, which, in turn, die at a high rate. Other species produce few young and invest heavily in their care, resulting in high rates of juvenile survival. Still other species show intermediate patterns of reproductive rate, parental care, and juvenile survival. In response to practical challenges of discerning patterns of survival, ecologists use bookkeeping devices called **life tables** that list the births, the survivorship, and the deaths, or *mortality*, in populations. In this chapter we will focus on the mortality component of life tables; births will be added in chapter 12, allowing for estimation of population growth rates.

Estimating Patterns of Survival

There are three main ways of estimating patterns of survival within a population. The first and most reliable way is to identify a large number of individuals that are born at about the same time and keep records on them from birth to death. In this context, a group born at the same time is called a **cohort,** and a life table made from data collected in this way is called a **cohort life table.** The cohort studied might be a group of plant seedlings that matured at the same time, or all the lambs born into a population of mountain sheep in a particular year.

While understanding and interpreting a cohort life table may be relatively easy, obtaining the data upon which a cohort life table is based is not. Imagine yourself lying face down in a meadow counting thousands of tiny seedlings of an annual plant. You must mark their locations and then come back every week for six months until the last member of the population dies. Or, if you are studying a moderately long-lived species, such as a barnacle or a perennial herb like a buttercup, imagine checking the cohort repeatedly over a period of several years. If your study organism is a mobile animal, such as a whale or falcon, or one that bites, such as a polar bear or cobra, the problems multiply. If your species is very long-lived, such as a giant sequoia, such an approach is impossible within a single human lifetime. When it is difficult or impossible to follow individuals through time, population biologists usually resort to other techniques.

A second way to estimate patterns of survival in wild populations is to go into the field for a narrow window of time and record the age at death of a large number of individuals. This method differs from the cohort approach because the individuals in your sample are born at different times. This method produces a **static life table**. The table is called *static* because the method involves a snapshot of survival within a population during a short interval of time. Estimating the age of death can be difficult, and its accuracy is critical to the value of the data generated with this approach. The most accurate method would be to tag individuals when they are born and then recover the tags after death. However, this is not practical in most circumstances, and instead the ecologist may somehow estimate the age of dead individuals. For instance, mountain sheep can be aged by counting the growth rings on their horns. There are also growth rings on the carapaces of turtles, in the trunks of trees, and in the "stems" of soft or hard corals.

A third way of determining patterns of survival is from the **age distribution.** An age distribution consists of the proportion of individuals of different ages within a population. You can use an age distribution to estimate survival by calculating the difference in proportion of individuals in succeeding age classes. This method, which also produces a static life table, assumes that the difference in numbers of individuals in one age class and the next is the result of mortality. What are some other major assumptions underlying the use of age distributions to estimate patterns of survival? This method assumes that a population is neither growing nor declining and that it is not receiving new members from the outside or losing members because they migrate away. Since most of these assumptions are often violated in natural populations, a life table constructed from this type of data tends to be less accurate than a cohort life table. Static life tables are often useful, however, since they may be the only information available for many populations.

High Survival Among Young Individuals

As we saw in the introduction, Adolph Murie studied patterns of survival among Dall sheep in what is now Denali National Park, Alaska. Murie estimated survival patterns by collecting the skulls of 608 sheep that had died from various causes. He determined the age at which each sheep in his sample died by counting the growth rings on their horns and by studying tooth wear.

Figure 11.3 summarizes the survival patterns for Dall sheep based on Murie's sample of skulls. The upper portion of the figure shows the static life table that Murie constructed. The first column lists the ages of the sheep, the second column lists the number surviving in each age class, and the third column lists the numbers dying in each age class. Notice that although Murie studied only 608 skulls, the numbers in the table are expressed as numbers per 1,000 individuals. This adjustment to 1,000 individuals is standard in population ecology and is made to ease comparisons with other populations. The upper portion of figure 11.3 also shows how to translate numbers of deaths into numbers of survivors.

The major assumption of this study is that the proportion of skulls in each age class represents the typical proportion of individuals dying at that age. For example, the proportion of skulls found belonging to sheep younger than age 1 was 199/1,000. But what if skulls of younger individuals are harder to find or weather faster than skulls of older individuals? This would mean that the ecologist's estimate that 19.9% of sheep die in their first year of life is lower than the actual value. Similarly, if the skulls of older individuals were harder to find or decay faster than skulls of younger individuals, then the estimate of 19.9% would be higher than the true risk of mortality in this population. Although the assumption that the rate of skull capture is exactly equal to the proportion of individuals that generally die during the first year may not be strictly true, the pattern of survival that emerges probably gives a reasonable picture of survival in the population, particularly when the sample is as large as Murie's.

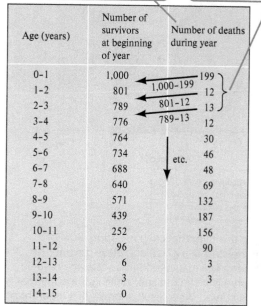

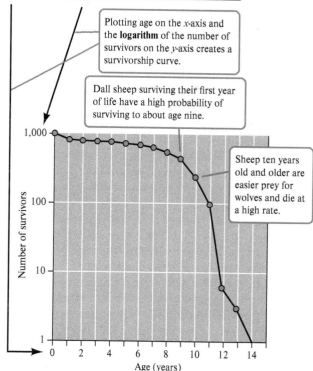

Figure 11.3 Dall sheep: from life table to survivorship curve.
Data from Murie 1944.

Plotting number of survivors per 1,000 births against age produces the **survivorship curve** shown in the lower portion of figure 11.3. A survivorship curve shows patterns of life and death within a population. You will notice that the y-axis of the survivorship curve is presented in a logarithmic scale. Why

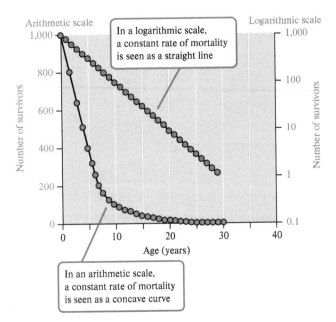

Figure 11.4   In this hypothetical population, 20% of individuals at the start of a given age class die prior to their next birthday. Using a logarithmic scale, the resulting survivorship curve is a straight line, while in the arithmetic scale the line is curved. As a result, the use of a logarithmic scale makes it easier to quickly understand mortality patterns in populations.

is this, and what happens if we use the arithmetic rather than logarithmic scale? First, it is important to understand why ecologists draw survivorship curves in the first place. Survivorship curves let us quickly determine whether mortality rates for a given population change with age by simply observing whether the resulting line is linear or curving. If we used the arithmetic scale, changes in slope would occur even without changes in survivorship rates (fig. 11.4). In the logarithmic scale, a straight line indicates that mortality rates do not change as a function of an individual's age.

Notice in figure 11.3 that in this population of Dall sheep, the survivorship curve has two areas where the slope is relatively steep: during the first year and during the period between 9 and 13 years. The increased steepness of the slope during those periods indicates that juvenile mortality and mortality of the aged are high in this population, while mortality in the middle years is relatively lower than these other age classes. The overall pattern of survival and mortality among Dall sheep is much like that for a variety of other large vertebrates, including red deer (*Cervus elaphus*), African buffalo (*Syncerus caffer*), and humans. The key characteristics of survival among these populations are relatively high rates of survival among the young and middle-aged and high rates of mortality among the older members.

This pattern of survival has also been observed in populations of annual plants and small invertebrate animals. Notice in figure 11.5 that patterns of survival in a population of a plant, *Phlox drummondii*, and a rotifer, *Floscularia conifera*, are remarkably similar to that of Dall mountain sheep. Following

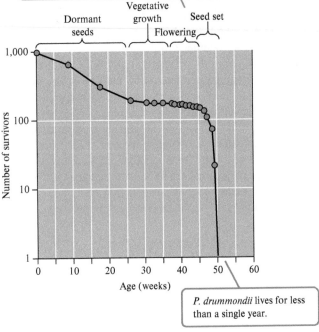

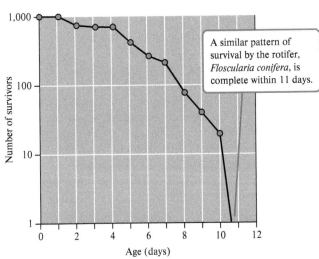

Figure 11.5   High rates of survival among the young and middle-aged in plant and rotifer populations.

an initial period of higher juvenile mortality, mortality is relatively low for a period, and then mortality is high among older individuals. In the *Phlox* population, however, this pattern of survival is played out in less than 1 year and in the rotifer population in less than 11 days. Thus, species of dramatically different longevity can express similar patterns of mortality. The notion of "young" and "old" will be relative to the lifespan of the organism being studied.

Survival patterns can be quite different in other species. In the next example, mortality is not delayed until old age but occurs at approximately equal rates throughout life.

Constant Rates of Survival

The survivorship curves of many species are nearly straight lines. In these populations, individuals die at approximately the same rate throughout life. This pattern of survival has been commonly observed in birds, such as the American robin (*Turdus migratorius*) and the white-crowned sparrow (*Zonotrichia leucophrys nuttalli*) (fig. 11.6). While birds are commonly known for showing a linear pattern of survival, many other taxa do as well. For instance, figure 11.6 also shows the same pattern of survival for a population of the northern water snake *Nerodia sipedon*. Though the water snake has a high rate of mortality during the first year of life, thereafter, survival follows a straight line.

As we shall see next, some organisms die at a much higher rate as juveniles than we have seen in any of the populations we have considered to this point.

Low Survival Among Young Individuals

Some organisms produce large numbers of young with very high rates of mortality. The eggs produced by marine fish, such as the mackerel *Scomber scombrus*, may number in the millions. Out of 1 million eggs laid by a mackerel, more than 999,990 die during the first 70 days of life, either as eggs, larvae, or juveniles. Survival rates are similar in populations of the prawn *Leander squilla* off the coast of Sweden. For every 1 million eggs laid by *Leander*, only about 2,000 individuals survive the first year of life. This period of high mortality among young prawns is followed by a fairly constant mortality over the remainder of the lifespan.

Similar patterns of survival are shown by other marine invertebrates and by fish and by plants that produce immense numbers of seeds. One of these plants is *Cleome droserifolia*, a desert shrub. Local populations of approximately 2,000 plants produce almost 20 million seeds each year (Hegazy 1990). Of these, approximately 12,500 seeds germinate and produce seedlings. Only 800 seedlings survive to become juvenile plants. Figure 11.7 traces this pattern of survival by *Cleome* expressed as survivors per million seeds. For each 1 million seeds produced, about 39 survive to the age of one year, a survival rate of only 0.0039%. Survival in this desert plant population contrasts sharply with that seen in Dall sheep. The striking difference in patterns of survival between populations such as *Cleome*, birds such as the American robin, and large mammals such as Dall sheep led early population biologists to propose a classification of survivorship curves.

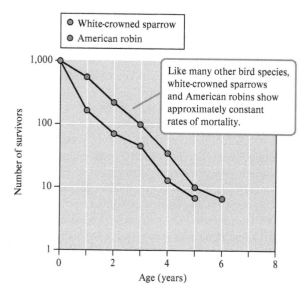

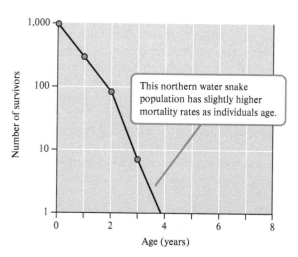

Figure 11.6 Constant rates of survival in sparrows and robins (*top*). Water snakes have higher juvenile survival rates than older individuals (*bottom*).

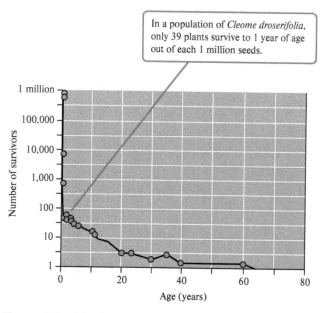

Figure 11.7 A high rate of mortality, and thus low survival, among the young of a perennial plant population.
Data from Hegazy 1990.

Three Types of Survivorship Curves

Based on studies of survival by a wide variety of organisms, population ecologists have proposed that most survivorship curves fall into three major categories (fig. 11.8*a*). A relatively high rate of survival among young and middle-aged individuals followed by a high rate of mortality among the aged is known as a **type I survivorship curve.** Constant rates of survival throughout life produce the straight-line pattern of survival known as a **type II survivorship curve.** A **type III survivorship curve** is one in which a period of extremely high rates of mortality among the young is followed by a relatively high rate of survival.

How well does this classification of survivorship represent natural populations? A team of researchers, including Phil Currie, the renowned paleontologist from the University of Alberta, summarized survivorship curves for several familiar vertebrate taxa (fig. 11.8*b*) (Erickson et al. 2006). Included in the table is the hypothesized type I survivorship curve of North American tyrannosaurs (Albertosaurs). Just as Adolph Murie has been able to infer patterns of survivorship from estimating the age of death from the skulls of sheep, so too has Currie been able to infer age of mortality from found bones (albeit much older). Consequently, though these extinct dinosaurs lived over 60 million years ago, they appear to demonstrate the same ecological patterns found in species today.

From figure 11.8*b*, you will see that most populations do not conform perfectly to any one of the three basic types of survivorship but show virtually every sort of intermediate form of survivorship between the curves. Even single species can show considerable variation in survivorship from one environment to another. For example, while human survivorship generally follows a type I survivorship curve, in difficult environments, human survivorship approaches a type II curve. This variation in patterns of human survival prompted G. Evelyn Hutchinson (1978) to muse, "One can only conclude that sometimes man is constrained to die randomly like a bird, but in other circumstances he may aspire to as ripe an old age as that of a wild sheep or an African buffalo" (p. 51). If survivorship can be so variable within species, what good are these idealized, theoretical survivorship curves? Their most important value, like most theoretical constructs, is that they set boundaries that mark what is possible within populations. Survivorship curves can be thought of as the "Coles Notes" of understanding patterns of mortality in natural populations. They do not include all of the fine details found in nature, but instead they serve as useful summaries of survival patterns within populations. They also generate hypotheses that can advance ecological theory. In chapter 9 we introduced allometry, including the non-linear scaling of metabolism to mass among mammals. Metabolic theory was introduced when Max Kleiber (1947) provided an empirical relationship of:

$$B = aM^{3/4}$$

where *B* is basal metabolism and *M* is body mass. This relationship (often referred to as metabolic theory) is believed to play a role in the evolution of life-history characteristics. You may have noticed in chapter 9, for instance, that animals that fit the

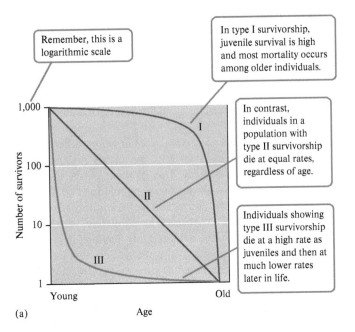

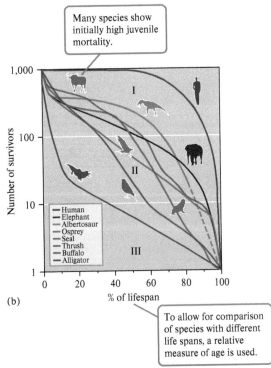

Figure 11.8 Three types of survivorship curves: (*a*) idealized forms; (*b*) comparisons among some familiar vertebrates.

(*b*) Modified from G. M. Erickson, P. J. Currie, B. D. Inouye, and A. A. Winn. 2006. Tyrannosaur life tables: An example of nonavian dinosaur population biology. *Science* 313:213–17. Reprinted with permission from AAAS.

MacArthur and Wilson (1967) model for K-selection strategists tend to be larger, longer-lived species. James Anderson (2018) recently developed a model to link body mass with longevity through cellular-level processes. The mathematical model combines metabolic theory with processes of cell aging and vitality theory. It predicts survivorship curves based on body mass, which can then be compared against empirical data. This approach provides a mechanistic understanding of how differences in metabolism imposed by allometric scaling to body size can affect evolution of the life-history traits of age-specific survivorship.

We now turn to the age distributions of populations, a topic closely related to survivorship.

ECOLOGY IN ACTION

Conservation of Sex Ratios

If you consider the many mammalian species with which you are familiar, you may recognize that sex ratios tend to be fairly even, ~1:1. In subsection 11.3, we'll talk about sex ratios and Ronald Fisher's (1930) argument that natural selection should favour a balanced sex ratio. Fisher's argument would seem to explain the pattern we see in many species. However, Robert Trivers (1972) and Dan Willard (1973) argue that under certain circumstances, natural selection might drive sex ratios away from 1:1. For example, in a polygynous species, a healthy male is likely to mate with many females while an unhealthy male is unlikely to mate at all. A female, in turn, will mate with only a single male and will do so whether she is healthy or not. If a mother is healthy, she is more likely to have healthy offspring. Her fitness will be greater in producing healthy sons, who will, in turn, mate with multiple females. If the mother is unhealthy, her fitness is greater if she produces daughters. Any sons will be unlikely to mate, whereas any daughter, even if unhealthy, will have a good chance of mating. Evolution should favour females in polygynous species having some control over sex ratios of offspring, and, indeed, that is what we see in many such species of birds and mammals.

In species that are not polygynous, deviations in sex ratios can limit opportunities for individuals to reproduce. Sex ratios can be influenced by a variety of environmental factors, and, for many species, localized populations may have sex ratios that differ from 1:1.

Green sea turtles are highly endangered and highly charismatic. They have complex habitat requirements that make them vulnerable to threats on the beach and at sea. These include predators and people harvesting or crushing eggs, the trade in turtles and turtle products, beach development and recreational use, plastic debris and other waste

in the ocean, and fishing nets. Adding to this is a new demographic stress: sex ratios that are out of whack.

In many amphibians and reptiles, sex determination is temperature dependent. A number of recent studies have sounded a clarion call about the threats of climate change on sex ratios, specifically that feminization of species that have temperature dependent sex determination (e.g., Refsnider and Jansen 2016) could jeopardize the long-term viability of these populations (Laloe et al. 2016, Valenzuela et al. 2019). Sea turtles are capable of responding to temperature changes by changing nesting patterns and locations, which could ensure nesting sites are within the characteristic range for the species. However, along a longitudinal gradient from the northern end to the southern end of Australia's Great Barrier Reef, there is a marked gradient in sex ratios of green turtles (*Chelonia mydas*) (Jensen et al. 2018).

Dominic Tilley, Annette Broderick, and a group of collaborators (Tilley et al. 2019) have explored the question of whether the green sea turtle shows evidence of local adaptation to the thermal properties of their nesting sites. Ascension Island is a small volcanic island midway between Africa and South America and has one of the world's largest green turtle rookeries. More than half of the nesting activity occurs on two beaches: Long Beach (LB) and North East Bay (NEB). These two beaches have different sands: LB has pale sand, and NEB has dark grey volcanic sand. The difference in colour means that these beaches have very different albedos (chapter 1) and different thermal properties. Sand temperatures in NEB are about 2°C warmer than in LB.

At each beach, clutches were selected at random while the females were actively laying eggs. For LB, a total of 23 clutches were selected in 2015 and 2016 seasons, and in NEB a total of 21 clutches were selected in each year. The research team placed temperature loggers into the centre of each selected clutch after the female had laid about 50 eggs. When she completed laying eggs, she then buried the loggers along with her eggs. The team built corrals around each clutch, and monitored for hatchlings. When hatchlings emerged, a random sample of 10 hatchlings were sexed, and all hatchlings were then released outside the corral. In a parallel laboratory study, eggs collected from a number of clutches on each beach were sampled at the time of laying. For each beach, an egg from each of the sampled clutches was pooled and co-incubated. Eggs were incubated at temperatures from 26 to 33°C, and the hatchlings were sexed to determine the proportion that were female, as well as the proportion of eggs that successfully hatched.

The laboratory incubations revealed an expected pattern: as temperature increased, the proportion of hatchlings that were female increased. This was true for both LB and NEB hatchlings (fig 11.9a). This temperature-dependent sex ratio also played out in the field experiment (fig 11.9b). The range of temperatures on the beaches was higher (29.5°C to 33.5°C) than lab incubations, and the proportion of female hatchlings was >70% in all nests. Clutches incubating at LB were cooler, on average, compared with NEB (average of 31°C at LB versus 33°C at NEB). This increased temperature at NEB was enough that all hatchlings there were female! An important outcome of the study was that the beach of origin (LB vs. NEB) did not affect the pivotal temperatures

for sex determination or hatching success, suggesting that these two populations are not locally adapted to differences in temperature regime. This seeming inability to adapt to local regime could greatly complicate conservation efforts as climate change pushes temperatures higher, and an already endangered species experiences even greater demographic pressures: a lack of males.

Beyond temperature, other environmental factors can disrupt sex ratios in natural populations. An interesting example is the effects of exogenous estrogens and androgens on sex differentiation in fish. High levels of these male and female hormones may enter water when we discharge our waste, either from sewage or industry. This may cause local hotspots of endocrine disruption and sex ratio anomalies. For example, in Berlin's waterways, 70% of the fish are female (Hansen et al. 1998), and in the Mississippi River at St. Paul, Minnesota, male carp downstream of a sewage treatment plant produce vitellogenin, an egg yolk precursor protein normally produced only by females (Folmar et al. 1996). Sewage is a complex mixture of chemicals. Stephanie Tamschick, Matthias Stock, and their colleagues (Tamschick et al. 2016) have recently shown that three species of amphibians—the African clawed frog (*Xenopus laevis*), the European tree frog (*Hyla arborea*), and the European green toad (*Bufo viridis*)—can undergo sex reversal (genetic males expressing female phenotypes) at

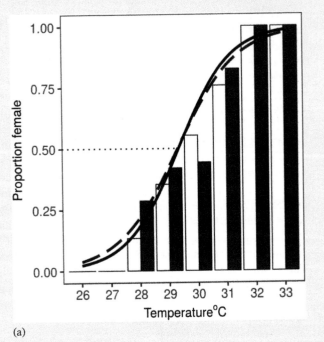

(a)

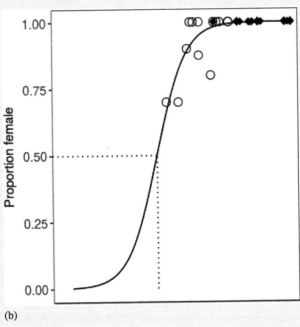

(b)

Figure 11.9   Relationship between incubation temperature and the proportion of female hatchlings in the laboratory and in the field. Data binned by 1° C increments. *(a)* White fill, solid trend line represents Long Beach (LB) eggs incubated in the lab; black fill, dashed trend line represents North East Bay (NEB) eggs. *(b)* Open circles represent LB eggs incubated in the field; filled diamonds represent NEB eggs.

From D. Tilley, S. Ball, J. Ellick, B. J. Godley, N. Weber, S. B. Weber, A. C. Broderick. 2019. No evidence of fine scale thermal adaptation in green turtles. *Journal of Experimental Marine Biology and Ecology* 514–515:110–17. Reprinted with permission from Elsevier.

concentrations of 17a-ethinylestradiol (EE2), which can be found in treated sewage outflow to surface waters. EE2 is a major constituent of contraceptive pills.

Joakim Larsson and colleagues (2000) studied embryonic sex ratios in a population of eelpout (*Zoarces viviparous*), a species of fish that resides in streams and rivers in Sweden and that is **viviparous.** Previous studies of pulp mill effluents had suggested that these might contain androgenic compounds. Gravid females were captured in a river at reference locations upstream of a pulp mill and at locations of varying distances from the mill. In the reference sites, the sex ratio was approximately 1:1, or 50% female (fig. 11.10). Immediately upstream or downstream, the sex ratio was strongly male biased, becoming progressively more balanced with distance (and presumably dilution) from the mill. Interestingly, exogenous hormones might not only affect sexual differentiation of embryos but may even cause sex reversal in adults. In carefully controlled laboratory experiments, a team of researchers, including Michael van den Heuvel (presently, University of Prince Edward

Island) and Lynda McCarthy (Ryerson University), exposed adult female mosquitofish to effluent from a New Zealand pulp and paper mill. The team observed a high degree of sex reversal, with females producing male reproductive structures and exhibiting typical male mating behaviour (Ellis et al. 2003). Such a phenotypic reversal has interesting implications for future sex ratios of these localized populations. In fish where sex is normally determined by sex chromosomes, a female (XX) might mate with a functional (as opposed to genetic) male (XX) and produce all offspring that are genetic females (XX).

Disruptions of sex ratio can make some threatened populations of aquatic vertebrates vulnerable to collapse. What might we do to better protect these populations? Recently, there have been many initiatives to separate urine from sewage and treat it separately. There are a number of different reasons this might be done, such as to improve phosphorus recovery and nutrient recycling, and to decrease the volume of sewage produced. This would benefit water and energy conservation, as the volume of waste to be pumped might be reduced. Another potential advantage from an aquatic species protection lens would be removal of estrogens and androgens. Wastewater treatment facilities are the major source to the environment of these exogenous hormones, and urine is the main excretion route. As much as 95% of estrogen may be excreted in urine (Combalbert and Hernandez-Raquet 2010). Conventional wastewater treatment is not particularly good at removing hormones, meaning that most of the estrogens excreted in urine will find their way into surface waters after passing through wastewater treatment plants. Advanced treatment processes, such as reverse osmosis or ozone treatment, can effectively remove nearly all of these chemicals, but treating bulk sewage with these processes is not practical. Urine, in contrast, is only 1% of the sewage volume, and treatment by ozonation or reverse osmosis would not be complicated by organic matter and solids. Urine, then, might effectively be treated in next-generation wastewater plants. Increasingly, the case is being made for waste diversion toilets—toilets that would separate urine and feces at the source, in your bathroom (Lamichhane and Babcock 2012). You may, in the near future, find yourself fighting the good fight for fish and amphibian demographics whenever you flush.

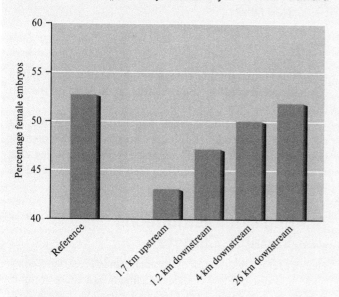

Figure 11.10   Sex ratios of eelpout (*Zoarces viviparous*) embryos, expressed as percent female. The reference is a composite value for all four reference sites upstream of the mill. Distances refer to distance downstream of the mill for each of the sampling locations.

11.2   Age Distribution

The age distribution of a population reflects its history of survival, reproduction, and potential for future growth. Population ecologists can tell a great deal about a population by studying its age distribution. Age distributions indicate periods of successful reproduction, periods of high and low juvenile and adult survival, whether the older individuals in a population are being replaced by younger individuals, and whether a population is declining. By studying the history of a population through describing its age distribution, population ecologists can make predictions about its future.

Stable and Declining Tree Populations

In 1923, R. B. Miller published data on the age distribution of a population of white oak (*Quercus alba*) in a mature forest in Illinois. In his study, Miller first determined the relationship

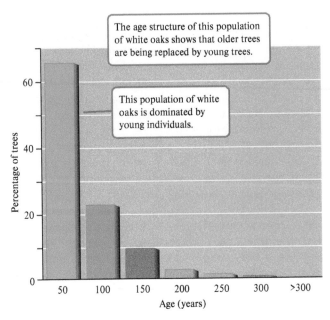

Figure 11.11 The age distribution of a white oak (*Quercus alba*) population in Illinois.
Data from Miller 1923.

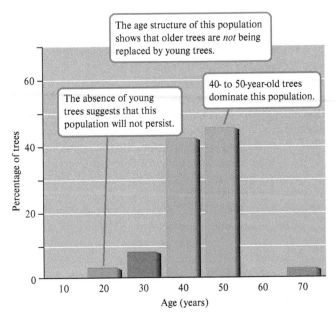

Figure 11.12 The age distribution of a population of Rio Grande cottonwoods (*Populus deltoides* ssp. *wislizeni*) near Belen, New Mexico.
Data from Howe and Knopf 1991.

between the age of a white oak and the diameter of its trunk. To do this, he measured the diameters of 56 trees of various sizes and then took a core of wood from their trunks. By counting the annual growth rings from each of the cores, he could determine the ages of the trees in his sample. With the relationship between oak age and diameter in hand, Miller used diameter to estimate the ages of hundreds of trees.

Most white oaks in Miller's study forest were concentrated in the youngest age class of 1 to 50 years, with progressively fewer individuals in the older age classes (fig. 11.11). In other words, the age distribution of white oak in this forest was biased toward the young trees. What might we infer from this age distribution? The age distribution suggests that reproduction is sufficient to replace the oldest individuals in the population as they die.

The age distribution of this white oak population contrasts sharply with the age distributions of populations of Rio Grande cottonwoods (*Populus deltoides* ssp. *wislizeni*). The most extensive cottonwood forests remaining in the southwestern United States grow along the Middle Rio Grande in central New Mexico. However, studies of age distributions indicate that these populations are declining. In contrast to the white oak population in Illinois, the Rio Grande cottonwood population is dominated by older individuals. Older trees are not being replaced by younger trees. At the study site, there has been no successful reproduction for over a decade (fig. 11.12).

Why have Rio Grande cottonwoods failed to reproduce? As we discussed in chapter 6, regeneration by cottonwoods depends upon seasonal floods, which play two key roles. First, floods create areas of bare soil without a surface layer of organic matter and without competing vegetation. Floods also keep these areas of bare soil moist until cottonwood seedlings can grow their roots deep enough to tap into the shallow water

table. The annual rhythm of seed bed preparation and seeding has been interrupted by the construction of dams on the Rio Grande.

The age distributions of tree populations change over the course of many decades or centuries. Meanwhile, other populations can change significantly on much shorter timescales. One of these dynamic populations has been thoroughly studied on the Galápagos Islands.

Shifting Age Distributions in a Variable Climate

Here we return to the work of Rosemary and Peter Grant (chapter 9) and discuss how changes in climate can cause shifts in aspects of population structure, including age distributions (Grant and Grant 1989). One of the Grants' most thorough studies focused on the large cactus finch (*Geospiza conirostris*). The study took place on the island of Genovesa, which lies in the northeastern portion of the Galápagos archipelago, approximately 1,000 km off the west coast of South America. The Galápagos Islands have a highly variable climate, which is reflected in the highly dynamic populations of the organisms living on the islands, including populations of the large cactus finch.

The age distributions of the large cactus finch during 1983 and 1987 show that the population can be very dynamic (fig. 11.13). The 1983 age distribution shows a fairly regular distribution of individuals among age classes, suggesting frequent years of successful reproduction. However, although there were many 5-year-olds and many 7-year-olds, there were no 6-year-old individuals in the population. A missing age group in a population can often be a sign that some environmental factor had an unusual influence during a certain time

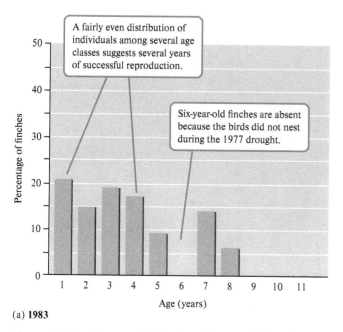

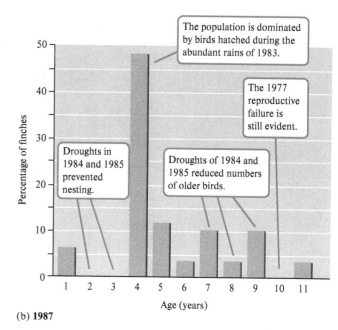

Figure 11.13   The age distribution of a population of large cactus finches (*Geospiza conirostris*) on the island of Genovesa in the Galápagos Islands during (*a*) 1983 and (*b*) 1987.
Data from Grant and Grant 1989.

period. In this case, the gap is due to a drought in 1977, during which no finches reproduced. Now, compare the 1983 and 1987 age distributions. The distributions contrast markedly, though they are for the same population separated by only four years! Such a dramatic change in population structure is a clear sign that something important changed during this time period.

The 1977 gap is still present in the 1987 age distribution and another has been added for two- and three-year-old finches. This second gap is the result of two years of reproductive failure during a drought that persisted from 1984 to 1985. Another difference is that the 1987 age distribution is dominated by four-year-old birds that were fledged during 1983. The 1983 class dominates because wet weather that year resulted in very high production of food that the finches depend upon for reproduction. The 1987 age distribution also shows evidence of high mortality among older finches, perhaps associated with the 1984–85 drought. Whatever the cause of these declines, the reproductive output of this population of large cactus finches is dominated by birds hatched in one exceptionally favourable year, 1983. This long-term study of the large cactus finch population of Genovesa Island demonstrates the responsiveness of population age structure to environmental variation.

In this section, we have seen that an age distribution tells population ecologists a great deal about the dynamics of a population, including whether a population is growing, declining, or approximately stable. Looking even more closely at populations, we can find differences among populations in the relative frequency of different sexes within the populations. In the next section we will find these differences are often the result of natural selection.

CONCEPT 11.2 REVIEW

1. Can a healthy population that is not in danger of extinction have an age structure that shows years of reproductive failure?

2. The last major natural reproduction by Rio Grande cottonwoods, which produced the large number of 40- and 50-year-old trees documented by Howe and Knopf (1991), occurred before the last major dam was built on the river. Is there any evidence for reproductive failure before that dam was built?

11.3   Sex Ratios

Population sex ratios can change depending upon the relative fitness of different sexes within a population. By studying patterns of mortality and age distributions, ecologists are able to understand many processes that are occurring within populations. Another pattern of population structure that can help ecologists learn about the factors influencing natural populations is the relative frequency of alternative sex types (chapter 8) within a population. Sexual reproduction is widespread among plant and animal species, and there can be strong evolutionary advantages to sexual recombination. However, if we look closely at sex types in the populations of many species, we find a puzzling pattern: although species and populations differ in many attributes, such as population growth rates and size, males and females are frequently found in approximately

(a)   (b)

Figure 11.14   (a) Male and (b) female individuals of the banded Uromastyx (*Uromastyx flavofasciata*) are different colours. Most natural populations of animals have equal numbers of males and females.
(a), (b): Douglas Dix.

equal numbers. As a result, many populations of many species have 1:1 **sex ratios** (fig. 11.14). Sex ratios can be defined as the relative frequency of each sex type (e.g., male, female) in a population. What factors influence the sex ratio of a population?

Fisher (1930) was among the first to suggest that sex ratios could be the result of natural selection. The logic he used was elegant in its simplicity. Imagine a population that had 100 individuals, 1 of which was female, and 99 of which were male. Some of you may find such a scenario attractive, while others most assuredly would not. Nonetheless, this hypothetical scenario can inform our understanding of how natural selection influences sex ratios. Let us take away the complication of mate choice, and assume that mating is random among individuals but that each male can only mate with one female (and vice versa). In this scenario of a 1:99 sex ratio, the lone female will most assuredly be able to mate, while the males will experience strong competition for access to the female. As a result, the parents of the female will have a high fitness (as they will have grandchildren), while the parents of nearly all the males will have zero fitness (no grandchildren). If the ability to produce males or females has at least some additive genetic variance (chapter 4), then the relative frequency of female-producing individuals will increase in subsequent generations. As the relative frequency of females approaches a 1:1 sex ratio, the fitness benefit for producing females instead of males decreases. If the population contains more females than males, then the selection will favour the production of sons, and not daughters. This process is a form of **frequency-dependent selection,** where the relative fitness of producing males or females is not inherent in the gender of the offspring itself but, instead, is dependent upon the relative frequency of both alternative phenotypes. Through this process of frequency-dependent selection, populations should reach equilibrium at approximately a 1:1 sex ratio.

Although we do not generally consider the gender of one's offspring as a factor under evolutionary control, there is

substantial research identifying a variety of specific genes and processes that increase or decrease the likelihood of producing males or females. The most obvious examples are in cases of environmental sex determination where species lack sex chromosomes (e.g., XY), and instead the gender of an offspring is determined by the environmental conditions in which the embryo develops. Those conditions can be under parental control. For example, the sex of many reptile species is determined by the temperature of incubation of the egg during the middle trimester of development. This is controlled in many species by changes in nest construction and egg burial depth. In other species, the relative motility of "male" and "female" sperm differs, potentially contributing to the likelihood of a male's producing male or female offspring. In other species, including some human populations, infanticide can be biased among the sexes, such that either male or female offspring are more likely to be cared for and reared than the alternative gender. In other words, there are a variety of mechanisms by which parents are able to influence the likelihood of raising male or female offspring.

Although Fisher's theoretical model may be useful in explaining the many populations that do have 1:1 sex ratios, it fails to explain the many populations that have biased sex ratios. This issue has not escaped the attention of many biologists over the last several decades, and here we will discuss just a few of the mechanisms that can cause unequal sex ratios. First, differential mortality of the sexes can cause sex ratios to vary among age classes within a population. For example, in human populations across the world there is a bias toward males at birth (Central Intelligence Agency 2007), with 1.07 males born for every female. However, for people older than 65, there is a female bias, with 0.78 males remaining alive to every female. Across all age classes, the sex ratio is 1.01:1, very close to Fisher's theoretical prediction of 1:1. And of course, you have probably heard recent reports on differences among human populations in sex ratios based upon gender selection by parents, either through use of contraception after a desired number of sons are born or through selective abortions. Such distortions in human sex ratios are becoming apparent in a number of countries, primarily in Asia and Africa. The most extreme example of sex ratio bias toward males is in China with 1.19 male births for every female birth (Bongaarts 2013). Although the behaviours driving this sex ratio distortion ultimately reduce parental fitness, ratios will not be corrected by frequency-dependent selection, as the behaviours creating distortions are cultural, not heritable.

Second, for many species, the body sizes of the different sexes are different, even at birth. As a result, so too is the energetic cost of producing a son or a daughter. In general, natural selection will favour producing more individuals of the least costly sex, such that if males cost twice as much to produce as females, the population sex ratio should be female-biased. Fisher's model assumed that all individuals had an equal probability of mating, but as we saw in chapter 8, there are many mating systems found in plant and animal species where this assumption is not met. For example, in harem-forming systems, dominant males generally receive more than an equal share of mating opportunities, while subordinate males receive few, if any, opportunities. If only the biggest and healthiest males become dominant in a population, then there should be selection against producing small sons, but not against producing smaller females (nearly all females will mate regardless of size in most harem mating systems). This can then result in increased

costs in producing males relative to females (as described above), or instead it could result in only the healthiest females producing sons. In both scenarios, sex ratios should be female biased. Finally, in the introduction to this chapter, Dave Boag and Jan Murie described female-biased sex ratios in a ground squirrel population (Boag and Murie 1981). This was caused both by increased mortality experienced by the males, as well as an increased tendency of the males, but not females, to disperse away from their natal population.

In chapter 12, we'll discuss population dynamics and growth. As you will see, the ratio of females to males in a population will be an important determinant of how populations grow.

CONCEPT 11.3 REVIEW

1. Is frequency-dependent selection likely to influence the sex ratio of individual populations or the average ratio among all populations of a species? Why?

2. How can a sex ratio of 2:1 males:females be stable? Is such a skewed sex ratio an indication of extinction risk for a population?

ECOLOGICAL TOOLS AND APPROACHES

Using Population Structure to Assess the Impact of Human-Mediated Change

As we describe throughout the book, humans are modifying the landscape and environment in a number of ways. These changes have no impact on populations of many species and substantial impacts on others. One impact of humans that is difficult to see directly is associated with the production of pollutants that comes with industrialization. As we show below, some ecologists are using shifts in population structure of flagship species as a tool to indicate and draw awareness to ongoing ecological change.

Many scientists are studying the effects of sublethal concentrations of pollutants (concentrations too low to kill within a short period of time) on the population biology of a diverse set of organisms. Recently, there has been increased attention given to the potential of pollution to impact organisms located in arctic habitats. At first glance, it is difficult to understand why researchers in the Arctic would be concerned about pollutants, as the Arctic is far removed from areas of high industrial development. However, as we saw in chapters 2 and 3, global patterns of air and water movement bring large quantities of pollutants

to these seemingly isolated areas. Of particular concern is the movement of persistent organic pollutants (POPs), such as polychlorinated biphenyls (PCBs), and heavy metals, such as mercury (Hg). POPs are able to volatize in warmer southern latitudes and move north through global air circulation. As these POPs reach colder air, they condense and become re-deposited in the Arctic, resulting in high pollutant concentrations in arctic communities (Barrie et al. 1997). Similar effects are found in alpine communities (Blais et al. 1998), where the POPs carried in warm air from lower elevations condense in the cool air at higher elevations. POPs are particularly troublesome because they are hydrophobic, and thus they tend to accumulate rapidly in biological (i.e., fatty) tissues. These compounds can be ingested or absorbed at higher rates than they can be excreted or detoxified. As a result, toxin concentrations gradually increase within an individual through the process of **bioaccumulation.** If the contaminated individuals are consumed (e.g., when a seal eats a fish), the predator gains both the nutritive value and toxin load of its prey. Because bioaccumulation has resulted in the prey item's having elevated toxin levels compared to its environment, the levels in the predator will become even greater, through a process called **biomagnification.** This process continues up the food chain, where the top predators have very high concentrations of pollutants due to the consumption of prey items with lower levels of pollutant concentrations. Arctic food webs generally include species with particularly high fat reserves (e.g., seal, walrus, etc.), making them particularly prone to accumulation of POPs. These pollutants enter the systems of all individuals that consume polluted prey species. For example, PCB concentrations in human breast milk of individuals from Inuit communities can be much higher than those found in southern areas, where PCBs are actually used and produced (Dewailly et al. 1989). There is some thought that this is related to processes of bioaccumulation and biomagnification. A detailed discussion of the potential effects of pollution in the north on human populations is beyond the scope of this text, and we will instead focus on the potential, and documented, impacts on nonhuman populations.

One of the central themes running through the ecological study of pollution is the attempt to connect the effects of pollutants on animal physiology with their effects on populations. An energy balance equation provides the key to bridging physiological and population ecology:

Energy assimilated = Respiration + Excretion + Production

In this equation, the amount of energy assimilated by an animal equals the sum of that expended in respiration, the amount of energy excreted (perspiration, urination, defecation, etc.), and the amount of energy available for production. This production energy is the amount of energy that an organism can use for growth and reproduction.

How does this equation connect the physiological effects of pollutants with their effects on populations? The connection derives from the principle of allocation we have already discussed in the text. The principle of allocation assumes that energy supplies available to organisms are limited, and it predicts that any increase in the allocation of energy to any one of life's functions decreases the amount of energy available to other functions. In terms of our energy balance equation, if an organism is exposed to a toxin that induces physiological stress, energy expended in respiration generally increases. This increased respiration includes energy expended to excrete the toxin, to convert the toxin into a nontoxic chemical form, and to repair cellular damage caused by the toxin. The important point is that the processes that increase the energy spent for respiration decrease the energy available for growth and reproduction. This trade-off between reproduction and respiration provides the bridge between physiological and population ecology. Of course, we are not suggesting the principle effect of toxins on organisms will be to increase respiration. They may have more consequential effects, but

the increase in energy spent to cope with toxins is an additional stress, and one that is a common response to most stressors.

Now that we understand the reasons why pollutants might alter mortality or other aspects of population structure, what information is needed to determine whether such effects are actually occurring? Three critical pieces of information are needed: (1) identification of a pollutant in a population of interest, (2) evidence that observed concentrations have a negative physiological effect on individual performance, and (3) evidence that the level of pollutants in all individuals in the population will alter population parameters.

POPs and heavy metals have been found in the blood and tissues of a disappointingly large number of wild species (Gamberg et al. 2005; Evans et al. 2005; Braune et al. 2005); however, documenting causal effects of these pollutants on aspects of population structure can be logistically difficult. It is in trying to meet criteria numbers 2 and 3 where desired scientific information comes into conflict with scientific ethics and the difficult logistics associated with field work in remote locations.

As we discussed in chapter 1, experiments are useful tools for determining the direct effects of a factor of interest. For example, if we wanted to understand the impacts of PCBs on polar bears, the scientifically cleanest approach would be a controlled experiment in which different individuals are exposed to different amounts of PCBs and the resulting changes measured. This is exactly the approach routinely used in toxicology labs, though typically centred on model species such as lab mice and rats. It is not a viable option for many wild species for a variety of reasons, including naturally low population densities, where removing individuals for study could put the population at risk; the inability of many species to thrive in captivity; and the extreme expenses associated with large-scale and long-term experiments. Instead, in the study of pollution in wild species, a correlative approach is generally used in which correlations are found between factors (such as PCB levels in individuals and their fertility), and causality is inferred. So what have ecologists learned about pollutants in northern and alpine populations over the last few decades? To address this issue we will focus on one well-studied and dramatic example, the polar bear (*Ursus maritimus*) (fig. 11.15).

Polar bears are the largest extant land predator and are at the top of the food chain in the Arctic. Males often weigh more than 450 kg, and females generally weigh less than 400 kg. Polar bears can be found throughout the Arctic, with their range limited to areas where sea-ice persists for much of the year. Ringed seals are their primary food source, and polar bears tend to preferentially consume the fatty tissues over the protein. This preference for consuming fat makes sense from an evolutionary perspective, given that nearly 50% of the calories of a seal are in the fat tissues, but it poses a potential risk due to the accumulation

Figure 11.15   Polar bears feed upon a number of marine mammals. They are currently at the centre of international efforts to understand the impact of bioaccumulation and biomagnification on marine mammal populations in the Arctic. Ian Stirling.

of lipophilic POPs. As a result, the bears preferentially consume the parts of the seal that contain the highest levels of pollutants. Additionally, these levels of pollutants are magnified in the seals as they themselves consume fish and other prey items that contain pollutants. By understanding the basic aspects of the ecology of this species and the system, it is reasonable to believe that this species is particularly at risk for detrimental effects of pollution on its population dynamics. So what have ecologists learned?

Over the last several decades, teams of researchers from Canada, Russia, Norway, Sweden, and the United States have been investigating POP impacts on polar bears. A variety of POPs, including PCBs and pesticides, have been found in tissue samples of polar bears from many populations (Verreault et al. 2005). There were complex spatial patterns in terms of which populations had high levels of specific compounds, though in general PCB concentrations were higher in the eastern populations from Svalbard, Norway, and Eastern Greenland than from the western populations of Alaska. Even within a single population there is substantial variation in PCB concentrations among individuals.

Olsen et al. (2003) conducted a study to explore potential causes of this variation in which they tagged 54 female polar bears from around Svalbard with transmitters to monitor bear movement. At the end of the study, they found that the size of the home range of individual bears was the strongest predictor of total PCB levels found within the bear, with bears with larger home ranges having higher

PCB levels. Why might this be the case? Going back to our theory of allocation, if an animal is moving a lot, it either needs to burn existing fat reserves for energy or it needs to eat more food, both of which can influence the amount of PCBs found in the blood. By eating more food, the animal may simply be consuming more pollutants contained in its prey, and the authors believe that was likely occurring in their study. However, what happens when an animal burns fat for energy? Lipophilic compounds previously stored in the fat, such as PCBs, become liberated and can now affect the physiology of the animals. These results show that not only can regional differences in pollutant levels cause large-scale gradients in PCB concentrations, but the behaviour of individual animals can influence their own pollutant levels. If PCBs reduce an individual's fitness, do you think natural selection would favour larger or smaller home range sizes?

Now that we have established that POPs are found in wild polar bear populations, what evidence is there that they have any physiological effect on the bears? Polar bear females, like all mammals, feed their cubs milk postpartum. Where does the energy for that milk come from? In large part, it comes from the stored fat reserves. In this process, PCBs and other POPs are liberated, and high concentrations of these pollutants are found in the milk itself (Polischuk et al. 2002). Not all cubs will survive, and there is some evidence that the POP concentrations in the milk of mothers whose cubs were lost are higher than the POP concentrations of mothers who kept their cubs (Polischuk et al. 2002). This provides us with a hint that there may be a reproductive cost to POP concentrations on cub survival. However, without a decisive experiment, it is difficult to refute alternative explanations, and more research is needed.

Other studies by Lie et al. (2004, 2005) suggest that PCBs and other POPs can negatively impact the immune system of adult bears. In these studies, the authors captured bears in Canada and Norway and measured their POP levels and collected blood samples for in vitro immunological assays (e.g., lymphocyte proliferation). They also gave the bears immunizations for a variety of compounds, such as influenza virus, and upon recapture they measured antibody levels. They found that for many variables, the level of immune response was negatively correlated with the level of PCBs in the bear. In other words, it appears that high PCB concentrations can increase the risk of infection of polar bears. If infection is a natural cause of mortality for these bears, then this again suggests that POP pollution can negatively impact population dynamics.

The final piece of this puzzle requires us to see if there is a link between POPs and population dynamics, and here the data are fairly sparse. The best study to date comes from Andy Derocher, at the University of Alberta, and his colleagues (Derocher et al. 2003). They measured POP contents in polar bear blood samples that were collected and stored from the Svalbard population in 1967, and then related those values to observed patterns in population age distributions. In 1973, hunting of polar bears was banned in Svalbard, and in the absence of pollutants, populations were expected to show growth during the last 30 years. During this same time period, Derocher et al. (2003) found an increase in PCBs, potentially posing an increased stress to this population. By measuring the age distribution of individuals within the Svalbard population, they found there were fewer older females (> 16 years) compared to other polar bear populations where hunting is also restricted. Additionally, this age distribution more closely resembles a Canadian population, which is managed for maximal harvest yet experiences relatively little pollution. These data suggest that although the Svalbard population has grown following the hunting ban, its rate of growth is well below that expected, and mortality and decreased reproduction associated with pollution is likely a contributing factor.

In this example, Derocher and colleagues used age distributions to identity a population-level consequence of a human-mediated activity: the release of POP into the atmosphere. In a separate study (Derocher et al. 1997), Derocher was able to show how other human activities could influence sex ratios within populations of polar bears in Western Hudson Bay. Derocher and his colleagues examined a long-term data set on this population of bears, including information on every bear that was hunted, killed due to human–wildlife conflict, sent to a zoo, or died during handling associated with research (Ecology in Actionin chapter 9). Between 1966 and 1992, an average of 42 bears were removed from the population each year by humans, the vast majority of which were part of a regulated harvest by Inuit peoples. At least two-thirds of the animals harvested or killed as problem animals were male, while those sent to zoos or killed during handling had a slight tendency to be female. Derocher and colleagues (1997) suggest that this male-biased harvest contributes to this population's having a strongly female-biased sex ratio (over 60% female by the end of the study). However, they also point out that this level of a biased sex ratio is not necessarily detrimental to the long-term prospects of this population, as the mating system of this species is such that all females are likely to mate, even if there are fewer males.

What you can see in these studies is not the end product of decades of research, which have resulted in a firm and certain conclusion, but, instead, a view of what science-in-progress looks like. There are hints that humans can alter aspects of population structure of these long-lived organisms through direct management and long-term poisoning of the environment. But the data are not completely firm. There are great scientists hard at work trying to fill in the missing pieces, but the inherent difficulty in working with large and dangerous animals in remote locations under often brutal conditions makes this an expensive and slow process. However, these are important questions being addressed, with significant implications for this species. It is only through continued work by future ecologists that we can hope to further unravel these and related questions.

The implications of the work of these researchers goes well beyond the effects of particular pollutants on particular animal species. Their results suggest that organisms that are seemingly isolated from industrial development and large human population centres are connected through global patterns of water and air circulation, and through the actions of Indigenous peoples. Their work also raises concern in the context of global warming, which is placing additional stresses on many species of the north. How these populations will respond to multiple stressors remains the future work of ecologists. It is also significant that this research at the population level is rooted in phenomena at the level of the individual organism. This successful bridging between physiological and population ecology suggests that similar connections exist between the population level and higher organizational levels that we examine in the later sections of the book.

SUMMARY

11.1 A survivorship curve summarizes the pattern of survival in a population.

Patterns of survival can be determined either by following a cohort of individuals of similar age to produce a cohort life table or by determining the age at death of a large number of individuals or the age distribution of a population to produce a static life table. Life tables can be used to draw survivorship curves, which generally fall into one of three categories: (1) type I survivorship, in which there is low mortality among the young but high mortality among older individuals; (2) type II survivorship, in which there is a fairly constant probability of mortality throughout life; and (3) type III survivorship, in which there is high mortality among the young and low mortality among older individuals (fig. 11.16).

11.2 The age distribution of a population reflects its history of survival, reproduction, and potential for future growth.

Age distributions indicate periods of successful reproduction, high and low survival, and whether the older individuals in a population are replacing themselves or the population is declining. Population age structure may be highly complicated in variable environments, such as that of the Galápagos Islands. Populations in highly variable environments may reproduce

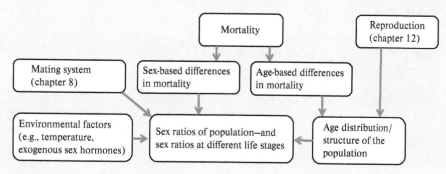

Figure 11.16 Concept map for chapter 11.

episodically. Population age structure is a function of age-specific mortality rates and reproduction (chapter 12).

11.3 Population sex ratios can change depending upon the relative fitness of different sexes within a population.

Many populations contain approximately equal numbers of males and females. This balanced sex ratio can be the result of frequency-dependent selection, in which there should be selection favouring the rarer sex. In species in which there are complicated mating systems, sex-dependent survivorship differences, or differential costs associated with producing offspring of each gender, sex ratios can diverge from 1:1. Differences in male versus female mortality rates, overall and at different life stages,

may affect sex ratios. Environmental factors, such as exogenous hormones and temperature-dependent sex determination, and mating systems may affect sex ratios in a population (fig. 11.16).

Ecologists are studying the impacts of pollutants on the population dynamics of many species in arctic communities. Working with wild species imposes constraints on the methods available to physiological and population ecologists, and correlative rather than experimental approaches are often used. Pollutants can alter population-level processes by changing the physiology of individual organisms. The results of this research suggest that variation in population growth rates for some species can be an indicator for pollutant levels, though much more research is needed before making broad conclusions.

REVIEW QUESTIONS

1. Compare cohort and static life tables. What are the main assumptions of each? In what situations or for what organisms would it be practical to use either?

2. Of the three survivorship curves, type III has been the least documented by empirical data. Why is that? What makes this pattern of survivorship difficult to study?

3. Population ecologists have assumed that populations of species with very high reproductive rates, those with offspring sometimes numbering in the millions per female, must have a type III survivorship curve even though very little survivorship data exist for such species. Why is this a reasonable assumption? In general, what is the expected relationship between reproductive rate and patterns of survival?

4. Draw hypothetical age structures for growing, declining, and stable populations. Explain how the age structure of a population with highly episodic reproduction might be misinterpreted as indicating population

decline. How might population ecologists avoid such misinterpretations?

5. Persistent organic pollutants (POPs) have the potential to greatly impact the population dynamics of many species of the arctic and alpine environments. Why are species so far removed from industry at risk from an industrial pollutant? Draw a hypothetical graph relating the levels of PCBs you would expect in a polar bear population as a function of latitude, and explain why.

6. Which aspects of our understanding of the impacts of POPs on polar bear populations came from manipulative experiments, and which came from correlative studies? What are the strengths and weaknesses of each approach?

7. Suppose you measure the sex ratio of a population and find 1.2 males per female. Is this an indication of a skewed sex ratio? What additional information would you seek to help determine whether this result is due to chance events or due to stabilizing selection?

Getty Images/DAL.

CHAPTER 12   POPULATION DYNAMICS AND GROWTH

CHAPTER CONCEPTS

Given suitable environmental conditions, populations will grow rapidly. Each spring, in temperate seas and lakes around the planet, populations of diatoms explode as these single-celled organisms survive, mature, and reproduce. Populations of zooplankton respond to the "spring blooms" of diatoms, on which they feed, by increasing their own numbers (fig. 12.1). Later in the annual cycle, the numbers of individuals in the diatom and zooplankton populations decrease, responding to decreases in sunlight and nutrients and increases in competition and predation. Populations are dynamic: increasing, decreasing, and responding to changes in the biotic and abiotic environments.

In this chapter, we examine the factors that determine rates and patterns of population growth. We will look at population growth in the presence of abundant resources, growth where resources are limiting, and how the environment can act to change birth and death rates within populations. Understanding the processes that influence changes to population size and being able to predict future population sizes are fundamental goals of population ecologists. The accuracy of these predictions has significant economic and conservation implications. Many organisms are harvested for food, fun, or profit. As we will discuss in this chapter, harvest quotas are often determined through a combination of information derived from ecological models, as well as through political and economic considerations. In chapter 10 we discussed species rarity and Canada's Species at Risk Act. A critical aspect of this federal law was the development of recovery plans designed to increase the population sizes of threatened species. Once again, ecological models of population growth form the foundation of many of these plans.

In this chapter we discuss two approaches to understanding populations. One approach uses mathematics to model population growth. The second approach focuses on studies of laboratory and natural populations. Our knowledge of population growth has progressed through an interplay between modelling and observations of actual populations. We begin with a general discussion of the factors that can affect population growth.

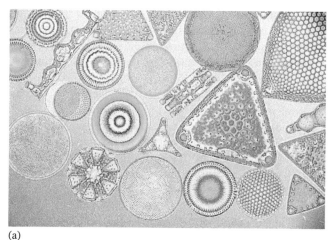

(a)

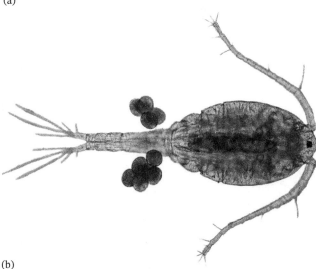

(b)

Figure 12.1 Lake plankton populations undergo explosive population growth each spring in mid- and high-latitude lakes as a result of favourable environmental conditions. Shown here are (*a*) diatoms and (*b*) a copepod.

(a) © M.I Walker/Science Source; (b) Photo 89484786 © Puntasit Choksawatdikorn–Dreamstime.com.

12.1 BIDE (Birth, Immigration, Death, Emigration) Dynamics

Population size changes as a function of birth rates, death rates, immigration, and emigration. These processes may be either density independent or density dependent. In this chapter, we will present a number of equations that describe population growth under different conditions. It is easy to let the numbers and equations obscure the underlying biology, and it is easy to become overwhelmed by equations. However, at its core, understanding how populations change over time is very simple, as there are only four factors that can cause a population to change in size: births of new individuals, immigration into the population, deaths, and emigration out of the population.

Population biologists use the term *birth* to refer to any process that produces new individuals in the population. In populations of most species of birds, fish, and reptiles, births are usually counted as the number of eggs laid. In plants, the number of births may be the number of seeds produced or the number of shoots produced during asexual reproduction. In bacteria, the birth rate is measured as the rate of cell division. Immigration and emigration are the consequence of dispersal, a topic discussed in chapter 10. Death is both inevitable and self-evident, which was discussed in chapter 11.

As a group, the number of births, immigrants, deaths, and emigrants that occur within a population over some time span are described as the BIDE dynamics (pronounced *bye-dee*). BIDE dynamics can explain changes in the size of all populations on this planet and, likely, on any others. This can be seen by constructing a simple equation:

$$N_{t+1} = N_t + B + I - D - E$$

In this equation, N_{t+1} is the size of a population at some future time (one time step in the future), and N_t is the size of the population at time t. The time interval, "+1," may be one year, day, hour, or second, depending upon the biology of the organism of interest and the personal preference of the ecologist. B, I, D, and E represent the number of individuals that were born, immigrated, died, or emigrated during this time interval. If the number of individuals born plus those that immigrate is greater than the number of individuals that die plus those that emigrate, the population grows. If it is less, the population decreases. This is the essence of understanding population dynamics, and it is no different than understanding any other system of accounting.

Although this equation is a useful way to determine whether population size is changing over time, complexity arises when we want to compare differences among populations or when we want to understand why changes are occurring. The first step in making these comparisons is to recognize the difference between **per capita rates** of birth, death, immigration, and emigration, and the *total number* of individuals that are born, die, immigrate, or emigrate. A per capita rate is the rate of some ecological process (e.g., births) divided by the number of individuals in a population. For example, in a population of 100 individuals that produces 10 offspring during a time interval, the per capita birth rate would be 0.10 offspring per individual per time interval. By using per capita rates, we can modify the above equation as:

$$N_{t+1} = N_t + N_t b + N_t i - N_t d - N_t e$$

which can be further rewritten as:

$$N_{t+1} = N_t + N_t(b + i - d - e)$$

where b, i, d, and e represent per capita birth, immigration, death, and emigration rates, respectively. Per capita rates allow us to understand how and why population size changes over time. For example, simply multiplying each of these four per capita rates by the total number of individuals in a population allows us to determine the magnitude of population change. If we want to understand differences in population growth among populations or changes in growth rates over time, we again need to focus on per capita rates. One factor that frequently alters per capita rates is the density of a population.

Density Dependence and Density Independence

Most of us could recite an impressive list of factors that can affect the size of populations. Such lists generally include food, competitors, shelter, rainfall, disease, floods, and predators—a mixture of abiotic and biotic factors. Ecologists have long been concerned with the effects of factors such as these on populations. Out of this concern came a long period of debate between the champions of the importance of abiotic factors in limiting population growth and those who argued for the importance of biotic factors as growth-limiting factors. Because the effects of some factors, such as competition, disease, and predation, are often influenced by population density, biotic factors are typically referred to as **density-dependent factors** (fig. 12.2b). Meanwhile, abiotic factors, such as floods and extreme temperature, can exert their influences independently of population density and are often called **density-independent factors** (fig. 12.2a).

Figure 12.2 illustrates what we mean by density independence and dependence for two processes that influence population growth: per capita birth rates and per capita death rates. In figure 12.2a, b and d are constant over the entire range of population sizes (N), which in words indicates that per capita birth and death rates are *independent* of population size. In figure 12.2b, per capita birth rates decrease and per capita death rates increase as population size increases, indicating that the rate of each of these processes is *dependent* upon population size.

Although in these examples we drew both processes as either density independent or density dependent, in natural populations it is possible to have one process dependent and the other independent. It is also possible that immigration and emigration may be density dependent. For example, offspring

Figure 12.2 Per capita rates of births and deaths as a function of population size with (a) density independence and (b) density dependence. Though not drawn, both immigration and emigration rates may also be either density dependent or density independent.

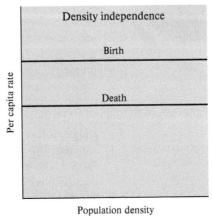

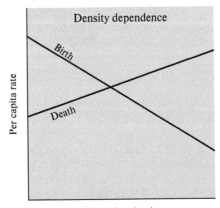

may be more likely to disperse from their natal habitat (e.g., emigrate) at high population densities than at low population densities. Although immigration and emigration are important for population dynamics, we will focus on birth and death rates throughout the remainder of this chapter. These rates are most easily measured, most often used, and allow us to calculate a number of critical measures of population growth. Before that, however, let us explore some evidence for density dependence and independence in a natural population.

Roughly categorizing abiotic factors as having density-independent effects and biotic factors as having density dependent effects on populations is a useful first approximation. However, many ecologists were (and are) quick to point out that abiotic factors can also influence populations in a density-dependent fashion. For instance, think of the effect of an unusually cold period on mortality. At low population density, most of the individuals may be able to find sheltered sites, and thus mortality may be low. However, at high population densities, a larger proportion of the population will inhabit less sheltered sites, and so mortality rate in the population may be greater at high population density than at low population density. Similarly, biotic factors, such as disease, can affect populations in a density-independent way—for example, the virulent pathogen Dutch elm disease causes total mortality in infected populations regardless of their local density. The significance of biotic and abiotic factors on populations has been well demonstrated by studies of Galápagos finches.

Environment and Birth and Death Among Galápagos Finches

We return to the Galápagos Islands and the studies of Peter and Rosemary Grant (chapters 9 and 11). Here we focus on long-term records describing highly variable rainfall, responsive plant populations, and abiotic effects on birth and death rates in these finches (fig. 12.3).

In 1976, Peter Boag was a graduate student working with Peter Grant at McGill University. Now a professor at Queen's University, Boag began his research career with detailed studies of Darwin's finches. Among his early studies was one on the populations of Darwin's finches inhabiting Daphne Major, an island of only 0.4 km^2 situated in the middle of the Galápagos Archipelago (Boag and Grant 1984). The numerically dominant finch on Daphne Major at the beginning of the study was the medium ground finch (*Geospiza fortis*), with about 1,200 individuals. In 1977, a drought struck the Galápagos Islands, and by the end of the year the population of *G. fortis* had fallen to about 180 individuals, a decline of about 85% in just one year!

Though a few birds may have emigrated to other nearby islands, most of this population decline was due to starvation. During the drought, the plants that normally produce an annual crop of seeds upon which the finches depend for food failed to do so. From 1977 to 1982, the population of *G. fortis* on Daphne Major averaged about 300 individuals. Then in 1983, about 10 times the average amount of rainfall fell, and the population grew to about 1,100 individuals (fig. 12.4). This population growth was due to an increased birth rate as a consequence of an abundance of seeds that the adult finches eat and an abundance of caterpillars that the finches feed to their young (fig. 12.5). As you can see, *G. fortis* populations declined in 1977 because deaths due to starvation far exceeded births. However, the situation was reversed in 1983, when, in the presence of abundant food, the number of births greatly exceeded the number of deaths.

Over this same period, Rosemary Grant and Peter Grant (1989) were studying a population of the large cactus finch (*Geospiza conirostris*) on Genovesa, a small, highly isolated island in the extreme northeastern portion of the Galápagos Archipelago. The study continued from 1978 to 1988, long enough for the researchers to observe the effects of two droughts and two wet periods on reproductive biology. In this

(a)

(b)

Figure 12.3 The abundant rains of 1983 (*a*) greatly increased plant growth on the Galápagos Islands compared to (*b*) periods of lower rainfall.

(a), (b) © Peter R. Grant, Princeton University.

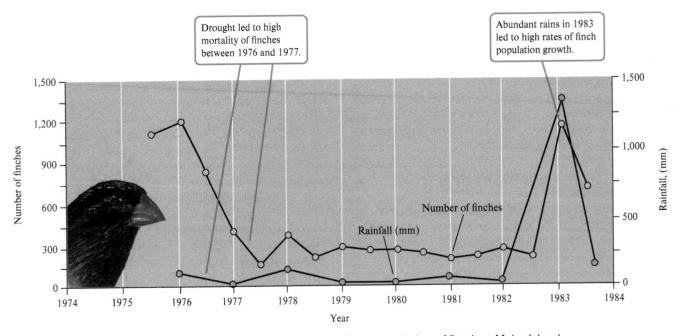

Figure 12.4   Rainfall and the medium ground finch (*Geospiza fortis*) population of Daphne Major Island. Gibbs and Grant 1987.

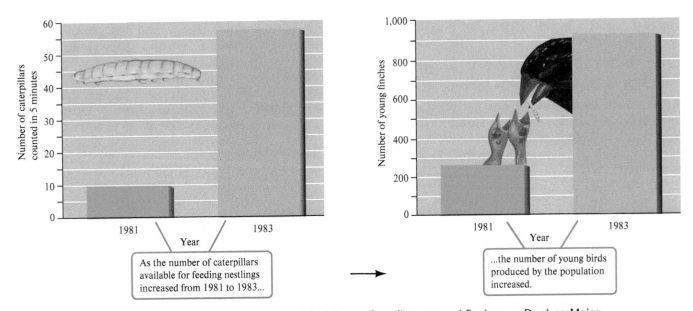

Figure 12.5   Availability of caterpillars and number of fledglings of medium ground finches on Daphne Major. Gibbs and Grant 1987.

population of cactus finches, there was a positive correlation between the number of clutches of eggs laid by birds and the total annual rainfall (fig. 12.6). Unusual weather (drought years and wetter than normal years) was clearly a factor influencing finch population size. Was the effect of weather density dependent or density independent? It depends on your reference population. For the plant populations, rainfall was arguably a density independent factor. However, from the perspective of the bird population, the rainfall patterns affected food supply, and the size of the finch population relative to food supply influenced the finches' birth and death rates. Had the population of finches been small, there might have been enough food to permit a higher rate of survival during years of drought. The response of finches to rainfall was, then, dependent on the population density and linked to rainfall by its effect on food supply.

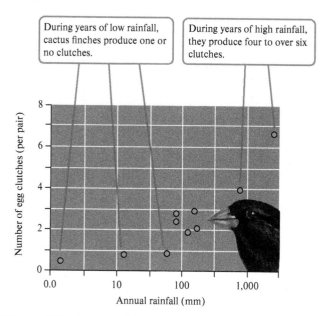

During years of low rainfall, cactus finches produce one or no clutches.

During years of high rainfall, they produce four to over six clutches.

Figure 12.6 Relationship between annual rainfall and the number of egg clutches produced by large cactus finches (*Geospiza conirostris*) on Genovesa Island.

Data from Grant and Grant 1989.

CONCEPT 12.1 REVIEW

1. Why can BIDE dynamics be said to govern population growth of all populations on the planet?

2. Why are abiotic factors often considered to have density-independent effects on per capita rates of birth, death, immigration, and emigration?

3. Why might medium ground finch population responses to short-term, episodic increases in rainfall differ from their responses to increases in rainfall lasting for years or decades?

12.2 Rates of Population Change

A life table combined with a fecundity schedule can be used to estimate net reproductive rate (R_0), geometric rate of increase (λ), generation time (T), and per capita rate of increase (r). Now that we understand what processes can be involved in causing population sizes to change over time, we need to understand how an ecologist can actually measure these rates in natural populations. We can then use that information to predict changes in population growth. To do this, we return to chapter 11, where we introduced *life tables* as a means to demonstrate age-specific mortality. Here we will expand life tables to also include birth rates.

Tracking birth rates in a population is similar to tracking survival rates. In a sexually reproducing population, the biologist needs to know the average number of births per female for each age class and the number of females in each age class. In practice, the ecologist counts the number of eggs produced by birds or reptiles, the number of fawns produced by deer, or the number of seeds or sprouts produced by plants. The numbers of offspring produced by parents of different ages are then tabulated. The tabulation of birth rates for females of different ages in a population is called a **fecundity schedule**. It may seem a bit surprising that population biologists primarily focus on the reproduction of females, rather than of both males and females. However, for most species it is quite simple to determine maternity, while, as we discussed in chapter 8, paternity can be more difficult to establish. Male per capita reproduction can be estimated for the population based upon female per capita reproduction and the sex ratio, but this would tell us little about the distribution of individual reproductive output (do all males have equal chance, or is reproduction dominated by a small number of males?) or age distribution for male reproduction. As a result, though information on paternity would improve population modelling, high-quality paternity data is often difficult and expensive to obtain, and so most population ecologists focus on female reproduction. Besides, population growth is limited by female per capita reproduction rather than male. Once a fecundity schedule is obtained, it can be combined with the other information in a life table and used to estimate several important characteristics of populations. To a population ecologist, one of the most important things to know is whether a population is growing or declining.

Estimating Rates for a Short-Lived Plant

Figure 12.7 combines survivorship with seed production by the plant *Phlox drummondii* (fig. 12.8). The first column in figure 12.7, x, lists age intervals in days. The second column, n_x, lists the number of individuals in the population surviving to each age interval. The third column, l_x, lists survivorship, the proportion of the population surviving to each age x. The fourth column, m_x, lists the average number of seeds produced by each individual in each age interval. Finally, the fifth column, $l_x m_x$, is the product of columns 3 and 4.

Let us first explore the first two columns in figure 12.7, x and n_x. For this species, the ecologist has chosen to use days as the time interval of interest. Why not months or years? You will notice that in the 355–362 age class, there are no surviving individuals ($n_x = 0$). Even without seeing this species grow, we have been able to learn that it is an annual plant species, completing its life cycle in less than one year—thus, years would have been a poor choice for age intervals. Looking more closely, you will notice that all of the mortality of the individuals occurs in a very narrow age-window, between ages 299 and 362—a span of only 63 days. Thus, using months as an age interval would be too coarse a measure to understand the age-specific processes that are occurring. Let us now turn to the other columns in this life table.

We have already used the data in column 3, l_x, to construct the survivorship curve for this species (see fig. 11.5). Now, let's combine those survivorship data with the seed production for *P. drummondii*, m_x, to calculate the **net reproductive rate (R_0)**. The calculations of reproductive rates in this section

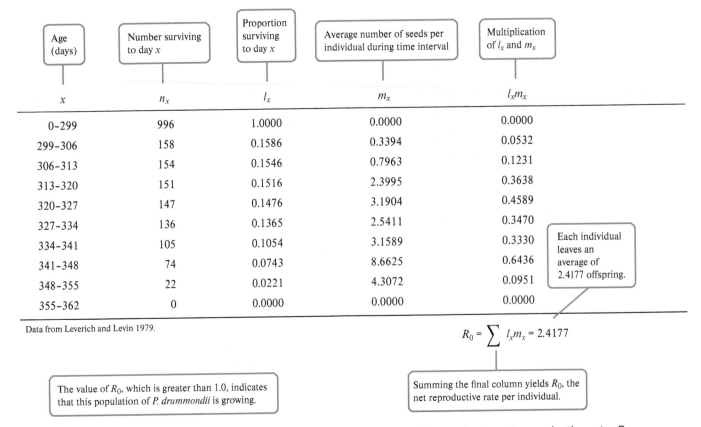

Age (days) x	Number surviving to day x n_x	Proportion surviving to day x l_x	Average number of seeds per individual during time interval m_x	Multiplication of l_x and m_x l_xm_x
0–299	996	1.0000	0.0000	0.0000
299–306	158	0.1586	0.3394	0.0532
306–313	154	0.1546	0.7963	0.1231
313–320	151	0.1516	2.3995	0.3638
320–327	147	0.1476	3.1904	0.4589
327–334	136	0.1365	2.5411	0.3470
334–341	105	0.1054	3.1589	0.3330
341–348	74	0.0743	8.6625	0.6436
348–355	22	0.0221	4.3072	0.0951
355–362	0	0.0000	0.0000	0.0000

Each individual leaves an average of 2.4177 offspring.

Data from Leverich and Levin 1979.

$$R_0 = \sum l_xm_x = 2.4177$$

The value of R_0, which is greater than 1.0, indicates that this population of *P. drummondii* is growing.

Summing the final column yields R_0, the net reproductive rate per individual.

Figure 12.7   Combining survivorship with seed production by *P. drummondii* to estimate net reproductive rate, R_0. Leverich and Levin 1979.

Figure 12.8   *Phlox drummondii.*
© Argenlant I Dreamstime.com.

assume that birth rates and death rates for each age class in a population are constant and that the population under study has a **stable age distribution**. In a population with a stable age distribution, the proportion of individuals in each of the age classes is constant. In general, the net reproductive rate is the average number of offspring produced by an individual in a population during its lifetime or per generation. In the case of the annual plant *P. drummondii*, the net reproductive rate is the average number of seeds left by an individual. You can calculate

the net reproductive rate from figure 12.7 by adding the values in the final column. The result is:

$$R_0 = \sum l_xm_x = 2.4177$$

To calculate the total number of seeds produced by this population during the year of study, multiply 2.4177 by 996, which was the initial number of plants in this population. The result, 2,408, is the number of seeds that this population of *P. drummondii* will begin with the next year.

Since *P. drummondii* has pulsed reproduction, we can estimate the rate at which its population is growing with a quantity known as the **geometric rate of increase (λ)**. The geometric rate of increase is the ratio of the population size at two points in time:

$$\lambda = \frac{N_{t+1}}{N_t}$$

In this equation, N_{t+1} is the size of the population at some future time, and N_t is the size of the population at some earlier time (fig. 12.9). The time interval t may be years, days, or hours; which time interval you use to calculate the geometric rate of increase for a population depends on the organism and the rate at which its population grows.

Let's calculate λ for the population of *P. drummondii*. What time interval should we use for our calculation? Since *P. drummondii* is an annual plant, the most meaningful time interval would be one year. The initial number of *P. drummondii*

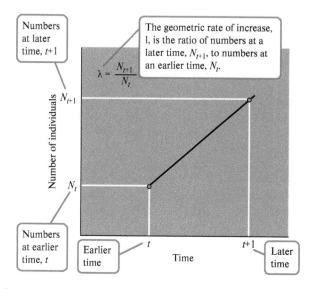

Figure 12.9   The geometric rate of increase.

x (years)	l_x	m_x	$l_x m_x$	$x l_x m_x$
0	1.0000	0	0	0
1	0.4000	0	0	0
2	0.1640	0	0	0
3	0.1000	0	0	0
4	0.0640	5.5400	0.3547	1.4188
5	0.0307	6.7600	0.2078	1.0388
6	0.0148	7.8100	0.1152	0.6913
7	0.0071	8.8900	0.0629	0.4406
8	0.0034	9.1000	0.0309	0.2474
9	0.0016	9.2400	0.0151	0.1357

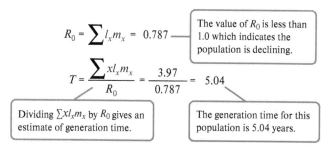

$$R_0 = \sum l_x m_x = 0.787$$

The value of R_0 is less than 1.0 which indicates the population is declining.

$$T = \frac{\sum x l_x m_x}{R_0} = \frac{3.97}{0.787} = 5.04$$

Dividing $\sum x l_x m_x$ by R_0 gives an estimate of generation time.

The generation time for this population is 5.04 years.

Figure 12.10   Calculating net reproductive rate, R_0, and generation time, T, for a population of the northern water snake (*Nerodia sipedon*).

in the population, N_t, was 996. The number of individuals (seeds) in the population at the end of a year of study was 2,408. This is the number in the next generation, which is N_{t+1}. Therefore, the geometric rate of increase for the population over the period of this study was:

$$\lambda = \frac{2,408}{996} = 2.4177$$

This is the same value we got for R_0. But, before you jump to conclusions, you should know that R_0, which is the number of offspring per female per generation, does not always equal λ. In this case, λ equalled R_0 because *P. drummondii* is an annual plant with pulsed reproduction. Consequently, parents always die before their offspring germinate, meaning that the generations are discrete and non-overlapping. If a species has overlapping generations and continuous reproduction, R_0 will usually not equal λ. Do you think λ will be greater than R_0 or less than R_0 in species with overlapping generations? It will depend upon the life stage of the species. How long do you think this plant can continue to reproduce at the rate of λ, or $R_0 = 2.4177$? Not long, as you will see later in this chapter. Before we get to that, let's do some calculations for organisms with overlapping generations.

Estimating Rates When Generations Overlap

The population of the northern water snake (*Nerodia sipedon*), whose mortality we examined in figure 11.6, contrasts with the *P. drummondii* population in various ways. Let's examine some of the details of this snake to better understand life tables. The data presented in figure 12.10 were collected in a marsh near Queen's University Biological Station in Ontario. Snakes were captured, marked, and recaptured regularly over a period of nine years. Approximately 70% of adult females will breed in any particular year. In contrast to annual plants, individual snakes do not die following breeding; thus, there is overlap in

survival among generations (parents and children coexist). Further complicating matters, individuals can mate multiple times in their life. Females are not generally sexually mature until age four, and even then larger females tend to produce larger litters than smaller females. To determine age-specific fecundity rates (m_x), the average number of eggs laid by females of each age class was multiplied by 0.7 (since only 70% of females reproduce each year, on average). This product was then multiplied by 0.5, since on average, half of the offspring will be male, and half will be female. Population biologists generally keep track of only female offspring, as the population of females has greater influence on potential population growth (although recall the threats of feminization discussed in 11.1, Ecology in Action). The values calculated are represented in figure 12.10 under the m_x column for each age class.

Figure 12.10 includes the life table information used to construct figure 11.6 plus the fecundity information estimated during the study. The sum of $l_x m_x$ provides an estimate of R_0, the net reproductive rate of females in this population. In this case, $R_0 = 0.787$. We can interpret this number as the average number of daughters produced by each female in this population over the course of her lifetime. If this number is correct, the mothers in this population are not producing enough daughters to replace themselves. What value of R_0 would suggest a stable snake population? In a stable population, R_0 would be 1.0, which means that each female would replace just herself during her lifetime. In a growing population, such as the population of *Phlox*, R_0 would be greater than 1.0.

Population ecologists are also interested in several other characteristics of populations. One of those is the **generation time, T**, which is the average age at which a female gives birth to her offspring. Or, put another way, a population's generation time represents the average time it takes to go from egg to egg, seed to seed, and so forth. We can use the information in figure 12.10 to calculate the average generation time for the northern water snakes of Barb's Marsh as:

$$T = \frac{\sum x l_x m_x}{R_0}$$

In this equation, x is age in years. To calculate T, sum the last column and divide the result by R_0. The result shows that the average generation time is 5.04 years.

How could you tell if 5.0 years is an unusually long or short generation time? Figure 12.11 plots the generation time against body size for a broad range of organisms. As we saw for population density in chapter 10, there is a significant positive correlation between body size and generation time. The largest organisms tend to have the longest generation times, while the smallest have the shortest. While this relationship might not be particularly surprising, its consistency across such a wide range of organisms is impressive. In addition, the relationship is not restricted to a narrow taxon, such as herbivorous mammals. John Bonner (1965) found that the trend shown in figure 12.11 is rooted in the bacteria and extends all the way to the largest organisms in the biosphere, the giant sequoia (*Sequoiadendron gigantea*). Humans and water snakes lie somewhere in the middle range of the distribution.

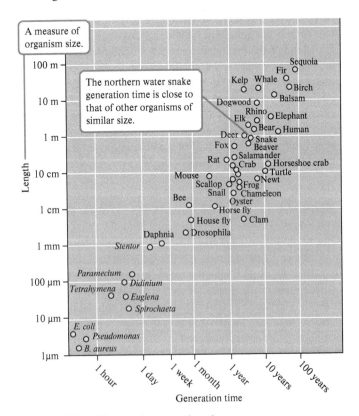

Figure 12.11 Size and generation time.

J. T. Bonner. 1965. *Size and Cycle: An Essay on the Structure of Biology.* Princeton, NJ: Princeton University Press.

Knowing R_0 and T allows us to estimate r, the **per capita rate of increase** for a population (where ln is the base of the natural logarithms):

$$r = \frac{\ln R_0}{T}$$

We can interpret r as per capita birth rate minus per capita death rate: $r = b - d$. Using this method, the estimated per capita rate of increase for the northern water snake population is:

$$r = \frac{\ln 0.787}{5.04} = -0.048$$

The negative value of r in this case indicates that birth rates are lower than death rates and that the population is declining. A value of r greater than 0 would indicate a growing population, and a value equal to 0 would indicate a stable population. While there are ways to make more accurate estimates of r, this method is accurate enough for our discussion.

In this section we have seen how a life table combined with a fecundity schedule can be used to estimate net reproductive rate, R_0, geometric rate of increase, λ, generation time, T, and per capita rate of increase, r. We will next use r to model population growth.

CONCEPT 12.2 REVIEW

1. Suppose that you are managing a population of an endangered species that has been reduced in numbers throughout its historic range and that your goal is to increase the size of the population. What values of R_0 would meet your management goals?

2. Both R_0 and r indicate that the water snake population at Barb's Marsh is in decline. Is there any way that this population could persist, without human intervention, for many generations even with such negative indicators?

3. Life tables can be intimidating. Imagine you found another population of water snakes that had the same l_x values as in figure 12.10, but whose m_x values were doubled for each age class. Recalculate r.

12.3 Geometric and Exponential Population Growth

In the presence of abundant resources, populations can grow at geometric or exponential rates. Suppose a population had access to abundant resources, such as food, space, nutrients, and so forth. Imagine that birth, death, immigration, and emigration rates are all density independent and that births are much greater than deaths. How fast could that population grow? Imagine a plant, animal, or bacterial population reproducing at its maximum reproductive rate and experiencing relatively little mortality. What would be the resulting pattern of

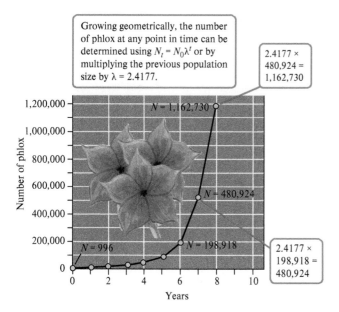

Growing geometrically, the number of phlox at any point in time can be determined using $N_t = N_0\lambda^t$ or by multiplying the previous population size by $\lambda = 2.4177$.

$2.4177 \times 480,924 = 1,162,730$

$2.4177 \times 198,918 = 480,924$

$N = 1,162,730$

$N = 480,924$

$N = 996$ $N = 198,918$

Number of phlox

Years

Figure 12.12   Geometric growth by a hypothetical population of *Phlox drummondii*.

population growth? (Think back to the BIDE equation.) Regardless of the species you choose, the pattern will be the same. A population growing at its maximum rate will add a few new individuals at first and then increasingly more at each later time step. In other words, population growth accelerates, producing a characteristic *J-shaped curve* (fig. 12.12). This is the outcome of density independence, if per capita emigration and death rates are continually lower than the rates of birth and immigration (fig. 12.2a).

When growing at their maximum rates, some populations are said to grow *geometrically,* and others, *exponentially.* We examine what causes these two ways of modelling population growth in this section.

Geometric Growth

Because it is an annual plant, populations of *Phlox drummondii* grow in discrete annual pulses. Populations of insects that produce a single generation a year also grow in pulses. Growth by any population with pulsed reproduction can be modelled as **geometric population growth**, in which successive generations differ in size by a constant ratio.

We can use the population of *Phlox* studied by Leverich and Levin (1979) to build a model of geometric population growth. You may recall that we calculated a geometric rate of increase, $\lambda = N_{t+1}/N_t$, for this population of 2.4177, which was equivalent to the net reproductive rate (R_0) for this annual plant (figure 12.7). At the end of that discussion, we asked rhetorically how long the *Phlox* population could continue growing at this rate. Let's address that question here.

We can compute the growth of a population of organisms whose generations do not overlap by simply multiplying λ times the size of the population at the beginning of each generation. The initial size of the population studied by Leverich and Levin

was 996, and the number of offspring produced by this population during their year of study was:

$$N_1 = N_0 \times \lambda, \text{ or } 996 \times 2.4177 = 2,408$$

Now let's repeat this calculation for a few generations. The population size at the beginning of the next generation, N_2, would be $N_1 \times \lambda$. However, because

$$N_1 = N_0 \times \lambda, \text{ then } N_2 = N_0 \times \lambda \times \lambda, \text{ or } N_0 \times \lambda^2$$

then, at the second generation, N_2 equals

$$996 \times 2.4177 \times 2.4177 = 5,822.$$

At the third generation, N_3 equals

$$N_0 \times \lambda^3 = 14,076$$

and, in general, the size of a population growing geometrically at any time, t, can be modelled as

$$N_t = N_0\lambda^t$$

In this model, N_t is the number of individuals at any time, N_0 is the initial number of individuals, λ is the geometric rate of increase, and t is the number of time intervals or generations. The interpretation of this model and the definitions of each of its terms are summarized in figure 12.13. We can use this model to project the future size of our hypothetical *Phlox* population. Notice in figure 12.12 that in only eight years the population has grown from 996 to 1.16×10^6, to over 1 million individuals. By 16 years, the population would be over a billion, by 24 years the population would top 1 trillion individuals, and by year 40 it would increase to over 10^{18}, or 1 billion billion individuals.

We can get a feeling for how large this hypothetical *Phlox* population would be by calculating how much space the growing population would occupy. Since the *Phlox* population studied by Leverich and Levin was from Texas, let's confine our hypothetical population to North America and scale population growth against the area of the North American continent, which is about 24 million km^2. Assuming a uniform density across the continent, by 32 years our population would reach a density of nearly 80 million individuals per square kilometre, or about 80 individuals per square metre across the entire continent, from southern Mexico to northern Canada and Alaska.

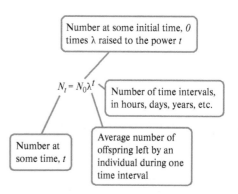

Number at some initial time, *0* times λ raised to the power *t*

$N_t = N_0\lambda^t$

Number of time intervals, in hours, days, years, etc.

Number at some time, *t*

Average number of offspring left by an individual during one time interval

Figure 12.13   Anatomy of the equation for geometric population growth.

Eight years later, the density would be nearly 90,000 individuals per square metre!

There are many reasons why this exercise is unrealistic, and we would reasonably expect density to alter birth and death rates. This population would soon be so dense that plants would die because they lacked sufficient nutrients, light, and water; and the population would soon spread beyond the physical climates to which *P. drummondii* is adapted. In other words, we would expect per capita death rates to increase with density, and, likely, per capita birth rate to decrease due to reduced access to energy and food with which one could produce offspring. However, out of this unrealistic exercise comes an important fact about the natural world. Natural populations have a tremendous capacity for increase, and geometric population growth cannot be maintained in any population for very many generations. You may also recognize how this realization influenced the development of the theory of natural selection (chapter 4). It is apparent that populations cannot grow without bounds for extended periods of time; thus, the relative performance of individuals within a population will have strong influences on their overall fitness.

Now let's consider population growth by organisms such as bacteria, forest trees, and humans, which have overlapping generations. Because growth by these populations can be continuous, the geometric model is usually not appropriate.

Exponential Growth

Continuous population growth in an unlimited environment can be modelled as **exponential population growth**:

$$\frac{dN}{dt} = rN$$

The exponential growth equation (fig. 12.14) expresses the rate of population growth, dN/dt, which is the change in numbers of individuals with change in time, as the per capita rate of increase, r, times population size, N. The exponential model is appropriate for populations with non-pulsed reproduction because it represents population growth as a continuous process. In the exponential model, r is a constant, while N is a variable. Therefore, as population size, N, increases, the rate of population increase, dN/dt, gets larger and larger. The rate of increase gets larger because the constant r is multiplied by a larger and larger population size, N. Consequently, during exponential growth, the rate of population growth increases over time.

For a population growing at an exponential rate, the population size at any time (t) can be calculated as:

$$N_t = N_0 e^{rt}$$

In this form of the exponential growth model, N_t is the number of individuals at time t, N_0 is the initial number of individuals, e is the base of the natural logarithms, r is the per capita rate of increase, and t is the number of time intervals. Notice that this form of the exponential model of population growth is virtually the same as our equation for geometric growth but with e^r taking the place of λ. The two forms of the exponential growth equation are presented and explained in figure 12.14.

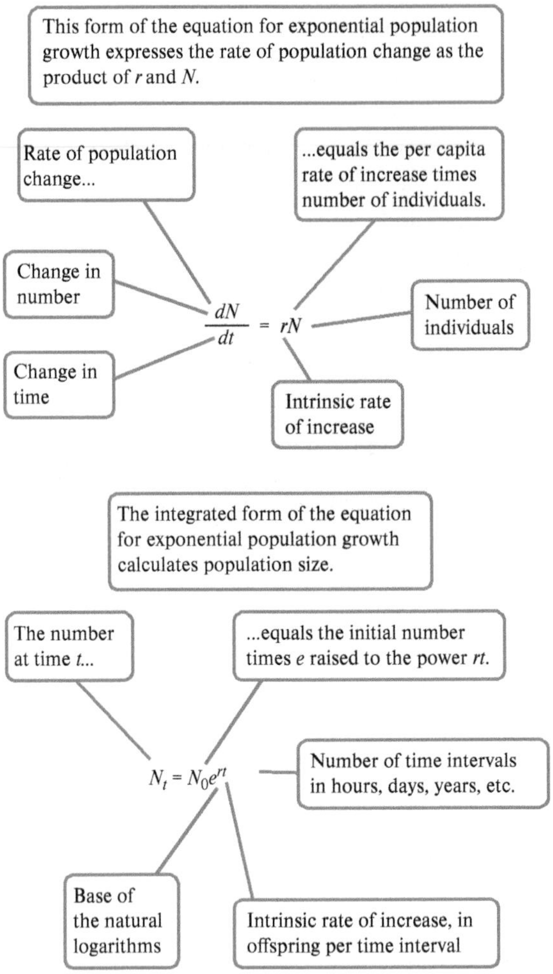

This form of the equation for exponential population growth expresses the rate of population change as the product of r and N.

Rate of population change...

...equals the per capita rate of increase times number of individuals.

Change in number

Change in time

$$\frac{dN}{dt} = rN$$

Number of individuals

Intrinsic rate of increase

The integrated form of the equation for exponential population growth calculates population size.

The number at time t...

...equals the initial number times e raised to the power rt.

$$N_t = N_0 e^{rt}$$

Number of time intervals in hours, days, years, etc.

Base of the natural logarithms

Intrinsic rate of increase, in offspring per time interval

Figure 12.14 Anatomy of equations for exponential population growth. The first equation is the derivative of the second.

A common question that is asked when a population grows exponentially is this: How long will it take for the population to double in size? When the population doubles, N_t will equal $2 \times N_0$, or $N_t/N_0 = 2$. Doubling time can be calculated by rearranging the integrated equation as:

$$2 = e^{rt} \text{ or } (\ln 2)/r = t$$

A population that has a per capita rate of increase of 0.3 per year, for example, will double in size in 2.3 years. Of course, this assumes the population will still be growing exponentially in 2.3 years. As we will discuss in subsection 12.4, this may not be the case.

Exponential Growth in Nature

Some of the assumptions of the exponential growth model, such as a constant rate of per capita increase, may seem a bit unrealistic. Do populations in nature ever grow at an exponential rate? The answer is a qualified yes. Natural populations may grow at exponential rates for relatively short periods of time in the presence of abundant resources.

Exponential Growth by Tree Populations

As we saw in chapters 1 and 10, as the last ice age was ending, tree populations in the Northern Hemisphere followed the retreating glaciers northward. Ecologists have documented these movements by studying the sediments of lakes, where the pollen of wind-pollinated tree species is especially abundant. The appearance of pollen of a tree species in the lake sediment is a record of its establishment near the lake. The date of each establishment can be determined using carbon-14: carbon-12 in organic matter to determine its age along a sediment profile.

Pollen records have also been used to estimate the growth of several post-glacial tree populations in Britain. K. Bennett (1983) estimated population sizes and growth by counting the number of pollen grains of each tree species deposited within lake sediments. By counting the number of pollen grains per square centimetre deposited each year, Bennett was able to reconstruct changes in tree population densities in the surrounding landscape. This approach is a bit different from going out in a forest and estimating population density directly by counting trees. What is the main assumption of this method? Bennett's assumption was that the rate of pollen deposition is proportional to the size of tree populations around a lake. This assumption, which seems reasonable, leads to an interesting picture of growth by postglacial tree populations in the British Isles. Populations of the tree species studied grew at exponential rates for 400 to 500 years following their initial appearance in the pollen record. Figure 12.15 shows the exponential increase in abundance of Scots pine (*Pinus sylvestris*), which first appeared in the pollen record of the study lake about 9,500 years ago.

Conditions for Exponential Growth

Natural populations of organisms as different as diatoms, birds, and trees can grow at exponential rates. However, as different as these organisms are, the circumstances in which their populations grow at exponential rates have a great deal in common. All begin their exponential growth in favourable environments at low population densities. The trees studied by Bennett began at low densities because they were invading new territory previously unoccupied by the species. Spring blooms of planktonic diatoms are also the result of exponential population growth in response to seasonal increases in nutrients and light.

The whooping crane provides another example of exponential growth following protection and careful management (fig. 12.16). Hunting and habitat destruction had reduced the population of whooping cranes to 15 individuals by 1941–42. At that time it was known that this remnant population of whooping cranes wintered on the Texas Gulf Coast, but its northern breeding grounds were unknown. It was later discovered that they breed in Wood Buffalo National Park in Alberta. Under full protection and careful management in both Canada and the United States, the migratory whooping crane population has grown exponentially from 22 individuals in 1942 to 383 birds in 2010 (fig. 12.17). However, continued tar sands development in northern Alberta may present risk to these populations by the loss of suitable habitat, potential impacts on migratory pathways, and the creation of large tailings ponds. But as a species protected by the Migratory Bird Treaty, there are significant legal consequences for inadequate protection of this species.

These examples suggest that exponential population growth may be very important to populations during the process of establishment in new environments; during exploitation of transient, favourable conditions; and during the process of recovery from some form of exploitation. However, as we saw with *P. drummondii*, geometric or exponential growth cannot continue indefinitely. In nature, population growth eventually slows and population sizes level off. There are limits to how large a population can grow based on environmental constraints. This density dependence of population size is incorporated into another model of population growth called **logistic population growth**, which will we examine next.

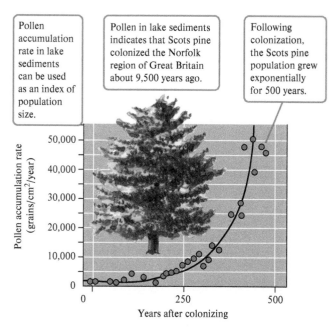

Figure 12.15 Exponential growth of a colonizing population of Scots pine (*Pinus sylvestris*).
Data from Bennett 1983.

Figure 12.16 Whooping cranes in the breeding grounds found within Wood Buffalo National Park, Alberta.
© Grayfoxx1942 | Dreamstime.com.

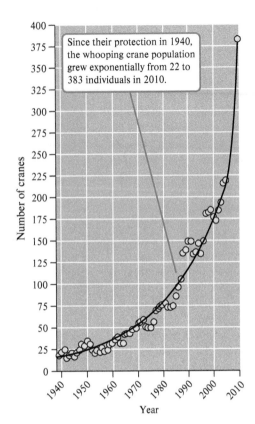

Figure 12.17 Hunting and habitat destruction reduced the whooping crane, which is endemic to North America, to a single natural population. Protection and intensive management of this population have led to its dramatic recovery.

Data from USGS 2010, USFWS Whooping Crane Coordinator.

(graph annotation: Since their protection in 1940, the whooping crane population grew exponentially from 22 to 383 individuals in 2010.)

CONCEPT 12.3 REVIEW

1. What was the major assumption underlying Bennett's (1983) use of pollen deposited in lake sediments to estimate the postglacial population size of Scots pine?

2. Populations of exotic species, such as zebra mussels in the Laurentian Great Lakes or collared doves in Europe, may grow at exponential rates for some time following their introduction into a new environment. Why are these populations able to grow exponentially?

3. African annual killifish live in temporary pools, where their populations survive the dry season as eggs that lie dormant in the mud, developing and hatching only when the pools fill each wet season. In contrast, the guppy, a common aquarium fish, lives in populations consisting of mixed-age classes in which reproduction occurs year-round. Which model of population growth, exponential or geometric, would be most appropriate for each of these fish species?

12.4 Logistic Population Growth

If resources become limited, population growth rate slows and eventually stops; this is known as logistic population growth. Exponential growth cannot continue indefinitely. Resource limitation, competitors, predators, pathogens, and other factors all act to reduce the rate of population growth. As we will see, the basic models of exponential growth can be modified to represent these biotic influences on population growth. One challenge that nearly all populations will encounter is a limited supply of resources, and that is the topic we use here to demonstrate how exponential models of population growth can be expanded to include other ecological interactions.

Eventually, populations run up against environmental limits to further increase. The effect of the environment on population growth is reflected in the shapes of population growth curves. As population size increases, growth rate eventually slows and then ceases as population size levels off. This pattern of growth produces a **sigmoidal**, or "*S-shaped*," **population growth curve** (fig. 12.18). The population size at which growth stops is generally called the **carrying capacity**, or K, which

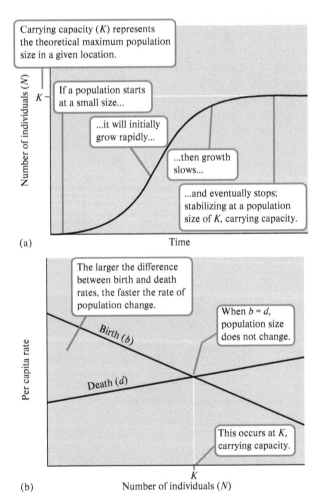

Figure 12.18 (*a*) Sigmoidal, or logistic, population growth results from environmental limitation on population size acting in a (*b*) density-dependent manner.

is the number of individuals of a particular species that the local environment can support. What causes *K* to exist? Since the only factors that can affect population growth are births, deaths, immigration, and emigration, we should have a good idea. In general, *K* is reached when per capita birth + immigration rates equal per capita death + emigration rates. However, immigration and emigration are generally low relative to births and deaths and are excluded from the models we are discussing here. Thus, with density dependence, carrying capacity is the outcome of per capita birth rates equalling per capita death rates, resulting in zero net population growth (fig. 12.18).

Sigmoidal growth curves have been observed in a wide variety of populations. In the course of his laboratory experiments, G. F. Gause (1934) obtained sigmoidal growth curves for populations of several species of yeast (fig. 12.19) and protozoa (fig. 12.20). Similar patterns of population growth have been recorded for other populations, including barnacles (fig. 12.21) and African buffalo (fig. 12.22).

What causes these populations to slow their rates of growth and eventually stop growing at carrying capacity? The idea behind the concept of carrying capacity is that a given environment has a fixed supply of food, space, light, or other limiting resources and, thus, can support only so many individuals of a particular species. For the barnacles studied by Connell (1961*a*, 1961*b*), carrying capacity was largely determined by the amount of space available on rocks for attachment by new barnacles. For African buffalo, Tony Sinclair of the University of British Columbia found carrying capacity depends upon the amount of grass available as food (Sinclair 1977). Yeast feed on sugars and produce alcohol. As the density of a population of yeast increases, their environment contains less and less sugar and more and more alcohol, which is toxic to them. So, yeast populations are eventually limited by their own metabolic waste products. For most species, carrying capacity is likely determined by

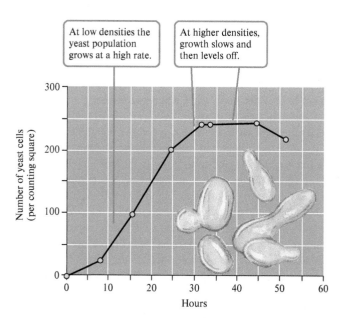

Figure 12.19   Sigmoidal growth by a population of the yeast *Saccharomyces cerevisiae*.

Data from Gause 1934.

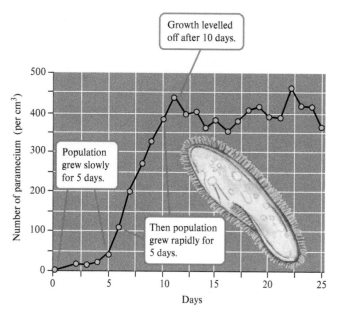

Figure 12.20   Sigmoidal growth by a population of *Paramecium caudatum*.

Data from Gause 1934.

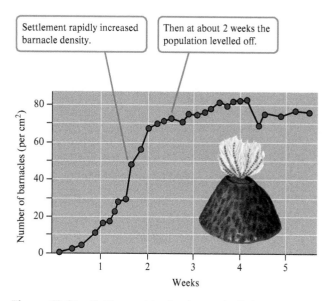

Figure 12.21   Settlement by the barnacle *Balanus balanoides* in the intertidal zone.

Data from Connell 1961a.

a complex interplay among factors such as food, parasitism, disease, and space. While we can discuss these factors in a general way, the mathematical models of population biology help us to discuss population processes in a more precise way.

The logistic model was proposed to account for the patterns of growth shown by populations as they begin to deplete environmental resources. Population ecologists built the logistic growth model by modifying the exponential growth model:

$$dN/dt = r_{max}N$$

Notice that here, the per capita rate of increase, *r*, has a subscript *max*. The subscript indicates that this is the *maximum*

When rinder pest, a disease of cattle and their relatives, was eliminated from the Serengeti, the buffalo population began to grow.

Buffalo population levels off within a decade.

Rinder pest eliminated.

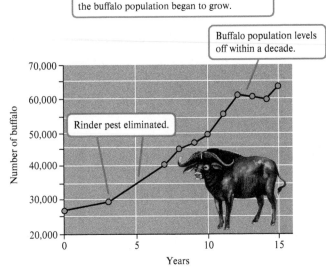

Figure 12.22 Sigmoidal population growth by African buffalo (*Syncerus caffer*) on the Serengeti Plain.

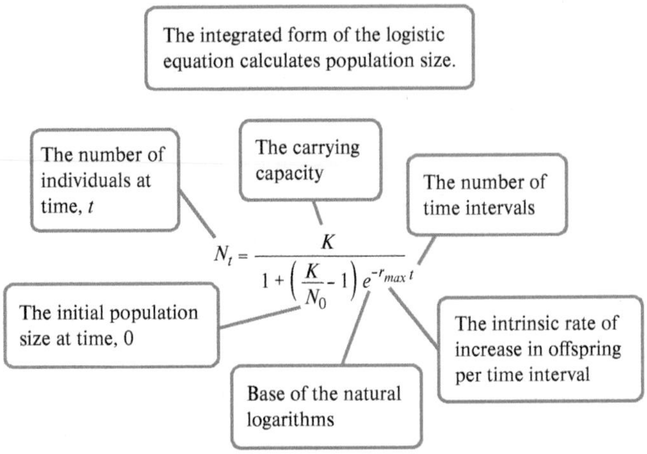

The integrated form of the logistic equation calculates population size.

The number of individuals at time, t

The carrying capacity

The number of time intervals

$$N_t = \frac{K}{1 + \left(\frac{K}{N_0} - 1\right) e^{-r_{max} t}}$$

The initial population size at time, 0

Base of the natural logarithms

The intrinsic rate of increase in offspring per time interval

Figure 12.23 The integrated form of the logistic equation.

per capita rate of increase, achieved by a species under ideal environmental conditions, where birth rates, death rates, and age structure are constant. The per capita rate of increase attained under such circumstances, r_{max}, is called the **intrinsic rate of increase**. When we calculated the rate of increase from a life table earlier in this chapter, we determined r, the *realized* or *actual* per capita rate of increase. As we saw, realized r may be positive, zero, or negative, depending on environmental conditions. Because natural populations are usually subject to factors such as disease, competition, and so forth, the actual per capita rate of increase, realized r, is generally less than r_{max}. It is this maximum value, r_{max}, that is used in this section, as opposed to the realized value of r that was used previously.

The exponential model of population growth can be modified to produce a model in which population growth is sigmoidal. The simplest way to do this is to add an element that slows growth as population size approaches carrying capacity, K:

$$\frac{dN}{dt} = r_{max}N\left(\frac{K-N}{K}\right)$$

The inventor of this equation for sigmoidal population growth, P. F. Verhulst, called it the **logistic equation** (Verhulst and Quetelet 1838). Rearranging the logistic equation shows more clearly the influence of population size, N, on rate of population growth:

$$\frac{dN}{dt} = r_{max}N\left(\frac{K-N}{K}\right) = r_{max}N\left(\frac{K}{K} - \frac{N}{K}\right) = r_{max}N\left(1 - \frac{N}{K}\right)$$

In the logistic equation, the rate of population growth, dN/dt, slows as population size increases because the difference $(1 - [N/K])$ becomes a smaller and smaller value as N approaches K. Imagine a population in which N is very low, while K is very high. What impact would $1 - (N/K)$ have on population growth? Very little. Now imagine that N equals K. In this case, $1 - (N/K) = 0$, and population growth will stop. Therefore, as population size

increases, the logistic growth rate becomes a smaller and smaller fraction of the exponential growth rate. When $N = K$, population growth ceases. By taking the integral of this equation (fig. 12.23) we can calculate population size at a given time period.

The ratio N/K has been called the "environmental resistance" to population growth. As the size of a population, N, gets closer and closer to carrying capacity, environmental factors increasingly impede further population growth.

In the logistic growth model, the *realized* per capita rate of increase, which is $r = r_{max}(1 - N/K) = r_{max} - r_{max}(N/K)$, depends upon population size. Therefore, when population size, N, is very small, the per capita rate of increase is approximately r_{max}. As N increases, however, realized r decreases until N equals K. At that point, realized r is zero.

Modelling population growth is all well and good, but how do we know a population's carrying capacity (K) or intrinsic rate of increase (r_{max})? In most cases, we need to determine these empirically from data on population size over time, determining the combination of r_{max} and K that best fits the data. But if we know the population's pattern with respect to time, why do we need to know K and r_{max}? Wouldn't this be simply modelling the known? Often we can apply what we learn from one population to another population where we expect similar growth characteristics and for which we do not have a clear picture. For example, if we determine r_{max} for one population of white-tailed deer, we might assume another population would have similar r_{max} (if the ability to grow is inherent to the species). If the second population is still growing, we might be able to look at its pattern of growth and model carrying capacity for the habitat. It should not escape your notice that many wildlife conservation decisions are based upon modelling population sizes using the best, yet imperfect, estimates of these key parameters (see Ecology in Action). It is also worth noting that the carrying capacity of an environment is not a stable constant but changes with environmental conditions, and modelling population growth may need to account for this dynamic. Improving our estimates of population parameters by carefully designed study of vulnerable populations is critical for making better conservation decisions.

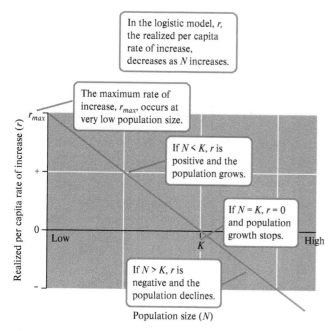

Figure 12.24 The relationship between population size, *N*, and realized per capita rate of increase, *r*, in the logistic model of population growth.

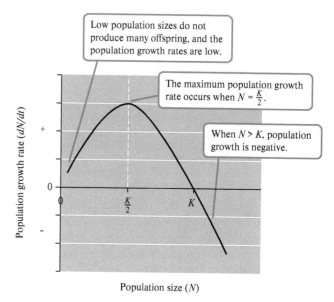

Figure 12.25 Relationship of population growth rate, *dN/dt*, as a function of population size, *N*, in the logistic model of population growth.

The relationship between realized *r* and population size in the logistic model, which follows a straight line, is shown in figure 12.24. If, according to the logistic equation, per capita growth rates are highest at low population sizes, when will population growth itself be greatest? Or, put another way, at what population size will the largest number of individuals be added during a given time interval? We know the answer cannot be at population sizes above *K*, as that results in either zero or negative population growth (fig. 12.24). What about at the other extreme, when population sizes are very low? Under these conditions, *r*, the realized per capita growth rate (the value that we measured in the life tables of chapter 11), is at its highest point, equal to r_{max} (fig. 12.24). However, because the population size is low, although the population is growing rapidly on a per capita basis, it is not increasing rapidly in absolute numbers. Instead, the growth rate of a population, *dN/dt*, is influenced both by population size, *N*, and the realized per capita growth rate. If a population is demonstrating logistic growth, *dN/dt* is greatest when $N = K/2$ (fig. 12.25), which is also population size at the inflection point of a sigmoidal growth curve.

When working with mathematical models, it is always useful for the ecologist to keep the biology behind the model firmly in mind. A mathematical model is only a formal description of an idea. It's not magic, it's not law, it's just an idea. These equations can be very helpful in trying to understand and predict changes in population sizes. In the case of models of population growth, we should remember that *r* is the difference between birth and death rates in a population. Let's think about figure 12.18 from this perspective. At very low population size, the per capita birth rate, *b*, greatly exceeds the per capita death rate, *d*. As population size increases, the logistic model assumes that per capita birth rates will decrease and per capita

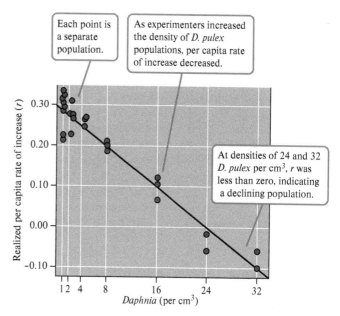

Figure 12.26 Relationship of density to per capita rate of increase in populations of *Daphnia pulex*.
Data from Frank, Boll, and Kelly 1957.

death rates will increase. Then, when population size reaches carrying capacity, or *K*, *b* = *d*, and since *b* − *d* = 0, population growth stops.

The response of per capita rate of increase by *Daphnia pulex*, a water flea, to population density closely matches the assumptions of the logistic growth model. When *D. pulex* are grown at densities ranging from 1 to 32 individuals per cubic centimetre, *r* decreases with increasing population size (fig. 12.26). As assumed by the logistic growth model, per capita rate of increase was highest at the lowest population densities.

Per capita rate of increase was positive in *D. pulex* populations with densities of 16 individuals per cubic centimetre or lower. However, at densities of 24 and 32 individuals per cubic centimetre, per capita rate of increase was negative.

Ultimately, the environment limits the growth of populations by modifying birth and death rates. In the following Ecology in Action, we examine in detail a few examples of environmental effects on population growth.

 **ECOLOGY IN ACTION**

Fisheries

Commercial fishing has a long history in Canada, serving as the economic and social foundation of many communities on the Atlantic, Pacific, and Northern coasts, as well as many inland communities that rely on freshwater fisheries. In 2016, Canada exported $6.6 billion (Cdn) in fish and seafood products, with over 80% of that coming from the Atlantic fisheries. The single largest contributor was the lobster, with a net export of $2 billion. However, Atlantic fish harvests declined from around 1.2 million tonnes annually in the late 1980s to about 850,000 tonnes annually in the early 2000s. Hidden within these numbers are harvests of a diversity of species, some of which have shown dramatic declines in population sizes over a relatively short time period. For example, the cod harvest in Newfoundland and Labrador declined from approximately 250,000 tonnes (valued at approximately $133 million) in 1990 to 20,000 tonnes (valued at approximately $27 million) in 2002. Clearly, these changes carry significant challenges for the local and national economies. Underlying collapses of fisheries are big changes in the population dynamics of species of commercial interest. We begin here with a general discussion of fisheries management and the potential influence that ecologists can have in the collection and interpretation of data. We will then provide a more detailed analysis of the Atlantic cod fishery collapse off the coast of Newfoundland and Labrador.

What is a fishery? A fishery includes fish, fishers, the marketplace, local communities, and other related industries. Fisheries are themselves embedded in natural ecosystems that influence the population dynamics of the fish, and they are influenced by local and national governments. A principle goal of sustainable fishery management is to provide the maximum long-term economic return while also maintaining a stable fish population. Successful fisheries will combine sound ecological and scientific knowledge with accurate local knowledge, helping to construct appropriate governmental policies that provide incentives to protect the resource while also allowing for the economic viability of communities and industry. This is not an easy task, and over the last 50 years, 366 of the world's 1,519 fisheries have experienced a collapse (Mullon et al. 2005), and many more fisheries are likely to collapse in the upcoming decades. Daniel Pauly and Johanne Dalsgaard from the University of British Columbia,

along with colleagues from the Philippines, have documented that over the last several years there has been a global move to "fish down the food chain" (Pauly et al. 1998). In a survey of catches from fisheries across the globe, they found that there has been a shift away from large piscivorous fish toward small planktivorous fish and invertebrates. This pattern is likely due to rapid population declines of the "desired" species, causing a shift in the fishing effort toward fish that historically did not support commercial fisheries. Global changes in fishing efforts suggest a general failure in managing these "renewable" resources. Why? Critical to the management of a sustainable fishery is a sound understanding of the ecology of the species of interest as well as knowledge of the factors that influence population growth. It also is dependent upon governments and individuals choosing to maintain long-term sustainability, even at the cost of short-term profits. This is complicated by the fact that many marine species migrate through the territorial waters of many countries; thus, international cooperation is often necessary. Global politics is a bit beyond the scope of this book, and instead we limit ourselves to a simpler question: What do ecological theory and population ecology tell us about sustainable harvest levels?

If we believe that a population is following the logistic growth curve, then we already know a few pieces of information that may help us manage the fishery. Although there are countless numbers of fishery models currently in use (Caddy 1999), we will talk about the most basic idea of the maximum sustainable yield (MSY). MSY represents the maximum harvest (catch) of a population that can occur without decreasing population growth rates (fig. 12.27). In an ideal population, such as one that follows the very simple and easy to understand logistic model of population growth, MSY is achieved when harvests maintain population densities at $N = K/2$. Why this value? When $N = K/2$, population growth rates are highest (fig. 12.25)! If harvests are greater than that, then dN/dt is reduced because there are relatively few individuals in the population left to reproduce. If harvest rates are lower than that, then dN/dt is reduced because density-dependent factors will reduce per capita reproduction (fig. 12.24), and thus population growth rates are suppressed. It is important to recognize that MSY is generally higher than the optimum sustainable yield (OSY) (fig. 12.27).

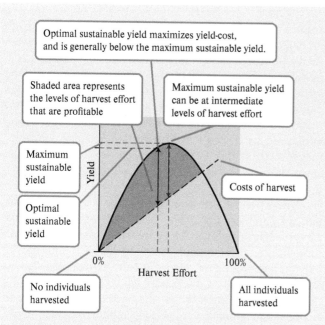

Figure 12.27   By integrating harvest intensity, costs, yields, and population growth, fishery managers can develop predictions of maximum and optimal sustainable yields. The dark-green shaded area represents the levels of harvest effort that are profitable. The straight dashed line represents costs of harvest. The black arrow indicates the harvest effort at which optimal sustainable yield is achieved. The red arrow indicates the harvest effort at which maximum sustainable yield is achieved.

OSY incorporates economics of harvesting as well as population growth rates, with the OSY being at the point that maximizes the difference between total revenue and total costs. The exact shape of the cost and revenue curves will depend on the value of the fish, as well as on the type of equipment and intensity of harvest.

This all sounds so simple, yet why do fisheries so frequently collapse? We need to remember that fisheries are set within a social context, and the actions of individuals and governments are not necessarily those that will result in a sustainable harvest. In many cases, local economic pressures to maximize economic returns over the short term, even at the risk of fishery collapse, can place significant political pressures to set harvest targets that are not biologically justified. At the same time, the logistic growth model has a variety of assumptions built into it that, if not true, means the resulting predictions are also not true. For example, to calculate *dN/dt*, you need actual numbers for *r*, *K*, and *N*, and these are not necessarily easy to get for large populations of deep-ocean fish. Inaccurate assessments of these measures, or of age of maturity, generation time, and sample size, can result in equally inaccurate predictions of MSY and OSY. Additionally, mathematical models of population growth are simply that—models. Sometimes, despite the best efforts of population biologists, the models that are

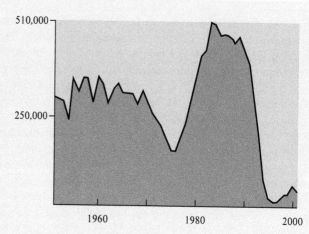

Figure 12.28   A 50-year time series of harvest of Atlantic cod in Canada.

constructed are simply wrong for a given species of interest. When this is the case, even accurate measures of population parameters will result in inaccurate predictions of population dynamics. Taking into consideration that faulty data, misguided governmental decisions, selfish behaviour, and incomplete ecological knowledge can all lead to fishery collapses, it may be less surprising that many of the world's fisheries are not particularly healthy. We end this section with one specific example, the recent collapse of cod (*Gadus morhua*) fisheries off the coast of several Atlantic provinces in eastern Canada.

During the late 1980s and early 1990s there was a dramatic collapse in cod fisheries off the coasts of Nova Scotia and Newfoundland and Labrador (fig. 12.28), leading to a fishing moratorium declared in the early 1990s. Particularly striking about this collapse was that the decades prior showed relatively little variation in harvests. This fishery is rapidly becoming a model for study among ecologists, with the exact reasons behind the collapse still an issue of intense social debate. The central question for ecologists to answer is whether this collapse was the result of natural events (e.g., shifting habitats, altered climate, increase in natural predation rates, etc.), or if it was due to overexploitation through commercial fishing.

The population density of cod has historically been measured by recording the catch rate. This methodological choice is based upon the assumption that there is a linear relationship between fish population density and catch rate (proxy measure). Figure 12.28 clearly shows that catch rates were constant just prior to the fishery collapse. Does this mean that the population densities were themselves constant? Jeffrey Hutchings (1996) suggests otherwise and instead argues that the data imply that population densities off the coast of Newfoundland and Labrador were decreasing since the middle 1980s, and thus the apparent sudden collapse had longer-term biological explanations. Hutchings found that the cod population appears to have become more clumped as fishing mortality increased and population size decreased throughout the 1980s. By focusing fishing efforts primarily in areas of high fish density, commercial catch rates did not decrease substantially, even though the underlying fish population was experiencing a substantial decline. The idea of the population becoming more clumped assumes there is a fitness benefit to cod's being part of a group, such as increased foraging success, predator avoidance, or increased mating success. Another risk of relying on catch rates as a measure of population size is that technical advances in fishing can cause increases in catch rates even when the underlying population is declining.

It is difficult to overestimate the political and social sensitivities to the idea that fishing caused the collapse of the cod fishery, and it is important to point out that several other hypotheses exist. Here we briefly discuss one of the more commonly discussed hypotheses: the idea that the fishery collapse was due to increased predation by seals, rather than due to fishing. Caihong Fu and colleagues at the Department of Fisheries and Oceans conducted a set of mathematical analyses designed to determine the relative impacts of several factors on the collapse of a cod population off the coast of Nova Scotia (2001). Of particular interest was the role of seals, which are natural predators of the Atlantic cod. The researchers simulated the effects of

seal on cod populations by developing a population growth model for the fish. More specifically, this model accounted for different sources of mortality and rates of increase in different age classes. In their analyses, they manipulated the values given to the different parameters to determine the overall sensitivity of cod populations to each value. They found no evidence that predation by seals was strong enough to cause the initial population collapse. However, they found that the intensity of seal predation has increased since 1993, and seals may in part be responsible for a failure of this fish population to recover.

Understanding the population dynamics of natural populations can have significant consequences for many local communities. There can be competing pressures between maximizing instantaneous rates of harvest and providing good stewardship of a long-term sustainable fishery. Responding to all of the actions taken by people are the fish, whose population growth and evolutionary trajectories will be a direct function of changes in birth and death rates. Ecologists are essential to any hopes of reducing the pressures put on natural fisheries throughout the world. Without accurate data and scientific understanding of population growth, there will be no hope for maintaining healthy fish stocks as human populations continue to grow, placing even higher demands on wild fish stocks.

Lags and Dynamic Population Growth

To this point, we have discussed what might be considered single-cycle population growth patterns, for example, the geometric growth of a hypothetical population of *P. drummondii* (fig. 12.12) or the exponential growth of Scots pine (*Pinus sylvestris*) (fig. 12.15). We extended the discussion to logistic growth models and considered the growth patterns of yeast, ciliates, barnacles, and buffalo (fig. 12.19–12.22) as their populations grew to equilibrium (or pseudo-equilibrium). Many populations, however, are much more dynamic. These populations may experience cyclic periods of rapid growth (with patterns describing geometric or exponential growth), followed by sharp population declines. This is fairly common in *r*-selected species with high intrinsic reproduction rates. Why does this happen?

Many ecosystems are characterized by pulsed resources. A food resource may be available in abundance but for only a short time. Reproductive events of many species track these pulsed events of resource availability (Ostfeld et al. 1996). A species that is *r*-selected (see chapter 9, subsection 9.2) may respond quickly to exploit the resource while it is available. However, a key feature of this interaction between food availability and reproduction is a lagged response. Reproduction may continue at a high rate even as the food resource is declining. As a result of the lag, juveniles may enter a population when resources are scarce, reducing their ability to survive (White 2008). The

population may outgrow available food resources; the large population becomes unsustainable and collapses. These boom-bust patterns in response to a pulsed resource, or other short-term environmental phenomena, can reverberate through a biological community, affecting predator or prey populations, and we will consider those dynamics in chapter 14.

The populations of many small mammals follow these boom and bust cycles based upon pulsed resources. Dany Garant's laboratory at Université de Sherbrooke studied population dynamics of the eastern chipmunk (*Tamias striatus*), a beech seed predator (Bergeron et al. 2011). Seed failures in 2005 and 2007 resulted in no reproduction by the chipmunks. However, the chipmunks did reproduce in 2006 and 2008 during years with successful beech seed production (masting). Interestingly, the chipmunks reproduced not only in response to masting but in anticipation of masting. Juveniles were entering the population as seeds were maturing and becoming available to the chipmunks. Overall, population growth correlated well with seed production over the duration of the study. The growth in the chipmunk population was dynamic, with increased numbers slightly lagging seed production, although reproduction in anticipation of the resource, rather than strictly in response to it, minimized this lag. This anticipatory reproductive effort suggests that it is triggered by some environmental variable other than seed availability, but one that correlates with success in beech seed production (e.g., seasonal weather conditions).

ECOLOGICAL TOOLS AND APPROACHES

The Human Population

Most of the environmental concerns expressed by human society trace their origins to the effects of the human population itself on the environment. Therefore, students of ecology should be familiar with the history, current state, and projected growth of human populations. This knowledge serves as a critical tool in understanding the root cause of many ecological issues that students may be called upon to fix in the future. Let's use some of the conceptual tools we discussed in chapters 10 and 11 and in this chapter to review patterns of human distribution and abundance, population dynamics, and growth.

Distribution and Abundance

One of the most distinctive features of the human population is its distribution. Our species is virtually everywhere. We occupy all the continents—even the Antarctic includes a population of scientists and support staff—and most oceanic islands. What other species, other than those dependent upon humans, is so ubiquitous? Except for the Antarctic population, the current distribution of humans did not require modern technological advances. People with stone-age technology nearly reached the present limits of our distribution over 10,000 years ago. Colonization of only the most isolated oceanic islands had to await the development of sophisticated navigational techniques by the Polynesians and Europeans.

Like other populations, human populations are highly clumped at large scales (see chapter 10). In 2019, 59.2% of the global population, or about 4.5 billion people, were concentrated in Asia (fig. 12.29). In turn, most Asians live in two countries: China and India, the most populous countries on the planet. The remainder of the human population is spread across Africa (17.0%), Europe (9.9%), North America (4.9%), and South and Central America and the Caribbean (8.5%). The remainder (0.5%) live in Oceania (Australia, New Zealand, and scattered oceanic islands).

Within continents, human populations attain their highest densities in eastern, southeastern, and southern Asia. Other areas of high population density include western and central Europe, northern and western Africa, and eastern and western North America. The patterns shown in figure 12.30 suggest that the highest human population densities are in coastal areas and along major river valleys.

There is even more variation in human population density if viewed on a smaller scale. Within Asia, Singapore has a population density of over 6,900 persons per square kilometre, while Mongolia has a population density of only 2 persons per square kilometre. This is slightly less than the density on the continent of Australia, which is 2.8 persons per square kilometre. Within Europe, the Netherlands harbours nearly 500 persons per square kilometre, while Greece has population densities of about 80 per square kilometre. In North America, Canada has an average population density of about 3.7 people per square kilometre. However, this population is concentrated in the southern part of the country, with nearly three-quarters of the population living within 200 km of the southern border with the United States. Within Canada, population densities are lowest in Nunavut (0.02 people per square kilometre) and highest in Prince Edward Island (24.5 people per square kilometre). In contrast, the United States has an average population density of about 30 per square kilometre. This ranges from nearly 450 people per square kilometre in New Jersey to less than 1 person per square kilometre in Alaska. Again, on a large scale, human populations are highly clumped; as a consequence, population density is highly variable. Other aspects of human populations also vary a great deal.

Population Structure and Dynamics

Population dynamics vary widely from region to region and from country to country. Let's examine the age distributions, birth rates, and death rates of three countries that have stable, declining, and rapidly growing populations. As we saw in chapter 11, population ecologists can surmise a great deal about a population by examining its age distribution. In 2019, there were over 36 million people living in Canada. When we look at the age structure of Canada, we see an age distribution that is approximately the same width near

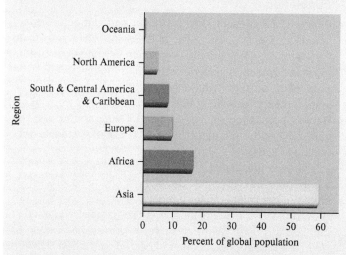

Figure 12.29   Distribution of the human population by region in 2019.

Data from the U.S. Bureau of the Census, International Data Base 2019.

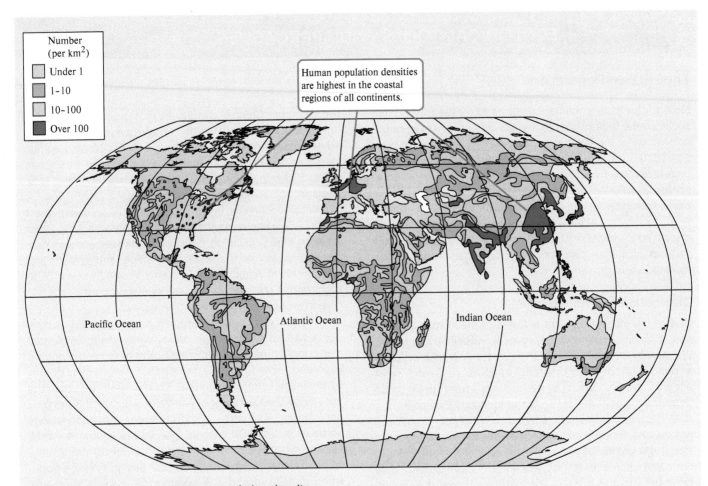

Figure 12.30 Variation in human population density.
Data from the United Nations Population Information Network.

its base as it is higher up (fig. 12.31*a*). Across all age classes, Canadian birth rates are slightly higher than death rates, and thus the population is slightly increasing. Compare this distribution with that of Hungary (fig. 12.31*b*). The age distribution of Hungary's population is much narrower at its base, which indicates a declining population. In contrast, the very broad base of Benin's age distribution indicates a rapidly growing population (fig. 12.31*c*).

The impressions we get by examining the age distributions of these three countries are confirmed if we calculate their birth and death rates. In 2019, the annual per capita birth rate, *b*, of Canada's population was 0.010, slightly higher than Canada's death rate, *d*, which was 0.009. If we subtract Canada's death rate from its birth rate (0.010 – 0.009), the result is a per capita rate of increase, *r*, of 0.001. In contrast, Hungary's birth rate (0.009) was lower than its death rate (0.013), which results in a per capita rate of increase, *r*, of −0.004. This negative value for *r* confirms our impression that Hungary's population is declining. At the other end of the population dynamics spectrum, Benin's population has a birth rate that is nearly five times its death rate. As a consequence, this country's annual per capita rate of increase is 0.027, which is strongly positive growth. Let's move from these estimates of the present

rates of change to examine the longer-term population trends in these countries.

Population Growth

Figure 12.32 presents the historical and projected populations of Canada, Hungary, and Benin. While growth in Canada is slowing, and the population in Hungary is declining, the population in Benin is growing rapidly. In 1950, the population of Benin was only 12% that of Canada's population and approximately 18% that of Hungary's population. Benin's population exceeded that of Hungary around the year 2012 and is projected to be 54% that of Canada's population in 2050.

How is the global human population changing? While the populations of many developed countries are either stable or declining, those of most developing countries are growing, and the trend for the entire global population is continued growth. While the rate of growth has begun to slow, the global population is expected to exceed 9 billion by the middle of the twenty-first century (fig. 12.33).

There are signs that global population growth is slowing. While the global population continues to grow, it is no longer growing exponentially. The *rate* of global population growth has declined substantially over the

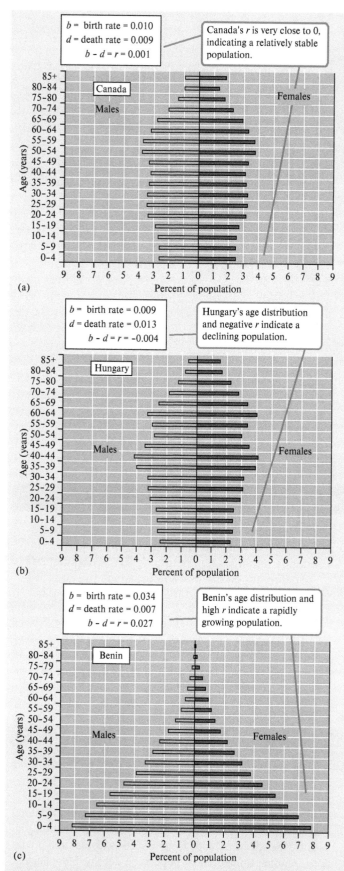

b = birth rate = 0.010
d = death rate = 0.009

$b - d = r = 0.001$

Canada's r is very close to 0, indicating a relatively stable population.

(a)

b = birth rate = 0.009
d = death rate = 0.013

$b - d = r = -0.004$

Hungary's age distribution and negative r indicate a declining population.

(b)

b = birth rate = 0.034
d = death rate = 0.007

$b - d = r = 0.027$

Benin's age distribution and high r indicate a rapidly growing population.

(c)

Figure 12.31 Age distributions for human populations in countries with (*a*) stable, (*b*) declining, and (*c*) rapidly growing populations.

Data from the U.S. Bureau of the Census, International Data Base, 2019.

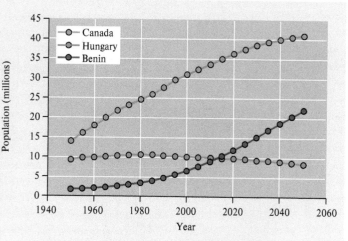

Figure 12.32 Historical and projected human populations of countries with growing, declining, and stable populations.

Data from the U.S. Bureau of the Census, International Data Base, 2016.

past 40 years, as shown in figure 12.33*b*. The size of the global population is not rising as steeply as it once was and is projected to level off sometime after the middle of the twenty-first century. Figure 12.33*b* also displays the proximate cause of this levelling off in population size, a decline in annual growth of the global population. The rate of annual growth by the global population rose steadily from 1950 to 1957 and then took a sharp dip during a major famine in China that lasted from 1958 to 1961, resulting in the deaths of an estimated 16 to 33 million Chinese. Annual growth rate, which peaked from 1962 to 1963 at 2.19%, has been decreasing in the four decades since, reaching 1.15% in 2008. The global growth rate is projected to decline to less than 0.5% by 2050. However, this is a projection based on current conditions and recent dynamics of the global and regional populations. Since rates of growth in human populations are currently very dynamic, projections of future global population sizes are frequently being adjusted. During the past five years, most of these adjustments have produced lowered estimates of future global population size. However, while the cost that the present human population exacts upon the global environment is already substantial (see chapter 23), size alone is insufficient for estimating the environmental impact of a population. Such impact results from a combination of population size and per capita resource consumption. If you factor in resource use, populations of developed countries, on average, use natural resources at a rate eight times higher than the populations of developing countries (WWF 2006). One of the greatest environmental challenges of the twenty-first century will be to establish a sustainable global population, and good ecological data and theory will be critical to our prospects for success.

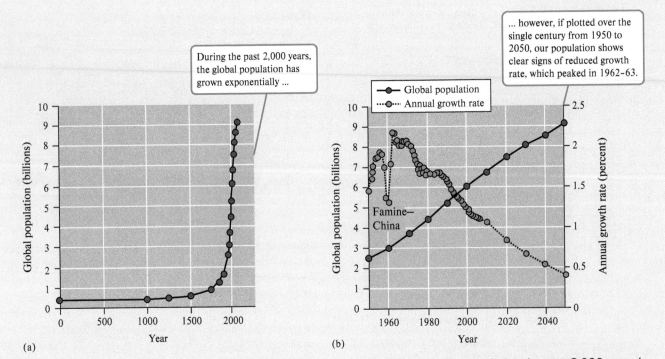

Figure 12.33 Temporal perspectives on global population growth: (*a*) exponential growth during the past 2,000 years is evident, but (*b*) the past 40 years have been a period of slowing growth by the global human population; growth is projected to continue to slow over the next half century.

(a), (b): United Nations Population Information Network and the U.S. Bureau of the Census, International Data Base, 2006.

CONCEPT 12.4 REVIEW

1. How could you test the hypothesis that carrying capacity for the *Paramecium* population shown in figure 12.20 was set by the availability of their main food—yeast cells?

2. Why might a manager of an exploited population, such as a commercially important fish, want to keep fish population size near one-half *K* and not much lower?

3. What might be an adaptive advantage in reproduction in anticipation of a food resource abundance rather than in response to the abundance? What might be the risk against which the adaptive advantage is weighed?

 ## SUMMARY

12.1 Population size changes as a function of birth rates, death rates, immigration, and emigration. These processes may be either density independent or density dependent.

Changes in population size can only occur through changes in the number of births, deaths, immigrants, and emigrants within a population (fig. 12.34). These BIDE processes provide a useful framework for understanding population dynamics. Underlying

these factors are ecological mechanisms that include biotic factors, such as food, disease, competitors, and predators, and abiotic factors, such as rainfall, floods, and temperature. Because the effects of biotic factors, such as disease and predation, are often influenced by population density, biotic factors are often referred to as density-dependent factors. Meanwhile, abiotic factors, such as floods and extreme temperature, can exert their influences independently of population density and

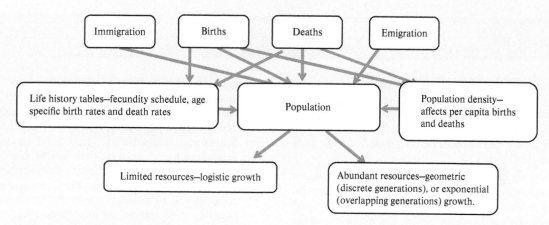

Figure 12.34   Concept map for chapter 12.

so are often called density-independent factors. Both abiotic and biotic forces have important influences on populations. The significant effects of biotic and abiotic factors on populations have been well demonstrated by studies of Galápagos finches and their major food sources.

12.2 A life table combined with a fecundity schedule can be used to estimate net reproductive rate (R_0), geometric rate of increase (λ), generation time (T), and per capita rate of increase (r).

Because these population parameters form the core of population dynamics, it is important to understand their derivation as well as their biological meaning. Net reproductive rate, R_0, the average number of offspring left by an individual in a population, is calculated by multiplying age-specific survivorship rates, l_x, times age-specific birth rates, m_x, and summing the results:

$$\sum l_x m_x$$

The geometric rate of increase, λ, is calculated as the ratio of population sizes at two successive points in time. Generation time is calculated as:

$$T = \frac{\sum x l_x m_x}{R_0}$$

The per capita rate of increase, r, is related to generation time and net reproductive rate. The per capita rate of increase may be positive, zero, or negative depending on whether a population is growing, stable, or declining.

$$r = \frac{\ln R_0}{T}$$

12.3 In the presence of abundant resources, populations can grow at geometric or exponential rates.

Population growth by organisms with pulsed reproduction can be described by the geometric model of population growth. Population growth that occurs as a continuous process, as in human or bacterial populations, can be described by the exponential model of population growth. Examples of exponential growth from natural populations suggest that this type of growth may be very important to populations during establishment in new

environments; during recovery from some form of exploitation; or during exploitation of transient, favourable conditions (fig. 12.34).

12.4 If resources become limited, population growth rate slows and eventually stops; this is known as logistic population growth.

As population size increases, population growth eventually slows and then ceases, producing a sigmoidal, or S-shaped, population growth curve. Population growth stops when populations reach a maximum size called the carrying capacity, the number of individuals of a particular population that the environment can support (fig. 12.34). Sigmoidal population growth can be modelled by the logistic growth equation, a modification of the exponential growth equation that includes a term for environmental resistance. In the logistic model, per capita growth rates decrease linearly with increasing population density. In contrast, the growth rate of the population itself, dN/dt, shows a unimodal relationship with density, with maximal population growth when $N = K/2$. Population growth is a function both of per capita growth rates and population size. Research on laboratory populations indicates that zero population growth at carrying capacity can be due to a variety of combinations of reduced birth rates and increased death rates.

The present state of the human population can be examined using the conceptual tools of population biology discussed in chapters 10, 11, and 12. Though humans live on every continent, their population density differs by several orders of magnitude in different regions. In 2019, 59.2% of the global population, or about 4.5 billion people, were concentrated in Asia. The remainder of the human population was spread across Africa (17.0%), Europe (9.9%), North America (4.9%), South America (8.5%), and Oceania (0.5%). Population densities in different regions vary from less than 1 person per square kilometre to nearly 7,000 persons per square kilometre. While the populations of some countries are stable and some are declining, the global population is expected to continue growing past the year 2050. One of the greatest environmental challenges of the twenty-first century will be to establish a sustainable global human population.

REVIEW QUESTIONS

1. For what types of organisms is the geometric model of population growth appropriate? For what types of organisms is the exponential model of population growth appropriate? In what circumstances would a population grow exponentially? In what circumstances would a population not grow exponentially?

2. In chapters 10, 11, and 12 we have presented a number of mathematical models that describe natural populations. Why are models used extensively in population biology? How can models enhance, or hinder, understanding of the underlying concepts of population biology?

3. How do you build the logistic model for population growth from the exponential model? What part of the logistic growth equation produces the sigmoidal growth curve?

4. In question 3, you thought about how the logistic growth equation produces a sigmoidal growth curve. Now, let's think about nature. What is it about the natural environment that produces sigmoidal growth? Pick a real organism living in an environment with which you are familiar, and list the things that might limit the growth of its population.

5. What is the relationship between per capita rate of increase, r, and the intrinsic rate of increase, r_{max}? In chapter 11, we estimated r from the life tables and fecundity schedules of two species. How would you estimate r_{max}?

6. Both abiotic and biotic factors influence birth and death rates in populations. Make a list of abiotic and biotic factors that are potentially important regulators of natural populations.

7. Population biologists may refer to abiotic factors, such as temperature and moisture, as density-independent because such factors can affect population processes independently of local population density. At the same time, biotic factors, such as disease and competition, are called density-dependent factors because their effects may be related to local population density. Explain how abiotic factors can influence populations in a way that is independent of local population density. Explain why the influence of a biotic factor is often affected by local population density. Now, explain how the impact of an abiotic factor may also be affected by the local population density, that is, may behave at least partly as a density-dependent factor.

8. What factors will determine the earth's carrying capacity for *Homo sapiens*? Explain why the earth's long-term (thousands of years) carrying capacity for the human population may be much lower than the projected population size for the year 2050. Now argue the other side. Explain how the numbers projected for 2050 might be sustained over the long term.

9. What role can ecologists play in developing a sustainable fishery? Does the source of harvest mortality (e.g., seals vs. people) have differential impacts on population growth and/or evolution?

10. Use the integrated form of the logistic equation to calculate the size of a population seven years from now if the current population size is 300 individuals, the population's intrinsic rate of increase is 0.035 y^{-1}, and the carrying capacity for the population is 620 individuals.

Sylvain Cordier/Photodisc/Getty Images.

SECTION 4   INTERACTIONS

Interactions among species can take a variety of forms and can have varying effects on an organism's fitness, population dynamics, and community structure. In this section, we explore several types of ecological interactions common in natural and managed systems: competition, predation, herbivory, mutualism, disease, and parasitism. These topics build on our understanding of populations (section 3) and are critical to our ability to understand how communities are structured, the topic of section 5.

Chris Cheadle/All Canada Photos/Getty Images.

CHAPTER 13   COMPETITION

CHAPTER CONCEPTS

13.1 Individuals can compete with other individuals, of their own species and of different species, in a number of different ways.

Concept 13.1 Review

13.2 Field and mesocosm studies show that resource limitation and competition are widespread.

Concept 13.2 Review

13.3 Mathematical and laboratory models provide a theoretical foundation for studying competitive interactions in nature.

Concept 13.3 Review

13.4 Competition can have significant effects on species coexistence and the direction of evolution.

Ecology in Action: The Role of Competition in Forest Management

Concept 13.4 Review

Ecological Tools and Approaches: Identifying the Mechanisms by Which Plants Compete

Summary

Review Questions

One spring day, when my daughter was three, we planted a crab apple tree in the front yard. The digging turned up a lot of worms, springtails, and a variety of insect larvae. One of my favourite memories from that spring is lying on the ground next to Norah and watching her watch a worm dig its way back into the soil. A robin sang from the nearby ash tree, probably hoping we would leave the worm-minding to him. While we were watching the worm, Norah poked at some of the small holes made by white grubs and at some of the larger holes made by our neighbourhood skunks, who hunt the grubs at night. The grubs and skunks have made quite a job of a lawn that was already far from the suburban dream, a patchwork of two different clover species, a few other broadleaf plants, and the remnants of the blue grass and fescue that some past owner had probably tended with love. We dug out a few grubs so that Norah could see what had made the holes. Meanwhile, it took the worm about 20 minutes to completely disappear, at which point Norah asked if I could dig it out so that we could watch it do it all again.

Like much of central Canada, we've been hit hard by the invasive emerald ash borer beetle. A robin was perched in a tree that would be dead before the end of that summer. I pulled back a piece of loose bark to show Norah the tracks made by the beetle larvae as they burrowed their way through the vascular tissue just under the bark. We had a lot of ash trees in the neighbourhood, many of them planted in the wake of the deaths of elm trees. Elms were lost throughout their range due to a fungal blight, interestingly also spread from tree to tree by beetle larvae burrowing under the bark. The loss of the ash trees in the neighbourhood has opened up the canopy, which, in the long term, will release some of the younger trees planted in the past few years. But in the meantime, the loss has reduced the available nesting habitat for other bird species and squirrels.

The species in my yard are not related (taxonomically), but they have relationships. They interact with each other through a diverse array of ecological interactions. Some are exploitative, such as the skunk preying upon the grubs or the grubs feeding on the shallow roots of grasses; others are competitive. Competition, the subject of this chapter, was exemplified by the different species of grasses, clover, and other broadleaf plants competing with each other for soil nutrients, physical space, soil moisture, and light.

Ecologists, like all scientists, like to create order in the face of chaos, and we can arrange the diversity of ecological interactions into a grid based upon the costs and benefits of an interaction to each participation (fig. 13.1). If we consider any two of the plant species that are competing to be our lawn, they will have a "−, −" interaction. That is, the presence of one clover species will come at a cost to the other, and vice versa. Given the chance, or our temporary distraction, the robin would have eaten the worm. This exploitative interaction is "+, −" and such interactions will be the focus of chapter 14. Had we dug out a clover plant and looked at the roots, we might have seen the nodules that contain nitrogen-fixing bacteria; they might be particularly prominent since we don't fertilize. The bacteria in these nodules provide ammonium to the clover and support its growth (nitrogen is often a limiting nutrient). In return, the clover provides organic carbon to the bacteria, supporting their growth. The clover and nitrogen-fixing bacteria have a mutualistic or "+, +" interaction, the subject of chapter 15.

Though competition, exploitation, and mutualism are the interactions we discuss most in this book, **commensalism**, **neutralism**, and **amensalism** are all also common in natural systems. The ash tree provided a home for the robin's nest, as well as other bird species and a few squirrels. This interaction comes at no cost to the tree but is a great benefit to its resident birds and squirrels; this is an example of commensalism (+, 0). Amensalisms are less well studied, and many may be a form of competition. For example, if we focus only on light and ignore soil resources, we can find amensalism when we consider the ash tree and the lawn plant species. The tree shades (or did) part of the lawn, harming some of the lawn species while not being harmed (or benefited) in return, a "−, 0" relationship. Interestingly, the shading effect of the tree may have been more detrimental to some lawn plant species than to others. Death of the tree may change the competitive interactions among those grasses, clovers, and other plant species, altering the composition of our lawn. Neutralisms are the vanilla ice cream of community ecology. Species regularly come into contact with other species, passing by without more than a sniff or a wave. These "0, 0" interactions may be common, but they are likely hard to get research funding support to study them!

Although I am partial to my home, there is nothing special about the plants and animals and fungi found there. Walk

		What effect does the interaction with species A have on species B?		
		Positive (+)	**Neutral (0)**	**Negative (−)**
What effect does the interaction with species B have on species A?	**Positive (+)**	Mutualism	Commensalism	Exploitation (e.g., predation, parasitism, herbivory)
	Neutral (0)	—	Neutralism	Amensalism
	Negative (−)	—	—	Competition

Figure 13.1 Ecological interactions can be roughly characterized based upon the impacts of those interactions on each of the participants.

out your own door and be still for a while. If you look carefully, you will see many different species of plants and animals, many of them very small. If you watch carefully, you'll start to appreciate what these plants and animals are doing. We tend to think of ecology as something that happens "out there" in the forests and oceans far from our doorsteps. But every city, farm, or suburban yard has its own community of living things that interact in complex and often fascinating ways. If you can do so without being stepped on or run over, flop down in your front yard and watch for a while. Observe what is happening.

Having now provided an overview of types of interactions that occur in natural systems, we focus our attention on just one: competition. We begin by describing what, exactly, is meant by *competition*.

13.1 Forms of Competition

Individuals can compete with other individuals, of their own species and of different species, in a number of different ways. Careful observation and experimentation reveals competition among species in nature. For example, along coral reefs in the Caribbean, fish such as blennies (fig. 13.2) live in high densities and vigorously defend their small territories. Damselfish on these same reefs may guard territories of less than 1 m². These territories are dispersed regularly across the reef and contain most of the resources upon which the damselfish depend: nooks and crannies for shelter against predators, tended patches of fast-growing algae for food, and, in the territories of males, an area of coral rubble kept clean for spawning. The damselfish constantly patrol and survey the borders of their territories, vigorously attacking any intruder that presents a threat to their eggs and developing larvae, or to their food supply. Not all members of the population have a territory, and some damselfish live

in marginal areas around the territorial members, wandering from one part of the reef to another, waiting and watching for their opportunities.

If you create a vacancy on the reef by removing one of the damselfish holding a territory, other damselfish appear within minutes to claim the vacant territory. Some of the new arrivals are threespot damselfish like the original resident, and some are cocoa damselfish, which generally live a bit higher on the reef face. These new arrivals fight fiercely for the vacated territory. The damselfish chase each other, nip each other's flanks, and slap each other with their tails. The new resident, which may have driven off a half-dozen rivals, is usually another threespot damselfish.

This example demonstrates several things. First, individual damselfish maintain possession of their territories through ongoing competition with other damselfish, and this competition takes the form of *interference competition* (chapter 8), which involves direct aggressive interactions between individuals. Second, though it may not appear so to the casual observer, there is a limited supply of suitable space for damselfish territories, a condition that ecologists call **resource limitation**. Here, the limited resource is space on the reef rather than a direct limitation of food items. Third, the threespot damselfish engage in both **intraspecific competition** (competition with members of their own species) and **interspecific competition** (competition between individuals of different species).

The effects of competition on the fitness of the competitors are not necessarily the same for all individuals. Instead, competitive effects can be asymmetric, where some individuals are harmed (the losers) while others (the winners) are not, or at least are less severely harmed. Competition is not always as dramatic as fighting damselfish, nor is it always resolved so quickly. In the white pine forests of New Hampshire, tree roots grow throughout the soil, taking up nutrients and water as they provide support. In 1931, J. Toumey and R. Kienholz designed an experiment to determine whether the activities of these tree roots suppress the activities of other plants. The researchers cut a trench, 0.92 m deep, around a plot 2.74 m by 2.74 m in the middle of the forest. In so doing, they cut 825 roots, which removed potential competition by these tree roots for soil resources. They also established control plots on either side of the trenched plot and then watched as the results of their experiment unfolded. The experiment continued for eight years, with the plot retrenched every two years, cutting over 100 roots each time. By retrenching, the researchers maintained their experimental treatment—suppression of potential root competition.

In the end, this eight-year experiment yielded results as dramatic as those with the damselfish. Vegetative cover on the section of forest floor that had been released from root competition was 10 times that present on the control plots. Apparently the roots of white pines exert interspecific competition for limited supplies of nutrients and water that is strong enough to suppress the growth of forest floor vegetation (fig. 13.3). In addition, the growth of young white pines was much greater within the trenched plots than in the control

Figure 13.2 Territorial reef fish, such as blennies (pictured) and damselfish, can compete intensely for space.
© Jodi Jacobson/Photolibrary/Getty Images.

Figure 13.3 Competition in a forest can be as intense as competition on a coral reef. However, much of the competition in a forest takes place underground, where the roots of plants compete for water and nutrients.
© National Geographic/Getty RF.

plots, demonstrating that considerable intraspecific competition was occurring.

In both the forest floor and damselfish examples, individuals are competing for limited resources. A critical difference is that the damselfish compete by actively attacking other individuals, in the hopes of preventing access to the desired resource contained on the reef. In the forest example, the plants are not competing by preventing access to the soil nutrients and water. Instead, competition occurs when some individuals acquire these resources before other individuals are able to capture the resources. The damselfish demonstrate interference competition, while the plants demonstrate **exploitative competition** (fig. 13.4). Both plants and animals are able to demonstrate exploitative and interference competition, depending upon the details of the specific competitive interaction.

Ecologists have long thought that competition is pervasive in nature, and in many circumstances competitive interactions can affect fitness and evolution of species. In the next section, we provide some evidence that competition for resource occurs in diverse communities, with often predictable consequences.

CONCEPT 13.1 REVIEW

1. Competitive interactions among co-occurring individuals can be either direct or indirect. What aspects of how individuals compete determine whether the competition is direct or indirect?

2. How does the logistic model of population growth (see chapter 12, subsection 12.4) explicitly assume that intraspecific competition is occurring? (Is it by interference or exploitative competition?)

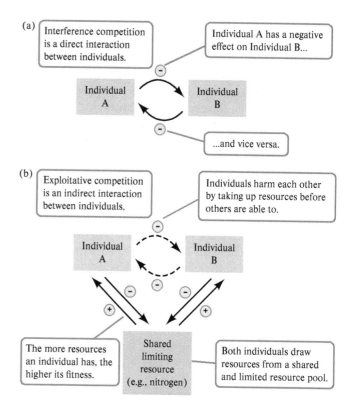

Figure 13.4 Competition can be (*a*) direct interaction or (*b*) indirect interaction among individuals of the same or different species.

13.2 Evidence of Competition in Natural Systems

Field and mesocosm studies show that resource limitations and competition are widespread. In chapter 12, we saw that slowing population growth at high densities produces a sigmoidal, or S-shaped, pattern in which population size levels off at carrying capacity. Our assumption in that discussion was that intraspecific competition for limited resources plays a key role in slowing population growth at higher densities. In fact, the effect of intraspecific competition was explicitly included in the model of logistic population growth as $(K - N)/K$. But is competition truly widespread in natural systems? If so, then we should be able to observe it most commonly among individuals of the same species, individuals with identical or very similar resource requirements.

Intraspecific Competition in Plant and Planthopper Populations—Exploitative

The development of a stand of plants from the seedling stage to mature individuals suggests competition for limited resources. Each spring as the seeds of annual plants germinate, their population density often numbers in the thousands per square metre. However, as the season progresses and individual plants grow, population density declines. This same pattern occurs in the development of a stand of trees. As the stand of trees develops, more and more biomass is composed of fewer and fewer individuals. In populations of long- or short-lived plants, this process is often referred to as **self-thinning**. Importantly, this term does not imply that the plants are actively eliminating themselves from the population to benefit the others that remain. Instead, self-thinning indicates that even in the absence of outside agents (e.g., people with chainsaws!), the number of individual plants found within a stand decreases as the average size of the plants within the stand increases.

Driving this process is intraspecific competition for limiting resources. As a local population of plants develops, individual plants take up increasing quantities of nutrients, water, and space for which some individuals compete more successfully than others. The losers in this exploitative competition are unable to continue to grow, and many die, reducing population densities over time. As the population is thinned, it is composed of fewer and fewer large individuals.

One way to represent the self-thinning process is to plot total plant biomass (the sum of the biomasses of all individuals in the population) against population density. If we plot the logarithm of total plant biomass against the logarithm of population density, the slope of the resulting line is often around $-1/2$ (fig. 13.5). In other words, there is an approximately one-unit increase in total plant biomass with each two-unit decrease in population density. We can illustrate self-thinning if we imagine two possible different initial populations, imaginatively labelled A and B (fig. 13.5). Population A lies below the regression line. At this population density, there is little intraspecific competition, and there are sufficient resources in the environment for each of the individual trees to grow and add biomass. This is indicated by the vertical arrow. Eventually, the trees will grow large enough that they begin to compete with one another, and the population will follow the vectors along the regression line. In other

words, intraspecific competition will begin to cause some mortality and thinning. As this happens, the remaining trees grow larger still. Population B lies above the regression line. At this population density, intraspecific competition is intense. Before individual trees grow larger, many trees will die, decreasing population size. This is indicated by the arrow. When enough thinning has occurred, the individual trees can begin to grow larger. As they do, further thinning of the population will occur, following the vectors along the regression line.

Recent analyses have shown that self-thinning in some plant populations deviates significantly from the $-1/2$ slope. However, regardless of the precise trajectory followed by different plant populations, self-thinning of plant populations, as a consequence of intraspecific competition, has been demonstrated repeatedly. The **self-thinning rule** appears to apply to most plant species tested.

If intraspecific competition is the norm for plant species, is it also the norm for animals? Ecologists have often failed to demonstrate that insects, particularly herbivorous insects, necessarily compete for limiting resources; instead, other factors limit their populations. However, one group of insects in which intraspecific competition has been repeatedly demonstrated is the Homoptera, including the leafhoppers, planthoppers, and aphids. Robert Denno and George Roderick (1992), who studied interactions among planthoppers (Homoptera, *Delphacidae*), attribute the prevalence of competition among the Homoptera to their habit of aggregating around mobile food supplies (plant fluids) coupled with rapid population growth that can quickly lead to exhaustion of local resources.

Denno and Roderick demonstrated intraspecific competition within populations of the planthopper *Prokelisia marginata*, which lives on the salt marsh grass (*Spartina alterniflora*) along the Atlantic and Gulf coasts of the United States. The population density of *P. marginata* was controlled by enclosing the insects with *Spartina* seedlings at densities of 3, 11, and 40 leafhoppers per cage—densities that are within the range at which they live in nature. At the highest density, *P. marginata* showed reduced survivorship, decreased body length, and increased developmental time (fig. 13.6). These signs of intraspecific competition were probably the result of reduced food quality at high leafhopper densities. Plants heavily populated by planthoppers show reduced concentrations of protein, chlorophyll, and moisture. Therefore, competition among these leafhoppers was probably the result of limited resource supplies. However, as demonstrated in the following example, interference competition may occur in the absence of obvious resource limitation.

Intraspecific Competition Among Song Sparrows—Interference

Peter Arcese (1987) conducted a field study on Mandarte Island, British Columbia, to determine how male song sparrows (*Melospiza melodia*) defend their territories. These sparrows are primarily monogamous. Starting at age one, males set up territories in which they sing and present visual displays to attract females as potential mates. However, appropriate space for territories is limited, and many males are left without established

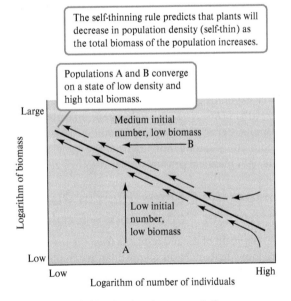

Figure 13.5 Self-thinning in plant populations.
Data from Westoby 1984.

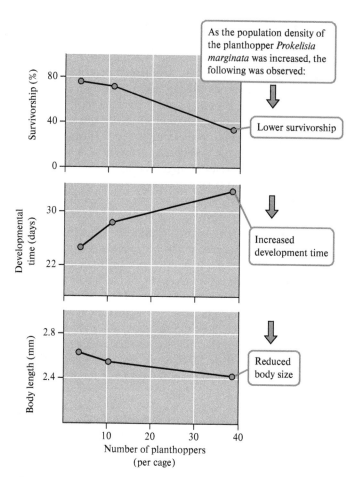

Figure 13.6 contains the following annotations:

As the population density of the planthopper *Prokelisia marginata* was increased, the following was observed:

Lower survivorship

Increased development time

Reduced body size

Figure 13.6 Population density and planthopper performance.

Data from Denno and Roderick 1992.

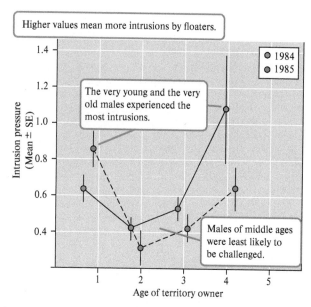

Higher values mean more intrusions by floaters.

The very young and the very old males experienced the most intrusions.

Males of middle ages were least likely to be challenged.

Figure 13.7 Intrusion pressure by floaters varies as a function of the age of the territorial male.

Reprinted from P. Arcese. 1987. Age, intrusion pressure and defense. *Animal Behaviour* 35:776. © 1987 with permission from Elsevier.

territories (around 20% of males on this island). These males, called *floaters*, live within the territories of other males, rarely singing or perching on visually obvious branches. In other words, they generally hide, waiting for the territorial male to die, thus allowing them to take over the territory; or they challenge the territorial male in the hope of winning the contest and claiming the territory. When a territorial male sees a floater intruding in his territory, there is a rapid and obvious response of a song followed by a chase, a clear example of interference competition.

For 10 years prior to Arcese's study, the sparrows on this island had been extensively studied, with every bird individually marked. Arcese and his field crew then spent 294 hours over the course of two years observing the behaviour of many floaters and territorial males. Of particular interest to Arcese were intrusions by the floaters into the territories of other males; he wondered whether some territorial males were more likely to be intruded upon than others.

Intrusion pressure was not related to territory size, nor was it related to the presence of fertile females in the territory. Instead, there was a strong relationship between the age of the territory owner and intrusion pressure (fig. 13.7). This was consistent with prior research that suggested that territory size, male age, and male health may all influence the likelihood of intrusion by a floater. The sparrows in Arcese's study typically

live up to four years, and both the youngest and the oldest males were most likely to be challenged by floaters. These intrusions appeared to come at a real cost to the resident males, as the youngest and oldest males held on to their territories for a shorter duration than two- and three-year-old males. In many cases, the physical chase that ensued resulted in broken limbs or other injuries, often leading to declining health or death of older dispossessed males. The one-year-olds that were dispossessed did not generally show physical handicaps. Arcese reasoned that they were not physically harmed by the intrusion; these males were simply less experienced and less able to defend a territory than were slightly older males.

Overall, Arcese's field study shows that interference competition can occur in a natural setting, with potentially strong consequences for the competing individuals. He also shows that, like exploitative competition, a variety of factors can influence the strength of competition experienced by different individuals in the population. In this case, it appears that the floating males were choosing to challenge the weakest or most inexperienced males while generally avoiding the stronger, experienced males. These results show that for some organisms, behavioural choices also can influence competitive interactions. Next we will provide a more general discussion of evidence for competition in natural systems.

Interspecific Competition among Small Rodents

One of the most ambitious and complete field experiments that ecologists have conducted on interspecific competition among mammals focused on desert rodents in the Chihuahuan Desert near Portal, Arizona. This experiment, initiated by James H. Brown and his students and colleagues (Munger and

Figure 13.8 Aerial photo showing the placement of 24 study plots, each 50 m by 50 m, in the Chihuahuan Desert near Portal, Arizona.

© James Brown.

Brown 1981, Brown and Munger 1985, Heske et al. 1994), began in 1977 and is ongoing. The experiment was conducted at a large scale—a 20-hectare study site, including 24 study plots, each 50 m by 50 m (fig. 13.8)—and has been well replicated, both in space and in time.

The rodent species living on the Chihuahuan Desert study site can be divided into groups based upon size and feeding habits. Most members of the species are **granivores**, rodents that feed chiefly on seeds. The large granivores consist of three species of kangaroo rats (fig. 13.9*a*) in the genus *Dipodomys*: *D. spectabilis*, 120 g; *D. ordii*, 52 g; and *D. merriami*, 45 g. In addition, the study site is home to four species of small granivores (fig. 13.9*b*): *Perognathus penicillatus*, 17 g; *P. flavus*, 7 g; *Peromyscus maniculatus*, 24 g; *Reithrodontomys megalotis*, 11 g. It is also home to two species of insectivorous rodents: *Onychomys leucogaster*, 39 g; and *O. torridus*, 29 g.

Brown and his colleagues set out to determine whether large granivorous rodents (*Dipodomys* spp.) limit the abundance of small rodents on their Chihuahuan Desert study site and whether the rodents might be competing for food. The researchers enclosed the 50 m by 50 m study plots with mouse-proof fences. The fences were constructed with wire mesh with 0.64 cm openings, which were too small for any of the rodent species to crawl through. They also buried the fencing 0.2 m deep so the mice couldn't dig under it, and they topped the fences with aluminum flashing so the mice couldn't climb over it. This may sound like a lot of work, but to answer their questions, the researchers had to control the presence of rodents on the study plots.

The researchers next cut holes 6.5 cm in diameter in the sides of some of the fences to allow all rodent species to move freely in and out of the study plots. With this arrangement in place, the rodents in these study plots were trapped live and marked once a month for three months. The expectation was that these plots would have populations of the individual rodent species that were comparable to the broader habitat (the Chihuahuan Desert floor). Following this initial monitoring period, the holes on some of these study plots were reduced to 1.9 cm, small enough to exclude *Dipodomys*, the large granivores in this system. *Dipodomys* were then trapped and removed from all enclosures, although they could readily re-enter the control plots where 6.5 cm holes in the fence remained.

(a)

(b)

Figure 13.9 Two species of granivorous rodents living in the Chihuahuan Desert: (*a*) the kangaroo rat (*Dipodomys* spp.), a large granivore; and (*b*) a pocket mouse (*Perognathus* sp.), a small granivore.

(a), (b) © Dr. James H. Brown.

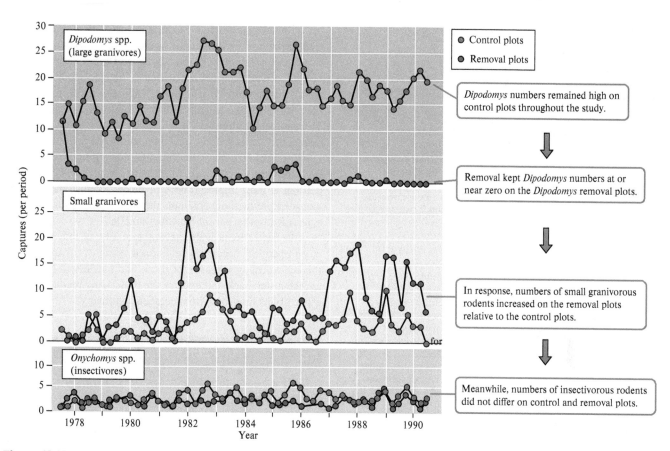

Figure 13.10 Responses by small granivorous and insectivorous rodents to removal of large granivorous *Dipodomys* species. Data from Heske, Brown, and Mistry 1994.

If *Dipodomys* competes with small rodents, how would you expect populations of small rodents to respond to its removal? The density of small rodent populations should increase, right? If food is the limiting resource, would you expect granivorous and insectivorous rodents to respond differently to *Dipodomys* removal? The researchers predicted that if competition among rodents is mainly for food, then small granivorous rodent populations would increase in response to *Dipodomys* removal while insectivorous rodents would show little or no response.

The results of the experiment were consistent with the predictions. During the first three years of the experiment, small granivores were approximately 3.5 times more abundant on the *Dipodomys* removal plots compared to the control plots, while populations of small insectivorous rodents did not increase significantly (fig. 13.10). The results supported the hypothesis that *Dipodomys* spp. competitively suppress populations of small granivores.

Is Interspecific Competition a Common Ecological Interaction?

Darwin himself focused our attention on the potential importance of competition to the ecology and evolution of natural species; thus, this issue has been the subject of substantial research effort. Many of the questions about whether competition plays

an important role in natural populations were raised by animal ecologists. As you will see in later chapters (section 5), animals are generally rare on the landscape relative to plants, and direct encounters between individuals are not as frequent in comparison to a plant living its life rooted next to another. Plants generally grow in very close proximity to their neighbours, and their leaves and roots likely interact for their entire lives. The impact of these interactions can be obvious, as all gardeners know if they don't pull weeds from their strawberry beds. So for plant ecologists, the big question about competition is not whether it occurred but, rather, if competition is strongest when resources are rare or when resources are common.

This debate originated with Phil Grime, who developed one of the theories of plant life history strategies we discussed in chapter 9. Grime (1973) argued that competition among plants will be unimportant in unproductive areas, areas of low resource availability and little plant growth. Edward Newman (1973) and, later, David Tilman (1987) disagreed with this position and argued that competition will be important at both high and low resource availability. What will differ, they hypothesized, is that in unproductive environments competition will be primarily below ground, while in productive environments competition will be predominantly above ground (fig. 13.11). Of course, is it really too surprising that people who study competition for a living are often themselves embroiled in advancing competing hypotheses?

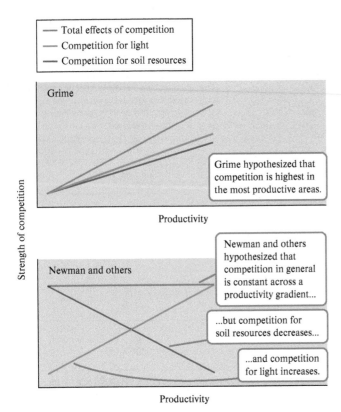

- Total effects of competition
- Competition for light
- Competition for soil resources

Grime hypothesized that competition is highest in the most productive areas.

Newman and others hypothesized that competition in general is constant across a productivity gradient...

...but competition for soil resources decreases...

...and competition for light increases.

Figure 13.11 Contrasting theories about the relationship between plant competition and productivity.

Throughout the 1980s and early 1990s, numerous experiments were designed to resolve this debate, generally with conflicting results. One concern was that most relevant experiments were conducted over a relatively small spatial scale, and thus differences observed could have been due to site-specific differences. Richard Reader, of the University of Guelph, initiated an ambitious study to try to finally resolve what had been a long-standing and combative debate among ecologists. Reader assembled a team of 20 researchers located throughout the world (Canada, United States, the Netherlands, Sweden, and Australia). The team conducted identical experiments at each of 12 study sites, allowing a broad test of the research question (Reader et al. 1994). To minimize variation among sites, they used similar types of communities (grasslands and abandoned fields) in all locations, and they chose sites that had naturally occurring variation in productivity (an indirect measure of resource availability). Within each site they laid out a number of plots, from which they either removed the neighbouring vegetation by spraying a herbicide or left the neighbouring vegetation intact. They then transplanted one individual of the species *Poa pratensis* (Kentucky bluegrass) into every plot, measuring its growth over the course of the season. This sort of design is called a *focal plant study*, in which measures are taken from a specific individual within each plot (the transplanted bluegrass seedlings).

The strength of competition can be measured in several ways but is most widely reported as some function of the growth of the focal plants when neighbours were present relative to their growth when neighbours were removed. Using this relative measure of competition, Reader and his colleagues found no evidence that competition varied in intensity along this intercontinental productivity gradient. They also found that within their study there was substantial variation in the relationship between competition and productivity among study sites. The results of Reader's study would generally seem to support the hypothesis of Newman and Tilman—that strength of competition does not vary along a productivity gradient. Where competition is most intense (above or below ground) may change along the productivity gradient, although Reader's study did not explicitly test this part of Newman's model.

We have now provided several examples of different forms of competition occurring in natural systems. To understand the ecological significance of these findings, it will be helpful to take a step back and explore the underlying predictions and expectations that come from competition theory.

CONCEPT 13.2 REVIEW

1. The self-thinning rule appears to apply to most species of plants; however, there is some variation in slope. What factors about a species' biology are likely to influence the slope of the relationship between population density and population biomass?

2. What does the increase in small granivore populations but the lack of response by populations of insectivorous rodents suggest about the nature of competition between rodents in Brown's Arizona study area?

3. Richard Reader and his colleagues (1994) found no overwhelming evidence that, across a broad geographic gradient, competition among plants varied as a function of productivity. How is it possible that even when resources vary, competition may stay constant?

13.3 Mathematical and Laboratory Models

Mathematical and laboratory models provide a theoretical foundation for studying competitive interactions in nature. Ecologists have used both mathematical and laboratory models to explore the ecology of competition. Models are generally much simpler than the natural circumstances the ecologist wishes to understand and, thus, can lead to an understanding of key principles. Though modelling sacrifices realism, its simplicity offers a degree of control that ecologists would not have in most natural settings. Models also generate hypotheses that ecologists can then test with cleverly designed experiments.

In this section we will present an influential approach to modelling interspecific competition that is an extension of the logistic equation. In our experiences teaching ecology to literally thousands of students over the years, we appreciate that models can be intimidating. However, with patience and practice, a deeper understanding of ecology will emerge. Another benefit to taking the time to understand the following material is that we will present similar models in both chapters 14 and 15, so you might as well learn them now!

Modelling Interspecific Competition

Models of competition typically try to predict one thing: How do competitors influence population growth rates? If we go back to the exponential growth models presented in chapter 12, we see what happens when a population grows without any restriction. One "brake" to this unrealistic situation was introduced in the model of logistic population growth by including a term for intraspecific competition, $(K - N)/K$. This approach to modelling competition is quite simple: take a model we already know (e.g., exponential growth), and add a new term (e.g., representing intraspecific competition). We will now take this approach one step further, and add an additional term representing *interspecific* competition.

Lotka–Volterra Model of Interspecific Competition

The first person to modify the logistic equation to incorporate interspecific competition as an additional brake on population growth was Vito Volterra (1926). Volterra's specific interest was to develop a theoretical basis for explaining changes in the composition of a marine fish community in response to reduced fishing during World War I. Alfred Lotka (1932a) independently repeated Volterra's analysis and extended it using graphics to represent changes in the population densities of competing species during competition. Because of their independent efforts and the great importance of their findings, ecologists have named the resulting equations the "Lotka–Volterra Model of Competition."

Let's retrace the steps of Lotka's and Volterra's modelling exercise, beginning with the logistic model for population growth discussed in chapter 12:

$$\frac{dN}{dt} = r_{max}N\left(\frac{K - N}{K}\right)$$

The logistic equation is great when we have a single species, but by definition interspecific competition involves multiple species. The first step, then, is to express the population growth of multiple species of potential competitors with multiple equations. Here, we will limit our discussion to two species, though this model can be expanded to include more species. Subscripts 1 and 2 refer to model parameters that are characteristic of species 1 or 2, respectively. The basic logistic equation describes change in population growth of species 1 as

$$\frac{dN_1}{dt} = r_{max1}N_1\left(\frac{K_1 - N_1}{K_1}\right)$$

and change in population growth of species 2 as

$$\frac{dN_2}{dt} = r_{max2}N_2\left(\frac{K_2 - N_2}{K_2}\right)$$

where N_1 and N_2 are the population sizes of species 1 and 2, K_1 and K_2 are their carrying capacities, and r_{max1} and r_{max2} are the intrinsic rates of increase for species 1 and 2. In these models, population growth slows as N increases due to increased intraspecific competition. The relative level of intraspecific competition can be expressed as the ratio of current population size to carrying capacity, either N_1/K_1 or N_2/K_2. The assumption here is that resource supplies will diminish as population size increases due to intraspecific competition for resources. We can continue that logic and assume that resource levels can also be reduced by interspecific competition.

This is where the math gets a bit more complicated, but it is important to understand that the logic is simple: the logistic equation works by including a brake on population growth that represents *intraspecific* competition. Lotka and Volterra added an additional brake to represent the effects of *interspecific* competition. The way they achieved this was by introducing new terms called **competition coefficients**, which we define below. The resulting equations are:

$$\frac{dN_1}{dt} = r_{max1}N_1\left(\frac{K_1 - N_1 - \alpha_{12}N_2}{K_1}\right)$$

and

$$\frac{dN_2}{dt} = r_{max2}N_2\left(\frac{K_2 - N_2 - \alpha_{21}N_1}{K_2}\right)$$

In these equations, the rate of population growth of a species is reduced both by intraspecific competition and interspecific competition. The effect of interspecific competition is incorporated into the Lotka–Volterra model by introducing the terms $-\alpha_{12}N_2$ and $-\alpha_{21}N_1$. The terms α_{12} and α_{21} are the competition coefficients and express the interspecific competitive effects of species 1 and species 2. To understand this model, it is important to understand exactly what these competition coefficients represent.

α_{12} is the effect that one individual of species 2 has on the rate of population growth of species 1, while α_{21} is the effect of one individual of species 1 on the rate of population growth of species 2. In other words, these coefficients describe the *per capita* effects of species 2 on the population growth of species 1, and the *per capita* effects of species 1 on the population growth of species 2. Think about this in terms of a trade-off: at a given population size for species 1, it may be possible to add more individuals of species 1 or more of species 2. But, adding an individual of species 1 may not be equivalent to adding an individual of species 2. If, for example, $\alpha_{12} = 3$, this means that adding one individual of species 2 would have the same effect as adding three individuals of species 1 on the population growth of species 1. Species 2 may have a relatively greater impact because it uses resources less efficiently, or perhaps it competes with species 1 by interference (or interference and exploitation). If, on the other hand, $\alpha_{12} = 0.5$, then the competitive effect of one individual of species 2 on the population growth of species 1 is equivalent to one-half of an individual of species one. By multiplying α_{12} and α_{21} by N_2 and N_1, respectively, we move away from *per capita* effects and measure population level effects of one species on another.

There is another way of looking at competition coefficients. Why does the logistic equation cause a reduction in population growth? Let us imagine a scenario in which $r_{max1} = 0.5$, $K_1 = 200$, and $N_1 = 50$. What would dN_1/dt equal if only intraspecific competition were occurring?

$$\frac{dN_1}{dt} = 0.5 * 50\left(\frac{200 - 50}{200}\right) = 18.75$$

In this scenario, species 1 would increase at a rate of 18.75 individuals per unit time. Now let us add interspecific competition by assuming $\alpha_{12} = 3$ and $N_2 = 25$. As you see below, the competition coefficients translate the population size of one species into "population equivalents" of its competitor, based upon its effectiveness as a competitor.

$$\frac{dN_1}{dt} = 0.5 * 50\left(\frac{200 - 50 - (3 * 25)}{200}\right) = 25\left(\frac{200 - 50 - 75}{200}\right)$$
$$= \left(\frac{200 - 125}{200}\right) = 9.375$$

In this example, the presence of an interspecific competitor reduced population growth of species 1 from 18.75 to 9.375 individuals per unit time. This happened because the 25 individuals of species 2 were equivalent to 75 individuals of species 1 in the numerator of the brake in the logistic equation. It might be interesting for you to calculate population growth of species 1 if you instead had 25 more individuals of species 1 rather than 25 individuals of species 2. The difference may help you better understand the importance of the competition coefficient (α_{12}). In fact, we think we will make this a question in Concept 13.3 Review.

The next step is to move from solving the equations for specific combinations of parameter values and toward understanding what general patterns emerge across all possible combinations of parameters. It is here that we find the true value of theory.

Under most circumstances, the Lotka–Volterra model predicts that interspecific competition will cause the local extinction (population size = 0) of one of the two species. We will develop this prediction of *competitive exclusion* more thoroughly in the next section. Although exclusion is often predicted, species coexistence can also occur, particularly if interspecific competition is weaker than intraspecific competition for both species. How do we know this? How can you use this theory to predict that species will co-exist under some conditions, while not under other conditions? The answer to this question involves a bit of mathematical rearrangement, and we begin by determining the conditions under which the population growth of both species is zero.

Populations of species 1 and 2 stop growing when:

$$\frac{dN_1}{dt} = r_{max1}N_1\left(\frac{K_1 - N_1 - \alpha_{12}N_2}{K_1}\right) = 0$$

and

$$\frac{dN_2}{dt} = r_{max2}N_2\left(\frac{K_2 - N_2 - \alpha_{21}N_1}{K_2}\right) = 0$$

We can exclude the $r_{max}N$ situations outside the bracket as not being relevant scenarios, and instead focus on the numerator inside the bracket. Why? If N or $r_{max} = 0$ for either species, it is already extinct! Remember, r_{max} represents the *maximum potential* population growth rate, and all extant populations must at some point have had positive growth. Therefore, we can further simplify the biologically meaningful conditions at which population growth rates will equal 0 to:

$$(K_1 - N_1 - \alpha_{12}N_2) = 0 \text{ and } (K_2 - N_2 - \alpha_{21}N_1) = 0$$

Or, further rearranging these equations, we predict that population growth for the two species will stop when:

$$N_1 = K_1 - \alpha_{12}N_2 \text{ and } N_2 = K_2 - \alpha_{21}N_1$$

Here is some good news: the resulting equations describe two straight lines. These lines follow the format of y = y-intercept + slope(x). We will ultimately want to plot these two lines on the same plane, with N_1 on the x-axis and N_2 on the y-axis. To accommodate this, the first equation will actually follow the format of x = x-intercept + slope(y), where the x-intercept is K_1 and slope is α_{12}. The line will intercept the x-axis where $N_1 = K_1$, and will intercept the y-axis where $N_1 = 0$. When $N_1 = 0$, $K_1 = \alpha_{12}N_2$; therefore, this y-intercept is where $N_2 = K_1/\alpha_{12}$ (fig. 13.12a). The line described by the second equation will intercept the y-axis at K_2 and will intercept the x-axis when $N_2 = 0$, which is when $K_2 = \alpha_{21}N_1$; therefore, the x-intercept occurs where $N_1 = K_2/\alpha_{21}$ (fig. 13.12b). At any point along the line described by the first equation, the growth of population 1 is zero. Likewise, the growth of population 2 is zero for any point along the line described by the second equation. These lines are called **isoclines of zero population growth**.

At every point along these lines, population growth is stopped:

$$\frac{dN_1}{dt} = 0 \text{ and } \frac{dN_2}{dt} = 0$$

Figure 13.12 displays the isoclines of zero population growth for population 1 (*a*) and population 2 (*b*). If we consider first population 1 (species 1), point "A" represents a scenario where there are individuals of both species 1 and species 2. Although there are only 60 individuals of species 1, and this is below carrying capacity (K_1), the point is to the right of the isocline (or above the triangle described by the isocline). This tells us there are more individuals of species 1 than the environment can support (given the number of individuals of species 2 present). As a result, the total population size of species 1 will decrease ($dN_1/dt < 0$), represented by the arrow pointing left toward the isocline. Point "B" represents a scenario where there are again individuals of both species. However, in this scenario, the point is to the left of the isocline (or within the triangle described by the isocline), and the number of individuals of species 2 does not prevent growth of species 1. The population of species 1 will grow ($dN_1/dt > 0$). Point "C" represents a combination of species 1 and species 2 where population 1 will not change ($dN_1/dt = 0$).

If we next consider population 2, point "D" lies within the triangle described by the isocline, and represents a combination of individuals of species 1 and species 2 where there are still sufficient resources for the species 2 population to grow

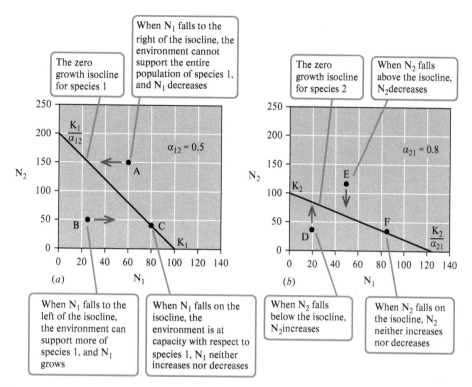

The zero growth isocline for species 1

When N_1 falls to the right of the isocline, the environment cannot support the entire population of species 1, and N_1 decreases

The zero growth isocline for species 2

When N_2 falls above the isocline, N_2 decreases

When N_1 falls to the left of the isocline, the environment can support more of species 1, and N_1 grows

When N_1 falls on the isocline, the environment is at capacity with respect to species 1, N_1 neither increases nor decreases

When N_2 falls below the isocline, N_2 increases

When N_2 falls on the isocline, N_2 neither increases nor decreases

Figure 13.12 Graphical representation of the isoclines of zero population growth derived from the Lotka–Volterra competition models for (*a*) species 1 and (*b*) species 2. N_1 and N_2 (the population sizes of species 1 and 2) are the x- and y-axes for both panels.

($dN_2/dt > 0$). This growth is represented by the vertical arrow, pointing upward toward the isocline. Point "E" lies above the isocline (outside the triangle described by the isocline) and represents a combination where there are more individuals of species 2 than the environment can sustain (given the number of individuals of species 1). Species 2 population will decline ($dN_2/dt < 0$), represented by the arrow pointing downward toward the isocline. And, finally, point "F" represents a combination where population 2 neither grows nor shrinks ($dN_2/dt = 0$).

You will notice in figure 13.12 that N_1 is always on the x-axis, and N_2 is always on the y-axis. This is the conventional way of drawing these isoclines, and will make understanding exclusion and coexistence easier. For now, it is important to remember that changes in population size of species 1 are indicated by left/right movement and changes in species 2 are indicated by up/down movement. *Highlight this in your notes, as forgetting this point is among the most common student mistakes in interpreting these graphs.*

The isoclines of zero growth show how the environment can be filled up or, in other words, show the relative population sizes of species 1 and species 2 that will deplete the critical resources. Looking at the isocline of zero growth for species 1, at one extreme species 1 completely fills the environment and species 2 is absent. This occurs where $N_1 = K_1$. At the other extreme, the environment is saturated entirely by species 2, while species 1 is absent. This occurs where $N_2 = K_1/\alpha_{12}$. In between these extremes, the environment is saturated with a

mixture of species 1 and 2. The graph of the isocline for zero growth for species 2 can be interpreted in a similar way.

When we combine these two graphs, there are four possible arrangements of the isoclines. Putting the isoclines of zero growth for the two species on the same axes allows us to predict if one species will exclude the other or whether the two species will coexist. The prediction depends upon the relative orientation of the two isoclines. The first two arrangements depict conditions where isoclines do not cross (fig. 13.13). Under these conditions, the Lotka–Volterra model predicts that one species will exclude the other. If the isocline for species 1 lies above that of species 2, species 1 will eventually exclude species 2. This exclusion occurs because all growth trajectories lead to the point where $N_1 = K_1$ and $N_2 = 0$ (fig. 13.13*a*). In the figure, red arrows represent the prediction for each species, while the blue arrows represent the vector predicted for species 1 and 2 collectively. Points "A" and "B" predict decrease and increase (respectively) for each species population until the populations reach one of the zero growth isoclines. Combinations of population 1 and population 2 that lie between the isoclines (e.g., point "C") are predicted to have a decrease in the population of species 2, and an increase in the population of species 1. Points lying on either the population 1 or the population 2 zero growth isocline (e.g., points "D" and "E") are predicted to move toward K_1, where N_1 is at carrying capacity and N_2 is 0. Figure 13.13*b* portrays the opposite situation in which the isocline for species 2 lies completely above that of species 1. In this case, all trajectories of population growth lead to the point where $N_2 = K_2$ and $N_1 = 0$.

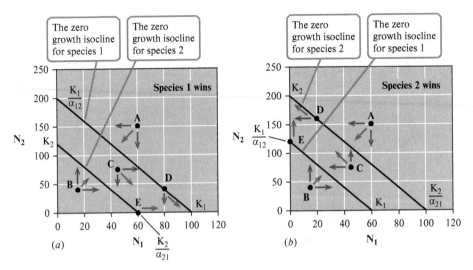

Figure 13.13 Graphical representation of isoclines for zero population growth and the outcome of competition according to the Lotka–Volterra competition model in scenarios where (*a*) the population 1 isocline is above the population 2 isocline, and (*b*) the population 2 isocline is above the population 1 isocline.

Coexistence is predicted only in the situations in which the isoclines cross. However, only one of the two such situations leads to stable coexistence. In figure 13.14*a*, $K_1 > K_2/\alpha_{21}$ and $K_2 > K_1/\alpha_{12}$. A combination of the two populations lying above the isoclines (e.g., point "A") will see a decrease in the size of each population. A combination lying below the isoclines (point "B") will see an increase in the size of each population. In either case, the change in population sizes may move the point toward the intersection of the two isoclines. At this intersection, neither population 1 nor population 2 will change. This represents an equilibrium where the two species can coexist. However, it is not a stable equilibrium. At points lying between the intersections (e.g., points "C" and "D"), the populations will tend toward either K_1 (in the region where the population 1 isocline is above the population 2 isocline), or K_2 (where the population 2 isocline is above the population 1 isocline).

Figure 13.14*b* shows the situation where $K_2/\alpha_{21} > K_1$ and $K_1/\alpha_{12} > K_2$. In this scenario, the population sizes will approach

the intersection of isoclines, starting from any point where neither N_1 nor $N_2 = 0$. No matter what population sizes of species 1 and 2 you start with, they will always end up at the point where the isoclines cross. This represents a stable equilibrium where the populations can coexist. In this situation, each species is limited more by members of its own species than it is by members of the other species. In other words, the Lotka–Volterra model predicts that species coexist when *intraspecific* competition is stronger for both species than is *interspecific* competition. These are relatively restricted conditions for coexistence. Are they likely to be met? Well, two members of the same species will have fully overlapping niche requirements, while two individuals of different species are likely to have only partial overlap. This will, in many cases, cause intraspecific competition to be more intense than interspecific competition.

The Lotka–Volterra model is but one of many different models that describe competitive interactions among species. An alternative theoretical framework was presented by David

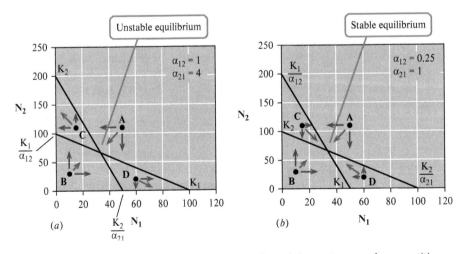

Figure 13.14 The orientation of isoclines for zero population growth and the outcome of competition according to the Lotka–Volterra competition model in scenarios where (*a*) $K_1 > K_2/\alpha_{21}$ and $K_2 > K_1/\alpha_{12}$, and (b) $K_2/\alpha_{21} > K_1$ and $K_1/\alpha_{12} > K_2$.

Tilman (Tilman 1982), commonly referred to as the "resource-ratio" model. The main difference between these two modelling approaches is that Lotka–Volterra's model does not include any biological mechanism and instead is based simply upon changes in population sizes. In other words, it does not include the resources that are actually the subject of competition. Tilman's model is substantially more explicit in terms of resource supply and uptake and is easily expanded to address competition under different conditions. However, a detailed description of his model is beyond the scope of this text. In the simplified version of his model, he finds a result very similar to that of Lotka and Volterra: when interspecific competition is weaker than intraspecific competition, species tend to coexist. This is a central finding of competition theory, and it is supported by the results of laboratory experiments on interspecific competition.

Laboratory Models of Competition

Experiments with Paramecia

G. F. Gause (1934) was among the first to use laboratory experiments to test the major predictions of the Lotka–Volterra competition model. Among the most well known of Gause's experimental subjects were paramecia: small, freshwater, ciliated protozoans. Since protozoans are small, they can be kept in large numbers in a small space, and some of their natural habitats are fairly well simulated by laboratory aquaria. In addition, paramecia feed on microorganisms that can be easily cultured in the laboratory and provided in any concentration desired by the experimenter.

In one of his most famous experiments, Gause studied competition between two species: *Paramecium caudatum* and *P. aurelia*. He wanted to know whether one of these two species would drive the other to extinction if grown together in microcosms where they were forced to compete with each other for a limited food supply. In other words, would you get competitive exclusion or coexistence?

Gause demonstrated resource limitation by growing pure populations of *P. caudatum* and *P. aurelia* in the presence of two different concentrations of their food, the bacterium *Bacillus pyocyaneus*. If food supplies limit the growth of laboratory populations of these paramecia, what kind of population growth would you expect them to show? As you probably expect, Gause observed sigmoidal growth with a carrying capacity at both full- and half-strength concentrations of the food supply (fig. 13.15). When grown in the presence of a full-strength concentration of food, the carrying capacity of *P. aurelia* was 195. When food availability was halved, the carrying capacity of this species was reduced to 105. *P. caudatum* showed a similar response to food concentration, with carrying capacity of 137 and 64 under high and low resource conditions. The nearly one-to-one correspondence between food level and the carrying capacities of these two species provides evidence that, when grown alone, the carrying capacity was determined by intraspecific competition for food. These results set the stage for Gause's experiment to determine whether interspecific competition for food, the limiting resource in this system, would lead to the exclusion of one of the competing species.

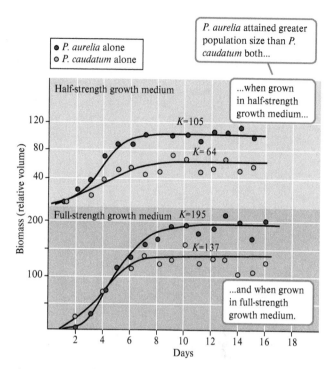

Figure 13.15 Population growth and population sizes attained by *Paramecium aurelia* and *P. caudatum* grown separately.
Data from Gause 1934.

When grown together, *P. aurelia* survived, while the population of *P. caudatum* quickly declined (fig. 13.16). The difference in results obtained at the two food concentrations supports the conclusion that competitive exclusion results from competition for food. At full-strength food concentrations, the decline in the *P. caudatum* population approached exclusion by 16 days, but exclusion was not complete. In contrast, at a half-strength food concentration, *P. caudatum* was entirely eliminated by day 16. What does this contrast in the time to exclusion suggest about the influence of food supply on competition? It suggests that reduced resource supplies increase the intensity of competition.

Competitive Exclusion Principle and Mechanisms of Coexistence

The results of Gause and the predictions of Lotka and Volterra contributed to the development of the **competitive exclusion principle**, which in its simplest form states that "complete competitors cannot coexist" (Hardin 1960). What does this actually mean? Quite simply, it states that if two species that are nearly identical in their basic ecology (feeding, nesting, etc.) come into competition, one of them will persist while the second will go locally extinct. This idea has become a central tenet in ecological theory. However, like all theories, the world is full of exceptions. For example, if you go for a walk in a field, you may find 20 different species of plants growing within a metre of where you are standing. These plants may appear similar in their basic ecology, all needing

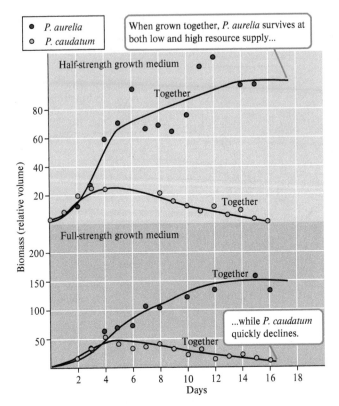

Figure 13.16 Population growth and population sizes attained by *Paramecium aurelia* and *P. caudatum* grown together.

light, nitrogen, and water, and yet they appear to coexist. As we will see in later chapters, one obvious explanation is that competition is not occurring in all communities, and thus competitive exclusion should not occur. For example, in many communities the struggle for existence of individuals within a population may be primarily with extreme environmental conditions rather than interspecific competitors. Populations may also be limited through predation and disease (chapters 14 and 15) rather than competition. Even with these exceptions, we can still find a large number of situations where species coexist *and* competition is occurring among the species. How is this possible if the competitive exclusion principle is true? For the last several decades, ecologists have tried to determine what mechanisms allow for the coexistence of competing species. Many potential mechanisms have been proposed and demonstrated in the literature; here we will discuss only a few.

In the Lotka–Volterra equations, stable coexistence can occur when interspecific competition is low relative to intraspecific competition. What does this mean in the context of the competitive exclusion principle? In short, species are unlikely to cause the extinction of similar species if they don't compete very strongly with them. This leads to the first of our potential mechanisms of coexistence: *spatial heterogeneity in the strength of competition*. As we saw in Gause's work, the speed with which *P. caudatum* went extinct was a function of the amount of food provided. If we think more broadly and consider two species that have overlapping distributions

across a landscape, we could imagine that in some areas resources will be limiting, and in other areas resources may be abundant. A requirement of exploitative competition is that resources must be limiting, and thus in areas of high resource abundance competition will be low or nonexistent, and the species can coexist. In areas of lower resources, competition may be more intense and one species will go locally extinct. The heterogeneity in resources and competition can allow for coexistence on the landscape, even if not within every single patch on the landscape.

Varied resource levels are not the only factor that can cause variation in the strength of competition. Instead, we could imagine that disease, predation, herbivory, extreme climatic conditions, and countless other factors will influence population growth, densities, behaviour, and ultimately the strength (or lack thereof) of competition. If there is heterogeneity on the landscape in any of these factors, we can then expect species coexistence in some locations, even if they compete strongly elsewhere on the landscape.

The second mechanism of coexistence we will discuss here is that of *non-equilibrium conditions*. Competitive exclusion is not instantaneous but, rather, is a process that may take many generations to occur. Both Gause (1934) and Thomas Park (1954, experiment described further below) found that for fast-growing species, exclusion took weeks or even years to occur. What this means is that prior to exclusion, coexistence occurred—it just wasn't stable. In many communities, the environment may be variable and unlikely to ever allow population dynamics to reach equilibrium. At the same time, we must keep in mind that competition can alter the fitness of the individuals that are competing, and this may cause an evolutionary response. Most models of competition, such as Lotka–Volterra, are based upon the assumption that competitive ability is a fixed trait of a species. Park, however, has shown how this isn't true when you have variation in climate.

A third, and related, mechanism of coexistence is *incomplete exploitation of resources*. Two competing species may fail to approach their carrying capacities for a variety of reasons, including predation or disease (as will be elaborated in chapters 14 and 15). The effect of this will be to depress N_1 and N_2, preventing each species from fully using the resources available. In the context of the Lotka–Volterra model, the combination of N_1 and N_2 may perpetually lie below the zero growth isoclines for the two species (e.g., the point represented by "B" in fig. 13.13–13.14).

A fourth mechanism of coexistence is the idea of *competitive equivalence*. We have so far been assuming that, under some conditions, one species is able to displace another, causing competitive exclusion. But in some situations species may be completely equal in their competitive abilities, such that the outcome of competition is not predictable. Although individually one species may win or lose a competitive contest, on average, across a landscape, these species should win and lose an approximately equal number of times. As a result, coexistence in the landscape should occur.

A final mechanism that can permit species coexistence in the face of competition is *variation in competitive ability within a species*. The Lotka–Volterra model assumes that the competition coefficients are fixed values for each species. However, this is not always the case, and often many factors influence competitive abilities, including local environmental conditions and even the genotype of the individuals engaged in competition. Why might climate alter a species' competitive ability? As we discussed in section 2, there are trade-offs in the ability to perform different physiological and ecological functions, including competitive ability. In 1954, Thomas Park published a classic laboratory study demonstrating the role that variation in the local microclimate can have on competitive outcomes.

Tribolium beetles infest stored grains and grain products. Since all of the life stages of *Tribolium* live in finely milled flour, small containers of flour provide all the environmental requirements necessary to sustain a population; as a result, *Tribolium* are ideal subjects of laboratory research. Thomas Park (1954) worked extensively on interspecific competition between two species, *T. confusum* and *T. castaneum*, under varied levels of temperature and humidity. Under hot (34°C) and wet (70% RH) conditions, and without competition, both species were able to maintain populations for the duration of the experiment (fig. 13.17a). However, when grown together under these conditions, *T. castaneum* usually caused competitive exclusion of *T. confusum* (fig. 13.17b). In contrast, cool-dry conditions generally favoured *T. confusum*, with *T. castaneum* going extinct under these conditions even without competition (fig. 13.18). These results demonstrate that competitive outcomes can be influenced by altered climatic conditions. If such

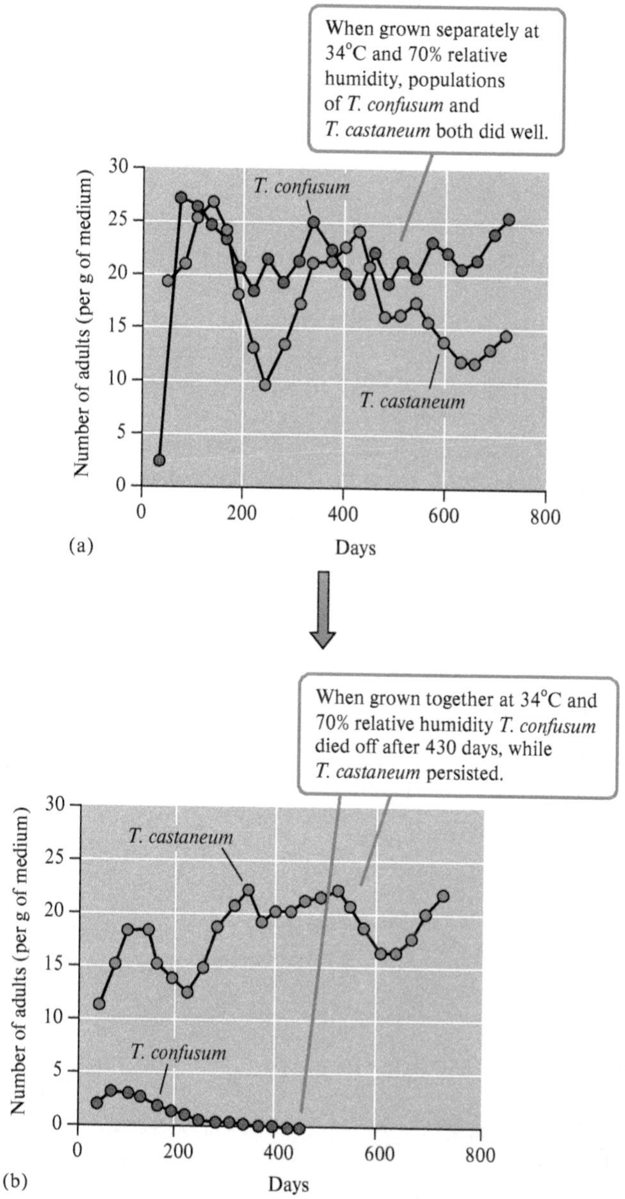

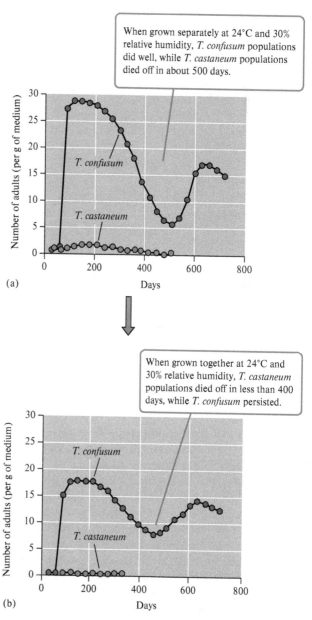

When grown separately at 34°C and 70% relative humidity, populations of *T. confusum* and *T. castaneum* both did well.

(a)

When grown together at 34°C and 70% relative humidity *T. confusum* died off after 430 days, while *T. castaneum* persisted.

(b)

Figure 13.17 Populations of *Tribolium confusum* and *T. castaneum* grown (a) separately and (b) together at 34°C and 70% relative humidity.
Data from Park 1954.

When grown separately at 24°C and 30% relative humidity, *T. confusum* populations did well, while *T. castaneum* populations died off in about 500 days.

(a)

When grown together at 24°C and 30% relative humidity, *T. castaneum* populations died off in less than 400 days, while *T. confusum* persisted.

(b)

Figure 13.18 Populations of *Tribolium confusum* and *T. castaneum* grown (a) separately and (b) together at 24°C and 30% relative humidity.

variation exists in natural settings (think about the temperature and humidity differences you experience sitting under a tree versus sitting in an open field), then coexistence should occur across the landscape.

Next we will discuss how competition can cause evolutionary changes, which may themselves promote coexistence.

CONCEPT 13.3 REVIEW

1. *Paramecium aurelia* and *P. caudatum* coexisted for a long period before competitive exclusion when fed full-strength food compared to when they were fed half that amount. What does this contrast in time suggest about the role of food supply on competition between these two species?

2. In this section, we gave an example of how to calculate the change in population size where $N_1 = 50$, $r_{max} = 0.5$, and $K_1 = 200$ ($dN_1/dt = 18.75$). We then demonstrated how to calculate this change in population size when there is a second species with population size of 25 ($N_2 = 25$), and a competition coefficient (α_{12}) of 3. In this case, $dN_1/dt = 9.38$. Now, calculate dN_1/dt if you instead had 25 more individuals of species 1 rather than 25 individuals of species 2 (i.e., $N_1 = 75$, $N_2 = 0$).

3. Competitive exclusion can, but does not necessarily, occur when species interact. How can competitive equivalence among species prevent exclusion?

4. Using the isoclines in figures 13.13*a* and 13.13*b*, is there any way that predation on one of the two competing species could alter the outcome of competition?

13.4 Competition and Niches

Competition can have significant effects on species coexistence and the direction of evolution. Species have both fundamental and realized niches (chapter 9). The fundamental niche represents the range of conditions under which a species has the capacity to survive, while the realized niche represents the conditions under which that species is typically found. One of the dominant factors causing realized niches to be smaller than fundamental niches is interspecific competition. As we discussed above, a species' competitive ability may vary with environmental conditions, and we might expect a species to be a most effective competitor only under a narrow set of environmental conditions (perhaps near the performance optima; chapter 5). As a result, competition can have short-term ecological effects on species' distributions by restricting them to realized niches, which would likely only include the portion of the fundamental niche (the range of

conditions) under which the species is an effective competitor (fig. 9.23). Under most conditions, these changes will be restricted to the ranges of individual populations based upon resource distributions (ecological shifts). However, in some circumstances, competitive interactions may be strong and pervasive enough to produce an evolutionary response, causing a change in the dimensions of the fundamental niche. In this section, we explore the evidence for the effects of competition in structuring both the realized and fundamental niches of natural populations.

Niches and Competition Among Plants

A. Tansley (1917) conducted one of the first experiments to test whether competition was responsible for the separation of two species of plants on different soil types. In the introduction to his paper, Tansley pointed out that while the separation of closely related plants had long been attributed to mutual competitive exclusion, it was necessary to perform manipulative experiments to demonstrate that this interpretation is correct. That is exactly what Tansley did to account for the mutually exclusive distributions of *Galium saxatile* and *G. sylvestre* (now *G. pumilum*), two species of small perennial plants (fig. 13.19). In the British Isles, *G. saxatile* is largely confined to acidic soils; and *G. sylvestre*, to basic limestone soils.

Tansley conducted his experiment at the Cambridge Botanical Garden from 1911 to 1917, where seeds of the two species of plants were sown in planting boxes (i.e., a **mesocosm**) of acidic and basic soils. The seeds were sowed in single-species plantings and in mixtures of the two species, similar to the experiments of Gause and Park. Both species germinated on both soil types, in both single- and mixed-species plantings (fig. 13.20). Both *Galium* species established healthy populations on both soil types when grown by themselves, and these single-species plantings persisted to the end of the six-year

Figure 13.19 These two species of bedstraw grow predominately on different soil types: *Galium saxatile* (shown here) grows mainly on acidic soils, while *G. sylvestre* (*G. pumilum*) grows mainly on basic limestone soils.

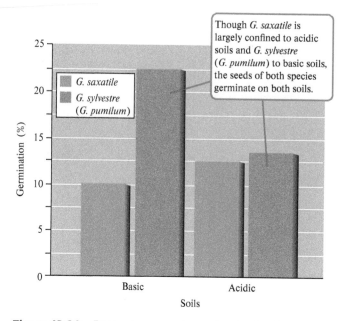

Though *G. saxatile* is largely confined to acidic soils and *G. sylvestre* (*G. pumilum*) to basic soils, the seeds of both species germinate on both soils.

Figure 13.20   Percentage seed germination by *Galium saxatile* and *G. sylvestre* (*G. pumilum*) in basic calcareous soils and acidic peat soil.
Data from Tansley 1917.

study. This indicates that the fundamental niche of each species includes both soil types, and thus observed differences in species distribution cannot be explained purely by physiological limitation. However, as the two species grew in mixed plantings, Tansley observed clear competitive dominance by each species on the soil type in which each species typically grows.

On limestone soils, *G. sylvestre*, the species naturally found on limestone soils, overgrew and eliminated *G. saxatile*, the acidic soil species, by the end of the first growing season. On acidic soils, the relationship was reversed and *G. saxatile* was competitively dominant but competitive exclusion was not completed. Growth by both species was so slow on the acidic soils that it took until the end of the six-year experiment for *G. saxatile* to completely cover the planting boxes containing acidic soils, a density attained by *G. sylvestre* on limestone soils in just one year. Tansley was one of the first ecologists to use experiments to demonstrate the influence of interspecific competition on the niches of species. The fundamental niche of both species of *Galium* included a wider variety of soil types than they inhabit in nature. The results of this experiment suggest that interspecific competition restricts the realized niche of each species to a narrower range of soil types.

Niche Overlap and Competition Between Barnacles

The barnacles *Balanus balanoides* and *Chthamalus stellatus* are restricted to predictable bands in the intertidal zone. We saw in chapter 10 that adult *Chthamalus* along the coast of Scotland are restricted to the upper intertidal zone, while

adult *Balanus* are concentrated in the middle and lower intertidal zones. Joseph Connell's observations (1961a, 1961b) indicate that *Balanus* is limited to the middle and lower intertidal zones because it cannot withstand the longer exposure to air in the upper intertidal zone. However, physical factors only partially explain the distribution of *Chthamalus*. Connell noted that larval *Chthamalus* readily settle in the intertidal zone below where the species persists as adults but that these colonists die out within a relatively short period. In the course of field experiments, Connell discovered that interspecific competition with *Balanus* plays a key role in determining the lower limit of *Chthamalus* within the intertidal zone.

Because barnacles are sessile, small, and grow in high densities, they are ideal for field studies of survivorship. Their exposure at low tide is an additional convenience for the researcher. Connell established several study sites from the upper to the lower intertidal zones, where he kept track of barnacle populations by periodically mapping the locations of every individual barnacle on glass plates. He established his study areas and made his initial maps in March and April of 1954, before the main settlement by *Balanus* in late April. He divided each of the study areas in half and kept members of one of the halves free of *Balanus* by scraping them off with a knife. Connell determined which half of each study site to keep *Balanus*-free by flipping a coin.

By periodically remapping the study sites, Connell was able to monitor interactions between the two species and also monitor the fates of individual barnacles. The results showed that in the middle intertidal zone, *Chthamalus* survived at higher rates in the absence of *Balanus* (fig. 13.21). *Balanus* settled in densities up to 49 individuals per square centimetre in the middle intertidal zone and grew quickly, crowding out the second species in the process. In the upper intertidal zone, removing *Balanus* had little effect on survivorship by the second species because the population density of *Balanus* was too low to compete seriously. Connell's results provide direct evidence that *Chthamalus* is excluded from the middle intertidal zone by interspecific competition with *Balanus*.

How does interspecific competition affect the niche of *Chthamalus*? In the absence of *Balanus*, it can live over a broad zone from the upper to the middle intertidal zones. Using the terminology of Hutchinson (1957), we can call this broad range of physical conditions the fundamental niche of *Chthamalus*. In fact, *Chthamalus* survives better in the middle intertidal zone than in the upper intertidal zone, suggesting that this portion of its fundamental niche is closer to its optimum. However, competition largely restricts *Chthamalus* to the upper intertidal zone, which is a more restricted and marginal portion of the fundamental niche but one that constitutes *Chthamalus's* realized niche (fig. 13.22).

Does variation in interspecific competition completely explain the patterns seen by Connell? At the lowest levels in the lower intertidal zone, *Chthamalus* suffered high mortality even in the absence of *Balanus*. What other factors might contribute to high rates of mortality by *Chthamalus* in the lower intertidal zone? Experiments have shown that this

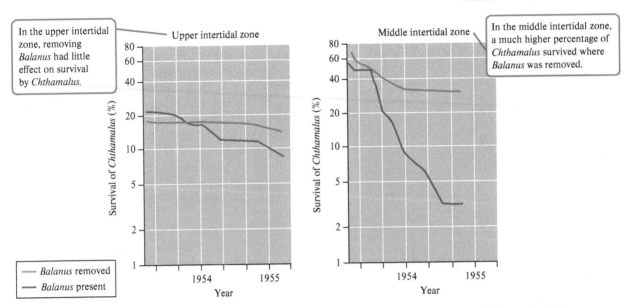

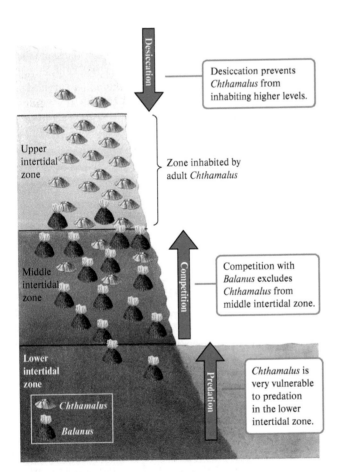

Figure 13.21   A competition experiment with barnacles: removal of *Balanus* and survival by *Chthamalus* in the upper and middle intertidal zones.
Data from Connell 1961a, 1961b.

Figure 13.22   Environmental factors restricting the distribution of *Chthamalus* to the upper intertidal zone.

species can withstand periods of submergence of nearly two years, so it seems that it is not excluded by physical factors. It turns out that the presence of predators in the lower intertidal zone introduces complications that we will discuss in chapter 14 when we examine the influences of predators on prey populations.

Character Displacement

Because competition can reduce an individual's fitness, it can exert selective pressure within a population. If this pressure is strong enough, it can cause evolutionary changes, including (1) selection favouring improved competitive abilities and increasing the rewards of competition to the "winners," or (2) selection favouring reduced niche overlap and reduced competition (and thus the cost of competition). Here, we will focus on evolution of niche divergence (reduced niche overlap) in the face of competition, an evolutionary process called **character displacement**.

The idea of character displacement was presented by Brown and Wilson in 1956, where they suggested that two species that live apart (allopatric) may be nearly identical in form and function, although when these species live together (sympatric) competition will cause the evolution of some meaningful differences between them. Although the idea that evolution can cause a reduction in competition seems to be a modest proposal, it resulted in a prolonged and often inflammatory debate among ecologists. At the core of the debate were broad concerns that competition was being used as a mechanism to explain observed patterns without sufficient data. These issues were presented most succinctly in a paper by Joseph Connell (1980) in which he criticized the invoking of the "Ghost of Competition Past." He pointed out that just because one observes morphological differences between sympatric species does not prove that competition caused those differences. Connell's paper, and others, contributed to concerns about whether there was truly any strong evidence for character displacement in natural systems. To help resolve this issue, Dolph Schluter and John McPhail (1992) compiled a list of criteria that would be necessary to vigorously show that character displacement has occurred:

1. Chance should be ruled out as an explanation for the differences in phenotypes among allopatric and sympatric populations.
2. Phenotypic differences must have a genetic basis.
3. Phenotypic differences in sympatry should be the outcome of evolutionary shifts, and not just the inability of

similar-sized species to coexist (e.g., because of competitive exclusion).

4. Phenotypic differences should be related to differences in resource use.
5. Sites of sympatry and allopatry should not differ in food or major environmental features.
6. There should be evidence that similar phenotypes actually compete for food.

You can see how difficult demonstrating character displacement can be, and you can see the rigours of doing good, strong science. We will end this section by discussing a set of studies that provides one of the best examples of character displacement, starring the threespine stickleback (following the Ecology in Action).

ECOLOGY IN ACTION

The Role of Competition in Forest Management

Competition is not an abstract scientific concept with little relevance to broader society; instead, the effects of competition on the growth of economically important species can result in economic losses in the millions, and maybe even billions, of dollars. The economics of competition have not escaped the attention of farmers, ranchers, fishers, and foresters. Modifying the strengths of intra- and interspecific competition is often an integral aspect of resource management. Canada is home to numerous researchers studying the impacts of competition on crop production and developing management strategies to reduce the economic cost of this ecological process. For example, Paul Cavers of Western University links population ecology and the study of interspecific competition by focusing his research on understanding how weed species use temporal dispersal (a seed bank) to escape competition from crop plants. His work also explores how crop litter may suppress future weed growth. There are numerous other examples of ecological research being applied to agricultural systems; however, here we will focus on another important "crop" grown in Canada: trees.

Approximately 50% of the Canadian land base is covered by forests and woodlands (396 million hectares). On a global scale, Canada is home to nearly 30% of the world's boreal forest and about 10% of all global forests. Within Canada, approximately 767,000 hectares of forest were harvested in 2016, with a total value of nearly $25 billion ($Cdn) (Canada, Natural Resources Canada 2019). In short, Canada is home to a large reserve of forests, and the harvest of this area makes a significant contribution to the national and local economies. The

impacts of forestry on local communities are also important, providing jobs to nearly 317,000 people. At the same time, logging activities dramatically alter the landscape, both through logging itself as well as through construction of roads and movement of large, heavy equipment, causing habitat fragmentation. Forests are also home to countless numbers of species in addition to the commercially desired trees. These can include other harvested species, such as deer and moose, and the much more diverse and abundant group of non-harvested species. These understory plants, mosses, insects, birds, mammals, fungi, and other species represent a large proportion of Canada's biodiversity.

Forests provide much more than wood, and there is often conflict between continued expansion of the forest industry and the conservation of existing forests. The realities of Canadian society are such that forest activities are likely to continue for the foreseeable future; thus, forest biologists and ecologists are actively working on ways to both reduce the environmental damage associated with logging and allow sustainable forestry practices that yield good economic returns. This research has led to changes in tree-planting programs, minimization of soil disturbance, reduced road development, and changes in the methods used for harvesting timber. Our understanding of succession in the boreal forest, a topic we discuss in chapter 18, greatly influences these efforts. Here we focus on efforts to increase yields in regrowth forests (forests that have been logged). In theory, the overall footprint of logging activity can be kept smaller if we are able to increase the yields from the areas we currently harvest. Competition plays an important role in determining yields

Figure 13.23   Open space is found in a lodgepole pine stand after thinning.
Photo by Brett Purdy.

by causing a reduction in the harvestable biomass in Canada's forests.

To understand the impact of competition in stand development and forestry, it is first important to understand what an area that has been recently logged looks like (fig. 13.23). The removal of the tall over-story trees causes a dramatic increase in light reaching the soil floor, and the dead roots and leaf litter often result in a flush of nutrients. In other words, conditions are ideal for the establishment of large numbers of *r*-selected (Pianka 1970) or ruderal (Grime 1979) species (chapter 9). At the same time, forestry practices often involve a replanting effort, generally with economically desirable tree species. As you can imagine, it would be very easy for the ruderal species to rapidly overtake the plantings, causing high tree mortality and slower wood production. In other words, competition by "weeds" can kill and stunt trees desired by the

forest industry, causing a loss of wood production and economic benefit. We use the term "weed" for a specific reason. Weeds are species that a person does not want in a certain location at a certain point in time. If our goal is to maximize harvestable biomass of trees, then species that reduce this are undesired weeds. However, if our goal is instead to maximize biodiversity, then those same species would be desired and, thus, would not be called weeds. In other words, a weed is a human designation of a species based upon what people want; it is not an inherent characteristic of a species.

Foresters have learned how to use the self-thinning law to increase harvestable biomass from forests. Rather than waiting for the trees and other plants to shade out the smaller individuals, unwanted plants can be managed through a variety of practices, including applying herbicide, grazing, burning, and other methods of weed removal. Because all of these practices cost money, it is not surprising that several long-term studies are testing whether vegetation management practices (i.e., reducing interspecific competition) result in increased tree growth and economic benefit. Responses can be large. Full removal of neighbouring vegetation increased growth of lodgepole pine 150% over 15 years in British Columbia; balsam fir in New Brunswick increased 250% after 28 years; and white spruce in Ontario increased by up to 90% over 30 years (Wagner et al. 2006).

Whether these increases in yield offset the cost of the vegetation management itself depends upon market conditions (e.g., price of timber, labour costs, etc.), and is beyond the scope of ecology. What is clear is that applying knowledge of ecological processes such as competition can have significant impacts on the harvest and management of Canada's natural resources.

Numerous species of closely related sticklebacks (*Gasterosteus aculeatus* complex) live in small lakes. Some sympatric species appear to exhibit character displacement such that one species feeds on benthic organisms in the littoral zone, with the second species feeding on planktonic species in the littoral zone. These species are morphologically dissimilar, with the benthic species having few, short gill rakers and a wide gape, and the limnetic species having many, long gill rakers and a narrow gape. Prior work indicates that these phenotypes improve efficiency at capturing specialized food items. What is particularly interesting is that when these species live allopatrically, they demonstrate intermediate phenotypes and feed in both the littoral and benthic zones. Knowing these pieces of natural history, it becomes easy to understand why Schluter would believe this to be a potential case of character displacement. But is it? To answer this, we will work through the list of criteria that Schluter published.

Detailed work on these populations has shown that the phenotypic variations found between sympatric and allopatric populations are greater than expected by chance (criterion #1, Schluter and McPhail 1992), that these phenotypes have a heritable component (criterion #2), and that the phenotype influences feeding (criterion #4). To address the remaining three criteria, Schluter (1994) designed an elegant experiment in which he controlled environmental conditions (addressing criterion #5), tested whether there was competition for food (criterion #6), and tested whether there was directional selection due to sympatry (criterion #3). Schluter reasoned that a prediction of character displacement would be that if you put a species with an intermediate phenotype in the same pond as a limnetic species, there should be directional selection on the species with intermediate phenotype towards a benthic form. In other words, those individuals of the species with intermediate phenotype that were most similar to its competitor (the limnetic species) would have lower fitness than those individuals that were most dissimilar to the competitor.

To see if this actually occurred, Schluter constructed two experimental ponds on the campus of the University of British Columbia. He divided each pond in half, placing individuals of the species with intermediate form into both halves of both ponds. On one half of each pond, he also added individuals of a limnetic species. After three months, he harvested all the remaining fish and was able to measure growth rates. As predicted by theory, individuals of the species with intermediate phenotype that most resembled the competitor species had the lowest growth rates (fig. 13.24). Since these fish all grew under identical environmental conditions, this directional selection cannot be due to any factor other than competition, providing clear and convincing evidence that competition can cause evolutionary shifts in populations over short ecological timescales.

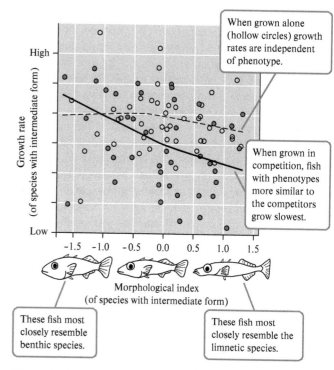

Figure 13.24 Growth rates among the species of stickleback with intermediate phenotype varied as a function of phenotype and the presence of a competitor species.

From Dolph Schluter. 1994. Experimental evidence that competition promotes divergence in adaptive radiation. *Science* 266:798–801, Figure 1. Copyright 1994 AAAS. Reprinted with permission from AAAS.

CONCEPT 13.4 REVIEW

1. What do you think would have happened to the *Galium sylvestre* on acidic soil if Tansley had continued his experiment for a few more years?

2. Why do phenotypic differences among populations need to be partly heritable to believe character displacement may have occurred?

ECOLOGICAL TOOLS AND APPROACHES

Identifying the Mechanisms by Which Plants Compete

Discussions of competition often centre on the consequences of competition, such as reduced fitness, altered population dynamics and distributions, or changes in community structure. However, there is another side of competition that ecologists explore, and this is the study of the mechanisms by which individuals actually compete. This research is most actively pursued by plant ecologists, and we will explore two case studies in which the researchers were trying to identify the factor(s) that influence competitive ability in plants.

Size Does Matter

One of the pioneers in the study of mechanisms of competition among plants is Paul Keddy, formerly of the University of Ottawa. For the past several decades, he and a large number of students and post-docs have published a series of papers designed to understand which plant traits are most closely associated with competitive ability in plants. When

Keddy began his work, the standard experimental approach was to choose one or just a few species and study them intensely. The hope was that by understanding the specific ecology of one species, you would gain an understanding of many species. However, by using this approach the literature rapidly filled with a series of special cases without a clear understanding of general processes across large numbers of taxa. Keddy understood that to make truly broad generalizations about the relationship between plant traits and competitive abilities, he would need to develop a unique methodological approach.

Keddy, along with graduate student Connie Gaudet (Gaudet and Keddy 1988), developed a comparative method in which they could study large numbers of species simultaneously. In their study, they chose 44 species of plants found in the wetlands near the campus of the University of Ottawa. One of the first problems they faced was deciding how to conduct an experiment from which they could determine a standard measure of competitive performance. If they used two species, this would be easy, as they would simply need to put these plants together in a pot or grow them individually. With three species, it is still manageable; pair-wise contests result in only three competition treatment (species A vs. B, A vs. C, B vs. C). However, the number of pair-wise contests is equal to $N(N - 1)/2$, where N is the number of species used. With 44 species, this would result in 946 different competition treatments. Clearly this was not feasible, no matter how many undergraduate assistants they hired! Gaudet and Keddy instead used what is now called a *phytometer*. They chose one species, *Lythrum salicaria*, which would compete against all 44 species. By measuring the growth of the phytometer against the different competitors, they could then establish which species were strong competitors and which were weak. In other words, if *Lythrum* was small in a pot, it was against a strong competitor. It if was large, it was against a weak competitor. By using this approach, Gaudet and Keddy were able to reduce the size of the experiment from 946 treatments to 44. This was a major advance in competition studies, and is widely used today.

Now that they had measures of competitive ability, they needed a way to determine which plant traits were most likely the cause of enhanced competitive ability. To assess this, they measured a variety of traits of each of their study species, such as above- and below-ground biomass, height, leaf shape, canopy diameter, etc. Using a multiple regression analysis (appendix A), they were able to explain most of the variation in competitive abilities of the species (74%) using their measures of plant traits. In other words, if they knew what a plant looked like (quantitatively), they were fairly accurate in predicting its competitive ability. Looking at the traits individually, plant biomass was most strongly associated with competitive ability (fig. 13.25), with the largest plants being the best competitors.

Numerous studies have been conducted since Gaudet and Keddy. Plant size remains one of the major correlates of competitive ability in plants. However, as we see in the next example, size is not the only weapon available to plants.

Perceiving One's Environment Allows for Adaptation

As we saw in section 2, plants exhibit a diverse set of mechanisms that allow them to adapt to changes in their abiotic environment. They do not simply "sit and take it" but instead are able to change their morphologies and physiologies to be better suited to the specific microenvironment they find themselves rooted in. From an evolutionary perspective, this makes sense, as selection will favour those genotypes (plants or animals) with the highest fitness within a population. Using the same logic, there is no reason to believe that plants should just suffer the consequences of competition, with no evolutionary response. Instead, if competition is strong, it should favour a response by the competing plants. Such a response is obvious when animals compete, as you

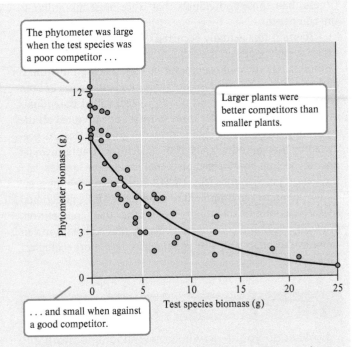

Figure 13.25 Results of Gaudet and Keddy's experiment investigating the relationship between plant traits and competitive ability.

can see one bird attacking another, but what can plants do? The major difference in responses between plants and mobile animals is that plants respond by altered morphology, while many animals respond with movement. However, both approaches can be adaptive and can have a genetic basis. Johanna Schmitt and her students have published a series of papers describing one response in plants: shade avoidance.

Many plants exhibit an interesting trait: in response to low light levels, they grow taller than they would under high light conditions. More specifically, many plants are not just responding to low light levels, but instead they are responding primarily to light that has low levels of red wavelengths (relative to far-red wavelengths). Why? First, we can ask, what makes leaves green? Leaves are green because chlorophyll reflects green light, absorbing red and blue. That means that light that travels through a leaf will have a lower R:FR ratio than light that has not passed through another plant. (Recall the discussion in chapter 7 on plants changing light quality, and the "green twilight" of the forest floor.) This physical fact results in a signal that many plants are able to perceive: if low R:FR light hits their leaves, that means a neighbouring plant is above them. This is potentially bad news for the plant, and a common response is for the lower plant to grow tall quickly, trying to overtop its neighbour. This process is mediated through the phytochrome system, which is extremely sensitive to changes in R:FR ratios and influences a variety of aspects of plant growth and development. Theory predicts that plants that exhibit this shade avoidance response have the potential to access direct sunlight at the top of the canopy, while plants that are unable to exhibit this response are likely doomed to subordinate status where they will receive very little light. Although this response is well documented, and the logic behind its adaptive advantage makes sense, Schmitt realized that tests to determine whether it actually was an adaptive behavioural response were lacking.

Schmitt and colleagues (1995) reasoned that support for the adaptive hypothesis would require demonstrating that elongated plants have higher fitness in a dense stand than unelongated plants in a dense stand. However, Schmitt immediately reached an impasse: if all plants in a population elongate in response to being part of a dense stand, there is no way of measuring the fitness of short and tall individuals! Schmitt and her colleagues devised a novel solution and were among the first researchers to incorporate transgenic plants in ecological research. Schmitt and her colleagues developed two transgenic strains of tobacco (*Nicotiana tabacum*), in which they inserted a gene

from oats, which greatly reduces the shade avoidance response. By doing this, they produced plants that even in deep shade were unable to elongate, and thus they could now begin their experiment. The experimental design was very straightforward, growing plants at low and high density in both monocultures and mixtures. As expected, the transgenic plants exhibited a reduced shade avoidance response at high density. After the plants had experienced significant competition for light, the transgenic plants were smaller than the wild type plants when grown at high density. As we know from Keddy's work, reduced size could further reduce a plant's competitive ability. Small size is also commonly associated with reduced survival and fecundity, and thus this reduction in size likely is a demonstration of a real fitness cost of not possessing the shade-avoidance response.

These results support the adaptive hypothesis. Even more importantly, the creative experimental design by Schmitt and her colleagues shows that by blending molecular biology with traditional approaches in ecology, researchers are able to find answers to questions that previously were impossible to address.

SUMMARY

Species exhibit a diversity of interactions with other species in natural systems. Species interactions can be roughly characterized based upon the effects of these interactions on each of the participants. Competition is a form of interaction in which all individuals are harmed.

13.1 Individuals can compete with other individuals, of their own and of different species, in a number of different ways.

Competition is generally divided into *intraspecific competition*—competition between individuals of the same species—and *interspecific competition*, which is competition between individuals of different species. Competition can take the form of interference competition, which consists of direct aggressive interactions between individuals, or exploitative competition, in which individuals interact indirectly through use of a shared and limiting resource (fig. 13.26).

13.2 Field and mesocosm studies show that resource limitation and competition are widespread.

Experiments under field and semi-natural conditions (mesocosms) show that competition occurs outside the laboratory. Growing plant populations can experience self-thinning, in which the average plant size varies with plant density (fig 13.26). Resource competition among leafhoppers also varies with population density and results in reduced survivorship and

growth of the competing individuals. A field study with song sparrows shows that even in the absence of a clear limiting resource, interference competition can occur, with individual birds choosing to enter or avoid competitive encounters due to the relative experience and health of their potential competitor. Several large reviews show that competition is widespread in natural systems but is not omnipresent. Plant ecologists have investigated the roles of resource availability and habitat productivity on the strength of competition and have developed contrasting models. An intercontinental field experiment was conducted to try to provide a critical test, lending support to the idea that competition is strong across a broad resource gradient.

13.3 Mathematical and laboratory models provide a theoretical foundation for studying competition in nature.

Lotka and Volterra independently expanded the logistic model of population growth to represent interspecific competition. In the Lotka–Volterra competition model, the growth rate of species depends both upon numbers of conspecifics and numbers of the competing species (fig. 13.26). In this model, the effect of one species upon another is summarized by competition coefficients. In general, the Lotka–Volterra competition model predicts coexistence of species when interspecific competition is less intense than intraspecific competition. Competitive exclusion of one species by another is a common outcome of laboratory experiments. However, changes to experimental conditions

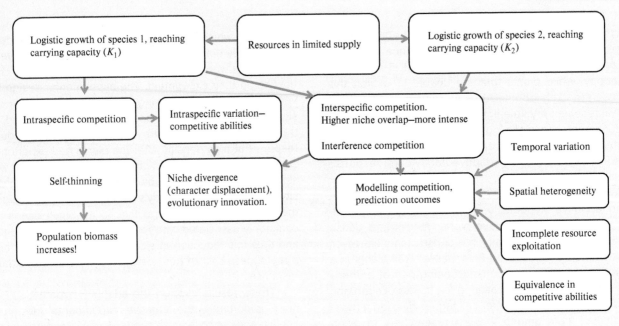

Figure 13.26   Concept map for chapter 13.

can impact the outcome of competition, enhancing the possibility of coexistence. Observations in nature suggest that the competitive exclusion principle is not inviolate. Competition theory suggests that competing species can coexist if there is spatial heterogeneity in resources or in the strength of competition, if the natural system is not at equilibrium, if other factors such as predation or disease (Chapters 14 and 15) prevent full exploitation of resources by the competing species, if there is equivalence in competitive ability among species, or if there is variation in competitive abilities within a species.

13.4 Competition can have significant effects on species coexistence and the direction of evolution.

Field experiments involving a diversity of organisms have demonstrated that competition can restrict the niches of species to a narrower set of conditions than they would otherwise occupy in the absence of competition. Natural selection can lead to divergence in the niches of competing species, a phenomenon called character displacement (fig 13.26). Stringent requirements for a definitive demonstration of character displacement have

limited the documented number of cases. However, studies like those of the threespine stickleback indicate that character displacement does occur under natural conditions. After many decades of work on competition, we can conclude that competition is a common and strong force operating in nature, but not always and not everywhere.

Due to the potential importance of competition to ecologists, foresters, farmers, fishers, ranchers, and other members of society, it is not surprising that the study of competition continues to be a major focus of attention by ecologists. At the core of resolving genuine scientific and societal issues in science is a strong scientific method and creative experimental designs. Ecologists have incorporated theory, laboratory studies, observations, and experiments to develop a body of knowledge about competition. Continued improvements are gained through novel approaches, such as using phytometers in comparative studies and incorporating transgenic plants to address ecological questions. Continued expansion of research methodologies will allow for improved understanding of this topic, which is central to much of ecology and society.

REVIEW QUESTIONS

1. How can the results of greenhouse experiments on competition help us understand the importance of competition among natural populations? How can a researcher enhance the correspondence of results between greenhouse experiments and the field situation?

2. Explain how self-thinning in field populations of plants can be used to support the hypothesis that intraspecific

competition is a common occurrence among natural plant populations.

3. Explain why species that overlap a great deal in their fundamental niches have a high probability of competing. Now explain why species that overlap a great deal in their realized niches and live in the same area probably do not compete significantly.

4. Draw the four possible ways in which Lotka's (1932a) isoclines of zero growth (see fig. 13.13 and fig. 13.14) can be oriented with respect to each other. Label the axes and the points where the isoclines intersect the horizontal and vertical axes. Explain how each situation represented by the graphs leads to either competitive exclusion of one species or the other or to stable or unstable coexistence.

5. How was the amount of food that Gause (1934) provided in his experiment on competition among paramecia related to carrying capacity? In Gause's experiments on competition, *P. aurelia* excluded *P. caudatum* faster when he provided half the amount of food than when he doubled the amount of food. Explain.

6. Discuss how mathematical theory, laboratory models, and field experiments have contributed to our understanding of the ecology of competition. List the advantages and disadvantages of each approach.

7. One of the conclusions that seems justified in light of several decades of studies of interspecific competition is that competition is a common and strong force operating in nature, but not always and not everywhere. List the environmental circumstances in which you think intraspecific and interspecific competition would be most likely to occur in nature. In what circumstances do you think competition is least likely to occur? How would you go about testing your ideas?

8. The study of competition has been filled with contentious debates among researchers, such as was seen in the study of character displacement. Schluter and McPhail (1992) compiled a list of criteria that would be necessary to convincingly show that character displacement had occurred. Develop a similar list of criteria to convincingly show that competition is a strong influence on the current distribution of any particular species.

9. The study of competition can increase economic benefits associated with forestry. This, in turn, has the potential to increase forest activity by making previously marginal forests economically viable for harvest. What role do ecologists have in deciding how their results are used by industry and science, and should ecologists advocate specific policy positions?

10. Discuss potential reasons why we observe competitors coexisting in natural systems when the competitive exclusion principle predicts that this should not occur.

Robert Postma/First Light/Getty Images.

CHAPTER 14   HERBIVORY AND PREDATION

CHAPTER CONCEPTS

14.1 Herbivory is a widespread ecological interaction and has caused the evolution of a diversity of plant defence strategies.

Ecology in Action: Invasive Species and Exploitative Relationships

Concept 14.1 Review

14.2 Prey populations are influenced by food availability, by consumption by predators, and by nonconsumptive effects of predators.

Concept 14.2 Review

14.3 The population consequences of exploitative relationships can be explored with theoretical models.

Concept 14.3 Review

14.4 Prey populations can persist in the presence of predators through the use of display and refugia.

Concept 14.4 Review

Ecological Tools and Approaches: Evolution and Exploitation

Summary

Review Questions

In nature, the consumer eventually becomes the consumed. A willow tree grows during the summer months, consuming mineral resources and water and using the energy from the sun to produce new tissues and biomass. During the winter, when snow covers the ground and there is little else to graze, a moose browses on the twigs and buds of the willow (fig. 14.1), taking stored energy from the plant and adding it to its own reserves to get through the cold winter. Then, a familiar scent catches the moose's attention, and, startled, it runs. A blur of bounding forms dashes after—a pack of wolves in pursuit of their own meal. The moose has experienced this chase many times, each time successfully getting away. This time, however, the moose isn't so fortunate, and, after a fierce struggle, the wolves settle in to feed.

Some of the strongest ecological interactions in natural systems are based upon *exploitation* of one organism by another. Here we find the herbivore (moose) benefiting from the exploitation of the willow, and the predator (wolf) benefiting from the exploitation of the moose. But we must remember that predators do more than just consume their prey. Even when they are unsuccessful in the hunt, and they usually are, they may change the behaviour of their potential prey. They may increase the prey's stress hormones and affect its fitness even when it escapes from the chase. These, too, are the effects of exploitative interactions.

There are somewhere of the order of 350,000 species of photosynthetic plants, and some unknown number of autotrophic bacteria. Combined, these make up the majority of biomass on the plant but just a fraction of the number of species, which means that most species obtain essential resources through some sort of exploitative relationship with other species. It is perhaps, then, no surprise that ecologists have focused on many aspects of these exploitative relationships, using terms like plant–animal interactions, tri-trophic interactions, predator–prey, herbivore–host, disease–host, and others to describe the branch of ecology in which they work.

Predation and herbivory are not the only forms of exploitative relationships we have encountered. Recall from chapter 8 that some social interactions are manipulative, such as the cowbirds that lay eggs in the nests of other species. Parasitic interactions in general are considered exploitative, and they, along with a closely related form of interaction called mutualism, will be discussed in chapter 15. Competition, the subject of chapter 13, occurs due to interference or due to common exploitation of a limiting resource, such as the willows' consumption of soil nitrate. It is important to understand that we are distinguishing common exploitation of a resource from exploitative relationships. In exploitative relationships, one participant exploits another, which is different than competition, where all participants exploit a shared pool of resources. As you will see, this is much more than a subtle difference in wording. And what of detritivores? These organisms are certainly exploitative and ecologically important. However, they feed on organisms that are already dead or dying, so these relationships will generally not shape the species they exploit. In chapters 13–15, we focus on relationships that can affect the evolution of both member species.

Let's consider some of the most common types of exploitation. *Herbivores* consume live plant material but do not usually kill plants. Common herbivores include caterpillars, aphids, and ungulates. **Predators** kill and consume other organisms. Typical predators are animals that feed on other animals—wolves that eat moose, snakes that eat mice, and people that eat cattle.

As clear as these definitions may seem, they are fraught with semantic problems. Once again, we are faced with capturing the full richness of nature with a few restrictive definitions. For instance, not all predators are animals: a few are plants, some are fungi, and many are protozoans. When a herbivore kills the plant upon which it feeds, should we call it a predator? If an ant eats a seed, thereby killing a baby plant, is it a herbivore or a predator? If a herbivore does not kill its food plants, would it be better to call it a parasite? The point of these questions is not to argue for more terminology but to argue for fewer, less restrictive terms. Let's recognize the diversity and continuous variation facing the ecologist, put the restrictive definitions aside for the moment, and recognize what is common to all these interactions: **exploitation** of one organism at the expense of another. We begin by discussing one of the most common ecological interactions: herbivory.

14.1 Herbivory and Plant Defence

Herbivory is a widespread ecological interaction and has caused the evolution of a diversity of plant defence strategies. The effect of a successful predation event on a prey is pretty obvious: death. The effect of an act of herbivory on the host plant is less clear. Herbivory rarely immediately kills a plant, and following the departure of the herbivore, many plants appear to recover very well. Under some conditions, herbivory

Figure 14.1 This moose exploits the twigs and buds of woody plants for the food it needs to survive a cold northern winter. Eventually, wolves may prey upon the moose for their own survival.
© Mark Newman/Science Source.

may actually stimulate plant growth. However, to find out what typically happens, Christine Hawkes and Jon Sullivan (2001) decided to comb through the extensive literature on herbivory and determine whether there were any general patterns. They summarized a total of 81 cases in which growth or reproduction were measured on plants grown with and without herbivory under experimental conditions. When averaged across all species, they found that herbivory typically harms plants through reduced plant growth and reproduction. However, the exact effects of herbivory varied among plant species, with monocots (e.g., grasses) generally increasing their growth rates following herbivory when nutrients were abundant. So, although herbivory is detrimental for a "typical" plant, there will be times in which herbivory may stimulate growth. We will look first at how herbivory may reduce growth, not of plants but of algae, in streams. We will then discuss some more complicated effects of herbivory in subarctic wetlands.

A Herbivorous Stream Insect and Its Algal Food

The herbivorous larval stage of the caddisfly *Helicopsyche borealis* (order Trichoptera) lives in streams across most of North America. It is most notable for the type of portable shelter it builds as a larva. The larvae cement sand grains together to form helical portable homes that look like small snail shells. In fact, the species was originally described as a freshwater snail. Larval *Helicopsyche* graze on the algae and bacteria growing on the exposed surfaces of submerged stones. This feeding habit requires that *Helicopsyche* spend considerable time out in the open, where they would be far more vulnerable to predators were it not for their case.

Gary Lamberti and Vincent Resh (1983) found that larval *Helicopsyche* grow and develop through the summer and fall, attaining densities of over 4,000 individuals per square metre

in Big Sulphur Creek, California. At this density, they make up about 25% of the total biomass of benthic animals. A consumer that reaches such high population densities clearly has the potential to reduce the density of its food supply. However, while *Helicopsyche* is the most abundant herbivore in the stream, there are others. So how could Lamberti and Resh know if *Helicopsyche* was affecting algae, and how could they separate the effect of this one species from the combined effects of all herbivores?

The researchers used an exclusion experiment to test for the effect of *Helicopsyche*, specifically on its food supply. They placed unglazed ceramic tiles in two 3-by-6 grids of 18 tiles each. One grid was placed directly on the stream bottom, while the other was placed on a metal plate supported by an upside-down J-shaped metal bar. This arrangement raised the tiles 15 cm above the bottom but still 35 cm below the stream surface. This allowed colonization of the raised tiles by algae and most invertebrates while preventing colonization by *Helicopsyche*. *Helicopsyche* could not colonize the tiles because their heavy snail-shaped cases confine them to the stream bottom. To reach the tiles, *Helicopsyche* would have to crawl up the J-shaped support bar, out of the water, and then back down; most other invertebrates could colonize by either drifting downstream with the current or by swimming to the raised tiles. Lamberti and Resh coated the above-water parts of the bar with an adhesive to prevent adult *Helicopsyche* from crawling down to the tiles to deposit their eggs. This design was effective at excluding *Helicopsyche* while allowing large numbers of other invertebrates to colonize the raised tiles (as well as the tiles on the stream bed).

The results of this experiment show that *Helicopsyche* reduce the abundance of their food supply. Figure 14.2 shows that the tiles without *Helicopsyche* supported higher abundances of both algae and bacteria. The large effect of *Helicopsyche* on their food supply is apparent from paired photos of the experimental and control tiles at the beginning and the end

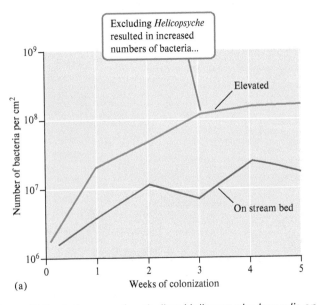

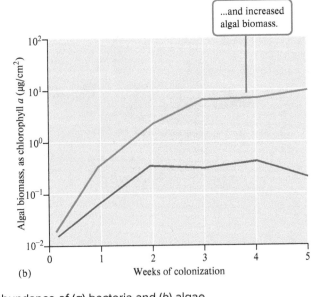

Figure 14.2 Influence of excluding *Helicopsyche borealis* on abundance of (*a*) bacteria and (*b*) algae. Data from Lamberti and Resh 1983.

(a)

(b)

Figure 14.3 Effects of excluding *Helicopsyche borealis* on benthic algal biomass: (*a*) two sets of tiles at the beginning of the experiment, exclusion tiles in foreground; (*b*) same tiles five weeks into the experiment.
(a), (b) Gary Lamberti.

of the experiment (fig. 14.3). This experiment supported an intuitive outcome of herbivory—that the herbivore can reduce the **standing biomass** of the primary producer (here algae, rather than a plant). The next example will demonstrate that the response of a primary producer can be more complicated if we also consider productivity.

Snow Goose Grazing and a Subarctic Salt Marsh

Until his death in 2009, Bob Jefferies, of the University of Toronto, was a global leader in the study of the ecological consequences of herbivory in natural systems. For decades Jefferies brought a team of students to the subarctic wetlands at La Pérouse Bay, Manitoba. La Pérouse Bay is at the northern limit of the boreal forest, just east of Churchill, Manitoba. These wetlands are the summer home to large numbers of herbivores, whose feeding behaviour has the ability to change the landscape. When we think of herbivores, it is often images of bison, caterpillars, and deer that come to mind. However, in La Pérouse Bay and other wetlands of the North, geese are the

dominant herbivores, having the potential to completely devegetate areas (fig. 14.4).

Within La Pérouse Bay, there is a large expanse of marsh dominated by two plant species, *Puccinellia phryganodes* and *Carex subspathacea*. These two species alone make up nearly 95% of all plant biomass in the marsh, and thus changes in their growth indicate changes in the overall biomass production of this community. In 1979–80 there were approximately 4,000 nesting pairs of snow geese, along with many more non-breeding geese. The birds graze heavily, often leaving only 1–2 cm of vegetation unclipped (Cargill and Jefferies 1984). One of the first questions that Jefferies and his colleagues asked was quite simple: What is the effect of this grazing on the growth of these plant species? As he was to find out over several decades of research, the answer isn't as simple as "negative."

To determine the effects of geese grazing on plant growth, Jefferies and colleagues created areas of the marsh that were protected from the herbivores. By building a series of 5 × 5 m *exclosures* out of wood and chicken wire, they were able to keep geese out of their study plots. Some of these exclosures were temporary, and some were permanent, allowing them to

(a)

(b)

Figure 14.4   (*a*) Geese are the dominant herbivores in many northern wetlands, such as this marsh at La Pérouse Bay, Manitoba. (*b*) Exclosures can be used to experimentally manipulate grazing intensity.

(a), (b) David Hik.

determine both the short- and longer-term consequences of grazing on plant growth. They then measured plant biomass inside and outside the exclosures over the course of the growing season for two years. No one was surprised when they found that grazing reduced above-ground biomass. What was surprising, however, was that when they added up all the biomass production from the plots over the entire summer, taking into account the amount of biomass the geese ate, the grazed plots actually had higher primary productivity than the ungrazed ones! Jefferies found that herbivory increased plant productivity, even though standing biomass was reduced. This is an example of **overcompensation**, where growth following herbivory is greater than growth without herbivory.

Overcompensation may seem very counterintuitive. How can plant productivity increase when plants are being consumed? Jefferies and his students have explored this issue, finding that this pattern is much more complex than it first appears. David Hik (now at Simon Fraser University) and Jefferies conducted an experiment designed to understand why overcompensation occurs (Hik and Jefferies 1990). Researchers quickly zeroed in on three ideas that could influence plant recovery. (1) Not all grazing is of the same potential impact to the plant. Minor grazing could be beneficial if herbivores consumed dead/dying parts of the plant, increasing light availability to the rest of the plant. At high levels of herbivory, however, herbivores may consume the whole plant, with negative impact. (2) Grazers don't just eat; they also defecate. As a result, the geese may be converting nitrogen into a form that plants can take up, stimulating growth. (3) Plants may be more vulnerable to grazing at different times of the year, and early-season grazing may give plants the most opportunity to recover.

Hik and Jefferies conducted a series of experiments where they manipulated the duration of grazing and altered the timing of herbivory. To do this, they used *enclosures*, rather than exclosures. The difference here is that they added geese inside

the enclosures, permitting them to graze for known durations during different times of year, thereby controlling the level of herbivory experienced by the plants. To manipulate nutrient remobilization, they also removed feces by hand from several plots and left them behind in others (yeah, ecology can be glamorous).

Hik and Jefferies found that overall productivity increased in response to light grazing and when feces were present. This response was greatest early in the summer and absent later. When the plants were grazed heavily, growth was reduced. When feces were removed, growth was reduced. When herbivory happened late in the season, plants couldn't recover. In short, overcompensation only occurred if a very narrow set of conditions were met. If these conditions were not met, herbivory reduced not only standing biomass but also primary productivity.

One may think of this as a nice story about the balance of nature and how these geese are able to coexist with their food resources, increasing the production of the food they depend upon, with all members living happily ever after. Unfortunately, nature is not so simple and not always so harmonious. The "balance" that may have once existed between the geese and their food has now mostly collapsed. Peter Kotanen, from the University of Toronto, and Jefferies have shown that there has been a significant shift in the dynamics of this plant–animal interaction in much of the subarctic wetland (Kotanen and Jefferies 1997). At the heart of this change has been rapid population growth of geese: the numbers of breeding pairs of lesser snow geese at La Pérouse Bay increased from fewer than 2,000 in 1968 to over 20,000 in 1990. This population growth has a variety of causes, though it is primarily driven by decreased mortality on the geese's wintering grounds in the United States, due to increased food availability in agricultural fields and to reduced hunting activity. As you might imagine, this population growth has resulted in an increase in the intensity of grazing in the breeding grounds. Knowing what we do from the work of Hik and Jefferies, it should come as no surprise that during this period there has been nearly a 65% decrease in the abundances of *Puccinellia* and *Carex*, the two dominant plant species in the late 1970s. In their place have emerged carpets of moss, plants the geese do not eat, and large expanses of completely devegetated soil. In other words, changes in human behaviour and agricultural practices thousands of kilometres away have significant consequences for a very local ecological interaction. One consequence for the snow geese may be that, although food-rich wintering grounds may have allowed the population to grow, they may ultimately become starved of food in summering grounds.

These studies by Jefferies and his colleagues show that herbivory isn't inherently bad for plant growth. Instead, its effects will depend upon a variety of issues, such as nutrient relations, plant phenology, and the intensity of the grazing event. The potential for overcompensation notwithstanding, herbivory is widespread and often carries negative consequences for the plant. It will probably come as no surprise to you that natural selection has favoured a variety of traits that allow plants to defend themselves against herbivory. Plants are passive recipients of whatever ecological challenges they face. As you will see next, a diversity of defences are actively and passively employed by plants.

Plant Defences

Plants are subject to natural selection, just like every other living thing on this planet. If being eaten reduces the reproductive output and/or survival of an organism, there can be selection for traits that make the individual less likely to be eaten (*resistance*) or reduce the harm associated with being

eaten (*tolerance*). For example, imagine there is a caterpillar that can eat only one species of plant. When it finds the plant, it will consume a large portion of the leaves, reducing the plant's photosynthetic capacity and potential to produce seeds. Some aspects of this interaction are likely related to the plant's genotype; and with genetic variation in the plant population, there can be variation in the fitness consequences of this association. Some plants may produce a toxin that reduces feeding, others may grow smaller and be harder to find, while still others may produce leaves of low nutritive value, decreasing the cost of replacement. These are all examples of possible adaptations that increase the resistance to exploitation or increase the ability of the organism to tolerate exploitation. As you might recognize, these changes would then have impacts on the herbivore, potentially resulting in a co-evolutionary response (see Ecological Tools and Approaches).

In this section we will discuss common mechanisms of plant defence. We will also discuss some evolutionary consequences of long-term herbivore–host relationships, further demonstrating that ecological interactions have the potential to profoundly alter species, populations, and communities.

We have already discussed how plants have high C:N ratios (chapter 7), resulting in a low nutritive value for animals that need nitrogen for growth and reproduction. Maintaining relatively low nutritional value leaves may itself be seen as one defence against herbivores, though certainly herbivory is not the only cause of a plant's C:N ratios. One consequence of poor nutrition in any given leaf is that for a herbivore to obtain sufficient nitrogen for its own growth, it will need to consume large amounts of plant tissues. As a result, herbivores are forced to come in contact with many other defences employed by the plants.

ECOLOGY IN ACTION

Invasive Species and Exploitative Relationships

One of the most ecologically damaging activities that humans regularly engage in is the intentional and accidental release of organisms into novel habitats. These activities occur through the introduction of new horticultural plants, in ballast water released near shore, as contaminants to imported agricultural products, and as simple stowaways in our cars and backpacks as we leave our houses for cottages or decide to see how long it really takes to travel from St. John's to Nanaimo. Most of these introduced (i.e., exotic or non-native) species will quickly flounder before they establish a sustainable population. Perhaps the new home is too hot, too cold, or too crowded. Others will establish and maintain small populations, being simply another minor component of a complex ecological system. In fact, nearly one-third of all vascular plant species in Canada are non-native. A small subset of introduced species will not

only establish populations but rapidly expand, reducing the abundance and diversity of the pre-existing native species. These invasive species are an issue of global concern (Mack et al. 2000) and are the second leading contributor (after habitat loss) to declining biodiversity. Ecologists throughout the world are actively pursuing research designed to understand both the causes of species invasion and potential ways to control their spread.

What allows introduced species to establish in novel habitats? What allows some introduced species to become invasive and spread? In a classic view of ecological systems, ecologists have often thought of all species as being essential components of the system, where bending one part will cause bends elsewhere. In this model, the community was also viewed as closed, where all the available niches were full and competitive exclusion (chapter 13) would keep out new species. We realize now that this model was woefully incorrect. Introduced species are able to establish in nearly every ecological community across the planet. How is this possible? Why don't the regular processes of exploitation and resource limitation keep these species in check? We will discuss here the "enemy release hypothesis," one of several explanations for the spread of species into new communities.

One of the interesting findings that researchers have uncovered is that many species that spread in novel habitats are typically relatively minor members of the community in their native environments. The enemy release hypothesis suggests that at home, population growth is reduced due to exploitation. In new habitats, these species do not bring with them their native predators and herbivores, nor are they eaten extensively by the predators and herbivores in their new home; thus, their populations grow, restricted only by resources. Making things even worse is that with enemy release, organisms may grow a bit bigger and have increased vigour, making them better able to compete with the native organisms. In other words, by not bringing along their pests, these new species do not suffer the costs of exploitation and may actually accrue the benefit of increased competitive ability. But does this really occur?

Peter Kotanen (see earlier in this chapter) and his colleague Anurag Agrawal were skeptical of this idea. They conducted a large field experiment at the Koffler Scientific Reserve at Jokers Hill, north of Toronto (Agrawal and Kontanen 2003). They planted seeds of 30 plant species into a plowed field, measuring rates of herbivory on each plant at the end of the growing season. Making this study particularly well designed is that these species were divided into different pairs of congeneric species, such that within each pair, one species was native to Jokers Hill while its congener was introduced. By using this taxonomic pairing, they controlled for a variety of confounding effects that could be associated with differences among species. In contrast with the enemy release hypothesis, they found that leaf damage by herbivores was about 40% higher on exotic species compared to their native relatives! Importantly, they also found that overall levels of herbivory were low (around 6% leaf damage). They suggest that not only is the pattern opposite to that which was predicted, the low magnitude of leaf damage suggests that herbivory itself is not a significant stressor on most of the species they tested. In other words, if herbivory doesn't hurt plants too much, being released from herbivory is not likely to be of much benefit.

A similar result was found by Elizabeth Elle's research group (Stastny et al. 2005). While Michael Stastny was an undergraduate student with Elle at Simon Fraser University, they conducted an experiment in Switzerland with the plant *Senecio jacobaea,* which is native to much of Europe.

(a)

Figure 14.5
*(a) Senecio jacobaea;
(b) Longitarsus
jacobaeae.*
(a), (b) Ken Puliafico.   (b)

Senecio has been introduced and has become invasive to rangelands throughout North America, Australia, and New Zealand. The researchers were interested in whether the genotypes that invaded new habitats were less susceptible to damage by the specialist herbivore *Longitarsus jacobaeae,* a flea beetle (fig. 14.5), than the genotypes commonly found in the native habitat. To do this, they collected seed from eight populations of *Senecio* from their introduced and native ranges. The plants were then planted into a meadow in Switzerland, where *Senecio* and *Longitarsus* naturally occur. They measured herbivory and growth of the plants throughout the growing season. They found that the introduced genotypes grew larger, had greater reproductive output, *and* were eaten more than the native genotypes. These results also are not consistent with the enemy release hypothesis. The researchers suggest that the increased vigour of the introduced species allows them to tolerate the increased levels of herbivory, which, as in the Agrawal and Kotanen study, are thought not to be of a magnitude great enough to reduce fitness. This is another example of the importance of both understanding the diversity of ecological interactions that individuals encounter, and not assuming that increased levels of herbivory will necessarily reduce plant fitness.

These findings have significant implications for the management of invasive species in natural and managed systems. Invasive species can be managed in a variety of ways, including ignoring them, removing them mechanically (i.e., weeding), using herbicides, and using biocontrol. Biocontrol is the deliberate introduction of some agent (herbivore, pathogen, etc.) that will exploit an invasive species, reducing its population size. You can see that the ideas presented in this chapter lend some support to this approach:

under some conditions, exploitation can reduce population growth. However, you likely also recognize that information in this chapter raises significant questions about how effective these programs will be and whether there will be any nontarget effects. Nontarget effects are changes to species other than the intended invasive target. It may come as no surprise that there is substantial divide among ecologists as to whether biocontrol is an environmentally responsible, or reckless, idea (Louda et al. 2003). On one side, proponents of biocontrol programs point out that once an agent is identified, it is inexpensive to use, self-replicates, and reduces the need to use potentially toxic compounds. There is also substantial evidence that biocontrol can be effective in reducing populations of many species.

In a review of the effects of herbivores on plant population growth, John Maron and Elizabeth Crone (formerly of the University of Calgary) report that biocontrol agents have a seven times stronger negative effect on plant population growth than do native herbivores (Maron and Crone 2006). Clearly, biocontrol agents can be effective in reduced plant growth. However, there are serious ecological risks associated with using biocontrol agents (Louda et al. 2003), including the following: (1) there is substantial evidence indicating that relatives of the target species are also likely to be attacked, including endangered native species; (2) biocontrol agents have undesired cascading effects on the trophic dynamics of ecological communities; and (3) in many cases, exploitation is not of a magnitude sufficient to cause declines in abundance of the invasive species. In other words, if, as in the examples above, enemy release is not the driver of a species' spread, it is unlikely that the introduction of an enemy will slow it down. Finally, there is often a difference of goals, with many biocontrol agents designed to tackle agricultural pests, where success is measured as reduction in weed densities and increased crop yield, while many ecologists are concerned about what happens when these organisms spread outside the fields and into native communities.

Understanding the causes of species invasion, as well as mechanisms of control, is a critical issue for the current and next generation of ecologists. By identifying which aspects of a species' life history limits, or encourages, population growth, one may be able to design more appropriate control measures. However, it is clear that the world isn't as simple as saying that enemies control growth. The outcome of one interaction is dependent upon other interactions, and only by understanding these connections can we hope to learn how to control species invasion.

Many plants also possess a variety of morphological defences, such as thorns, which deter herbivores (fig. 14.6). These defences are generally small and nonlethal—an irritant rather than a real risk to the large herbivores they deter. Why do thorns reduce herbivory? As we discussed previously (chapter 7), animals engage in some sort of optimal foraging in which they increase energy (or nutrition) uptake per unit time. To eat a thorny plant, the animal will need to move its head and body more precisely, which slows down the rate of feeding. It may be more energetically advantageous for the animal to keep walking and find a less prickly bush than to stop walking and feed slowly. In other words, thorns work as defences because plants are able to use animal behaviour to their own advantage.

Although morphological defences are widespread among plants, plants also contain a variety of chemical defences that can be roughly divided as (1) toxins, and (2) digestion-reducing substances. Toxins are chemicals that kill, impair, or repel most would-be herbivores. The compounds are widely used by humans as medicines, and include such compounds as cocaine, morphine, digitalis, and others. Digestion-reducing substances are generally phenolic compounds, such as tannins, that bind to plant proteins and inhibit their breakdown by digestive enzymes. This in turn further reduces the value of plants as food for the herbivore. Humans are familiar with tannins as the bitter taste one gets when eating an unripe banana, or as the dark coloration in a cup of Earl Grey tea.

Chemists have isolated thousands of toxins from plant tissues, and the list continues to grow. The great variety of plant

Figure 14.6 Herbivores must overcome the wide variety of physical and chemical defences evolved by plants.
©Chestertonjp/Getty Images RF.

toxins defies easy description and generalization. However, one interesting pattern is that more tropical plants contain toxic alkaloids than their temperate counterparts. Despite these higher levels of chemical defence, herbivores appear to remove approximately 11%–48% of leaf biomass in tropical forests but only about 7% in temperate forests. These higher levels of herbivore attack on tropical plants suggest that natural selection for chemical defence is more intense in tropical plant populations. At risk of muddying the waters by introducing concepts from future chapters, some plants are defended by toxins produced by other organisms. The leaves of many plant species are invaded by endophytic fungi. The fungi produce compounds that deter herbivores. This may be seen as a mutualistic relationship (chapter 15) when it modifies an exploitative relationship (herbivory): the plant benefits from the fungus by its protection against the herbivore, while the fungus benefits from photosynthetic products of the plant. When herbivory pressure is low, the plant–fungus relationship may be better characterized as parasitic—but more on parasitism in the next chapter.

Plant chemical defences often work against some herbivores but not all. Just as herbivory puts selective pressures on plants, resulting in the variety of defensive adaptations described above, defensive adaptions put selective pressure on herbivores, resulting in novel adaptations that allow them to exploit the plants. The tobacco plant uses nicotine, a toxic alkaloid, to repel herbivorous insects, most of which die immediately upon ingestion. However, several insects specialize in eating tobacco plants and manage to avoid the toxic effects of nicotine. Unfortunately, humans cannot do the same, yet some keep trying. Some of the specialist insects avoid such harm by excreting nicotine, while others convert it to nontoxic molecules. Similarly, toxins and repellents produced by plants in the cucumber family repel most herbivorous insects but attract the spotted cucumber beetle. This beetle is a specialist that feeds mainly on members of the cucumber family. Some specialized herbivores go even further by using plant toxins as a source of nutrition. Even more amazing is that some species, such as the monarch butterfly and the dogbane leaf beetle, are able to sequester plant toxins, using these as chemical deterrents against their own natural enemies, such as predators. Adaptations that allow herbivores to feed on these toxic plants allow them to exploit resources for which there is limited competition from other herbivores.

As we have seen with competition and foraging, plants are able to alter their physiology and morphology in response to a change in their environment, such as a pulse of nutrients or the presence of a competitor. Plants show similar plasticity in response to herbivores. Many morphological and chemical defences are **constitutive defences**, produced continuously, independent of what happens to a plant. Many, however, are also **induced defences**, where concentrations of defensive chemicals (or even morphological defenses) increase rapidly in response to the first indication of herbivore damage. Such induced defences make sense in the context of the theory of allocation, where allocating energy and limited resources to defences when insects are not around seems maladaptive. It seems likely that the benefit of producing constitutive or induced defences will depend upon the likelihood of a plant's being attacked.

The world may appear green to us, but for a herbivore not all that is green is food. Plant defences and the adaptations of herbivores that overcome those defences are complex.

CONCEPT 14.1 REVIEW

1. In many natural communities, there are a number of herbivore species feeding simultaneously. How did Lamberti and Resh determine the specific effects of *Helicopsyche* on algal biomass?

2. How can geese cause an increase in productivity but a decrease in standing biomass in La Pérouse Bay?

3. Plants can possess traits that make them resistant to herbivores or tolerant of herbivory. Are the same plant traits likely to confer both of these abilities? Why?

14.2 Impacts of Predators on Prey Populations

Prey populations are influenced by food availability, by consumption by predators, and by nonconsumptive effects of predators. In the previous section we saw how herbivores can affect the plants they feed upon, with the plants also impacting the herbivores. In this section we move to understanding the interactions between predators and their prey. We will begin with an overview of a landmark experiment led by Canadian researchers. We then discuss more general aspects of effects predators can have on prey populations, including both consumptive and nonconsumptive effects. We now look to the north, where the population sizes of many animals appear to cycle, sparking decades of ecological research on predation.

Cycles of Abundance in Snowshoe Hares and Their Predators

Population cycles are well documented for a wide variety of animals living at high latitudes, including lemmings, voles, muskrats, red fox, arctic fox, ruffed grouse, and porcupines. We have already seen (in chapter 10) how periodic outbreaks of voles lead to local increases in the abundance of avian predators due to *numerical responses* by owls and hawks (Korpimäki and Norrdahl 1991). And in chapter 11 we talked about how Adolph Murie was hired to determine what effect wolves were having on Dall sheep populations in Alaska. There has been a long history in ecology of studying how predation would alter prey populations.

One of the best-studied cases of animal population cycles is that of the snowshoe hare (*Lepus americanus*) and the lynx (*Lynx canadensis*), one of the snowshoe hare's chief predators

Figure 14.7 Lynx–hare interactions have served as a model system for the study of the effects of predation on population dynamics.
FLPA/Alamy Stock Photo.

(fig. 14.7). The population cycles of these two species are especially well documented because the Hudson Bay Company kept trapping records during most of the eighteenth, nineteenth, and twentieth centuries. Drawing on this unique historical record, ecologists were able to estimate the relative abundances of Canada lynx and snowshoe hare over a period of about 200 years. That record, shown in figure 14.8, demonstrates a remarkable match in the cycles of the two populations.

The regularity of the pattern struck the imagination of many ecologists, and several hypotheses were proposed to explain these and other cycles among northern populations. One of the first ideas was from Charles Elton (1924), who thought the system was driven by plants, not predators. He proposed that variation in intensity of solar radiation—associated with sunspot cycles—altered plant growth, directly affecting snowshoe hares, and that lynx populations then responded to

the changing abundance of the snowshoe hare, their main prey. The sunspot hypothesis was rejected by D. MacLulich (1937) and P. Moran (1949), who showed that sunspot cycles do not match snowshoe hare population cycles.

The second group of hypotheses, which Lloyd Keith (1963) referred to as "overpopulation theories," suggested that periods of high population growth are followed by (1) decimation by disease and parasitism, (2) physiological stress at high densities leading to increased mortality as a consequence of nervous disorders, and (3) starvation due to reduced quantity and quality of food at high population densities. An alternative to the overpopulation hypothesis was that population cycles are driven by predators. According to this hypothesis, predators increase in number in response to increasing prey availability and then eventually reduce prey populations.

Keith observed that none of these hypotheses completely accounts for population cycles in snowshoe hare and other northern populations. He went on to say that "the 10-year cycle is not likely to become better understood by further theorizing. Clearly the present need is for comprehensive long-term investigations by a diversified team of specialists" (p. 116). As you will see, population cycles of predators and prey occur through a number of co-occurring mechanisms.

The Role of Food Supply

Snowshoe hares live in the boreal forests of North America, an area dominated by a variety of coniferous and deciduous trees (chapter 2). Within the boreal forest, snowshoe hares associate with dense growths of understory shrubs, which provide both cover and winter food, the most critical portion of the snowshoe hare's food supply.

Hares can "breed like rabbits," with estimated geometric rate of increases (chapter 12) during the growth phase of a hare population cycle averaging as high as 2.0. In other words, snowshoe hare populations can double in size each generation. As a result of potentially high growth rates, snowshoe hares have the potential to reduce the quantity and quality of their food supply.

Local population densities are highly dynamic. Keith cites 100-fold fluctuations in snowshoe hare densities in some areas and found 10- to 30-fold fluctuations to be common. Snowshoe hares spend the long northern winter (six to eight months) browsing on the buds and small stems of shrubs and tree saplings. Over the winter, each hare requires about 300 g of these stems each day. In some areas, however, snowshoe hares have been observed to remove over 1,500 g of food biomass per day. Feeding at these rates, one population of snowshoe hares reduced food biomass from 530 kg per hectare in late

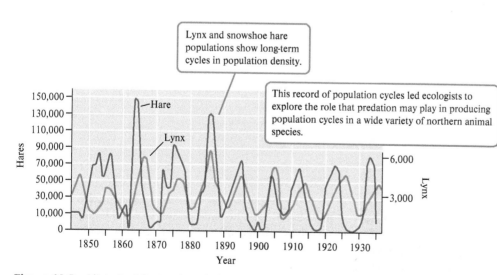

Figure 14.8 Historical fluctuations in lynx and snowshoe hare populations based on the number of pelts purchased by the Hudson Bay Company.
Data from MacLulich 1937.

November to 160 kg per hectare by late March. Many ecologists have demonstrated food shortages during winters of peak snowshoe hare density.

Snowshoe hares also influence the quality of their food supply. Feeding by snowshoe hares induces chemical defences in their food plants, like those we discussed previously. Shoots produced after browsing contain elevated concentrations of terpene and phenolic resins, defensive chemicals that repel mammals. Elevated concentrations of plant defensive chemicals can persist for up to two years after browsing by hares, reducing *usable* food supplies for the hare during the population decline.

The Role of Predators

The long historical record of lynx population cycles may have distracted ecologists from the fact that lynxes are only one of several predators that feed on snowshoe hares. Other major predators of snowshoe hares include goshawks (*Accipiter gentilis*), great horned owls (*Bubo virginianus*), mink (*Mustela vison*), long-tailed weasels (*Mustela frenata*), red foxes (*Vulpes vulpes*), and coyotes (*Canis latrans*). Populations of these predators are known to cycle synchronously with snowshoe hare populations. Though the lynx is a specialist on snowshoe hares, the diet of a generalist predator, such as the coyote, may also depend heavily on snowshoe hares. This is particularly true when snowshoe hare populations are at peak density. Arlen Todd and Lloyd Keith (1983) report that snowshoe hares made up 67% of the coyote diets in central Alberta. Ecologists have estimated that predation by this diverse group of predators may account for 60% to 90% of snowshoe hare mortality during peak densities.

Research by a team of ecologists from British Columbia, Alaska, the Yukon, Alberta, and Argentina (O'Donoghue et al. 1997, 1998) provides clear evidence of *functional* and *numerical responses* to increased hare densities. You may recall that a functional response relates the density of prey to the feeding rate of a predator (fig 7.21). O'Donoghue and colleagues found that lynx show a clear type 2 functional response to increasing hare densities, reaching a maximum predation rate of 1.2 hares per day (per lynx). This maximum occurs at intermediate hare densities, such that further increases in hares have no effect on how many hares an individual lynx can predate. In contrast, over the range of hare densities they observed, coyotes show type 1 functional response, with a predation rate of 2.3 hares per day (per coyote) at the highest hare densities. Even at that level, the coyote functional response showed no signs of levelling off. At high hare densities, coyote and lynx predation rates greatly exceeded their daily energetic needs. Coyotes killed more hares early in the winter, caching many and retrieving them later in the season.

In chapter 10 we first mentioned *numerical responses*, which describe how predator populations increase in relation to prey population increases. Increases in predator populations can be due to two major mechanisms: (1) movement of more predators into areas where more prey are found (i.e., immigration rates increase), and (2) increased reproductive rates of predators due to increases in food availability (i.e., birth rates increase). O'Donoghue and his colleagues found both coyote and lynx demonstrated significant numerical responses to hare populations, with six- to seven-fold more predators present

when hares were at high density than at low hare density. As both per-capita feeding rates and predator population sizes increase with increasing hare densities, O'Donoghue and colleagues demonstrate there is great potential for lynx and coyote to have strongly negative effects on high-density snowshoe hare populations.

In summary, several decades of research provided evidence that both predation and food can make substantial contributions to snowshoe hare population cycles (Haukioja et al. 1983, Keith 1983, Keith et al. 1984). The food availability and predation hypotheses are complementary, not mutually exclusive, alternatives. As hare populations increase, they reduce the quantity and quality of their food supply. Reduced food availability, which leads to starvation and weight loss, would itself likely produce population decline. This potential decline is ensured and accelerated by high rates of mortality due to predation. As hare population density is reduced, predator populations decline in turn, plant populations recover, and the stage is set for another increase in the hare population. This scenario was tested through a series of long-term experiments.

Experimental Test of Food and Predation Impacts

Charles J. Krebs, now an emeritus professor at the University of British Columbia (UBC), along with several colleagues from UBC, University of Alberta, and the University of Toronto (Krebs et al. 1995) conducted a large-scale, long-term experiment designed to sort out the tangle of conflicting evidence regarding the impacts of food and predation on snowshoe hare population cycles. Over a period of eight years, Krebs and colleagues conducted one of the most ambitious field experiments to date.

What do we mean by a large-scale experiment? In this study, each experimental plot was a 1 km² block of undisturbed boreal forest near Kluane, Yukon. In total they used nine such blocks, each separated from other experimental blocks by a minimum of 1 km. Three blocks served as controls and were left unmanipulated. To test whether food availability limited hare densities, hares were given unlimited supplemental food in two experimental blocks during the entire period of the study. To test whether plant tissue quality limited hare numbers, the researchers applied a nitrogen-potassium-phosphorus fertilizer from the air to two of the experimental blocks. To explore the role of predators on hare numbers, they built electric fences around two of the 1 km² blocks, which excluded mammalian predators (but not hawks and owls). One of these predator reduction blocks also received supplemental food. The fences on both predator reduction areas (8 km of fence) had to be checked every day through the winter, when temperatures would sometimes dip as low as −45°C. Krebs's research team maintained these experimental conditions through one full cycle of snowshoe hare numbers. Due to maintenance requirements (and limited budget) of such a large project, they could not replicate the predator reduction and predator reduction + food experimental manipulations.

During the eight years of the experiment, the researchers observed an increase in hare numbers to a peak, followed by

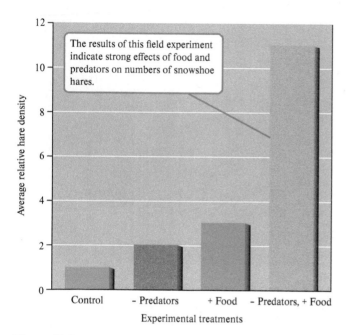

The results of this field experiment indicate strong effects of food and predators on numbers of snowshoe hares.

Figure 14.9 The densities of snowshoe hares averaged from the peak in hare density through the period of declining density observed during the study. Hare densities are expressed relative to the densities on the control plots where no experimental manipulation was applied.

Data from Krebs et al. 1995, 2001.

a decline on all the study plots, regardless of the treatments imposed. However, the treatments had diverse effects on the magnitude and duration of these peaks. For example, fertilizer application increased plant growth but did not increase the numbers of snowshoe hares. However, hare numbers increased substantially in the food addition, predator reduction, and predator reduction + food addition plots. Averaged over the peak and decline phases of the study, reducing predators doubled hare density, adding food tripled hare density, and excluding predators and adding food increased hare density to 11 times that of the control plots (fig. 14.9). Krebs and his colleagues found that these higher hare densities were the result of both increased per capita rates of survival and reproduction.

After approximately 70 years of research, we can conclude that the population cycle of snowshoe hares is the result of an interaction between three trophic levels: (1) the hares, (2) the plants upon which they feed, and (3) the predators that feed upon them. In other words, different forms of exploitation interact to create the cycles of hares that have puzzled scientists for decades.

Krebs and colleagues (2001) point out that to understand the controls on hare numbers, researchers have had to work with all three trophic levels simultaneously. In addition, the critical experiment had to be done on a large scale and in the field. Still, this experiment leaves a number of questions unanswered, such as why does artificial rabbit food increase hare densities but increased natural food (plants) does not? Perhaps an even more interesting set of questions comes when one recognizes that predators do much more to prey than kill them. Fear itself matters.

Nonconsumptive Effects of Predators: The Ecology of Fear

We live in a culture fascinated by fear. Go to an amusement park and you'll find that the line for the Scrambler ride is longer than the line for the Teacups. And the box office success of recent horror films is definitely not driven by the storyline, acting, or production value. Presumably, we would be less thrilled if the danger were real. If you were the hare and were fortunate enough to hop away from an encounter with a lynx, you would probably not be excited to gather your hare friends for *Lynx 2: The Next Encounter.* We can indulge in fear only because it's safe, but we choose to indulge because of the rush. Fear triggers a physiological response. However, the stress of prolonged fear triggers a different suite of physiological responses.

Encounters with predators in which prey escape are common. In fact, for individual encounters, escape is more common that not. Even when predation is successful, predators generally kill and consume only a fraction of the entire prey population. As a result, the direct **consumptive effects of predation** influence only a small number of prey at any particular point in time. Consumptive effects of predation are the direct effects that predators have on prey populations through the capture and consumption of living prey. This is what Lord Alfred Tennyson was commenting on in his famous line, "nature, red in tooth and claw" (Tennyson, "In Memoriam A.H.H.," canto 56). But predators do much more than kill, and there is evidence that **nonconsumptive effects of predation** have significant consequences on prey population dynamics.

Nonconsumptive effects of predators are those changes to the prey that occur as a consequence of predators being present, even when the prey are not killed. These changes include shifts in morphological traits, stress physiology, and altered behaviour. Because it is easy to imagine how we ourselves would feel when chased by a predator, or even when knowing predators are present, the study of these nonconsumptive effects of predation is commonly referred to as "the ecology of fear." This phrase was first applied to natural systems by Joel Brown and colleagues (Brown et al. 1999) and has led to a renewed interest in predator–prey dynamics. Though we have no idea whether prey actually feel fear, we do know that the presence of a predator causes biologically significant effects on prey populations.

Rudy Boonstra, of the University of Toronto, was interested in whether the snowshoe hares exhibited stress in response to predators and whether this could influence population cycling. Boonstra and colleagues (Boonstra et al. 1998) worked within the larger lynx-hare experiment described above, focusing primarily on the hares during the decline phase of their population cycle. During this population decline, nearly every hare in the control plots that died was killed by a predator, suggesting that most hares see predators occasionally; thus, "fear" is likely rampant throughout the hare population. The research team recognized that stress can cause predictable physiological responses, often indicated by shifts in blood cortisol levels and general shifts in hormonal physiology. Over time, prolonged stress can lead to changes in a number of factors related to fitness, including reduced energy storage and reduced allocation of energy to reproduction, growth, and immune response. To test whether the hares were experiencing stress associated with repeated predator encounters, the research team collected blood samples from hares during different years of the decline (early versus late) and from the plots with predators and those without.

The results Boonstra found were convincing. Blood cortisol levels were higher in hares when predation rates were high than in a year with lower predation. They were also higher in plots in which predators were present than when predators were experimentally removed. In other words, hares were exhibiting the physiological signature of stress, due to the presence of predators, well before they died. Boonstra had evidence that this chronic stress had negative impacts on the hares, as female hares exposed to predators had reduced reproductive rates, among other changes (Boonstra et al. 1998). These results suggest that in addition to the consumptive effects that predators would have on hare populations, these nonconsumptive effects would cause an even faster drop in hare populations. In other words, the predators seem to be causing both increases in hare per capita rates of mortality *and* decreases in per capita birth rates. Evidence of nonconsumptive effects of predators on prey have now become common in the literature, in both terrestrial and aquatic systems.

Tiger sharks are a top predator of marine mammals throughout much of their range, including Shark Bay, Australia (fig. 14.10*b*). Larry Dill and a team of students from Simon Fraser University, along with colleagues around the world, have been studying what role fear may be playing in the behavioural decisions of the shark's potential prey. One common prey are dugongs (*Dugong dugon*), large herbivorous mammals that feed upon seagrass beds (fig. 14.10*a*). Dill and his colleagues found that dugongs altered the location of where they feed as a function of the density of tiger sharks (Wirsing, Heithaus, and Dill 2007). When sharks were relatively absent, the dugongs were more likely to occupy shallow areas of high seagrass density. However, when tiger sharks were more abundant, the dugongs increased their use of the deeper areas, even though food availability was lower. Dill and his colleagues suggest that the dugongs are faced with a food vs. safety trade-off, yet another example of a nonconsumptive effect of predators.

How important are these nonconsumptive effects in general? Evan Preisser and colleagues conducted a meta-analysis comparing the relative effects of consumptive and nonconsumptive effects of predators on prey populations (Preisser et al. 2005). In studies that measured both effects, nonconsumptive effects were, on average, approximately equal in magnitude to the more commonly studied consumptive effects. Or, put another way, the vast majority of research in predator–prey interactions has focused on one organism eating another. It appears that what happens to those animals not (yet) eaten is just as important if one wants to understand prey population dynamics. There is substantial research to be done, and there are great opportunities for the next generation of ecologists.

Understanding prey population dynamics is a critical goal of many branches of ecology, with significant societal implications. To do this requires generalization beyond specific cases studies. To achieve this, ecologists again turn to theoretical and laboratory studies for help.

(a)

(b)

Figure 14.10   Dugongs (*a*) adjust their foraging behaviour as a function of whether or not tiger sharks (*b*) are hunting in the area.

(a) David Peart/arabianEye/Getty Images; (b) Alastair Pollock Photography/Getty Images.

CONCEPT 14.2 REVIEW

1. When the coupled cycling of lynx and snowshoe hare populations (see fig. 14.8) was first described, many concluded that lynx control snowshoe hare populations. Why do we now know that the story is not that simple?

2. In a study by Mark Ohman (1990), a copepod (*Pseudocalanus newmani*) exhibited vertical daily migration in the water column, but only to avoid a predator when one was present. Is this a consumptive or nonconsumptive effect of predation on the population? How can this behaviour affect fitness of individual copepods?

3. How can nonconsumptive effects of predators alter prey population dynamics?

14.3 Predator–Prey Dynamics in a Mathematical Model

The population consequences of exploitative relationships can be explored with theoretical models. As we discussed in chapter 13, mathematical and laboratory models offer ecologists the opportunity to manipulate variables that they cannot control in the field, in an attempt to understand underlying principles about ecological interactions. For example, the Lotka–Volterra competition model contributed to the identification of the competitive exclusion principle and described necessary conditions for species coexistence. As discussed above, predator–prey dynamics in natural systems often cycle through time. If we rip away the specific details of individual systems, can models provide a general explanation for these coupled predator–prey dynamics?

We will begin this section by viewing predation as a potential "brake" that limits the growth rate of prey. Once again, we find Lotka (1925) and Volterra (1926) independently developing a mathematical solution to the problem of population cycles. Both researchers built their models based on observations of interactions among natural populations. Lotka was impressed by the reciprocal oscillations of populations of moth and butterfly larvae and the parasitoids that attack them. Volterra was inspired by the response of marine fish populations to cessation of fishing during World War I. Volterra observed that the response of fish populations was uneven. Predaceous fish, particularly sharks, increased in abundance, while the populations upon which they fed decreased. This reciprocal change in numbers suggested that predators have the potential to reduce the abundance of their prey. In this single observation, Volterra somehow saw the potential for predator–prey population cycles. With these observations in mind, Lotka and Volterra set out to build mathematical models that would produce the cycles that they thought occurred in nature. It is worth mentioning at the start that in contrast to other models we have presented, the parameters of the Lotka–Volterra predator–prey models are represented by different letters by nearly every researcher and textbook author. We emphasize the key to learning ecological models is to understand the concepts they represent, rather than focusing solely on the equation. If concepts are learned, then you will be able to understand the model even if different letters are used in different situations. Here we refer to the prey as "H" (you could think "host" or "herbivore") and the predator as "P." This model also applies to host-pathogen interactions (chapter 15), though we limit discussion here to predator–prey dynamics.

We start by describing what factors might influence the population growth of the prey. The basic Lotka–Volterra predator–prey model assumes that in the absence of predators, prey populations grow at an exponential rate:

$$\frac{dN_h}{dt} = r_h N_h$$

Here, N_h represents prey population size (as mentioned above, h represents prey) and r_h represents the prey's per capita growth rate (r_{max}). You should see something unusual here, in that this

model assumes there is no intraspecific competition among the prey. The equation is the exponential, rather than the logistic, model of population growth. Instead of intraspecific competition, Lotka and Volterra suggested that the prey's population size will be limited by its predators through the inclusion of another set of parameters:

$$\frac{dN_h}{dt} = r_h N_h - b N_h N_p$$

In the Lotka–Volterra model, exponential growth by the host population is opposed by deaths due to predation, which is represented by $-b N_h N_p$. Again, N_h is the number of hosts, or prey, and N_p is the number of predators. The new term, b, is the capture efficiency of the prey by the predators. So, we have one part of the equation describing how many prey are created as a function of per capita prey growth rates multiplied by the number of prey, and a second part that describes how many prey are killed by predators as the product of the frequency of encounters between predator and prey ($N_h N_p$) and the proportion of those encounters that result in prey death (b).

The Lotka–Volterra model assumes that the rate of growth by the predator population is determined by the rate at which it converts the hosts it consumes into offspring (new predators) minus the predator's per capita mortality rate:

$$\frac{dN_p}{dt} = cb N_h N_p - d_p N_p$$

Here again, N_h and N_p are the numbers of hosts and predators, respectively. The rate at which the predators convert hosts into offspring is $cb N_h N_p$. This term is the product of the number of prey killed by the predator as described in the prior equation ($b N_h N_p$) multiplied by a new term, c, which represents a conversion factor of how many dead prey it takes to create one new predator. For example, if five prey need to be consumed to create one new predator, then $c = 0.20$. The growth rate of the predator population is opposed by predator deaths, $d_p N_p$, where d_p represents the per capita death rate of the predators. Once again, Lotka and Volterra have assumed no intraspecific competition among the predators, as per capita death rates are a constant. Thus, in these models, prey densities are determined by predator numbers along with some constants, and predator densities are determined by prey densities, along with some constants. The Lotka–Volterra predator–prey model is summarized in figure 14.11.

Now let's reflect on the behaviour of this model. To do this, we will follow the same approach as in chapter 13, and solve these coupled equations at the point of equilibrium, when dN_h/dt and dN_p/dt each equal 0. This results in:

$$\frac{dN_h}{dt} = 0 \text{ when } r_h N_h - b N_h N_p = 0$$

This can be reduced and rearranged such that prey population growth will be zero when:

$$N_p = r_h/b$$

And for the predator:

$$\frac{dN_p}{dt} = 0 \text{ when } cb N_h N_p - d_p N_p = 0$$

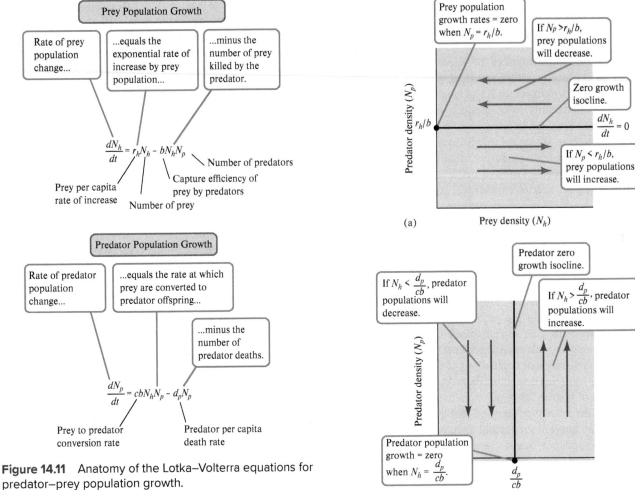

Figure 14.11 Anatomy of the Lotka–Volterra equations for predator–prey population growth.

This can be reduced and rearranged such that predator population growth will be zero when:

$$N_h = \frac{d_p}{cb}$$

You may recognize what we have just done. We now have the ability to draw the zero-growth isoclines for the predator and prey populations (fig. 14.12), as we did for competing species in chapter 13. These graphs represent the conditions under which either predator or prey populations are predicted to change based upon the Lotka–Volterra model. We can combine these onto a single graph, and make predictions about the dynamics of the coupled systems (fig. 14.13).

Figure 14.13 represents the combined model when both predators and prey have populations densities > 0. We can see in this figure the basis for population cycles. Initially, both prey and predator populations are small. Predation pressure (bN_hN_p) is low since the frequency of encounter (N_hN_p) is small. The prey population grows at an exponential rate (quadrant A). Its population growth accelerates with increasing population size (N_h). However, this acceleration with increasing N_h is opposed by the increasing rate of predation (bN_hN_p). This happens because as the prey population grows, the frequency of encounters with predators (N_hN_p) must also increase. In the Lotka–Volterra model, predation, bN_hN_p, is translated directly and immediately

Figure 14.12 Zero-growth isoclines for (a) prey and (b) predator populations derived from the Lotka–Volterra predator–prey model.

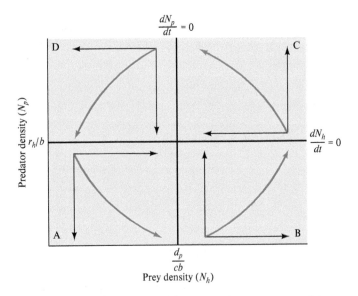

Figure 14.13 The Lotka–Volterra predator–prey model predicts cycling of predator and prey populations.

into more predators by cbN_hN_p (quadrant B). An increase in the number of predators (N_p) further increases the rate of predation (bN_hN_p). Growth of the predator population eventually reduces the prey population. This, in turn, decreases the frequency of encounters and, therefore, the rate of predation (quadrant C). This reduction in predation leads to declines in the predator population (quadrant D). So, like the prey, exploiter success carries the seeds of its own destruction. Finally, a decrease in the predator population permits release of the prey from predation pressure, and the prey population again begins an exponential increase (quadrant A).

These reciprocal effects of host and exploiter (or prey and predator) produce oscillations in the two populations, which we can represent in two ways. In Figure 14.14*a*, population oscillations are presented as we looked at them in snowshoe hare and lynx populations (see fig. 14.8), while Figure 14.14*b* gives an alternative representation. The time axis has been eliminated and the two remaining axes represent the numbers of predators and prey. When we plot population data in this way, we see that the Lotka–Volterra model produces oscillations in predator and prey populations that follow an elliptical path whose size depends upon the initial sizes of host and prey populations. Whatever the ellipse size, however, the predator and prey populations just go round and round on the same path forever.

The prediction of eternal oscillations on a very narrowly defined path is obviously unrealistic. Another unrealistic assumption is that neither the host nor the exploiter populations are subject to carrying capacities. Another is that changes in either population are instantaneously translated into responses in the other population. This model also does not allow for any nonconsumptive effects. Despite these unrealistic assumptions, Lotka and Volterra made valuable contributions to our understanding of predator–prey systems. They showed that simple models with a minimum of assumptions produce reciprocal cycles in populations of predator and prey analogous to those that can occur in natural populations. They demonstrated that exploitative interactions themselves can, in theory, produce population cycles without any influences from an outside force, such as climatic variation. Other researchers have taken their basic models and expanded them, allowing for more biological realism. Most notably, Michael Rosenzweig and Robert MacArthur (1963) modified the Lotka–Volterra model to account for density dependence in prey and predator species, and Roger Arditi and Lev Ginzburg (1989) suggested that the trophic function of predator–prey models (per capita consumption) could better be represented by the predator–prey ratio, rather than as a function of prey density. John Fryxell at the University of Guelph has been influential in the field of behavioural ecology (chapter 8). Fryxell and his colleagues (2007) have addressed some of the limitations in theoretical ecology as it pertains to modelling predator–prey dynamics, where models assume mass action, with random movement of individual predators and prey. In the Lotka–Volterra model, encounter frequencies are a simple function of population densities. This may not hold true when animals (predator or prey) form social groups. Fryxell and colleagues have developed an alternative approach that treats the social groups, rather than individuals, as the fundamental units for predator–prey interactions. These models have been very influential in community ecology and have led to greater realism in predator–prey models, but a more detailed discussion is beyond the scope of this book. One of the great uses of a simple model is the ability to expand it, allowing researchers to test whether the addition of more biological complexity alters our basic understanding of biological processes.

Although there has been some success in laboratory models to reproduce Lotka–Volterra-type oscillations, most attempts have failed. Instead, most laboratory experiments have led to extinction of the predator or prey population in a fairly short period of time. To sustain oscillations even for a short period, the prey had to have some sort of protection from the predators.

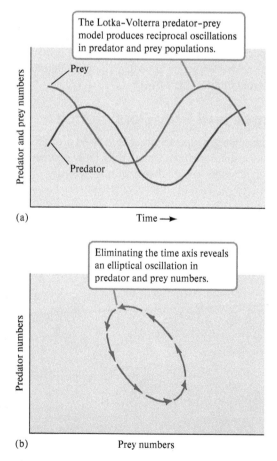

(a)

(b)

Figure 14.14 A graphical view of the Lotka–Volterra predator–prey model.

Data from Gause 1934.

14.4 Predator Avoidance

Prey populations can persist in the presence of predators through the use of display and refugia. Despite all of the potential negative effects that predators can have on prey populations, we do find a world in which potential prey exist. Here, we will discuss an evolutionary solution involving animal display, and then we discuss *refugia*, situations in which members of an exploited population have some protection from predators.

Animal Display

Most prey species are masters of defence, one of the most basic means of which is *camouflage*. Quite simply, predators cannot eat prey they cannot find. There are many examples of visual camouflage in the natural world, some more elaborate than others (fig 14.15). Camouflage may include not only visual displays but also olfactory "displays." The puff adder (*Bitis arietans*), for example, can use chemical crypsis to avoid detection by meerkats (*Suricata suricatta*), which hunt snakes using olfactory cues (Miller et al. 2015). The coral-feeding filefish (*Oxymonacanthus longirostris*), meanwhile, can sequester dietary elements of the corals on which it feeds. As a result, the filefish smells like the coral to predatory cod, making it harder for these olfactory hunters to detect (Brooker et al. 2015) their prey. Interestingly, while many organisms have evolved strategies to hide from predators, for other organisms being noticed is the best defence.

Many prey species are coloured to be extremely visually apparent. This can be seen in the striking colours displayed by many butterflies, snakes, and nudibranchs. How can prey persist with such coloration? Many of these animals are toxic. Prey that carry a threat to predators often advertise that fact, usually by being brightly coloured or conspicuous in some other way. The conspicuous colours, or **aposematic coloration**, of many distasteful or toxic animals warn predators that "feeding on me may be hazardous to your health." However, such a signal is not perfect. Many predatory species need to learn to associate coloration with toxicity. Only for a subset of species is this "knowledge" an innate trait of the species. The curious predator is not the only potential threat to species with warning coloration.

In **Batesian mimicry**, a harmless (nontoxic) species will exhibit coloration similar to that of a noxious species that lives in the same area. For example, king snakes mimic the poisonous coral snakes, viceroy butterflies mimic the noxious monarch butterfly, and syrphid flies mimic stinging bees. Batesian mimics elude predation not through the actual ability to defend themselves from attack but instead by using the learned (and innate) abilities of predators to associate harm with particular colours and patterns. What do you imagine might happen if in a given community the frequency of mimics exceeds the frequency of actually toxic models?

Müllerian mimicry is also common and can enhance the learning by potential predators associated with aposematic coloration. Müllerian mimics are *all* toxic/noxious and share similar coloration. For example, you may have noticed that many stinging flies, wasps, and bees, three distantly related taxa, have superficially similar appearances that include yellow and black stripes. These are Müllerian mimics. One likely advantage of similar coloration is that potential predators are likely to encounter toxic/noxious organisms with similar coloration more frequently than if only one species has such coloration. As a result, it is thought that Müllerian mimicry systems enhance the rate at which predators learn to associate a particular colour/pattern with risk, thereby reducing predation risk for these species. You may also have noticed that some flies share the same coloration yet do not sting. These are Batesian mimics of Müllerian mimics (fig. 14.16).

Refuges and Prey Persistence

Although some prey species are able to avoid predation through appearance, many are not. Nonetheless, these prey can be found on the landscape, co-occurring with a diversity of potential

(a)

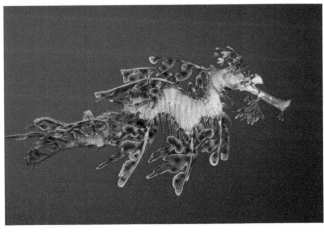

(b)

Figure 14.15 *(a)* An algal symbiont in the sloth's fur makes the sloth harder to spot among the tree leaves, and *(b)* the lobed appendages on the sea dragon resemble fronds, helping it hide among the kelp.

(a)

(b)

Figure 14.16   (*a*) Poisonous Müllerian (a stinging bee), and (*b*) nonpoisonous Batesian (a non-stinging hoverfly) mimics.
(a) Seraphzheng/Dreamstime.com/GetStock.com; (b) Evelyng23/Dreamstime.com/GetStock.com.

predators. However, recreating coexistence between predator and prey in a lab setting has proven to be surprisingly difficult. Gause (chapter 13) was among the first to realize that creating Lotka–Volterra oscillations in the lab was a challenge. He established a simple system involving *Paramecium caudatum* and one of its predators, another aquatic protozoan called *Didinium nasutum*. When Gause grew these organisms together, *Didinium* quickly consumed all the *Paramecium* (fig. 14.17), and thus there was no coexistence. Gause responded by putting some sediment on the bottom of his microcosm to provide a refuge for *Paramecium*. In this case, once *Didinium* had eaten all of the *Paramecium* not hiding in bottom sediments, it starved and became extinct. Following the disappearance of *Didinium* and the removal of predation pressure, the population of *Paramecium* quickly increased. Here, a simple refuge for the prey population led to extinction of the predator.

Gause was able to maintain oscillations in predator–prey populations only if he periodically restocked the populations from his laboratory cultures. In this experiment, the microcosm contained no refuges for *Paramecium*, but every three days Gause would take one of each organism from his pure laboratory cultures and add them to the experimental microcosm. Using these periodic immigrations, he was able to produce Lotka–Volterra–type predator–prey oscillations (see fig. 14.17).

Are these experimental requirements entirely artificial, or do they correspond with anything we already know about natural populations? Gause's experimental results match many of our observations in natural populations. In chapter 10, we saw that on larger scales, populations show clumped distributions. Most species are much more common in some parts of their range than in others. Then in chapter 11, we saw how dispersal is an important contributor to population dynamics and that some local populations are maintained entirely by dispersal from other areas. Some biologists have combined observations such as these to hypothesize the existence of population sources and population sinks. Local populations may be maintained, entirely or in part, by immigration from source populations. Local populations

may also be maintained by dispersal from areas of high localized density, such as from social groups. In Gause's experiment, the pure laboratory cultures were population hot spots, or sources, while the microcosms where predator and prey interacted were population sinks. The requirements of Gause's experiment are also consistent with the results of later experiments.

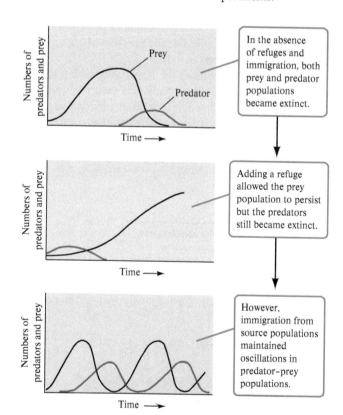

Figure 14.17   Refuges and the persistence of predator–prey oscillation in laboratory populations of prey (*Paramecium caudatum*) and predators (*Didinium nasutum*).
Data from Gause 1935.

C. Huffaker (1958) set out to test whether Gause's results could be reproduced in a situation in which the predator and prey are responsible for their own immigration and emigration among patches of suitable habitat. Huffaker chose the six-spotted mite (*Eotetranychus sexmaculatus*)—a mite that feeds on oranges—as the prey, and the predatory mite *Typhlodromus occidentalis*—which attacks *E. sexmaculatus*—as the predator. Huffaker's experimental setups, or "universes" as he called them, consisted of various arrangements of oranges, or combinations of oranges and rubber balls, separated by partial barriers to mite dispersal consisting of discontinuous strips of petroleum jelly.

An important point of natural history is that the predatory mite had to crawl to disperse from one orange to another, while the herbivorous mite can disperse either by crawling or by "ballooning," a means of aerial dispersal. A mite balloons by spinning a strand of silk that can catch wind currents. Huffaker gave the herbivorous mite the chance to balloon by providing small wooden posts that could serve as launching pads and by having a fan circulate air across his experimental setup.

While Huffaker's simpler experimental universes did not produce predator–prey oscillations, his most elaborate setup of 120 oranges did. Huffaker observed three oscillations that spanned about six months (fig. 14.18). They were maintained by the dispersal of predator and prey among oranges in a deadly game of hide-and-seek, in which the prey managed to keep ahead of the predator for three full oscillations. These results are similar to those obtained by Gause, but we need to remember that Huffaker did not directly manipulate dispersal. In Huffaker's experiment, both predator and prey moved from patch to patch under their own power.

Lotka (1932b) recognized the importance of refuges and incorporated them into his mathematical theory of predator–prey relations. The starting point for his discussion was the set of Lotka–Volterra predator–prey equations that we discussed previously:

$$\frac{dN_h}{dt} = r_h N_h - b N_h N_p \text{ and } \frac{dN_p}{dt} = cb N_h N_p - d_p N_p$$

Lotka pointed out that while it may be reasonable to assume that b is a constant for a particular environment, its value should change from one environment to another if the environments differ structurally, particularly if there is a difference in the availability of refuges in the two environments. Specifically, b should be lower where the prey, or hosts, have access to more refuges. This refinement of the Lotka–Volterra predator–prey model anticipated recent theoretical analysis of the role that refuges and spatial diversity in general play in the persistence of predator–prey and parasite–host systems. While Lotka's analysis concentrated on physical refuges that could shelter terrestrial prey, he recognized the wide variety of forms that refuges could take. He pointed out, for instance, that flight is a refuge for birds from terrestrial predators.

Exploited Organisms and Their Wide Variety of "Refuges"

Space

Most of our discussion has focused on what we might call "spatial" refuges, places where members of the exploited population have some protection from predators. Many forms of spatial refuge are familiar: burrows, trees, air, water (if faced with terrestrial predators), and land (if faced with aquatic predators). However, some spatial refuges differ in subtle ways from other areas.

St. John's wort (*Hypericum perforatum*) persists in refuges in the face of attacks by the beetle *Chrysolina quadrigemina*, one of the chief enemies of *Hypericum* in the Pacific Northwest region of the United States. *Hypericum* was introduced into areas along the Klamath River around 1900, and its population quickly grew to cover about 800,000 hectares by 1944. Following the release of the beetles, the area covered by St. John's wort was reduced to less than 1% of its maximum coverage. This remnant population of the plant was concentrated in shady habitats, where, though it grows more poorly than in sunny areas, it is protected from the beetles, which avoid shade.

Protection in Numbers

Living in a large group provides a type of refuge. Aside from the potential of social groups to intimidate would-be predators, numbers alone can reduce the probability that an individual prey or host will be eaten. We can make this prediction based solely on the work of C. S. Holling (1959) on the responses of predators to prey density. Holling is a fellow of the Royal Society of Canada and has worked at the University of British Columbia and the Department of the Environment for the Canadian government. His research on predator–prey relationships has been central to the theoretical understanding of this ecological process. In chapter 7 we looked at the functional responses of several predators and herbivores. Briefly, predator functional response results in an increasing rate of food intake as prey density increases. Eventually, however, the predator's feeding rate levels off at some maximum rate. In chapter 10, we looked at numerical response, a second component of predator response to prey density that results in increased predator density as prey

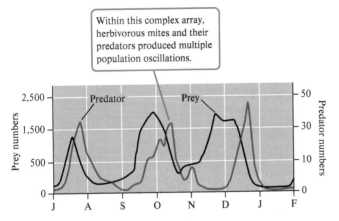

Within this complex array, herbivorous mites and their predators produced multiple population oscillations.

Figure 14.18 Environmental complexity and oscillations in laboratory populations of a herbivorous mite and a predatory mite.

Data from Huffaker 1958.

density increases. As with functional response, the numerical response eventually levels off at the point where further increases in prey density no longer produce increased predator density.

Now let's put functional response and numerical response together to predict the predator's **combined response** to increased prey density. We can combine the two responses by multiplying the number of prey eaten per predator (functional response) times the number of predators per unit area (numerical response):

$$\frac{\text{Prey consumed}}{\text{Predator}} \times \frac{\text{Predator}}{\text{Area}} = \frac{\text{Prey consumed}}{\text{Area}}$$

By dividing the prey consumed per unit area by the population density of the prey, we can determine the percentage of the prey population consumed by the predator. If we plot the percentage of the prey consumed against prey density over a broad range of prey densities, the prediction is that the percentage of the prey population consumed will be lower at high prey densities (fig. 14.19).

Why should the percentage of the prey consumed by the predator decline at high prey densities? The answer to this question, which may not be obvious at first, lies in the predator functional and numerical responses. We see this effect because both numerical and functional responses level off at intermediate prey densities; that is, beyond a certain threshold, further increases in prey density do not lead to either higher predator densities or increased feeding rates. Meanwhile, the density of the prey population continues to increase and the proportion of the prey eaten by predators declines. This work by Holling suggests that prey can reduce their individual probability of being eaten by occurring at very high densities. It appears that this defensive tactic, called **predator satiation**, is employed by a wide variety of organisms, from insects and plants to marine invertebrates and African antelope.

Protection in Numbers—Predator Satiation by Periodical Cicadas

Periodical cicadas (*Magicicada* spp.) emerge as adults once every 13 years in the southern part of their range in North America, and once every 17 years in the northern part of their range. Though these insects emerge only once every 13 or 17 years in any particular area, virtually every year sees a brood emerging somewhere in eastern North America. An emergence of periodical cicadas produces a sudden flush of singing insects whose density can approach 4×10^6 individuals per hectare, which translates into a biomass of 1,900 to 3,700 kg of cicadas per hectare, the highest biomass of a natural population of terrestrial animals ever recorded.

Periodical cicadas are insects of the order Homoptera, which includes the leafhoppers and aphids. Like their relatives, cicadas make their living by sucking the fluids of plants. Cicadas spend either 13 or 17 years of their life as nymphs underground, where they feed on the xylem fluids in roots. When mature, nymphs dig their way to the soil surface, where they shed their nymphal skin and emerge as winged adults. This emergence is so synchronized that millions of adults emerge over a period of only a few days. Following emergence, males fly to the treetops where they sing the mating songs to which females are attracted. After they mate, females lay their eggs in living twigs of shrubs and trees. When the nymphs hatch in about six weeks, they immediately drop to the ground and burrow down to a root, where they begin to feed, moving around very little for the next 13 or 17 years. A mass emergence of periodical cicadas, one of the most memorable biological phenomena nature has to offer, appears aimed at predator satiation.

Kathy Williams and her colleagues (1993) tested the effectiveness of predator satiation in a population of 13-year periodical cicadas in northwest Arkansas. They monitored emergence of cicadas using conical emergence traps constructed of plastic mesh and inverted their traps to measure predation rates (fig. 14.20).

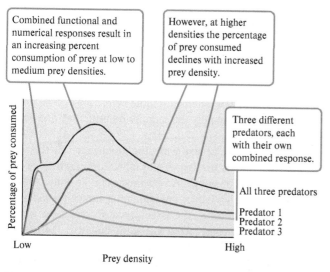

Figure 14.19 Prey density and the percentage of prey consumed due to combined functional and numerical responses.

Data from Holling 1959a, 1959b.

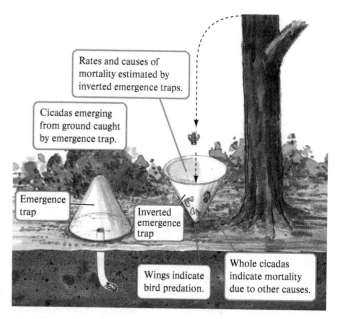

Figure 14.20 Estimating cicada population size and predation rates by birds.

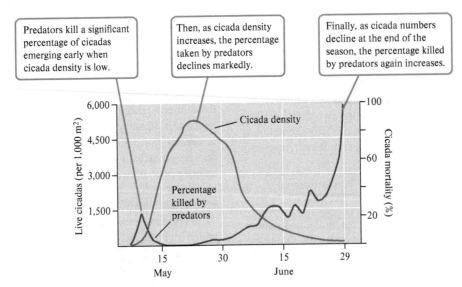

Figure 14.21   Cicada population density and their percent mortality due to predation.
Data from Williams, Smith, and Stephen 1993.

Nymphs emerging from the ground below the traps could be counted to estimate the numbers of emerging nymphs. Then, as adult cicadas died from a variety of factors, including physical factors, senescence, and pathogens, they fell from the trees to the ground, where some were caught in the inverted traps. Because the major predators were birds, predation rates could be estimated because birds discard the wings of cicadas as they feed upon them. The wings falling into the inverted traps gave an estimate of predation rates.

Patterns of mortality and predation rates relative to population size support the predator satiation hypothesis. Williams and her colleagues estimated that 1,063,000 cicadas emerged from their 16 hectares study site and that 50% of these emerged during four consecutive nights. Cicada abundance peaked in late May and then declined rapidly during the first two weeks of June. Part of this decline was due to mortality from severe thunderstorms during the first week of June. Figure 14.21 shows that losses due to birds were low throughout the period of peak cicada abundance and then climbed to 100% as cicada populations declined during June. These results indicate that the predator satiation tactic was sufficiently effective to reduce cicada losses to birds to only 15% of the total population.

Size as a Refuge

We first encountered size-selective predation in chapter 7 among bluegills (*Lepomis macrochirus*), and pumas (*Felis concolor*). However, many other organisms select their prey by size. In fact, average prey size shows a significant correlation with predator size across taxa ranging from lizards to small mammals. The reason for size-selective predation among such a diverse array of organisms is that prey capture and consumption are mechanical problems. As we saw in chapter 7, size can influence the time required to handle prey and therefore the

Figure 14.22   Large size can provide a refuge from predators. While young African elephants may be vulnerable to predation by African lions, mature elephants are not.
© Gregory G. Dimijian/Science Source.

rate of energy intake. The bottom line is that for a given predator, some prey are simply too large to be profitable and so are not attacked.

Now let's look at size from the perspective of the prey. If large individuals are ignored by predators, then large size may offer a form of refuge. An obvious example is the African savanna. While a variety of predators may attack the calves of elephants or rhinoceros, the same predators avoid the adults, which have been observed to kill adult lions (fig. 14.22). On a smaller scale, Robert Paine (1976) found that the sea star *Pisaster ochraceus* does not consume the largest individuals in populations of one of its chief prey species, the mussel *Mytilus californianus*. Figure 14.23 shows that the maximum size of mussels eaten by sea stars is a function of sea star size.

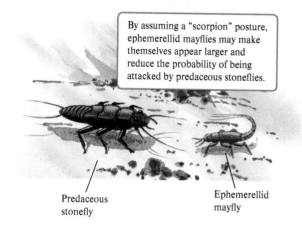

By assuming a "scorpion" posture, ephemerellid mayflies may make themselves appear larger and reduce the probability of being attacked by predaceous stoneflies.

Predaceous stonefly

Ephemerellid mayfly

Figure 14.24 Posturing by an ephemerellid mayfly confronted by a predaceous stonefly.

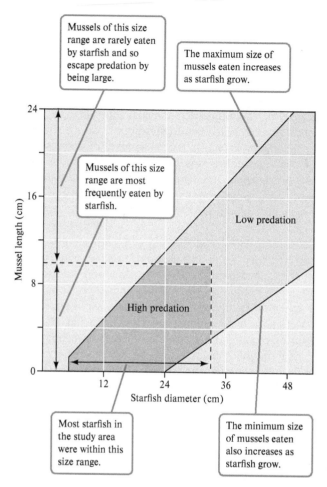

Mussels of this size range are rarely eaten by starfish and so escape predation by being large.

The maximum size of mussels eaten increases as starfish grow.

Mussels of this size range are most frequently eaten by starfish.

Low predation

High predation

Most starfish in the study area were within this size range.

The minimum size of mussels eaten also increases as starfish grow.

Figure 14.23 Large mussels are eaten infrequently by the sea star *Pisaster ochraceus*.
Data from Paine 1976.

Notice that most of the successful predation observed by Paine involved small- to medium-sized sea stars attacking mussels less than 11 cm long. Most sea stars cannot eat the largest mussels, and the largest sea stars that can were limited to a few areas of coastline in the study area. What this means is that if a mussel can manage to escape predation long enough to reach 10 to 12 cm in length, it will be immune from attack by most sea stars.

If predators pass up prey above a particular size threshold, might natural selection favour organisms that project a "large" body size to some would-be predators? It appears that some aquatic insects have been selected to do just that. Barbara Peckarsky (1980, 1982) observed that mayflies in the family Ephemerellidae would stand their ground in the face of a foraging predatory stonefly. In fact, they would not only stand their ground, they would curve their abdomens over their backs and point the tips of their abdominal cerci into the face and antennae of a stonefly, a behaviour Peckarsky called a "scorpion" posture (fig. 14.24). Usually a stonefly greeted in this way does not attack. While many other stream ecologists had seen this behaviour in ephemerellid mayflies, Peckarsky was the first to suggest that the scorpion posture was a defensive tactic in which

the mayfly projected a larger image to a tactile, size-selective predator.

Why should a large stonefly avoid large ephemerellid mayflies? Large ephemerellids have been observed attacking stoneflies trying to prey on them, and so like lions that avoid rhinoceros, stoneflies that avoid ephemerellids may be protecting themselves from injury. Most ephemerellids, however, present no danger to large predaceous stoneflies, so self-protection only partially answers our question. For the bulk of encounters between stoneflies and ephemerellid mayflies, large apparent size would probably indicate low profitability, low E/T in terms of optimal foraging theory (see chapter 7), and send the predator looking for a prey that would yield a higher energy return. It may be that the display by ephemerellids is not a bluff, however, since they require an exceptionally long handling time for a prey of their size. The scorpion posture of ephemerellids may be a case of "truth in advertising." As you will see in chapter 15, organisms possess a variety of mechanisms of defence against predators and herbivores.

In section 5 (Communities and Ecosystems), we will explore how scientists are beginning to understand the evolutionary consequences of this widespread ecological interaction.

CONCEPT 14.4 REVIEW

1. Why might Mullerian mimicry among a group of species contribute to the evolution of Batesian mimicry in other species?

2. Why should there be strong selection on periodical cicadas for highly synchronous emergence?

3. Why should a large predaceous stonefly avoid ephemerellid mayflies that assume a scorpion posture to project a large appearance?

ECOLOGICAL TOOLS AND APPROACHES

Evolution and Exploitation

Research in the ecology of exploitation can take place at a variety of spatial and temporal scales. At the shortest and smallest scales, an ecologist might be interested in understanding which insect species feed on which plant species. Another ecologist may be interested in understanding how herbivory by insects affects the biomass and growth of the plant. At a deeper time scale, an ecologist might be interested in host shifts, as an insect species moves from using one host plant to another. On a longer time scale still, an evolutionary ecologist may be interested in how these host shifts, followed by specialization, may contribute to differentiation and ultimately speciation of herbivorous insects. Aspects of the evolutionary ecology of exploitation can be explored through a variety of tools, including molecular genetics. But as we'll see, there remains an important role for conceptual models that help guide the application of such tools. We'll look at the relationships between plant hosts and phytophagous insects (those that feed on plants), and consider how ecologists might consider the role of host specialization by insects on their diversification.

Although only a fraction of insect species are described in science, a current estimate suggests that there are around 5–10 million insect species, with perhaps 35%–40% of these being plant-eating, or phytophagous, species (Ødegaard 2000). The number of phytophagous insect species alone is greater than the total number of birds, fish, and mammal species combined (9,000 species of birds, 20,000 species of fish, and 4,500 species of mammals). This level of diversity has led many researchers to wonder whether there is something about the herbivore–host interaction that could cause such high levels of diversity. Of particular interest was the realization that although many insects are generalists, feeding upon a diverse set of host plants, other species are specialists, feeding upon a more restricted diet—perhaps limited to even a single plant species. Could this specialization lead to speciation?

When ecologists began to explore this issue, it soon became apparent that a single species of insect could form host races, genetically distinct subpopulations that are differentiated as a function of the host species. For example, *Rhagoletis pomonella,* the apple maggot, forms two main host races. One of these feeds upon the common apple, while a second feeds upon a related species, the hawthorn. Such differentiation may be the first step in the evolution of isolating mechanisms that could lead to sympatric speciation (chapter 4). What is unclear, however, is how common such differentiation is among herbivores. Unfortunately, broad surveys of large numbers of species have not yet been conducted, and there is not enough information to make a conclusive statement. However, Steve Heard at the

University of New Brunswick and colleagues in Iowa used a different approach, leading them to conclude that host differentiation may, in fact, cause the levels of diversity we see.

Heard and colleagues decided to address this question in a novel way (Stireman et al. 2005). Rather than focus in-depth on a single insect species, they instead chose two common host plants (*Solidago altissima* and *S. gigantea*) and looked at many of the herbivore species that feed upon these plants. These two plant species are ideal for such a study, as they are found growing together over most of southern Canada and the United States, and thus there is substantial opportunity for host-race formation. They found nine common herbivores, which include leaf-feeding beetles and gall-forming midges, flies, and moths (fig. 14.25). To test for divergence, they collected insects from both plant species throughout much of Canada and the United States. They flash-froze the insects in the field, allowing them to later sequence segments of mitochondrial DNA. Divergence was then estimated by looking at the differences in sequences for a given species as a function of its two hosts. In other words,

(a)   (b)

Figure 14.25   Adult moths oviposit within stems of *Solidago,* forming (*a*) galls. (*b*) Within the galls are the developing larvae of the moths.

(a), (b) Courtesy of Stephen Heard, and Chris Kolaczan.

was a particular insect species genetically homogeneous or genetically distinct across the two host plant species?

They found that four of their nine insect species showed evidence of genetic divergence among host plants. This high number supports the idea that variation among host species can lead to genetic specialization, which could be the first step toward speciation. In a follow-up study, the authors show that such differentiation is not limited to the plant and herbivore but can also extend to the parasitoids of the herbivores (Stireman et al. 2006). They again sampled a broad geographic range, this time focusing exclusively on the common gall-forming insects of these plant species. Many of these insects will themselves serve as host to a variety of parasitoid species. Again using genetic analysis, Heard and his colleagues were able to show that the parasitoid populations themselves were genetically differentiated as a function of the plant species that their host insect was feeding upon, even though the parasitoid had no direct interactions with the plant itself. They suggest that host-race formation can cascade to these top predators, potentially contributing to increased diversity for them as well.

The studies by Heard and colleagues leave many questions unanswered, such as what are the mechanisms for differentiation of phytophagous insects on different host species. More recently, Heard (2012) has developed a conceptual model for how phytophagous insects may use plant host trait space which could explain initial plant host shifts, and subsequent genetic diversification of insect populations on separate hosts. This model, called the gape and pinch model, incorporates four independent, testable hypotheses which represent four successive stages in the process of host shift and genetic differentiation of insects.

To understand trait space, it can be thought of as the subset of phenotypic traits within a host plant species that a phytophagous insect can use. For example, an insect feeding on a species of golden rod may use some plants, but not others. The insect may preferentially use larger plants, or those with higher water content. There is phenotypic variation within the golden rod population, and some plants are more suitable hosts than others. The entire trait space of the plant host is not used by the insect, only the space defined by plants with sufficient water and size. Another species of plant, perhaps even another species of golden rod, will also have phenotypic variation with respect to size and water content. The two plant species may have areas of overlap or adjacency with respect to the traits important to the insects. If the portion of the original host's trait space that is used by the insect happens to be similar to, or adjacent to, the trait space of the new plant species, the insect might make use of the new plant.

Heard's model includes the following four hypotheses: (1) Adjacency favours host shifting, or what Heard calls the *adjacent errors hypothesis*. (2) Adjacency persists after host shifting (*adjacent oligophagy hypothesis*). For a period of time after host shifting, the insect will use both plant species, specifically those individuals of each plant species that have adjacent trait spaces. (3) Distance permits genetic isolation (*trait distance-divergence hypothesis*). After a host shift, insects may begin to use other portions of the new host plant's trait space that is not adjacent to the original plant's trait space. As this happens, an individual insect will stop using both plants. Populations can become isolated. Finally, (4) other isolating mechanisms reduce importance of trait-space distance (*distance relaxation hypothesis*).

Heard has also presented a framework for testing these hypothesis, and the call is open. As yet, there are relatively few data to test these hypotheses, but the power of the conceptual model is that it provides a road map to future ecologists to help answer fundamental questions about the co-evolution of plant–herbivore interactions, and species diversification of insects.

SUMMARY

Predator–prey and host–herbivore interactions are two common forms of exploitation that occur among species (fig. 14.26). These interactions increase the fitness of one member at the expense of the other and can have significant consequences on population dynamics and evolutionary trajectories.

14.1 Herbivory is a widespread ecological interaction and has caused the evolution of a diversity of plant defence strategies.

Most plants experience some degree of herbivory during their life. Feeding by herbivores typically has negative fitness consequences for the plant and positive benefits for the consumer. However, light grazing by geese can cause overcompensation in a subarctic salt marsh, while heavy grazing by the same geese can cause reductions in plant growth. Herbivorous stream insects can control the density of their algal and bacterial food. Plants often contain numerous morphological and chemical defences that deter feeding or cause illness in the herbivore if consumed (fig. 14.26). Some of these defences will be constitutive, while others will be induced following an attack.

14.2 Prey populations are influenced by food availability, by consumption by predators, and by nonconsumptive effects of predators.

Populations of a wide variety of predators and prey show highly dynamic fluctuations in abundance, ranging from days to decades. A particularly well-studied example of

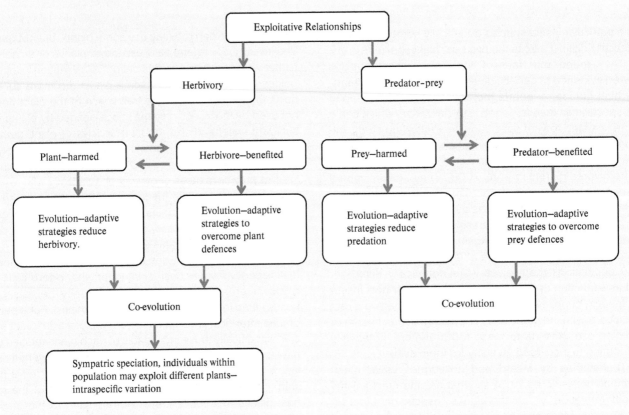

Figure 14.26   Concept map for chapter 14.

predator–prey cycles is that of snowshoe hares and their predators, which have been shown to result from the combined effects of the snowshoe hares on the food and of the predators on the snowshoe hare population. In addition to direct consumptive effects on prey populations, predators can significantly impact prey populations through nonconsumptive effects (fig. 14.26). The study of these effects is commonly referred to as the "ecology of fear." By altering stress physiology of hares, lynx can cause reduced health and reproduction of the hares that have not been killed, with implications for future population growth. In a large meta-analysis, such nonconsumptive effects appear to be at least as important in determining prey population dynamics as are consumptive effects.

14.3 The population consequences of exploitative relationships can be explored with theoretical models.

Mathematical models of predator–prey interactions by Lotka and Volterra suggest that exploitative interactions themselves can produce population cycles without any influences from outside forces, such as weather. This model assumes that no intraspecific competition is occurring and that prey population growth is limited only by predation. Though these assumptions are unrealistic, this model is a useful starting point for understanding general principles related to predator–prey population dynamics.

14.4 Prey populations can persist in the presence of predators through the use of refugia and a diversity of defence strategies.

Prey need a way to avoid predators, or else their populations will tend to crash. Many animal species are Batesian mimics, in which they display the warning coloration that is associated with a toxic model species. Other animal species are Müllerian mimics, in which there has been convergence toward a common warning coloration for unrelated toxic species, such as the black and yellow stripes of stinging insects. Another method of avoiding predation is the use of refugia. The refuges that promote the persistence of hosts and prey include secure places to which the exploiter has limited access. However, living in large groups can be considered as a kind of refuge since it reduces the probability that an individual host or prey will be attacked. It appears that predator satiation is a defensive tactic used by a wide variety of organisms. Growing to large size can also represent a kind of refuge when the prey species is faced by size-selective predators. Size is used as a refuge by prey species ranging from stream insects to the rhinoceros.

Exploitative interactions can cause evolution in the prey species. In predator–prey or plant–herbivore relationships, there may be no clear winner as the exploited species evolves innovations to reduce vulnerability while the exploiter species evolves innovations that permit it to overcome these defences. Populations of herbivores can become genetically subdivided if they feed upon multiple host species. This could be the first step toward sympatric speciation, and may contribute to the large number of phytophagous insect species that exist on the planet.

REVIEW QUESTIONS

1. Predation is one of the processes by which one organism exploits another. Others are herbivory, parasitism, and disease. What distinguishes each of these processes, including predation, from the others? We can justify discussing these varied processes under the heading of exploitation because each involves one organism making its living at the expense of another. By what "currency" would you measure that expense (e.g., energy, fitness)?

2. Researchers have suggested that predators could actually increase the population density of a prey species heavily infected by a pathogenic parasite (Hudson et al. 1992). Explain how predation could lead to population increases in the prey population.

3. Explain the roles of food and predators in producing cycles of abundance in populations of snowshoe hare. Populations of many of the predators that feed on snowshoe hares also cycle substantially. Explain population cycles among these predator populations.

4. What contributions have laboratory and mathematical models made to our understanding of predator–prey population cycles? What are the shortcomings of these modelling approaches? What are their advantages?

5. We included spatial refuges, predator satiation, and size in our discussions of the role played by refuges in the persistence of exploited species. How could time act as a refuge? Explain how natural selection could lead to the evolution of temporal refuges.

6. Joseph Culp and Gary Scrimgeour (1993) studied the timing of feeding by mayfly larvae in streams with and without fish. These mayflies feed by grazing on the exposed surfaces of stones, where they are vulnerable to predation by fish, which in the streams studied are size-selective feeders and feed predominantly during the day. In the study streams without fish, both small and large mayflies have a slight tendency to feed during the day, but feed at all hours of the day and night. In the streams with abundant fish populations, small mayflies fed around the clock, while large mayflies fed mainly at night. Explain these patterns in terms of time as a refuge and size-selective predation.

7. Batesian mimics confer an advantage from the toxicity of the model species, yet do not incur any of the energetic costs associated with the actual production of the toxic chemical. Why do the Batesian model species allow this to happen?

8. Having induced, rather than constitutive, plant defences seems like a very cost-effective mechanism to protect oneself against attack. However, many plant species contain constitutive defences. Why?

9. Snow geese can cause either positive or negative changes in the growth of their food plants, depending upon the intensity of grazing. When grazing is most severe, a variety of low-growing moss species becomes dominant. Why aren't these moss species dominant when grazing is light? How can grazing alter competitive interactions among these plant species?

10. Ecological interactions, such as exploitation, can have significant evolutionary consequences, such as host-race formation. To understand this, it is critical that researchers be able to blend techniques from different disciplines, such as evolutionary biology and ecology. Are ecology and evolution truly distinct disciplines, or do they look at similar questions but in different time scales?

Photograph by Francois Teste.

CHAPTER 15 — MUTUALISM, PARASITISM, AND DISEASE

CHAPTER CONCEPTS

hances are that at some point in a high school or first year university biology course, you have seen *Paramecium bursaria* under a microscope. This ciliate differs from most other members of its genus in the characteristic presence of endosymbiotic algae, or zoochlorellae (fig. 15.1). The presence of the zoochlorellae give *P. bursaria* a photosynthetic quality and it is able to use the carbon fixed by the algae to grow and to produce energy. And, like other species of *Paramecium*, it can feed heterotrophically, sweeping particles into its oral grove and engulfing them into vacuoles.

Imagine having that same flexibility in nutrition. You could forage, but when the cupboard is bare, you could then just make your own food. For many protists and marine invertebrates, this is their reality. Many of these organisms enjoy the advantages of **mixotrophy** conferred by the presence of endosymbiotic algae or cyanobacteria. But these advantages and the nature of the relationship between host and endosymbiont may change with context.

The algae that find themselves inside the body of a host may receive protection from grazing and access to a rich source of nutrients and CO_2. The algae may also find themselves exploited for the carbon they produce. For the host, the advantage gained when food is scarce and light is available disappears if there is plenty of food, or if a predator drives the host to take refuge in the dark. In these contexts, the endosymbiont may become a liability. Some portion of the carbon consumed by the host will go to maintain the algae when they are not able to fix their own carbon.

Context will then determine whether these types of relationships are mutualistic or parasitic, and context will determine which organism is being exploited. Some endosymbiotic relationships are facultative. When the context no longer favours a host, the relationship may be terminated. *P. bursaria* can be grown in the dark but will expel their zoochlorellae. Both the ciliate and the algae are capable of independent growth. However, when conditions change, for example when the *P. bursaria* are brought back into the light and the context again favours the relationship, zoochlorellae may be reincorporated.

In a long and highly specific co-evolutionary association between a host and an endosymbiont, selection may reduce intrinsic redundancies. The host may assume control over the dispensable metabolic functions of the symbiont, and the relationship may become progressively more obligate, for the symbiont, the host, or both. Lynn Margulis at Boston University drew upon this analogy in her hypothesis regarding the evolution of eukaryotic cells. She postulated that the origins of the mitochondria, chloroplasts, and cytoskeletal elements lay in initially symbiotic relationships among prokaryotes that became progressively more obligate.

The bacterial origin of eukaryotic organelles had been proposed as early as 1910 by Konstantin Mereschkowski. Margulis presented a "plausible scheme" for the sequential origins of aerobic metabolism, evolution of the mitochondrion, mitotic cell division, and finally the chloroplast from prokaryotic ancestors (Sagan 1967). Her scheme drew upon cytological, biochemical, and paleontological evidence, and proposed testable hypotheses

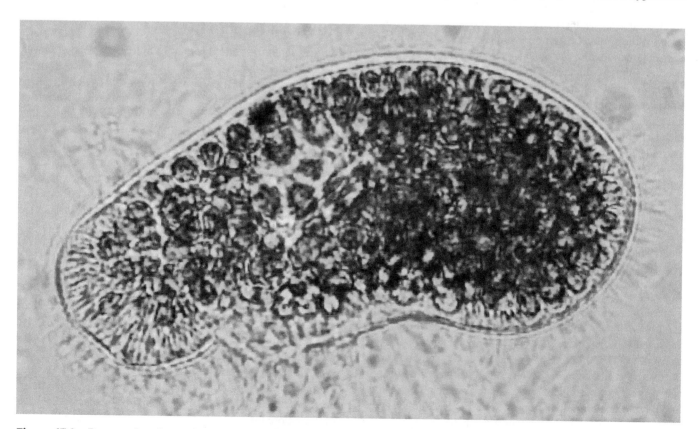

Figure 15.1 *Paramecium bursaria* is a mixotroph that can exploit endosymbiotic zoochlorellae.
Andrew Laursen.

that would later substantiate the prokaryotic origins of eukaryotic organelles.

The evolution of eukaryotic cells dramatically changed the course of biology and was considered by evolutionary biologist Ernst Mayr as "perhaps the most important and dramatic event in the history of life" (Mayr 2001). Without the evolution of eukaryotes, I would not be writing this chapter, nor would you be reading it. Our current understanding of this origin and by extension insights into symbiotic relationships are largely owed to Lynn Margulis. Moreover, Margulis provides a great example of the importance of creative insights coupled with perseverance in science. By her own account, her seminal paper was rejected about 15 times before finally being accepted for publication in the *Journal of Theoretical Biology*. Were the relationships among prokaryotes that led to eukaryotic cells mutualistic or parasitic? The evolutionary outcome, which we would consider very positive, may cloud our view of the nature of these original interactions.

In this chapter we will discuss mutualism and parasite–host relationships and why many ecologists are moving away from the idea that parasitism and mutualism are fundamentally different types of interactions. Instead, there is an increasing understanding that these are simply different points on a continuum of possible interactions and that ecological context can modify the nature of an interaction between species. These types of interactions have historically received less attention from community ecologists than competition or predator–prey/plant–herbivore interactions. However, as we will see they can be important in shaping biological communities. Without mutualisms, the biosphere would be entirely different. We can erase the Great Barrier Reef, the largest biological structure on earth. Deep sea life around ocean floor hydrothermal vents would not exist (chapter 7), and we would have no sunflowers, apples, or other animal-pollinated plants and produce. We would still have many wind-pollinated plants, such as conifers and grasses. However, without their mycorrhizae they might be in a very sorry state. Even if the grasses remained, the large herbivores, such as bison, elephants, and camels, and even the smaller rabbits and caterpillars would not. They have a variety of mutualistic relationships with microbes in their guts that allow them to eat plants. If we remove predators from a system, there will be some shifts in population dynamics. If we remove mutualists, natural systems as we know them would collapse.

If you ask a child to name her favourite animals, I will lay odds that she will name horses or dogs or cats before mentioning tapeworms. Apart from the fact that tapeworms are not particularly cuddly and make lousy pets, we rarely think about parasites when we are considering the diversity of life. However, most animal species on earth are parasites. Humans alone can host well over 100 endo- and ectoparasites, many of which are specific to humans or have a very limited range of potential alternate hosts. Other free-living species could likely boast (or bemoan) a similarly impressive guest list. Animals are not special in this respect, and all known organisms, including plants, fungi, bacteria, and protists appear to host at least one species of specialist parasite and several species of generalist parasites.

Mutualisms and parasitic relationships may be ephemeral, relationships of chance and convenience, or they may be highly specialized and obligate relationships for one or both members. The relationships that gave rise to eukaryotic cells lay at one extreme end of this continuum. We will consider other examples of both mutualistic and parasitic relationships that fall along the continuum and will discuss their ecological importance. This will include a discussion of parasites as agents of disease that play an ecological role in shaping populations.

15.1 Complex Interactions

There is great diversity in the types of parasitic and mutualistic interactions that exist, defying easy generalization. Analogies have been drawn between parasitism and predation as exploitative interactions that may control a host or prey population. However, as we will see there is tremendous variation in the natures of different parasitic relationships, and, again, the same relationship between two species may be mutualistic, commensal, amensal, or parasitic depending upon the ecological context. These relationships, then, defy generalization. They cannot be represented as effectively in conceptual mathematical models as competition and predation (chapters 13 and 14). It is impossible to present the full diversity of these interactions in a single section of a chapter, and instead we present just a few examples that demonstrate the variability that exists in nature. We will begin with mutualisms, then move into examples of parasitic relationship, leading to subsection 15.2 on ecology of disease.

Mutualism: Protection of Bullhorn Acacia by Ants

Writing about the natural history of mutualism, Daniel Janzen (1985) included "plant–ant protection mutualisms" as one of his general categories of mutualism. Janzen (1966, 1967a, 1967b) himself is responsible for studying one of the best known of these mutualisms, the mutualism between ants and swollen thorn acacias in Central America.

Worldwide, the genus *Acacia* includes over 700 species. Distributed throughout the tropical and subtropical regions around the world, acacias are particularly common in drier tropical and subtropical environments. The swollen thorn acacias are restricted to the New World, where they are distributed from southern Mexico, through Central America, and into Venezuela and Colombia. Swollen thorn acacias show several characteristics related to their association with ants, including enlarged thorns with a soft, easily excavated pith (fig. 15.2); year-round leaf production; enlarged foliar nectaries; and leaflet tips modified into concentrated food sources called Beltian bodies. The thorns provide living space for ants, while the foliar nectaries provide a source of sugar and liquid. Beltian bodies are a source of oils and protein.

Ants of the genus *Pseudomyrmex* (subfamily *Pseudomyrmecinae*) form mutualistic relationships with swollen thorn acacias. This subfamily of ants is dominated by species that have evolved close relationships with trees, and shows several characteristics that Janzen suggests are associated with arboreal living. They are generally fast and agile runners, have good vision, and forage independently. The *Pseudomyrmex* spp. associated with swollen thorn acacias, or "acacia-ants," maintain large colony sizes and exhibit 24-hour activity outside the nest. Workers in the colony are highly aggressive. They will attack, bite, and sting nearly all insects they encounter on their home plant or any large herbivores, such as deer and cattle, that attempt to feed on the plant. They will also attack and kill any vegetation encroaching on the home tree. These activities keep other plants from growing near the base of the home tree and prevent other trees, shrubs, and vines from shading it. Consequently, the home plant's access to light and soil nutrients is increased.

Newly mated *Pseudomyrmex* queens move through the vegetation searching for unoccupied seedlings or shoots of bullhorn acacia. When a queen finds an unoccupied acacia, she excavates an entrance in one of the green thorns or uses one carved previously by another ant. The queen then lays her first eggs in the thorn and begins to forage on her newly acquired home plant. She gets nectar for herself and her developing larvae from the foliar nectaries and gets additional solid food from the Beltian bodies. Over time, the number of workers in the new colony increases, and the queen shifts to a mainly reproductive function. Once a colony reaches a size of about 1,200 workers, it begins producing a more or less steady stream of winged reproductive males and females, which fly off to mate. The queens among them may eventually establish new colonies on other bullhorn acacias or on one of the other Central American swollen thorn acacias.

Janzen's detailed natural history of the interaction between bullhorn acacia and ants suggests interactions of mutual benefit to both partners; however, the strength of these benefits had not been experimentally tested. It was clear that the ant needs swollen thorn acacias, but do the acacias need the ants? Janzen's experiments concentrated on the influence of ants on acacia performance. He also tested the effectiveness of the ants at keeping acacias free of herbivorous insects. Janzen removed ants from acacias by clipping occupied thorns or by cutting out entire shoots with their ants. He then measured the growth rate, leaf production, mortality, and insect population density on acacias with and without ants.

Janzen's experiments demonstrated that ants significantly improve plant performance. Differences in plant performance were likely the result of increased competition with other plants and increased attack by insects faced by acacias without their tending ants. Suckers (basal shoots) growing from stumps of acacias occupied by ants lengthened at seven times the rate of suckers without ants (fig. 15.3). Suckers with ants were also more than 13 times heavier than suckers without ants and had more than twice the number of leaves and almost three times the number of thorns. Suckers with ants also survived at twice the rate of suckers without ants (fig. 15.4).

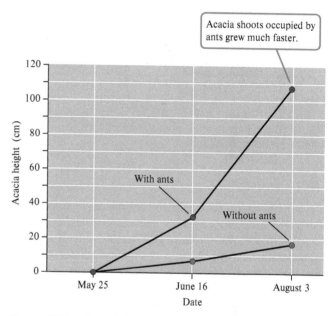

Figure 15.3 Growth by bullhorn acacia with and without resident ants.
Data from Janzen 1966.

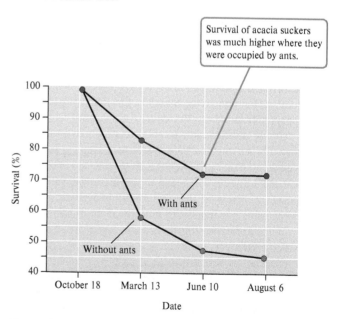

Figure 15.4 Survival of bullhorn acacia shoots with and without resident ants.
Data from Janzen 1966.

Figure 15.2 Split thorn of a bullhorn acacia, revealing a nest of its ant mutualists.
© Robert & Linda Mitchell.

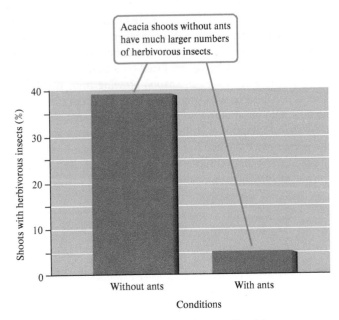

Acacia shoots without ants have much larger numbers of herbivorous insects.

Figure 15.5 Ants and the abundance of herbivorous insects on bullhorn acacia.
Data from Janzen 1966.

What produces the improved performance of acacias with ants? One factor appears to be reduced populations of herbivorous insects. Janzen found that acacias without ants had more herbivorous insects on them than did acacias with ants (fig. 15.5). Janzen's experiments provide strong evidence that bullhorn acacias need ants nearly as much as the ants need the acacia.

Mutualism or Exploitation? Corals and Zooxanthellae

Because of the importance of mutualism in the lives of reef-building corals, it appears that the ecological integrity of coral reefs depends upon mutualism. Coral reefs show exceptional productivity and diversity. Recent estimates put the number of species occurring on coral reefs at approximately one-half million, and coral reef productivity is among the highest of any natural ecosystem. As we saw in chapter 3, the paradox is that this overwhelming diversity and exceptional productivity occur in an ecosystem surrounded by nutrient-poor tropical seas. The key to explaining this paradox lies with mutualism: in this case, between reef-building corals and unicellular algae called zooxanthellae, members of the phylum Dinoflagellata. Most of these organisms are free-living unicellular marine and freshwater photoautotrophs. Together, these organisms create the foundation ecosystem.

Zooxanthellae live within coral tissues at densities averaging approximately 1 million cells per square centimetre of coral surface. Like plants, the zooxanthellae need inorganic nutrients, which they receive from their animal partner. In return, the coral polyps, which are heterotrophs, receive organic compounds synthesized by zooxanthellae during photosynthesis.

One of the most fundamental discoveries concerning the relationship between corals and zooxanthellae is that the release of organic compounds by zooxanthellae is controlled by the coral partner. Corals induce zooxanthellae to release organic compounds with "signal" compounds, which alter the permeability of the zooxanthellae cell membrane. Zooxanthellae grown in isolation from corals release very little organic material into their environment. However, when exposed to extracts of coral tissue, zooxanthellae immediately increase the rate at which they release organic compounds. This response appears to be a specific, chemically mediated communication between corals and zooxanthellae. Zooxanthellae do not respond to extracts of other animal tissues, and coral extracts do not induce leaking of organic molecules by any other algae that have been studied.

Corals not only control the secretion of organic compounds by zooxanthellae, they also control the rate of zooxanthellae population growth and population density. In corals, zooxanthellae populations grow at rates one-tenth to one-hundredth the rates observed when they are cultured separately from corals. Normally, unicellular algae show balanced growth, growth in which all cell constituents, such as nitrogen, carbon, and DNA, increase at the same rate. However, zooxanthellae living in coral tissues show unbalanced growth, producing fixed carbon at a much higher rate than other cell constituents. Moreover, the coral stimulates the zooxanthellae to secrete 90% to 99% of this carbon, which the coral uses for its own respiration. Carbon secreted and diverted for use by the coral could otherwise be used to produce new zooxanthellae, which would increase population growth.

If zooxanthellae grow at slower rates and exhibit unbalanced growth, are there benefits to their relationship with corals? The main benefit appears to be access to higher levels of nutrients, especially nitrogen. Corals feed on zooplankton, which gives them a means of capturing nutrients, especially nitrogen and phosphorus. When corals metabolize the protein in their zooplankton prey, they excrete ammonium as a waste product. L. Muscatine and C. D'Elia (1978) showed that coral species such as *Tubastrea aurea* that do not harbour zooxanthellae continuously excrete ammonium into their environment, while corals such as *Pocillopora damicornis* do not excrete measurable amounts of ammonia (fig. 15.6). What happens to the ammonium produced by *Pocillopora* during metabolism of the protein in their zooplankton prey? Muscatine and D'Elia suggested that this ammonium is immediately taken up by zooxanthellae as the coral excretes it. In addition to internal recycling of the ammonium produced by their coral partner, zooxanthellae also actively absorb ammonium from seawater. By absorbing nutrients from the surrounding medium and leaking very little back into the environment, corals and their zooxanthellae gradually accumulate substantial quantities of nitrogen. So, as in tropical rain forests, large quantities of nutrients accumulate on coral reefs and are retained in living biomass.

As an aside, the relationship between corals and zooxanthellae is not obligate, and algae may abandon the corals (or corals may expel the algae). The loss of algae from coral polyps is referred to as "bleaching" and occurs when corals are under physiological stress, such as thermal stress. Ove Hoegh-Guldberg and colleagues describe predicted feedback on coral reefs from rapid climate change and attendant ocean acidification (2007). Increased ocean temperatures are expected to increase the incidence of coral bleaching. In combination with acidification, this could lead to functional collapse of many carbonate reef systems. We'll discuss this issue in greater depth in chapter 23. But for here, we note that changing environmental conditions can alter or end a mutualism that underpins an entire ecosystem.

Parasite Infestation: Ghost Moose and Winter Ticks

Moose (*Alces alces*) are found throughout most of Canada (fig. 15.7*a*) and are the subject of many myths, legends, and stories. One of the more common stories is about the "ghost moose," white moose seen walking across the landscape (fig. 15.7*b*). Bill Samuel, of the University of Alberta, has studied these "ghost" moose and has been able to show the cause: winter ticks (Samuel 2004).

Dermacentor albipictus is a tick that can feed on a variety of hosts, including moose, elk, and white-tailed deer (fig. 15.7*c*). Winter ticks are unique compared to all other ticks in Canada in that the larval, nymph, and adult stages feed upon the blood of a single host. This is in contrast to parasites such as *Plagiorhynchus,* described below, which alternates between hosts during different stages of its own development. *Dermacentor albipictus* are found throughout most of the southern range of moose in North America. Although these ticks are large relative to other ticks, reaching 1.5 cm in length as a blood-engorged adult, their size is dwarfed in comparison to an adult moose, standing nearly 2 m in height. How is it possible that this little parasite can cause a dramatic shift in the appearance and health of this large animal? Think of Gulliver's encounters with the diminutive Lilliputians (Swift 1726). The answer lies primarily in numbers.

Over the years, Samuel and his students examined the hides of hundreds of moose collected in the winter. On 214 hides collected from western Canada, there was an average of 33,000 winter ticks per moose, with 3% of the moose having in excess of 100,000 ticks. As a point of reference, 50,000 ticks correspond to approximately 3.0 ticks per cm² on a moose calf (Samuel 2004). Samuel compared tick densities on co-occurring hosts in Elk Island National Park, Alberta, and found tick densities to be more than 25 times greater on moose than on elk, deer, or bison. In other words, these ticks infest this particular host, even though other hosts are available in the area.

The consequences of this infestation can be severe. Using estimates on the amount of blood that individual female ticks can consume, Samuel (2004) made some rough calculations about blood loss. He estimated that naturally occurring tick densities consume approximately 17% of the blood volume of a bull moose, 11% of the blood volume of cows (though this is during the last trimester of pregnancy), and 58% of the blood volume of calves. Aside from blood loss, high densities of these

(a)

(b)

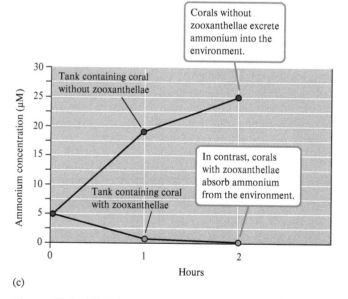

(c)

Figure 15.6 (*a*) *Tubastrea aurea* does not harbour zooxanthellae, while (*b*) *Pocillopora damicornis* does. (*c*) Harbouring zooxanthellae by corals reduces ammonium flux compared to corals without zooxanthellae.

(a), (b), (c) Aquanaut4/Dreamstime.com, Mychadre77/Dreamstime.com. Data from Muscatimne and D'Elia 1978.

(a)

(b)

(c)

Figure 15.7   (*a*) With few ticks, moose retain a brown coat. (*b*) At high numbers of ticks, moose self-groom, destroying the winter coat of hair and giving the whitish image of a "ghost" moose. (*c*) Winter ticks can occur at extremely high densities on the skin of a moose.

(a) David Ponton/Design Pics RF/Getty Images; (b) Photo 89934982 © Amelia Martin–Dreamstime.com; (c) © Brian Peterson/*Minneapolis Star Tribune*/ZUMA Wire/Alamy Live News.

parasites cause a behavioural shift in the moose—increased grooming.

Grooming of moose includes biting and licking, scratching with hind hooves, and rubbing against trees. In a study of captive moose, Samuel found that tick-infested moose groom up to two hours each day in March through April, the period in which the ticks are most actively feeding. In contrast, tick-free moose groom less than five minutes per day. The direct outcome of this high level of grooming is hair loss (Mooring and Samuel 1999). The "ghost" moose have broken off the dark outer portion of their hair on over 80% of the body surface, exposing the white-coloured lower portion, giving rise to an overall whitish appearance.

Knowing what you do about the theory of allocation and physiological ecology (section 2), it should be readily apparent that increased expenditure of energy to replace blood, increased time spent grooming, and decreased insulative properties of the coat likely increase stress and reduce the health of infested individuals. For nearly a century, ticks have been seen as reducing the strength of moose and as a likely source of mortality. Samuel (2004) lists a variety of accounts throughout Canada linking moose die-offs to tick numbers. Within Elk Island National Park, Samuel found that moose and tick numbers tracked in synchrony, similar to what we saw with predator–prey dynamics in chapter 14. The average number of ticks found on moose appears to be tightly linked to the number of moose present the previous year. We now turn to a different example to demonstrate that parasites can not only affect physiology of the host but also alter host behaviour.

Parasites Modify Host Behaviour

A number of parasites alter the behaviour of their hosts in ways that benefit transmission and reproduction of the parasite. Acanthocephalans, or spiny-headed worms, change the behaviour of amphipods, small aquatic crustaceans, in ways that make it more likely that infected amphipods will be eaten by a suitable vertebrate host. Janice Moore (1983, 1984a, and 1984b) studied a parasite–host interaction involving an acanthocephalan, *Plagiorhynchus cylindraceus*; a terrestrial isopod, or pill bug, *Armadillidium vulgare*; and the European starling (*Sturnus vulgaris*). In this interaction, the pill bug serves as an intermediate host for *Plagiorhynchus*, which completes its life cycle in the starling (fig. 15.8).

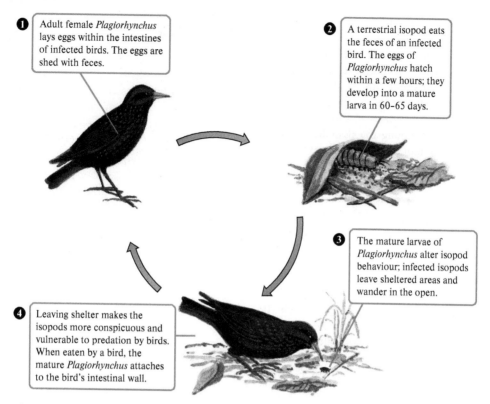

① Adult female *Plagiorhynchus* lays eggs within the intestines of infected birds. The eggs are shed with feces.

② A terrestrial isopod eats the feces of an infected bird. The eggs of *Plagiorhynchus* hatch within a few hours; they develop into a mature larva in 60–65 days.

③ The mature larvae of *Plagiorhynchus* alter isopod behaviour; infected isopods leave sheltered areas and wander in the open.

④ Leaving shelter makes the isopods more conspicuous and vulnerable to predation by birds. When eaten by a bird, the mature *Plagiorhynchus* attaches to the bird's intestinal wall.

Figure 15.8 The life cycle of *Plagiorhynchus cylindraceus*, an intestinal parasite of birds.

At the outset of her research, Moore predicted that *Plagiorhynchus* would alter the behaviour of *Armadillidium*. She based this prediction on several observations. One was the relative frequency of infection of *Armadillidium* and starlings by *Plagiorhynchus*. Field studies had demonstrated that even where *Plagiorhynchus* infected only 1% of the *Armadillidium* population, over 40% of the starlings in the area were infected. Something was enhancing the rates of transmission to the starlings, and Moore predicted that it was altered host behaviour. Moore thought that the size of *Plagiorhynchus* might also be a factor. At maturity, the infective cystacanth stage of *Plagiorhynchus* grows to about 3 mm, a substantial fraction of the internal environment of an 8 mm pill bug!

Moore brought *Armadillidium* into the laboratory and established two populations: an uninfected control group and an infected experimental group. Moore found that *Plagiorhynchus* alters the behaviour of *Armadillidium* in several ways. Infected *Armadillidium* spend less time in sheltered areas and more time in low-humidity environments and on light-coloured substrates. These changes in behaviour would increase the time an *Armadillidium* spends in the open, where a bird could easily see it. In other words, infected *Armadillidium* behave in a way that increases the probability of discovery by foraging birds.

A critical step in this research was to determine whether the changed behaviour of infected *Armadillidium* translates into their being eaten more frequently by wild birds. Moore collected the arthropods that starlings feed to their nestlings and

from these collections estimated the rate at which they delivered *Armadillidium*—about one every ten hours. Using this delivery rate and the proportion of the *Armadillidium* population infected by *Plagiorhynchus* (about 0.4%), she was able to predict the expected rate of infection among starling nestlings if the adults capture *Armadillidium* at random from the natural population. The proportion of infected nestlings was 32%, about twice the rate of infection predicted if starlings fed randomly on the *Armadillidium* population. These results support Moore's hypothesis that the altered behaviour of infected *Armadillidium* increases their probability of being eaten by starlings.

Moore emphasized that *Plagiorhynchus* does not just alter *Armadillidium's* behaviour—it does so in a way that increases the rate at which the final host of the parasite, starlings, is infected. Altering the behaviour of the *Armadillidium* to increase their susceptibility to predation is then adaptive for the *Plagiorhynchus*. As parasites can affect host physiology and health, and can alter host behaviour, it will come as no surprise that parasites can alter the host's interactions with other species. We'll see in the next example how parasites may modulate competitive interactions.

Parasites Modify Outcome of Competition

During their work on competition among flour beetles, Thomas Park and his colleagues (Park 1948, Park et al. 1965) uncovered one of the very first examples of competitors eating each other. As we saw in chapter 13, the outcome of competition between *Tribolium castaneum* and *T. confusum* depended upon temperature and moisture. It turns out that the presence or absence of a protozoan parasite of *Tribolium, Adelina tribolii*, also influences the competitive balance between flour beetle species. The effects of this parasite are also entangled with predation among the flour beetles and with cannibalism, which we might think of as a form of intraspecific exploitation.

Of the two species, *T. castaneum* is the most cannibalistic; however, it preys on the eggs of *T. confusum* at an even higher rate than it cannibalizes its own eggs. In light of its predatory behaviour, it is not surprising that *T. castaneum* eliminated *T. confusum* in 84% of 76 competition experiments spanning a period of about 10 years. This predatory strategy works best, however, in the absence of *Adelina*.

Several biologists before Park had noted that *Adelina* caused sickness and death among *Tribolium* populations. It was Park, however, who demonstrated that *Adelina* reduces the density of *Tribolium* populations and can alter the outcome of competition between *T. confusum* and *T. castaneum*. *Adelina* strongly reduces the population density of *T. castaneum* populations but has little effect on *T. confusum* populations. In the absence of the parasite, *T. castaneum* won 12 of 18 competitive contests against *T. confusum*. When the parasite was included, however, *T. confusum* won 11 of 15 contests (fig. 15.9). In other words, parasitism can completely reverse the outcome of competitive interactions between species.

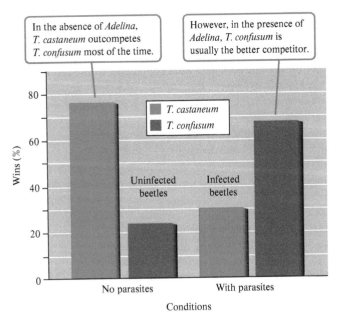

Figure 15.9 The influence of the protozoan parasite *Adelina tribolii* on competition between the flour beetles *Tribolium castaneum* and *T. confusum*.

Data from Park 1948.

CONCEPT 15.1 REVIEW

1. There is a big difference between describing an interaction and experimentally showing that the interaction has a potential fitness consequence. Why were Janzen's experiments effective in demonstrating that mutualisms do have fitness consequences under natural conditions?

2. Many parasites cause their hosts to alter their behaviour. What impact can this have on the parasite's ability to complete its life cycle?

3. The previous question relates to how altered host behaviour may affect fitness of the parasite. How might altered host behaviour affect fitness of the host?

15.2 Ecology of Disease

Basic ecological principles can be applied to our understanding of disease, and the population dynamics of pathogens can be predicted using a compartmental model. In 2016, the Zika virus was a major news story, bursting onto the news scene when a causal link was suggested between maternal infections during pregnancy and microcephaly. There is now scientific consensus that Zika virus infection is a cause of microcephaly. Interestingly, as big a story as this was in 2016, I have probably heard the word *Zika* fewer than 10 times in the past year, and I think 5 of those were from my own lips. Why is that? Yes, in part it speaks to our short attention span, but it also relates to the dynamic nature of pathogen outbreaks.

Zika was first isolated in 1947, with sporadic infections associated with relatively mild symptoms, including fever and rash. The epidemic in Brazil that captured our attention in 2016 began in Micronesia back in 2007, then spread throughout Oceania, arriving in the Americas in 2014–15. In 2016, there were 5,168 reported Zika cases in the United States, with 224 presumed local transmissions. It was these local transmissions that raised the spectre of the virus becoming endemic in North America. However, by 2017 the epidemic was in decline, with 452 cases in the U.S., and 15 presumed local transmissions. In 2018, there were 15 cases, with no local transmissions, and as of May 2019, there has been 1 reported case in the U.S.: a traveller who had been to a country where the virus is endemic. The decline in the U.S. mirrors a general decline in new cases elsewhere, but like populations of hares, we should reasonably expect to see periodic increases in the "population" of the virus, reflected as new outbreaks.

To understand Zika (and through Zika, other viruses), we should understand its ecology. Zika is caused by an arboviral pathogen. You may be more familiar with other diseases caused by arboviruses, such as dengue, yellow fever, and chikungunya.

Like these other viruses, Zika is transmitted by mosquito vectors, principally *Aedes aegypti* and *Aedes albopictus*. These two mosquito species are rapidly expanding their global distributions and, in the process, the distributions of the viruses. *A. albopictus* is more cold tolerant and is expanding into eastern North America. Both *Aedes* species are cosmopolitan and do well in rural or urban environments where water containers provide habitat for larvae. Does this mean outbreaks of Zika or dengue are likely to emerge and become endemic in North America? While you may think of this as a global health question, it is also fundamentally an ecology question.

Diseases are atypical conditions in living organisms that cause some sort of physiological impairment. Diseases can be caused by a number of factors, including genetic abnormalities, exposure to toxins, or parasitic organisms. While parasites will all cause some degree of stress to a host, not all will cause disease. Those parasites that do cause disease are referred to as pathogens. In the case of Zika, the virus is an endoparasite, and since it is the disease-causing agent, it is also a pathogen. The *Aedes* species are ectoparasites. They are not pathogens; however, they are vectors that transmit pathogens. The prospects for Zika to spread into North America will depend on complex ecological interactions among three species (virus, mosquito, and human) and between the vector species and the environment.

Pathogens are themselves living organisms, just like the caribou, pine trees, and whales that are more often associated with ecology. Although there are certainly debates about which types of pathogens are alive (bacteria, fungi, etc.) and which are not (viruses), ecological principles can be applied to our understanding of disease whether the pathogen is living or non-living. Natural selection is not dependent upon the pathogen's being "alive." As you may recall from chapter 4, evolution by natural selection requires traits to be heritable (the pathogen must be able to reproduce or replicate), and there need to be different levels of fitness (rates of reproduction or replication) among genotypes (or heritable units). This applies to viruses, such as the Zika virus, as much as it applies to wolves.

What influences the population size of pathogens? Some factors will be processes within the host (e.g., immune response, competition with other pathogens), and others will occur outside the host (e.g., transmission rates). Those heritable traits in the pathogen that increase its fitness (e.g., increase transmission) will tend to increase in frequency, while those that reduce fitness will tend to be selected against. The core mechanism of this, as with natural selection in general, is ecology.

Pathogens differ greatly in a number of critical life-history parameters, with significant implications for the growth of these agents, as well as host populations. As you will see, the efficiency with which disease-causing agents are transferred from host to host has important implications for the host's population dynamics. Transmission can be *direct*, such as through touching an infected individual, or *indirect*, such as when an uninfected individual touches a surface that has become infected. Pathogens also differ as a function of whether they are horizontally or vertically transmitted. **Horizontal transmission** is the transfer of pathogens among different individuals of the same generation, such as the spread of H1N1 flu virus through university campuses. **Vertical transmission** is the transfer of a pathogen from parent to offspring. The differences in transmission, as well as a number of other factors that influence the spread and growth of pathogens, will influence the disease dynamics in host populations. At the core, these differences are life-history differences among different disease-causing agents. Studying the interactions between pathogen and host is simply another form of exploitative ecological interactions, and so understanding disease is within the domain of ecology.

Taking an ecological approach to understanding disease also provides insights that may be helpful in reducing the spread of disease through a population of concern, whether the members are human or wildlife. In an influential paper titled "The Dawn of Darwinian Medicine," evolutionary biologists George Williams and Randolph Nesse (1991) argued that human health could be better improved by understanding the evolutionary and ecological basis of disease. How so?

Quite simply, the goal of disease management programs is to reduce the spread of pathogens and the incidence of disease among the host population. Some of our population management decisions (such as many medical treatments) may reduce pathogen growth rates, while others may not. In human populations, public health interventions (e.g., immunizations, quarantine) can be expensive and invasive to individuals, although the cost of not intervening may be much greater. As a result, there is a strong desire to apply such intervention measures only if there is evidence that they will be effective in reducing the spread of disease within the population. You may recall from chapters 12–14 that ecologists have developed a number of models to study population dynamics. It should then come as no surprise that these models have been modified for application to the study of disease.

To understand disease models, we first need to understand what factors actually influence the population growth of pathogens. Though disease is widespread across all species, here we focus on humans.

Compartmental Models

In chapter 12 we introduced the concept that populations, given unlimited resources and no enemies, would grow exponentially. However, natural populations rarely encounter such conditions, and instead a variety of ecological processes serve as brakes to population growth. Limited resources cause intraspecific competition within a population, a process that can be modelled with the logistic model. Interspecific competition was added to that model in chapter 13, and predator–prey dynamics used a similar modelling framework in chapter 14.

Although there is conceptual similarity among competition, predation, and disease in terms of their effects in reducing population growth, the ecology of disease has a number of specific differences that require a new modelling framework. One unique aspect of disease is that there are two scales at which pathogen populations can grow: pathogen levels within the body of a single host (e.g., viral load) and the number of new hosts a pathogen is able to colonize. As you will see, it is often the rate of spread to new hosts that most severely limits the spread of disease, rather than the population size of disease-causing agents within a single host. Because of the population-level importance of transmission, this life-history characteristic of the disease-causing agent is often a main target of vaccination and quarantine programs. The modern approach to understanding the impacts of disease on host populations was presented in a foundational paper by Roy Anderson and Robert May (1979).

At the core of this modelling approach are a series of "compartments" that represent different subpopulations of the host, connected through a series of arrows and parameters that represent disease transmission, recovery, and mortality (fig. 15.10). This modelling approach is an elegant way of showing how these basic aspects of pathogen population growth are connected to host population dynamics, allowing researchers to address questions of great public concern. But what exactly is being represented, and how can these be used?

In the centre of figure 15.10 are three compartments: susceptible, infected, and immune. These compartments represent different subpopulations of the hosts. This may seem vaguely familiar, as we discussed subpopulations in the subsection describing metapopulations (chapter 10). In fact, the math underlying both compartmental models and many of the traditional metapopulation models is nearly identical. The core difference is that here, subpopulations represent individuals that differ not in location (as in metapopulation models) but, instead, in health status with respect to the disease of interest. Susceptible hosts are those individuals in the population that have the potential to acquire the disease. Infected hosts already have the disease and, thus, are no longer susceptible. Some individuals may have acquired immunity, either naturally through recovery or through an intervention, such as a vaccination program. In either case, immune individuals are a discrete subpopulation.

What determines the size of each of these subpopulations? Though we are focused on disease, we cannot forget the basic factors that influence population dynamics of all populations: births, immigration, deaths, and emigrations. For simplicity, we will ignore immigration and emigration in figure 15.10, though these can be added if needed. Each of the host compartments is connected to another compartment labelled "death." These represent the number of susceptible, infected, and immune individuals that die. All individuals have a background per capita mortality rate, d. Infected individuals may die at a higher rate (depending upon the disease), and thus we can modify their mortality rate to be $d + \alpha$, where α represents the change in per capita mortality associated with the disease, generally called *virulence* of the pathogen. Highly virulent pathogens cause the presentation of many symptoms in the host and can lead to high rates of mortality. Pathogens with low virulence may result in hosts that are asymptomatic, with very low rates of mortality. It is worth considering this issue a bit more, from the perspective of the pathogen. All else being equal, what is likely to confer the greatest fitness to a pathogen, high or low virulence? If a pathogen quickly kills its host, it has less time to find a new host, and thus its growth rate is likely lower than a pathogen whose host persists longer. In other words, high rates of virulence are often counter to the best interests, evolutionarily, of a disease. In fact, many pathogens are highly virulent when they first jump to a new host species but become less virulent over time, likely due to natural selection within the pathogen's population.

All subpopulations of hosts also exhibit a background per capita birth rate, here represented as b. This rate may be altered in infected individuals through the addition of another term, σ (negative values would indicate reduced birth rates of infected individuals). It this model, all newborn individuals enter the susceptible subpopulation, indicating horizontal disease transmission. If a vertically transmitted disease was being modelled, births from individuals within infected subpopulation would go directly into the infected subpopulation.

Missing from the model at this point is the likelihood of individuals transitioning directly among the three main subpopulations. The probability of a susceptible individual becoming infected will be a function of the ability of the pathogen to move from one host to another. Some pathogens are particularly good at this and have very high transmission rates, ß, while others are less efficient at this, and have lower transmission rates. Pathogens with a high ß will move quickly through a host population and will tend to have, at least for a short time, a high population growth rate. Depending upon the disease and the population being modelled, some infected individuals will recover and gain immunity, thereby entering the immune subpopulation. Here, that occurs at a rate v. Depending upon the disease, immunity may decay over time, resulting in some individuals in the immune subpopulation moving into the susceptible subpopulation at a rate γ.

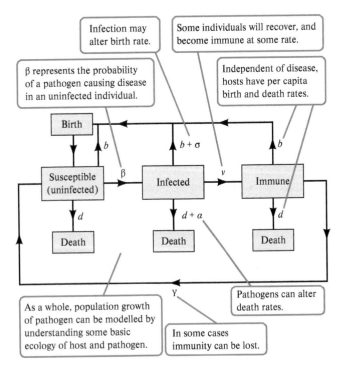

Figure 15.10 A compartmental model of the population growth of a disease-causing organism.

Reprinted by permission from Macmillan Publishers Ltd: NATURE. Roy M. Anderson and Robert M. May. 1979, August 2. Population biology of infectious diseases: Part I: A compartmental model of the population growth of a disease-causing organism. *Nature* 280:361–7. Used with permission via Rightslink.

Once a compartmental model is constructed, each of these parameters can be estimated. This allows the ecologists (or public health officials) to determine the likely progression of the disease through populations and, most importantly, to assess the potential impacts of any health interventions on the size of each subpopulation. Next, we will consider vaccination as a brake on the production and spread of pathogens, the efficacy of which can be estimated in compartmental models.

Using Vaccination to Provide Herd Immunity

Why do humans spend billions of dollars annually on immunization programs? There are two main answers. At the individual level, people are concerned about individuals they know contracting a variety of diseases, many of which have significant negative consequences for individual health. However, many of the diseases that we currently vaccinate for are actually rare in Canada, though that was certainly not always the case. What is the point in vaccinating for a rare disease, one that even an unvaccinated individual is unlikely to contract? An answer to this question came home to us in 2014–15 when more than 500 Canadians contracted measles, a disease that has been virtually eradicated in North America since the 1970s due to immunization programs. In spite of the success of these programs, or perhaps because of their success and our cultural amnesia of preventable disease, vaccination rates have dropped in recent years. There are a variety of social factors contributing to this decline, but my head might explode if I discuss them here. Unfortunately, the measles virus still finds a home in other parts of the world lacking universal vaccination programs. With global travel and a growing susceptible human population, it should not be surprising that we saw this outbreak.

Vaccination programs provide a significant benefit to public health by modifying the growth rates of diseases. At the extreme, an effective vaccination program can lead to negative pathogen population growth rates, such that the pathogen goes extinct in that host population (e.g., Canada). At that tantalizing point, **herd immunity** has been achieved and a great public health objective has been met. Why does this work? Let us go back to our basic compartmental model (fig. 15.10). How would we account for vaccination? A simple solution would be to include a new arrow linking the susceptible subpopulation with the immune subpopulation. By moving previously susceptible hosts to an "immune" subpopulation, vaccination will reduce the number of potential hosts for the pathogen, with direct negative consequences for the rate of pathogen growth.

Unfortunately, herd immunity is unlikely to be achieved for every population of every disease. And herd immunity once achieved must be maintained, as the measles outbreak demonstrates. What types of diseases do you think are more likely to be effectively controlled? Pathogens with naturally low levels of transmission have low population growth rates and are most susceptible to vaccination programs. Polio, for example, has a relatively low R_0 (5–7) and has been eradicated throughout many countries by using aggressive vaccination programs. This happened not because every person in a population was vaccinated but, rather, because the rates of vaccination were high enough to cause negative population growth of the disease. In contrast, measles has a very high R_0 (12–18) and is unlikely to ever be fully eliminated through vaccinations, and herd immunity requires a higher minimum percentage of the population to be vaccinated (83–94%).

CONCEPT 15.2 REVIEW

1. Why is life not a necessary condition for application of ecological models of population growth to diseases?
2. Why are the terms for per capita birth and death rates modified to account for infection in compartmental models of population growth?
3. Why is herd immunity hard to achieve for diseases with high transmission rates?

15.3 Mutualist–Exploiter Continuum

Many interactions can switch from parasitic to mutualistic depending upon the specific conditions of the local environment. So far in this chapter we have seen what appears to be a static portrayal of parasitic and mutualistic interactions. Similarly, we have presented examples that generally involve few individuals, such as the ant–acacia mutualism, where there are highly specialized adaptations that link species. Although this view is helpful in contrasting different types of ecological interactions, they give a skewed perspective of the complexity that actually exists in nature. To understand that mutualism and parasitism are actually different points on a continuum of possible ecological interactions, we must first recognize that most mutualistic interactions are facultative, not obligatory. Additionally, the more common mutualisms generally involve sets of species, rather than single species pairs, such as the ant–acacia example. Two examples we will discuss here, pollination and mycorrhizae, are typical of the complexity of mutualisms. Only in rare exceptions can a single flower be pollinated by a single animal; instead, most animal-pollinated flowers can be serviced by a diversity of insects (fig. 15.11). Similarly, insects are not usually dependent upon a single plant host for nectar or other food but instead often have a broad selection to choose from. The fact that multi-species interactions are involved, rather than the simpler idea of one-to-one interactions, has required ecologists to take a fresh look at mutualistic and exploitative interactions. We begin, once again, with natural selection.

Recall from chapter 8 that altruism and cooperation required stringent conditions to be evolutionarily stable. There is strong selection against an individual decreasing its fitness, as cheaters in the population would gain benefits from others

Figure 15.11   Mutualisms, such as those that occur among plants and pollinators, generally involve large numbers of species. Here are three pollinators of *Camassia quamash*, a plant found throughout southwestern Canada.
Sandra Gillsepie.

while expending no cost. This same logic applies to facultative mutualisms. Individuals are selected most strongly based upon traits that increase their own fitness, not the fitness of others. If an individual in the population sacrifices a portion of its fitness to an individual of another species, and receives less than that amount in fitness return, that behaviour will be selected against. Mutualisms are not "friendly" interactions that occur among species but instead are exploitative interactions that happen to be reciprocal. In these examples, we highlight that interactions can switch from parasitic to neutral to mutualistic depending on which species are participating, on the local environmental conditions, and even on the energetic status of the individuals involved.

Pollination: Optimal Foraging vs. Pollen Movement

Let us imagine pollination for a minute. Most of us will picture a sunny summer day, a field of flowers, and bees moving from one flower to the next, fertilizing the plants and, in turn, receiving nectar from the flowers. We can, however, look at it another way. Plants that undergo sexual reproduction have a problem: they cannot move. As a result, they are unable to actively pursue potential mates and instead require a **pollen vector** to move pollen from the anther to a stigma. In many cases, this pollen vector is abiotic, such as the wind moving the pollen of grasses and many boreal and temperate tree species. These vectors are non-specific in where they carry the pollen, as you will know when you see clouds of pollen during late spring. Plants that use these vectors put energy into producing lots of pollen such that some of it finds the mark (another plant of the same species). Other plant species use a biotic pollen vector, such as bees, flies, ants, birds, butterflies, or even small mammals. It is this group of "animal-pollinated" plants that we will discuss here. Animal pollination improves targeting and reduces the amount of pollen a plant needs to produce, but it comes with its own costs. Plants must invest energy to attract pollinators.

From the plant's perspective, traits that (1) increase visitation rates by pollinators, (2) enhance rates of pollen deposition, and (3) ensure that pollen moves from one individual to another individual of the same species at a minimum energetic cost should all be favoured by natural selection. Let us now look at it from the perspective of a pollinator, perhaps a bee. The bee is not interested in pollination; instead it is searching for food while trying to spend the minimum amount of energy foraging (chapter 5.2). Traits that help the bee locate food efficiently and reduce handling time will be favoured. This presents a problem. For the bee, it is best to fly from one flower to another on a single plant, as this will reduce travel time. Additionally, the bee should spend very little time on each flower, just taking the nectar and leaving. Unfortunately, for the plant, it is best if the bee visits very few flowers on a single plant (or else there is a good chance of inbreeding), and spends some time at each flower (ensuring pollen deposition). We clearly see that the mutualism of pollination is the outcome of conflicting exploitative interactions: the plants need sex, the bees need food. I don't think this is what parents have in mind when they teach their children about the "birds and the bees."

These conflicts of interest have been extensively studied and show how the evolutionary self-interest of members of mutualistic associations drives these exploitative interactions. Let us first consider an example of a non-obligate pollination mutualism and the issue of how long flowers "should" stay open. Plant species vary greatly in how long their flowers stay open, with some lasting a few hours, others several weeks. Why? Tia-Lynn Ashman, a distinguished professor at the University of Pittsburgh, addressed this issue while a post-doc of Daniel Schoen at McGill University (Ashman and Schoen 1994, 1997). She began by developing a model based upon the potential costs and benefits of keeping flowers open for different lengths of time.

What does a plant gain from having its flowers open? Only when open is there a chance that a pollinator will bring or remove pollen, and thus the male and female function of

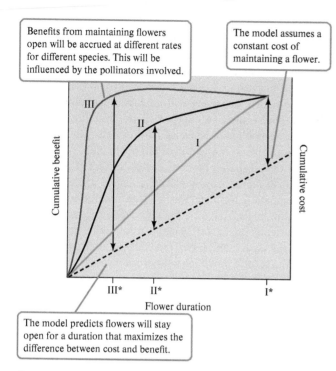

Benefits from maintaining flowers open will be accrued at different rates for different species. This will be influenced by the pollinators involved.

The model assumes a constant cost of maintaining a flower.

The model predicts flowers will stay open for a duration that maximizes the difference between cost and benefit.

Figure 15.12 Cost-benefit analyses can be helpful in trying to understand mutualisms, such as the optimal time for a plant to keep its flowers open. Roman numerals represent different rates of fitness accrual. The frequency of visits or the behaviour of the pollinator may result in rapid fitness accrual for the plant (III) or slow accrual (I).

the plant is dependent upon the flower's being open. But this lasts only to a point. Although not all pollen is removed during a single visit by a pollinator, nor all ovules generally fertilized, the fitness gained from subsequent visits by a pollinator is likely less than that gained on the first visit. In other words, there are diminishing returns from staying open longer (fig. 15.12). At the same time, there are a variety of costs associated with keeping flowers open, such as increased evaporation of nectar, increased respiration costs, and even increased risk of acquiring a sexually transmitted disease. The shapes of the cost and benefit curves will vary among species, but the point is the same. Maintaining open flowers is a balance between potential rewards and costs. In experimental work, they showed that seed set decreases when flowers are fertilized long after opening as opposed to soon after opening (Ashman and Schoen 1997), supporting their model. From the pollinator perspective, having the plant close flowers is not in the insect's best interest but is a perfectly understandable "selfish" behaviour of the plant, one that is likely favoured by natural selection. Any thoughts as to what selective pressures this would place on the pollinators?

The costs and benefits of mutualisms to each partner are variable, even within an obligate mutualism. John Addicott, of the University of Calgary, has spent decades unravelling details of the obligate mutualism occurring between the yucca plant and its pollinator, the yucca moth. Yuccas are a group of species (*Yucca* spp.) common throughout the dry areas of the western United States, also existing as small populations in southern

Alberta, and are common to gardens throughout Canada. Yuccas are pollinated by specialist moths (*Tegeticula* spp.). This is a highly specialized system where neither the plant nor the moth can complete its life cycle without the other (fig. 15.13).

(a)

(b)

Figure 15.13 (a) *Yucca baccata* in full flower; (b) a yucca moth, *Tegeticula altiplanella*, ovipositing on a yucca flower.

(a), (b) Dashingstock/Shutterstock, Natural History Archive/Alamy Stock Photo.

We begin in spring, when the moths emerge from cocoons in the soil and quickly mate. The gravid females fly to a nearby yucca plant, which is now in bloom. The moth enters the flower and picks many packets of pollen. Using specialized appendages, she forms the pollen into a ball and carries it with her out of the flower. She flies to a new flower and lays her eggs in its ovary. She then moves to the stigma of the flower and inserts the pollen ball, ensuring fertilization of the ovules of the plant. The moth larvae emerge from their eggs, consuming many of the developing seeds within the yucca fruit. Fall eventually arrives, and the fruits split open, releasing whatever seeds were not consumed. The fruit falls to the ground, and soon the moth larvae will crawl out, go below ground, and form a cocoon, repeating this cycle in the spring. Some yucca–yucca moth pairs are species specific, some yuccas can be pollinated by a few species of the moth, and some moths can pollinate a few species of yucca. However, yucca cannot be pollinated by anything other than yucca moths, and these moths cannot complete their life cycle without yucca plants.

You may recognize in this description that there are a variety of places where cheating could happen. The plant could drop fruits that are being eaten, the pollinator could lays eggs without pollinating the plant, or larvae could eat all of the seeds rather than only some. Over the years, Addicott and his students have been able to learn much about this system, including the frequency of cheating.

One of his initial discoveries was that though most yucca plants and yucca moth associations are similar in terms of their general mode of operation, there is substantial variation in the potential costs and rewards of this mutualism among *Yucca* species. The morphology of the moth greatly influences its ability to place pollen on the stigma, and the morphology of the plant's reproductive structures influences the moth's ability to successfully lay her eggs. Variation in these traits can lead to variations in benefit to the plant, and to the moth. Variation can also lead to cheating, receiving benefit from the mutualistic partner while not providing a service in return. In fact, upon closer examination of several species, Addicott (1996) found that cheating was common in the yucca–yucca moth system. After capturing a number of female yucca moths, he was able to show that a number of the females of this "mutualist" species were lacking the specialized appendages necessary to move pollen! These females continued to lay their eggs in the ovules of the yucca ovary but did not display any of the behaviour associated with pollen ball formation and deposition.

As it turns out, these cheaters are common and can represent 30% of all larvae in the fruits of at least five Yucca species. Needless to say, such cheaters represent an increased cost for these *Yucca* species, one for which no apparent reward is obtained. This is a further example of how the field of ecology has moved away from viewing mutualism as associated species that "do things" for each other, to seeing mutualisms as cases of reciprocal exploitation. There are a number of questions left unanswered: How common can cheaters be in a population before yucca populations decline? Do cheater females lay eggs in flowers they know have been pollinated by other moths? If not, how do their offspring get fed?

Cheaters are not unique to the obligate mutualism of yucca plants and the yucca moths. The next time you are in a field full of flowers, sit down and look closely. You will likely see many animals, ants, flies, wasps, bees, beetles, and bugs, moving in and out of the flowers. Some of these will be carrying or leaving pollen, but many will not. These are called **nectar robbers**, who exploit an energy-rich resource (nectar) while providing no pollination services. This exploitation is not limited to insects; plants may deceive their pollination "partners." A variety of orchid species produce flowers similar in shape, size, and odour to reproductively receptive female wasps, inducing pseudocopulation by male wasps. These males land on the flowers and "mate," taking away and depositing pollen in the process. Clearly the plant benefits from these services provided by the wasp. I will leave it to your own imagination as to whether the plant is providing a service or instead taking advantage of the wasp.

Pollination services are of enormous economic importance in Canada, contributing millions of dollars annually to the economy as a critical aspect of the successful production of many agricultural crops. At the core of this critical agricultural process is a familiar ecological theme: exploitation. What we learn in ecology does not just apply to our national parks and wilderness areas. These processes affect our lives every day. We see in this next example that exploitation is common in another interaction that involves plants: mycorrhizae.

Mycorrhizae: Nutrient Gain vs. Carbon Gain

The study of mutualisms has largely centred on interactions between plants and other organisms. This is in part because plants are the dominant life form on land. It would be no exaggeration to say that the integrity of the terrestrial portion of the biosphere depends upon plant-centred mutualisms. However, there is another reason so much research has been done on plant mutualisms: plants make very good experimental subjects. Researchers can often learn much more, more quickly, by being able to experimentally alter environmental conditions and thus the potential costs and benefits of associations, and plants are ideally suited for this. We thus continue our discussion on mutualisms, once again involving plants, but now move from the colourful flowers and diverse pollinators to a less well-understood web of interactions in the soil.

The fossil record shows that mycorrhizae arose early in the evolution of land plants, perhaps as long as 400 million years ago. Over evolutionary time, a relationship between plants and some fungi evolved in which mycorrhizal fungi provide plants with greater access to inorganic nutrients while feeding off the root exudates of plants. The two most common types of mycorrhizae are: (1) **arbuscular mycorrhizal fungi (AMF)**, in which the mycorrhizal fungus produces **arbuscules**, sites of exchange between plant and fungus comprised of fungal **hyphae** and **vesicles**, and fungal energy storage organs within root cortex cells; and (2) **ectomycorrhizae (ECM)**, in which the fungus forms a mantle around roots and a net-like structure around root cells (fig. 15.14). Mycorrhizae are

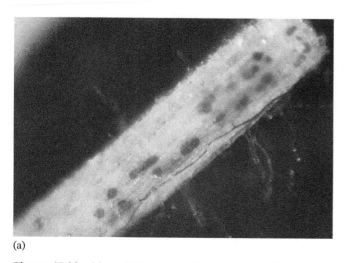

(a)   (b)

Figure 15.14   Mutualistic associations between fungi and plant roots: (*a*) arbuscular mycorrhizal fungus stained so that fungal structures appear blue; and (*b*) ectomycorrhizae, which give a white fuzzy appearance to these roots.

(a), (b) © Dr. Nancy Collins Johnson, © Dr. Jeremy Burgess/Science Source.

especially important in increasing plant access to phosphorus and other immobile nutrients (nutrients that do not move freely through soil).

Mycorrhizae and the Water Balance of Plants

Mycorrhizal fungi appear to improve the ability of many plants to extract soil water. Edie and Michael Allen (1986) studied how mycorrhizae affect the water relations of the grass *Pascopyrum smithii* by comparing the leaf water potentials of plants with and without mycorrhizae. Figure 15.15 shows that *Pascopyrum* with mycorrhizae maintained higher leaf water

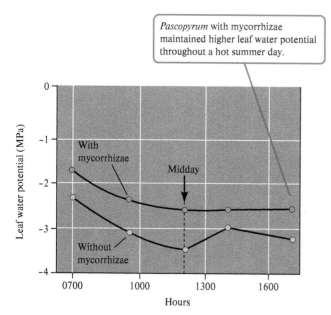

Pascopyrum with mycorrhizae maintained higher leaf water potential throughout a hot summer day.

Figure 15.15   Influence of mycorrhizae on leaf water potential of the grass *Pascopyrum smithii*.

Data from Allen and Allen 1986.

potentials than those without mycorrhizae. This means that when growing under similar conditions of soil moisture, the presence of mycorrhizae helped the grass maintain a higher water potential. Does this comparison show that mycorrhizae are directly responsible for the higher leaf water potential observed in the mycorrhizal grass? No, it does not. These higher water potentials may be an indirect effect of greater root growth resulting from the greater access to phosphorus provided by mycorrhizae.

Plants with greater access to phosphorus may develop roots that are more efficient at extracting and conducting water; mycorrhizal fungi may not be directly involved in the extraction of water from soils. Kay Hardie (1985) tested this hypothesis directly with an experimental manipulation of plant growth form and mycorrhizae. First, she grew mycorrhizal and non-mycorrhizal red clover (*Trifolium pratense*) in conditions in which their growth was not limited by nutrient availability. These conditions produced plants with similar leaf areas and root:shoot ratios. Under these carefully controlled conditions, mycorrhizal red clover showed higher rates of transpiration than non-mycorrhizal plants.

Hardie then removed the hyphae of mycorrhizal fungi from half of the red clover with mycorrhizae. She controlled for possible side effects of this manipulation by using a tracer dye to check for root damage, and by handling and transplanting all study plants, including those in her control group. Removing hyphae significantly reduced rates of transpiration (fig. 15.16), indicating a direct role of mycorrhizal fungi in the water relations of plants. Hardy suggests that mycorrhizal fungi improve water relations of plants by giving more extensive contact with moisture in the rooting zone and providing extra surface area for absorption of water.

So far, it seems that plants benefit from mycorrhizae. That may not always be the case, however. Environmental conditions may change the flow of benefits between plants and mycorrhizal fungi.

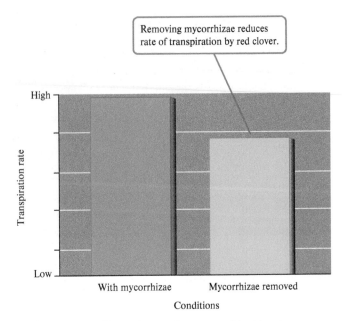

Figure 15.16 Effect of removing mycorrhizal hyphae on rate of transpiration by red clover.
Data from Hardie 1985.

Nutrient Availability and the Balance Sheet

Mycorrhizae supply inorganic nutrients to plants in exchange for carbohydrates, but not all mycorrhizal fungi deliver nutrients to their host plants at equal rates. The relationship between fungus and plant ranges from mutualism to parasitism, depending on the environmental circumstance and mycorrhizal species or even strains within species.

Nancy Johnson (1993) performed experiments designed to determine whether fertilization can select for less mutualistic mycorrhizal fungi. We have to first ask what would constitute a "less mutualistic" association. In general, a less mutualistic relationship would be one in which there was a greater imbalance in the benefits to the mutualistic partners. In the case of mycorrhizae, a less mutualistic mycorrhizal fungus would be one in which the fungal partner received an equal or greater quantity of photosynthetic product in trade for a lower quantity of nutrients. Assessing this from the fungal side is relatively challenging, so Johnson viewed this relative imbalance through the lens of the plant, specifically responses in shoot growth and production of flowers.

Johnson pointed out that there are several reasons to predict that fertilization would favour less mutualistic mycorrhizal fungi. The first is that plants vary the amount of soluble carbohydrates in root exudates as a function of nutrient availability. Plants release more soluble carbohydrates when they grow in nutrient-poor soils and decrease the amount of carbohydrates in root exudates as soil fertility increases. Consequently, fertilization of soils should favour strains, or species, of mycorrhizal fungi capable of living in a low-carbohydrate environment. Johnson suggested that the mycorrhizal fungi capable of colonizing plants releasing low quantities of carbohydrates will probably be those that are aggressive in their acquisition of carbohydrates from their host plants, perhaps at the expense

of host plant performance. Therefore, mycorrhizal fungi in soil with high fertility might be less mutualistic, and nearer the parasitic end of the continuum.

Johnson used greenhouse experiments to assess how these differences in the composition of mycorrhizal fungi might affect plant performance. She chose big bluestem grass (*Andropogon gerardii*) as a study plant that is well adapted to nutrient-poor soils of the area. Seedlings of *Andropogon* were planted in pots containing sand. Plants received an inoculum of mycorrhizal fungi from fertilized plots, from unfertilized plots, or no inoculum (control). In each case, the inoculum came in the form of a composite soil sample: half from the unfertilized plot, and half from the fertilized plot. To inoculate a pot with only "fertilized" mycorrhizae, Johnson used 15 g of soil from a fertilized plot mixed with 15 g of sterilized soil from an unfertilized plot. To inoculate with only "unfertilized" mycorrhizae, Johnson used 15 g of soil from an unfertilized plot mixed with 15 g of sterilized soil from a fertilized plot. Finally, for the control, Johnson combined 15 g of sterilized soil from a fertilized plot with 15 g soil from an unfertilized plot (fig. 15.17).

Johnson found that *Andropogon* inoculated with mycorrhizal fungi from unfertilized soils showed faster shoot growth and sexual maturation during early stages relative to control plants (no mycorrhizae) or to plants inoculated with mycorrhizae

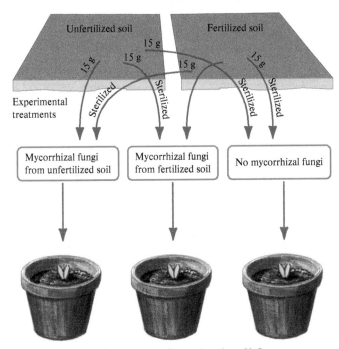

Figure 15.17 Testing the effects of long-term fertilizing on interactions between mycorrhizal fungi and plants on agricultural lands.

from fertilized soil. It appears from her results that altering the nutrient environment does also alter the mutualistic balance sheet; the mycorrhizae from fertilized soil may form a less mutualistic, more parasitic association with the plants. The way in which such environmental factors affect the nature of the plant–mycorrhizae relationship is of importance to agricultural practice.

John Klironomos, from the University of Guelph, has also delved into the complex world of plant–fungal interactions. He found that the form of interaction between plants and fungi is even more variable and complex than people had imagined. Klironomos (2003) asked a very important question: Are AMF generally mutualists, or parasites? In an elegantly simple experiment, he subjected individual plants of 64 species to one of two treatments: plants were planted in a greenhouse pot with either propagules of one species of AMF (*Glomus etunicatum*), or sterile soil. He used 10 replicates of each plant species × AMF combination, resulting in 1,280 pots. After 16 weeks, he measured plant biomass, comparing growth with and without AMF. The results were dramatic. The growth of most species did not differ between the AMF and sterile soil treatments! In other words, this relationship was generally neutral—neither mutualistic nor parasitic. However, across this broad range of species, Klironomos found a variety of plant responses; for some species the interaction was strongly parasitic; and for others, strongly beneficial. Ecological interactions, like mycorrhizae, fall along a continuum of effect for the partners. Understanding why requires us to look a bit at the evolution of mutualisms.

ECOLOGY IN ACTION

Impacts of Mycorrhizae on Forest Sustainability

As we have discussed, mycorrhizae have the potential to impact a plant's life positively or negatively, and the position along the mutualism–exploitation continuum depends upon the exact costs and benefits at any particular time. This issue has enormous implications for agriculture and forestry, and here we will discuss two examples in which mycorrhizal interactions may have significant consequences for forest regeneration and community composition.

Suzanne Simard, of the University of British Columbia, has extensively studied the ecology of ectomycorrhizae and their potential impact on forest dynamics. Forest dynamics are an important issue for the forest industry, and having a detailed understanding of the factors that influence regeneration can be of broad economic importance. One of the interesting aspects of mycorrhizae is that many of the fungi involved are generalists, able to colonize the roots of different species of plants. This aspect of fungal biology is not restricted to pots in a greenhouse but can occur in the field, where you can regularly find one individual fungus associated with the roots of many individual plants—simultaneously. Simard developed an elegant design to test whether these shared connections could result in sugar moving toward or away from some plants (Simard et al. 1997). In other words, could some plants partially parasitize others through these shared mycorrhizal connections? Her study used three focal species—paper birch (*Betula papyrifera*), Douglas fir (*Pseudotsuga menziesii*), and western redcedar (*Thuja plicata*) (fig. 15.18)—all of which are important to the forestry industry of British Columbia. Simard planted young plants of these three species together in forest soil and, after some time, fed the leaves of the plants with ¹³C or ¹⁴C. Why did she use these tracers? To follow the carbon. For example, if she fed *Betula* with ¹³C but found ¹³C in the other plants, that would tell her the carbon moved from *Betula* to these other plants. But does that mean it moved through

Figure 15.18 A number of tree species can be interconnected by mycorrhizal fungi in the forests of British Columbia.
Barbara Zimonick.

hyphae? No. It is certainly possible that the carbon went from the leaves, to the roots, and then entered the soil as dead roots, or root exudate. Part of the elegance of her design is that she included *Thuja* in her study. This species does not share fungal species with *Betula* and *Pseudotsuga,* so the amount of labelled carbon in *Thuja* would indicate how much passed from plant to plant through the soil rather than through ectomycorrhizae. If carbon passed from *Betula* to *Thuja* and *Pseudotsuga* only through soil, then transfer to each species should be the same. However, if *Pseudotsuga* received more of this carbon than *Thuja*, it would suggest the transfer was facilitated through mycorrhizal connections to *Betula*.

Why did she use two tracers in this study? She was not interested in simply whether carbon moved from one plant to another (as prior studies have shown it could); instead, she wanted to find whether there was *net* movement from one plant to another. Net movement, if it occurs, would indicate parasitism by the recipient on the host and would be quite a surprise to many forest biologists! So, in a single trial she would feed *Betula* with one tracer and *Pseudotsuga* with the other. In her analyses, she was particularly interested in knowing the net movement of sugars into, or out of, *Pseudotsuga*. Net movement could be measured as the difference in tracer concentrations between *Pseudotsuga* and *Betula*. For instance, if *Betula* was labelled with ^{13}C and *Pseudotsuga* with ^{14}C, net movement would be the difference between the ^{14}C found in *Betula* and the ^{13}C found in *Pseudotsuga*.

What did Simard find? There was very little tracer in western redcedar (*Thuja*), indicating the plant-to-soil pathway was not likely important. However, there was substantial net movement of sugars to Douglas fir (*Pseudotsuga*), indicating it was exploiting paper birch (*Betula*)! Even more interesting, the amount of parasitism expressed increased when she shaded *Pseudotsuga*, reaching up to 6% of its entire carbon budget. Why would *Betula* feed this unrelated host? We can once again return to our understanding of mutualisms as reciprocal exploitation. Not everything that happens in such an interaction is "good" for each member; instead, the net effect is positive. So, in this example it is possible that the potential benefit *Betula* receives from this mutualism with the fungus is greater than the costs of feeding the fungus and, by extension, other plants. But there is also an alternative explanation. Perhaps *Pseudotsuga* simply cannot do anything about it, and at this point in the evolution of this interaction, the parasite is winning! We cannot lose site of the fact that parasites, be they fungal or plant, are also subject to natural selection and will certainly evolve traits that allow them to circumvent the defence systems of the host organisms.

So what does this mean for forests' sustainability? The answer to that question is unknown. Many ecologists continue to work in this area, with a growing realization that it is much more complicated than simply saying mycorrhizae are "good" for the forests. Although there may be some feeding going on through mycorrhizae, it remains unclear whether that is greater than the negative effects of competition for light and nutrients. In other words, resource sharing is yet another type of interaction among species, one that happens in addition to the other forms of interaction we have already discussed. Because of the enormous potential impact on forest regeneration, it is fair to say we will hear more of this story in the years to come.

CONCEPT 15.3 REVIEW

1. What similarities do nectar robbers and "cheating" yucca moths share? What risk may they encounter if they represent a large proportion of the insects that visit the host flowers?

2. Explain why plants and pollinators have competing interests about how long flowers should be kept open.

3. Why should selection favour mycorrhizal fungi that are "less mutualistic" when soil nutrients are high?

15.4 Evolution of Mutualism

Theory predicts that mutualism will evolve where the benefits of mutualism exceed the costs. We have reviewed several complex mutualisms. There are many others, every one a fascinating example of the intricacies of nature. Ecologists not only study the present biology of those mutualisms but also seek to understand the conditions leading to their evolution and persistence.

We have also seen evidence that interactions are not fixed in time but can vary according to changes in local conditions. Theoretical analyses point to the relative costs and benefits of a possible relationship as a key factor in the evolution of mutualism.

Modelling of mutualisms has generally taken one of two approaches. The earliest attempts involved modifications of the Lotka–Volterra equations to represent the population dynamics of mutualism. The alternative approach has been to model mutualistic interactions using cost-benefit analysis to explore the conditions under which mutualisms can evolve and persist. In chapters 13 and 14, where we discussed models of competition and predation, we focused on the population dynamic approach to modelling species interactions. Here, we concentrate on cost-benefit analyses of mutualism.

Kathleen Keeler (1981, 1985) developed models to represent the relative costs and benefits of several types of mutualistic interactions. Among them are two of the mutualistic interactions we discussed in this chapter: ant–plant protection mutualisms and mycorrhizae. Keeler's approach requires that we consider a population polymorphic for mutualism containing three kinds of individuals: (1) *successful mutualists*, which give and receive measurable benefits to another organism; (2) *unsuccessful mutualists*, which give benefits to another organism but, for some reason, do not receive any benefit in return; and (3) *nonmutualists*, neither giving nor receiving benefit from a mutualistic partner. The bottom line in Keeler's approach is that for a population to be mutualistic, the fitness of successful mutualists must be greater than the fitness of either unsuccessful mutualists or nonmutualists. In addition, the combined fitness of successful and unsuccessful mutualists must exceed that of the fitness of nonmutualists. Why do we have to combine the fitness of successful and unsuccessful mutualists? Remember that both confer benefit to their partner, but only the successful mutualists receive benefit in return. If these conditions are not met, Keeler proposed that natural selection will eventually eliminate the mutualistic interaction from the population.

Keeler represents the fitness of mutualists as:

$$w_m = pw_{ms} + qw_{mu} \tag{1}$$

where:

p = the proportion of the population consisting of successful mutualists

w_{ms} = the fitness of successful mutualists

q = the proportion of the population consisting of unsuccessful mutualists

w_{mu} = the fitness of unsuccessful mutualists.

We can represent Keeler's conditions for the evolution and persistence of a plant–ant mutualism as:

$$w_m > w_{nm} \tag{2}$$

or

$$pw_{ms} + qw_{mu} > w_{nm} \tag{3}$$

where:

w_{nm} = the fitness of nonmutualists

The analysis is more convenient if we think of these relationships in terms of **selection coefficients (s)**, the relative selective costs associated with being either a successful mutualist, an unsuccessful mutualist, or a nonmutualist:

$$s = 1 - w \text{ and } w = (1 - s)$$

Using selection coefficients, Keeler expressed the selective cost of being a successful mutualist, an unsuccessful mutualist, or a nonmutualist as:

$$s_{ms} = (H)(1 - A)(1 - D) + I_A + I_D \tag{4}$$

$$s_{mu} = (H)(1 - D) + I_A + I_D \tag{5}$$

$$s_{nm} = H(1 - D) + I_D \tag{6}$$

where:

H = the proportion of the plant tissue damaged in the absence of any defences

D = the amount of protection given to the plant tissues by defences other than ants (e.g., chemical defences); so, 1 – D is the amount of tissue damage that would occur in spite of these alternative defences

A = the amount of herbivory prevented by ants (so, again, 1 – A is the amount of herbivory that occurs in spite of ants)

I_A = the investment by the plant in benefits extended to the ants

I_D = investment in defences other than ants

Using these selective coefficients, we can express Keeler's conditions for evolution and persistence of the ant–plant mutualism as:

$$p(1 - s_{ms}) - q(1 - s_{mu}) > 1 - s_{nm}$$

into which Keeler substituted the relationships given in equations (4), (5), and (6). By simplifying the resulting equation, she produced the following expression of benefits relative to costs:

$$p[H(1 - D)A] > I_A$$

where:

$$p[H(1 - D)A] = \text{benefits}$$
$$I_A = \text{costs}$$

Facultative Ant–Plant Protection Mutualisms

Keeler applied her cost-benefit model to facultative mutualisms involving plants with extrafloral nectaries and ants that feed at the nectaries and provide protection to the plant in return. Her model is not appropriate for obligate mutualisms like that between swollen thorn acacias and their mutualistic ants but instead applies to situations in which both the plant and ant can live without its partner. In addition, Keeler wrote her model from the perspective of the plant side of the mutualism. Let's step through the general model and connect each of the terms with the ecology of facultative plant–ant protection mutualisms.

In this model, w_{ms} is the fitness of a plant that produces extrafloral nectaries and that successfully attracts ants effective at guarding it, while w_{mu} is the fitness of a plant that produces extrafloral nectaries but that has not attracted enough ants to mount a successful defence. For example, these plants may be too far from an ant nest. In addition, Keeler includes the fitness of nonmutualistic plants, w_{nm}, which would be the fitness of individuals of a plant that does not produce extrafloral nectaries. Are there such individuals in natural populations? We do not know, but that is not the point. The reason Keeler includes nonmutualists in her model is to provide an assessment of the potential costs and benefits of such a strategy against which she can weigh the mutualistic strategy. This is analogous to the approach used in game theory in chapter 8.

Keeler's model represents potential benefits to the host plant as:

$$p[H(1 - D)A]$$

where:

p = the proportion of the plant population attracting sufficient ants to mount a defence

Keeler's model represents the plant's costs of mutualism as:

$$IA = n[m + d(a + c + h)]$$

where:

    n = the number of extrafloral nectaries per plant

    m = the energy content of nectary structures

    d = the period of time during which the nectaries are active

    a = costs of producing amino acids in nectar

    c = costs of producing the carbohydrates in nectar

    h = costs of providing water for nectar

Again, Keeler's hypothesis is that for mutualism to persist, benefits must exceed costs. In terms of her model:

$$p[H(1 - D)A] > I_A$$

This model proposes that for a facultative ant–plant mutualism to evolve and persist, the proportion of the plant's energy budget that ants save from destruction by herbivores must exceed the proportion of the plant's energy budget that is invested in extrafloral nectaries and nectar.

The details of Keeler's model offer insights into what conditions may produce higher benefits than costs. First, and most obviously, I_A, the proportion of the plant's energy budget invested in extrafloral nectaries and nectar, should be low. This means that plants living on a tight energy budget, for example, those living in a shady forest understory, should be less likely to invest in attracting ants than those living in full sun. Higher benefits result from (1) a high probability of attracting ants, p; (2) a high potential for herbivory, H; (3) low effectiveness of alternative defences, D; and (4) highly effective ant defence, A.

The task for ecologists is to determine how well these requirements of the model match the values of these variables in nature. By finding the conditions under which mutualisms are or are not most likely to occur, ecologists can begin to unravel the complexity of interactions that occur in the natural world.

CONCEPT 15.4 REVIEW

1. Suppose you discover a mutant form of plant that does not produce extrafloral nectaries. What does Keeler's theory predict concerning the relative fitness of these mutant plants and the typical ones that produce extrafloral nectaries?

2. According to Keeler's theory, under what general conditions would the mutant, lacking extrafloral nectaries, increase in frequency in a population and displace the typical plants that produce extrafloral nectaries?

ECOLOGICAL TOOLS AND APPROACHES

Mutualism and Humans

Mutualism has been important in the lives and livelihood of humans for a long time. Historically, much of agriculture has depended upon mutualistic associations between species, and much of agricultural management has been aimed at enhancing mutualisms, such as nitrogen fixation, mycorrhizae, and pollination, to improve crop production. Agriculture itself has been viewed as a mutualistic relationship between humans and crop and livestock species. However, there may be some qualitative differences between agriculture as it has been generally practised and mutualisms among other species. How much of agriculture is pure exploitation and how much is truly mutualistic remains an open question. When we discuss mutualisms in agriculture, the previous qualifier notwithstanding, we are generally discussing relationships between plant species or between plants and fungi that we are able to exploit. We stand as the exploitative beneficiary of the mutualistic relationship. However, there is at least one relationship in which humans are a direct member of a mutualistic pair.

Mutualism joins the traditional honey gatherers of Africa with the greater honeyguide (*Indicator indicator*) (fig. 15.19). Honey gathering has long been an important aspect of African cultures, important enough that there are scenes of honey gathering in rock art painted over 20,000 years ago (Isack and Reyer 1989). No one knows how long humans have gathered honey in Africa, but it is difficult to imagine the earliest hominids resisting such sweet temptation. Whenever honey gathering began, humans have apparently had a capable and energetic partner in their searches.

The Honeyguide

Honeyguides belong to the family Indicatoridae in the order Piciformes, an order that also includes the woodpeckers. The family Indicatoridae includes a total of 17 species, 15 of

Figure 15.19 The greater honeyguide (*Indicator indicator*).
©Nigel Dennis/Science Source.

which are native to Africa. Honeyguides have the unusual habit of feeding on waxes of various sorts—most feed on beeswax and insects. Of the 17 species of honeyguides, only the greater honeyguide (*I. indicator*) is known to guide humans and a few other mammals to bees' nests.

The greater honeyguide is found throughout much of sub-Saharan Africa. It avoids only dense forests and very open grasslands and desert, and its distribution corresponds broadly with the distributions of tropical savanna and tropical dry forest. Like all of the honeyguides, the greater honeyguide is a brood parasite that, like cuckoos, lays its eggs in the nests of other birds. This way of life is reflected in the early morphology of nestling honeyguides, which retain "bill hooks" on their upper and lower bills for the first 14 days of life that they use to lacerate and kill their nest mates. However, nests sometimes contain two honeyguide nestlings, so apparently there is some mechanism by which nestlings of the same species can coexist. After the deaths of their nest mates, honeyguide nestlings receive all the food brought by their foster parents, which continue to feed young honeyguides until they are completely independent, approximately 7 to 10 days after leaving the nest.

Greater honeyguides are capable of completely independent life without mutualistic interactions with humans, so we would classify their mutualism as facultative. Living independently, honeyguides feed on beeswax and on the adults, larvae, pupae, and eggs of bees. They also feed on a wide variety of other insects. Greater honeyguides show highly opportunistic feeding behaviour and sometimes join flocks of other bird species foraging on the insects stirred up by large mammals. The most distinguishing feature of the greater honeyguide, however, is its habit of guiding humans and ratels, or honey badgers, to bees' nests.

Guiding Behaviour

The first written report of the guiding behaviour of *I. indicator* was authored in 1569 by João Dos Santos, a missionary in the part of East Africa that is now Mozambique. Dos Santos first noticed honeyguides because they would enter the mission church to feed upon the bits of beeswax on candlesticks. He went on to describe their guiding behaviour by saying that when the birds find a beehive, they search for people and attempt to lead them to the hive. He noted that the local people eagerly followed the birds because of their fondness for honey, and he observed that the honeyguide profits by gaining access to the wax and dead bees left after humans raid the hive. Dos Santos's report of this behaviour was confirmed by other European visitors to almost all parts of Africa for the next four centuries. However, it was not until the middle of the twentieth century that the mutualism of honeyguides with humans was examined scientifically. The foundation work of these studies was that of H. Friedmann (1955), who reviewed and organized the observations of others, including those of Dos Santos, and who conducted his own extensive research on the honeyguides of Africa.

Friedmann's report of some of the African legends surrounding the greater honeyguide suggests that a wide variety of African cultures prescribed rewarding the bird for its guiding behaviour and that native Africans recognized the need for reciprocity in their interactions with honeyguides. One proverb reported by Friedmann was, "If you do not leave anything for the guide [*I. Indicator*], it will not lead you at all in the future." Another proverb stated more ominously, "If you do not leave anything for the guide, it will lead you to a dangerous animal the next time." Friedmann also observed that many African cultures forbid killing a honeyguide and once "inflicted severe penalties" for doing so. These observations suggest long association between humans and honeyguides and that the association has been consciously mutualistic on the human side of the balance sheet.

The mutualistic association between humans and honeyguides may have developed from an earlier association between the bird and the ratel, or honey badger (*Mellivora capensis*). The honey badger is a powerful animal, well equipped with strong claws and powerful muscles to rip open bees' nests, that readily follows honeyguides to bees' nests. The honey badger, though secretive, has been observed often following honeyguides while vocalizing. African honey gatherers also vocalize to attract honeyguides, and Friedmann reported that some of their vocalizations imitate the calls of honey badgers.

The most detailed and quantitative study of this mutualism to date is that of H. Isack of the National Museum of Kenya and H.-U. Reyer of the University of Zurich (Isack and Reyer 1989), who studied the details of the interaction of the greater honeyguide with the Boran people of northern Kenya. The Boran regularly follow honeyguides and have developed a penetrating whistle that they use to attract them. The whistle can be heard over 1 km away, and Isack and Reyer found that it doubles the rate at which Boran honey gatherers encounter honeyguides. If they are successful in attracting a honeyguide, the average amount of time it takes to find a bees' nest is 3.2 hours. Without the aid of a honeyguide, the average search time per bees' nest is about 8.9 hours. This is an underestimate of the true time, however, since Isack and Reyer did not include days in which no bees' nests were found in their analysis. The benefit of the association to the bird seems apparent from Isack and Reyer's analysis, since they report that 96% of the nests to which the Boran were guided would have been inaccessible to the birds without human help.

The greater honeyguide attracts the attention of a human by flying close and calling as it does so. Following this initial attention-getting behaviour, the bird will fly off in a particular direction and disappear for up to one minute. After reappearing, the bird again perches in a conspicuous spot and calls to the following humans. As the honey gatherers follow, they whistle, bang on wood, and talk loudly to "keep the bird interested." When the honey gatherers approach the perch from which the honeyguide is calling, the bird again flies off, calling and displaying its white tail feathers as it does so, only to reappear at another conspicuous perch a short time later. This sequence of leading, following, and leading is repeated until the bird and the following honey gatherers arrive at the bees' nest.

Isack, who is a Boran, interviewed Boran honey gatherers to determine what information they obtained from honeyguides. The main purpose of the study was to test assertions by the honey gatherers that the bird informs them of (1) the direction to the bees' nest, (2) the distance to the nest, and (3) when they arrive at the location of the nest. The data gathered by Isack and Reyer support all three assertions.

Honey gatherers reported that the bird indicated direction to the bees' nest on the basis of the direction of its guiding flights. One method used by Isack and Reyer to test how well flight direction indicated direction was to induce honeyguides to guide them from the same starting point to the same known bees' nest on five different occasions. Figure 15.20a shows the highly restricted area covered by these five different guiding trips. Another approach was to

induce the bird to guide them to a bees' nest from seven different starting points (fig. 15.20b). The result was a consistent tendency by the bird to lead directly to the site of the bees' nest.

The Boran honey gatherers said that three variables decrease as distance to the nest decreases: (1) the time the bird stays out of sight during its first disappearance following the initial encounter, (2) the distance between stops made by the bird on the way to the bees' nest, and (3) the height of the perch on the way to the nest. Data gathered by Isack and Reyer support all three statements (fig. 15.21).

The honey gatherers also report that they can determine when they arrive in the vicinity of a bees' nest by changes in the honeyguide's behaviour and vocalizations. Isack and Reyer observed several of these changes. While on the path to a bees' nest, a honeyguide emits a

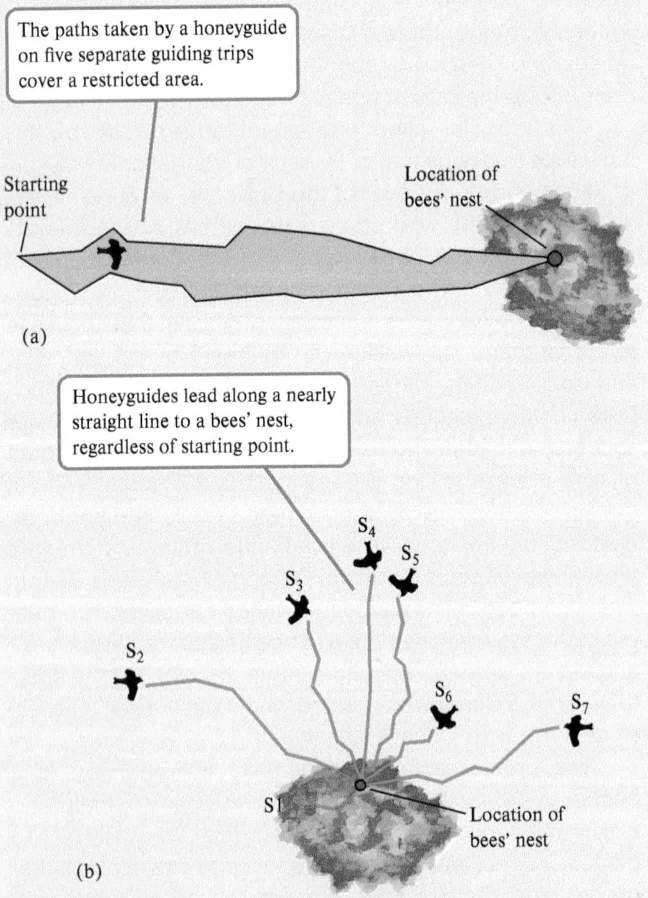

The paths taken by a honeyguide on five separate guiding trips cover a restricted area.

Starting point

Location of bees' nest

(a)

Honeyguides lead along a nearly straight line to a bees' nest, regardless of starting point.

S_4

S_5

S_3

S_2

S_6

S_7

S_1

Location of bees' nest

(b)

Figure 15.20 Paths taken by honeyguides leading people to bees' nests.

Data from Isack and Reyer 1989.

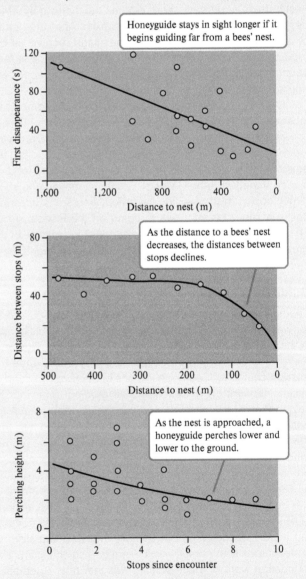

Honeyguide stays in sight longer if it begins guiding far from a bees' nest.

First disappearance (s)

Distance to nest (m)

As the distance to a bees' nest decreases, the distances between stops declines.

Distance between stops (m)

Distance to nest (m)

As the nest is approached, a honeyguide perches lower and lower to the ground.

Perching height (m)

Stops since encounter

Figure 15.21 Changes in behaviour of the honeyguide as it nears a bees' nest.

Data from Isack and Reyer 1989.

distinctive guiding call and will answer human calls by increasing the frequency of the guiding call. On arriving at a nest, the honeyguide perches close to the nest and gives off a special "indication" call. After a few indication calls, it remains silent and does not answer to human sounds. If approached by a honey gatherer, a honeyguide flies in a circle around the nest location before perching again nearby.

Isack and Reyer observe that their data do not allow them to test other statements by the Boran honey gatherers, including that when bees' nests are very far away (over 2 km), the honeyguide will "deceive" the gatherers about the real distance to the nest by stopping at shorter intervals. Isack and Reyer add, however, that they have no reason to doubt these other statements, since all others have been supported by the data they were able to collect. What these data reveal is a rich mutualistic interaction between wild birds and humans. It remains unclear how widely mutualisms alter human behaviour. Using ecological tools and methods of study may provide further insights into the social biology of people.

SUMMARY

Many interactions between individuals are difficult to classify, and range along a continuum of relative benefit from exploitation. Mutualisms, interactions between individuals that benefit both partners, are common in nature, and form the foundation of most of life as we know it within the biosphere. These can be viewed as mutual exploitations, where the benefit to each species in exploiting the other is greater than the cost of being exploited (fig. 15.22). Whether the relationship between two species is mutualistic or parasitic may change with ecological context. Mutualisms can be divided into those that are facultative, where species can live without their mutualistic partners, and obligate, where species are unable to complete their life cycle without their partner. Parasitic relationships are those in which the net benefits of exploitation are positive for one species and negative for the other.

15.1 There is great diversity in the types of parasitic and mutualistic interactions that exist, defying easy generalization.

Despite the ubiquity of mutualistic interactions, most species on the planet are parasites. The specific interactions between parasites and hosts and between mutualistic partners are extremely diverse. Many pathogens alter behaviour of their hosts in ways that increase the transmission rate of the pathogen. Such changes can have negative consequences for the host, such as increased predation rates and altered competitive abilities (e.g., outcome for Species 3 in fig. 15.22) Some parasites, such as winter ticks, can infest their hosts, causing shifts in appearance, behaviour, and likely population dynamics. Other interactions appear to benefit both partners, such as the obligate mutualism that occurs between ants and acacia trees. Acacia trees provide food and housing for ants, which provide protection from herbivores and potential competitors for the tree. The mutualism between zooxanthellae and corals results in the construction of the foundation of an entire ecosystem, coral reefs. The zooxanthellae live within their animal partners (the coral), receiving nutrients from the coral while returning organic compounds for the coral to synthesize.

15.2 Basic ecological principles can be applied to our understanding of disease, and the population dynamics of pathogens can be predicted using a compartmental model.

Disease can be viewed as an exploitative interaction between a host and a pathogen. Population growth of the disease can be modelled by the use of a compartmental model. One key

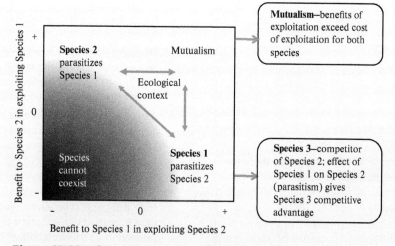

Figure 15.22 Concept map for chapter 15.

parameter is the transmission rate of the disease, which is a measure of how efficiently an infected host can infect a susceptible member of the population. Virulence is a measure of how symptomatic an infection is, along with any increased mortality. Population growth of a disease is highest when transmission rates are high and virulence low, and natural selection often favours decreased virulence over time. Humans can use these models to control the spread of disease within human populations. Basic ecological data on common human diseases allow public health professionals to design vaccination programs to provide herd immunity to the target population.

15.3 Many interactions can switch from parasitic to mutualistic, depending upon the specific conditions of the local environment.

Although many mutualisms appear as though individuals are doing things "for each other," mutualisms are better viewed as reciprocal exploitation. Most mutualisms are facultative, and the net effect can be parasitic, neutral, or mutualistic, depending on the specific environmental conditions and species involved (fig. 15.22). For example, plants modify flower longevity to maximize their own fitness, even though this comes at the cost of reduced foraging opportunities for their "partners," the pollinators. Even in the obligate mutualism of yucca–yucca moths, the costs and benefits of the interaction can vary greatly among populations. Many populations contain high densities of cheater phenotypes of the moths, which do not possess the physical ability to pollinate their host plants. Pollination services are of great importance to the economy of Canada and to the sustainability of natural systems. This interaction is based upon an exploitative interaction that is generally reciprocal.

Mycorrhizae are another form of mutualism involving plants, also with enormous economic importance. Mycorrhizae, which are mostly either arbuscular mycorrhizae or ectomycorrhizae, are important in increasing plant access to water, nitrogen, phosphorus, and other nutrients. In return for these nutrients, mycorrhizae receive energy-rich photosynthate. Experiments have shown that the balance sheet between plants and fungi can be altered by nutrient availability, and that the net effects of mycorrhizae on plant growth vary greatly among plant species. These results further emphasize the idea that interactions fall along a continuum of net effects.

15.4 Theory predicts that mutualism will evolve where the benefits of mutualism exceed the costs.

Keeler built a cost-benefit model for the evolution and persistence of facultative plant–ant protection mutualisms in which the benefits of the mutualism to the plant are represented in terms of the proportion of the plant's energy budget that ants protect from damage by herbivores. The model assesses the costs of the mutualism to the plant in terms of the proportion of the plant's energy budget invested in extrafloral nectaries and the water, carbohydrates, and amino acids contained in the nectar. The model predicts that the mutualism will be favoured where there are high densities of ants and potential herbivores and where the effectiveness of alternative defences are low.

Humans have developed a variety of mutualistic relationships with other species, but one of the most spectacular is that between the greater honeyguide and the traditional honey gatherers of Africa. In this apparently ancient mutualism, humans and honeyguides engage in elaborate communication and cooperation with clear benefit to both partners. The mutualism offers the human side a higher rate of discovery of bees' nests, while the honeyguide gains access to nests that it could not raid without human help. Careful observations have documented that the honeyguide informs the honey gatherers of the direction and distance to bees' nests as well as of their arrival at the nest.

REVIEW QUESTIONS

1. Why do scientists view mutualisms as one point along an exploitation–mutualism continuum? Why can some interactions switch from parasitic to mutualistic?

2. Why don't individuals "do things for each other," even if at a cost to their own fitness? Simard's studies with mycorrhizae suggest that in some cases this may occur. How can you reconcile your understanding of ecology and natural selection with her finding that one tree feeds unrelated individuals of another species?

3. Outline the experiments that Johnson (1993) designed to test the possibility that artificial fertilizers may select for less mutualistic mycorrhizal fungi. What evidence does Johnson present in support of her hypothesis?

4. Explain how mycorrhizal fungi may have evolved from ancestors that were originally parasites of plant roots. Is there any evidence that present-day mycorrhizal fungi may act like parasites to plants or animals? Be specific.

5. Janzen (1985) encouraged ecologists to take a more experimental approach to the study of mutualistic relationships. Outline the details of Janzen's own experiments on the mutualistic relationship between swollen thorn acacias and ants.

6. Explain how human diseases can be viewed as an ecological interaction. What benefits may come from using ecological models to describe population growth of a pathogen? Is medicine connected to ecology?

7. How are the coral-centred mutualisms similar to the plant-centred mutualisms we discussed in this chapter? How are they different? The exchanges between mutualistic partners in both systems revolve around energy, nutrients, and protection. Is this an accident of the cases discussed or are these key factors in the lives of organisms?

8. Outline the benefits and costs identified by Keeler's (1981, 1985) cost-benefit model for facultative ant–plant mutualism. From what perspective does Keeler's model view this mutualism—from the perspective of plant or ant? What would be some of the costs and benefits to consider if the model was built from the perspective of the other partner?

9. How could you change the Lotka–Volterra model of competition we discussed in chapter 13 into a model of mutualism? Would the resulting model be a cost-benefit model or a population dynamic model?

10. Outline how the honeyguide–human mutualism could have evolved from an earlier mutualism between honeyguides and honey badgers. In many parts of Africa today people have begun to abandon traditional honey gathering in favour of keeping domestic bees and have also begun to substitute refined sugars bought at the market for the honey of wild bees. Explain how, under these circumstances, natural selection might eliminate guiding behaviour in populations of the greater honeyguide. (In areas where honey gathering is no longer practised, the greater honeyguide no longer guides people to bees' nests.)

SECTION 5 COMMUNITIES AND ECOSYSTEMS

In this section we move beyond specific interactions among individuals and local environmental conditions and discuss broader topics in community and ecosystem ecology. In chapter 16 we discuss what communities are, how ecologists describe them, and how community structure and genetic diversity influence ecological function. In chapter 17 we show how species interactions can influence community assembly. In chapter 18 we discuss how disturbances influence communities, causing changes to species interactions and resulting in a process of succession. We end this section with chapters 19 and 20, in which we describe ecosystems, with an emphasis on the flow of energy and the cycling of elements such as carbon and various nutrients among the biotic and abiotic components of these systems.

Stephen Frink/The Image Bank/Getty Images

CHAPTER 16

COMMUNITY STRUCTURE AND FUNCTION

CHAPTER CONCEPTS

ifferent areas within the same geographic region may differ substantially in the number of species they support. Vast areas of flat or gently sloping land in the hot deserts of North America are often dominated by a single species of shrub, the creosote bush (*Larrea tridentata*). While grasses and forbs grow in the spaces between these shrubs, creosote bushes make up most of the biomass in these systems. In some areas, you can travel many kilometres and see only subtle changes in a landscape dominated by this single species (fig. 16.1).

The uniformity of the creosote flats contrasts sharply with the diversity of other places in these hot deserts (fig. 16.2). For instance, a rich variety of plant species cover Organ Pipe Cactus National Monument in southern Arizona. Here grow ocotillo, consisting of several slender branches 2 to 3 m tall originating from a common base; palo verde trees with green bark and tiny leaves; and mesquite that reach the size of medium-sized trees. In addition, there are cacti, such as the low-growing prickly pears and the shrub-like teddy bear chollas. The most striking are the column-shaped squat barrel cactus; the organ pipe cactus, with its densely packed slender columns; and the saguaro, a massive cactus that towers over all the other plant species. Among these larger plants also grow a wide variety of small shrubs, grasses, and forbs.

The creosote flats, dominated by one species of shrub, convey an impression of great uniformity. The vegetation of Organ Pipe Cactus National Monument, consisting of a large number of species of many different growth forms, gives the impression of high diversity. The ecologist is prompted to ask, what factors control this difference in diversity? Digging deeper, the ecologist may also ask whether these diversity differences have any functional consequences for the delivery of ecological services upon which people, and other species, rely. In chapters 13 to 15 we focused on competition, predation, mutualism, and disease, primarily between pairs of species. In this section, we consider patterns and processes that involve a larger number of species. A **community** is an association of potentially interacting species inhabiting some defined area, at some particular scale, over some particular span of time. Communities generally consist of many species that potentially interact in all of the ways discussed in chapters 13 to 15. At the same time, species within a community must continue to cope with the abiotic environment, and thus the issues discussed in chapters 5 to 9 also influence the patterns we observe, and the functions we measure, within communities.

Before immersing ourselves in the complexity of ecological communities, let us first ask a simple question: If we understand population ecology, why do we need to bother measuring communities? Isn't it possible to simply scale up from single populations and pairwise interactions to a general understanding of more diverse communities? The short answer is no, or at least not often. Due to high levels of diversity, complexity, and indirect interactions among co-occurring species, it is very difficult—if not impossible—to understand the behaviour of communities by simply scaling up from understanding individual populations. Or, put another way, understanding population-level processes is critical to understanding population-level patterns. However, this is not sufficient for understanding communities.

An even more important explanation as to why ecologists study communities is because many of the most urgent environmental pressures and issues of societal concern, in Canada and abroad, occur at the community level. For example, we are in the midst of a massive loss of global biodiversity (chapter 23) due to numerous anthropogenic causes. As species are lost from a community, there is the potential for both a loss of **ecological function** and increased invasion by non-native species, with additional negative consequences. As we will discuss in this chapter, communities (and ecosystems), perform a number of ecological functions that result in the delivery of services critical to human society. These include the basic requirements of human society, such as biomass production (i.e., food, fuel, building materials), water filtration, and nutrient cycling. As we will also discuss in this chapter, properties of the community influence a community's ability to perform different functions.

Figure 16.1 Desert landscape dominated by the creosote bush (*Larrea tridentata*).
© Charlie Ott/Science Source.

Figure 16.2 Species-rich Sonoran Desert landscape.
© Doug Sherman/Geofile RF.

A key starting point in the study of communities is to define what is meant by **community structure**. This concept includes attributes such as the number of species, the relative abundance of species, and the kinds of species comprising a community. Not surprisingly, ecologists have developed a number of metrics to help translate concepts into measurable variables, allowing for comparisons and understanding. This is similar to ecologists describing population structure through differences in sex ratios, ages, and numbers of individuals. As with most topics in ecology, measures of the community are scale-dependent, and this is particularly important when discussing patterns of diversity. Additionally, although society typically focuses on species diversity, ecologists do not focus on species diversity exclusively. Instead, there is growing recognition that other forms of diversity, including genetic diversity, have substantial impact on ecological function.

We begin this chapter by discussing some general patterns observed in communities and some means by which ecologists are able to quantify community structure.

16.1 Species Abundances and Diversity

A combination of the number of species and their relative abundance defines species diversity. What is diversity? This seemingly simple question can prove extraordinarily complex to answer. To begin to simplify this, we will focus on biological diversity rather than on social and abiotic aspects of diversity. This, however, still leaves us with many options. Diversity could represent variation in genotypes among individuals, differences in the physical structure of communities (e.g., low-growing peatland vs. tall forest), variation in the types of organisms found (mites, springtails, plants, etc.), or perhaps variation in the species that are found in a community. It is this latter form of diversity, **species diversity**, that community ecologists study most frequently and that we discuss first. However, it is important to recognize that species diversity represents just one type of diversity and that other forms of diversity (e.g., genotypic) are also important.

The number of species found within a community, called **species richness**, is one of the most fundamental aspects of community structure. It is such a common measure in ecology that it even has a standard abbreviation, *s*. How does one calculate this metric? Though in theory it is as simple as going into a community and counting the unique number of species observed, there are a few complications. On the technical side, determining what is a species is straightforward for vertebrates but complicated for other taxa, such as bacteria. (Ask your local microbial ecologist why!) Even when one has a working concept of "species," counting species is not always easy (see Ecological Tools and Approaches), particularly when the species are cryptic or as-of-yet unidentified to science. An additional concern is that the spatial scale at which one measures diversity will influence the results obtained. Consequently, ecologists typically refer to three scales of diversity: alpha, beta, and gamma. The differences among these

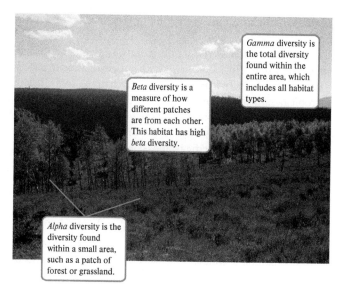

Figure 16.3 Aspen Parkland regions, such as that found outside Edmonton, consist of forest and grassland patches. As is true for all habitat types, the scale of interest influences one's estimate of diversity.
NPS Photo by William S Keller.

can be described using Canada's Aspen Parkland region as an example (fig. 16.3).

In the Prairie provinces, the Aspen Parkland is an ecological tension zone, situated between the boreal forest to the north and grasslands to the south. Within the Parkland, one will find aspen stands, complete with forest understory plants and forest-dwelling animals. However, these forests tend to be restricted toward the wetter areas (e.g., lowlands and north-facing slopes), while patches of grassland, complete with the expected complement of plant and animal species, are found in the drier upland areas. Combined, this region is a savanna habitat, with the relative mixture of grassland and forest community types a function of precipitation, fire history, and grazing activities. So, what is its diversity?

If we measured the diversity of the entire region (or at least some defined area), we would measure forest and grassland communities, along with some shrubland and wetland patches. Such measures would indicate *gamma diversity*. If instead we were to measure only the diversity of the grassland, or forest, or shrubland, or wetland areas, we would measure *alpha diversity*. In other words, alpha diversity is a measure of local diversity, while gamma diversity is a measure of regional or landscape diversity. *Beta diversity* has traditionally been viewed as a measure of the differences among communities within the region or landscape, such that it could be calculated as β = gamma/alpha (Whittaker 1972). However, beta diversity can have other meanings and metrics within community ecology (Anderson et al. 2011). But in general it represents a measure of variation in diversity among locations.

Regardless of what type of diversity is being measured, it is rare for an ecologist to measure all species found within a location, and instead we typically work with taxonomically restricted groups of organisms, for example, vascular or nonvascular plants, mammals, butterflies, beetles, or birds. Some community ecologists restrict their focus even more by studying **guilds**. A guild is a group of organisms that all make their living in a similar way. Examples include the seed-eating animals in the boreal forest, the fruit-eating birds in a tropical rain forest, or the filter-feeding invertebrates in a stream. Some guilds consist of closely related species, while others are taxonomically diverse. For instance, the fruit-eating birds on many South Pacific islands consist mainly of pigeons, while the seed-eating guild in the boreal forest includes mammals, birds, and ants. The term *guild* is most commonly used by community ecologists studying animals. Plant ecologists may instead use other terms such as **life-form**, meaning a body pattern or growth form characterizing a kind of organism (such as emergent macrophytes, or algae), or **functional group**, meaning a collection of organisms with similar ecological, morphological, physiological, or behavioural features or trophic characteristics.

Studying all species or a restricted group, ecologists quickly realized that within natural systems there is substantial variation in the population sizes of each species within a community. Early ecologists soon discovered repeating patterns in the relative abundances of species in natural communities, allowing them to propose that there were some general rules governing community structure.

Patterns of Species' Abundances

One of the first patterns ecologists observe when studying a new community is whether or not there is evidence of **dominance** by one or a few species. A species is *dominant* when it is substantially more common than the other species in the community. Decades of study have routinely shown that within most communities, most species are moderately abundant; few are very abundant or extremely rare. This property is so fundamental that George Sugihara (1980) referred to it as "minimal community structure."

Often, dominance will be visually obvious, as most individuals will tend to be of a single (or few) species. Such was the case with the creosote bush in the example at the start of this chapter. However, dominance can also occur within the more cryptic parts of a community, such as among mycorrhizal fungi, ants, and herbivorous insects. The actual measurement of dominance can be done using a variety of means, including counting individuals, estimating biomass, or estimating basal area occupied by sessile organisms (e.g., barnacles on a rocky shore). These different forms of measurement can be important, depending on what questions the ecologist is asking. For example, a forester is likely most interested in whether a single species dominates a stand of trees by biomass rather than as a count of individuals. Some species, such as the trembling aspen that grows throughout much of the boreal forest, are clonal, spreading partly through asexual reproduction as they spread across the landscape. For such species, counts of individuals are intellectually challenging, and ecologists often rely on measures such as basal area or biomass. Regardless of what part of the community you measure, and the exact units of measurement

you use, ecological dominance can have important implications for natural communities. If most individuals within a community are a single species, then that particular species will drive most interactions within that community. Thus if an ecologist, or society, is interested in the functions that a community provides (e.g., wood production, food, recreation), then understanding dominance helps explain whether these functions are likely the result of many, or few, species.

Looking at whole communities, and not just the dominant species, we find that there tend to be regularities in the relative abundance of species in communities that hold true whether you examine plants in a forest, moths in that forest, or algae inhabiting a nearby stream. If you thoroughly sample groups of organisms such as these, you will come across a few abundant species and a few that are very rare. Most species in most communities will be moderately abundant. This pattern was first quantified by Frank Preston (1948, 1962a, 1962b), who carefully studied the relative abundance of species in collections and communities. Preston worked throughout the Canadian Prairies, and his "distribution of commonness and rarity" among species is one of the best documented patterns in natural communities.

Preston focused on understanding the abundances of different species in relative, rather than absolute, terms, for example, describing one species as twice as abundant as another, rather than as having 200 vs. 100 individuals. This form of comparison is well suited to logarithmic scales, specifically log base 2. In this way, Preston was able to graph the frequency distributions of a number of species of a given relative abundance, with each level on the x-axis corresponding to twice the number of individuals as the previous level. When the relative abundance of species was plotted in this way he consistently obtained results like those shown in figure 16.4. Figure 16.4a shows the relative abundance of 86 species of birds breeding near Westerville, Ohio, over a 10-year period (Preston 1962a). Notice that few species were represented by over 64 individuals or by a single individual. Figure 16.4b shows the relative abundance of desert plants. Robert Whittaker (1965) plotted these abundances using coverage rather than numbers of individuals, which accords well with our discussions in chapter 10 of how to represent the relative abundance of plants. Notice that few plant species were represented by more than 8% cover or less than 0.15% cover. Most species had intermediate coverage.

Both of these data sets show the most distinctive feature of Preston's distributions, that is, they are approximately bell-shaped, or normal. Since abundance is plotted on a log scale, Preston's curves are called lognormal distributions. However, in many cases, only a portion of a bell-shaped curve is apparent, suggesting variations to Preston's distribution. For instance, in figure 16.5b, a sample of moths from Lethbridge, Alberta, comes closer to a complete curve than does figure 16.5a, a sample of moths from Saskatoon, Saskatchewan. Preston suggested that much of the difference between the two curves results from a difference in sample size. While the sample of moths from Saskatoon contained approximately 87,000 individuals belonging to 277 species, the sample from Lethbridge contained an incredible 303,251 individuals belonging to 291 species. If

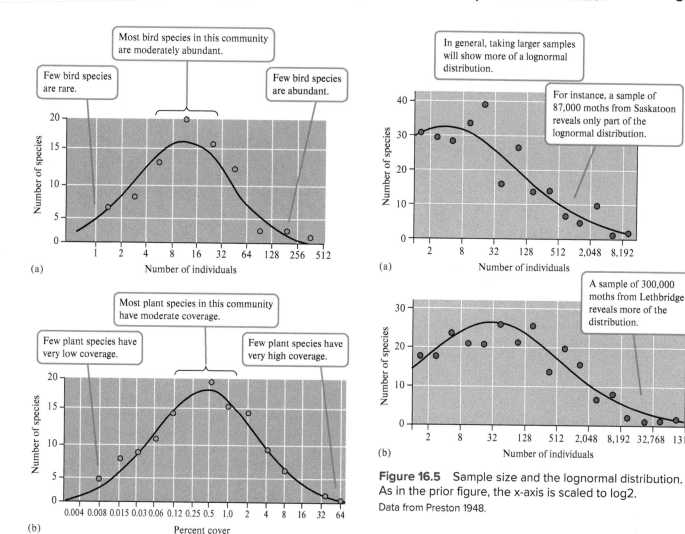

Figure 16.4 Lognormal distributions of (*a*) forest birds, and (*b*) desert plants. Note that in both graphs, the x-axis is scaled to log2. Thus, each step from left to right is a doubling of population size.
Data from Preston 1962a; Whittaker 1965.

Figure 16.5 Sample size and the lognormal distribution. As in the prior figure, the x-axis is scaled to log2.
Data from Preston 1948.

the sample from Saskatoon had contained 300,000 individuals, it would have likely contained more rare species, producing a more complete lognormal curve. Ecologists have found that the more you sample a community, the more species you will find. Common species show up in even small samples, but a great deal of sampling effort is needed to capture the rare species. As a result, our typical sampling schemes result in an underrepresentation of the rare species that live within natural communities. This is unfortunate, as more and more ecologists are realizing that rarity is itself common among species in a community. Thus, in order to have an accurate estimate of these species-abundance patterns, ecologists need to conduct substantial sampling.

So, how do ecologists explain the lognormal distribution of commonness and rarity? Robert May (1975) proposed that the lognormal distribution is the product of many random environmental variables acting upon the populations of many species. In other words, the lognormal distribution is

a statistical expectation. Is the lognormal distribution just a mathematical artifact, or does it reflect important biological processes? George Sugihara (1980) suggested that the lognormal distribution is a consequence of the species within a community subdividing niche space, and this alone could result in there being relatively few very abundant species. However, regardless of its origins, the lognormal distribution is important because it allows us to predict the distribution of abundance among species. As you see next, species abundances and species richness can be combined to describe other patterns of community structure.

An Integrative Index of Species Diversity

Previously, we discussed species richness as one measure of diversity. However, ecologists typically define species diversity on the basis of two factors: (1) species richness, and (2) the relative abundance of the different species within a community, or **species evenness**. Evenness can be thought of as the inverse of *dominance* as we described it in the prior section. A community that is "even" is one without an obviously dominant species. The influence of species richness on community diversity is clear: a community with 20 species is obviously less diverse than one

Communities *a* and *b* both contain five tree species. However, because community *b* has greater species evenness, it has higher diversity.

Community *a* is dominated by one of its five species and so has lower diversity than...

...community *b*, which has the same five species but in equal proportions.

(a)

Lower species evenness

(b)

Higher species evenness

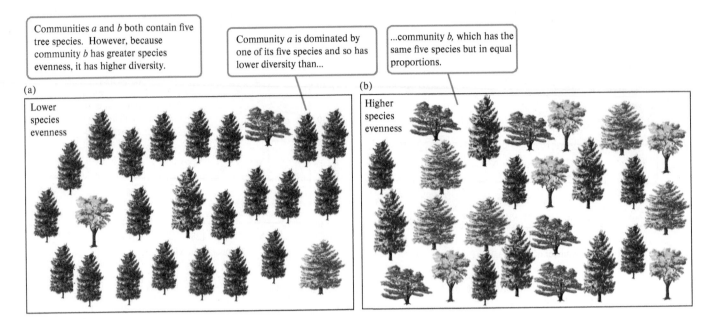

Figure 16.6   Species evenness and species diversity.

with 80 species. The effects of species evenness on diversity are more subtle but easily illustrated.

Figure 16.6 contrasts two hypothetical forest communities. Both forests contain five tree species, so they have equal levels of species richness. However, community *b* is more diverse than community *a* because its species evenness is higher. In community *b*, all five species are equally abundant, each comprising 20% of the tree community. In contrast, 84% of the individuals in community *a* belong to one species, while each of the remaining species constitutes only 4% of the community. In other words, community *a* is dominated by a single species. As a result, when walking through the two forests you would almost certainly form an impression of higher species diversity in community *b*, despite equal levels of species richness in the two forests.

This issue is of critical importance to understanding and describing communities. Diversity is generated through an increase in the number of species *and* through an increase in the evenness among those species. Different factors can affect species numbers and evenness, and these two measures of diversity may themselves differentially affect other community and ecosystem processes. Because of the importance of this issue, it should come as no surprise that these measures of diversity have been incorporated into a single index of diversity.

Getting ecologists to agree on the best index for species diversity is slightly less difficult than herding cats. A quick search through the literature will yield a diversity of indices seemingly as great as the diversity of the species they are intended to describe. These indices go by the names of Simpson's index (Edward, not Homer), Margalef's index, and Brillouin's index of diversity, to name just a few. These indices all share a core trait: their values depend upon levels of species richness and evenness. The most commonly used of these indices was first proposed by Claude Shannon (1948) working

in the field of communication theory at Bell Laboratories. You may also find reference to the Shannon-Wiener index or the Shannon-Weaver index, which creates some confusion and consternation among ecologists, but they are all the same thing. In way of brief explanation, Shannon first published his index in 1948, and in the paper he acknowledged that "communication theory is heavily indebted to the mathematician Norbert Wiener for much of its basic philosophy and theory" (p. 34), citing several of Wiener's papers that were foundational in development of the Shannon index. In 1949, Shannon co-authored a book with Warren Weaver that included much of the same content as the 1948 paper. So, while the confusion is understandable, Shannon independently proposed the index that we use here:

$$H' = -\sum_{i=1}^{s} p_i \ln p_i$$

where:

H' = the value of the Shannon diversity index

p_i = the proportion of the *i*th species

$\ln$ = the natural logarithm of p_i

s = the number of species in the community

The minimum value of H' is 0, which is the value of H' for a community with a single species, and increases as species richness and species evenness increase.

Figure 16.7 shows how to calculate H' for our two hypothetical forest communities. The different values of H' for the two communities reflect the difference in species evenness that we see when we compare the two forests depicted in figure 16.6. H' for community *b*, the community with higher species evenness, is 1.610, while H' for community *a* is 0.662.

The Shannon index is one way to get a snapshot of the diversity of the community, capturing aspects of both the

Calculating species diversity (H′) for two hypothetical communities of forest trees

Community a

Species	Number	Proportion (p_i)	$\log_e p_i$	$p_i \log_e p_i$
1	21	0.84	−0.174	−0.146
2	1	0.04	−3.219	−0.129
3	1	0.04	−3.219	−0.129
4	1	0.04	−3.219	−0.129
5	1	0.04	−3.219	−0.129
Total	25	1.00		−0.662

$$H' = -\sum_{i=1}^{s} p_i \log_e p_i = 0.662$$

Community b

Species	Number	Proportion (p_i)	$\log_e p_i$	$p_i \log_e p_i$
1	5	0.20	−1.609	−0.322
2	5	0.20	−1.609	−0.322
3	5	0.20	−1.609	−0.322
4	5	0.20	−1.609	−0.322
5	5	0.20	−1.609	−0.322
Total	25	1.00		−1.610

$$H' = -\sum_{i=1}^{s} p_i \log_e p_i = 1.610$$

Figure 16.7   Calculating species diversity (*H′*) for two hypothetical communities of forest trees.

number and evenness of species. However, sometimes an ecologist may be interested in these two components of diversity individually. There are many metrics used to measure evenness, including Pielou's *J*. This index was named after the Canadian ecologist Evelyn Pielou, who was a scientist with the Canadian Department of Agriculture and later a professor at Queen's University, Dalhousie University, and University of Lethbridge. Pielou was influential in developing mathematical tools to answer questions in community ecology. Her influence in the field was in part evidenced by the naming of an annual award by the Statistical Ecology section of the Ecological Society of America and given to graduate students in her honour. Pielou's measure of evenness, *J*, is key to many studies of biodiversity. The simplicity of the measure itself is evidence of the elegance of Pielou's research, as *J* is developed and supported by a large body of mathematical research in information science (Pielou 1966), yet has been presented in a very usable form. Simply:

$$J = \frac{H'}{H_{\max}}$$

where:

H' = the value of the Shannon diversity index

$H_{\max}$ = the total possible *H* for the number of species in the sample

$H_{\max}$ is calculated by assuming all individuals in a sample are evenly distributed among the species contained in the sample. For example, if there were five species ($s = 5$), then you would assume each has a p_i of 0.20, and calculate *H* accordingly. As Pielou shows, $H_{\max}$ will equal log *s*, and thus you can rewrite the equation for evenness as:

$$J = \frac{H'}{\ln s}$$

By this equation, as evenness increases, *J* approaches 1. For example, in our hypothetical forest populations, species richness was 5, so $H_{\max} = \ln(5) = 1.61$. In community *a*, the Shannon index (*H′*) was 0.662; therefore, $J = 0.41$. In community *b*, each species made up an equal proportion of total individuals.

H' in community $b = 1.61$, $H_{\max}$ is again equal to ln(5), or 1.61; therefore, $J = 1$. By using these equations, both evenness and species richness can be directly measured, providing ecologists with more tools for understanding communities. As you will see next, we can also use a graphical approach to contrast communities.

Rank-Abundance Curves

We can portray the relative abundance, dominance, and diversity of species within a community by plotting the relative abundance of species against their rank in abundance. The resulting **rank-abundance curve** provides us with important information about a community, information accessible at a glance. Figure 16.8 plots the abundance rank of each tree

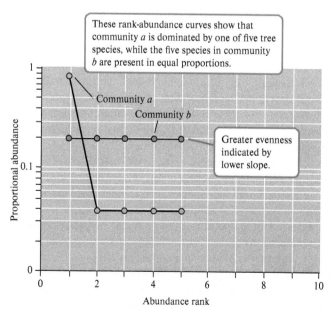

Figure 16.8   Rank-abundance curves for two hypothetical forests.

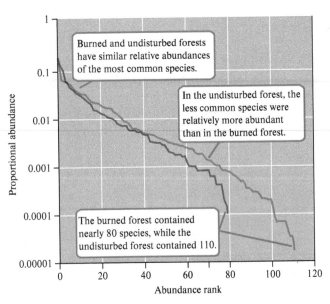

Figure 16.9   Rank-abundance curves for burned (red) and undisturbed (blue) forests near Thunder Bay, Ontario.
Data courtesy of Eric Lamb.

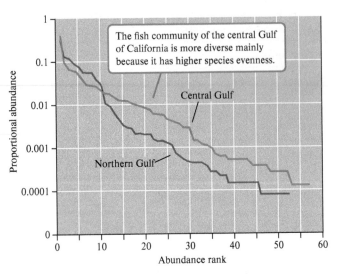

Figure 16.10   Rank-abundance curves for two reef fish communities in the Gulf of California.
Data from Molles 1978; Thomson and Lehner 1976; and courtesy of D. A. Thomson and C. E. Lehner 1976.

species in communities *a* and *b* (see fig. 16.6) against its proportional abundance. The rank-abundance curve for community *b* shows that all five species are equally abundant, while the rank-abundance curve for community *a* shows its dominance by the most abundant tree species.

Figure 16.9 shows rank-abundance curves for the understory vegetation found in burned and unburned forests just north of Thunder Bay, Ontario (Lamb et al. 2003). These data were collected by Eric Lamb, now at the University of Saskatchewan, while he was a graduate student at Lakehead University. Lamb wanted to determine the effects of forest burning on plant diversity, so he measured the diversity and abundance of vegetation in areas that were burned about four years prior to data collection and in areas with no recent history of fire. From the rank-abundance curve, you can see the undisturbed forest contained 110 species, while the burned forest held only 79. Additionally, you will notice that although the proportional representation of the common species was similar in both forest types, the less common species were found at a lower abundance in the burned forest than in the undisturbed forest.

Two reef fish communities from the Gulf of California further demonstrate the usefulness of rank-abundance curves (fig. 16.10). Using these curves, one is quickly able to see that the two reef fish communities contained similar numbers of species (52 vs. 57) but differed substantially in species evenness. The community of the central Gulf of California showed a more even distribution of individuals among species.

Combined, the great usefulness of rank-abundance curves is that they allow ecologists to visually describe dominance and diversity patterns within a single community or when comparing communities. Often, such visual representations are more useful than numerical summaries.

CONCEPT 16.1 REVIEW

1. Why do smaller samples result in only part of the bell-shaped curve that is characteristic of the log-normal distribution?

2. What do measures of evenness describe about community structure that cannot be captured by measures of species richness?

3. Describe the differences between alpha and gamma diversity.

16.2 Environmental Complexity and Species Diversity

Species diversity is higher in complex environments. Describing patterns of community structure is only the first step in understanding communities. As scientists rather than natural historians, ecologists strive to understand what causes the observed patterns in community structure and why they can vary among locations and through time. In chapter 17, we will discuss the role of species interactions in influencing community structure. Here, we focus on a more basic issue: the effects of environmental complexity and heterogeneity on the diversity of communities. In general, species diversity increases with environmental complexity or heterogeneity. However, aspects of environmental structure important to one group of organisms may have no effect on other groups. Consequently, you must know something about the ecological requirements of species to predict how environmental structure affects their diversity. In other words, you must know something about niches and natural history to understand ecological processes.

Structural Complexity, the Niche, and Bird Species Diversity

As we have discussed throughout the text (chapters 9 and 13), the fundamental niche is the multi-dimensional set of conditions an organism needs to survive. However, competitors can cause the exclusion of a species under some sets of conditions, and thus the realized niche will tend to represent a smaller set of suitable conditions than that described by the fundamental niche. Over time we might expect competition to decrease, due to either competitive exclusion or an evolutionary response (e.g., character displacement). In either case, the competitive exclusion principle leads us to predict that coexisting species will have different niches. As we saw in chapter 1, that is what Robert MacArthur (1958) found when he examined the ecology of five species of warblers that live together in the forests of northeastern North America.

What does MacArthur's study of warbler niches have to do with the influence of environmental complexity on species diversity? MacArthur's results suggest that since these species forage in different vegetative strata, the vertical structure of the vegetation may influence their distributions. He explored this possibility on Mount Desert Island, Maine, where he measured the relationship between volume of vegetation above 6 m and the abundance of warblers (fig. 16.11). The number of warbler species at the study sites increased with forest stature. The study sites with greater volume of vegetation above 6 m supported more warbler species. These results formed the

foundation of later studies of how foliage height diversity influences bird species diversity.

MacArthur was one of the first ecologists to quantify the relationship between species diversity and environmental heterogeneity. He quantified the diversity of species and the complexity of the environment using the Shannon index, H'. He measured environmental complexity as foliage height diversity, which increased with the number of vegetative layers and with an even distribution of vegetative biomass among three vertical layers, 0 to 0.6 m, 0.6 to 7.6 m, and > 7.6 m. MacArthur's foliage height diversity, like species diversity, increases with richness (the number of vegetative layers) and evenness (how evenly vegetative biomass is distributed among layers).

Robert MacArthur and John MacArthur (1961) measured foliage height diversity and bird species diversity in 13 plant communities in northeastern North America, Florida, and Panama. The vegetative communities included in their study ranged from grassland to mature deciduous forest, with foliage height diversity that ranged from 0.043 to 1.093. Plant communities with greater foliage height diversity supported more diverse bird communities (fig. 16.12). MacArthur and his colleagues went on to study the relationship between foliage height diversity and bird species diversity in a wide variety of temperate, tropical, and island settings, from North America to Australia. They again found a positive correlation between foliage height diversity and bird species diversity. The combined weight of the evidence from North and Central America and Australia suggests that the relationship is not one of chance but reflects something about the way that birds in these environments subdivide space.

How is environmental complexity related to the diversity of other organisms besides birds? Ecological studies have

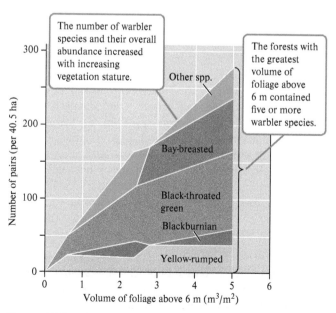

Figure 16.11 Stature of vegetation and number of warbler species.
Data from MacArthur 1958.

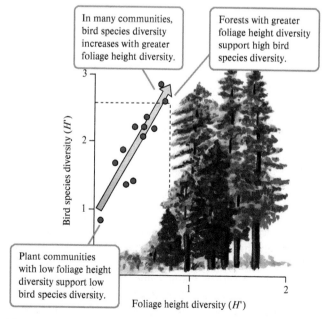

Figure 16.12 Foliage height diversity and bird species diversity.
Data from MacArthur and MacArthur 1961.

shown positive relationships between structural complexity and species diversity for many groups of organisms, including mammals, lizards, plankton, arthropods, marine gastropods, reef fish, and many other groups of animals. It will probably not surprise you to learn, in the examples below, that environmental complexity likewise affects diversity of plants.

Niches, Heterogeneity, and the Diversity of Algae and Plants

The existence of approximately 300,000 species of terrestrial plants presents a multitude of opportunities for specialization by animals. Consequently, high plant diversity can explain much of animal diversity. However, how do we explain the diversity of primary producers? G. Evelyn Hutchinson (1961) described what he called "the paradox of the plankton." He suggested that communities of phytoplankton present a paradox because they live in relatively simple environments (the open waters of lakes and oceans) and compete for the same nutrients (nitrogen, phosphorus, silica, etc.), yet many species can coexist without competitive exclusion. This situation seemed paradoxical because it appears to violate the competitive exclusion principle. Hutchinson argued that much of the paradox could be explained by taking into consideration the substantial heterogeneity in abiotic conditions and resource distributions, even though the essential resources needed by the planktonic species remain constant. The diversity of terrestrial plants presents a similar paradox, and it too can be (partly) explained by focusing on species' niches and environmental heterogeneity.

The Niches of Algae and Terrestrial Plants

The niches of algae appear to be defined by their nutrient requirements, and this was most clearly elucidated by David Tilman (1977). This name may sound familiar, as we discussed his resource-based model of competition in chapter 13. Tilman conducted a set of 76 long-term competition experiments on freshwater diatoms. His work is important not only in showing competitive exclusion but also in showing sets of conditions that allowed coexistence of diatom species. Exclusion or coexistence depended not upon the absolute amount of essential resources in the environment, but instead it depended upon the ratio of two nutrients: silicate, SiO_2^{-2}, and phosphate, PO_4^{-3}.

When Tilman grew the diatoms *Asterionella formosa* and *Cyclotella meneghiniana* by themselves, they each were able to establish and maintain stable populations at all resource ratios and flow rates (representing the rate of nutrient turnover). When grown together, the outcome of Tilman's experiments depended upon the ratio of silicate to phosphate (fig. 16.13). At high ratios (representing an abundance of Si relative to P), *Asterionella* eventually excluded *Cyclotella*. At lower ratios, the two species coexisted. At the lowest ratio, *Cyclotella* was numerically dominant over *Asterionella*.

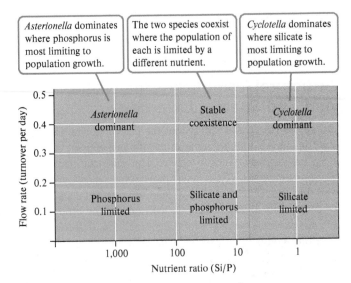

Figure 16.13 The ratio of silicate (SiO_2^{-2}) to phosphate (PO_4^{-3}) and competition between the diatoms *Asterionella formosa* and *Cyclotella meneghiniana*.
Data from Tilman 1977.

How can we explain Tilman's results? It turns out that *Asterionella* takes up phosphorus at a much higher rate than does *Cyclotella*. Tilman reasons that at high ratios of silicate to phosphate, *Asterionella* is able to deplete the environment of phosphorus and consequently eliminate *Cyclotella*. However, when ratios are low, silicate limits the growth rate of *Asterionella* and it cannot deplete phosphate. Consequently, when ratios are low, *Asterionella* cannot exclude *Cyclotella*. At these low ratios, silicate limits the growth rate of *Asterionella*, while phosphate limits the growth rate of *Cyclotella*. Consequently, in the presence of low ratios of silicate to phosphate, the two diatoms coexist.

What do the results of Tilman's experiments have to do with the relationship of environmental complexity to species diversity? A general prediction from his work is that as Si/P ratios go from high to low, the abundance of *Cyclotella* relative to *Asterionella* should increase. To test whether his predictions were consistent with reality, Tilman (1977) was able to access data on water samples taken from Lake Michigan. Among samples, Si:P ratios ranged from approximately 600 to 1. The relative abundance of *Cyclotella* changed as predicted: from nearly absent at high Si:P ratios to nearly 100% at lower ratios. Thus, Tilman's landmark work clearly shows that heterogeneity in resource ratios, one form of environmental complexity, has important consequences for community structure.

Effects of Environmental Heterogeneity on Terrestrial Plants

Light, water, and a diversity of nutrients are essential for plant growth, and plant responses to different levels of these resources form the dominant niche axes for most terrestrial plant species. However, unlike structural complexity, it is not visually obvious to the researcher the degree to which resources vary within a community. As it turns out, there is substantial variation, at

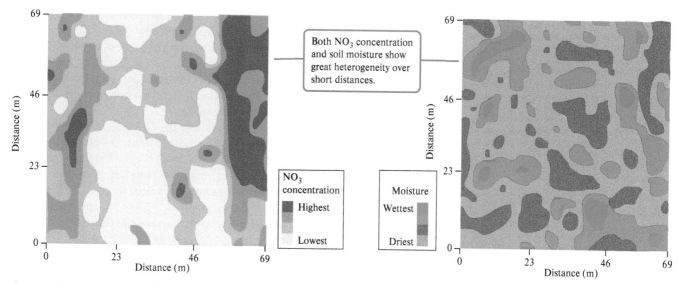

Both NO₃ concentration and soil moisture show great heterogeneity over short distances.

Figure 16.14   Variation in nitrate (NO₃) and soil moisture in a 4,761 m² area in an old agricultural field. Data from Robertson et al. 1988.

a diversity of spatial scales, with impacts on plant growth and community structure.

G. Robertson and a team of researchers (Robertson et al. 1988) quantified variation in nitrogen and moisture across an old field, abandoned from agricultural use for nearly 60 years. Robertson and his colleagues focused their measurements on a 0.5 hectare (69 m × 69 m) subplot within the old field, in which they measured several soil variables, including nitrate concentration and soil moisture, at 301 sampling points. This large number of sampling points over a small area provided sufficient data to construct a detailed map of soil properties. Figure 16.14 shows considerable patchiness in both nitrate and moisture. Both variables show at least tenfold differences across the study plot. In addition, nitrate concentration and moisture do not appear to correlate well with each other; hot spots for nitrogen were not necessarily hot spots for moisture. The researchers concluded that soil conditions show sufficient spatial variability to affect the structure of plant communities, particularly if the distribution of other soil parameters were also considered. Since this initial study by Robertson, many other ecologists have found similar results in a diversity of communities, ranging from dry grasslands to wet forests. Now let's examine how spatial heterogeneity in these resources may affect the distribution and diversity of plants.

Influences of Environmental Heterogeneity on the Diversity of Forest Sedges

Graham Bell, Martin Lechowicz, and Marcia Waterway of McGill University teamed up to identify the factors that influence the distribution of sedges in the deciduous forests of Quebec (Bell et al. 2000; fig. 16.15). The research team chose to focus on sedges, more specifically the genus *Carex*, as there are more *Carex* species in forest and wetland habitats of these northern areas than any other genus of seed plant, including over 50 within the 1,000 hectare study site used by the research team. In

other words, this is an ideal group of organisms to explore the linkages between heterogeneity and diversity.

The research team collected several healthy individuals of 11 *Carex* species. These plants grow by forming numerous *ramets*, genetically identical modules of the plant. The team separated each individual into its ramets, planted those individually, and ended up with a large number of clones for each of their 11 species. They then went back to the field and laid out three 1,000 m transects (along a lake, in a gorge, and along a cliff), planting one individual of each species every 10 m. By ensuring they only used a single genetic individual of a given plant species on a single transect, they could say that any variation in performance of the plants they found was due to environmental, not genetic, influences—very clever, and once again wonderful evidence as to why plants make such excellent study organisms for ecological research.

Figure 16.15   McGill University's Gault Nature Reserve on Mont-Saint-Hilaire, Quebec.
Martin Duval.

After a year, the research team members went back to their sites and recorded which plants were alive and which had died. They found substantial spatial variation in the number of species surviving along each transect. In addition to the number of survivors at each point on a transect, the researchers recorded the identity of the survivors. Why? Just because five species may have survived at each of two locations does not necessarily mean they were the same five species. Shifts in the **species composition** of a community, even without shifts in species richness, would indicate a shift in community structure.

What does this variation in survival (and composition) indicate? Since the use of clones allowed the research team to rule out genetic factors, they can conclude that there was biologically meaningful variation in the environment that affected the competitive outcomes of these species.

The work here by Bell, Lechowicz, and Waterway provides an example of how focusing on a single, but diverse, group of related species, *Carex*, can reveal patterns of community structure. In the next section, we explore the role of another factor in altering community composition: disturbance.

CONCEPT 16.2 REVIEW

1. Does Tilman's finding that *Asterionella* and *Cyclotella* exclude each other under certain conditions but coexist under other conditions violate the competitive exclusion principle?

2. Suppose you discover that the fish species inhabiting small isolated patches of coral reef use different vertical zones on the reef face—some species live down near the sand, some live a bit higher on the reef, and some higher still. Based on this pattern of zonation, can you predict how reef structure should affect the diversity of fish living on such reefs?

3. Why did Bell et al. (2000) use plants as indicators of heterogeneity rather than rely on measures of abiotic variables, such as light and nitrogen?

16.3 Functional Consequences of Diversity

Ecological functions performed by communities are dependent upon community structure. Globally, there is significant concern about the rapid rate of biodiversity loss, often associated with human disturbances. This concern arises for many reasons, including aesthetic, moral, and even functional ones. It is this latter issue, the impact of loss of biodiversity on ecological function and the delivery of **ecological services**, that we discuss here. Ecological services represent the processes and resources provided by ecological systems that are of value to humans, including biomass production, nutrient cycling, water filtration, carbon sequestration, recreation, and pollination of crops. If function is diminished, then so too is the quality of the service. Thus, independent of any moral or aesthetic argument, humans benefit directly from healthy ecological systems. As we will discuss in chapter 23, these benefits are beginning to be included in development plans, emphasizing the potential economic value.

Ecosystem function and the delivery of services does not imply intent by the ecosystem; instead, the function is a natural by-product of ecological and biogeochemical interactions within the ecosystem. Some of these functions will directly impact humans. For example, if a large wetland along a coastal region buffers tidal surges, then the loss of that ecosystem service (tidal dissipation) costs humans through risk of personal and property damage. A grassland that produces substantial amounts of plant matter has the potential to be more economically viable for a rancher than one that produces little. In other words, the services provided by ecological systems directly alter the economic well-being and personal safety of humans. As a result, there is substantial interest in understanding what factors control the efficiency of ecosystem services so that some processes can be protected or even augmented to enhance or restore the delivery of these services. We begin our discussion by focusing on species diversity and its impact on the delivery of ecosystem services.

Impacts of Biodiversity on Delivery of Ecological Services

Let us imagine a number of hypothetical communities that fall within some landscape. As we all love learning about plants, let us focus only on plant diversity and a key ecological function, biomass production. Why biomass production? Quite simply, plant biomass = food, fuel, and habitat (be they buildings for us or homes for other species). We notice that some of our hypothetical plant communities contain large numbers of plant species, some few, and some an intermediate number. What relationship between species diversity and biomass production is to be expected?

In recent years there has been an explosion of research activity trying to answer this question. These studies have taken place in the computer lab, in the greenhouse, and in the field. The standard experimental design is to grow "synthetic communities" of varying levels of diversity. To achieve this, the researcher typically decides on some overall pool of species (i.e., gamma diversity among all experimental plots). Each plot is then assigned some varying combination of numbers of species from this pool, thereby varying alpha diversity among plots. After some period of time, the researcher measures ecological function in the plots, using regression or other analyses to determine the nature of the relationship between diversity and function. Peter Reich and colleagues (including David Tilman, mentioned previously in this chapter) have synthesized the results of two such experiments (Reich et al. 2012).

BioDIV and BioCON are two independent experiments established in a Minnesota grassland in the 1990s, and each

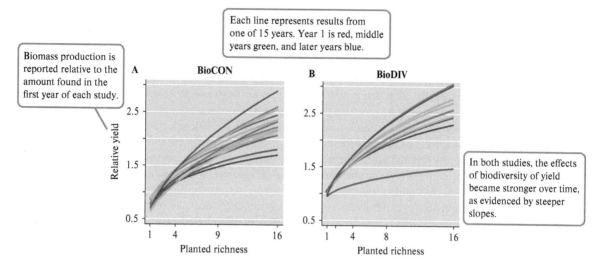

Figure 16.16 The effects of species diversity on biomass production became stronger over time in two parallel experiments (BioCON and BioDIV) in a Minnesota grassland. Each curve represents a single year (15 total) with colour gradient from red (Year 1) to blue (Year 15).

Peter B. Reich, David Tilman, Forest Isbell, Kevin Mueller, Sarah E. Hobbie, Dan F. B. Flynn, and Nico Eisenhauer. 2012, May 4. Impacts of biodiversity loss escalate through time as redundancy fades. *Science* 336(6081):589–92, Figure 1. Reprinted with permission from AAAS.

have run for over a decade. Each team set its species pool to 16, although there were some differences in which species were used in each experiment. The results obtained between these two studies are striking (fig. 16.16). In both experiments, not only did biomass production increase with increased species diversity, but the magnitude of this diversity effect grew stronger the longer the experiment ran. As strong as these results are, there are some important limitations. First, gamma diversity for each was only 16, while the true gamma diversity for the surrounding grassland area is well over 100. Second, the maximum diversity within each plot was limited to 16, a value lower than the maximum diversity of equally sized areas in the surrounding grassland. Third, though these experiments were run independently of each other, they do share species and are in similar geographic areas and, thus, do not represent completely independent tests. What is needed to address the generality of the effects of diversity of ecological function would be additional studies in geographically diverse locations, with independent species pools. Fortunately, such data are available.

As a sign of the increased importance this topic has gained over the years, there were fewer than five experiments investigating biodiversity–function relationships in 1995, and about 40 just 10 years later in 2004. This remains an active area of ecological research, with more than 40 papers on biodiversity–function relationships as recently as 2018. Patricia Balvanera and colleagues have synthesized the findings from 103 studies, allowing us to draw some general conclusions (Balvanera et al. 2006).

Across the studies they sampled, increased plant diversity caused a significant increase in primary production, consistent with Reich's (2012) results. Interestingly, manipulating the diversity of mycorrhizal fungi has nearly as large an impact on primary production as does manipulating the plants directly!

The effects of plant diversity manipulation were not limited to the plants. Increased plant diversity also caused an increase in insect herbivore biomass and enhanced litter decomposition in most studies in which they were measured. Though plant diversity increased herbivore biomass, there was little effect on the biomass of the predators that eat the herbivores. These findings are a clear indication that aspects of community structure, such as plant species diversity, impact the functioning of the local community and local ecosystem.

What Causes Diversity–Function Relationships?

The consistency with which different research groups find functional benefits of species diversity suggests there are some general mechanisms at play. There are three main mechanisms proposed to explain how biodiversity could enhance productivity (or other ecological functions), although there remains substantial debate regarding which mechanisms are most prominent (van Ruijven and Berendse 2005).

The first mechanism, *complementarity,* comes from niche theory (chapter 9). The basic logic is that a given ecological service will be highest/fastest in a community in which all resources/microenvironments are being exploited or occupied. If a single species has a single niche, then one might expect it only to be able to exploit a fraction of the potential niche space that might be available in a location that has multiple microhabitats. Similarly, a single species may have limited growth (e.g., shallow roots), or narrow diet, thereby consuming only a fraction of the available food/resources within a community. Consequently, though the habitat has the potential to host multiple species without competitive exclusion, alpha diversity is too low to allow for full exploitation of the environment. However, as new species are added, some will have different niche requirements and the ability to exploit different microhabitats, coexisting without exclusion. As a result, more of the niche space and resources in the community gets exploited, and ecological function should increase. This can continue as you add species, until all niche space and resources are exploited, at which point there should be no increased function due to addition of new species.

A second mechanism of diversity effects is *facilitation.* In this model, some species enhance the growth of others, perhaps by reducing soil salinity or modifying the thermal environment. This mechanism may be particularly important in stressful environments where, for example, nurse plants may create microhabitats that are suitable for seed germination or survival of other plants, including plants of other species. Plants of one species may provide shelter, protecting individual plants of other species from herbivores or desiccation. Plants may even provide suitable substrate for epiphytic species to grow. By modifying the environment on a very localized scale, one species of plant may create suitable niche space that another species can occupy.

A third means by which biodiversity can enhance ecological function is through the *sampling effect,* also called species selection. This mechanism is based upon the idea that species differ in their inherent rates of delivery of some ecological service. For example, some plant species are more productive than others; some microbes result in faster nitrogen cycling than others. As the number of species in a community increases, the odds of the community containing at least one species with enhanced function increases, resulting in an overall pattern of increased function with increased diversity. Thus, sampling is not a benefit of diversity itself, as much as increased odds of having the most productive species.

Although these three mechanisms have been presented as distinct, there is no reason to expect them to be exclusionary. In fact, a number of statistical tools exist allowing researchers to quantify what proportion of an observed diversity effect is due to the different mechanisms. For example, Cardinale estimated that 17% of his observed responses were due to species selection, while the remaining 83% were due to a combination of complementarity and facilitation (Cardinale et al. 2002). Reich and his colleagues (2012) were able to show that complementarity effects increased in strength over time for both the BioCON and BioDIV studies; selection effects did not.

It is also important to remember that diversity of a given taxonomic group can have simultaneous impacts on many ecological services, and these may result in positive feedback. For example, within the BioCON study (Reich et al. 2012), species diversity increased soil fertility, with the magnitude of these effects growing over time. Thus, not only did plant diversity increase plant biomass through increased complementarity of the plant species, but it also resulted in increased microbial activity, leading to more nitrogen in the soil and further enhancing plant growth. Or, put another way, communities are complex and interconnected biological systems; changing one component, such as biodiversity, can have functional consequences throughout the system. As we see next, species diversity is not the only level of complexity that is functionally important.

CONCEPT 16.3 REVIEW

1. What are ecological services, and how do they relate to the structure of communities?

2. Why is species selection a statistical, rather than biological, mechanism to explain diversity–function relationships?

3. How does complementarity relate to niche theory?

ECOLOGY IN ACTION

Indicators of Human Impacts

A running theme of this book has been a discussion of the impacts that humans are having on natural systems, and how ecologists are using a data-driven approach to reduce, mitigate, and recover from the environmental harm that comes from anthropogenic activities. When focused on a single species, the work of the ecologist is often relatively straightforward (even if politically charged). For example, to set quotas for the harvest of cod requires a detailed understanding of cod populations; to decide whether hunters can go after grizzly bears requires good data on bear populations. In neither case does the information the ecologist provides to government necessarily require a detailed description of the entire community and all the species found within it. However, suppose one wanted different types of questions answered, such as these: Following a disturbance, how do we know a wetland has recovered to a natural state? Is a particular human activity reducing the ecological integrity of a location? These questions are decidedly more difficult to answer, as they require comparisons among communities (i.e., populations of many species) as opposed to changes in the population of only one species (e.g., cod or grizzlies). Here, we discuss a few examples of how ecologists are able to simplify the data needed to answer these questions, making answers more accessible for government and those in need of assessing change.

Ecological "integrity," "intactness," and "health" are all terms commonly used in government documents and regulation, both as things to protect as well as goals for recovery following development. However, to a scientist these are awfully "squishy" concepts—they are easy to conceptualize but difficult to quantify. For example, imagine a forest with thousands of species of plants and animals. How do we know if it is intact or not? We could perhaps compare one forest with another, but do we need to measure the populations of thousands of species? Later in the book we will discuss some ways ecologists do compare diverse communities (e.g., ordinations); however, here we focus on finding a simpler answer. Why? From a regulatory perspective, measuring entire systems is very expensive because it requires detailed taxonomic expertise and substantial sampling over multiple seasons, if not years or decades. Consequently, ecologists frequently identify indicators as a rapid means of assessing human impacts and the condition of ecological communities. An indicator can be any species or group of species whose abundance or condition is representative of the overall condition of the community or ecosystem. You may immediately see the potential benefits; with an accurate indicator, a measure of ecological integrity or health may be obtained by measuring only a small component of a complex system.

Not all species can serve as effective indicators, and a poor choice has significant societal, economic, and environmental consequences. In an influential paper, Université de Moncton ecologists Marc-André Villard and his former graduate student Vincent Carignan suggest that valuable indicators will possess a number of characteristics (Carignan and Villard 2002). For example, the characteristics have the ability to provide early warnings of impending change, are relatively inexpensive to measure, and can be accurately measured by nonspecialists. However, they also highlight several potential limitations to the value of some indicators. For example, ecological theory suggests that no two species are likely to share the same niche, and thus no two species likely respond exactly the same when conditions change. Species with shorter generation times likely show effects of disturbance faster than do species with slower generation times, and thus a slowly changing indicator may underestimate degradation of ecological integrity. In addition, an indicator likely has a limited range of conditions over which it responds, a range narrower than the potential degree of human influence. Further, good indicators need to respond as quickly to positive change in the environment as they do to negative change; otherwise, the impacts of environmental improvements may not be properly assessed. Here we offer two examples of how indicators are being used in Canada to (1) measure urban pollution, and (2) monitor wetland recovery associated with oil sands development.

Using Lichens to Estimate Vehicular Pollution

Lichens rarely get any love (fig. 16.17). They are small, excruciatingly difficult to identify, and often appear more as a background in a nice photo than as the point of focus.

Figure 16.17 Trees are home to a diversity of lichens.
Jurik Peter/Shutterstock.

Despite popular indifference, they are both biologically intriguing (they are the product of a mutualism between a fungus and an alga, or a cyanobacterium), and they are well known to be very sensitive to air pollution. Critical to water and nutrient balance in lichens is the ability to absorb essential resources directly from air and water. They have neither the filtration systems found in vascular plants nor the detoxification pathways common in insects. Consequently, pollutants that harm biological systems often have rapid and pronounced effects on lichens. That's bad news for lichens but great news for someone searching for indicators of pollution. L. Paige Wright, an independent researcher on Prince Edward Island, recently collaborated with scientists at Environment and Climate Change Canada, Trent University, and Alberta Environment and Parks on a review of bioindicators and biomonitors of atmospheric pollution (Wright et al. 2018). The review found that lichens are repeatedly indicated as effective monitors for atmospheric nitrogen deposition and polyaromatic hydrocarbons exposure.

Though lichens have been used as indicators of pollution for decades in many locales (Conti and Cecchetti 2001), their response specifically to vehicular pollution has not been well understood. Two ecologists from Carleton University have recently published a study to help fill this knowledge gap (Coffey and Fahrig 2012).

Heather Coffey and her MSc supervisor Lenore Fahrig conducted a survey of 420 trees within Ottawa, measuring lichen abundance and species richness on each. The sites were distributed throughout the city and included areas that varied in vehicular pollution, moisture, and colonization potential by new propagules. For use as an indicator of pollution, Coffey and Fahrig reasoned that measures of lichen abundance and/or richness need not be *influenced* only by pollution. Instead, pollution needs to have a stronger effect than abiotic factors, such as moisture. Overall, they identified 18 macrolichen species, three of which were found in nearly all sites. At a given site, the total abundance of lichens was most strongly (and negatively) influenced by vehicular pollution within 300 m of the location measured. As expected, local moisture and availability of colonization sources were also important (and positive), though their influence was low relative to vehicular pollution. In contrast, though macrolichen species richness was also negatively influenced by vehicular pollution, richness was most strongly influenced by moisture and the availability of colonization sources.

Combined, these results support the use of lichens as indicators of very localized levels of vehicular pollution. For use as an indicator, their results suggest that species level identification is not needed, which is very good news. More specifically, with only minor training, individuals could rapidly (and inexpensively) measure lichen cover. For those of you interested in finding a simple research project, you might consider testing the generality of Coffey and Fahrig's results near your school!

Wetlands and Oil Sands

As you may have heard, there is a bit of oil sands development occurring in Alberta. Much of this oil extraction involves surface mining, rather than the classic image of oil wells and pumps. The vast majority of the oil sands reserves of Alberta occur within the boreal forest and, more specifically, in areas covered by wetlands. Rebecca Rooney (now at the University of Waterloo) and her former Ph.D. supervisor, Suzanne Bayley (from the University of Alberta), published a study proposing a few indicator species to help set targets for reclamation (Rooney and Bayley 2011).

Rooney and Bayley (2011) point out that due to a variety of regulations, companies involved in surface mining are not required to restore the landscape; instead, reclamation activities must return the landscape to an equivalent land capability. Though there is substantial debate over what exactly that means, there is no doubt that there will be (and currently is) substantial effort toward wetland reclamation following surface mining (fig. 16.18). Though several companies have conducted reclamation activities, specific targets have not been set by the government. Consequently, it is unclear when reclamation is done—a frustrating situation for industry, conservation groups, and everyone involved in development. Rooney and Bayley set out to help define targets for wetland reclamation in this region.

Figure 16.18   Reclamation activities attempt to return the landscape to equivalent land capability.
© Bill Brooks/Alamy.

The researchers measured the vegetation in 63 wetlands, 25 of which were reclaimed and 38 of which were undisturbed and represented the best case for that region. As these were wetlands, simply laying out transects and walking a path was not an option. Instead, key research gear included kayaks and a rake—the latter allowing them to sample the submerged vegetation.

Across all sites, they identified 26 species. Using a variety of complex statistical approaches (e.g., ordination), they were able to identify seven types of wetlands, each of which could be described by a single indicator species. Of these seven wetland types, two of them (marsh and marsh-fen) were most typical among the undisturbed sites, and Rooney and Bayley suggest that they represent suitable targets for reclamation. Unfortunately, all 25 of the reclaimed wetlands do not resemble either of these targets and instead most closely resemble the five alternative wetland types, each of which is rare among undisturbed wetlands. Thus, though substantial reclamation activity is underway, data to date suggest that the community types being reclaimed differ from those common on the undisturbed landscape. Whether this still meets the requirement of "equivalent land capability" is unclear, and that answer will require measures of large numbers of potential ecological services.

16.4 Genetic Diversity and Ecological Processes

Genetic variation of species within a community influences ecological function. You may have noticed that discussions of evolution have been generally lacking throughout this chapter, at least in contrast to its more thorough integration into previous sections of the text. Such omission is not limited to this book alone but instead fairly reflects the traditional approach used by ecologists in describing communities. In the last decade, however, there has been rapid growth in research devoted to integrating evolutionary biology and community ecology. Here we will focus on the functional importance of genetic diversity.

Functional Consequences of Genetic Diversity in Communities

Population biologists have long recognized the value of genetic diversity among their species of interest. For example, it is a general tenet in conservation biology that genetic variation is critical to the long-term viability of populations (e.g., Lacy 1997). The value of genetic diversity is also clear from agricultural studies. For example, in a classic study investigating the effects of genetic diversity within rice crops and the spread of a devastating crop disease, mixed-genotype plantings (in contrast to traditional genetic monocultures) were so effective at reducing disease that fungicide application was not needed (Zhu et al. 2000). Community ecologists have since been able to show functional consequences of the genetic diversity of the species within a community. We begin with a study that asks a simple question: Does community structure depend upon the genetic diversity of the species within the community?

Rosemary Booth and Phil Grime (2003) designed an elegant experiment to address the question of whether the genetic diversity of the plants within the community influenced plant community structure. Again, plants make excellent subjects for studies of genetic diversity. Most plant species have the ability to be cloned, either from single cells or through cuttings. Consequently, by taking one individual (of a single genotype) and using effective horticultural skills, one is able to rapidly cultivate many individuals (still of a single genotype). By repeating this procedure on different individuals, one can generate multiple individuals of a number of different genotypes. This is the research equipment needed in any study in which genetic diversity needs to be known and manipulated. In contrast, it is very hard to clone animals, and nearly all university ethics boards would not be keen on reading a proposal in which one takes cuttings in an attempt to try!

The experiment that Booth and Grime conducted was straightforward in its approach. They used 36 experimental communities into which they planted the same 16 individuals of each of 11 plant species. However, these 36 communities were each assigned one level of genetic diversity: low, intermediate, and high. In the low diversity treatment, each of the 16 individuals of a single species were of the same genotype. In the intermediate treatment, they used four individuals of each of four genotypes per species. In the highest diversity treatment, all 16 individuals were of different genotypes. Thus, this experimental design allowed Booth and Grime to manipulate genetic diversity while keeping species richness and evenness constant.

To allow the plants time to interact and work out any competitive differences, they measured community composition during five consecutive years (1998–2002). Over the course of the experiment, there was an overall drop in the Shannon index, due to both species loss and increased dominance (fig. 16.19); both of these are common in long-term mesocosm experiments. Of more interest is the effect of genetic diversity at the end of the study: increased genetic diversity resulted in higher community diversity by reducing the overall rate of species loss. Or put another way, just as genetic diversity of a single species leads to increased viability of that population, increased genetic diversity of species appears to lead to increased species diversity within a community. Why? Genotypes likely differ in how they acquire resources, where they put the roots and leaves, and their susceptibility

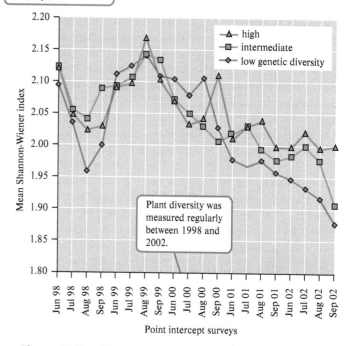

Figure 16.19 Changes in high, intermediate, and low genetic diversity over time, as a function of the genetic diversity of species.

Rosemary E. Booth and J. Philip Grime. 2003, October. Effects of genetic impoverishment on plant community diversity. *Journal of Ecology* 91(5):721–30, Figure 4. Reprinted by permission of John Wiley & Sons Inc. via Rightslink.

to competition and other processes. This is the same as saying an individual's genotype influences the exact form of an individual's niche and how it occupies habitat. Therefore, genetic diversity should lead to niche complementarity, similar to that previously described for species diversity.

The effects of plant genetic diversity are not restricted to impacts on the plants alone. Instead, as part of a connected ecological system they can cascade to impact herbivores and the predators of the herbivores. This was most clearly shown by meticulous work by Greg Crutsinger, now at the University of British Columbia (Crutsinger et al. 2006), while he was a graduate student.

Common throughout much of eastern North America are abandoned agricultural fields in various stages of succession (chapter 18). In many cases, species of *Solidago* (goldenrod) can become dominant, serving as food and foraging ground for a diversity of insect herbivores and predators. To tease apart the impacts of genetic diversity of this dominant plant on a number of aspects of the community, Crutsinger cultivated clones of 21 genotypes of *Solidago altissima*. He then planted 12 individuals from a total of 1, 3, 6, or 12 genotypes into 1 m² plots in a field. Thus, all plots started with the same number of species (1), the same number of plants (12), but different numbers of genotypes (1–12). As a result, any differences at the end of the study can be attributed to differences in genetic diversity.

Arthropods *loved* his research plots—so much so that Crutsinger and his crew counted 36,997 individuals from over 130 species in his plots over the course of a single growing season! However, arthropods seemed to prefer the high diversity plots, as Crutsinger counted over 25% more individuals in the 12-genotype plots than in the genetic monocultures (Crutsinger et al. 2006). This increase in arthropod diversity was due to increases in both herbivores and predators, as their diversities each increased with increases in plant diversity (fig. 16.20). Why? One possible contributor to increased insect abundance was the observed 36% increase in plant abundance with increased plant genetic diversity (fig. 16.20). In other words, genetic diversity led to increased plant growth, which could have caused increased herbivore and predator abundances. However, what led to increased plant growth? Once again, niche complementarity and sampling effects are likely explanations. It is comforting when a single set of theories can be used to explain a diversity of results! Importantly, it is also possible that complementarity was occurring among the arthropods, though future studies would be needed to know why they may have been using different components of niche space and/or habitat.

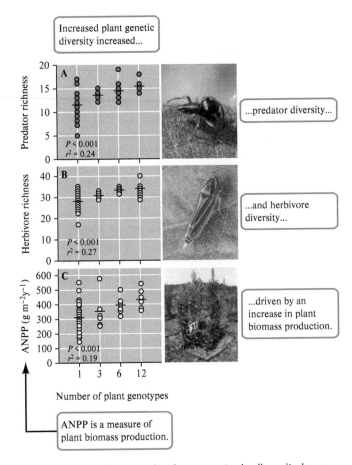

Figure 16.20 Changes in plant genotypic diversity have cascading effects of herbivore and predator diversity. From Gregory M. Crutsinger, Michael D. Collins, James A. Fordyce, Zachariah Gompert, Chris C. Nice, and Nathan J. Sanders. 2006, August 18. Plant genotypic diversity predicts community structure and governs an ecosystem process. *Science* 313(5789):966–8. Reprinted with permission from AAAS.

CONCEPT 16.4 REVIEW

1. Why might genetic diversity impact processes at the community level?
2. Why are plants so often used in studies of genetic diversity?

ECOLOGICAL TOOLS AND APPROACHES

Sampling Communities

At the heart of community ecology is the need to accurately and reliably measure the composition of a community. This may seem to be a trivially easy task, as we all know that ecology professors simply go out into the field, lay down a few transects or plots, write down a few numbers, and then return home ready to devise a difficult exam for the undergraduates in their introductory courses. Except for that last part, this is a woefully inaccurate overview of how community ecology is actually done, taking no account of the numerous pitfalls that lie along the way.

In the previous section, we discussed the growing recognition of how important genetic diversity can be within natural communities. In chapter 4, we described new innovations in molecular biology and how these tools were

revolutionizing ecological research. Few areas of ecology are more influenced by the adoption of molecular tools than studies involving genetic diversity. However, as do most ecologists of my generation, I will put aside further discussion of the specific ways that diversity is measured. Instead, the focus here is on species.

The question of how many species are found in a community is one of the most fundamental questions an ecologist can ask. With increasing threats to biodiversity, species richness is also one of the most important community attributes we might measure. Estimates of species richness are critical for determining areas suitable for conservation, for diagnosing the impacts of environmental change on a community, or for identifying critical habitat for rare and threatened species. However, determining species richness of an actual community is not simple. Sound estimates require a carefully designed, standardized sampling program and great accuracy when collecting and handling the data. This section will focus on several fundamental aspects of study design.

One of the positions that Evelyn Pielou advocated was that advancement in ecology would come through integration of models, lab studies, and data-rich studies from the field. Mathematical ecology would then serve a critical role in "processing large bodies of observational data in such a way that interesting regularities, hitherto buried from sight, become apparent" (Pielou 1977, p. 4). This approach by Pielou is important in that it emphasizes a link between question development (modelling, lab studies) and testing in real-world conditions (field studies confronted with statistics). Over the decades, ecologists have grappled with developing the appropriate research methods that provide society not only with large volumes of data but, more importantly, with large volumes of high quality and accurate data. In chapter 1 we presented a general overview of the scientific method. Here we explore some of the issues that ecologists face when they work at that point between research idea and statistical analysis (fig. 16.21).

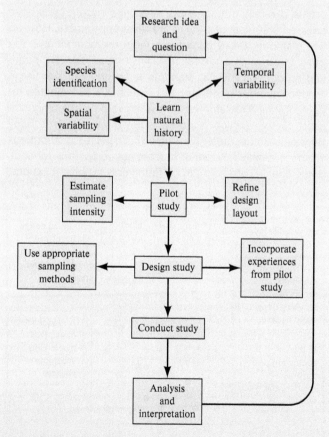

Figure 16.21 Much time and effort occurs between the development of a research idea and the statistical analysis of the data.

Where, When, Who, and How Much?

It is impossible to conduct accurate field work in community ecology unless you know how to identify species. It is really that simple—inaccurate identifications of birds, bats, butterflies, bears, and beetles result in meaningless data and a large waste of time and money. It is beyond the scope of this book to describe how to identify species, but we can lead you in a few directions: (1) get outside and look around—closely, (2) take courses in systematics and biodiversity from your college or university, and (3) get back outside and apply your knowledge. Accurate species identification is a difficult skill to acquire, particularly for species-rich groups. Nonetheless, it is the foundation of real-world ecology.

Once you are able to accurately identify the species in your area, a critical next step in doing community ecology is knowing exactly where and when you should sample. For some projects, this may be trivially easy. For example, if you are contracted to measure the number of native plant species growing in your parents' flower garden, and there is only one weekend left before you return to campus for the fall term, then this study has clearly defined boundaries, in both space and time. However, suppose your contract was to measure the number of plant species found in gardens throughout your home town. If you live in a very small town, with only a handful of gardens, it is possible that you would be able to measure every single garden and get an actual count of species richness. However, suppose you lived in Windsor, Ontario. It simply is not possible to measure every garden over the entire summer, let alone during your last weekend home. Instead, you will need to sub-sample. Additionally, because the growing season in Windsor is longer than a single weekend, there is going to be variation in which species you see at different points of the year; thus, sampling only in the fall is likely inadequate to measure the actual diversity of the system. Measuring only in that one weekend may result in a failure of fulfilling your contractual obligations.

Timing

We will first discuss a few issues related to deciding when and how often you should sample. In general, you want to sample with a frequency that allows you to accurately identify all species that are likely present. What that frequency is will depend upon the organisms. For example, you likely only want to sample for flying insects during the months and times of day that they are active. If you are working with plants, there is little value in sampling during the winter months throughout much of the Northern hemisphere. However, some regions around the world are too hot to support plant growth during the summer, and thus are best surveyed during the winter. Some groups of organisms are likely to have little change in species composition over their period of activity (e.g., small mammals over summer), while others may change substantially. As a result, you will need to sample high-turnover taxa more frequently than low-turnover

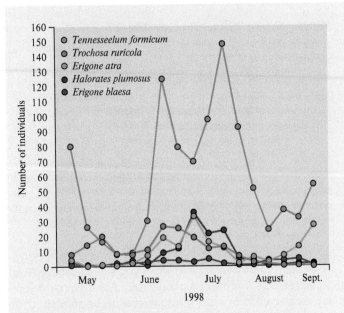

Figure 16.22   The abundances of five co-occurring species of spiders can vary greatly over the summer.

E. Bolduc et al. 2005. Ground-dwelling spider fauna (Araneae) of two vineyards in south Quebec. *Environmental Entomology* 34:635–45. Reprinted with permission.

taxa. For example, Elise Bolduc and her colleagues at McGill University sampled the diversity of ground-dwelling spiders in vineyards in southern Quebec (Bolduc et al. 2005). Their data show that the abundances of five of the more common species vary greatly over the summer months, and thus if they used a single snapshot of the community, they would have missed several of these species (fig. 16.22). It is clearly important to sample when your species are active! At the same time, you do not want to oversample your community, as this would be wasted effort, costing you money and loss of time, and even increasing risk to your study populations for little scientific value. Whether the right frequency means you should sample once a week, once a month, or once a year will depend on the organisms you work with; once again, having a strong basis in natural history is critical to doing good ecological research.

Location

Deciding where to sample poses difficulties similar to deciding when to sample. If all species were distributed evenly across a community, the life of a field ecologist would be quite simple, as we could simply throw down a quadrat, and what we would find would be representative of every other location in the community. The real world, however, is much more heterogeneous. As we have discussed throughout the text, different species have different niche requirements and even more restricted realized niches; thus, only a narrow set of locations within a community are likely suitable for growth for any particular species. As a result, even if we placed two quadrats down on the forest floor, separated only by 1–2 m, and measured the diversity of plant species in each, there is

a very good chance we would not find identical results. If we assume that it is not possible to sample every square inch of the forest floor, we need to instead use sub-samples. Where do we lay them? How many do we use?

Let's suppose we have the time, energy, and budget to sample the vegetation of only 100 m² of a 10 hectare forest community, or 0.1% of the actual community. How do we decide what size plots we should use and where to lay them? (It is worth noting that many ecological questions can also be measured using plotless sampling techniques, though that is beyond the scope of this text.) The most basic consideration given to determining the size of study plots is the size of the organisms you are going to study. Plots need to be larger than many individuals of all the species you are measuring. In other words, you can use a 50 × 50 cm plot if you are measuring mosses, but not if you are measuring trees. Second, your plot size needs to be small enough that you can accurately measure all the individuals within the plot. For organisms such as mosses that are very small, large plots result in substantial error. You learn the appropriate size of the plot for your system through experience and through conversations with graduate students and professors. However, even then a solid grounding in natural history is again critical to good ecological research.

We will now suppose that you are focusing your work on the diversity of understory seedlings and that you have decided that plots of 1 × 1 m are most appropriate. How do you distribute those plots throughout the community? You have three main choices: random, systematic, and stratified random (fig. 16.23). Random is simply that. You use a random number generator to develop XY coordinates for each of your 100 samples. This will give a completely unbiased sample (which is good), sometimes (which is bad). Why only sometimes? We know that species distributions are not typically random or at least not completely random. Some species are going to be found only in some locations,

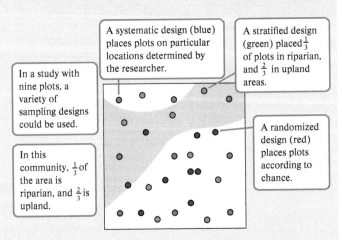

Figure 16.23   Systematic, random, and stratified sampling in a community where one-third of the area is riparian, and two-thirds of the area is upland.

particularly those that have very narrow niche requirements. When you randomly assign plots to locations, the plots may—by chance—aggregate in certain areas of the community. It is important to recognize that *random* is not the same as *even*. Random distributions of plots work best in communities that do not have any obvious major subcommunities within them. For instance, random plot assignments might work well in a homogeneous forest but not in one that has a stream going through it, as you would expect differences in species composition as a function of distance to the stream.

So does this mean that we should generally place our plots in certain places, using instead some sort of systematic plot design? In this study you could devise a grid with 100 evenly spaced intersections, sampling in each location. However, this design would introduce a new bias, one that is based upon the natural distribution of the organisms in the system. For example, imagine that competition for light results in a recurring pattern of tall tree—small tree—tall tree—small tree. Sampling on a grid that overlays a regular spatial pattern might cause a biased sample, overestimating the number of either large or small trees. As a result, systematic designs are generally avoided, unless substantial prior research is available showing that such underlying patterns do not exist.

The final design, and one that is often used, particularly when only a few plots are available, is the stratified random design. This approach takes the best parts of both the randomized and systematic design, without falling prey to their statistical traps. Quite simply, suppose you are working in a forest that has riparian and upland habitats, and you think that these subcommunities will contain different species. You can stratify your study into two parts, upland and riparian, and then you assign plots to those strata in proportion to their abundance on the landscape. For example, if 30% of the area was riparian, you would assign 30 of your 100 plots to riparian, and the remaining 70 to upland. Within a given strata, you would randomly locate those 30 (or 70) plots. This design is very commonly used and works best when a community is subdivided into a few strata, allowing for many plots within each.

The Need for Pilot Studies

In this section we have only briefly discussed a few of the common issues field ecologists encounter when they attempt to sample communities. Many more problems exist that we have not yet even touched upon. For example, how do we know when we have sampled enough or too little? Pilot studies will reveal some of the basic patterns in your study system so you can know the answer. Moreover, practice does not make perfect in science, but it does make more competent. Pilot studies can help you practise and validate identifications (if that is required your study), as well as practise sample collection, preparation, and processing. And, if you know Murphy's Law, you might guess that Murphy was a field ecologist. When you have complicated field experimental design, a heterogeneous landscape, a diverse biological community, sophisticated equipment (or contraptions built from bits and bobs from Home Hardware), and then you throw in the logistics of working in remote areas, unaccommodating wildlife, and, oh, let's not forget the weather, much can go wrong. A pilot study gives you a good rehearsal so that you can anticipate the challenges you will face and plan your full experiment to best effect.

SUMMARY

A *community* is an association of interacting species inhabiting some defined area. Examples of communities include the plant community on a mountainside, the insect community associated with a particular species of tree, or the fish community on a coral reef. Community ecologists often restrict their studies to groups of species that all make their living in a similar way. Animal ecologists call such groups *guilds,* while plant ecologists use the terms *life-forms* and *functional groups.* The field of community ecology concerns how the environment influences community structure, including the relative abundance and diversity of species, the subjects of this chapter.

16.1 A combination of the number of species and their relative abundance defines species diversity.

Diversity can be measured at different scales. *Alpha* diversity represents the most local scale, while *gamma* diversity represents a landscape scale. *Beta* diversity indicates the variability among locations within the landscape. In natural communities, most species are moderately abundant; few are very abundant or extremely rare. Frank Preston (1948) graphed the abundance of species in collections as distributions of species abundance, with each abundance interval twice the preceding one. Preston's graphs were approximately bell-shaped curves and are called lognormal distributions. Lognormal distributions, which describe the relative abundance of organisms ranging from algae and terrestrial plants to birds, may result from many random environmental variables acting upon the populations of a large number of species or may be a consequence of how species subdivide resources. Regardless of the underlying mechanisms, the lognormal distribution is one of the best-described patterns in community ecology.

Two major factors define the diversity of a community: (1) the number of species in the community, which ecologists usually call *species richness*; and (2) the relative abundance of

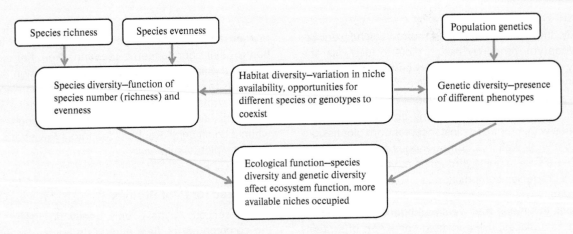

Figure 16.24   Concept map for chapter 16.

species, or *species evenness* (fig 16.24). One of the most commonly applied indices of species diversity is the Shannon index:

$$H' = -\sum_{i=1}^{s} p_i \ln p_i$$

Species evenness is generally measured with Pielou's *J*. The relative abundance and diversity of species can also be portrayed using *rank-abundance curves*. Accurate estimates of species richness require carefully designed sampling programs.

16.2 Species diversity is higher in complex environments.

Robert MacArthur (1958) discovered that five coexisting warbler species feed in different layers of forest vegetation and that the number of warbler species in North American forests increases with increasing forest stature. Various investigators have found that the diversity of forest birds increases with increased foliage height diversity. Heterogeneity in physical and chemical conditions across aquatic and terrestrial environments can account for a significant portion of the diversity among planktonic algae and terrestrial plants (fig. 16.24).

16.3 Ecological functions performed by communities are dependent upon community structure.

Ecological communities perform a number of functions, such as nutrient cycling and biomass production. These functions result in the delivery of services of value to people. Changes in the structure of natural communities can influence the efficiency of these ecological processes, and thus have societal impact. One of the most well studied examples is the relationship between species diversity and plant biomass production, where increased

plant diversity usually causes increased biomass production. Similar patterns have been found for other species and trophic groups. Underlying these patterns are explanations based upon niche theory (complementarity), species interactions (facilitation), and probability theory (sampling).

16.4 Genetic variation of species within a community influences ecological function.

Similar to the patterns found for species diversity–function relationships, recent studies are finding significant ecological consequences of genetic diversity for community-level functions (fig. 16.24). Again, by studying plants, ecologists have discovered that increased genetic diversity can lead to increased plant diversity. Additionally, these effects of plant diversity can impact herbivore and predator diversity, highlighting the complexity of natural systems. The integration of genetics and evolutionary biology is a rapidly growing area within ecology.

Studies in community ecology are complicated by variation in the distributions of species in both space and time. A common strategy when addressing real-world issues is to try and find species, or groups of species, that can serve as indicators of overall community condition. However, in all studies of community ecology, appropriate study designs require detailed knowledge of the natural history of the study system and the organisms that live within it. It is critical to consider aspects of the timing and frequency of measurements, as well as the shape, number, and distribution of study plots. Designs not founded in an understanding of the study system are likely to result in biased findings. In order to learn how to conduct field research, it is critical to do field research.

REVIEW QUESTIONS

1. What is the difference between a community and a population? What are some distinguishing properties of communities? What is a guild? Give examples. What is a plant life-form? Give examples.

2. Draw a typical lognormal distribution. Include properly labelled horizontal (x) and vertical (y) axes. You can use the lognormal distributions included in this chapter as models.

3. Suppose you are a biologist working for an international conservation organization concerned with studying and conserving biological diversity. On one of your assignments you are sent out to explore the local biotas of several regions. As part of your survey work you are to take large quantitative samples of the copepods of the North Atlantic, the butterflies of central New Guinea, and the ground-dwelling beetles of southwest Africa. Using the lognormal distribution, predict the patterns of relative abundance of species you expect to see within each of these groups of organisms.

4. What are species richness and species evenness? How does each of these components of species diversity contribute to the value of the Shannon diversity index (H′)? How do species evenness and richness influence the form of rank-abundance curves?

5. Why is it important that the ecologist be familiar with the niches of study organisms before exploring relationships between environmental complexity and species diversity?

6. Consider an ecosystem service that might be provided by a plant community, such as carbon sequestration in soil. How important do you think genetic diversity may be in the provision of this service? How would you expect this to compare with the importance of species diversity? Consider your answer in the context of complementarity.

How might you design an experiment to test the relative importance of each?

7. The study of diversity–function relationships has been led predominantly by plant ecologists. However, this does not mean these patterns do not apply to vertebrates or other taxa. Given the constraints associated with working with vertebrates, design a study to test whether guilds of seed-eating birds show facilitation in mixed species assemblages.

8. Suppose you are being paid to increase the long-term biomass production of a field. How would you determine whether it is economically important to take into consideration plant species and genotypic diversity in your management?

9. You have been contracted to determine the diversity of the species of your favourite group of organisms in your favourite part of the world. Money is tight, and you can only sample 1% of the area of your study community. Design a sampling protocol that is most likely to give an unbiased estimate of the number of species in the community. How would you know if you are right?

10. Draw hypothetical landscapes in which (a) beta diversity is low but gamma diversity is high, and (b) alpha diversity is high and beta diversity is high.

Manamana/Shutterstock.

CHAPTER 17 SPECIES INTERACTIONS AND COMMUNITY STRUCTURE

CHAPTER CONCEPTS

So far in this book we have presented a number of isolated facts: mutualisms, herbivory, parasitism, and competition are some of the ways species can interact; population growth can be exponential or regulated; species richness and evenness are two measures of biodiversity; more biodiverse communities may deliver ecosystem services more efficiently. However, if we want to understand *why* we see the patterns in communities that are commonly described, we need to integrate this information. In chapter 16 we discussed the functional consequences of community diversity as a component of community structure. In this chapter we explore more explicitly how complex interactions among diverse groups of species result in changes in community structure.

Feeding relationships provide some of the most visually obvious examples of interactions in communities. For example, around the Antarctic waters we can see krill, shrimp-like crustaceans named *Euphausia superba*, feeding upon large numbers of diatoms. The krill are themselves prey to many other species, including crabeater seals, penguins, seabirds, many fish and squid, as well as the large baleen whales that migrate to these waters (fig. 17.1). The krill-eating fish and squid are eaten by other predators, including emperor penguins, other fish, and Weddell and Ross seals. These penguins and seals are themselves fed upon by leopard seals, and all of these are fed upon by orcas. How do we go beyond this verbal description to one that more accurately summarizes these feeding relationships? This question is at the heart of one of the earliest approaches to studying communities, descriptions of who eats whom. Since the beginning of the twentieth century, ecologists have meticulously described the feeding relationships of hundreds of communities, each producing a tangle of relationships called a **food web**. These summaries of feeding interactions within a community can reveal many basic aspects of community structure, serving as a portrait of a community.

Food webs, however, are just one example of a larger category of **ecological networks**. An ecological network is a description of the interactions that occur among species in a community. They can be thought of as describing a community not based upon taxonomic affiliation but instead upon some ecological process in which the organisms participate. Ecological networks are typically divided into three main categories: (1) *trophic networks*, (2) *host–parasitoid networks*, and (3) *mutualistic networks*. Trophic networks describe interactions based upon feeding relationships, such as the food web described above. Host–parasitoid networks describe the interconnectedness of hosts and their parasites, diseases, and parasitoids. Mutualistic networks focus on interactions such as pollination and mycorrhizae, and emphasize that most mutualisms involve many species and differing degrees of specialization.

Networks are complicated but only because communities themselves are complicated. Fortunately, with close study a number of general patterns and principles emerge. One approach to identifying the key mechanisms that drive community structure is to determine whether any **community assembly rules** are occurring in a given location. Community assembly rules can occur within or across trophic levels and describe the processes that limit or promote coexistence. Though originally presented as a very specific set of rules that governed which species could, or could not, co-occur (Cody and Diamond 1975), assembly rules are now typically used in a more general way (Weiher and Keddy 1999).

Ecological interactions can cause predictable patterns, many of which can be described through the use of networks and the creation of assembly rules. In this chapter we will explore this complexity of nature and describe some aspects of how species interactions influence community structure. We first return to feeding relationships to describe what one type of ecological network looks like.

17.1 Ecological Networks Across Trophic Boundaries: Food Webs

A food web summarizes the feeding relationships in a community. The trophic networks described by food webs are difficult to construct but, when done well, serve as a bridge between community and ecosystem ecology. They incorporate aspects of the biology of the organism and describe the direction of movement of energy and resources within, or even between, communities. Here we focus on the underlying biology of food webs, leaving the study of energy and nutrient flow for chapters 19 and 20.

The earliest food webs concentrated on simplified communities. In 1927, Charles Elton pointed out that the number of well-described food webs, which he called food cycles, could be counted on the fingers of one hand. One of the first of those food webs described the feeding relations on Bear Island, off the coast of Northern Norway in the High Arctic (fig. 17.2). Summerhayes and Elton (1923) studied the feeding relations there because they believed that the high Arctic, with few species and thus reduced complexity, would be the best place to begin the study of food webs.

Figure 17.1 A marine food web in action: feeding baleen whales.

©John Tunney/Shutterstock RF.

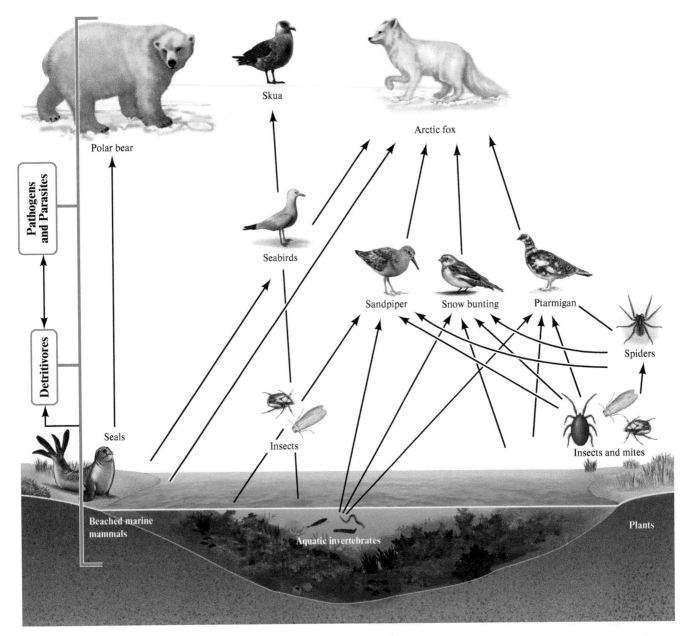

Figure 17.2   Simple food web of an arctic island. *Note:* The indication of detritivores and pathogens was not part of Elton's original food web. They are added to indicate that parasites, pathogens, and detritivores feed on organisms of all trophic levels.

Summerhayes and Elton used a food web to present the feeding relations on Bear Island in a single picture. The primary producers in the Bear Island food web are terrestrial plants and aquatic algae. These primary producers are fed upon by several kinds of terrestrial and aquatic invertebrates, which are in turn consumed by birds. The birds on Bear Island are attacked by arctic foxes. Arctic foxes also feed on marine mammals that have washed up onto the beaches and on the dung of polar bears. The polar bears of Bear Island consume seals and beached marine mammals. Seabirds harvest food from the sea around Bear Island but enter the Bear Island food web because they are attacked by foxes, feed on beached marine animals and on the freshwater invertebrates of Bear

Island, and contribute dung that fertilizes the primary producers of the island.

Ralph Bird was another pioneer in the study of community trophic relationships. Bird published a paper in 1930 titled "Biotic Communities of the Aspen Parkland of Central Canada." Bird travelled throughout the Parkland region and provided the first detailed survey of the feeding relationships among species in each of the major community types of the parkland: prairie, Aspen forest, and willow stands. Beyond sketching out the feeding relationships within community types, Bird recognized that some animals transcended the boundaries of the three community types. In other words, some animals fed within two or more of these parkland communities. Bird's food web drawings included the connections he observed among species in different communities. This is critical, as it shows that as early as 1930 ecologists recognized that community boundaries are fuzzy and that there can be direct interactions of species among communities. This issue has received substantially more attention among ecologists in recent decades, and it is now recognized that feeding relations across communities (e.g., streams and forests) can play a substantial role in energy and nutrient cycles (chapters 19 and 20).

Typically, these early depictions of food webs include information on who eats whom but not on the relative strength of these interactions or the abundance of the organisms depicted. These factors will be important when we consider the flow of energy through ecosystems, and we'll return to this in chapter 19. In addition to more quantitative information on flow of energy and taxonomic abundance, more recent food web studies have included (1) greater taxonomic refinement, moving away from the taxonomic bias toward charismatic animals; and (2) inclusion of decomposers and detritivores as part of the community.

As an example of greater taxonomic refinement, Kirk Winemiller (1990) constructed food webs describing the feeding relations of freshwater fish. While not doing this seminal study full justice, we introduce just one of his food webs here to illustrate the great, messy complexity of food webs. Winemiller studied the aquatic food webs at two locations in the savannas, or *llanos*, of Venezuela and at two other sites in the lowlands of Costa Rica. His study sites supported from 20 to 88 fish species. One of Winemiller's least species-rich study sites was a medium-sized stream called Caño Volcán. In one depiction of this food web, he included only the common fish species whose aggregate abundance comprised 95% of the individuals in his collections. These common-fish webs excluded many rare species. Winemiller also excluded the weakest trophic links, those comprising less than 1% of the diet. This "simplified" food web, containing only the 10 most common fish species, remains remarkably complex (fig. 17.3). While the figure shows trophic interactions among some fish species, most of the nodes in the figure represent other, non-fish, food sources. The disaggregation of these non-fish food sources provides a greater understanding of the complexity of communities and their trophic structure than we could appreciate in the earlier studies by Summerhayes, Elton, and Bird.

Given the complexity of food webs depicted in figure 17.3, you may wonder how Winemiller determined who ate whom. There are a variety of approaches when we want to construct trophic relationships, and these are discussed in the Ecological Tools and Approachesin this chapter. In Winemiller's study, the approach involved dissection of the fishes' digestive tracts and painstaking work with a microscope. You can probably see how following this approach makes is easier to determine the diets of large animals than of small ones, contributing to the historical bias against small organisms in food web depictions.

Returning to the High Arctic food web first described by Summerhayes and Elton, a group of researchers (Hodkinson and Coulson 2004) found a diversity of interactions lacking from the web of Elton (fig. 17.2). One of the major additions that Hodkinson and Coulson made to this web was the inclusion of

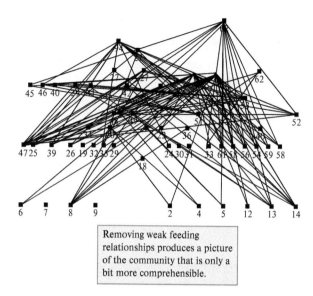

Removing weak feeding relationships produces a picture of the community that is only a bit more comprehensible.

Figure 17.3   Food web representing the feeding relations of the 10 most common fish species and other non-fish food resources at Caño Volcán, Venezuela, with weak feeding relationships excluded. Fish species are represented in the figure by the 10 nodes labelled 73 to 92. Data from Winemiller 1990.

soil organic matter, decomposers, and detritivores. Everything dies eventually, and the energy contained in these formerly living things does not simply leave the system; instead, it becomes food. Or, put another way, most of the feeding that occurs in even this simple system is hidden from view, occurring in and on the soil. As we will discuss in more depth in chapters 19 and 20, most biomass in a community is consumed only after death, not as a predation or herbivory event. The work of Winemiller and of Hodkinson and Coulson helps to redress the taxonomic bias toward larger animals, mentioned earlier. Very little of the planet's biological diversity is reflected by the relatively few large herbivores and carnivores. The links that connect the bulk of biomass to its consumers pass through the small, historically overlooked and traditionally aggregated members of the community. The current reality is that the ecology of parasites, pathogens, microbes, and other small consumers remains woefully understudied. These disciplines in ecology will remain open areas of research for enterprising students for decades to come. Because our understanding of the details of these aspects of food webs is so incomplete, we must ignore them for now, but we will come back to some of these aspects when we discuss decomposition in chapters 19 and 20.

We will return to the idea—implicit in Bird's work and explicit in Winemiller's models—that some interactions are more functionally important than others in influencing community structure. Let's first return to the idea of competition. Similar to what we see for feeding relations, there can be predictable linkages of competition across species. From this, a number of assembly rules emerge that, under certain circumstances, better enable us to understand community structure. Here we try to understand community within a single trophic group, focusing on the role of competition.

17.2 Community Assembly: Competitive Asymmetries

Strong competitors can alter community structure. In chapter 13, we discussed competition, describing many of the potential effects it could have on populations and species coexistence. We also talked about the most extreme impact of competition in a community: competitive exclusion. Under a narrow set of conditions, the competitive exclusion principle leads to an assembly rule: functionally identical species sharing a limited resource cannot coexist. However, we know that this rule does not always apply, as a number of ecological mechanisms do allow for competing organisms to coexist (chapter 13). This leaves us a bit unclear about whether competition can actually influence community structure. In this section we provide several examples in which competition has clear effects on community structure.

Competition and Diversity

What should happen to species diversity within a community if the strength of competition increases over time? The answer is going to be dependent upon whether species are similar in their competitive abilities (competitive equivalence) or whether communities contain **competitive hierarchies**. A competitive hierarchy is a very simple idea: some species are consistently better competitors than other species; thus, species can be ranked in the order of their competitive abilities. For example, if there were four species in a community (A, B, C, and D), and if a competitive hierarchy existed, then you could rank their competitive abilities as A > B > C > D. You may notice that this hierarchy is also transitive (think back to introductory algebra!), meaning that if A > B and B > C, then A > C. This is the most extreme possible version of a hierarchy, and one could imagine others, such as A > B = C > D. Regardless of the details of the rankings, the implications of hierarchies and transitivity for community structure are broad. If there is no competition in the community, then a hierarchy is irrelevant and competitive exclusion will not occur. Similarly, if intransitivity occurs (such that a complete hierarchy is not formed), species coexistence can also occur, even if competition is strong (Laird and Schamp 2006). However, if competition is strong and transitivity occurs,

then in the above example A, B, and C will start to squeeze out species D, potentially causing it to be lost from the community. If competition continues to increase, the community may lose species C, and perhaps even B, resulting in a community consisting only of species A. In other words, if the species of a community differ consistently in their competitive abilities, then increased competition should cause a drop in species diversity. That sure sounds like an assembly rule! Does it actually occur?

Competitive Hierarchies

We once again turn to plants. Much of the best data on the impacts of competition on community structure were collected by plant ecologists. Moreover, as we discussed in chapter 16, the diversity of animals in a community often varies as a function of the heterogeneity of the plants. As a result, changes to plant community structure due to competition can cause changes in animal community structure, even if the animals themselves are not competing with each other. This critical issue is often overlooked when examining the impact of competition on community structure.

Bill Shipley, of the Université de Sherbrooke, has spent many years combining mathematical and community ecology. He has been quite interested in the importance of competitive hierarchies in plant communities. In fact, he contributed to the initial concept of competitive transitivity (Keddy and Shipley 1989), which he then refined (Shipley 1993). In his 1993 paper, Shipley developed an analytical method allowing one to test whether competitive relationships among plants are, or are not, transitive. At that time, Shipley was able to find 10 published studies of matrices that recorded the competitive relationships (analogous to trophic networks described by food webs) (fig. 17.4) of different species of plants. In nine of ten cases, relationships were transitive, supporting the idea that competition has the potential to alter plant community structure.

As we will see next, the idea of competitive hierarchies can be combined with the theory of allocation (chapter 7) and an understanding of physiological ecology (chapters 5 and 6), leading to a theory that could be helpful in explaining the distribution of plant species along environmental gradients.

Centrifugal Organization of Species

Paul Keddy, formerly of the University of Ottawa, developed the concept of "centrifugal organization of plant communities." In

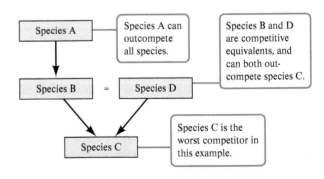

Figure 17.4 Competitive relationships among species can be displayed in a manner similar to that of food webs.

the freshwater wetlands in Ontario he kept observing a repeating pattern: much of the area would be dominated by a single genus of grass, *Typha*, while many other species could be found nearby in small patches of much higher diversity. What caused these reoccurring patterns in this system? Answering this question has served as the foundation of research for many students and postdocs from the Keddy lab.

The theory of centrifugal organization of species is most thoroughly explained in a 1992 paper by Irene Wisheu and Paul Keddy, titled "Plant Competition and Centrifugal Organization of Plant Communities: Theory and Test." The theory is based on the idea that both core and peripheral habitats exist within a landscape. The core habitat is the prime real estate in the community, with few abiotic stresses, lots of resources, and few pests or pathogens. In short, the core habitat meets the requirements of the fundamental niche for nearly all species of the community. However, because species differ in competitive abilities, and there exists a competitive hierarchy in this system, not all species will be able to occupy the core habitat. Instead, the core habitat will be dominated by the best competitor, which in these wetlands is *Typha*. But why do we find so many other species in this system?

As we discussed in chapter 16, the world is a heterogeneous place. Some places will freeze up and be subjected to frequent ice scouring. Other areas will be sandy and low in nutrient content. Others will be near beaver dams and subjected to repeated flooding. Some will be exposed to brackish water and have saline soils. In the theory of centrifugal organization of species diversity, Keddy makes the assumption that plants require specific adaptations to perform well under these less-than-ideal conditions. He further assumes that not all plants are able to perform at their optimum under all environmental conditions and that, instead, there will exist trade-offs between competitive ability and the ability to cope with the different types of environmental stresses. As we saw in our discussion of life histories (chapter 9), this assumption is quite reasonable.

As a result of these trade-offs, Keddy argues that you will find the competitively inferior species occupying areas that are dominated by these stresses, as under those conditions either they are able to outcompete *Typha*, or competition itself no longer occurs. Each community will have its own set of stress gradients along which stress-competition trade-offs will occur, and Keddy would expect a predictable arrangement of species along each of those gradients. These gradients can be arranged graphically (fig. 17.5), with the core habitat in the centre, and each stress gradient radiating out. If you have a detailed understanding of the species of the system, you can then include likely species found along each of these gradients. Once this is developed, you could then go out to a community, identify which stressors are, or are not, occurring in a given location, and then see whether you find the species you expect to occur. In other words, this relatively simple model of community organization, based on the ideas of competition and the theory of allocation, is a powerful tool to explain observed patterns of species occurrence.

Of course, this model is just one of many possible models to explain species distributions, and several assumptions are

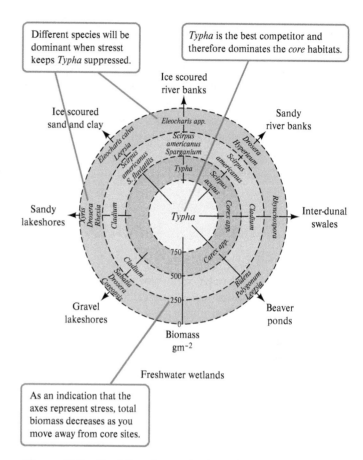

Figure 17.5 Centrifugal organization of the biotic and abiotic factors that influence community structure within a freshwater wetland. Note that this diagram is a representation of a set of concepts, rather than a specific map of a specific wetland.

I. C. Wisheu and P. A. Keddy. 1992. *Journal of Vegetation Science* 3:147–56, Figure 4. Reprinted with permission. Original source for 17.5, as adapted by Wisheu and Keddy: Reprinted from D. R. J. Moore et al. 1989. Conservation of wetlands—Do infertile wetlands deserve a higher priority? *Biological Conservation* 47:203–17. Copyright 1989, with permission from Elsevier.

built into it. For example, species hierarchies and trade-offs between competitive ability and stress tolerance are key aspects of the model. There will certainly be examples of communities where these assumptions are not met, and thus this model would not apply. However, there are other communities, such as the wetlands that Keddy has studied, that seem to be very well described by this model (Wisheu and Keddy 1992); as a result, it is an important tool to help ecologists understand how species interactions can alter community structure.

But the story does not end here. Although feeding relations and competitive interactions can both influence community structure, we need to recognize that these processes do not occur in isolation of each other. Instead, organisms will potentially need to deal with prey, predators, and competitors simultaneously. As we will see in the next section, interactions between feeding relations and competition can be critical to structuring some communities.

17.3 Community Assembly: Keystone Species

The activities of a few keystone species may control the structure of communities. Robert Paine (1966, 1969) proposed that the feeding activities of a few species have disproportionately strong influences on community structure. He called these **keystone species**. Paine's keystone species hypothesis emerged from a chain of reasoning. First, he proposed that predators might keep prey populations below their carrying capacity. Next, he reasoned that the potential for competitive exclusion would be low in populations kept below carrying capacity. Finally, he concluded that if keystone species reduce the likelihood of competitive exclusion, their activities would increase the number of species that could coexist in communities. In other words, Paine predicted that some predators may increase species diversity due to reduced competition among the prey species. We introduced this concept in chapter 13 when we discussed mechanisms by which competing species might coexist in a community. Implicit in that discussion was that a predator, by virtue of its own population density, could control the density of a prey population. Keystone species are unusual in having strong influence on prey populations even at low relative density. The idea of keystone species is an important one, and a great deal of ecological research has resulted in a clearer understanding of what being a keystone species entails.

Food Web Structure and Species Diversity

Paine began his studies by examining the relationship between overall species diversity within food webs and the proportion of the community represented by predators. He cited studies that demonstrated that as the number of species in marine zooplankton communities increases, the proportion that are predators also increases. For instance, the zooplankton community in the Atlantic Ocean over continental shelves includes 81 species, 16% of which are predators. In contrast, the zooplankton community of the Sargasso Sea contains 268 species, 39% of which are predators. Paine set out to determine if similar patterns occur in marine intertidal communities.

Paine described a food web from the intertidal zone near Neah Bay, Washington, which lies in the north temperate zone at 49° N. This food web is typical of the rocky shore community along the west coast of North America (fig. 17.6), including regions of the BC coast. The base of this food web consists of algae and phytoplankton. However, Paine was particularly interested in the dominant intertidal invertebrates. These included 11 primary consumers, a predatory snail (*Thais*), and a sea star (*Pisaster*). *Thais* is a middle level predator primarily eating barnacles (90% of its diet), while *Pisaster* is a top predator, obtaining 90% of its energy from a mixture of chitons (41%), mussels (37%), and barnacles (12%). Some of the remaining 10% of its energy comes from eating *Thais*.

Paine also described a subtropical food web (31° N) from the northern Gulf of California, a much richer web that included 45 species. Like the food web in Washington, the subtropical web was topped by a single predator, the starfish *Heliaster kubiniji* (fig. 17.6). However, six predators occupy middle levels in the subtropical web, compared to one middle level predator near Neah Bay. Because four of the five species in the snail family Columbellidae are also predaceous, the total number of predators in the subtropical web is 11. These predators feed on the 34 species that form the base of the food web. Despite the presence of many more species in this subtropical web, the top predator, *Heliaster*, obtains most of its energy from sources similar to those used by *Pisaster* near Neah Bay. *Heliaster* obtains 74% of its energy directly from a mixture of bivalves, herbivorous gastropods, and barnacles.

Paine found that as the number of species in his intertidal food webs increased, the proportion of the web represented by predators also increased. As Paine went from Washington to the northern Gulf of California, overall web diversity increased from 13 species to 45 species, a 3.5-fold increase. However, at the same time, the number of predators in the two webs increased from 2 to 11, a 5.5-fold increase. Expressed another way, as the number of predator species in a community increased, the local species diversity increased. Paine hypothesized that predation pressure could prevent competitive exclusion among prey species by preventing any prey species from becoming dominant and monopolizing resources. A community with many predator species having diverse feeding preferences might have less competitive pressure among prey species and, therefore, greater species diversity than a community with few predator species.

Does this pattern confirm Paine's predation hypothesis? No, it does not. First, Paine studied a small number of webs—not enough to make broad generalizations. Second, while the patterns described by Paine are consistent with his hypothesis, they may be consistent with a number of other hypotheses. To evaluate the keystone species hypotheses, Paine needed a direct experimental test.

Experimental Removal of Starfish

For his first experiment, Paine removed the top predator from the intertidal food web near Neah Bay and monitored the response of the community. He chose two study sites in the middle intertidal zone that extended 8 m along the shore and 2 m vertically. One site was designated as a control and the other as an experimental site. He removed *Pisaster* from the experimental site and relocated them in another portion

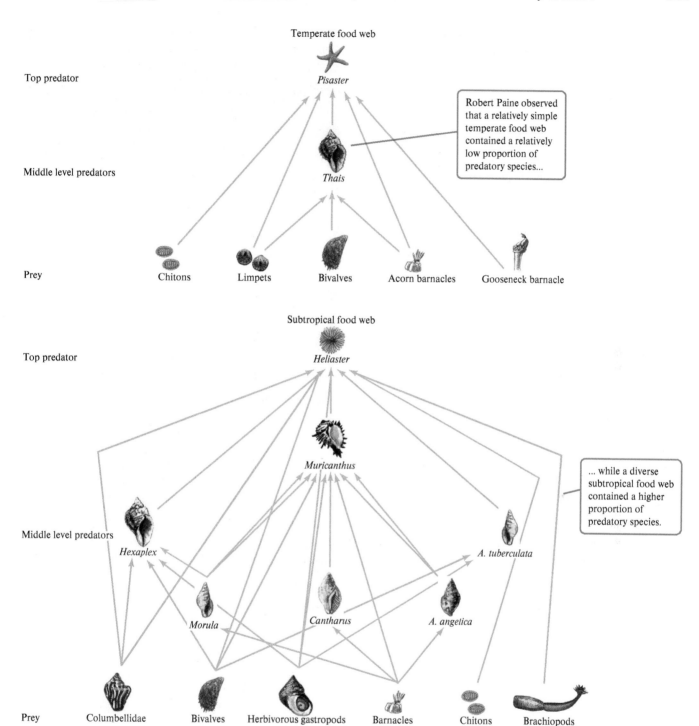

Figure 17.6 Roots of the keystone species hypothesis: Does a higher proportion of predators in diverse communities indicate that predators contribute to higher species diversity? Algae and phytoplankton are not included in these diagrams.

of the intertidal zone. Each week Paine checked the experimental site for the presence of *Pisaster* and removed any that might have colonized since his last visit.

Paine followed the response of the intertidal community for two years. Over this interval the diversity of intertidal invertebrates in the control plot remained constant at 15, while the diversity within the experimental plot declined from 15 to 8, a loss of 7 species. This reduction in species diversity supported Paine's keystone species hypothesis. However, if this reduction

was due to competitive exclusion, what was the resource over which species competed?

The most common limiting resource in the rocky intertidal zone is space. Within three months of removing *Pisaster* from the experimental plot, the barnacle *Balanus glandula* occupied 60% to 80% of the available space. One year after Paine removed *Pisaster*, *B. glandula* was crowded out by California mussels (*Mytilus californianus*) and gooseneck barnacles (*Pollicipes polymerus*). Benthic algal populations also declined because of a lack of space for attachment, indicating that algae and animals compete for the same resources. The herbivorous chitons and limpets also left, due to a lack of space and a shortage of food. Sponges were also crowded out and a nudibranch that feeds on sponges also left. After five years, the *Pisaster* removal plot was dominated by two species: the mussel (*M. californianus*) and the gooseneck barnacle (*P. polymerus*).

This experiment showed that *Pisaster* can act as a keystone species. When Paine removed this relatively rare predator from his study plot, the community structure changed dramatically. As we see next, keystone effects occur in other systems as well.

Fish as Keystone Species in River Food Webs

Mary Power (1990) tested the possibility that predatory fish can significantly alter the structure of food webs in rivers. In early summer, the boulders and bedrock of the Eel River in Northern California are covered by a turf of the filamentous alga *Cladophora* (fig. 17.7). However, the biomass of the algae declines by midsummer and what remains has a ropy, prostrate growth form and a webbed appearance. These mats of *Cladophora* support dense populations of herbivorous larval midges in the fly family Chironomidae. One chironomid, *Pseudochironomus richardsoni*, is particularly abundant. *Pseudochironomus* feeds on *Cladophora* and other algae and weaves the algae into retreats, altering their appearance in the process.

Chironomids are eaten by predatory insects and the young (known as *fry*) of two species of fish: a minnow called the California roach (*Hesperoleucus symmetricus*) and threespine sticklebacks (*Gasterosteus aculeatus*). These small fish are eaten by young steelhead trout (*Oncorhynchus mykiss*). Steelhead and large roach eat predatory invertebrates, and large roach also feed directly upon benthic algae. These interactions form the Eel River food web pictured in figure 17.8.

Power asked whether or not the two top predators in the Eel River food web, roach and steelhead, significantly influence web structure. She tested the effects of these fish on food web structure by using 3 mm mesh to cage off 12 areas 6 m² in the riverbed. The mesh size of these cages prevented the passage of large fish but allowed free movement of aquatic insects and stickleback and roach fry. Power excluded fish from six of her cages and placed 20 juvenile steelhead and 40 large roach in each of the other six cages. These fish densities were within the range observed around boulders in the open river.

Significant differences between the exclosures and enclosures soon emerged. Algal densities were initially similar; however, enclosing predatory fish over an area of streambed significantly reduced algal biomass (fig. 17.9). In addition, the *Cladophora* within cages with fish had the same ropy, webbed appearance as *Cladophora* in the open river.

How do predatory fish decrease algal densities? The key to answering this question lies with the Eel River food web (fig. 17.8). Predatory fish feed heavily on predatory insects, young roach, and sticklebacks. Enclosures containing the predatory fish resulted in lower densities of these smaller predators, decreasing predation on chironomids (fig. 17.10). Higher

(a)

(b)

Figure 17.7   Seasonal changes in biomass and growth form of benthic algae in the Eel River, California: (*a*) in early summer, June 1989; (*b*) in late summer, August 1989.
(a), (b) © Mary E. Power.

chironomid density increased the feeding pressure of these herbivores on algal populations. By enclosing and excluding fish from sections of the Eel River, Power demonstrated that fish act as keystone species in the Eel River food web.

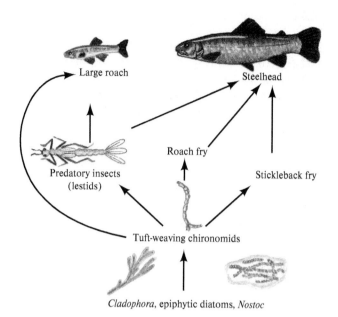

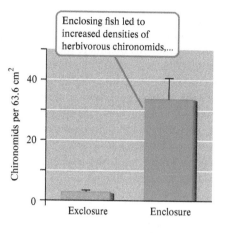

Enclosing fish led to increased densities of herbivorous chironomids,...

Figure 17.8 Food web associated with algal turf during the summer in the Eel River, California.

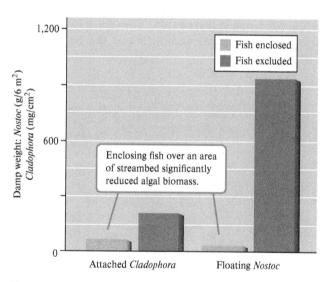

Enclosing fish over an area of streambed significantly reduced algal biomass.

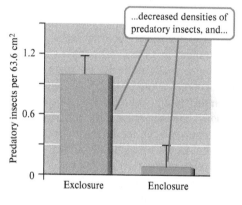

...decreased densities of predatory insects, and...

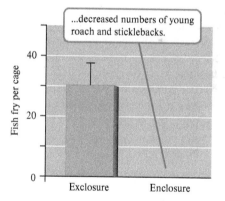

...decreased numbers of young roach and sticklebacks.

Figure 17.9 The influence of juvenile steelhead and California roach on benthic algal biomass in the Eel River. Data from Power 1990.

Figure 17.10 Effect of juvenile steelhead and roach on numbers of insects and young (fry) roach and stickleback. Data from Power 1990.

The examples discussed so far have been in aquatic communities, but a body of evidence indicates that keystone species exist in terrestrial systems as well. In the decades after Robert Paine's coining of the term "keystone species," ecologists came up with a long list of species that they deemed were keystone. It quickly became apparent that an explicit definition was needed.

Refining the Definition of Keystone Species

Many studies of food webs and keystone species have been done since Robert Paine's classic study of the intertidal food web. The studies have revealed a great deal of biological diversity, which

has prompted biologists to ask what traits characterize keystone species. This reflection is necessary, as the term *keystone species* has often been applied to indicate a species a person felt was important, as opposed to any specific scientific basis for this designation. To avoid the possibility that the term may become so inclusive that it becomes meaningless, a conference was organized to address the specific definition of *keystone species*.

Keystone species are those that, despite low biomass and low relative abundance in a community, exert strong effects on the structure of the communities they inhabit. In other words, keystone species are species whose effects on community structure are disproportionate to their abundance in the community. Important to this definition is the recognition that keystone species are not dominant members of communities (in terms of biomass or abundance), even if their actions or interactions dominate the direction of community assembly. This is in contrast to dominant species (or foundation species) that have a strong effect on community structure, but do so by virtue of their abundance, for example coniferous trees in a boreal forest.

Keystone species are not the only ones that can have strong impacts on how a community is structured. We see next that the actions of some organisms, even common ones, physically create the conditions necessary for communities to be formed. We begin with the humble beaver.

Ecosystem Engineers: Impacts of Beavers on Forest Communities

Castor canadensis, the North American beaver, is found throughout most of Canada and the United States (fig. 17.11). Beavers have been commercially exploited for their pelts, which has caused population crashes in part of their range, particularly in the southern and central United States. Across North America, reintroductions and legislative protections have resulted in increases in population densities over the last several decades.

Beavers fall into a very select grouping of species, generally referred to as **ecosystem engineers** (Jones et al. 1994). Ecosystem engineers are species who, by the nature of their activities, maintain and/or create new habitats for themselves and/or other species. For example, the coral-forming species of chapter 15 are a "poster-child" of ecosystem engineers. Without those species, coral reefs simply would not exist.

Beavers have effects on natural communities to a much greater extent than would be predicted based upon their relative abundance in a community. We can, then, consider beavers to be both ecosystem engineers and keystone species. This is in contrast to corals: the species that literally make up a coral reef are extremely abundant (within their community). Though

corals are certainly ecosystem engineers, we would not consider them to be keystone species. Jargon aside, what exactly are the impacts of beavers on natural communities?

Beavers cut down a variety of trees near the edges of streams and other water bodies, forming dams. These dams cause flooding and the formation of ponds, and they increase the amount of riparian area on the landscape. Dam building alters rates of stream flow and drainage and can alter various aspects of biogeochemical cycles (Naiman et al. 1994). The flooding and alteration of stream flow can change stream temperatures (Rosell et al. 2005). As we discussed in chapter 5, changes in water temperature can have significant effects on the growth of many aquatic organisms and thus can alter community structure. In the ponds that result from damming, the beavers build lodges. The reasons for this behaviour are not completely understood, but the isolation may provide some protection from predators and increased access to food sources. It is clear that beavers cause widespread changes to the aquatic communities in which they reside. What may be less obvious, however, is that beavers can also have strong effects on terrestrial communities.

Noble Donkor, of the University of Alberta, and John Fryxell, of the University of Guelph, explored the impacts of beavers on the vegetation in Algonquin Provincial Park, Ontario (Donkor and Fryxell 1999). They chose for their study 15 ponds, each less than 2 hectares in area, that had one active

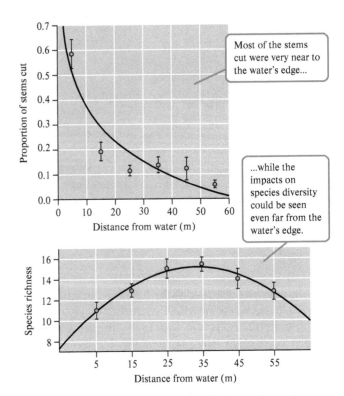

Figure 17.12   The intensity of exploitation and species richness both varied as a function of distance from the edge of a pond containing beavers.

Reprinted from N. T. Donkor and J. M. Fryxell. 1999. Impact of beaver foraging on structure of lowland boreal forests of Algonquin Provincial Park, Ontario. *Forest Ecology and Management* 118:83–92. Copyright 1999. With permission from Elsevier.

(a)   (b)

Figure 17.11   (*a*) The activity of beavers (*b*) can cause significant hydrological changes. Thus, beavers can have strong impacts as ecosystem engineers.

(a) Eastcott Momatiuk/The Image Bank/Getty Images; (b) William Smithey Jr./Photographer's Choice/Getty Images.

beaver lodge within it. They laid out several transects extending away from the pond and into the surrounding forest, along which they recorded beaver-cut stumps and the size and identity of woody vegetation.

In total, they found 1,841 tree stems cut by beavers, consisting of 20 plant species. However, 78% of the cut stems belonged to only six species (speckled alder, beaked hazel, red maple, trembling aspen, white birch, and beaked willow). Not surprisingly, the greatest proportion of stem cuts was found near the edge of the pond (fig. 17.12). As a result, there is a sharp

herbivory gradient from near the water's edge to the intact forest. Donkor and Fryxell found that, along this gradient, there was a unimodal relationship between species richness and distance (fig. 17.12), with maximum species diversity at an intermediate distance from the edge of the pond. Although certain plant species were most often cut down by beavers, these preferred tree species were also quick to re-sprout following cutting. Species less tolerant of cutting were less abundant near the water's edge. Deeper into the forest, there was less beaver activity. These areas tend to be dominated by species that are

 **ECOLOGY IN ACTION**

Keystone Species, Ecosystem Engineers, and Conservation Biology

The impacts of keystone species and ecosystem engineers on community structure have been of great interest to conservation biologists for many years, both in terms of conservation efforts and reintroduction of extirpated species. The logic behind such approaches is simple: if a natural community is maintained through the activities of only a few species, then removal of those species will cause a shift in community structure. As a result, conservation efforts to protect populations of those critical species should protect the overall structure of the community. Similarly, if human activities have caused the loss of a keystone or engineer within a community, reintroduction of that species should restore critical ecological services and community structure, right? The real world is not nearly that simple.

Tony Sinclair, of the University of British Columbia, argues in favour of viewing many large mammals as potential keystone species structuring communities (Sinclair 2003). However, he also acknowledges that there are difficulties in deciding what is, and what is not, a keystone species. For example, exactly how much does a community need to change by the introduction or removal of a species to consider that a critical species? Is 10% enough? 50%? 95%? Further, what do you actually measure? Species richness? Evenness? Biomass production? What trophic levels must be affected for a species to be keystone? For instance, if you add a predator, is it a keystone if that addition causes a decline in prey numbers, or does the effect have to continue on to the plants, decomposers, and soil systems? Further, when we look more closely, the default assumption that large animals are keystone is often not supported by data. Instead, the use of the keystone idea is often applied in conservation biology without consistency.

The potential advantage of focusing on keystone species in conservation efforts is also supported by Daniel Simberloff (1998). Simberloff argues that many historical approaches to conservation schemes (e.g., using umbrella,

flagship, and indicator species—all terms you may have learned in other classes) are ineffective and/or not well supported by actual data. Similarly, he argues that an ecosystem management approach has dangers in that the management goals are often vague, focusing on processes such as nutrient cycling rather than on protection of actual species. Simberloff suggests instead that research should be focused toward identifying keystone species and groups of species in natural communities. He readily acknowledges that not all communities will have such members, but in those that do, conservation efforts can be highly focused and potentially effective. Here we describe one example of how ecologists used the keystone species concept for a conservation goal: the reintroduction of wolves into Yellowstone National Park in the United States.

After 70 years of absence, grey wolves were reintroduced to Yellowstone National Park in the United States in 1995 (fig. 17.13). There were countless reasons justifying this reintroduction, including the argument that bringing back a top predator of this system should restore keystone

Figure 17.13   A wolf on the hunt in Yellowstone National Park. NPS photo by Barry O'Neill.

processes and alter many aspects of the community. More specifically, wolves were expected to alter predation pressures on a dominant herbivore (elk), which in turn would alter plant community organization. In other words, this single species (wolf) is viewed as keystone to the Yellowstone system. It is now nearly 25 years since the initial reintroduction, and data are available to begin to determine whether wolves are in fact keystone in this community.

Julie Mao and Evelyn Merrill at the University of Alberta collaborated with a team of researchers from the United States, following a number of radio-collared elk in Yellowstone and recording their locations as a function of both wolf densities in the area and a number of habitat characteristics (Mao et al. 2005). Mao and her coauthors, including Evelyn Merrill, found that elk population sizes changed very little over the course of the study, suggesting that wolves are not having major impacts on the total numbers of these large mammals. However, wolves are impacting where and when elk feed. In the summer months, elk primarily occupied areas of low wolf density, suggesting a behavioural response to predators. This may sound familiar, as it is another example of the nonconsumptive effects of predators on prey populations (chapter 14). Though few elk died through predation, the ecology of fear altered whole populations. Once again, the main effect of predators may not be mortality of individual prey but more subtle behavioural shifts. However, Mao found that the story was even more complicated.

In the winter, elk were found in high wolf density areas, indicating that the effects of wolves on elk movement are season-dependent. Mao and her coauthors argue that in the summer, food for elk is relatively abundant, and they are able to choose to feed in areas of low predator numbers. In the winter, food is scarce and the luxury to choose to feed in areas without predators does not occur. Instead, the elk need to feed wherever they find food.

Although Mao found that wolves influence elk behaviour, these results lend only limited support to the idea that wolves act as a keystone species. Clearly, if wolves alter where elk feed, this has the potential to alter plant communities. However, because habitat shifts as a function of wolves only occur part of the year, and it does not appear that elk numbers were suppressed by wolves, this study does not conclusively show keystone effects. We now turn to another study, where there is more evidence of such effects.

More than 10 years after Mao's study, it still appears that wolves are not having a substantial effect on elk population size, body condition, reproduction, or herbivory. A recent study by Michel Kohl and a research team that included Nathan Varley of University of Alberta considered the interactions between wolves and elk in Yellowstone in a "landscape of fear" context (Kohl et al. 2018). In concept, the landscape of fear is a map of the continuous change in predation risk that an animal perceives as it navigates its physical landscape (Brown and Kotler 2004). Kohl and his colleagues found that elk in Yellowstone are allocating time spent foraging in high-risk areas based on the diel rhythms of the wolves. Wolf movement tends to be crepuscular: they are most active at dawn and dusk. Elk avoid areas they recognize to be high risk during these times of day but will actively forage in these areas when the wolves are less active. This diel pattern of elk distribution, coupled with Mao's observations of seasonal distribution, may explain the limited response in the plant communities to the reintroduction of wolves in Yellowstone.

The studies by Mao et al. (2005) and Kohl et al. (2018) notwithstanding, Ripple and Beschta (2006) have found some indication that wolf reintroduction has affected a common group of riparian plant species in Yellowstone: willows (*Salix* spp.). Willows are of particular interest in this system because they serve as browse for elk and are habitat for a variety of bird species. As a result, a change in *Salix* would be an indication of potential keystone effects of wolves in this system. Ripple and Beschta analyzed a variety of photographs of *Salix* stands prior to wolf reintroduction and compared them to measured sizes following reintroduction. In upland habitats, wolves had no apparent effects on willow heights, while in lowland sites the results were quite dramatic. In the river valley populations, nearly all willow stands increased in height following wolf reintroduction, and this was related to a decrease in the frequency of browsing by elk.

As we have already discussed, a species is not viewed as keystone in a community if it simply alters some interactions (e.g., removes some prey, is food for some animals). It is considered a keystone if its impacts are large relative to the organism abundance in the system. The evidence to date that wolves serve a keystone role in Yellowstone is inconclusive. Fortunately, the wolves of Yellowstone are quite well established, and continued research by ecologists in this system will be able to provide an answer to whether wolves are important restoration tools that serve keystone roles, or whether the desire to reintroduce them should be based on other arguments, independent of any potential keystone effects.

The concept of keystone species and ecosystem engineers has implications for the management and restoration of natural areas. However, there are also many examples where the addition of what was perceived to be a keystone species did not actually alter communities. There is a growing realization that some changes to communities may be so severe that simple restoration efforts, such as a species reintroduction, will be insufficient to restore the community. It is also important to recognize that even if a species is not found to be keystone, it does not mean that reintroductions are not warranted. Instead, it means that using these concepts as the basis for reintroduction may not be appropriate in all cases. There is much research yet to be done to determine when individual species may, or may not, alter community structure.

good competitors for light or other resources but not generally tolerant of cutting. Diversity is likely highest at intermediate distances from the water's edge as this is the location where a mix of cutting-tolerant and competitively dominant species are likely to be found. It is also important to recognize that the beavers are creating soggy conditions for terrestrial plants near the water's edge, and this itself could contribute to reduced growth (or absence) of some species, as those conditions may be outside their niche requirements. Regardless of the mechanism of effect, the fact that beavers' activity can cause variation in terrestrial species composition clearly makes them a keystone species in this system.

The legacy of beaver dams extends well beyond the life of the dams themselves. Eventually, all beaver dams will be abandoned, and some time after that they lose structural integrity. When these dams "break," the stored water flows back into the streams, exposing land previously covered by water, initiating forest succession. The impacts of beavers can be seen for decades, even if the individual dams last only a few years.

So far we have focused primarily on negative interactions among species and their role in structuring communities. However, much more happens in communities than killing, fighting, and cutting down trees. As we discuss next, mutualisms and mutualistic networks can also play critical roles in determining community structure.

CONCEPT 17.3 REVIEW

1. Paine discovered that intertidal invertebrate communities of higher diversity include a higher proportion of predator species. Did this pattern confirm Paine's predation hypothesis?

2. How can beavers alter the growth of plants they do not eat?

3. What is the difference between a keystone and a dominant species?

17.4 Mutualistic Keystones

Mutualists can act as keystone species. While our earlier discussions of keystone species have emphasized the roles of predators as keystone species, many other kinds of organisms can act as keystone species. Returning to our refined definition of keystone species, the only requirements for keystone status is that the species in question have relatively low biomass in the community and a high impact on community structure. Increasingly, ecologists are discovering that many mutualistic species meet these requirements.

A Cleaner Fish as a Keystone Species

Many species of fish on coral reefs clean other fish of ectoparasites. This relationship, which involves the cleaner fish and its

clients, has been shown to be a true mutualism. One of the most widely distributed cleaner fish in the Indo-Pacific region is the cleaner wrasse (*Labroides dimidiatus*). The feeding activity of cleaner wrasses is intense. Alexandra Grutter of the University of Queensland, Australia, has shown that a single cleaner wrasse can remove and eat 1,200 parasites from client fish per day. She also performed experiments (Grutter 1999) that documented that fish on reefs without cleaner wrasses harbour approximately four times the number of parasitic isopods as those living on reefs with cleaner wrasses.

What effect might cleaning activity by *L. dimidiatus* have on the diversity of fish on coral reefs? This is the question addressed with a series of field experiments by Redouan Bshary of the University of Cambridge. Bshary studied the effects of cleaner wrasses on reef fish diversity at Ras Mohammed National Park, Egypt (Bshary 2003). The study area consists of a sandy bottom area approximately 400 m from shore, dotted with reef patches, in water depths from 2 to 6 m. Bshary chose 46 reef patches separated from other patches by at least 5 m of sandy bottom. He identified and counted the fish species present during dives on these reefs and noted the presence or absence of cleaner wrasses on each reef patch. Bshary recorded 29 natural disappearances or appearances of cleaner wrasses during his study. In addition, he performed experimental removals of cleaner wrasses from reefs and introductions of these cleaners to reef patches where there were none.

Bshary followed the responses of the fish community to natural disappearances and experimental removals and natural colonization and experimental introductions. In doing so, he gained insights into the influence of these tiny mutualists on reef fish diversity. Figure 17.14 summarizes the

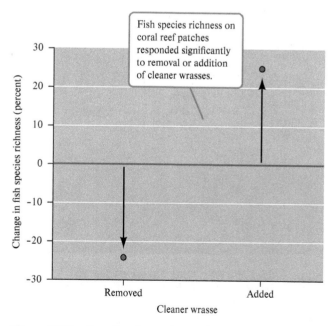

Figure 17.14 Results of experimental and natural removals or additions of cleaner wrasses (*Labroides dimidiatus*) to reef patches in the Red Sea.
Data from Bshary 2003.

responses of fish communities on reef patches four months following the natural or experimental addition or removal of cleaner wrasses. Bshary observed a median reduction in fish species richness of approximately 24% where cleaner wrasses disappeared or were removed. Where cleaner wrasses were added, either naturally or experimentally, he observed a median increase in fish species richness of 24%. Bshary's results indicate that the cleaner wrasse acts as a keystone species on the coral reefs of the Red Sea. Mutualists that act as keystone species have also been found on land.

Seed Dispersal Mutualists as Keystone Species

Ants that disperse seeds appear to have a significant influence on the structure of plant communities in the species-rich fynbos of South Africa. Caroline Christian (2001) observed that native ants disperse 30% of the seeds in the shrublands of the fynbos. The plants attract the services of these dispersers with food rewards on the seeds called elaiosomes. However, the Argentine ant (*Linepithema humile*) (fig. 17.15), which does not disperse seeds, has invaded these shrublands. Christian documented how the invading Argentine ants have displaced many of the native ant species in the fynbos, just as they have in other regions they've invaded. In addition, she discovered that the native ant species most impacted by Argentine ant invasion are those species most likely to disperse larger seeds.

Seed-dispersing ants are important to the persistence of fynbos plants because they bury seeds in sites where they are safe from seed-eating rodents and from fire. Fires are characteristic of Mediterranean shrublands, such as the fynbos, and

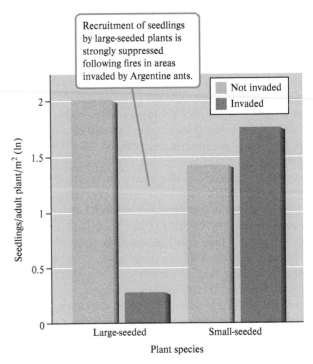

Figure 17.16 A comparison of recruitment of seedlings following fire in areas invaded by Argentine ants and areas not invaded shows the effects of the displacement of native seed-dispersing ants by Argentine ants.
Data from Christian 2001.

seeds are the only life stage of many fynbos plants to survive fires. Consequently, ant dispersal is critical to the survival of many plant species. In a comparison of seedling recruitment following fire, Christian found substantial reductions in seedling recruitment by plants producing large seeds in areas invaded by Argentine ants (fig. 17.16). Meanwhile, small-seeded plants, whose dispersers are less affected by Argentine ants, showed no reduction in recruitment following fire. Christian's results, like Bshary's, reveal the influence of mutualists acting as keystone species within the communities they occupy. Other studies are revealing the importance of other mutualists, such as pollinators and mycorrhizal fungi, as keystone species.

One of the things you may have noticed in several of the examples we have provided about keystone species is that not every case was actually a single species! Instead, studies often referred to some group of species, such as insect-eating birds or seed-dispersing ants, as providing ecological services that, if disrupted, can greatly alter natural communities. The issue of whether species or guilds/functional groups are most critical for ecosystem function is a topic of much debate among ecologists, and we will discuss this in later chapters. We end this chapter instead with a discussion of one more type of keystone species: humans. Humans are nearly everywhere on the planet, and to ignore their impact on community structure would greatly hinder our ecological understanding.

Figure 17.15 The Argentine ant (*Linepithema humile*) has invaded and disrupted ant communities in many geographic regions. In the fynbos of South Africa, invading Argentine ants are displacing keystone ant species, which threatens the exceptional plant diversity of the fynbos.
©Jesus Alberto Ramirez Viera/Getty Images RF.

17.5 Humans Can Be Keystone Species

Humans can act as keystone species. In chapters 2 and 3, and in various other places throughout the book, we have discussed the impacts humans can have on ecosystems and their biological communities. But have these examples shown humans to be keystone species? Sure, the urban landscape is very different from the biome from which it was carved, but are humans acting as keystone species or altering systems through sheer numbers? In some cases, the changes wrought are a function of large human population size. However, even at low population densities, humans can greatly alter biological communities. As we saw with the beaver, some species are ecosystem engineers. And no species engineers ecosystems more than humans do.

People have long manipulated food webs both as a consequence of their own feeding activities and by introducing or deleting species from existing webs. In chapter 4, we described how human harvesting of some species (e.g., bighorn sheep) could alter their evolutionary trajectories. Chris Darimont, of the University of Victoria, along with colleagues from Calgary and California, found that such changes were widespread across species (Darimont et al. 2009). Across 40 systems in which humans harvested some species (e.g., hunting, commercial fisheries, etc.), they found a 300% increase in phenotypic changes in the harvested species relative to systems in which the species were not harvested. These changes were most pronounced for size and life-history traits. Clearly, human harvesting has strong impacts on individuals and the direction of evolution. But what happens to the community if the species being harvested are keystone? Either consciously or unwittingly, people have, themselves, acted as keystone species in communities.

Hunters and Tropical Rain Forest Animal Communities

The current plight of the tropical rain forest is well known. However, Kent Redford (1992) points out that with few exceptions, most studies of human impact on the tropical rain forest have concentrated on direct effects of humans on vegetation, mainly on deforestation. Redford expands our view by examining the effects of humans on animals. The picture that emerges is that humans have so reduced the population densities of rain forest animals in many areas that they no longer play their keystone roles in the system, a situation Redford calls ecologically extinct.

Redford estimates that subsistence hunting, a major source of protein for many rural people, results in an annual death toll of approximately 14 million mammals and 5 million birds and reptiles within the Brazilian Amazon. He estimates further that commercial hunters, seeking skins, meat, and feathers, kill an additional 4 million animals annually. Consequently, the total take by hunters within the Brazilian Amazon is approximately 23 million individual animals. However, this figure underestimates the total number of animal deaths since many wounded animals escape from hunters, only to die. Including those fatally wounded animals that escape, Redford places the annual deaths within the Brazilian Amazon at approximately 60 million animals.

Hunters generally concentrate on a small percentage of larger bird and mammal species, however. For instance, Redford estimates that at Cocha Cashu Biological Station in Manu National Park, located in the Amazon River basin in eastern Peru, hunters concentrate on 9% of the 319 bird species and on 18% of the 67 mammal species. Because hunters generally concentrate on the larger species, this small portion of the total species pool makes up about 52% of the total bird biomass and approximately 75% of the total mammalian biomass around Manu National Park.

As impressive as all these numbers are, a critical question remains: Do hunters reduce the local densities of the birds and mammals they hunt? The answer is yes. Redford estimates that moderate to heavy hunting pressure in rain forests reduces mammalian biomass by about 80% to 93%; and bird biomass, by about 70% to 94%.

There may be cause for concern, however, that goes beyond the losses of these immense numbers of animals. As you might expect, many large rain forest mammals and birds may act as keystone species. If so, their decimation will have effects that ripple through the entire community. The first to suggest a keystone role for the large animals preferred by rain forest hunters was John Terborgh (1988), who presented his hypothesis in a provocative essay titled "The Big Things That Run the World."

Terborgh observed that in the absence of pumas and jaguars on Barro Colorado Island, Panama, medium-sized mammal species are over 10 times more abundant than in areas still supporting populations of these large cats. R. Dirzo and A. Miranda (1990) compared two forests in tropical southern Mexico, one in which hunting had eliminated most of the large mammals and one in which most of the large mammals were still present. The comparison was stark. In the absence of large mammals, such as peccaries, jaguars, and deer, the researchers found forests carpeted with undamaged plant seedlings and piled with uneaten and rotting fruits and nuts, signs of a changing forest. Such observations prompted Redford to warn, "We must not let a forest full of trees fool us into believing all is well." Tropical rain forest conservation must also include the large, and potentially keystone, animal species that are vulnerable to hunting by humans.

ECOLOGICAL TOOLS AND APPROACHES

Food Webs and the Development of Community Ecology

The University of Canberra in Australia curates a database of approximately 360 different food webs from diverse terrestrial and aquatic systems. The collection reflects the historical and scientific development of community ecology, including the seminal paper by Victor Summerhayes and Charles Elton (1923) describing the feeding relationships in an arctic community (Bear Island), focused on nitrogen transfer. The diagram outlining these relationships was reproduced in Elton's 1927 *Animal Ecology* textbook and may be the earliest published example of what we would recognize as a food web diagram.

The earliest food webs were built upon dogged observations, like those of Robert MacArthur in chapter 1, which described habitat partitioning by warblers. Ralph Bird, for example, used multiple lines of observational data in constructing the Aspen food webs described earlier in this chapter. Some evidence of feeding relationships came from gut content analysis, but other evidence came from watching animals feed. This included the strikes of raptors on rodent species and also the feeding behaviour of song birds, sweeping across meadows at particular times of day. Feeding of these latter birds were inferred from knowledge of the insect species active at given locations and times of day and knowledge of potential prey items. Further evidence came from examination of nests and from observation of the feathers or fur strewn around a nesting site.

The late 1960s saw maturation of theoretical community ecology, with growing interest in how interactions among populations could affect properties of the community. Robert May made important contributions by constructing theoretical interaction models and predicting how the nature of these interactions could influence a biological community's stability (to de discussed in greater detail in chapter 18). An important element was connectedness; communities in which species, on average, interacted with a larger number of other species were predicted to have greater stability. Stuart Pimm (1982), among others, brought these ideas into the study of food webs through greater operational definition of stability and connectedness. Pimm calculated connectedness as:

$$C = \frac{kn}{n(n-1)} = \frac{k}{n-1}$$

where C is connectedness, k is the average number of species with which any given species interacts, and n is the number of species within the web. The equation is based on Pimm's observation that $n(n-1)$ is the maximum number of interactions that are possible, excluding cannibalism. Consider a community in which a prey species is fed upon not by a single predator but by several different species.

Populations may be stochastic, and any number of factors, such as climate, disease, or migration, might dramatically change a predator's population density. If a prey species is fed upon by a single predator, its population may be volatile. When the predator becomes very abundant, the prey species may go locally extinct. Or, when the predator population collapses, the prey population may explode. From the predator side, feeding on several prey species rather than specializing in a single species may amount to bet hedging. Remember the boom–bust cycles of lynx and snowshoe hare? Having the ability to vary diet may allow the predator population to survive when the preferred prey population is low. The reduced pressure on the prey species may allow it to recover. Theory predicts that where trophic connectedness is high, predator and prey populations will be less volatile.

Another development in food web modelling was the recognition of trophic levels as falling along a continuum rather than occupying discrete strata. The earliest food webs depicted discrete pyramids with plants and other primary producers occupying a base level; herbivores, the next level; primary predators, the third level; secondary predators, the fourth level, etc. However, assigning an animal to one of these discrete levels proved problematic and did not provide a clear picture of an animal's ecological role. Consider a black bear that eats berries and other plant matter but that may also hunt herbivores or predatory fish. What trophic level would you assign? A lack of clarity can often stand in the way of effective conservation efforts.

S. M. Adams and colleagues (1983) introduced calculations that recognized the continuous distribution of trophic levels for predatory animals using the formula:

$$T_i = 1.0 + \sum_{j=1}^{n} T_j(p_{ij})$$

where T_i is the trophic level of predatory species, i; T_j is the trophic level of prey species, j; and p_{ij} is the proportion of prey species j (or aggregated species) in the diet of predator i, by volume. In calculating trophic levels, plants and other primary producers are assigned $T = 0$, while strict herbivores are assigned $T = 1$. Kirk Winemiller (1990) followed this approach in constructing the food webs presented in figure 17.3, with gut content analysis providing information on the proportion of various food resources consumed, and informing which links were strong and which were weak.

The brief history of food webs outlined above tracks the evolution of food webs from heuristic constructs of who eats whom to big picture descriptors of how communities function. However, the information that underpins the food webs described has certain limitations. There is a bias toward larger, more enigmatic animals that can be more easily observed in feeding or that are more amenable to gut content analysis. Gut content analysis itself has a bias toward larger or better preserved prey species. Food material that cannot be easily identified, or that does not leave behind a carapace (for example), may be under-represented in a food web's representation of predator diets. These biases make it very difficult to construct food webs for systems dominated by small invertebrate species. Finally, food webs constructed through observation of feeding behaviour or gut content analysis often provide snapshots of trophic relationships rather than an understanding of the longer-term integrated contribution of different food resources over an animal's life. We will next discuss some tools that address some of these issues and that have been useful in the evolution of food web models.

Stable Isotope Analysis as a Tool in Building Food Webs

Many elements come in more than one form, varying in the number of neutrons held in the nucleus. We refer to these different forms as isotopes. Some isotopes (e.g., ^{14}C) are unstable and undergo radioactive decay. However, others (e.g., ^{12}C and ^{13}C) are stable and do not decay. The relative abundance of stable isotopes in a substance can provide valuable information regarding its formation. When applied to living organisms, stable isotopes can yield clues about diet or sources of nutrients. Stable isotopes of different elements, including H, O, and S, can be useful in establishing geological origin of nutrients or trophic relationships. However, the most commonly used are isotopes of N and C.

Nitrogen is most abundant in the form ^{14}N; however, there is a smaller pool of ^{15}N. Similarly, carbon is most abundant as ^{12}C, with a smaller pool of ^{13}C. We express the relative abundance of isotopic forms in a substance (such as biological tissues) in terms of the rare isotope and relative to a universal standard with known isotopic composition. We use the notation $\delta^{15}N$ (‰) and $\delta^{13}C$ (‰) in describing isotopic composition. A biological tissue with a composition ($\delta^{15}N$) of 3‰, for example, has three parts per thousand more ^{15}N than atmospheric N_2.

When nitrogen is transferred from one trophic level to the next, or when a predator consumes prey or a herbivore eats a plant, the two different forms of N are not exactly equivalent. The lighter isotope is more easily excreted in waste, leaving behind the heavier isotope (DeNiro and Epstein 1981). As a result, the predator will retain a higher proportion of the heavy isotope in biomass, becoming isotopically enriched. We refer to this as isotopic discrimination, expressed as $\Delta^{15}N$. Suppose a prey species with $\delta^{15}N$ of 4‰ is consumed by a predator. Much of the prey's nitrogen is excreted, and some is retained in the predator's biomass, but there is isotopic discrimination. The predator

may end up with $\delta^{15}N$ of 7‰, or a discrimination ($\Delta^{15}N$) of 3‰. An influential paper by David Post (2002) combined new field data on isotopic discrimination with literature values encompassing diverse laboratory and field studies of organisms ranging in size "from copepods to polar bears." Post found $\Delta^{15}N$ associated with a one level trophic transfer to be 3.4 ± 1.0 ‰, and $\Delta^{13}C$ to be 0.4 ± 1.3 ‰. The value of 3.4‰ has become widely accepted and expected as a rate of N isotopic discrimination in establishing trophic relations, while predators or herbivores are generally expected to reflect the ^{13}C composition of their food.

When Karin Guiguer was a Ph.D. student under the supervision of David Barton at the University of Waterloo, she used isotopic analysis as a tool to better understand the relative importance of different food resources for *Diporeia* in Colpoys Bay, part of Georgian Bay in Lake Huron. *Diporeia* are amphipods and represent an important trophic link between benthos and the pelagic lake community. Guiguer and Barton (2002) wanted to understand if algae, primarily diatoms, sinking from the photic zone to the sediments were an important source of carbon (hence linking pelagic carbon production to the pelagic food web via a benthic feeder), or if *Diporeia* were using other sources of carbon, such as bacteria in sediment or allochtonous plant matter. Guiguer was also interested in how the relative importance of food sources might change seasonally. Figure 17.17 depicts a very limited subset of her data showing that *Diporeia* collected at 30 m depth had $\delta^{13}C$ similar to either sedimented diatoms or particulate organic matter. The epilithon and allochthonous plant matter had distinctly different isotopic C and did not appear to be important carbon sources. Nitrogen composition and other data showing a seasonal correspondence in $\delta^{13}C$ between particulate organic matter and *Diporeia* suggested that while they used diatoms when available, bacteria associated with sediments was a more significant source of food over the amphipod's life history.

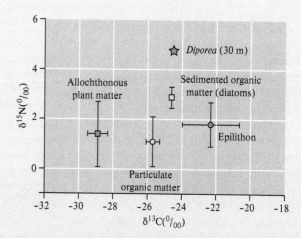

Figure 17.17   Isotopic composition of *Diporeia* and its potential food sources.
Modified from Guiguer and Barton 2002.

Bringing Molecular Biology to Bear on Resolving Food Web Structure

Tools developed in other disciplines have migrated into the realm of community ecology. In the previous section, we saw how tools grounded in geological sciences have migrated into ecology and helped to clarify trophic relationships. We are also seeing tools developed for molecular biology expand rapidly into the realm of ecology. High Arctic terrestrial communities tend to be relatively simple with fewer species and potential interactions than communities in temperate or tropical areas. This property has made High Arctic systems particularly ideal for exploring how DNA-based technologies may be used to supplement our understanding of trophic relationships.

In many High Arctic food webs, the dominant herbivores are Lepidoptera (butterflies and moths), and their major predators are Hymenoptera or Diptera parasitoids (wasps and flies). Parasitoids have free-living adult stages. Reproductive females pierce the exoskeletons of lepidopteran hosts and lay their eggs in the tissues. The larvae mature within the host and emerge, bursting from the host. When we consider the trophic relations between hosts and parasitoids, much of our knowledge comes from rearing experiments in which live hosts are captured and reared until a parasitoid emerges and can be identified. Helena Wirta at the University of Helsinki led an international research team that included Paul Hebert and Sean Prosser at the University of Guelph's Biodiversity Institute of Ontario. Wirta et al. (2014) used molecular evidence of trophic interactions by looking for parasitoid DNA in tissues of host butterflies and moths, and host DNA in adult parasitoids.

The research team used sweep netting, pitfall traps, and direct search and capture to collect a large and diverse sample of Lepidoptera and adult parasitoids. Tissues of individual animals were homogenized and DNA extracted. In the process of extracting DNA from a host, the DNA of any parasitoid feeding on that host would be incidentally extracted. Similarly, in the process of extracting DNA from a parasitoid, DNA from any host that the parasitoids fed upon would be extracted. Wirta et al. constructed a reference library of a highly variable region of the mitochondrial cytochrome c oxidase (CO1) gene for the known species in the community. They then used polymerase chain reaction (PCR) to amplify this region of CO1 in DNA extracted from each host or parasitoid, and sequenced the PCR products. Sequences were screened against the reference library to identify which parasitoids left DNA markers within host tissues, and which hosts' DNA was represented within the digestive tracts of parasitoids. Interaction webs were then constructed using data from rearing experiments, or data from rearing experiments supplemented with data from DNA.

The use of DNA evidence provided a much more complex, interconnected food web than emerged from

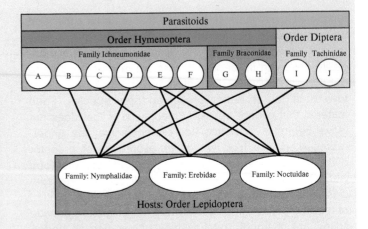

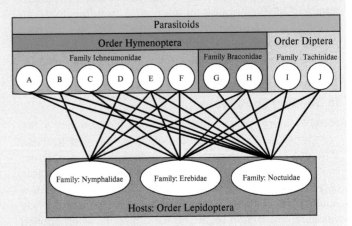

Figure 17.18   High Arctic food web with Lepidopteran hosts and parasitoid predators constructed based on (*a*) data gained in rearing experiments and (*b*) data gained in rearing experiments combined with DNA analysis of CO1 gene sequences of parasitoids in host tissue and host CO1 sequences in adult parasitoids. Circles A–J represent different subfamilies of parasitoids, including: A = Pimplinae, B = Ichneumoninae, C = Cryptinae, D = Banchinae, E = Campopleginae, F = Mesochorinae, G = Hormiinae, H = Microgastrinae, I = Exoristinae, J = Tachinidae.

rearing experiments. Overall, Wirta et al. found three times more trophic connections when molecular evidence was included. Figure 17.18 represents a very limited subset of the data depicted by Wirta, focusing on only three host nodes. However, it illustrates the increased connectedness of the web generated with DNA evidence for interaction. Rearing experiments may underestimate trophic interactions if larvae from different parasitoid species compete within the tissues of the host. A host may be infected simultaneously by several competing parasitoids, but rearing experiments would only capture the relationship with the winner.

The information provided by molecular analysis quite dramatically changed understanding of trophic relationships in the High Arctic. Of particular interest, it undermined our perception of the specificity of host–parasitoid relationships. It will be interesting to see how application of DNA in other food webs shapes this understanding going forward. Moreover, the tools of molecular biology may help us to better understand food webs dominated by small organisms where the classical tools of gut content analysis and

observation will not suffice. As with stable isotope analysis, DNA-based data should be viewed as complementary to other lines of evidence. Combining these various lines of evidence will allow construction of accurate food web models, useful in conservation biology and as broader macro descriptors of community function.

CONCEPT 17.5 REVIEW

1. A new housing development is built in an area of abandoned agriculture that is supporting a mixed grassland/shrubland biological community. This development will include 200 new homes. The construction and occupation of the homes will dramatically alter the pre-existing biological community. Is this an example of humans as keystone species? Explain.

2. Dirzo and Miranda found that hunting by a relatively small number of humans had greatly reduced the populations of large mammals, including jaguars, the top predator. Based on what you already understand about community ecology, what effects might this removal of the top predator have on the community?

SUMMARY

Community structure will be influenced by a diversity of interactions, all of which may be occurring simultaneously. A description of the patterns of species interactions in a community is called an *ecological network*. Different ecological interactions can result in predictable *assembly rules* that govern the structure of communities. Different ecological processes can interact among themselves, with potentially large consequences for the relative abundances of the component species.

17.1 A food web summarizes the feeding relationships in a community.

The earliest work on food webs concentrated on simplified communities in areas such as the Arctic islands. However, researchers such as Charles Elton (1927) soon found that even these so-called simple communities included very complex feeding relations. Ralph Bird (1930) showed that an added level of complexity exists when members of one community feed upon species primarily found in a different community. This work emphasizes that communities do not have discrete boundaries and that species connections can be very broad. Missing from most studies of food webs are parasites, pathogens, and decomposers.

17.2 Strong competitors can alter community structure.

Some communities will contain competitive hierarchies, in which certain species are continually able to suppress the abundance of other species. In such systems, competition can greatly limit species diversity, with the competitively subordinate species

being excluded from the community (figure 17.19). Paul Keddy combined the ideas of competitive hierarchies and the theory of allocation when he developed the theory of centrifugal organization of species. In this theory, core habitats are occupied by dominant competitors, while poorer competitors will be found in more stressful satellite habitats. The presence of the poorer competitors occurs because they are better able to deal with other stressors in the environment than are the dominant competitors.

17.3 The activities of a few keystone species may control the structure of communities.

Robert Paine (1966) proposed that the feeding activities of a few species have inordinate influences on community structure. He predicted that some predators may increase species diversity by reducing the probability of competitive exclusion. Manipulative studies of predaceous species have identified many keystone species, including starfish and snails in the marine intertidal zone and fish in rivers. On land, birds exert substantial influences on communities of their arthropod prey. Some keystone species, such as beavers, may also be ecosystem engineers. This designation is given to organisms whose activities result in the construction of a novel habitat. Keystone species are those that, despite low biomass, exert strong effects on the structure of the communities they inhabit (fig. 17.19).

17.4 Mutualists can act as keystone species.

Experimental studies have shown that cleaner fish, species that remove parasites from other fish, act as keystone species on

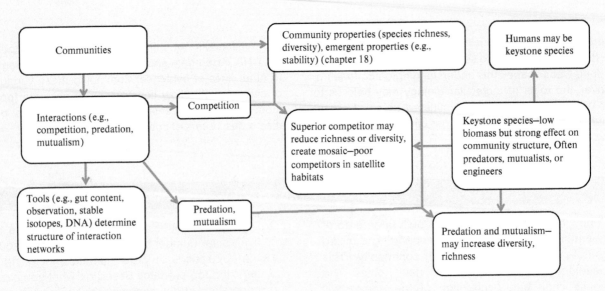

Figure 17.19   Concept map for chapter 17.

coral reefs. Removing cleaner fish produces a decline in reef fish species richness. Ants that disperse plant seeds in the fynbos of South Africa have been shown to have major influences on plant community structure. Where invading ants have displaced the mutualistic dispersing ants, the plant community suffers a decline in species richness following fires. Other mutualistic organisms that may act as keystone species include pollinators and mycorrhizal fungi.

17.5 Humans can act as keystone species.

People have long manipulated food webs both as a consequence of their own feeding activities and by introducing or deleting species from existing food webs. In addition, many of these manipulations have been focused on keystone species. Hunters in tropical rain forests have been responsible for removing keystone animal species from large areas of the rain forests of Central and South America.

REVIEW QUESTIONS

1. You could argue that the classical food web of Bear Island included several communities, each with its own food web. What were some of the different communities that Summerhayes and Elton (1923) included in their web? On the other hand, because the Bear Island food web includes significant movement of energy (food) and nutrients between what many ecologists might consider to be separate communities, what does their food web say about the distinctness of what we call communities?

2. What is a keystone species? How does Paine's experiment demonstrate this concept?

3. When Power (1990) excluded predaceous fish from her river sites, the density of herbivorous insect larvae (chironomids) decreased. Use the food web described by Power to explain this response.

4. Some paleontologists have proposed that overhunting caused the extinction of many large North American mammals at the end of the Pleistocene, about 11,700 years ago. The hunters implicated by paleontologists were a newly arrived predatory species, *Homo sapiens*. How might you expect directed extinctions of large mammals to have influenced community structure?

5. All the keystone species work we have discussed in this chapter has concerned the influences of animals on the structure of communities. Can other groups of organisms act as keystones? What about parasites and pathogens?

6. According to Paul Keddy's theory of the centrifugal organization of species, dominant species will displace poorer competitors from the best habitat in a community. There is evidence this occurs in the wetlands he has studied, at least among vascular plant species. How would you design a study to test whether this theory also applies to animal species?

7. Decomposition and parasitism are generally excluded from discussions of food webs. How might this practice give a biased view toward the relative importance of different ecological processes in structuring communities?

8. What evidence is necessary to make a firm declaration as to whether grey wolves are keystone species in Yellowstone National Park? If they are found not to be keystone, does this mean that there was no justifiable reason to reintroduce them to Yellowstone?

© Digital Vision/PunchStock

CHAPTER 18 DISTURBANCE, SUCCESSION, AND STABILITY

CHAPTER CONCEPTS

18.1 Intermediate levels of disturbance promote higher diversity.
Concept 18.1 Review
Ecology in Action: Using Disturbances for Conservation

18.2 Community stability may be due to lack of disturbance or community resistance or resilience in the face of disturbance.
Concept 18.2 Review

18.3 Community changes during succession include increases in species diversity and changes in species composition.
Concept 18.3 Review

18.4 Ecosystem changes during succession include increases in biomass, primary production, respiration, and nutrient retention.
Concept 18.4 Review

18.5 Mechanisms that drive ecological succession include facilitation, tolerance, and inhibition.
Ecological Tools and Approaches: Using Repeat Photography to Detect Long-Term Change
Concept 18.5 Review
Summary
Review Questions

The first recorded visit by a European to Glacier Bay gave no hint of its eventual contributions to our understanding of biological communities and ecosystems. In 1794, Captain George Vancouver visited the inlet, to what is today called Glacier Bay, Alaska (fig. 18.1). He could not pass beyond the inlet to the bay, however, because his way was blocked by a mountain of ice. Captain Vancouver (1801) described the scene as follows (remember that *f* was used in place of *s* at the time):

> Whilft the fhores of the continent, bounded by a continuation of thofe lofty frozen mountains, which extend fouth-eaftward from mount Fairweather, rofe abruptly from the water-fide, and were covered with perpetual fnow, whilft their fides were broken into deep ravines or vallies, filled with immenfe mountains of ice.

(a)

(b)

Figure 18.1   Glacier Bay National Park, Alaska, a laboratory for studying ecological succession. (*a*) The lower reaches of the Muir Glacier in August 1941. Note the bare terrain in the foreground of the photo. (*b*) The same scene 63 years later, in 2004, at which point the Muir Glacier had retreated 8 km up the valley and out of the view to the left, leaving open water where the ice had been hundreds of metres thick. Notice that the once bare foreground is now covered by thick vegetation.

(a) National Snow and Ice Data Center and Glacier Bay National Park and Preserve Archive/USGS; (b) Bruce Molnia/USGS.

In 1879, John Muir explored the coast of Alaska, relying heavily on Vancouver's earlier descriptions. Muir (1915) commented in his journal that Vancouver's descriptions were excellent guides except for the area within Glacier Bay. Where Vancouver had met "mountains of ice," Muir found open water. He and his guides from the Hoona tribe paddled their canoe through Glacier Bay in rain and mist, feeling their way through uncharted territory. They eventually found the glaciers, which Muir estimated had retreated 30 to 40 km up the glacial valley since Vancouver's visit 85 years earlier.

Though the surrounding mountains were filled with mature boreal forest, Muir found no such forests at the upper portions of the bay. He and his party had to build their campfires with the stumps and trunks of long-dead trees exposed by the retreating glaciers. Muir recognized that this fossil wood was a remnant of a forest that had been covered by advancing glaciers centuries earlier. He also saw that plants had quickly colonized the areas uncovered by glaciers and that the oldest exposed areas, where Vancouver had long ago met his mountains of ice, already supported forests.

Muir's observations in Glacier Bay were published in 1915 and read the same year by the ecologist William S. Cooper. Cooper saw Glacier Bay as the ideal laboratory for the study of ecological **succession**, the gradual community change in an area following *disturbance* (first introduced in chapter 9). As we discuss below, disturbances can be small or large, may remove a few individuals within a community, or may result in the creation of entirely new habitats. Glacier Bay was ideal for the study of succession because the history of glacial retreat could be accurately traced back to 1794 and perhaps further. Today, as the world becomes increasingly warmer, there is a net retreat of glaciers globally, and thus this process of succession is more than a lesson in ecological history. It is a way to understand the future of natural communities. Though species compositions will vary among locations, we can learn much from understanding the changes found in Glacier Bay.

When glaciers retreat, they do not leave behind soil, seeds, or living vegetation. Instead, they typically leave only water, rocks, sand, and silt. Such harsh conditions and lack of viable seed permit the growth of few plant species, and thus there tend to be few species able to colonize an area during the first few decades after it is exposed by the retreating glacier. These plants, the first in a successional sequence, form a **pioneer community**. The most common members of the pioneer community around Glacier Bay are horsetail (*Equisetum variegatum*), willow herb (*Epilobium latifolium*), willows (*Salix* sp.), cottonwood seedlings (*Populus balsamifera*), mountain avens (*Dryas drummondii*), and Sitka spruce (*Picea sitchensis*).

After another decade or so at Glacier Bay, the pioneer community gradually grades into a community dominated by mats of *Dryas*, a dwarf shrub. These *Dryas* mats also contain scattered alder (*Alnus crispa*), *Salix*, *Populus*, and *Picea*. This community then changes into a shrub-thicket dominated by *Alnus*. Soon after the closure of the *Alnus* thicket, however, *Populus* and *Picea* will grow above it, covering about 50% of the area on sites 50 to 70 years old.

In 75 to 100 years, succession at Glacier Bay leads to a forest community dominated by *Picea*. Mosses carpet the understory of this spruce forest, and here and there grow seedlings of western hemlock (*Tsuga heterophylla*) and mountain hemlock (*Tsuga mertensiana*). Eventually, the population of *Picea* declines and the forests are dominated by *Tsuga*. On landscapes with shallow slopes, these hemlock forests eventually give way to muskeg, a landscape of peat bogs and scattered tussock meadows.

Because succession around Glacier Bay occurs on newly exposed geological substrates not significantly modified by organisms, ecologists refer to this process as **primary succession**. Primary succession also occurs on newly formed volcanic surfaces, such as lava flows; in outflows of streams, where silt deposition can lead to the buildup of new land; and in any situation where new substrate is exposed or created. In contrast, when disturbance removes members from an existing community without destroying the soil or creating new substrate, **secondary succession** follows. For instance, secondary succession occurs after agricultural lands are abandoned, after a forest fire, or after a flood.

Succession may continue indefinitely (e.g., cyclic succession) or may end with a community whose populations remain stable until disrupted by subsequent disturbance. In the latter case, this final successional community is called the **climax community**. The nature of the climax community depends upon environmental circumstances. The communities we discussed in chapter 2—temperate forests, tundra, etc.—were essentially the climax communities for each of the climatic regimes that we considered. Other community types, such as grasslands, can be referred to as **disclimax communities**. Disclimax communities are maintained only through continual disturbances, such as grazing, drought, or fire. The climax community around Glacier Bay is determined by the prevailing climate and local topography. On well-drained, steep slopes the climax community is hemlock forest. In poorly drained soil on shallow slopes the climax community is muskeg.

Studies of succession show that communities and ecosystems are not static through time. In many cases, the general direction of change in community structure and ecosystem processes is predictable, at least over the short term. In other cases, the outcome of succession is not predictable, and instead it may end in a number of **alternative states**. Disturbances will not impact all communities equally, and instead some communities are less prone to change than others. These communities exhibit **stability**, the tendency to withstand or recover from disturbance. In this chapter we describe disturbance and the concept of equilibrium, some aspects of communities associated with increased stability, what succession looks like, and some of the mechanisms that cause it.

examined the role of disturbance in structuring natural communities, defined *disturbance* as "a discrete, punctuated killing, displacement, or damaging of one or more individuals (or colonies) that directly or indirectly creates an opportunity for new individuals (or colonies) to become established" (p. 356). P. S. White and S. Pickett (1985) defined *disturbance* as "any relatively discrete event in time that disrupts ecosystem, community or population structure and changes resources, substrate availability, or the physical environment" (p. 7). They also caution, however, that we must be mindful of spatial and temporal scale. For example, disturbance to bryophyte (mosses and liverworts) communities growing on boulders along the margin of a stream can occur at spatial scales of fractions of metres and at annual temporal scales that are irrelevant to the surrounding forest community. Consequently, a disturbance for one organism may have little or no impact on another, and the nature of disturbance may be quite different in different environments.

There are countless potential sources of disturbance to communities. White and Pickett listed 26 major sources of disturbance roughly divided into abiotic forces, such as fires, hurricanes, ice storms, and flash floods; biotic factors, such as disease and predation; and human-caused disturbances. How might we expect populations to respond to disturbances?

Attempts to understand species interactions, such as competition and predation, through mathematical modelling have often viewed populations as having more or less constant densities over time. In general, these models (chapters 13 and 14) predict that population densities will not change once **equilibrium** has been reached. In a system at equilibrium, stability is maintained by opposing forces such that if populations are altered by some event, they will soon return to the equilibrial state. However, as every ecologist knows, the abundances of real populations never remain exactly the same from year to year, or even season to season. Changes in the environment (abiotic conditions, food, etc.) cause changes to growth optima, carrying capacities, and the values of the other parameters of the models we have discussed. When environmental changes are sufficiently large, we call them disturbances, and these can have significant impacts on species diversity and ecosystem properties.

As we described above, some areas may move through a seemingly orderly series of community changes following a disturbance, resulting in a climax community. However, what happens to the diversity of the system before equilibrium is obtained? What happens if additional disturbances occur regularly, such that no equilibrium is ever reached? We begin by discussing disturbances and a **nonequilibrial theory** of species diversity.

18.1 Disturbance and Diversity

Intermediate levels of disturbance promote higher diversity. To understand why this may be true, we need to first ask this question: What is a disturbance? Wayne Sousa (1984), who

The Intermediate Disturbance Hypothesis

Joseph Connell (1975, 1978) proposed that disturbance is a prevalent feature of nature that influences the diversity of communities. This was a direct counter to the prevalent assumption

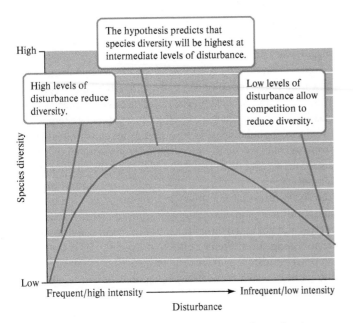

Figure 18.2   The intermediate disturbance hypothesis. Data from Connell 1978.

of equilibrial conditions made by most competition-based models of diversity. As you may recall from chapter 13, high levels of diversity are contrary to the predictions of the competitive exclusion principle, and thus substantial research was focused on ways in which organisms could persist even in the face of competition. Connell took a different approach, proposing that high diversity is a consequence of continually changing conditions, not of competitive accommodation at equilibrium. His "intermediate disturbance hypothesis" instead predicts that intermediate levels of disturbance promote higher levels of diversity (fig. 18.2).

Connell suggested that *both* high and low levels of disturbance lead to reduced species diversity. He reasoned that if disturbance is frequent and intense, the community will consist of those few species able to colonize and complete their life cycles between frequent disturbances (colonizers, pioneer species, *r*-selected species, ruderals, etc.). He also predicted that diversity will be low if disturbances are infrequent and of low intensity. Why? Connell reasoned that in the absence of significant disturbance, the community is eventually limited to the species that are the most effective competitors. Thus, at low disturbance, Connell's model predicts that one would find predominately the best competitors (also known as climax species, *k*-selected species, and competitors).

In the intermediate disturbance hypothesis, there is thus a shift in species composition from competitors to colonizers as disturbance intensity and/or frequency increases. Assuming that unique traits are needed to successfully perform each ecological strategy, low diversity is predicted at both extremes of the disturbance gradient. But why does Connell also predict that intermediate levels of disturbance promote higher diversity? Connell suggested that at intermediate levels of

disturbance there is sufficient time between disturbances for a wide variety of species to colonize but not enough time to allow competitive exclusion. Thus, at intermediate disturbances, species of all competition and colonization strategies may be found.

Importantly, although this model is based on continual disturbance and, thus, is inherently nonequilibrial, it does predict a fairly constant result—a certain number of species for a given level of disturbance. This model suggests that how species respond to disturbances might be predictable based upon the ecological principles we have discussed throughout the text.

Disturbance and Diversity in the Intertidal Zone

The most classic experimental test of Connell's intermediate disturbance hypothesis was performed by Wayne Sousa (1979a). Sousa studied the effects of disturbance on the diversity of marine algae and invertebrates growing on boulders in the intertidal zone. Disturbance to this community comes mainly from ocean waves generated by winter storms. These waves, which can exceed 2.5 m in height, are large enough to overturn intertidal boulders, killing the algae and barnacles growing on their upper surfaces. Meanwhile, the newly exposed underside of the boulder is available for colonization by algae and marine invertebrates.

Because boulders of different sizes turn over at different frequencies and in response to waves of different heights, Sousa predicted that the level of disturbance experienced by the community living on boulder surfaces depends upon boulder size. Smaller boulders are turned over more frequently and therefore experience a high frequency of disturbance, middle-sized boulders experience an intermediate level of disturbance, and large boulders experience the lowest frequency of disturbance.

Sousa quantified the relationship between boulder size and probability of being moved by waves. He established six permanent study sites, in which he measured the exposed surface area of each boulder and determined the force required to move each. He next mapped the locations of boulders by photographing the study plots and then checked for boulder movements by taking additional photographs monthly for two years. Sousa divided the boulders in the study sites into three classes based on the force required for movement: (1) ≤ 49 N, (2) 50 to 294 N, and (3) > 294 N. These classes translated into frequent movement (42% per month = frequent disturbance), intermediate movement (9% per month = intermediate disturbance), and infrequent movement (1% per month = infrequent disturbance).

The number of species living on boulders varied with frequency of disturbance (fig. 18.3). Most of the frequently disturbed boulders supported a single species, few supported five species, and none supported six or seven species. Most of the boulders experiencing a low frequency of disturbance supported one to three species, few supported six species, and none

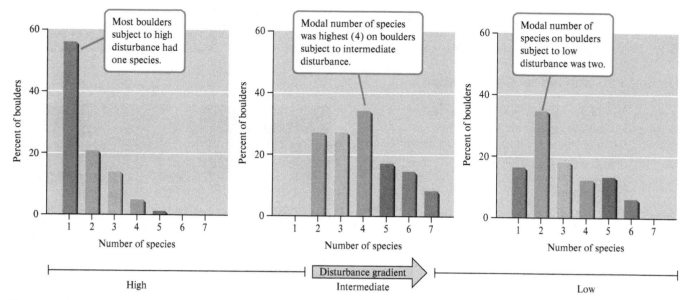

Figure 18.3 Levels of disturbance and diversity of marine algae and invertebrates on intertidal boulders. Data from Sousa 1979a.

supported seven. The boulders supporting the greatest diversity of species were those subject to intermediate levels of disturbance. Most of these supported three to five species, many supported six species, and some supported seven species.

Is the Intermediate Disturbance Hypothesis Generally True?

Though the intermediate disturbance hypothesis is a useful model for understanding how disturbances may alter species diversity, not all researchers find empirical support for the model's prediction. Robin Mackey and David Currie, of the University of Ottawa, conducted a meta-analysis on 116 published diversity–disturbance relationships (Mackey and Currie 2001). These examples include animals, plants, terrestrial systems, and aquatic systems. They found that unimodal relationships such as those proposed by Connell were surprisingly rare, occurring in less than 20% of the studies. Instead, most systems showed no significant relationship between diversity and disturbance, and many showed a negative significant relationship. Jeremy Fox, of the University of Calgary, has recently called the theory a "zombie idea," one that never seems to go away (Fox 2013). He argues that in addition to the empirical shortcomings, the model is theoretically flawed and ecologists should abandon it.

What does this mean? First, this is what science looks like. Though we textbook authors do our best to smooth out complexities in an effort to help students understand general concepts, the leading edge of science is full of uncertainty. Opinions are expressed, data is collected, and resolution eventually is reached . . . maybe. What we can say is that the relationship between diversity and disturbance is complex and cannot simply be described by any single line of any singular

form. Ecologists, and students of ecology, should not view this hypothesis as a law. Instead, the intermediate disturbance hypothesis is helpful in the same way that we use the Lotka–Volterra models or that physicists use models of Newtonian motion. For these models to be perfectly accurate requires a set of highly unrealistic interactions (e.g., only two species compete with each other; no friction or atmosphere). The value of such models is not to use them to predict outcomes for specific situations but to identify the core processes that may be important. By testing these models under diverse conditions, ecologists (and physicists) are able to eventually understand how natural systems work. Here, we see that the impacts of disturbance on diversity will be dependent upon both the biology of the organisms in a system, and the details of the disturbances they encounter. Once again, understanding basic natural history is important if we wish to understand complex ecological interactions.

As we will discuss next, not all communities are equally prone to change in response to disturbance.

CONCEPT 18.1 REVIEW

1. What is the difference between equilibrium and nonequilibrial models of diversity?

2. According to the intermediate disturbance hypothesis, how might you expect human population densities to relate to the species diversity of surrounding natural systems?

3. How does a species' life-history characteristics influence its response to disturbance?

ECOLOGY IN ACTION

Using Disturbances for Conservation

A variety of ecological topics routinely stimulate controversy in the public and among researchers. We have already discussed several of these, including issues related to fisheries, the Species at Risk Act, reintroduction of top predators, and impacts of hunting on evolution. Here we discuss another: the incorporation of disturbances into conservation programs. The goal of this section is not to suggest that all uses of disturbances are appropriate in all conservation programs. Instead, our intention is to show you how the basic information you have learned about succession has direct consequences for the conservation of Canada's wild areas.

Like ecologists, land managers have historically viewed communities as static, discrete entities. Each park was seen as an island, rather than as a piece connected to a larger whole and one that can itself change through time. At the core of this philosophical approach to communities has been the tendency to encourage the preservation of "pristine wilderness," areas free from any disturbances (Gillson and Willis 2004). In this mindset, natural communities were to be protected from disturbances, such as grazing and fire (Hobbs and Huenneke 1992). However, as we have seen in this chapter, communities are naturally dynamic, with substantial variation in species composition over space and time. If this is true for most communities, and current ecological thought believes it to be so, then the idea of trying to "protect" a community from change is at odds with basic ecological understanding.

In a summary of paleoecological work, Gillson and Willis (2004) were able to show that there have been interactions between humans and the environments in which they live for thousands of years, and these interactions are partially responsible for the landscapes we currently see and are trying to protect. A significant question emerges: if humans have caused a certain disturbance (e.g., sheep grazing in Europe) for thousands of years, what is natural: the continuation of this grazing or its cessation? In other words, the landscape we see now, shaped by disturbance, would not be the same one seen if we were to remove grazing (think succession!). Which landscape is the one we should preserve? This question is critical to governmental policy. For example, several governments in Europe pay landowners and occupants to regularly mow or graze grasslands, preventing succession to a forest community. Why? Because these fields have been covered with grasslands for thousands of years of human occupation, and the governments have chosen to preserve the historic human-maintained landscape, rather than a landscape without human intervention (that hasn't been seen for many centuries).

Figure 18.4   A controlled fire being set as part of ecosystem management.
Photo 53236919 © Jimmy Ostgard–Dreamstime.com.

It is issues like these that are shaking the foundations of many common practices in conservation biology. Should you manage a reserve to maintain the diversity of a single area or to maintain greater diversity on the landscape? As a reflection of this shifting mindset, fires are now routinely set in many of the National Parks of Canada (fig. 18.4), not to preserve a single community but instead to protect a *disturbance regime*. This, in turn, will result in the desired diversity of communities. For example, an aggressive anti-fire program over the last several decades has resulted in tree encroachment into alpine meadows, putting these habitats at risk. By reintroducing fire to these systems, park managers hope to restore these unique habitats.

There are few places where controversies regarding the use of disturbances as a conservation tool rage as strongly as they do in grasslands. As we have discussed, grasslands are a generally unstable habitat, often changing to forest or shrubland in the absence of disturbances. We generally view some combination of fire, drought, and grazing as necessary to maintain grassland habitats for extended periods of time. What are land managers supposed to do if they have been charged with the goal of protecting a grassland? Clearly, they cannot alter the frequency of droughts. As we have already seen, fire can be used under some conditions. Fire is less often a viable tool if the land being managed is near either private land and houses or major civic infrastructure (e.g., highways, bridges). The large native herbivores, such as bison, have been fairly efficiently removed from the grasslands of North America. The question that then faces the land manager is this: Do I allow cattle to graze on this conservation land? What do you think should happen? Is it justified to bring in an alien species (domesticated cattle) in an attempt to preserve a native habitat (grasslands)? If so, who gets to decide how many cattle and when they graze: the conservation organization or the ranchers that own the herd? Should the ranchers be paying for the right to graze, or should the conservation organization be paying to have its land grazed? These questions are not trivial and need to be resolved, as it is clear that the effects of herbivores on plant diversity and community structure can vary as a function of the types of herbivore and site conditions (Olff and Ritchie 1998).

Some ecologists are taking the issue of what is natural even further. Josh Donlan and colleagues have proposed re-wilding North America (Donlan et al. 2005). Donlan argues that humans have been, in part, responsible for the loss of a diverse mega-fauna that existed in North America

13,000 years ago. At that time there were species of camels, cheetahs, elephants, and lions throughout the Great Plains. Donlan argues that these species played critical roles in the ecology of these systems. (Think keystone species and ecosystem engineers, chapter 17.) By reintroducing their extant relatives (from Africa and Asia), they propose to reinstate the natural disturbance regime while also providing a new home to species that are likely to go extinct throughout parts of Asia and Africa. Needless to say, this proposal is controversial.

Hopefully, the points we have raised here have encouraged you to rethink some assumptions regarding the preservation of natural areas. If the plants and animals that appear there are always changing, can one ever succeed in preserving a single community without controlled disturbances? Clearly, the next generation of ecologists will be pivotal in further integrating current ecological understanding into the preservation of natural areas.

18.2 Community and Ecosystem Stability

Community stability may be due to lack of disturbance or community resistance or resilience in the face of disturbance. The simplest definition of *stability* is "the absence of change." In an ecological context, a community or ecosystem may be stable for a variety of reasons. Most obviously, in the absence of a disturbance, local conditions may remain constant over time. For instance, the benthic communities of the deep sea may remain stable over long periods of time because of constant physical conditions.

A second, and more interesting, situation occurs when communities and ecosystems may remain stable even when exposed to potential disturbance. Consequently, ecologists generally define *stability* as "the persistence of a community or ecosystem in the face of disturbance," rather than simply as "a lack of change." Stability may result from two very different characteristics of the community: (1) **resistance**, which is the ability of a community or ecosystem to maintain structure and/or function in the face of potential disturbance; or (2) **resilience**, which is the ability of a community to return to its original structure after a disturbance. A resilient community or ecosystem may be completely disrupted by disturbance but quickly return to its former state; thus, over long periods of time it may be relatively stable (fig. 18.5). We will note here without providing any useful advice that defining the time period is not trivial when we discuss stability and resilience, or the duration of a disturbance. Temporal (and spatial) scales relevant to the ecological question of interest need to be carefully considered.

One of the difficulties faced by ecologists studying stability is the need to conduct studies over a long period of time, and, again, this duration depends on the system and question of interest. Long-term data is critical, as stability—both resistance

and resilience—is something that can only be observed through time. Fortunately, long-term studies are becoming more common in ecology. We begin with one of the longest, the Park Grass Experiment.

Lessons from the Park Grass Experiment

The Park Grass Experiment is the prototype of all long-term experimental studies in ecology. Started at the Rothamsted Research in Hertfordshire, England, between 1856 and 1872, its purpose was to study the effects of several fertilizer treatments on the yield and structure of a hay meadow community. Because the Park Grass Experiment has continued without interruption for nearly one-and-a-half centuries, it provides one of the most valuable records of long-term community dynamics. That record provides some unique insights into the nature of community stability.

Jonathan Silvertown (1987) used data from the Park Grass Experiment to respond to the suggestion that existing studies do not conclusively demonstrate that any ecological community is stable. The composition of the plant community at the Park Grass Experiment has been monitored since 1862, and this record reveals at least one level of stability. Over this period, virtually no new species have colonized the meadow. Instead, changes in community composition occurred as a consequence of increases or decreases in species already present in the meadow at the beginning of the experiment. However, Silvertown was able to go much deeper into the data to understand stability.

Silvertown used variation in community composition as a measure of stability. He represented composition as the proportion of the community consisting of grasses, legumes, or other species. The analysis of composition was restricted to the period from 1910 to 1948 to avoid the early period of the experiment when the meadow community was adjusting to

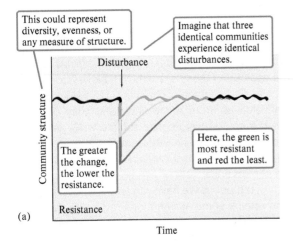

(a)

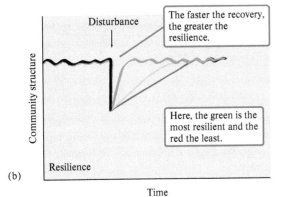

(b)

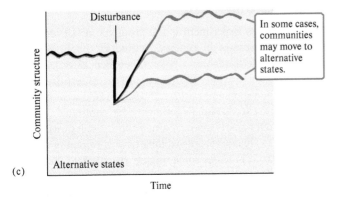

(c)

Figure 18.5 Visual representations of stability concepts. In all cases, imagine that three identical communities experience identical disturbances at identical points in time. The green communities are the most stable, the yellow exhibit intermediate stability, and the red are the least stable. (a) High resistance and high stability occur when the communities change very little in response to a disturbance. (b) High resilience and high stability occur when communities recover quickly to a pre-disturbance state. (c) In some situations, communities may never recover from a disturbance. Instead, community structure may stabilize at one of many alternative states.

the various fertilizer treatments (i.e., undergoing transient dynamics). Figure 18.6 shows the relative proportions of grasses, legumes, and other plants on plots receiving three different treatments: one with no fertilizer; one receiving P, K, Na, and

Mg; and one receiving N, P, K, Na, and Mg. The differences in vegetation on the three plots were mostly produced by the different fertilizer treatments and developed early in the Park Grass Experiment.

The proportion of grasses, legumes, and other plants in the study plots varied from year to year, mainly in response to variation in precipitation. Despite this annual variation, figure 18.6 indicates that the proportions of the three plant groups remained remarkably stable over the interval of the study. A quantitative analysis of trends in biomass revealed no significant changes in the biomass of the three plant groups in the plot receiving no fertilizer, nor in the plot receiving P, K, Na, and Mg. There was a minor, but statistically significant, decrease in the biomass of grasses on the plot receiving N, P, K, Na, and Mg.

Does the stability of Silvertown's three major groups of plants in the Park Grass Experiment hold up if we examine community structure at the species level? It turns out that while the proportions of grasses, legumes, and other species remained fairly constant, populations of individual species changed substantially. Mike Dodd and his colleagues (1995) used census data from 1920 to 1979 to examine plant population trends. The results of their analysis showed that some species increased in abundance, some decreased, some increased then decreased, and some showed no trend.

The contrasting results obtained by Silvertown and by Dodd's project suggest that whether a community or ecosystem appears stable may depend upon how we view it. At a very coarse level of resolution, the Park Grass community has remained absolutely stable. It was a meadow community when the Park Grass Experiment began in 1856, and it remains so today. When Silvertown increased the resolution to distinguish between grasses, legumes, and other species, the community again appeared stable. Silvertown measured stability at a level of aggregated functionality, lumping together species that played similar ecological roles. However, when Dodd and his colleagues increased the resolution still further and examined trends in the abundances of individual species, the Park Grass community no longer appeared stable. It is fair to ask which matters more, stability at the aggregated level, stability at the species level, or, if we go even further, stability at the genetic level? The answer will depend greatly on the context. If, for example, we are concerned with stability of a community function as an emergent property, such as primary production, or lignin decomposition, stability at the aggregate level may be of greater importance. This provides a natural lead-in to our next section, where we discuss how an aspect of the community itself can influence stability.

Biodiversity and Stability

In chapter 16 we discussed how species diversity was often positively associated with increased ecological function. It may thus come as no surprise that species diversity also can confer increased stability—both through increased resistance and resilience. The relationship between stability and diversity has a long history, which we cannot fully recapitulate here. The concept that stability and diversity were interrelated emerged in the

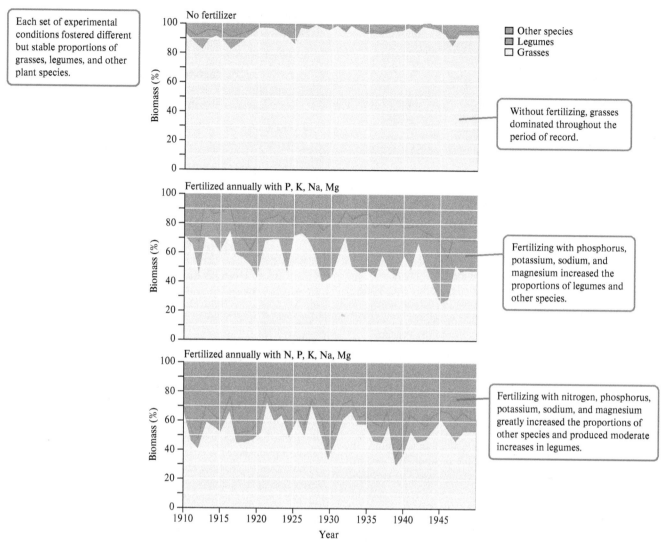

Each set of experimental conditions fostered different but stable proportions of grasses, legumes, and other plant species.

Without fertilizing, grasses dominated throughout the period of record.

Fertilizing with phosphorus, potassium, sodium, and magnesium increased the proportions of legumes and other species.

Fertilizing with nitrogen, phosphorus, potassium, sodium, and magnesium greatly increased the proportions of other species and produced moderate increases in legumes.

Figure 18.6 Proportions of grasses, legumes, and other plant species under three experimental conditions. Data from Silvertown 1987.

1950s with the first edition of Eugene Odum's *Fundamentals of Ecology* (1953). Several lines of evidence supporting a conceptual framework relating diversity and stability were outlined in Charles Elton's *The Ecology of Invasions by Animals and Plants* (1958). Robert MacArthur (1955) made an intuitive argument that community stability could be measured as a function of trophic diversity, which was seized upon by Hutchinson (1959) as an explanation for the stability of diverse communities. There are numerous studies testing for such diversity–stability relationships in many types of natural systems, and synthetic analyses have begun to emerge. The biodiversity–stability relationship has become a tenet of ecology, although Daniel Goodman (1975) provided a strong critique of this concept, concluding that neither theory nor empirical evidence provided compelling support. We'll refer you back to the section in this chapter titled "Is the Intermediate Disturbance Hypothesis Generally True?" (in subsection 18.1) and suggest that the stability–diversity relationship is also neither a law nor something that should be accepted dogmatically. Rather, it provides

a conceptual model for understanding how some communities may function.

Boris Worm, of Dalhousie University, and an international team of researchers (Worm et al. 2006) have compiled experimental and long-term observational data sets to explore the effect of marine biodiversity on stability of aquatic communities. Across 32 experiments in which researchers manipulated diversity (either species or genetic), increased stability (both resistance and resilience) typically resulted. In analyzing long-term data of economically and ecologically important marine species found within 12 coastal systems, areas of high regional (gamma) diversity had a smaller proportion of fisheries that have collapsed relative to areas of lower regional diversity (fig. 18.7). Why might this matter? One potential management implication is that fisheries in areas of lower diversity are at more risk of collapse than those from richer marine systems. Consequently, more care may need to be taken in the establishment of harvest quotas. Similar results are also found on land (Hooper et al. 2005). However, rather

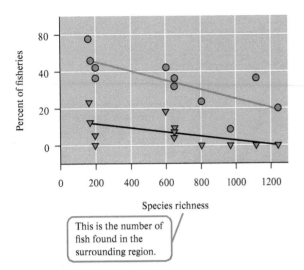

Figure 18.7   Increased regional species diversity is associated with reduced proportions of fisheries that have collapsed (circles) or that have gone extinct (triangles).

Fig 2b from Worm, B., Barbier, E. B., Beaumont, N., Duffy, J. E., Folke, C., Halpern, B.S., Jackson, J.B.C., Lotze, H. K., Micheli, F., Palumbi, S. R., Sala, E., Selkoe, K. A., Stachowicz, J.J., Watson, R. 2006. Impacts of biodiversity loss on ocean ecosystem services. *Science* 314:787–76. Reprinted with permission from AAAS.

than describe more patterns, let us talk about why diversity may confer increased stability.

Let us consider some disturbance, such as a drought in a grassland. If there is a single species present, the overall stability of the system is going to be determined by the performance of that single species. Thus, the system may be highly stable, or highly unstable, depending upon that single species' ability to cope with the disturbance. Let us now imagine another grassland with 50 species. These species represent functional redundancy in the system, that is, they fill a similar ecological role. The overall stability of that system will be determined by the combined performances of all of these species. The chance that some species will be able to cope with drought is increased, relative to there being only a single species present. This is the **insurance hypothesis**, in which diversity increases stability due to functional redundancy, with an increased probability of there being some species able to cope with any particular disturbance. Or, put another way, diversity buffers a community from the potential consequences of a disturbance or any environmental change. A key expectation of this idea is that a community's overall response is not driven by the same species every year; instead, different species should become important under different conditions. In a recent review of studies that was conducted by Forest Isbell of McGill University and colleagues (Isbell et al. 2011), it appears there is support for this idea. Isbell summarized the data from 17 biodiversity experiments conducted in grasslands, similar to those described in chapter 16. Combined, these studies contained 147 plant species. Overall, 84% of these species were found to be important to ecosystem function at some point in time, under some conditions, or in response to some disturbance.

18.3   Community Changes During Succession

Community changes during succession include increases in species diversity and changes in species composition. So far, we have discussed what disturbances are and how characteristics of the landscape and community may enhance stability. However, in many cases stability will be lost, and disturbances will significantly impact communities. In this section we focus on what happens next.

Some of the most detailed studies of ecological succession have focused on the studies of forests. Though primary and secondary forest succession require different amounts of time, the changes in species diversity that occur in each appear remarkably similar. Over the course of succession, nearly every aspect of community structure changes. There are shifts in dominance, evenness, species diversity, and composition, as well as changes to the abiotic environment. Underlying these shifts are the basic ecological interactions we have discussed throughout this book. Dispersal, niche requirements, competition, exploitation, and associated mutualists all influence when and if a species is found in a location undergoing succession. It is important to recognize that succession is the outcome of ecological processes; it is not a process itself. Communities do not act as a whole, moving from one form to another. Instead, individuals survive, thrive, or perish as a function of how well their biology is suited to local conditions. As these conditions change, so too do the species that become dominant. These changes are what we observe and call succession.

In some cases, changes during succession are highly predictable, and they appear to follow assembly rules (chapter 17) leading to a particular climax community. In many other cases, succession does not lead to a single end-point, and instead the outcome may be one of any number of alternative stable states (fig. 18.5c). We begin here by describing the classical form of succession.

Primary Succession at Glacier Bay

We return to Glacier Bay, Alaska, and look with a bit more depth at primary succession following glacial retreat. Succession can take a very long time—centuries or even millennia. This is well beyond the lifespan of even a young ecologist, let alone the length of a typical research grant! How, then, do we study

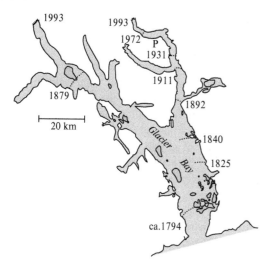

Figure 18.8 A map of Glacier Bay, showing the glacial extent since 1794.

Chapin, F. Stuart, Lawrence R. Walker, Christopher L. Fastie, and Lewis C. Sharman. 1994, May. Mechanisms of primary succession following deglaciation at Glacier Bay, Alaska. *Ecological Monographs* 64(2):149–75. Ecological monographs by ECOLOGICAL SOCIETY OF AMERICA. Reproduced with permission of ECOLOGICAL SOCIETY OF AMERICA, in the format Book via Copyright Clearance Center.

this process? A typical tool in succession research is the use of a **chronosequence**, which is a group of communities or ecosystems that represent a range of ages or times since disturbance. The idea is that if you know the time since disturbance at many locations, then by sampling different locations at the same time you can measure changes through succession. For example, figure 18.8 provides a map showing the approximate locations of the glacial extent since 1794. By measuring community structure at locations in which the glacier retreated 10, 100, and 1,000 years ago, we can swap space for time and infer successional changes. Though chronosequences require making many important assumptions (e.g., climate and gamma diversity have not changed over time), they are a key research tool in long-term ecological studies.

In their study of Glacier Bay, William Reiners and colleagues (1971) worked at sites that were carefully chosen for their similarity in physical features but that differed substantially in time since glacial retreat. Their eight study sites were below 100 m elevation; were on glacial till, an unstratified and unsorted material deposited by a glacier; and had moderate slopes. The study sites ranged in time since glacial retreat from 10 to 1,500 years. By minimizing site differences (e.g., slope and substrate), they give more confidence in the use of the chronosequence approach.

Their youngest site, which was approximately 10 years old, supported a pioneer community of scattered *Epilobium* (willowherbs), *Equisetum* (horsetails), and *Salix* (willows). Site 2 was about 23 years old and supported a mix of pioneer species and clumps of *Populus* (poplar) and *Dryas* (cushion forming evergreen dwarf shrubs). Site 3, which was approximately 33 years old, supported a mat of *Dryas* enclosing clumps of

Salix, *Populus*, and *Alnus* (alder). Site 4 was 44 years old and was dominated by a mat of *Dryas* with few open patches. Site 5, which was approximately 108 years old, was dominated by a thicket of *Alnus* and *Salix* with enough emergent *Populus* and *Picea* (spruce) to form a partial canopy. Site 6 was a 200-year-old forest of *Picea*. Using geological methods, Reiners and his colleagues dated site 7 at 500 years and site 8 at 1,500 years. Both sites were located on Pleasant Island, which, because it is located outside the mouth of Glacier Bay, had escaped the most recent glaciation. Site 7 was an old forest of *Tsuga* (hemlock) that contained a few *Picea*. Site 8 was a muskeg with scattered *Pinus contorta* (lodgepole pines).

The total number of plant species in the eight study sites increased with time since glacial retreat. As you can see in figure 18.9, species richness increased rapidly in the early years of succession at Glacier Bay and then more slowly during the later stages. However, not all groups of plants increased in diversity throughout succession. Though the species richness of mosses, liverworts, and lichens reached a plateau after about a century of succession (fig. 18.10), the diversity of low shrubs and herbs continued to increase throughout succession. In contrast, the diversity of tall shrubs and trees increased until the middle stages of succession and then declined in later stages.

The pattern of increased species richness with increased age of the stand that Reiners and his colleagues described for the successional sequence around Glacier Bay is typical of both primary and secondary succession. However, the tempo of succession can vary greatly among systems. The late successional climax community at Glacier Bay was 1,500 years old. In the following example of secondary succession, the climax forest community emerges in approximately one-tenth of that time.

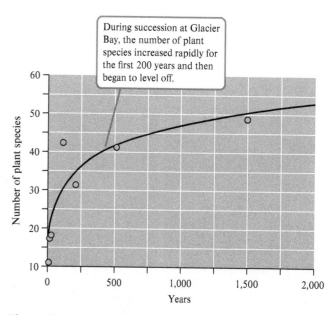

Figure 18.9 Change in plant species richness during primary succession at Glacier Bay, Alaska.

Data from Reiners, Worley, and Lawrence 1971.

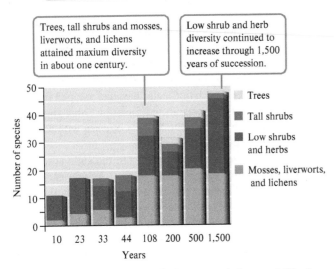

> The timing of increasing species richness differs among plant growth forms.

> Trees, tall shrubs and mosses, liverworts, and lichens attained maxium diversity in about one century.

> Low shrub and herb diversity continued to increase through 1,500 years of succession.

Figure 18.10 Succession of plant growth forms at Glacier Bay, Alaska. Timing of increased species richness differs among plant growth forms.

Data from Reiners, Worley, and Lawrence 1971.

Secondary Succession in Boreal Forest

Boreal forests are a dominant community type in Canada, and though we often think of the boreal as isolated areas of old forest, the reality is often very different. In addition to the ever-increasing pressures of oil and gas exploration, forestry, and peat extraction, the boreal forest is a dynamic community with frequent natural disturbances.

Fires are common throughout the boreal forest, with lightning strikes a frequent source of fire initiation. What exactly does fire do to a forest (fig. 18.11)? The answer depends upon the intensity of the fire: some fires are minor and affect only low-lying vegetation while others are severe and burn both the tops of the trees and through the accumulated litter on the forest floor to the soil. However, if we ignore the extreme ends of the fire intensity distribution, we find a few common consequences of fire. First, fire can kill plants. Death of canopy trees increases light penetration to the soil floors, allowing the recruitment and growth of smaller trees and seedlings that may have escaped the fire or plants that were able to quickly colonize through seed or clonal growth. Fire effects do not end with their immediate impacts on plant survival. Fire can cause increases in nutrient availability through the breakdown of organic matter and by stimulating microbial activity. In combination, these factors provide a high light environment with high resource availability. Following fire, recolonization by plants is rapid, with new plant growth occurring within days or weeks (unless it is winter!).

But how do plants know to colonize a burned area? Many plants possess life-history traits that facilitate regrowth following fire. These fire-tolerant species are widespread throughout the boreal forest. For example, although aspen stems can burn during a fire, the root systems generally survive. Soon after a fire, you will find thousands of young aspen sprouts emerging from these living root systems. This re-sprouting strategy is found in other species, such as paper birch, but rarely to the same density that is found with aspen. Other species may not be able to re-sprout, but fire may trigger seed dispersal or germination. For example, black spruce (*Picea mariana*) and jack pine (*Pinus banksiana*) produce seeds inside cones covered with a thick layer of pitch. The pitch burns off during fire, releasing the seeds. In other communities, compounds contained within smoke itself can serve as a stimulant promoting seed germination. The life-history trade-offs we discussed in chapter 9 are very relevant to understanding the process of succession. Species that invest in large numbers of seeds, which are able to disperse over great distances, are more likely to encounter the open environments of a post-burn fire. Following fire it is common to see species such as fireweed (*Chamerion angustifolium*),

1944   1916   1823   1760

Figure 18.11 Changes in boreal forest composition along a chronosequence in Quebec. Dates refer to the year of the last fire.
Danielle Charron.

blue-joint grass (*Calamagrostis canadensis*), and many other fast-growing species blanketing the forest floor until they are shaded out by trees. These species have life-history traits well suited to living in disturbed habitats but not as well suited for life within a mature forest. Knowing that some, but not all, species of the boreal forests have adaptations to recover following fire, what do you expect secondary succession in the boreal forest to look like?

Yves Bergeron of l'Université du Québec has been studying the secondary succession of southern boreal forests for decades. The work of Bergeron and his students has provided us with a much clearer understanding of how fire can alter plant community structure in the boreal forest. In one study (Bergeron 2000), we can see a general pattern in species change over time following fire. Bergeron conducted an extensive survey of forest composition in the southern extent of the boreal forest in Quebec, establishing a series of transects and study plots in the forests surrounding Lake Duparquet. These forests contain a mixture of dominant plant species, including jack pine, black and white spruce, balsam poplar, and paper birch. Bergeron wanted to know whether the distribution of these species on the landscape could be explained by fire. In other words, would you tend to find certain types of boreal species in areas that were recently burned and other species in areas that have not been burned for quite some time? Bergeron sampled forest stands that were established after different forest fires, with the most recent occurring in 1964 and the oldest in 1760. The results were striking. Bergeron found that prior to the fires there was substantial variation in forest composition and that following fire there was a regular pattern to successional changes over time (fig. 18.12). Soon after fire, forests were dominated by hardwood species, such as aspen, birch, willow, and pin cherry. These species were eventually replaced by white spruce and balsam fir, with white cedar becoming common even later. Bergeron found that these

dynamics were also influenced by periodic outbreaks of spruce budworms, once again emphasizing the point we made in chapter 17 that all communities will be influenced by multiple ecological factors. Despite this complexity, Bergeron was able to paint a portrait of secondary succession in the southern boreal forests of Canada. His interpretation of this process can help explain the observed heterogeneity in forest types within the boreal, as these areas may be in different stages of the long-term movement toward the local climax community.

As we see next, succession also is found in systems where animals, rather than plants, are among the dominant organisms covering the ground.

Succession in Rocky Intertidal Communities

When we discussed the influence of disturbance on local species diversity earlier in this chapter, we saw how an intertidal boulder stripped of its cover of attached organisms was soon colonized by algae and barnacles (fig. 18.13). Looking back

Figure 18.13 Succession in the intertidal zone involves colonization and competition for limited space among species as different as attached marine algae, sea anemones, mussels, and barnacles.
© Jim Zipp/Science Source.

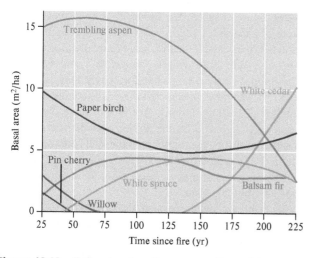

Figure 18.12 Following fire, the composition of the southern boreal forest changes over the course of secondary succession.

Data from Bergeron, P. 2000. Species and stand dynamics in the mixed woods of Quebec's southern Boreal forest. *Ecology* 81(6):1500–16, Figure 3. Reprinted with permission.

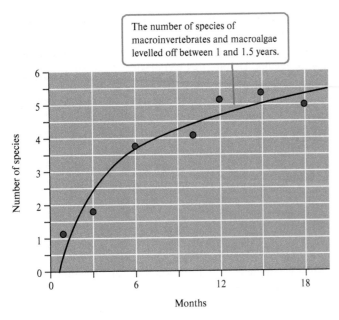

The number of species of macroinvertebrates and macroalgae levelled off between 1 and 1.5 years.

Figure 18.14   Succession in number of macroinvertebrate and macroalgae species on intertidal boulders.
Data from Sousa 1979a.

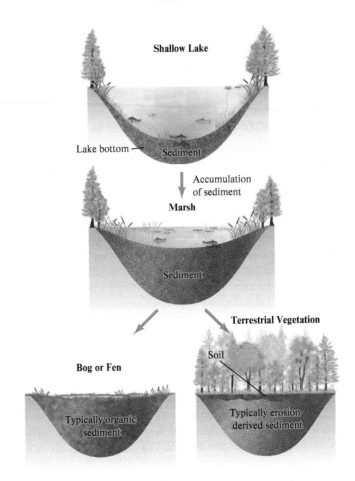

Figure 18.15   Shallow lakes can undergo succession. Terrestrialization is most common with accumulation of inorganic sediments, while transition to wetland habitats is more common with organic sedimentation.

on that pattern of community change, we can now see it as an example of ecological succession. Wayne Sousa (1979a, 1979b) showed that the first species to colonize open space on intertidal boulders were a green alga in the genus *Ulva* and the barnacle *Chthamalus fissus*. The next arrivals were several species of perennial red algae: *Gelidium coulteri*, *Gigartina leptorhynchos*, *Rhodoglossum affine*, and *Gigartina canaliculata*. Finally, if there was no additional disturbance for a few years, *G. canaliculata* grew over the other species and dominated 60% to 90% of the space.

Sousa explored succession on intertidal boulders with several experiments. In one of them, he followed succession on small boulders that he had cleaned and stabilized. As in forest succession, the number of species increased with time (fig. 18.14). Notice in the figure that the average number of species increased until about 1 to 1.5 years and then levelled off at about five species.

Primary forest succession around Glacier Bay may require about 1,500 years, and secondary forest succession in the boreal forest takes about 200 years. Meanwhile, the successional changes described by Sousa occurred within about 1.5 years. In highly dynamic systems, such as desert streams prone to flash flooding, secondary succession by algae and macroinvertebrates may occur in a matter of weeks (Fisher et al. 1982). As we'll see in the next examples, shallow lakes also follow predictable patterns of succession, encompassing two very different time scales.

Shallow Lake Succession

Freshwater lakes experience succession in two time scales. Over the short time scale of seasons or years there are changes in species composition following some disturbance, such

as flooding, freezing, or introduction of novel species. Such changes are similar in concept to what we have seen in the previous examples of succession in forests and streams. However, lakes also experience succession on a geological time scale. Most lakes, particularly small lakes, eventually disappear. This too is succession and involves predictable changes in species composition as a result of changing conditions in the lake (fig. 18.15). The mechanisms that drive lake succession vary as a function of local conditions. One form of lake succession is the process of *terrestrialization*, driven by **sedimentation**, the deposition of suspended matter onto the lake bottom. The composition of the sediment will vary among locations: it may be organic (e.g., peat), inorganic (e.g., sand), or some mixture of these and other materials.

We begin by imagining a small, shallow lake. Surrounding the lake will likely be a variety of mosses, cattails, and other plants that can grow in water-logged soils. As this is a shallow lake, there are likely to be substantial amounts of aquatic vegetation even far from the lake edge. Now ask yourself a question: What happens to all of the plant litter surrounding and inside the lake when it falls from the plants? Obviously, much of this will fall into the water and settle onto the bottom of the lake. In these cool regions, decomposition is generally slower than litter accumulations, such that the bottom of the lake gradually rises as litter is accumulated across years and decades. Sedimentation can also occur rapidly if the lake becomes eutrophied through inputs of fertilizers, which stimulates algal growth. When algae in lakes die, they too fall to the bottom, creating layers of detritus. An additional source of sediment may come from upland erosion, which may flow into and fill the bottom of the lake.

Sedimentation can eventually fill the lake bottom, leading to the conversion of the system into an alternative habitat type. The exact habitat will depend upon the type of sediment (organic vs. inorganic), lake depth, and other local conditions. Explaining how different wetland and upland habitat types are formed is well beyond the scope of this course, but we encourage those interested to take some courses in limnology!

In general, changes driven by accumulation of sediment can eventually result in a conversion of the lake into a marsh-like habitat with standing water surrounding dense vegetation. Depending upon the specific conditions (e.g., rate of water flow out of the lake, pH, etc.), continued organic sedimentation can convert the marsh into a fen or bog (chapter 3). In other conditions, particularly when sedimentation is from erosion rather than organic sources, the lake can develop into a drier upland forest community. A critical aspect of this form of succession is that it blurs the lines between aquatic and terrestrial systems. High levels of deposition from terrestrial vegetation into a shallow lake can cause succession from one to the other. As we have seen many times throughout the book, terms like *aquatic* and *terrestrial* are convenient for scientists to use to describe communities, but they mask the rich complexity of interconnections that actually exist.

It is important to also recognize that not all lakes will undergo this form of long-term succession. Deep lakes are unlikely to have large amounts of vegetation growing throughout the water; thus, relatively little sedimentation occurs. Similarly, lakes with steep, rock-lined boundaries are likely to experience little encroachment by the surrounding terrestrial vegetation, either slowing or preventing succession. Finally, a critical component of lake succession is that sedimentation rates are greater than decomposition rates. If microbial activity is high enough to decompose the litter or if there is sufficient outflow of water from the lake (carrying sediment), succession is less likely to occur.

It is also worth recognizing that many artificial lakes and ponds were designed specifically to undergo this succession or, at least, to begin this process. Wet retention ponds are a common storm water management feature. Their purpose is to collect sediment in storm water runoff, accumulate that sediment, and allow delayed release of clarified water to natural systems. They are worth mentioning here because, in many urban and suburban areas, they are the most prevalent type of aquatic system. Given their design and function, they tend to collect organically rich sediments, and decomposition may exhaust dissolved oxygen, accelerating sediment accumulation and contributing to aesthetic problems, such as odour. Slowing the process of succession and allowing these ponds to continue their function as ecosystems is an ongoing management challenge for municipalities and conservation authorities.

As we have just shown, ecological succession involves predictable changes in community structure. As you will see next, succession also leads to predictable changes in ecosystem structure and function.

CONCEPT 18.3 REVIEW

1. What are the primary differences in secondary succession rates in forest, rocky intertidal, and shallow lake communities?
2. How do life-history traits influence whether a species is likely to be found early or late in succession?
3. Why is lake succession toward a terrestrial system likely to occur in shallow lakes with low pH and cool temperatures?

18.4 Ecosystem Changes During Succession

Ecosystem changes during succession include increases in biomass, primary production, respiration, and nutrient retention. In the last section, we saw how plant and animal community structure changes during primary and secondary succession. However, as the species diversity and composition of communities change, they cause changes to a number of ecosystem properties. Further, time itself can influence ecosystem processes through a number of mechanisms, such as the weathering of bedrock. In this section, we review evidence that many ecosystem properties also change during succession. For instance, many properties of soils, such as the nutrient and organic matter content, change during the course of succession.

Ecosystem Changes at Glacier Bay

Again, we return to Glacier Bay in Alaska. Stuart Chapin and his colleagues (1994) documented substantial changes in ecosystem structure during succession at Glacier Bay. They focused on four study areas of approximately 2 km² each. Their first site had been deglaciated for about 5 to 10 years and was in the pioneer stage. Their second site had been deglaciated 35 to 45 years previously and was dominated by a mat of *Dryas*. *Dryas* had just begun to invade this site when it was studied by Reiners' group more than 20 years earlier. The third site had been deglaciated about 60 to 70 years before and was in the alder, *Alnus*, stage. This site was studied by Reiners when it was a young thicket of alder and by Cooper when it was in the pioneer stage. The fourth site studied by Chapin and his colleagues had been deglaciated 200 to 225 years earlier and was a forest of spruce, *Picea*.

Chapin and his research team measured changes in several ecosystem characteristics across these study sites, including the quantity of soil. Total soil depth and the depth of all major soil horizons all show significant increases from the pioneer

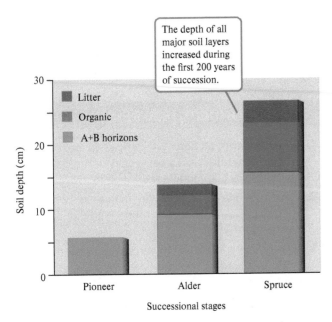

Figure 18.16 Soil building during primary succession at Glacier Bay, Alaska.

Data from Chapin et al. 1994.

community to the spruce stage (fig. 18.16). Chapin and colleagues found that the organic content and moisture concentrations of the soil had also increased substantially, while soil bulk density and phosphorus concentration decreased with time since glacial retreat.

Why are these changes in soil properties important? They demonstrate that succession involves more than just changes in the composition and diversity of species. Soils are the foundation upon which terrestrial ecosystems are built, and if the soil changes so too will many other aspects of the ecosystem. We can see from this study that the physical and biological properties of ecosystems are inseparable. Organisms acting upon mineral substrates contribute to the building of soils upon which spruce forests eventually grow around Glacier Bay. Soils, in turn, strongly influence the kinds of organisms that grow in a place.

Four Million Years of Ecosystem Change

The detailed knowledge of ecosystem change that has emerged through studies at Glacier Bay is impressive. However, the sequence of ages represented by the chronosequence are limited. In 1794, when Captain George Vancouver encountered a wall of ice at the mouth of Glacier Bay, the island of Kauai in the Hawaiian Island chain supported forest ecosystems growing on soils that had developed on lava flows that were over four million years old. The Hawaiian Islands have formed over a hot spot on the Pacific tectonic plate and have been transported on that plate to the northwest, forming a chain of islands that vary greatly in age. The youngest island in the group is the big island of Hawaii, which is currently growing over the hot spot. The big island is made up of volcanic rocks that vary from fresh lava flows to flows that are approximately 150,000 years old. Meanwhile, the islands to the northwest are sequentially older.

As in Glacier Bay, teams of ecologists have probed the chronosequence represented by the Hawaiian Island chain for information on ecosystem development. However, in Hawaii the chronosequence spans not hundreds of years but millions.

Lars Hedin and colleagues (2003) examined nutrient distributions and losses on a chronosequence of forest ecosystems on the islands of Hawaii, Molokai, and Kauai. The youngest ecosystems, which were on Hawaii, had developed on basaltic lava flows that were 300, 2,100, 20,000, and 150,000 years old. The study site on Molokai had developed on rocks that were 1,400,000 years old; and the oldest study site, which was on Kauai, was 4,100,000 years old. All sites currently have an average annual temperature of about 16°C and receive approximately 2,500 mm of precipitation annually. They also all support forest communities dominated by the native tree *Metrosideros polymorpha*.

Over the chronosequence represented by their six study sites, Hedin and colleagues encountered changes in a wide range of soil features. Earlier studies had demonstrated that primary production in the Hawaiian forest ecosystems is limited by nitrogen early in succession and by phosphorus later in succession. Organic matter, which is absent from fresh lava, increased in soils over the first 150,000 years of the chronosequence (fig. 18.17). Increases in soil organic matter also occur over the course of succession at Glacier Bay. However, in the Hawaiian chronosequence, organic matter was lower at the 1.4- and 4.1-million-year-old sites. Figure 18.17 also shows that changes in soil nitrogen content followed almost precisely the pattern exhibited by soil organic matter.

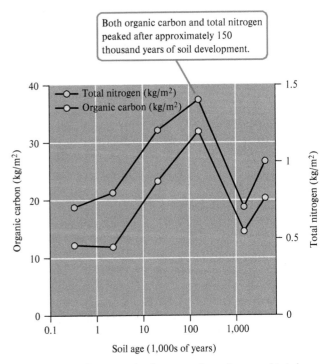

Figure 18.17 Changes in the organic carbon and total nitrogen content of soils developing on Hawaiian lava flows ranging in age from 300 years old to 4.1 million years old.

Data from Hedin, Vitousek, and Matson 2003.

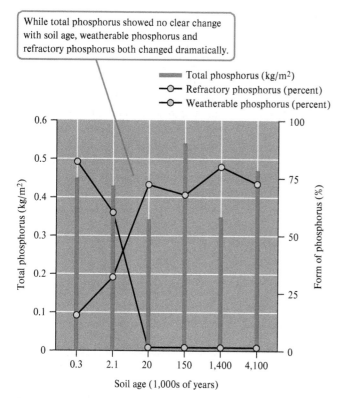

Figure 18.18 Changes in the total phosphorus and percentages of total phosphorus in weatherable and refractory (low availability) forms.
Data from Hedin, Vitousek, and Matson 2003.

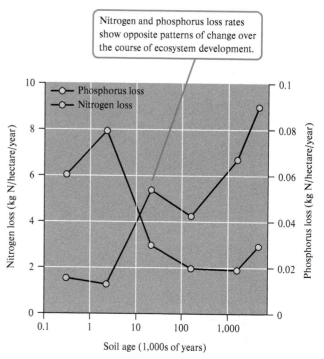

Figure 18.19 Nitrogen and phosphorus loss rates from soils developing on Hawaiian lava flows ranging in age from 300 years old to 4.1 million years old.
Data from Hedin, Vitousek, and Matson 2003.

The pattern of change in the total phosphorus content of soils was remarkably different (fig. 18.18). The total amount of phosphorus in soils showed no obvious pattern of change with site age. However, the forms of phosphorus changed substantially over the chronosequence. Weatherable mineral phosphorus was largely depleted by 20,000 years. Meanwhile, the percentage of soil phosphorus in refractory forms, which are not readily available to plants, increased, varying from 68% to 80% of total phosphorus across ecosystems that had developed on lava flows 20,000 years old or older. On these older soils, primary production is limited by phosphorus availability.

Hedin and colleagues found changes in rates of nutrient loss across the chronosequence. Over the course of four million years of ecosystem development, these tropical forest ecosystems show progressively higher rates of nitrogen loss but decreased rates of phosphorus loss (fig. 18.19). In other words, for approximately 2,000 years these ecosystems are highly retentive of nitrogen but as nitrogen content increases in their soils, they begin to lose nitrogen at a higher rate. Most losses are due to leaching to groundwater. In contrast, as phosphorus becomes progressively less available in these ecosystems, and eventually limiting to primary production, these ecosystems become more retentive of phosphorus. As we shall see in the next example, intact vegetative cover may play a key role in nutrient retention in forest ecosystems.

Recovery of Nutrient Retention Following Disturbance

Bormann and Likens (1981) monitored a control and an experimental stream catchment for three years in the Hubbard Brook Experimental Forest. This forest, located in New Hampshire, provides some of the best evidence of the ecosystem changes that occur during succession in forested communities. They were particularly interested in the effects of clear-cut logging on nutrient dynamics. As we have seen throughout the book, often the best way to study natural processes is through experimental manipulation. Here, they cut down the forest surrounding their experimental catchment, and they suppressed regrowth of vegetation with herbicides for three years (Likens et al. 1978). By suppressing vegetative growth, they delayed succession.

When herbicide applications were stopped, succession proceeded and nutrient losses by the forest ecosystem decreased dramatically. As you can see in figure 18.20, the herbicide suppressed vegetative growth on the experimental catchment for at least three consecutive years. It was during this period that the experimental catchment lost large quantities of nutrients, including calcium, potassium, and nitrate.

When herbicide applications stopped in 1969, Likens's group observed simultaneous increases in primary production and decreases in nutrient loss. However, the researchers point out that uptake by vegetation cannot account completely for reduced nutrient loss and that losses of calcium, potassium, and nitrate all peaked during the time when herbicide was still being applied. They suggest that some of the reduced losses

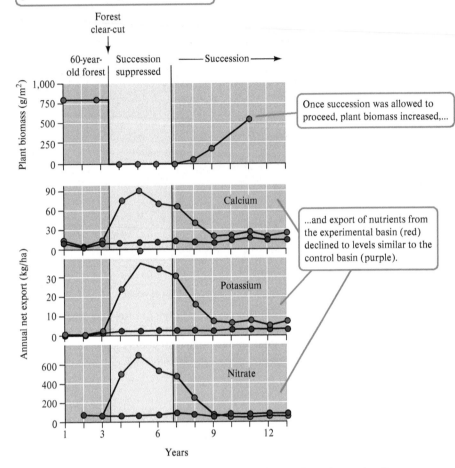

The Hubbard Brook deforestation experiment showed that succession can reduce losses of plant nutrients caused by disturbance.

Once succession was allowed to proceed, plant biomass increased,...

...and export of nutrients from the experimental basin (red) declined to levels similar to the control basin (purple).

Figure 18.20   Succession following deforestation and nutrient retention.

Data from Likens et al. 1978.

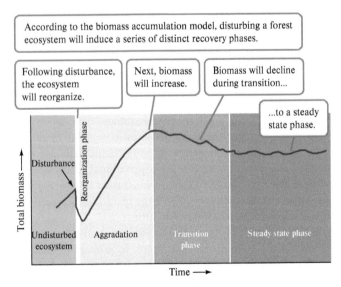

According to the biomass accumulation model, disturbing a forest ecosystem will induce a series of distinct recovery phases.

Following disturbance, the ecosystem will reorganize.

Next, biomass will increase.

Biomass will decline during transition...

...to a steady state phase.

Figure 18.21   The biomass accumulation model of forest succession.

Data from Bormann and Likens 1981.

during this period can be attributed to reduced amounts of these nutrients in the ecosystem. In other words, nutrient losses were reducing nutrient pools. However, vegetative uptake is clearly implicated since once succession was allowed to occur, nutrient losses from the experimental catchment declined rapidly. Though losses of nitrate returned to pre-disturbance levels within four years, calcium and potassium losses remained elevated above pre-disturbance levels even after seven years of forest succession.

A Model of Ecosystem Recovery

As a result of their observations on the Hubbard Brook Experimental Forest, Bormann and Likens (1981) proposed a model for recovery of ecosystems from disturbance (fig. 18.21). Their biomass accumulation model divides the recovery of a forest ecosystem from disturbance into four phases: (1) a reorganization phase of 10 to 20 years, during which the forest loses biomass and nutrients, despite accumulation of living biomass; (2) an aggradation phase of more than a century, when the ecosystem accumulates biomass, eventually reaching peak biomass; (3) a transition phase, during which biomass declines somewhat from the peak reached during the aggradation phase; and (4) a steady-state phase, when biomass fluctuates around a mean level.

How well does the biomass accumulation model represent the process of forest succession? Given the time scale of secondary succession in forests, this is difficult to assess. However, we might ask if the model can be generalized to other ecosystems. This can be tested on ecosystems that undergo rapid succession. Such ecosystems give the ecologist the chance to study multiple successional sequences. Do such ecosystems reach a steady state following disturbance (at least between disturbance events)? As we will see in the following example, the patterns of ecosystem change during succession on Sycamore Creek, Arizona, suggest that several ecosystem features eventually reach a steady state.

Succession and Stream Ecosystem Properties

Stuart Fisher and his colleagues studied successional events in Sycamore Creek, Arizona. This desert stream is prone to flash flooding events that remove algae and invertebrates and reset successional processes. Patterns similar to those proposed by the biomass accumulation model were recorded by Fisher's research group during just 63 days of post-flood succession in Sycamore Creek, Arizona (Fisher et al. 1982). Algal biomass

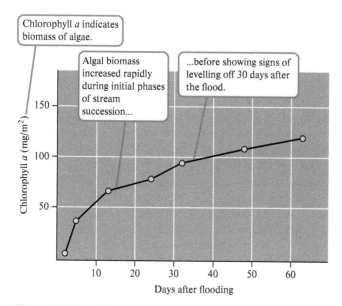

Figure 18.22   Changes in biomass during stream succession.

Data from Fisher et al. 1982.

increased rapidly for the first 13 days following disturbance and then increased more slowly from day 13 to day 63 (fig. 18.22). Sixty-three days after the flood, algal biomass showed clear signs of levelling off. The biomass of invertebrates, the chief animal group in Sycamore Creek, increased rapidly for 22 days following the flood and then, like the algal portion of the ecosystem, began to level off.

Ecosystem metabolic parameters showed even clearer signs of levelling off before the end of the 63-day study (fig. 18.23). Gross primary production (see chapter 19), measured as grams of O_2 produced per square metre per day, increased rapidly

until day 13, increased more slowly between days 13 and 48, and then levelled off between days 48 and 63. Total ecosystem respiration, measured as oxygen consumption per square metre per day, increased quickly for only five days after the flood and then began to level off. Respiration by invertebrates, which at its maximum represented about 20% of total ecosystem respiration, levelled off by day 63.

Nancy Grimm (1987) studied nitrogen dynamics in Sycamore Creek following floods that occurred from 1981 to 1983. As in the earlier studies by Fisher and his colleagues (1982), Grimm found that during succession, algal biomass and whole ecosystem metabolism quickly reached a maximum and then levelled off, as did the quantity of nitrogen in the system.

In addition, however, Grimm examined patterns of nitrogen retention during stream succession. She estimated the nitrogen budget in each of her study reaches by comparing the nitrogen inputs at the upstream end to nitrogen outputs at the downstream end. In the early stages of succession, approximately equal amounts of dissolved inorganic nitrogen entered and left Grimm's study reaches (fig. 18.24). What do equal levels of input and output indicate regarding nutrient retention? A balance between input and output means that the ecosystem shows no, or zero, retention. The level of retention increased rapidly during succession, levelling off at nearly 200 mg N per square metre per day, about 28 days after a flood. Then, between 28 days and 90 days after the flood, the study reach showed progressively lower retention until it eventually exported a little more dissolved inorganic nitrogen than came in with groundwater.

The results of Grimm's study raise several questions. First, what mechanisms underlie retention? Grimm attributes most retention by the Sycamore Creek ecosystem to uptake by algae and invertebrates, since levels of nitrogen retention are consistent with the rates at which nitrogen was accumulated by algal

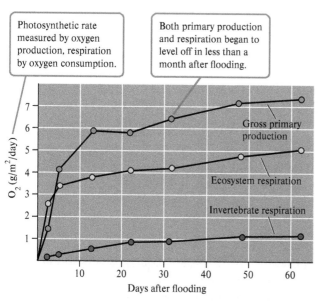

Figure 18.23   Ecosystem processes during succession in Sycamore Creek, Arizona.

Data from Fisher et al. 1982.

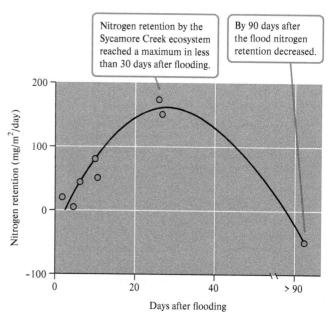

Figure 18.24   Nitrogen retention during stream succession.

Data from Grimm 1987.

and animal populations. What causes the stream reaches to eventually export nitrogen? Grimm suggested that at 90 days post-flood her study sites may have stopped accumulating biomass or may have even begun to lose biomass and, with it, accumulated nitrogen. A loss of biomass in the later stages of succession is consistent with the predictions of the Bormann and Likens biomass accumulation model.

The major point here is that succession, which produces changes in species composition and species diversity, also changes the structure and function of ecosystems, ranging from forests to streams. However, we are left with a major question concerning this important ecological process: What mechanisms drive succession? Ecologists have proposed that the mechanisms underlying succession may fall into one of three categories. Those mechanisms are the subject of the next section.

CONCEPT 18.4 REVIEW

1. Why are the changes in soil properties during the course of succession documented by Stuart Chapin and his colleagues ecologically significant?

2. What would equal levels of nitrogen input and output in the stream reaches (sections) studied by Nancy Grimm indicate?

3. How are the biomass accumulation model of Bormann and Likens (see fig. 18.21) and Fisher's observed patterns in metabolism during succession in Sycamore Creek (see fig. 18.23) compatible?

18.5 Mechanisms of Succession

Mechanisms that drive ecological succession include facilitation, tolerance, and inhibition. Succession occurs in terrestrial and aquatic environments in response to a diversity of disturbances. What are the underlying mechanisms that cause these changes? Over the last several decades there has been a move away from viewing succession as a process in and of itself, and toward a focus on the interactions of individuals within a community. By focusing on the individual, ecologists have been able to identify several general mechanisms that can cause successional change within a community. We begin, however, with some history.

An early model for successional change was proposed by Frederic Clements in 1916. Clements viewed succession as analogous to the development of an organism (1916, 1936) and saw the climax community as a kind of *superorganism.* (As a point of reference, *Superman* did not appear until 1938.) He argued that each wave of species in a successional sequence facilitated the establishment and growth of the next wave. This process of *serial replacement* would continue until the climax community was established, which, according to Clements, was then able to maintain itself in perpetuity or at least until another disturbance occurred.

Henry Gleason (1926, 1939) opposed this idea, arguing that species are distributed independently of each other, with overlaps in distribution the result of coincidence, not mutual interdependence. Gleason advocated an individualistic approach to understanding communities and succession, arguing that specific conditions and random events could alter the course of succession. By Gleason's model, the outcome of succession was not nearly as neat and orderly as that proposed by Clements, and instead local interactions and conditions would influence the pattern of community change that was observed. Gleason and Clements had a difficult professional relationship, and there was heated debate between them and among their supporters.

Today, most modern ecologists hold a view more similar to that of Gleason than Clements, although, interestingly, many members of the general public (and many ecology students) seem to fall (initially) toward the side of Clements. One of the key observations, in contrast to Clements's model, is that succession does not always result in the same climax community, even under similar environmental conditions. Instead, a system may have a number of alternative stable states, depending upon which specific mechanisms occur during succession. Substantial research has shown that a variety of processes—such as **dispersal limitation**, influence of herbivores and predators, and simple chance events—can have dramatic impacts on the direction and speed of successional pathways. Though the climax concept is useful in understanding the general concepts of succession, it should not be taken to imply that succession results in a specific community with deterministic distributions and abundances of species. Instead, although there are repeatable patterns in community structure, communities are groups of individuals rather than a *superorganism* that follows a predictable developmental pathway.

Frank Egler was among the first to clearly articulate the contrasting ideas related to succession presented by Gleason and Clements (Egler 1954), and, by doing so, Egler ushered in a new wave of research in community ecology. Egler presented two alternatives as to how succession might work in a given location. First was **relay floristics**, which was the name Egler gave to Clements's views of how succession operated. In relay floristics, one group of species colonizes an area immediately following disturbance. These pioneer species are then replaced by a second wave of species, and so on, until the climax community is reached. (Think of these waves of species like runners in a relay race, each handing off the baton to the next wave.) A critical point of this model is that each stage facilitates the establishment of the next wave, resulting in very little overlap of species distributions in the different successional stages. As an alternative model, Egler presented **initial floristics**. In this model, you still find that different species are dominant in different time periods following disturbance, but species occurrences can overlap greatly throughout succession. Most important is the idea that many species, even those we associate with late successional communities, may establish immediately following a disturbance. This pattern appears to occur in much of the western boreal forest in Canada. For example, white spruce (*Picea glauca*), a species

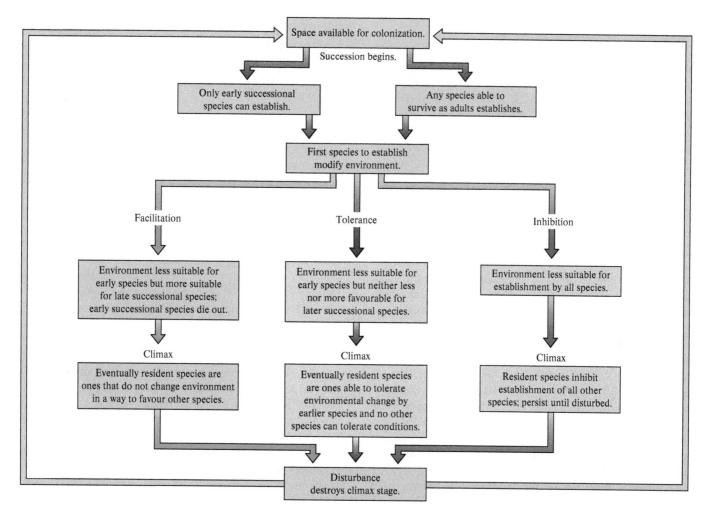

Figure 18.25 Alternative successional mechanisms.
Data from Connell and Slatyer 1977.

commonly associated with the climax community of the western mixedwood boreal forest, can often establish immediately following fires. The plants can remain as saplings for decades, when they may eventually become dominant species (Peters et al. 2006). Peters and his colleagues also show that in some boreal stands, establishment of spruce can occur decades after fire, supporting the idea of delayed regeneration. The fact that the same species of tree can show different patterns of regeneration in nearby forest stands is strong support for Gleason's individualistic concept and soundly refutes Clements's notion that species replacement is clean and orderly.

Following Egler, Joseph Connell and Ralph Slatyer (1977) provided what remains the unifying concepts for the mechanisms of succession. They presented three models of succession: (1) facilitation, (2) tolerance, and (3) inhibition (fig. 18.25). This paper has stimulated substantial research, and we explore the models here.

Facilitation

The **facilitation model** proposes that many species may attempt to colonize newly available space, but only certain species, with particular characteristics, are able to establish themselves. Species capable of colonizing new sites are called pioneer species. According to the facilitation model, pioneer species modify the environment in such a way that it becomes less suitable for themselves and more suitable for species characteristic of later successional stages. In other words, these early successional species facilitate colonization by later successional species, at the expense of themselves. Replacement of early successional species by later successional species continues in this way until resident species no longer facilitate colonization by other species. This final stage in a chain of facilitations and replacements is the climax community.

It is critical to understand that there is no "intent" on the part of early species to facilitate their own replacement. Instead, this facilitation is a consequence of their own niche requirements and the impacts of their growth on local conditions. For example, seeds that require high light levels to germinate will do well following a disturbance. However, the growth of those plants will reduce light levels, reducing their own ability to germinate underneath the maternal plants. Their growth would also facilitate the germination of plants that require low light levels for their seeds.

Tolerance

According to the **tolerance model**, the initial stages of colonization are not limited to a few pioneer species. Juveniles of species dominating at climax can be present at even the earliest stages of succession (e.g., initial floristics). In this model, species colonizing early in succession do not facilitate colonization by species characteristic of later successional stages. They do not modify the environment in a way that makes it more suitable for later successional species. Later successional species are simply those tolerant of environmental conditions created earlier in succession. The climax community is established when the list of tolerant species has been exhausted.

Inhibition

Like the tolerance model, the **inhibition model** assumes that any species that can survive in an area as an adult can colonize the area during the early stages of succession. However, the inhibition model proposes that the early occupants of an area modify the environment in a way that makes the area less suitable for both early and late successional species. Simply, early arrivals inhibit colonization by later arrivals. Later successional species can only invade an area if space is opened up by disturbance of early colonists. In this case, succession culminates in a community made up of long-lived, resistant species. The inhibition model assumes that late successional species come to dominate an area simply because they live a long time and resist damage by physical and biological factors.

Which of these models does the weight of evidence from nature support? As you will see in the following examples, most studies of succession support the facilitation model, the inhibition model, or some combination of the two.

Mechanisms of Succession Following Deglaciation

The complex mechanisms underlying succession were well demonstrated by the detailed studies of Chapin's research team (1994). They combined field observations, field experiments, and greenhouse experiments to explore the mechanisms underlying primary succession at Glacier Bay, Alaska. They found that no single factor or mechanism determines the pattern of primary succession at Glacier Bay, Alaska.

Figure 18.26 summarizes the complex influences of four successional stages on establishment and growth of spruce seedlings. During the pioneer stage, there is some inhibition of spruce germination. Any spruce seedlings that become established, however, have high survivorship but low growth rates. Spruce seedling growth rates and nitrogen supplies are increased somewhat during the *Dryas* stage. However, this facilitation during the *Dryas* stage is offset by poor germination and survivorship, along with increased seed predation and mortality.

Strong facilitation of spruce seedlings first occurs in the alder stage. During this stage, germination and survivorship remain low and seed mortality, root competition, and light competition are significant. However, these inhibitory effects are offset by increased soil organic matter, nitrogen, mycorrhizal activity, and growth rates. The net effect of alder on spruce seedlings is facilitation.

In the spruce stage, the net influence on spruce seedlings is inhibitory. Germination is high during the spruce stage but this is counterbalanced by several inhibitory effects. Growth rates and survivorship are low and nitrogen availability is reduced. In addition, seed predation and mortality, root competition, and light competition are all high.

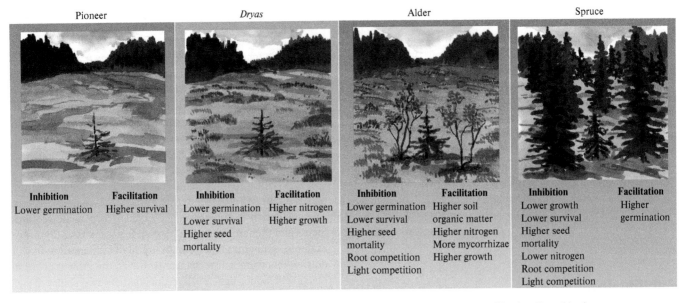

Figure 18.26 Inhibition and facilitation of spruce during the major successional stages at Glacier Bay, Alaska.
Data from Chapin et al. 1994.

These results remind us that nature is far more complex and subtle than models such as that proposed by Connell and Slatyer. However, even in other systems, we still find facilitation, inhibition, and tolerance to be useful categories for understanding the mechanisms of succession.

Successional Mechanisms in the Rocky Intertidal Zone

What mechanisms drive succession by algae and barnacles in the intertidal boulder fields studied by Sousa? The alternative mechanisms proposed by Sousa were those of Connell and Slatyer: facilitation, tolerance, and inhibition. Sousa used a series of experiments to test for the occurrence of these alternative mechanisms. He conducted his first experiments on 25 cm² plots on concrete blocks placed in the intertidal zone. In this experiment, Sousa explored the influence of *Ulva* on recruitment by later successional red algae by keeping *Ulva* out of four experimental plots and leaving four other control plots undisturbed. This experiment showed that *Ulva* strongly inhibits recruitment by red algae (fig. 18.27).

In a second set of experiments, Sousa studied the effects of the middle successional species *Gigartina leptorhynchos* and *Gelidium* on establishment of the late successional *Gigartina canaliculata*. He selectively removed middle successional species from a set of four experimental plots while simultaneously monitoring another set of four control plots. These experiments were conducted in 100 cm² areas on natural substrate, dominated by either *G. leptorhynchos* or *Gelidium*. When Sousa removed these middle successional species, the experimental plots were quickly reinvaded by *Ulva* and eventually by significantly higher densities of *G. canaliculata*, the late successional species. The effects of these successional algae support the inhibition model for succession.

The inhibition model of succession proposes that early successional species are more vulnerable to a variety of physical and biological factors causing mortality. If algal succession in the intertidal boulder fields studied by Sousa follows the

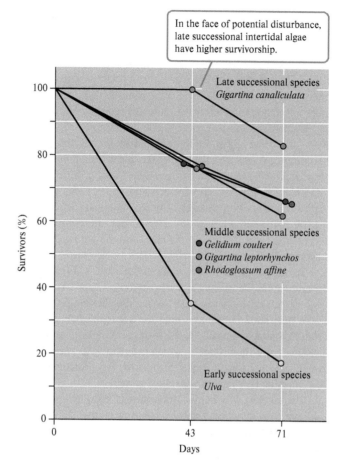

Figure 18.28 Survivorship of early, middle, and late successional species.
Data from Sousa 1979b.

inhibition model, then early successional species should be more vulnerable to various sources of mortality.

Sousa addressed the question of relative vulnerability of algal species with several experiments. In one, he studied the relative vulnerability of intertidal algae to physical stress, especially exposure to air, intense sunlight, and drying wind. He studied the vulnerabilities of the five dominant algal species in his study area by tagging 30 individuals of each species and monitoring their survivorship for two months during a period when low tide occurred during the afternoon, when air temperatures are highest. The results of this study show that the early successional species, *Ulva*, had lower survivorship than the middle or late successional species (fig. 18.28).

Sousa also designed several different field and laboratory experiments to explore differential vulnerability to herbivores. The results of all these experiments indicated that the early successional species *Ulva* is more vulnerable to herbivores than later successional species. These results and those of the several other manipulations performed by Sousa support the inhibition model of succession.

Some studies of intertidal succession, however, have demonstrated facilitation. Teresa Turner (1983) pointed out that the bulk of intertidal studies had supported the inhibition model

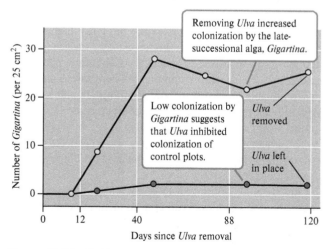

Figure 18.27 Evidence for inhibition of later successional species.
Data from Sousa 1979a.

and that the few studies documenting facilitation had shown that facilitation was not obligate. However, she went on to report a case of obligate facilitation during intertidal succession.

Turner described the successional sequence at her Oregon study site as follows. High waves during winter storms create open space in the lower intertidal zone. In May, these open areas are colonized by *Ulva*, the same early colonist of open areas in Sousa's study area, over 1,000 km south of Turner's study site. *Ulva* is eventually replaced by several middle successional species, especially the red algae *Rhodomela larix*, *Cryptosiphonia woodii*, and *Odonthalia floccosa*. Through this middle stage, the pattern of succession appears much as that in the intertidal boulder field studied by Sousa. However, in the lower intertidal area studied by Turner, the dominant late successional species was not an alga but a flowering plant, the surfgrass *Phyllospadix scouleri*.

Turner proposed that recruitment of *Phyllospadix* by seeds depends upon the presence of macroscopic algae. The seeds of *Phyllospadix* are large and bear two parallel, barbed projections. These projections hook and hold the seeds to attached algae. From this attached position, the seed germinates, first producing leaves and then roots by which the plant will anchor itself to the underlying rock. Once established, *Phyllospadix* spreads and consolidates space by vegetative growth.

Turner tested whether recruitment by *Phyllospadix* is facilitated by attached algae by clearing eight 0.25 m² plots of all attached algae. She then compared the number of new *Phyllospadix* seeds in these plots with the number in eight nearby control plots. The control plots remained undisturbed with their algal populations intact except that all *Phyllospadix* seeds were removed at the start of the study. When Turner checked the removal and control plots the following spring, she found a total of 48 seeds: 46 on the control plots (all attached to *Rhodomela*), and 2 on the removal plots (fig. 18.29). Both seeds on the removal plots were attached to two isolated branches of *Rhodomela* that had sprouted from remnant holdfasts.

During three years, Turner systematically searched an area of about 200 m² for *Phyllospadix* seeds and found a total of 298. All were attached to algae. These data support the hypothesis that middle successional algae facilitate recruitment and establishment of *Phyllospadix* and that this facilitation is obligate. As a consequence of Turner's study and others, we can say that facilitation and inhibition occur during intertidal succession. Other research, which we review in the next example, has shown that facilitation and inhibition also occur during forest succession.

Successional Mechanisms in Forests

We now turn from succession in the marine intertidal zone, a place where succession occurs in a matter of a few years, to succession in boreal forests. Forest succession takes hundreds of years to complete and so cannot be observed directly within the period of a typical research project. Therefore, most research on the mechanisms driving succession in forests has focused on the earliest stages.

Mechanisms of Succession in a Boreal Forest

We have already described how succession in boreal forests often results in a transition from hardwood species, such as aspen, toward dominance by softwood species, such as spruce and fir. Why? We can think of this issue from an evolutionary perspective. There is certainly no fitness benefit gained by aspen when it is replaced by spruce (rather than its own offspring), so why do aspen plants let it happen? The answer may seem familiar. Specific life-history traits possessed by aspen allow it to perform some ecological processes extremely well (such as recovery following fire), but, at the same time, it is unable to perform other ecological processes. Aspen, as it turns out, has seedlings that are shade-intolerant, while spruce has shade-tolerant seedlings (chapter 5). Aspen trees also produce very small seeds (for a tree) able to travel long distances. Following fire, the amount of sunlight reaching the forest floor is very high. Any existing aspen trees will re-sprout, and high dispersal ability of aspen seeds also means there is a good probability of seeds in the area that will quickly germinate. These seedlings and sprouts grow rapidly, soon casting deep shade onto the forest floor. During this period of rapid aspen (and other pioneer species) growth, there has been increased opportunity for the more poorly dispersed seeds to enter the community. Seeds of spruce and other species are able to germinate, and seedlings are able to establish themselves in this shade. Seeds of aspen and other species cannot. As a result, beneath the canopy of aspen, you will find young spruce and fir trees, not aspen. In other words, aspen recovery following fire actually results in inhibition of further aspen recruitment, but not of spruce.

At this point in the growth of the forest, two events may occur. First, the aspen trees can grow to maturity, and then, like all organisms, some individual trees will die. What happens in the wake of these deaths? The small spruce trees that have been growing beneath the aspen will quickly grow to fill the gap in the canopy made by the death of the aspen. Over time, this can lead to dominance by the softwood tree species. But, as we have

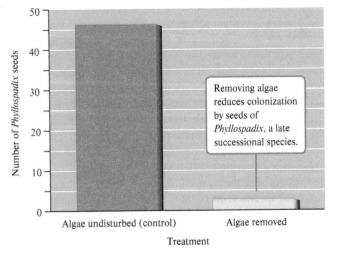

Figure 18.29 Evidence for facilitation of colonization by an intertidal plant, *Phyllospadix scouleri*.
Data from Turner 1983.

said before, succession is not inevitable and communities do not develop or progress. This is very similar to our understanding of evolution. Evolution does not move toward a particular goal (does not optimize traits), but it does result in change. In the boreal system, one clear reminder that succession is not inevitable is the reality that fire can burn the aspen stand well before spruce has become dominant. Thus the second event that may occur is fire.

If the forest burns again, the floor is once again an excellent place for re-sprouting and regrowth by the aspen. If spruce seeds are still available, seedlings will once again establish. The frequency of fires is critical in shaping the community structure. If fires are frequent, regions of the boreal forest may never become dominated by softwood species. If fires are rare, the hardwood species may be missing, replaced by softwood species. Because of variation in fire frequency, and because of interspecific differences in life histories, the boreal forest is a mosaic of different communities, interspersed throughout the landscape. We will discuss more about the role of landscapes in ecology in chapter 21.

As complicated as the dynamics of boreal forest succession may seem, we have yet to discuss one critical issue. What role do the plants themselves have in influencing whether there is a fire? At first, this may seem a ridiculous idea—lightning strikes are the dominant form of fire initiation, and these are driven by weather patterns. As important as plants are, they do not control the weather. However, Meg Krawchuk, while a graduate student at the University of Alberta, and her colleagues have shown that both climate and forest composition can influence the probability of fire initiation in the boreal mixedwoods (Krawchuk et al. 2006). The research team analyzed an 11-year database of fire histories for 91,000 km^2 of mixedwood forest in central-eastern Alberta. Using detailed information on for-est composition, meteorological records, and whether any fires occurred, they were able to construct statistical models that determined the relative contribution of both climate and forest composition on the probability of fire initiation. As expected, fires were more likely to occur in areas that were hotter and drier than those that were cooler and wetter. However, even after accounting for this climate effect, there was a substantial impact of forest composition. Specifically, the probability of fire initiation decreased as forests moved from spruce dominance toward aspen dominance. In other words, aspen were inhibiting fires, while spruce were facilitating them.

The result may be a bit surprising, particularly given that aspen can only successfully recruit following a disturbance! It may not be quite as hard to understand if we instead focus on the spruce. As we discussed previously, their seeds will establish soon after a fire, and in many cases cones cannot even open unless a fire occurs (lodgepole and jack pine also exhibit this interesting fire-dependence). It may make sense that spruce contains a variety of flammable resins and has a growth structure (fuels near the forest floor) that promotes fire, as fire itself is necessary for spruce to most efficiently complete its life cycle! The end result, however, is that spruce facilitates its own replacement, albeit temporary, by aspen. It is because of patterns like this that most ecologists do not believe in the concept of a single climax community and, instead, see communities as dynamic.

In fact, in many communities ecologists do not necessarily believe that there is even a single climax community; instead, depending upon local conditions and chance events, there may be alternative stable states. Under this model, a single piece of land can persist as alternative types of communities, depending upon some set of factors. This issue will be more fully explored in our discussion of landscape ecology, chapter 21.

ECOLOGICAL TOOLS AND APPROACHES

Using Repeat Photography to Detect Long-Term Change

While some graduate students look over their shoulders, Raymond Turner and Julio Betancourt of the U.S. Geological Survey carefully examine a photograph of a desert landscape taken about 100 years earlier. Their goal is to take another photograph of the same scene to document long-term change in the plant community. To do so they must return to the same location and take a photograph from exactly the same spot.

The larger landmarks, such as hills and ridges, will help them find the general location, but they need finer-scale reference points to locate the exact spot. Turner finally indicates a small boulder about 30 cm in diameter in the foreground, saying, "This should get us close and those small junipers will help orient the cameras." Betancourt agrees. The students are incredulous that someone should think that they can find a small boulder and two small trees after a century. However, long practice at repeat photography has taught Turner what can be found after a century in the arid lands of the American Southwest.

A field trip later takes the group to the general area of the site. After a careful search, Betancourt finds the remains of the two junipers. They have died sometime during the last half-century. Next, Turner finds the small boulder. They use a few more landmarks to orient the camera and then position it within about 1 m of the spot from which the century-old photo was taken.

Using techniques such as these, Ray Turner and his colleagues have produced a useful photographic record of vegetation changes from throughout the southwestern United States and northwestern Mexico. For instance, a series of repeat photographs beginning in 1907 document substantial vegetation change in MacDougal Crater in northern Sonora, Mexico (Turner 1990). The crater is about

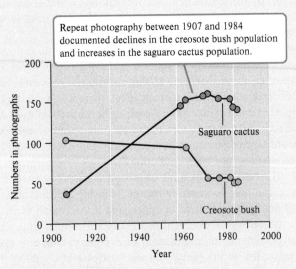

Repeat photography between 1907 and 1984 documented declines in the creosote bush population and increases in the saguaro cactus population.

Saguaro cactus

Creosote bush

Figure 18.30 Changes in populations of creosote bushes and saguaro cacti determined by repeat photography.

137 m deep and was formed by a volcanic eruption about 200,000 years ago. MacDougal Crater is protected by its steep walls from livestock and other human impacts. This protection removes the possibility that observed changes in vegetation might be the result of human influences.

With repeat photographs, Turner was able to quantify changes in the plant community of MacDougal Crater. One of the changes he documented was a decrease in the population of *Larrea* and an increase in the population of saguaros (fig. 18.30). From 1907 to 1986 the number of creosote bushes (*Larrea tridentata*) in Turner's study area decreased from 103 to 48. Over the same interval, the number of saguaros increased from 38 to 159 in 1972 and then declined to 140 by 1986.

Some of the most important questions asked by ecologists concern changes in the distribution and abundance of organisms. Repeat photography is an easily overlooked tool that is helping to document changes in plant distribution and abundance during the past century.

CONCEPT 18.5 REVIEW

1. What is the role of disturbance in the Connell and Slatyer succession model?

2. Suppose *Gigartina* had colonized the plots where Sousa had removed *Ulva* and where he had left

Ulva in place at the same rates. This result would be consistent with which successional model?

3. How does spruce inhibit its own replacement by aspen?

SUMMARY

Natural communities experience a diversity of disturbances, which can have immediate and prolonged impacts on community structure and ecological function. *Succession* is the gradual change in plant and animal communities in an area following disturbance or the creation of new substrate. *Primary succession* occurs on newly exposed geological substrates not significantly modified by organisms. *Secondary succession* occurs in areas where disturbance destroys a community without destroying the soil. Succession may end with a climax community whose populations remain stable until disrupted by disturbance. In other cases, communities may never recover, and instead persist in an alternative state.

18.1 Intermediate levels of disturbance promote higher diversity.

Joseph Connell (1975, 1978) proposed that high diversity is a consequence of continually changing conditions, not of competitive accommodation at equilibrium. He predicted that intermediate levels of disturbance would foster higher levels of diversity (fig. 18.31). At intermediate levels of disturbance,

a wide array of species can colonize open habitats, but there is not enough time for the most effective competitors to exclude the other species. Wayne Sousa (1979a), who studied the effects of disturbance on the diversity of sessile marine algae and invertebrates growing on intertidal boulders, found support for the intermediate disturbance hypothesis. Diversity in prairie vegetation also appears to be higher in areas receiving intermediate levels of disturbance. Across many systems there is no widespread support for a general relationship between disturbance and diversity. Instead, observed patterns are due to interactions among life-history traits of the resident species, and the details of the disturbance they encounter.

18.2 Community stability may be due to lack of disturbance or community resistance or resilience in the face of disturbance.

Ecologists generally define *stability* as the persistence of a community or ecosystem in the face of disturbance (fig 18.31). Resistance is the ability of a community or ecosystem to maintain structure and/or function in the face of potential disturbance.

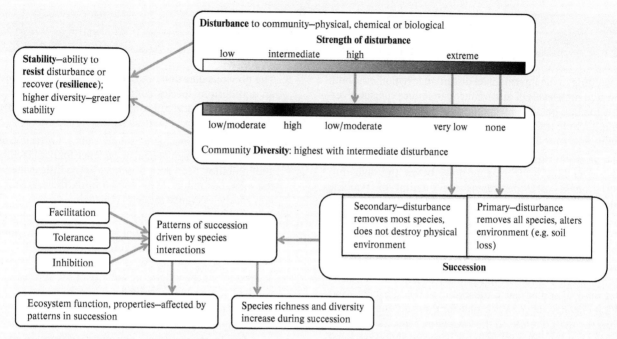

Figure 18.31 Concept map for chapter 18.

The ability to bounce back after disturbance is called resilience. A resilient community or ecosystem may be completely disrupted by disturbance but quickly return to its former state. Studies of the Park Grass Experiment suggest that our perception of stability is affected by the scale of measurement. Many studies suggest that resilience and resistance are higher in more biologically diverse communities, although this is not a universal pattern.

18.3 Community changes during succession include increases in species diversity and changes in species composition.

Primary forest succession around Glacier Bay may require about 1,500 years, while secondary forest succession on the Piedmont Plateau takes about 150 years. Meanwhile, succession in the boreal forest requires 100 to 200 years, and succession within a desert stream occurs in less than two months. Over even longer time periods, some lakes will undergo succession, becoming fens, bogs, or forests. Despite the great differences in the time required, all these successional sequences show increased species diversity over time.

18.4 Ecosystem changes during succession include increases in biomass, primary production, respiration, and nutrient retention.

Succession at Glacier Bay produces changes in several ecosystem properties, including increased soil depth, organic content, and moisture. Over the same successional sequence, several soil properties show decreases, including soil bulk density and phosphorus concentration. During ecosystem development on lava flows in Hawaii, organic matter and nitrogen content of soils increased over the first 150,000 years and then declined by 1.4 million years. Weatherable mineral phosphorus in soils was largely depleted on lava flows 20,000 years old. The percentage of soil phosphorus in refractory form made up the majority of phosphorus on lava flows 20,000 years old or older. Succession at the Hubbard Brook Experimental Forest increased nutrient retention by the forest ecosystem. A model of biomass accumulation in forest succession predicts that a forest will eventually reach steady state with respect to total biomass. The model may be applicable to other ecosystems, and was consistent with succession in Sycamore Creek, Arizona. Several ecosystem properties change predictably during succession in this creek, including biomass, primary production, respiration, and nitrogen retention.

18.5 Mechanisms that drive ecological succession include facilitation, tolerance, and inhibition.

Most studies of succession support the facilitation model, the inhibition model, or some combination of the two (fig. 18.31). Both facilitation and inhibition occur during intertidal succession. Facilitation and inhibition also occur during secondary and primary forest succession.

Succession is a very long process, and thus studies through time are critical. Ecologists use a diversity of techniques, including chronosequences, long-term longitudinal studies, and repeat photography.

REVIEW QUESTIONS

1. According to the intermediate disturbance hypothesis, both low and high levels of disturbance can reduce species diversity. Explain possible mechanisms producing this relationship. Include trade-offs between competitive and dispersal abilities in your discussion.

2. The dams that have been built on many rivers often stabilize river flow by increasing flows below the dam during droughts and decreasing the amount of flooding during periods of high rainfall. Using the intermediate disturbance hypothesis, predict how stabilized flows would affect the diversity of river organisms below reservoirs.

3. The successional studies in Sycamore Creek produced patterns of variation in diversity that differed significantly from those observed during primary succession at Glacier Bay or algal and barnacle succession in the intertidal zone. What may have been responsible for these different results? How might differences in the longevity of species have contributed to the different patterns observed by researchers? (Hint: Think about what we might observe in the other communities if they were studied for a longer period of time.)

4. If a landscape is disturbed, it will undergo secondary succession following a fairly predictable pathway with respect to process, but perhaps not with respect to equilibrium species composition. In other words, if the same landscape is disturbed and undergoes succession repeatedly, the equilibrium species composition may differ each time. These differences can represent alternative stable states. Why do these alternative states exist?

5. The previous question, and many others, presupposes that an equilibrium species composition is real. Is an equilibrium state a meaningful concept? If so, under what circumstances? And over what time scales?

6. In the studies of mechanisms underlying succession, ecologists have found a great deal of evidence for both facilitation and inhibition. However, they have found little evidence for the tolerance model. Why do you think there is little support for the tolerance model?

7. Species have come and gone in response to changing global climates during the history of the earth. Some of the mass extinctions of the past have resulted in the deaths of over 90% of existing species. What do these biological changes suggest about the long-term stability of the species composition of climax communities?

8. Succession seems to lead to predictable changes in community and ecosystem structure. Predict the characteristics of a frequently disturbed community/ecosystem versus a largely undisturbed community/ecosystem. What do your predictions suggest about a future biosphere increasingly disturbed by a growing human population? How does the intermediate disturbance hypothesis figure into your answer?

9. Describe the successional pathway of the boreal forest. Is there a climax community that is truly stable?

10. In lake succession, shallow lakes can be converted into bogs or fens, or into a drier terrestrial habitat, such as a forest. What factors do you think are likely to influence the direction of succession for a given body of water?

Photo 36026148 © Debra Tosca–Dreamstime.com.

CHAPTER 19   PRODUCTION AND ENERGY FLOW

CHAPTER CONCEPTS

19.1 Primary production is the gateway for energy and nutrients entering food webs. Energy and nutrients will be transferred and transformed as they flow through food webs.
Concept 19.1 Review

19.2 Terrestrial primary production is generally limited by temperature and moisture.
Ecology in Action: Interactions Across Community Boundaries
Concept 19.2 Review

19.3 Aquatic primary production is generally limited by nutrient availability.
Concept 19.3 Review

19.4 Energy losses limit the number of trophic levels in ecosystems.
Concept 19.4 Review

19.5 A variety of species can influence rates of primary production in aquatic and terrestrial ecosystems.
Concept 19.5 Review

Ecological Tools and Approaches: Using Stable Isotope Analysis to Trace Energy Flow Through Ecosystems Across Community Boundaries
Summary
Review Questions

For many of you, as you come toward the end of this book, spring may be in the air (if it's −20°C and spring is a long way off, know that we feel for you). As I write this, buds are on the trees, and the daffodils are trying their best to bloom. A few robins have been hopping around the backyard hunting worms, and that skunk I mentioned back in chapter 13 is tearing up the yard looking for grubs (fig. 19.1). When I walk down to the lakeshore, the winter waves have washed a lot of *Cladophora* ashore. As the weather starts to warm up, bacteria and fungi will cause the algae to decay. It's not too bad now, but anything that washes up during the height of summer will stink when it begins to rot.

When I drive up the Niagara escarpment into farm country, I don't see a lot of action yet. But there are quite a few dairy farms, and soon they'll be spreading manure. Growing up, I did the spreading so it's kind of a weirdly comforting smell to me, but the smell of ammonia and other nitrogenous wastes can drive most urbanites back to the cities, which have their own weird smells.

What are we really perceiving with these sights and smells of spring? These are the visual and olfactory cues that energy is flowing again. No, it never really stopped in winter, but it certainly slowed down. We are witnessing bursts of **primary production**, plants growing and turning carbon dioxide into biomass. We are witnessing **secondary production** with the first tentative nibbling of new plant growth by hungry herbivores that made it through winter. We are seeing evidence of energy flow from worm to robin, grub to skunk, and dead algae to bacteria and fungi. We are smelling the by-products of respiration, including the nitrogen waste. And, in some cases, we may be smelling the outcome of other modes of respiration, such as sulfate reduction generating sulfide and its attendant rotten egg smell.

Ironically, when I first broach the subject of energy flow in class, much of the class energy dissipates. It may seem boring at first glance because it is less clearly about what the bugs and bunnies do and more about the results of bugs and bunnies going about their business. But, if you give this topic a chance, I think you'll see how production and energy flow (this chapter)

and nutrient and elemental cycling (chapter 20) really underpin not only ecology but biology more broadly.

Ecosystem Processes: Flow of Energy and Nutrients

Primary production is the gateway for energy and nutrients entering food webs. Energy and nutrients will be transferred and transformed as they flow through food webs. The first thing all living things must do is eat, or they stop being living things. But even when they become dead things, they still participate in the flow of energy and nutrients we'll discuss here. We'll spend much of this chapter discussing primary production, which is the fixation of carbon by autotrophs in an ecosystem. Most commonly, these autotrophs are plants, algae, and cyanobacteria that carry out photosynthetic autotrophy, although in some ecosystems other modes of autotrophy may be important for fixing carbon and allowing chemical energy (as sugars) into the food web (chapter 7). We'll discuss these in more detail here and again in chapter 20 as they pertain to nutrient cycles.

Gross primary production is the total amount of energy fixed by all the autotrophs in the ecosystem, independent of any costs associated with either energy fixation or basal metabolism of the organisms. **Net primary production (NPP)** is the amount of energy left over after autotrophs have met their own energetic needs by primary producers, and it is the amount of energy available to the consumers in an ecosystem. In most systems, NPP is the difference between photosynthesis and respiration in net primary producers. Ecologists have measured primary production in a variety of ways but mainly as the rate of carbon uptake by primary producers or by the amount of biomass or oxygen produced.

Energy fixed through primary production eventually moves from the primary producers to other parts of the ecosystem. In chapter 7, we examined the biology of herbivores, detritivores, and carnivores. In chapters 14 and 15 we discussed the ecology of exploitation, and in chapter 17 we used food webs as a means of representing the trophic structure of communities. Ecosystem ecologists are also concerned with trophic networks, as the outcome of feeding is the movement of energy through an ecosystem. Ecosystem ecologists have simplified the trophic structure of ecosystems by typically arranging species into trophic levels based on the predominant source of their nutrition (i.e., where they get their energy). A **trophic level** is a position in a food web and is determined by the number of transfers of energy from primary producers to that level. We introduced this concept in chapter 17, including the fuzziness of trophic levels and how they are determined. We also discussed some of the advantages of aggregating feeding relationships in understanding community food webs. In ecosystem ecology, where we are primarily concerned with flow of energy and materials, there is some necessary simplification in how we represent trophic structure.

Figure 19.1   A skunk hunting for grubs.
©iStockphoto.com/Geoff Kuchera.

Primary producers occupy the first trophic level in ecosystems since they convert inorganic forms of energy, principally light, into biomass. Herbivores are often called *primary consumers* and occupy the second trophic level. The energy transferred as food from plants to herbivores supports the growth of herbivore biomass, or secondary production. Carnivores are *secondary consumers* and occupy the third trophic level. Carnivores that feed on other carnivores occupy a fourth trophic level. Since each trophic level may contain several species, in some cases hundreds, an ecosystem perspective simplifies trophic structure in comparison to trophic networks and food webs (fig. 19.2). Consuming members of all trophic levels are parasites and detritivores, which themselves are often prey for other consumers.

It is important to remember that such energetic descriptions of ecosystems are gross simplifications of what is actually found in natural systems. As we saw in chapter 17, food webs are complex; many animals feed at more than one level and so cannot themselves be placed into a discrete trophic level. Nonetheless, the trophic level approach is a useful means for organizing our understanding of energy flow within an ecosystem. Because of its importance and because rates of primary production vary substantially from one ecosystem to another, ecosystem ecologists study the factors controlling rates of primary production in ecosystems. In this chapter, we discuss the major patterns of variation in primary production in terrestrial and aquatic ecosystems and key experiments designed to determine the mechanisms producing those patterns. We then discuss how energy flows through different trophic levels, and how these processes can be altered through the activity of organisms within the ecosystem. Before we start this journey, however, we need to consider relationships between energy and nutrient flow, and why particular ecosystem processes happen.

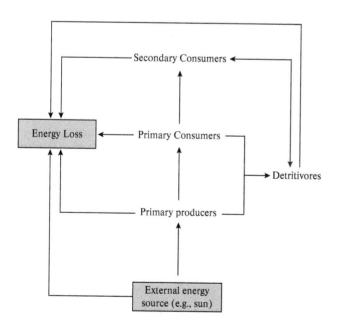

Figure 19.2   From an energetic perspective, food webs can be organized by understanding from where each trophic level obtains its energy. Presented here is a system containing three trophic levels.

Primary Production and the Redfield Ratio

Let's begin by understanding that plants are not altruistic. They do not fix carbon and produce energy for the benefit of herbivores. This is a simplification, and you know from chapter 15 that plants can form mutualistic relationships with animals and fungi, providing energy in exchange for nutrients or improved pollination efficiency. However, the reason plants fix carbon is often lost in the shuffle. Too often we think of plants as making organic carbon and animals as consuming it. But plants, like other organisms, need sugars as their fuel for making ATP and need organic molecules as their building blocks for producing biomass. We talk about the sun as the source of energy for plants, and it is, although indirectly. Sunlight is the source of energy used to oxidize H_2O, which is coupled to the reduction of CO_2 to produce sugars. The sugars are later oxidized to generate ATP through cellular respiration. The ATP is, then, the currency of energy used most commonly for driving cellular processes. Plants will fix more carbon than they need in order to support ATP production, and this extra energy is allocated to plant growth, reproduction, and maintenance—until animals come along and eat them.

Energy flow is usually considered in the context of primary production, respiration, and trophic transfer supporting secondary production. This usually begets a simplification. We talk about energy flow in a carbon context. The problem with this is that carbon cycling is intimately coupled with cycling of other elements. When new organic matter is produced (primary production), it always involves the flow of N, P, H, O, S, and other elements as well. So energy flow and nutrient cycling have to be considered together. In this chapter and in chapter 20, we admittedly fall into the simplification of discussing elemental cycles individually. We do so to help you understand them. But at the outset of this chapter, we wish to firmly plant the idea that these other elements are related to energy flow, and we will make these connections repeatedly in this chapter and in chapter 20.

You will be familiar with the basic photosynthetic equation:

$$6CO_2 + 6H_2O \rightarrow C_6H_{12}O_6 + 6O_2 \quad \Delta G = 686 \; kcal$$

or the reverse equation for aerobic respiration with a $\Delta G = -686 \; kcal$. The production of organic matter is not an energetically favourable process, as indicated by the positive value for change in free energy. It requires the input of energy—in this case, sunlight. The oxidation of organic matter during respiration, however, is energetically favourable, and the energy gained is used to do some work, such as producing ATP.

When plants are fixing carbon and building organic molecules, they are also incorporating other elements. Figure 19.3 shows a photosynthetic leaf and the various materials that it incorporates into biomass while carrying out photosynthesis. The plant then respires some of this organic matter to generate ATP. This regenerates inorganic carbon, nitrogen, phosphorus, and sulfur, which may be reused by the plant to make new biomass. When the plant is consumed by the cow (or any

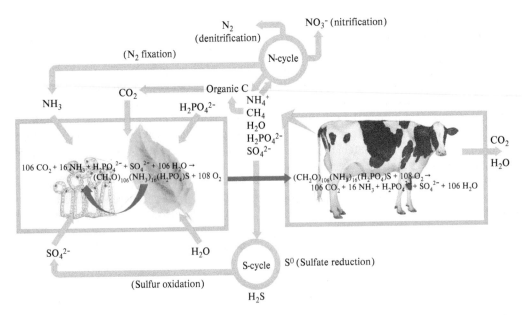

Figure 19.3 Energy flow and nutrient cycling are intimately coupled. Respiration will recycle the elements incorporated into biomass during primary production.
Leaf: Dorling Kindersley RF/Getty Images; Cow: GlobalP/Getty Images.

other animal), some of the plant biomass will be converted into bovine biomass (secondary production), but most will be respired by the cow to generate ATP. The cow, like the plant, is recycling N, P, and S.

Figure 19.3 includes a more comprehensive equation for primary production then we gave above. The figure is a bit complicated, but it is a good reference when we talk about alternate modes of primary production and respiration and when we talk about carbon, nitrogen, and sulfur cycles in chapter 20. You will notice that whenever new carbon is fixed, a smaller amount of N is also incorporated to build such macromolecules as amino acids and nucleotide bases. An even smaller amount of P and S are incorporated to produce phospholipids, nucleotides, amino acids, and other molecules. This is a general form equation. There is some variation in the ratio of these elements and in the form of the element used. For example, most bacteria, green algae, and many plants will most effectively use ammonium, while marine diatoms will primarily use nitrate.

So where do the elemental ratios in this photosynthesis equation come from, you ask? More than 80 years ago, Alfred C. Redfield reported measurements of nitrate, phosphate, and dissolved oxygen measured at various depths in the Atlantic, Pacific, and Indian Oceans. Despite the broad geographic and geophysical range across which samples were collected, the ratios among these elements had a striking consistency. Redfield inferred that this consistency in water chemistry might result "if the different samples contained the products of the complete disintegration and oxidation of organic matter of a similar composition" (Redfield 1934, p. 183). In other words, sea water might reflect the elemental ratio of organic matter. The Redfield ratio, 106C:16N:1P, has proven to be foundational for modern marine biogeochemistry. Redfield later proposed that

the key to the ratio's stability was the cycling of nitrogen into and out of bioavailable forms as other nutrients became more or less limiting to growth (Redfield 1958). A simplified version of the nitrogen cycle is included in figure 19.3. For example, if ammonia is used up, but there is enough P to support algal growth, marine diazotrophic bacteria might fix nitrogen, converting N_2 into a bioavailable form. This allows the full use of any available phosphate:

$$106\,CO_2 + 8N_2 + H_2PO_4^- + 130\,H_2O + H^+ \rightarrow (CH_2O)_{106} + 118\,O_2$$

While there is substantial variation in elemental ratios for some species, or across nutrient regimes, the Redfield ratio is a good first approximation for composition of not only marine algae biomass but terrestrial plant biomass as well. The ratio relates C, N, and P but has been extended to include other elements. Here, we have expanded it to include S. As an approximation, the Redfield ratio allows us to predict how much of various other elements might be swept up in the flow of energy from one trophic level to the next, and how much might be regenerated by respiration.

Alternative Modes of Primary Production

In photosynthesis, oxidation of H_2O is coupled with the reduction of CO_2. The net change in free energy is positive (not favourable), and so photosynthesis requires an input of photon energy to make it happen. However, other oxidation reactions can be paired with CO_2 reduction that are energetically favourable. For example, the free energy gained in oxidizing ammonium (NH_4^+) or methane (CH_4) can be used to make organic carbon and to support growth of nitrifiers and methanotrophs, respectively. Although these reactions are favourable, the bacteria or archaea that make their living this way are slow growers. But does this slow growth limit their ecological roles?

We usually consider the importance of nitrification from the standpoint of nitrogen cycling rather than primary production. Nitrification converts ammonium to nitrate. In agricultural fields, this makes nitrogen relatively less available to crops, as most crops use ammonium more effectively. In the oceans, it makes nitrogen relatively more available to diatoms, which use nitrate more efficiently. Nitrification is also studied as a source of the greenhouse gas N_2O, produced as a by-product of ammonium oxidation. However, nitrification can be an important pathway for carbon fixation. While doing a post-doc with Sybil Seitzinger at Rutgers University (now at the University of Victoria), one of this book's authors did a study of nitrogen biogeochemistry on the continental shelf of the eastern United States (Mid-Atlantic Bight). Nitrification rates measured in marine sediments at one site could account for 10–60% of total gross carbon fixation (Laursen and Seitzinger 2002).

Methane oxidation is most often viewed from a standpoint of the methane budget. As a potent greenhouse gas, accounting of methane flux is important for understanding how various ecosystems contribute to, or ameliorate, climate forcing. A large amount of methane is produced in deep sediments of aquatic systems. In lakes, for example, as much as half of the total primary production may decompose in sediments and be returned as methane (Fallon et al. 1980). Yet methanotrophic bacteria can be highly effective in trapping methane. Most of the methane produced in lake sediments is oxidized near the sediment surface, leaving little to escape to the atmosphere. In methanotrophic pathways, 1 mole of CO_2 is fixed for every 1 mole of CH_4 oxidized. This suggests that carbon fixation by methanotrophs in lakes may be ~25% of carbon fixation by photosynthesis. Methanotrophy is a nontrivial but mostly overlooked source of energy in the lake food web.

The oxidation of reduced sulfur (H_2S) can also be coupled with the reduction of CO_2, but this is not an energetically favourable reaction, and, like oxidation of H_2O, it requires an input of energy. Purple sulfur bacteria, for example, use the energy from sunlight to oxidize H_2S, much as plants use it to oxidize H_2O (fig. 19.4). Other sulfur oxidizing bacteria may use thermal energy, such as the endosymbiotic bacteria we discussed in chapter 7 that live within tube worms near deep sea vents. In those environments, sulfur oxidation is by far the most important pathway for primary production, supporting a unique food web.

Respiration Pathways—Flow of Energy and Regeneration of Nutrients

The cow in figure 19.3 uses aerobic respiration in producing ATP, releasing CO_2 and H_2O. However, you will also notice that the cow is releasing methane, an end-product of a strictly anaerobic process. How is the cow carrying out both aerobic and anaerobic respiration? The short answer is that the cow is not. But while the cow carries out aerobic respiration, some archaea in the anoxic recesses of its digestive system

Figure 19.4 Purple sulfur bacteria are photoautotrophs that use sunlight to oxidize H_2S, and couple this with fixation of CO_2.
Photo: Jennifer B. Glass, July 2008.

are carrying out methanogenic fermentation. You are probably aware of bovine flatulence as a contributor to climate change. Before you get mad at the cows, the culprits are these archaea.

Aerobic respiration is nearly universal among plants and animals. Even yeast and other fungi that can use fermentation to generate ATP will preferentially use aerobic respiration when oxygen is available. Many bacteria and archaea are capable of using other terminal electron acceptors in respiration, such as NO_3^-, Fe^{3+}, Mn^{4+}, or SO_4^{2-}. These other pathways can be important in the flow of energy and in conversion of organic carbon to ATP. The equation for nitrate respiration (denitrification) is provided as an example so that you can see how organic carbon is linked to nitrogen cycling:

$$(CH_2O)_{106} + 84.8\,HNO_3^- \rightarrow 106\,CO_2 + 42.4\,N_2 + 148.4\,H_2O$$

However, when oxygen is present, aerobic respiration will be the dominant pathway. There are a couple of reasons for this. The proximate cause is that oxygen may inhibit the expression of genes involved in other respiratory pathways. A distal cause is that aerobic respiration is more efficient, generating more energy (more ATP) per unit organic carbon (e.g., per mole glucose). Once oxygen is depleted, a relatively predictable sequence of anaerobic processes occurs, each generating successively less ATP, and each occurring at successively lower redox potential (fig. 19.5). The importance of each of these processes in an ecosystem depends on the relative abundance of the different electron acceptors. As we will see in chapter 20, denitrification may be a very important pathway for carbon degradation in some ecosystems, while in marine sediments sulfate reduction may be as important as aerobic respiration, not because it is a good way to generate ATP, but because there is just so much sulfate available.

With this foundation laid, we will spend the rest of this chapter discussing broad patterns of primary production. The

Electron acceptors

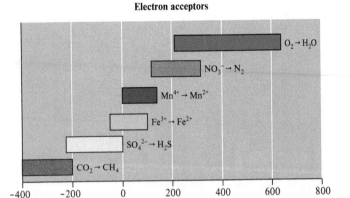

Figure 19.5 Electron acceptors supporting respiration of organic carbon. Oxygen is used preferentially until it is exhausted, with each successive electron acceptor yielding less ATP per mole of organic carbon.

focus will be on oxygenic photosynthesis, but remember that along with energy flow is the unspoken flow of nutrients. And as we discuss patterns of oxygenic primary production and aerobic respiration, there will be other modes of production and respiration operating.

CONCEPT 19.1 REVIEW

1. Gross primary production indicates the total amount of carbon fixed within an ecosystem over a period of time. Net primary production indicates the amount of fixed carbon that is available to herbivores and detritivores. Which is a better predictor of energy flow through an ecosystem?

2. In a system that has plenty of available Fe^{3+}, bacteria will still use oxygen until it is nearly depleted before any substantial iron-respiration begins. Why?

3. Suppose that in a pond, the molar ratios of available nitrogen (e.g., ammonium) to available phosphorus (e.g., ortho-phosphate) is 10:1. Which of these nutrients (nitrogen or phosphorus) might you expect to limit the flow of carbon from algae to higher trophic levels?

19.2   Patterns of Terrestrial Primary Production

Terrestrial primary production is generally limited by temperature and moisture. As we surveyed the major terrestrial biomes in chapter 2, you probably got a sense of the geographic variation in rates of primary production. Globally, the variables most highly correlated with variation in terrestrial

primary production are *temperature* and *moisture*. Highest rates of terrestrial primary production occur under warm, moist conditions.

The importance of temperature and moisture to net primary productivity (NPP) is illustrated by a map of primary productivity across Canada (fig. 19.6). This map was developed by Jing Chen and colleagues from the Canada Centre for Mapping and Earth Observation (formerly the Canada Centre for Remote Sensing) based at the University of Toronto (Liu et al. 2002). Describing patterns across a large geographic extent, such as the whole of Canada, cannot be done with traditional field samples. In chapter 1, we presented the idea that larger-scale sampling, often involving remote sensing done by satellites, has opened up an area of research unimaginable just a few decades ago.

Across Canada, Chen and colleagues found NPP was 1.22 gigatonnes of carbon (Gt C) per year (1 Gt = 1 billion tonnes). However, this production was highly spatially variable. It may surprise you that 78% of Canada's NPP occurs in the boreal forest, even though these forests occupy only 40% of the land base. Productivity is low in the northern regions of Canada, as well as along the Rocky Mountain and Pacific Coast mountain ranges in Alberta and British Columbia. This is probably not surprising, as mountain peaks and high latitudes are quite cold and dry, which limits plant growth. However, there is another large area of low productivity found primarily in southern Alberta and Saskatchewan. This region is commonly referred to as Palliser's Triangle, named after John Palliser, who in early surveys of the region deemed this region unsuitable for agriculture. The farmers of western Canada would beg to differ. This region is the northern extent of the Great Plains, and with warm summers it has become a major region of wheat and

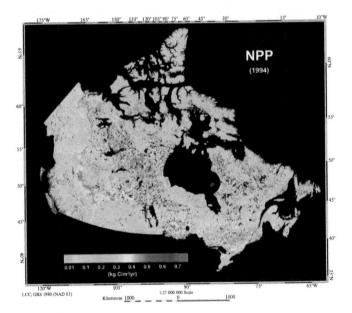

Figure 19.6 Estimated terrestrial net primary productivity across Canada.

J. Liu, J. M. Chen, J. Cihlar, et al. 2002. Net primary productivity mapped for Canada at 1-km resolution. *Global Ecology and Biogeography* 11:115–29. Reprinted with permission of John Wiley and Sons. Copyright Clearance Center.

canola production. In Palliser's Triangle, it is soil moisture, not temperature, that predominantly limits NPP, and agriculture in this region is highly vulnerable to drought.

While Canadian NPP is presented here as an example, temperature and moisture are strongly correlated with variation in NPP in most other regions of the world as well. Such patterns are so common that ecologists have developed a metric allowing them to more accurately understand the abiotic controls on NPP.

Actual Evapotranspiration and Terrestrial Primary Production

Michael Rosenzweig (1968) estimated the influence of moisture and temperature on rates of primary production by plotting the relationship between annual net primary productivity and annual actual evapotranspiration for many different terrestrial ecosystems. **Actual evapotranspiration (AET)** is the total amount of water that evaporates and transpires off a landscape during a given time period, measured in millimetres of water. Here, we are referring to AET over an entire year. AET is affected by both temperature and precipitation. Ecosystems with the highest AET are those that are warm and receive large amounts of precipitation. Conversely, ecosystems tend to have low levels of AET either because they receive little precipitation, are very cold, or both. Both hot deserts and cold tundra exhibit low levels of AET.

Figure 19.7 shows Rosenzweig's plot of the positive relationship between net primary productivity and AET for different ecosystems. Tropical forests show the highest levels of both net primary productivity and AET. At the other end of the spectrum, hot, dry deserts and cold, dry tundra show the lowest levels of AET and NPP. Intermediate levels occur in temperate forests, temperate grasslands, woodlands, and high-elevation forests.

Rosenzweig's analysis is useful in explaining variation in primary productivity across the whole spectrum of terrestrial ecosystems, and figure 19.7 suggests that AET can explain a large amount of the variation in NPP across diverse terrestrial ecosystems. What controls variation in primary productivity within similar ecosystems, such as two different grasslands? O. E. Sala and his colleagues (1988) explored the factors controlling primary productivity in the central grassland region of the United States. Their study was based on data collected by the U.S. Department of Agriculture Soil Conservation Service at 9,498 sites. To make this large data set more manageable, the researchers grouped the sites into 100 representative study areas.

The study areas extended from Mississippi and Arkansas in the east to New Mexico and Montana in the west and from North Dakota to southern Texas. Primary productivity was highest in the eastern grassland study areas and lowest in the western study areas. This east–west variation corresponds to the westward changes from tall-grass prairie to short-grass prairie that we reviewed in chapter 2. Sala and his colleagues found that this east–west variation in primary productivity among grassland ecosystems correlated significantly with the amount of rainfall (fig. 19.8).

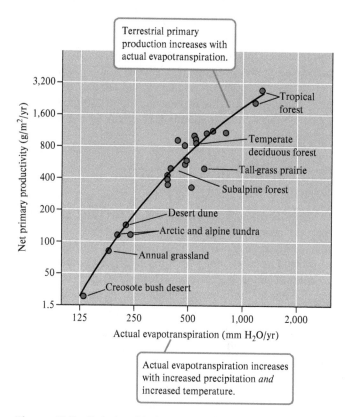

Figure 19.7   Relationship between actual evapotranspiration and net above-ground primary productivity in a series of terrestrial ecosystems. Data from Rosenzweig 1968.

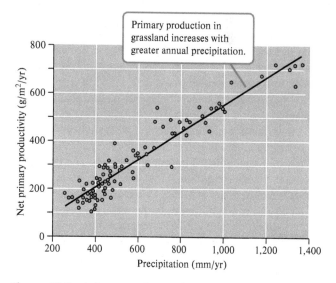

Figure 19.8   Influence of annual precipitation on net above-ground primary productivity in grasslands of central North America. Data from Sala et al. 1988.

These researchers found strong correlations between terrestrial primary productivity and AET across vastly different biomes, or between primary productivity and precipitation within grassland biomes. However, their models are unable to completely explain the variation in primary productivity among the study ecosystems. For instance, in figure 19.7, ecosystems with annual AET levels of 500 to 600 mm of water showed annual rates of primary production ranging from 300 to 1,000 g per square metre! In figure 19.8, grassland ecosystems receiving 400 mm of annual precipitation had annual rates of primary production ranging from about 100 to 250 g per square metre. Some of this variation will be driven by differences in soil fertility.

Soil Fertility and Terrestrial Primary Productivity

Farmers have long known that adding fertilizers to soil can increase agricultural production. However, it was not until the nineteenth century that scientists began to quantify the effects of specific nutrients, such as nitrogen (N) or phosphorus (P), on rates of primary productivity. Justus Liebig (1840) pointed out that nutrient supplies often limit plant growth. He also suggested that nutrient limitation to plant growth could be traced to a single limiting nutrient. This hypothetical control of primary productivity by a single nutrient was later called Liebig's Law of the Minimum. We now know that Liebig's perspective, though remaining influential, is also too simplistic. Usually several factors, including a number of nutrients, simultaneously affect levels of terrestrial primary production in natural systems. However, Liebig's work led the way to a concept that remains true today: variation in soil fertility can affect rates of terrestrial primary production.

Liebig's work, and most practical experience prior to Liebig, concerned the productivity of agricultural ecosystems. Do nutrients influence rates of primary production in other ecosystems, such as the tundra or deserts, where human manipulation has been less prominent? In short, yes. Ecologists have demonstrated the effects of nutrients on terrestrial primary production in many experiments and across a wide variety of terrestrial ecosystem types, including arctic tundra, alpine tundra, grasslands, deserts, and forests.

Gaius Shaver and Stuart Chapin (1986) studied the potential for nutrient limitation in arctic tundra. They added commercial fertilizer containing nitrogen, phosphorus, and potassium to several tundra ecosystems in Alaska. They made a single application of fertilizer to half of their experimental plots (control plots) and two applications to the remaining experimental plots (fertilized plots). Fertilization increased net primary production (by 23% to 300%) at all of the study sites, measured two to four years after nutrient addition. Four years after the initial application of fertilizer, NPP on Kuparuk Ridge was twice as high on the fertilized plots than on the control plots (fig. 19.9).

You may recall from chapter 14 that Canadian researchers conducted a large-scale experiment manipulating resources, prey, and predators in an attempt to understand the linkages between plants, hares, and lynx in the Yukon. As part of this study, Roy Turkington, of the University of British Columbia, along with researchers from the University of Alberta, Nova Scotia Agricultural College, University of Toronto, and University of Sussex, analyzed the response of the boreal vegetation to long-term nutrient additions (Turkington et al. 1998). The

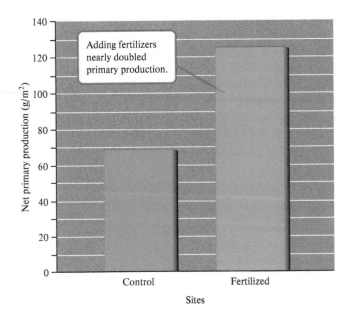

Figure 19.9 Effect of addition of nitrogen, phosphorus, and potassium on net above-ground primary production in arctic tundra.
Data from Shaver and Chapin 1986.

research team added fertilizer to two large (1 km²) plots, and monitored plant growth in these, and two control plots, for six years. Fertilizer was added each year, always including nitrogen, and in some years P and K were also added. The response they found varied more than what we saw on Kuparuk Ridge.

One of the great strengths of the Turkington study is that they did not simply measure total production in the plots but instead measured each of the major plant groups separately. By doing this, they found a rather interesting story. Overall, the biomass of the system increased, indicating soil fertility did in fact limit primary production. However, the exact effects of adding nutrients varied among the different plant types. The fast growing herbaceous species responded very quickly, while effects on tree growth became apparent only later in the study. Additionally, several plant species showed a reduction in growth due to fertilization. How is this possible if the boreal forest is nutrient limited? Not all plant species are equally limited by mineral nutrients. Instead, species differ in the shape of their performance curves related to nitrogen, light, or any other resource that occupies a niche-axis (chapter 9). Some species will have traits that allow them to grow and reproduce under low resource conditions, while others require higher resource levels. Under low nutrient conditions, stress-tolerant species (chapter 9) will do just fine. However, by adding nutrients, the stress has been removed, and now the faster growing and more competitively dominant species are able to take over. In other words, even though an ecosystem may be nutrient limited, this does not mean that all species increase in growth if nutrients are added. This is a critical point to understand about ecosystem ecology. The factors that limit NPP, or other ecosystem processes, do not necessarily limit the growth of all species within the ecosystem.

Experiments such as these have shown that despite the major influence of temperature and moisture on rates of primary production in terrestrial ecosystems, variation in nutrient availability can also have measurable influence. As we shall see in the next section, a variety of nutrients are often the main factors limiting primary production in aquatic ecosystems.

ECOLOGY IN ACTION

Interactions Across Community Boundaries

In chapter 18, we observed that there is growing acceptance that communities are not static entities but instead are constantly in a state of flux due to natural and human-induced disturbances. More progressive conservation programs generally try to incorporate some aspect of disturbance into the management plan. Here we will explore a related topic. The factors that influence the growth and ecosystem dynamics of a particular community (e.g., forest, lake, etc.) include not only those factors internal to the community that we have discussed (biodiversity, consumers) but also can include processes in the surrounding communities. There is an increasing realization that to preserve a particular community will require an understanding of nutrient inputs from the surrounding area, as changes in primary production can have cascading effects on competitive interactions, on herbivory, and on community structure.

Many communities receive **allochthonous inputs** of nutrients and biomass. Allochthonous inputs are derived/created within a community external to the one in which they are eventually deposited. For example, the nutrients and energy contained in leaves that fall from trees into a stream are an allochthonous input into the stream ecosystem. Thomas Reimchen and his colleagues and students at the University of Victoria have studied the role that bears feeding upon salmon have on the primary production of coastal forests (fig. 19.10). Coastal forests tend to be nitrogen-limited, and thus they are likely very sensitive to any additions of nitrogen into the system. Large numbers of salmon spawn in the rivers throughout coastal British Columbia, and enormous quantities of these fish are eaten by bears, wolves, and other animals. Let's look at this interaction from an ecosystem perspective. You have fish that leave the streams at a very small size and move into the ocean. There, they live for many years, growing to large size. The resources they use for this growth come from the marine environment. They then move back into freshwater, where they either are consumed by terrestrial animals or die in the streams. In either case, many of the nutrients they carried with them from the ocean are released onto land (as bear feces and urine or as decomposing fish carcasses) or on the stream edges (for fish that die in the stream), or they are swept with the currents into the ocean. The exploitative interaction between bear and salmon causes an allochthonous input of nutrients into coastal forests. Reimchen and

his group have been working to determine whether such nutrient inputs alter primary production of the forests.

As you will see in the Ecological Tools and Approaches section of this chapter, ecologists are able to use stable isotope analyses to determine the source of different nutrients in different trophic levels. We will not go into the details here; it is sufficient to understand that animal tissue that comes from marine habitats contains a higher percentage of ^{15}N than similar tissue from terrestrial habitats. As a result, if plants near the water's edge consume the nitrogen that comes from the ocean, rather than the nitrogen that is found on land, they should have more ^{15}N in their leaves than plants that do not have access to this marine-derived nitrogen source (MDN).

Reimchen and his colleagues (Mathewson et al. 2003) were able to test whether this was true by comparing ^{15}N levels of several riparian plant species collected in different positions along a stream, in each of two watersheds. Specifically, they recognized that some waterfalls are impenetrable barriers to salmon, such that plants below the waterfall would have access to MDN, while those above would not. When they measured the plant tissues, they found that their hunch was correct: most species tested were enriched in ^{15}N below the waterfall but not above it. More importantly, for most samples more than 30% of the nitrogen in the plant tissues came from the ocean! To put it mildly, this is strong evidence that the bear–salmon interaction has strong impacts on nutrient inputs on land. But does it actually alter the composition and production of these forests? Again, Mathewson and colleagues (2003) have data suggesting that, yes, it does. Plants generally associated with low-N soils were much more abundant above the waterfalls, while plants associated with high-N soils were much more abundant below the falls. This is initial evidence to suggest that not only do salmon alter nitrogen levels, they can alter the outcome of interactions among plant species! As an interesting aside, Reimchen's laboratory found that coat colour polymorphism in the black bear (*Ursus americanus kermodei*) can affect the efficiency with which bears capture salmon. On several small islands off the mid-coast of British Columbia, two distinct polymorphisms occur: (1) the black morph, and (2) the recessive white morph (Kermode, or spirit bear). Both morphotypes feed on salmon in the day and at night, but the white morph is much more effective

(a)

(b)

Figure 19.10   (*a*) Feeding by bear on salmon results in large allochthonous inputs of nutrients into (*b*) the forest surrounding salmon spawning grounds.

(a), (b) Wendy Shattil and Bob Rozinski/Oxford Scientific/Getty Images; Katie Christie.

at capturing salmon during the day (Klinka and Reimchen 2009). The salmon were better at evading ecologists dressed in black than those dressed in white (something to file away next time you go fishing), suggesting that avoidance behaviour by the fish accounts for the white morph's greater efficiency. It is fascinating to think that the persistence of this coat colour polymorphism may be the result of increased salmon hunting efficiency (and fitness) for the white bear. It is also interesting to consider that the population genetics of bears, specifically the proportion of the population with the recessive white phenotype, might influence something as superficially unrelated as the efficiency with which marine derived nutrients are transferred to forest ecosystems.

The idea that fish can influence plant competition and forest community composition has significant implications

for any conservation program of the coastal forests. It suggests that if you want to preserve the forest, you also need to protect the fish that feed the forest. Without the large number of salmon that die each year and that serve as fertilizer for the riparian forest, there will most certainly be a shift in plant species composition and a loss of the ecosystem we are trying to preserve. Realization of this concept serves as the foundation of ecosystem-based management, where the goal is to protect an entire set of interactions, rather than specific communities. A recent success story is the Great Bear Rainforest, a newly protected, five-million-acre expanse of coastal rain forest along the coast of British Columbia and Alaska. An understanding of the basic ecological principles occurring in nature serves as the foundation for such an ambitious conservation program.

CONCEPT 19.2 REVIEW

1. Why was precipitation alone, without temperature, sufficient to account for most of the variation in grassland net primary production across central North America?

2. Why are the desert dune ecosystem and the arctic and alpine tundra ecosystems indicated in figure 19.7 similar with respect to NPP?

3. Why do different plant species respond differently to nutrient addition, even if the net primary production, overall, is nutrient limited?

19.3 Patterns of Aquatic Primary Production

Aquatic primary production is generally limited by nutrient availability. Limnologists and oceanographers have measured rates of primary production and nutrient concentrations in many lakes, streams, and coastal and oceanic study sites. These studies have produced one of the best documented patterns in the biosphere: the positive relationship between nutrient availability and rate of primary production in aquatic ecosystems.

Patterns and Models

A quantitative relationship between phosphorus, an essential plant nutrient, and phytoplankton biomass was first described for a series of lakes in Japan (Hogetsu and Ichimura 1954, Ichimura 1956, Sakamoto 1966). The ecologists studying this relationship found a strong correspondence between total phosphorus and phytoplankton biomass.

Soon after the ecologists from Japan studied this relationship, two Canadian researchers emerged who further explored nutrient controls on aquatic productivity: Peter Dillon, now an Industrial Research Chairholder at Trent University, and Frank Rigler, formerly of University of Toronto. Rigler was an exceptionally influential person in the field of aquatic ecology, and today the Society of Canadian Limnologists has named its highest award, the Frank H. Rigler Award, in his honour. Since his work with Rigler, Dillon has continued to study nutrient issues in lakes, influencing governmental policy through ecological studies. In their work, Dillon and Rigler (1974) described a similar positive relationship between phosphorus and phytoplankton biomass for lake ecosystems throughout the Northern Hemisphere (fig. 19.11), as was found in Japan. Remarkably, the slopes of the lines describing the relationship between phosphorus and phytoplankton biomass for the Japanese and Canadian lakes were nearly identical.

The data from Japan and North America strongly support the hypothesis that nutrients, particularly phosphorus, control phytoplankton biomass in lake ecosystems. However, what is

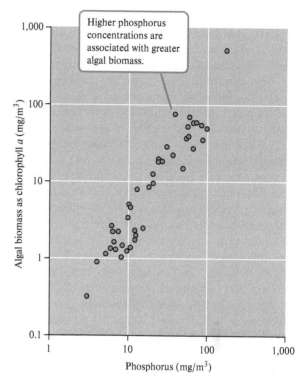

Figure 19.11 Relationship between phosphorus concentration and algal biomass in northern temperate lakes.
Data from Dillon and Rigler 1974.

the relationship between phytoplankton biomass and the rate of primary production? This relationship was explored by Val Smith (1979) for 49 lakes of the north temperate zone. The data from these lakes showed a strong positive correlation between chlorophyll concentrations (as a proxy for algal biomass) and photosynthetic rates.

The work of Hogetsu, Ichimura, Sakamoto, Dillon, Rigler, and Smith provided compelling evidence that algal biomass and, by extension, primary production were related to phosphorus concentrations in freshwater. Yet, although correlations are suggestive, they are not definitive. Experimentation was needed. During the late 1960s and early 1970s, there was a major effort to understand the cause of massive algal growth (eutrophication) of freshwater, and laboratory manipulations often gave conflicting results as to the cause of eutrophication. Some ecologists suggested that it was phosphorus; others, that it was nitrogen; and still others, that it was organic carbon or some combination of these. This conflict, and the importance of the question at a time of deteriorating water quality, set the stage for some of the most influential experiments in ecology. Canadian ecologists moved beyond correlation and lab-based studies and began whole-lake experimental manipulations.

Whole-Lake Experiments on Primary Production

In chapter 1, we introduced some experiments on primary production conducted at the Experimental Lakes Area by David Schindler and his colleagues. The Experimental Lakes Area was founded in northwestern Ontario, Canada, in 1968, as a place in which aquatic ecologists could manipulate whole-lake ecosystems (Mills and Schindler 1987, Findlay and Kasian 1987). Ecologists manipulated nutrient availability in a lake called Lake 226 using a vinyl curtain to divide Lake 226 into two 8-hectare basins, each containing about 500,000 m³ of water. Each half of Lake 226 was fertilized from 1973 to 1980. The researchers added a mixture of carbon in the form of sucrose and nitrate to one basin and carbon, nitrate, and phosphate to the other basin. They stopped fertilizing the lakes after 1980 and then studied the recovery of the Lake 226 ecosystem from 1981 to 1983.

Both sides of Lake 226 responded significantly to nutrient additions; however, the side that received phosphorus showed a much more dramatic increase in phytoplankton growth (fig. 1.5). Prior to the manipulation, Lake 226 supported about the same biomass of phytoplankton as two reference lakes (fig. 19.12). However, when experimenters began adding the nutrient mix that included phosphorus to Lake 226, phytoplankton biomass quickly surpassed that in the reference lakes (and in the other half of Lake 226 that did not receive phosphorus). Phytoplankton biomass remained elevated in Lake 226 until the experimenters stopped adding fertilizer at the end of 1980. Then, from 1981 to 1983 the phytoplankton biomass in Lake 226 declined significantly.

Correlations between phosphorus concentrations and primary productivity, as well as whole-lake experimental manipulation, support the generalization that nutrient availability controls primary productivity in freshwater ecosystems. The whole-lake manipulation results are also a good reminder that the scale at which experiments are conducted can be important. Results in a laboratory (e.g., observations that organic carbon might limit primary production) may be artifacts of scale. To be validated, lab experiments need to be supported by field studies, where the scale is relevant to the phenomenon being studied. Now, let's examine the evidence for a relationship between nutrient abundance and primary production in marine ecosystems.

Global Patterns of Marine Primary Production

The geographic distribution of net primary production in the sea indicates a positive influence of nutrient availability on rates of primary production. The highest rates of primary production by marine phytoplankton are generally concentrated in areas with higher levels of nutrient availability along the margins of continents over continental shelves and in areas of upwelling (fig. 19.13). Along continental margins, nutrients are renewed by runoff from the land and by biological or physical disturbance of bottom sediments. As we saw in chapter 3, the upwelling that brings nutrient-laden water from the depths to the surface is concentrated along the west coasts of continents and around the continent of Antarctica, areas that appear dark red in figure 19.13a, indicating high to very high rates of primary production. Meanwhile, the central portions of the major oceans show low levels of nutrient availability and low rates of primary production. The main source of nutrient renewal in the surface waters of the open ocean is vertical mixing. Vertical mixing is generally blocked in open tropical oceans by a permanent thermocline. Consequently, the surface waters of open tropical oceans contain very low concentrations of nutrients and show some of the lowest rates of marine primary production.

Figure 19.13b highlights that NPP patterns are not static but instead change over time. Between the periods of 1979–86 and 1997–2002, global marine NPP decreased 6%, attributed to changing temperatures and decreased atmospheric deposition of iron, an essential element for phytoplankton. However, these changes in NPP were not uniform. Oceans near coastlines, particularly near large urban centres, showed great increases in NPP. Decreases tended to be in the open oceans, particularly in northern latitudes.

What is the experimental evidence for nutrient limitation of marine primary production? There have been no experiments done in the marine environment that are equivalent to the whole-lake manipulations at the Experimental Lakes Area, in large part because ocean waters are interconnected. However, there have been a number of nutrient addition studies. For example, researchers were able to alter the nutrient inputs and concentrations in Himmerfjärden, Sweden, a brackish water coastal inlet of the Baltic Sea with a surface area of 195 km² (see fig. 19.14) (Granéli et al. 1990). (For comparison, the lake sub-basins manipulated in the whole-lake experiments were < 0.1 km².) The researchers combined this large-scale manipulation with small-scale culture flask experiments, providing critical data for understanding nutrient controls of production in a marine system. The results of this manipulative experiment indicate that the marine system was nitrogen limited but that this could be tipped to phosphorus limitation if nitrogen additions push N:P above the Redfield ratio. There is also substantial evidence that marine productivity can, at certain times and in

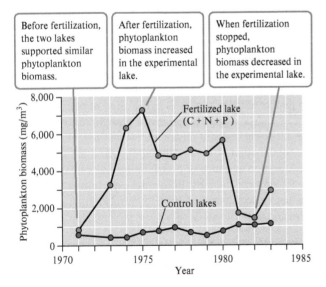

Figure 19.12   A whole-lake experiment shows the effect of nutrient additions on average phytoplankton biomass.

Data from Findlay and Kasian 1987.

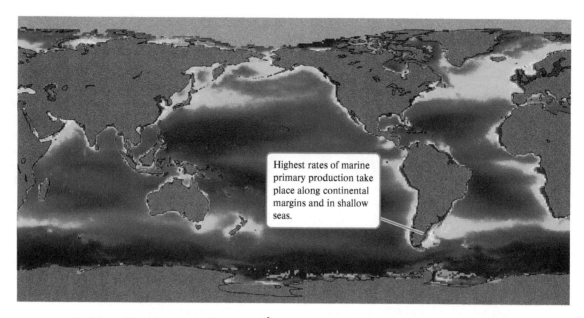

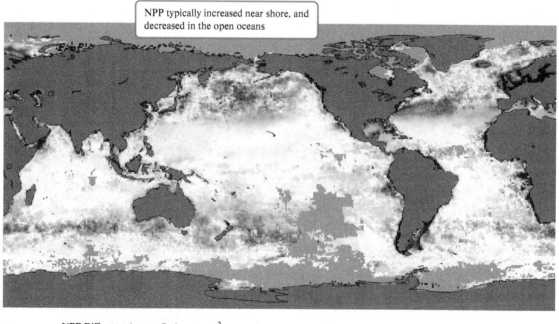

Figure 19.13 (*a*) Geographic variation in marine primary productivity (NASA Earth Observatory). (*b*) Change in ocean NPP between 1979–86 and 1997–2002.

(a), (b) Images by Robert Simmon, NASA GSFC Earth Observatory, based on data provided by Watson Gregg, NASA GSFC.

some locations, be influenced by dissolved iron concentrations (Moore et al. 2004).

Additional evidence for nutrient controls of marine primary production is found in the observation of increasing numbers and sizes of **dead zones** throughout the world's oceans. Dead zones are hypoxic areas (< 2mg/L oxygen), typically a consequence of pollution, eutrophication, and high rates of decomposition, that are essentially devoid of marine life. Diaz and

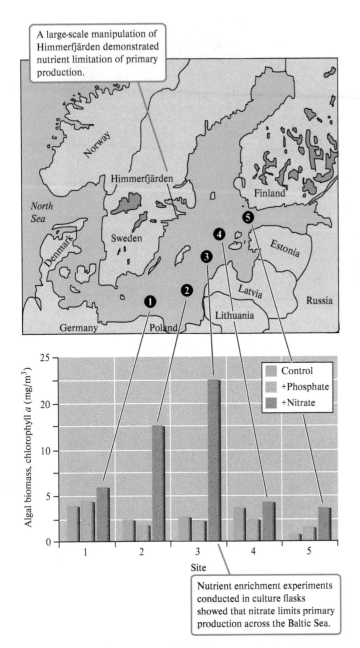

A large-scale manipulation of Himmerfjärden demonstrated nutrient limitation of primary production.

Nutrient enrichment experiments conducted in culture flasks showed that nitrate limits primary production across the Baltic Sea.

Figure 19.14 Nitrate control of primary production in the Baltic Sea.

Data from Granéli et al. 1990.

near the outflow of the Mississippi river. The size of the dead zone varies as a function of rainfall and other climatic conditions, and can exceed 15,000 km^2 in some years (Rabalais et al. 2002). Though a number of local factors influence whether a dead zone forms and whether it persists, the general sequence of events is one we have discussed before. High rates of limiting nutrients enter the marine system. In response, certain groups of organisms (typically algae and cyanobacteria) grow rapidly, forming an algal bloom. As these organisms die, microbial activity associated with decomposition increases. The heterotrophic organisms have substantial food (dead algae) and thus consume the available oxygen in respiration. Often this happens in deeper water since the biomass sinks, and the oxygen consumed cannot be replaced by re-equilibration with the atmosphere. This is particularly true if the water is thermally stratified. An outcome of this process is an area with oxygen levels too low to support other marine life. It is a common, though unfortunate, example of how marine primary production and ecosystem function can be affected by nutrients.

Ecologists have been able to identify major drivers governing primary production, both on land and in aquatic systems. However, ecologists also recognize that such general causes do not always apply to specific locations. Dillon and Rigler (1974) suggested that limnologists pay attention to the scatter of points around lines showing a relationship between nutrient concentrations and phytoplankton biomass (FAO 1972). We call that scatter of points residual variation. Residual variation is that proportion of variation not explained by the independent variable, in this case, by nutrient concentration. Dillon and Rigler suggested that environmental factors besides nutrient availability significantly influence phytoplankton biomass. One of those factors is the intensity of predation on the zooplankton that feed on phytoplankton. As we shall see in subsection 19.5, consumers can influence rates of primary production in both terrestrial and aquatic ecosystems, but first we will consider energy flow through the different trophic levels in biological communities (subsection 19.4).

Rosenberg (2008) compiled the global distribution of oceanic dead zones, finding evidence for over 400 locations. These zones are indicated in figure 19.15 as dots and are most prevalent along the coastlines of land masses where the human footprint is greatest (e.g., eastern United States, Europe, and East Asia). Paleoecological evidence suggests these areas are not typically recurring over long time scales; instead, the number of such zones reported has been doubling each decade for the last 50 years (Diaz and Rosenberg 2008). Major causes appear to be nutrient runoff (particularly nitrogen) associated with fertilization of agricultural fields within the surrounding watershed, as well as general nutrient-rich pollution being dumped into oceans. One of the largest dead zones is in the Gulf of Mexico,

CONCEPT 19.3 REVIEW

1. Suppose that when you add nitrogen to one-half of a lake, you observe no change in phytoplankton biomass, but when you add phosphorus to the other half of the lake, phytoplankton biomass more than doubles. What is the most likely explanation for your results?

2. Suppose you fertilize a region of an ocean with nitrogen only, another region with phosphorus only, and a third region with nitrogen plus phosphorus and observe no change in phytoplankton biomass. What is the most likely explanation of your results?

3. How does the global distribution of oceanic dead zones influence our understanding of what controls NPP in marine systems?

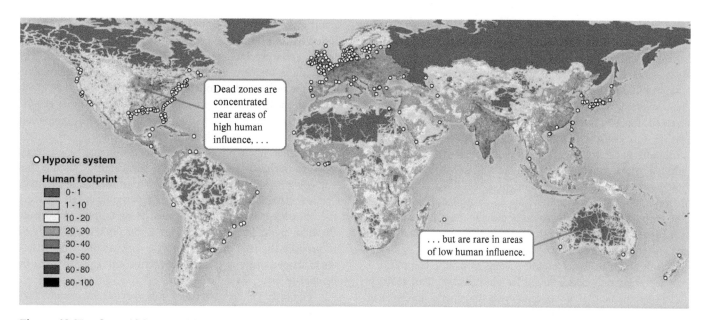

Figure 19.15   Over 400 eutrophication-associated dead zones have been identified around the world. Here, the extent of human influence on the land is reflected as the Human Footprint, reported as a percentage of the maximum possible score on a "human influence index."

From Robert J. Diaz and Rutger Rosenberg. 2008, August 15. Spreading dead zones and consequences for marine ecosystems. *Science* 321(5891):926–9. Reprinted with permission from AAAS.

19.4   Trophic Levels

Energy losses limit the number of trophic levels in ecosystems. An understanding of thermodynamics tells us that with each transfer or conversion of energy, some energy is lost. What are the consequences for these losses of energy in ecosystems? To answer this question, we first need to quantify the flow of energy through ecosystems. One of the very first ecologists to do this was Raymond Lindeman.

A Trophic-Dynamic View of Ecosystems

Raymond Lindeman (1942) published a revolutionary paper, *The Trophic-Dynamic Aspect of Ecology*. In this paper, Lindeman articulated a view of ecosystems centred on energy fixation, storage, and flows that remains influential to this day. Like Tansley before him, Lindeman pointed out the difficulty and artificiality of separating organisms from their environment and promoted an ecosystem view of nature. Lindeman concluded that the ecosystem concept is fundamental to the study of **trophic dynamics**, which he defined as the transfer of energy from one part of an ecosystem to another. Viewing organisms as simply stored energy will not come easily for everyone, except of course for science fiction fans, who are accustomed to the idea of sentient energy. For the rest of us, we have spent substantial time focusing on the details of species interactions, based upon a deep understanding of natural history; putting that aside requires an alternative way of viewing organisms. Such an approach is critical to understanding energy flow in natural systems.

Lindeman suggested grouping organisms within an ecosystem into trophic levels: primary producers, primary consumers, secondary consumers, tertiary consumers, and so forth. The concept of trophic levels, and unravelling trophic position, was introduced in chapter 17. In Lindeman's scheme, each trophic level feeds on the one immediately below it and is food for the level immediately above it. Energy enters the ecosystem as primary producers (typically) engage in photosynthesis and convert solar energy into biomass. As energy is transferred from one trophic level to another, energy is lost due to limited consumption and assimilation, respiration by consumers, and heat production. As a result of these losses, the quantity of stored energy in an ecosystem decreases with each successive trophic level.

This loss of energy is unavoidable and comes from basic physical properties described by the laws of thermodynamics (fig. 19.16). The first law is simple and explains that energy can only be transformed, not created. For example, plants can

---

Two Laws of Thermodynamics Relevant to Ecology

1. The total amount of energy in the universe is constant. Thus, energy can only be transformed, not created.

2. Heat energy will move from a warmer body to a cooler one. This is equivalent to the idea that entropy will tend to increase over time in a closed system.

Figure 19.16   There are several laws of thermodynamics critical to understanding physical processes. Two of those laws that are important for understanding the movement of energy among trophic levels are presented here.

convert sunlight into plant biomass, deer convert plant bio-mass (stored solar energy) into deer biomass (still stored solar energy), and wolves convert deer biomass into wolf biomass (yet again, stored solar energy). The only way for such a system to gain new energy is for it to come from the sun and, then, be converted by the plants. But even there, energy is not being created. Instead, nuclear and chemical reactions occur in and on the sun, converting other forms of stored energy into solar radiation. Back on Earth, we find that the deer's growth can be limited by plant biomass and that the wolf's growth can be limited by the deer. In theory, one might expect the deer to be able to eat 100% of the plants; thus, the amount of stored energy in the herbivore trophic level could be close to the amount fixed by the plants. This is where both the second law of thermodynamics and some basic ecology come into play.

Entropy, the focus of the second law, is a complicated concept, generally better suited for physics class than ecology. However, the bit that is relevant here is that energy, in the form of heat, will move from warm areas (e.g., a deer) to cool areas (e.g., night sky). Where did that heat energy come from? It was the product of metabolism within the deer, and its movement into the atmosphere means that some of the solar energy, transferred to the deer in the form of plant energy, is lost to the sky in the form of heat. It cannot be used to produce more deer biomass. All organisms warmer than ambient temperature suffer from this energy loss explained by the second law of thermodynamics. Actually, so too do inanimate objects, which is why my coffee is cooling as I write this. Though many organisms have a number of ways to minimize this loss of heat energy (chapter 5), some loss will still occur.

An additional reason why consumers do not contain 100% of the energy found in producers comes from our understanding of exploitation in chapter 14. Most of a plant that a deer may encounter is inedible, and thus the energy stored within it is inaccessible. Thick trunks and most woody structures, roots, and a variety of other plant parts simply are not edible by most organisms. Further, deer will never find all of the plants in an ecosystem; as a result, much of the potentially edible plant biomass will never be consumed. Combined, these ecological realities limit the potential size of the consumer trophic level, even were energy transfer to be completely efficient. The same thing happens as we move from consumer to predator, for example, from deer to wolf. In chapter 14, we talked about how refugia allow some prey to avoid predation. In an ecosystem context, this means that much of the consumer biomass is unavailable for conversion into predator biomass.

Because higher trophic levels cannot create new energy, because they lose heat energy, and because they cannot find and consume all potential food, there is an inevitable pyramid-shaped distribution of energy among trophic levels in *every* natural ecosystem. Lindeman called these **trophic pyramids** Eltonian pyramids, since Charles Elton (1927) was the first to propose that the distribution of energy among trophic levels is shaped like a pyramid. Both terms are regularly used by ecologists.

Figure 19.17 shows the distribution of annual primary production among trophic levels in Cedar Bog Lake and in Lake Mendota, Wisconsin. As predicted by Elton, the distribution of energy across trophic levels in both lakes is shaped like a pyramid. Note, too, that both lakes have fairly few trophic levels: Lake Mendota includes four trophic levels, while Cedar Bog Lake includes just three. Later, we will return to the topic of limits to the number of trophic levels found within an ecosystem.

Following Lindeman's pioneering work, many other ecologists studied energy flow within ecosystems. One of the most comprehensive of these later studies focused on the Hubbard Brook Experimental Forest we first discussed in chapter 18.

Energy Flow in a Temperate Deciduous Forest

James Gosz and his colleagues (1978) studied energy flow in the Hubbard Brook Experimental Forest, which is managed for research by the U.S. Forest Service. They concentrated their efforts on a stream catchment called watershed 6, which was left undisturbed so it could serve as a control for experimental

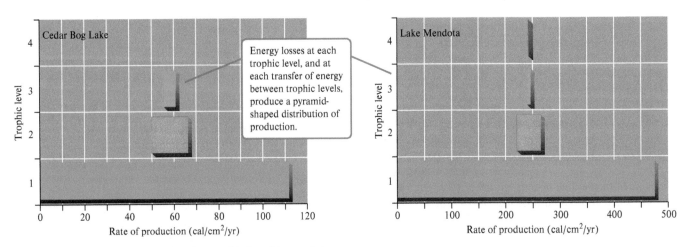

Figure 19.17 Annual production by trophic level in two lakes.
Data from Lindeman 1942.

studies on other stream catchments. The energy flow in the Hubbard Brook Experimental Forest was quantified as kilocalories (kcal) per square metre per year. The results of the analysis are shown in figure 19.18.

First, you will notice that figure 19.18 does not look anything like the trophic pyramids presented in figure 19.17! The pyramids are useful when one is trying to provide a rough snapshot of the energy distributions within an ecosystem. The energy budget that Gosz and colleagues provide is a much more detailed account of where all of the energy that enters the ecosystem goes. Both approaches are useful, albeit for answering slightly different questions.

Let's examine the distribution of organic matter among the major components of the Hubbard Brook ecosystem. The largest single pool of energy in the forest, 122,442 kcal/m^2,

occurred as dead organic matter. Most of the dead organic matter, 88,120 kcal/m^2, was in the upper 36 cm of soil. The remainder occurred as plant litter on the forest floor. Total living-plant biomass amounted to 71,420 kcal/m^2, of which 59,696 kcal/m^2 was stored in above-ground biomass; and 11,724 kcal/m^2 as below-ground biomass.

The total standing stock of energy occurring as dead organic matter and living-plant biomass was 193,862 kcal/m^2. This estimate by Gosz and his colleagues dwarfs the energy stored in all other portions of the ecosystem. For instance, the energetic content of a caterpillar population during a severe population outbreak amounted to only 160 kcal/m^2. However, even this amount far exceeds the total energetic content of all vertebrate biomass. The researchers estimated that the total energetic content of the most numerous vertebrates, including chipmunks,

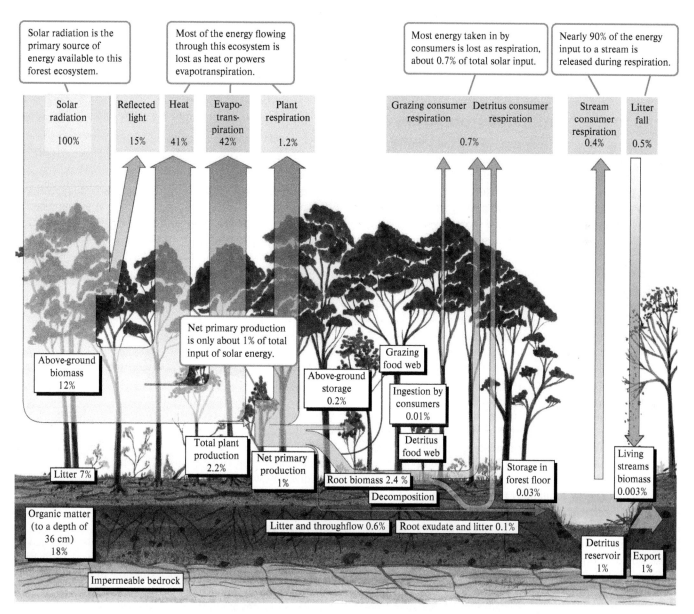

Figure 19.18   Energy budget for a temperate deciduous forest.
Data from Gosz et al. 1978.

mice, shrews, salamanders, and birds, amounted to less than 1 kcal/m². In other words, in this fairly typical ecosystem, animals make up an amazingly small fraction of the biomass, and in terms of energetic abundance, vertebrates are essentially absent. This is again a critical point to understand about ecosystems and energy flow: the study of energy in ecosystems is often the same as the study of the plants and the microbes that feed upon organic matter. Now that we have inventoried the major standing stocks of energy, let's look at energy flow through the Hubbard Brook Forest.

The main source of energy for the ecosystem is solar radiation. The total input of solar energy to the study area during the growing season was estimated to be 480,000 kcal/m² (expressed as 100% in figure 19.18). Of this total energy input, 15% was reflected, 41% was converted to heat, and 42% was absorbed during evapotranspiration. About 2.2% of the solar input was fixed by plants as gross primary production. Plant respiration accounted for 1.2%, leaving about 1% as net primary production. In other words, only about 1% of the solar input to the Hubbard Brook ecosystem was available to the herbivores and detritivores that made up the second trophic level. And of this, only about 1% NPP (or 0.01% of solar input) was consumed by herbivores.

Limits to the Number of Trophic Levels

One consistent feature of ecosystems across the planet is that all tend to have relatively few trophic levels, with three to five being typical. Some ecosystems will have more (seven to eight), but these tend to be rare. Why don't we tend to find systems with 10, 15, or even 25 trophic levels? Clear answers to this question still elude ecologists, though there are several hypotheses that have been put forward. Many hypotheses focus on energy loss, and that is where we begin.

The energy budget constructed by Gosz and his colleagues gives us a basis for understanding how energy loss can limit the number of trophic levels in natural ecosystems. Net primary production in the Hubbard Brook Forest ecosystem was less than 1% of the input of solar energy. In other words, over 99% of the solar energy available to the Hubbard Brook was unavailable for use by a second trophic level. Of the NPP available to consumers, approximately 96% is lost as consumer respiration. This leaves very little for a third trophic level. Such losses with each transfer of energy in a food chain will limit the number of trophic levels that can be supported in an ecosystem. As these losses between trophic levels accumulate, eventually there will be insufficient energy remaining to support a viable population of an even higher trophic level.

Although energy limitations may be an important factor restricting the number of trophic levels in an ecosystem, it is not the only hypothesis that has been put forward. Let us consider what a fifth or sixth or tenth trophic level actually represents. These would be organisms that primarily feed upon high level predators, not simply additional types of predators that feed upon primary consumers. These would be animals that hunt great white sharks, eagles, and cheetah. You may see some problems here. First, the prey for these hypothetical predators are going to be in extremely low abundance (the trophic pyramid is

still there!). At some point, natural selection operating through optimal foraging (chapter 7.3) would likely favour choosing more abundant prey at lower trophic levels. Why spend all that time hunting a rare, hard-to-catch, and expensive-to-handle prey if more abundant and less dangerous prey exist? Another issue may be an evolutionary constraint. Though we might imagine body designs that would catch these top predators, that does not mean that any putative ancestor possessed the raw genetic material that would allow for evolution of those traits.

Energy limitation can play a big role in determining the trophic structure of ecosystems. As we see next, a number of biotic processes can also be important.

CONCEPT 19.4 REVIEW

1. In the Hubbard Brook Forest ecosystem studied by James Gosz and colleagues, would you expect there to be a greater biomass of primary predators feeding on herbivores or of soil invertebrates feeding on bacteria and fungi? Why?

2. What are the relative amounts of net primary production consumed by herbivores versus plant litter-feeders (detritivores) living on the forest floor?

3. How do the laws of thermodynamics influence the number of trophic levels found in an ecosystem?

4. Related to question 3, suppose that you study two ecosystems. The two systems have similar gross primary production rates, but the first system has 30% more net primary production than the second system. Which ecosystem would you expect to support more trophic levels? Why?

19.5 Biotic Influences

A variety of species can influence rates of primary production in aquatic and terrestrial ecosystems. In subsection 19.2 of this chapter, we emphasized the effects of physical and chemical factors on rates of primary production. More recently, ecologists have discovered that primary production is also affected by a diversity of species interactions as well. For example, in chapter 16 we discussed how the genotypic and species diversity within a community enhanced primary production. Here, we focus on the impacts of herbivory and predation.

Ecologists refer to the influences of physical and chemical factors on ecosystems, such as temperature and nutrients, as **bottom-up controls**. Bottom-up controls are also reflected in our discussion of energy flow; the amount of energy at the base of the food web affects how much can flow to each successive trophic level. The influences of consumers on ecosystems are known as **top-down controls**. In the previous two sections, we discussed bottom-up controls on rates of primary production. Here, we discuss top-down control.

Piscivores, Planktivores, and Lake Primary Production

Stephen Carpenter, James Kitchell, and James Hodgson (1985) proposed that while nutrient inputs determine the potential rate of primary production in a lake, piscivorous and planktivorous fish can cause significant deviations from potential primary production. In support of their hypothesis, Carpenter and his colleagues (1991) cited a negative correlation between zooplankton size, which is an indication of grazing intensity, and primary production.

Carpenter and Kitchell (1988) proposed that the influences of consumers on lake primary production can extend to other levels throughout food webs. Since they visualized the effects of consumers coming from the top of food webs to the base, they called these effects on ecosystem properties trophic cascades. The trophic cascade hypothesis (fig. 19.19) is very similar to the keystone species hypothesis (chapter 17). However, notice that the trophic cascade model is focused on the effects of consumers on ecosystem processes, such as primary production, and not on their effects on species diversity.

Carpenter and Kitchell (1993) interpreted the trophic cascade in their study of lakes as follows: piscivores, such as largemouth bass, feed on planktivorous fish and invertebrates. In doing so, they indirectly affect populations of herbivorous zooplankton. By reducing populations of planktivorous fish, largemouth bass reduce predation pressure on zooplankton. Large-bodied zooplankton, the preferred prey of size-selective planktivorous fish (see chapter 7), soon dominate the zooplankton community. A dense population of large zooplankton reduces phytoplankton biomass and the rate of primary production. This interpretation of the trophic cascade is consistent with the negative correlation between zooplankton body size and primary production reported by Carpenter and his research team.

Carpenter and Kitchell tested their trophic cascade model by manipulating the fish communities in two lakes and by using a third lake as a control. Two of the lakes contained substantial populations of largemouth bass. A third lake had no bass, due to occasional winterkill, but contained an abundance of planktivorous minnows. The researchers removed 90% of the largemouth bass from one experimental lake and put them into the other. They simultaneously removed 90% of the planktivorous minnows from the second lake and introduced them to the first (fig. 19.20). They left a reference lake unmanipulated as a control.

The responses of the study lakes to the experimental manipulations support the trophic cascade hypothesis (fig. 19.20). Reducing the planktivorous fish population led to reduced rates of primary production. In the absence of planktivorous minnows, the predaceous invertebrate *Chaoborus* became more numerous. *Chaoborus* fed heavily upon the smaller herbivorous zooplankton, and the herbivorous zooplankton assemblage shifted in dominance from small to large species. In the presence of abundant, large herbivorous zooplankton, phytoplankton biomass and rate of primary production declined.

Adding planktivorous minnows produced a complex ecological response. Increasing the planktivorous fish population led to increased rates of primary production. However, though the researchers increased the population of planktivorous fish in this experimental lake, they did so in an unintended way. Despite the best efforts of the researchers, a few bass remained. So, by introducing a large number of minnows they basically fed the remaining bass. An increased food supply combined with reduced population density induced a strong numerical response by the bass population (see chapter 11). The manipulation increased the reproductive rate of the remaining largemouth bass 50-fold, producing an abundance of young largemouth bass that feed voraciously on zooplankton.

The lake ecosystem responded to the increased biomass of planktivorous fish (young largemouth bass) as predicted at the outset of the experiment. The biomass of zooplankton decreased sharply, the average size of herbivorous zooplankton decreased, and phytoplankton biomass and primary production increased.

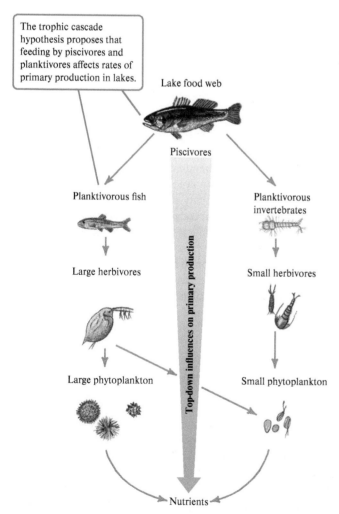

The trophic cascade hypothesis proposes that feeding by piscivores and planktivores affects rates of primary production in lakes.

Lake food web

Piscivores

Planktivorous fish

Planktivorous invertebrates

Large herbivores

Small herbivores

Large phytoplankton

Small phytoplankton

Top-down influences on primary production

Nutrients

Figure 19.19   The trophic cascade hypothesis proposes that feeding by piscivores and planktivores affects rates of primary production in lakes.

Experimental manipulations

Reduced piscivore (bass) biomass
Increased planktivore biomass

Increased piscivore (bass) biomass
Decreased planktivore biomass

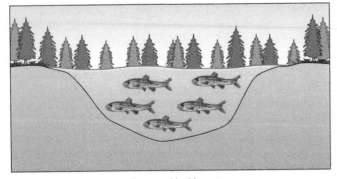

Decreased herbivores
Increased phytoplankton

Responses

Increased herbivores
Decreased phytoplankton

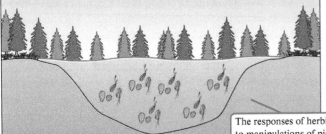

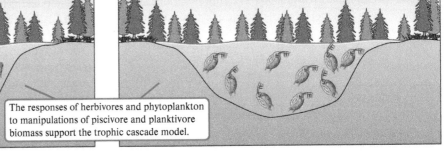

The responses of herbivores and phytoplankton to manipulations of piscivore and planktivore biomass support the trophic cascade model.

Figure 19.20   Experimental manipulations of ponds and responses.

The results of these whole-lake experiments show that the trophic activities of a few species can have large effects on ecosystem processes. However, most trophic cascades described by ecologists have been in aquatic ecosystems with algae as primary producers. This pattern prompted Donald Strong (1992) to ask, "Are trophic cascades all wet?" Strong suggested that trophic cascades most likely occur in ecosystems of lower species diversity and reduced spatial and temporal complexity. These are characteristics of many aquatic ecosystems. Despite these restrictions, consumers have significant effects on rates of primary production in some terrestrial ecosystems; one of those is the Serengeti grassland ecosystem.

Grazing by Large Mammals and Primary Productivity on the Serengeti

The Serengeti-Mara, a 25,000 km² grassland ecosystem that straddles the border between Tanzania and Kenya, is one of the last ecosystems on Earth where great numbers of large mammals still roam freely. Sam McNaughton (1985) reported estimated densities of the major grazers in the Serengeti that included 1.4 million wildebeest (*Connochaetes taurinus albujubatus*), 600,000 Thomson's gazelle (*Eudorcas thomsonii*), 200,000 zebra (*Equus quagga*), 52,000 buffalo (*Syncerus caffer*), 60,000 topi (*Damaliscus korrigum*), and large numbers of

20 additional grazing mammals. McNaughton estimated that these grazers consume an average of 66% of the annual aboveground primary productivity on the Serengeti. In light of this estimate, the potential for consumer influences on primary productivity seems very high.

Over two decades of research on the Serengeti ecosystem in Tanzania led McNaughton to appreciate the complex interrelations of abiotic and biotic factors there. For instance, both soil fertility and rainfall stimulate plant production and the distributions of grazing mammals. However, grazing mammals also affect water balance, soil fertility, and plant production.

As you might predict, the rate of primary production on the Serengeti is positively correlated with the quantity of rainfall. However, McNaughton (1976) also found that grazing can increase above-ground primary production. Similar to the methods used by Jefferies in chapter 14.1, McNaughton fenced in some areas in the western Serengeti to explore the influence of herbivores on production. The migrating wildebeest that flooded into the study site grazed intensively for four days, consuming approximately 85% of plant biomass. During the month after the wildebeest left the study area, biomass within the enclosures decreased, while the biomass of vegetation outside the enclosures increased (fig. 19.21). Similar to the geese in arctic wetlands, these mammals caused compensatory growth of many grass species. Compensatory growth was likely caused

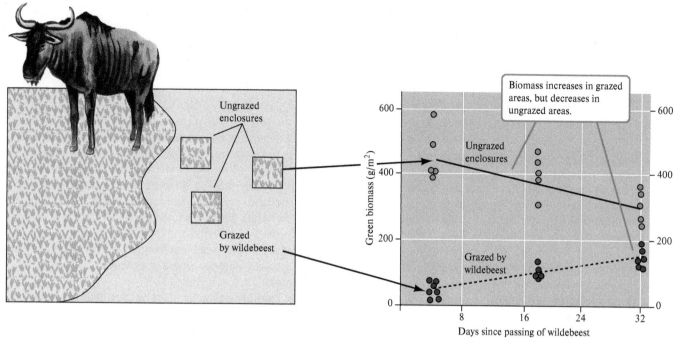

Figure 19.21   Growth response by grasses grazed by wildebeest.
Data from McNaughton 1976.

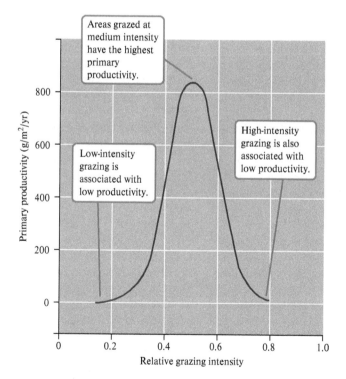

Figure 19.22   Grazing intensity and primary productivity of Serengeti grassland.
Data from McNaughton 1985.

by reduced self-shading and improved water balance due to reduced leaf area and reduced respiration. McNaughton (1985) found that compensatory growth was highest at intermediate grazing intensities (fig. 19.22). Apparently, light grazing is

insufficient to produce compensatory growth, and very heavy grazing reduces the plant's capacity to recover.

What McNaughton and his colleagues described is essentially a trophic cascade in a terrestrial environment where the feeding activities of consumers have a major influence on ecosystem properties. The Serengeti is now an exceptional terrestrial ecosystem, but it was not always so. As we saw in chapter 2, the extensive grasslands of North America and Eurasia too were once populated by vast herds of mammalian grazers. Historians estimate that the population of North American bison in the middle of the nineteenth century numbered up to 60 million. Such a dense concentration of grazers must have had significant influences upon the grassland ecosystems of which they were a part. It appears that terrestrial consumers, as well as the aquatic ones studied by Carpenter and Kitchell, can have important influences on primary production.

In the Ecological Tools and Approaches section, we review how ecologists can use stable isotope analyses to determine the trophic position of a species within an ecosystem.

CONCEPT 19.5 REVIEW

1. Since increased phytoplankton biomass decreases water clarity in lakes, how should fishing pressure on the bass population in a lake ecosystem impact water clarity?

2. Why is it more difficult to obtain evidence for trophic cascades in terrestrial ecosystems, as opposed to lakes?

ECOLOGICAL TOOLS AND APPROACHES

Using Stable Isotope Analysis to Trace Energy Flow Through Ecosystems Across Community Boundaries

How do ecologists study the flow of energy through ecosystems? First, they identify the organisms that make up the biological part of the ecosystem. Next, they determine who eats whom. They may identify consumers down to species or assign them broader taxonomic categories (e.g., insectivorous birds). Next, they assign organisms to trophic levels and determine (1) the biomass of each trophic level, (2) the rate of energy or food intake by each trophic level, (3) the rate of energy assimilation, (4) the rate of respiration, and (5) rates of loss of energy to predators, parasites, etc. Finally, ecologists combine their information on individual trophic levels to construct a trophic pyramid such as that constructed by Lindeman (see fig. 19.17) or an energy flow diagram such as that by Gosz and his colleagues (see fig. 19.18).

One of the fundamental steps in constructing a trophic pyramid or energy flow diagram is assigning organisms to trophic levels. While this task may sound easy, it is not. Most assignments are based on studies of feeding habits. If food items are easily identified and feeding habits are well studied and do not change significantly over time or from place to place, you may accurately identify feeding relations and assign organisms to trophic levels. However, if feeding habits are variable or if food items are difficult to identify, it may be difficult to assign organisms accurately to a particular trophic level. One of the most useful tools for making such assignments is stable isotope analysis (see chapter 6 and the Ecology in Action in this chapter).

Seasonal Shifts in the Diet of the Arctic Fox

In this book, we have presented food webs as static descriptions of the natural communities, but the composition of an individual's diet varies greatly over the course of its lifetime, as well as over the course of years, seasons, or even days. Further, individuals within a population of a single species may consume different prey, resulting in a diverse diet at the species level. The reasons for this are obvious: different food items become available at different times of year due to phenological patterns in plant growth, animal migration, and activity; and, just like people, different animals may specialize on and/or prefer different types of food. As we first introduced in chapter 17, stable isotopes can serve as a useful tool for deciphering the actual complexity of food webs.

James Roth has been studying the feeding behaviour of the animals near Churchill, Manitoba, for nearly a decade. Arctic foxes (*Vulpes lagopus*) are a common carnivore of the area, and they have a broad diet. The foxes are known to eat lemmings, bird eggs, and birds. However, some of these food items are available primarily during the summer,

while the foxes are year-round residents of the north. Additionally, lemmings have notoriously large population booms and busts; consequently, they will not always be available in high numbers as a food item. (And, no, this is not because they march themselves off cliffs for the good of the species. This myth comes about from their sometimes tragically careless habits during mass migration.) It has been hypothesized that in the winter the foxes can walk along the sea ice and scavenge seal meat from polar bear kill sites. Roth used a stable isotope approach to study seasonal shifts in the diets of the foxes (Roth 2002).

To measure seasonal shifts in diet, Roth needed samples from the foxes that would reflect short-term, rather than long-term, diet composition. In other words, he needed some animal tissue that grows rapidly. The Arctic foxes moult twice each year, and thus Roth was able to make the reasonable assumption that the dark brown hair produced at the start of spring would have the isotopic composition of their winter food, and the white hair produced at the start of winter would reflect their summer diet. Roth then took samples of fox hair over three years, as well as samples of the eggs of Canada geese, caribou, lemmings, and other possible food sources. Roth measured $^{13}C/^{12}C$ ratios for all samples.

There was a substantial shift in $^{13}C/^{12}C$ ratios across seasons (fig. 19.23), with substantially more ^{13}C in the winter diet than in the summer diet. This shift is consistent with a shift toward more marine-based food items in winter, as these animals tend to be enriched in ^{13}C relative to terrestrial animals. In a mark-recapture study, Roth found that the lemming population went from approximately 13 animals per hectare in 1994 to fewer than 4 animals per hectare in 1995, 1996, and 1997. Using a variety of analytical methods, Roth was able to estimate that when lemmings were abundant, marine food sources represented only about 17% of the foxes' diet. Immediately after the lemming population crash, marine food, such as leftovers scavenged from polar bear kills, represented over 40% of the foxes' diet.

This study is a great example of how stable isotopes allow ecologists to study complex phenomena, such as the relative contribution of different food items to the diet of animals. The results also have important implications for the future of the Arctic fox. Due to rapid global warming in the North, sea ice is forming later and breaking up earlier than it has over the last several decades. The impacts of this will most immediately be felt by polar bear populations, as their hunting grounds become less available. If this change results in decreasing numbers of polar bears and polar bear kill sites, it could mean a great reduction in a winter food source for the Arctic fox.

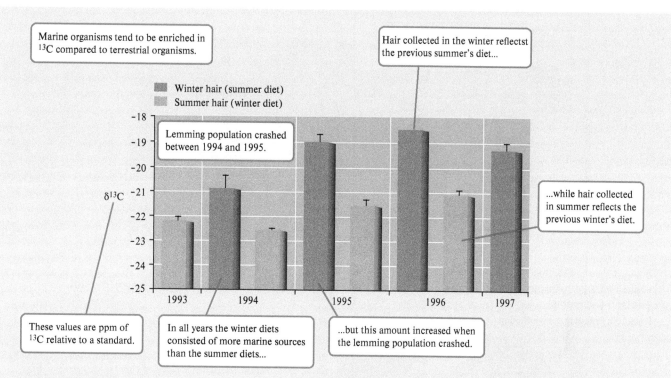

Marine organisms tend to be enriched in ^{13}C compared to terrestrial organisms.

Hair collected in the winter reflectst the previous summer's diet...

Winter hair (summer diet)
Summer hair (winter diet)

Lemming population crashed between 1994 and 1995.

...while hair collected in summer reflects the previous winter's diet.

$\delta^{13}C$

These values are ppm of ^{13}C relative to a standard.

In all years the winter diets consisted of more marine sources than the summer diets...

...but this amount increased when the lemming population crashed.

Figure 19.23 Isotopic composition of Arctic fox hair shifts with seasonal shifts in diet: hair collected in winter reflects the previous summer's diet, and hair collected in summer reflects the previous winter's diet.

From J. D. Roth. 2002. Temporal variability in Arctic fox diet as reflected in stable-carbon isotopes: The importance of sea ice. *Oecologia* 133:70–77. With kind permission from Springer Science and Business Media.

Using Stable Isotopes to Identify Sources of Energy in a Salt Marsh

The main energy source in a salt marsh in eastern North America is primary production by the salt marsh grass *Spartina*, most of which is consumed as detritus. The detritus of *Spartina* is carried into tidal creeks at high tide, where it is consumed by a variety of organisms, including crabs, oysters, and mussels. However, *Spartina* is not the only potential source of food for these organisms. The waters of the salt marsh also contain organic matter from upland plants and carry phytoplankton. How much might these other food sources contribute to energy flow through the salt marsh ecosystem?

Bruce Peterson, Robert Howarth, and Robert Garritt (1985) used stable isotopes to determine the relative contributions of *Spartina*, phytoplankton, and upland plants to the nutrition of the ribbed mussel (*Geukensia demissa*), a dominant filter-feeding species in New England salt marshes. The researchers pointed out that determining the trophic structure of salt marshes is not easy; detritus from different sources is difficult to identify visually because there are several potential sources of detritus and because organisms may frequently change their feeding habits. As a result, it is difficult to accurately quantify the relative contributions of alternative energy sources to a species like *Geukensia*

using traditional methods. Those methods will also probably miss transient dietary switches entirely.

As a solution to these problems, Peterson and his colleagues used the ratios of stable isotopes of carbon, nitrogen, and sulfur to assess the relative contributions of alternative food sources to the nutrition of the mussel. They used the stable isotopes of these three elements because their ratios are different in phytoplankton, upland C_3 plants (see chapter 7), and *Spartina*, a C_4 grass (fig. 19.24). Upland plants are the most depleted of ^{13}C while *Spartina* is the least depleted. Stable isotopes of sulfur and nitrogen are also distributed differently among these potential energy sources. For instance, *Spartina* has the lowest relative concentration of ^{34}S while plankton has the highest concentration of ^{34}S.

Because of these differences in isotopic concentrations, the researchers were able to identify the relative contributions of potential food sources to the diet of the mussel (fig. 19.25). Their analyses showed that *Geukensia* gets most of its energy from plankton and *Spartina* but that the relative contributions of these two food sources depend upon location. In the interior of the marsh, the mussel feeds mainly on *Spartina*, while near the mouth of the marsh it depends mainly on plankton. This is an example of how analyses of stable isotopes can provide us with a window to the otherwise hidden biology of species.

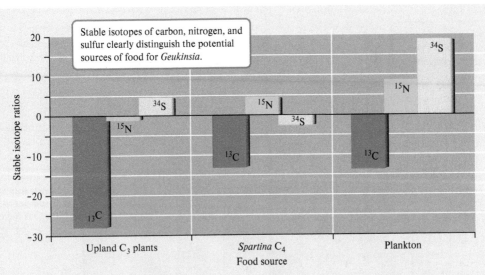

Stable isotopes of carbon, nitrogen, and sulfur clearly distinguish the potential sources of food for *Geukinsia*.

Figure 19.24   Isotopic content of potential food sources for the ribbed mussel (*Geukensia demissa*) in a New England salt marsh.

Data from Peterson, Howarth, and Garrit 1985.

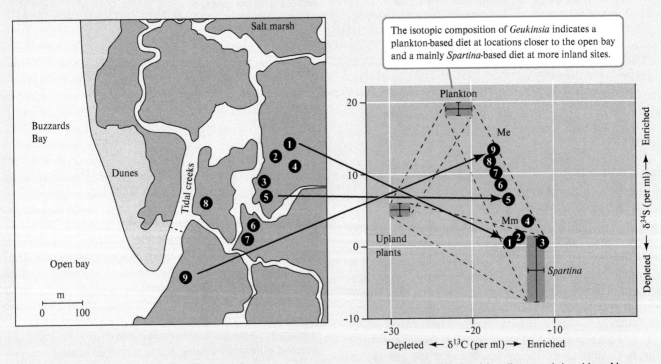

The isotopic composition of *Geukinsia* indicates a plankton-based diet at locations closer to the open bay and a mainly *Spartina*-based diet at more inland sites.

Figure 19.25   Variation in isotopic composition of ribbed mussels (*Geukensia demissa*) by distance inland in a New England salt marsh.

Data from Peterson, Howarth, and Garrit 1985.

SUMMARY

We can view a forest, a stream, or an ocean as a system that absorbs, transforms, and stores energy. In this view, physical, chemical, and biological structures and processes are inseparable. When we look at natural systems in this way we view them as ecosystems. An *ecosystem* is a biological community plus all of the abiotic factors influencing that community.

Primary production, the fixation of energy by autotrophs, is one of the most important ecosystem processes. The rate of primary production is the amount of energy fixed over some interval of time. Gross primary production is the total amount of energy fixed by all the autotrophs in the ecosystem. Net primary production is the amount of energy left over after autotrophs have met their own energetic needs.

19.1 Primary production is the gateway for energy and nutrients entering food webs. Energy and nutrients will be transferred and transformed as they flow through food webs.

Primary production is the biological fixation of inorganic carbon (CO_2 or HCO_3^-) forming organic matter. Organic molecules possess stored chemical energy that can be transferred from one trophic level to the next when, for example, a plant sheds its leaves and fungi decompose them, a herbivore eats a plant, or a parasite feeds on the herbivore (fig. 19.26). The flow of energy from one trophic level to the next is intimately coupled with the flow and transformation of nutrients, including N, P, and S. We generally focus on photosynthetic primary production, but chemolithotrophs may oxidize reduced nitrogen, sulfur, or carbon compounds. These alternate forms of autotrophy can contribute significantly to an ecosystem's primary production. The respiration and decomposition of organic matter fuels generation of ATP but also regenerates mineral forms of nutrients. Although aerobic respiration is most efficient for generating ATP, anaerobic forms or respiration may occur when oxygen is limiting. The use of nitrate or sulfate as terminal electron acceptors is another way in which energy flow is linked to nutrient cycling.

19.2 Terrestrial primary production is generally limited by temperature and moisture.

The variables most highly correlated with variation in terrestrial primary production are temperature and moisture. Highest rates of terrestrial primary production occur under warm, moist conditions (fig. 19.26). Temperature and moisture conditions can be combined in a single measure called annual actual evapotranspiration, or AET, which is the total amount of water that evaporates and transpires off a landscape during the course of a year. Annual AET is positively correlated with net primary production in terrestrial ecosystems. However, significant variation in terrestrial primary production results from differences in soil fertility.

19.3 Aquatic primary production is generally limited by nutrient availability.

One of the best documented patterns in the biosphere is the positive relationship between nutrient availability and rate of primary production in aquatic ecosystems. Phosphorus concentration usually limits rates of primary production in freshwater ecosystems, while nitrogen concentration usually limits rates of marine primary production. In many areas of high human impact, there are large marine dead zones, areas essentially devoid of life.

19.4 Energy losses limit the number of trophic levels in ecosystems.

Ecosystem ecologists have simplified the trophic structure of ecosystems by arranging species into trophic levels based upon the predominant source of their nutrition. A trophic level is determined by the number of transfers of energy from primary producers to that level. As energy is transferred from one trophic level to another, energy is lost due to limited assimilation, respiration by consumers, and heat production. As a result of these losses, the quantity of energy in an ecosystem decreases with each successive trophic level, forming a pyramid-shaped distribution of energy among trophic levels (fig. 19.26). As losses between trophic levels accumulate, eventually there is insufficient energy to support a viable population at a higher trophic level. Along with energy limitation, optimal foraging, evolutionary constraints, and decreasing stability may also limit the number of trophic levels in an ecosystem.

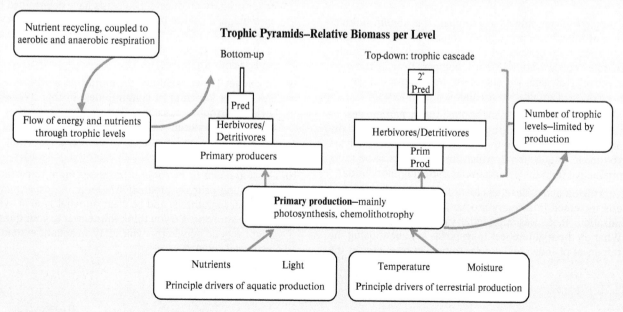

Figure 19.26 Concept map for chapter 19.

19.5 A variety of species can influence rates of primary production in aquatic and terrestrial ecosystems.

Trophic cascades can occur in terrestrial and aquatic ecosystems. Piscivorous fish can indirectly reduce rates of primary production in lakes by reducing the density of plankton-feeding fish, leading to increased densities of herbivorous zooplankton and decreased densities of phytoplankton (fig. 19.26). Intense grazing in the Serengeti can lead to compensatory growth by plants. These effects may also cascade up the food chain, increasing herbivore biomass.

Stable isotope analysis can be used to trace the flow of energy through ecosystems. The ratios of different stable isotopes of important elements such as nitrogen and carbon are generally different in different parts of ecosystems. As a consequence, ecologists can use isotopic ratios to study the trophic structure and energy flow through ecosystems.

REVIEW QUESTIONS

1. Population, community, and ecosystem ecologists study structure and process. However, they focus on different natural characteristics. Contrast the important structures and processes in a forest from the perspectives of population, community, and ecosystem ecologists.

2. M. Huston (1994) pointed out that the well-documented pattern of increasing annual primary production from the poles to the equator is strongly influenced by the longer growing season at low latitudes. The following data are from table 14.10 in Huston (1994). The data cited by Huston are from Whittaker and Likens (1975).

Forest Type	Annual NPP (t/ha/yr)	Length of Growing Season (months)	Monthly NPP (t/ha/mo)
Boreal forest	8	3	2.7
Temperate forest	13	6	?
Tropical forest	20	12	?

Complete the missing data to compare the *monthly* production of boreal, temperate, and tropical forests. How does this short-term perspective of primary production in high-, middle-, and low-latitude forests compare to an annual perspective? How does the short-term perspective change our perception of tropical versus high-latitude forests?

3. Many migratory birds spend approximately half the year in temperate forests during the warm breeding season and the other half of the year in tropical forests. Given the analyses you made in question 2, which forest appears to be more productive from the perspective of these migratory birds?

4. Turkington and colleagues (1998) found that although forests increased in primary productivity in response to fertilization, there was substantial variation among species. What do these differences in response say about using the responses of individual species to predict responses at the ecosystem level? What about the reverse: Can we predict the responses of individual species or growth forms from ecosystem-level responses?

5. Compare the pictures of trophic structure that emerged from our discussions of food webs in chapter 17 with those in this chapter. What are the strengths of each perspective? What are their limitations?

6. Over the last several decades, NPP near coastal areas has typically increased, while it decreased in open areas. Why might this pattern have emerged?

7. Suppose you are studying a community of small mammals that lives on the boundary between a riverside forest and a semidesert grassland. One of your concerns is to discover the relative contributions of the grassland and the forest to the nutrition of small mammals living between the two ecosystems. Design a research program to study this.

8. Most of the energy that flows through a forest ecosystem flows through detritus-based food chains, and the detritus consists mainly of dead plant tissues (e.g., leaves and wood). In contrast, most of the energy flowing through a pelagic marine or freshwater ecosystem flows through grazing food chains with phytoplankton constituting the major primary producers. Ecologists have determined that, on average, a calorie or joule of energy takes only several days to pass through the pelagic ecosystem but a quarter of a century to pass through the forest ecosystem. What explains this difference?

9. In chapter 17, we examined the influences of keystone species on the structure of communities. In this chapter, we reviewed trophic cascades. Discuss the similarities and differences between these two concepts. Compare the measurements and methods of ecologists studying keystone species versus those studying trophic cascades.

10. Are top-down or bottom-up processes more important in controlling primary production? Design an experiment to test your hypothesis, and be clear on what type of system you are studying. Do you think the answer to your question might depend on whether you study an aquatic system or a terrestrial system?

Radius Images/Alamy.

CHAPTER 20   NUTRIENT AND ELEMENTAL CYCLING

CHAPTER CONCEPTS

20.1 All common elements have global cycles that include biotic and abiotic pools.
Concept 20.1 Review

20.2 Decomposition rate is influenced by temperature, moisture, and chemical composition of litter and the environment.
Ecology in Action: How Decomposition Can Change the World
Concept 20.2 Review

20.3 Plants and animals can modify the distribution and cycling of nutrients in ecosystems.
Concept 20.3 Review

20.4 Human activities and natural disturbance can dramatically impact nutrient cycling.
Ecological Tools and Approaches: Altering Aquatic and Terrestrial Ecosystems
Concept 20.4 Review
Summary
Review Questions

When you pick up a handful of soil, you are holding tens of billions of microorganisms, representing millions of different species of bacteria, archaea, fungi, and protists. Not only are you holding tremendous genetic diversity, but you are holding enormous metabolic diversity. In your hands are microbes capable of fixing their own carbon using sunlight or oxidation of ammonium, sulfur, or methane. You have microbes capable of aerobic respiration, or respiration supported by nitrate, ferric iron, sulphate, or organic matter. You are holding microbes capable of degrading nearly any carbon compound that occurs naturally or that we are capable of producing. We have previously talked about the great diversity of flora and fauna in tropical rain forests, but it pales in comparison to the microbial diversity in your grasp.

The diversity of metabolic processes in a fairly small space has some interesting ramifications. One is a sharp gradient in oxidation/reduction potential (ORP), discussed further below. Microbial metabolism creates this gradient in ORP in water, soils, and sediment. In chapter 19, we talked about some different modes of respiration and how conditions affect what chemical species might be used as electron acceptors. Oxygen yields more energy per molecule of glucose than nitrate, and will be used first. Once oxygen is exhausted, nitrate will be used in respiration. Once nitrate becomes depleted, microbes may switch to using ferric iron, then to sulfate, and finally to fermentation (fig. 19.5). If you go from the surface of sediments (closest to a source of oxygen), ORP is positive and aerobic respiration predominates. As you go deeper into the sediments, away from oxygen, you see progressively more reducing conditions (negative ORP) and a change along this gradient to more hard-core anaerobic processes, such as fermentation and sulfate reduction.

The ORP is a measure of the tendency for a solution to gain or lose electrons. When we add a new chemical species, is it likely to gain electrons and become reduced or to lose electrons and become oxidized? A solution's ORP depends on the chemical composition of a solution. An abundance of oxidized species, such as O_2 and NO_3^-, contributes to high (positive) ORP. A new chemical species introduced would tend to lose electrons. But when microbes use up the oxygen and then the nitrate, ORP decreases. A new chemical species added would tend to gain electrons and become reduced. Microbial metabolism therefore affects ORP, and in turn ORP affects which microorganisms can grow and what metabolic pathways can occur.

Figure 20.1 is a sediment core, a plastic cylinder filled with pond sediment. An electrode was buried at 5 cm, and a second electrode is in the water above the sediment surface. The meter shows the difference in ORP at surface versus 5 cm depth as a voltage potential between the anode and cathode. This voltage potential is a direct result of the different metabolic pathways at different depths. It is a measure of electro-chemical energy that could be used to do work. This little core of sediment is never going to power my laboratory. While it is not a microbial fuel cell, it demonstrates how microbial fuel cells can produce electrical energy. Microbial fuel cells in general do not provide a great deal of electrical current. It is unlikely that they will

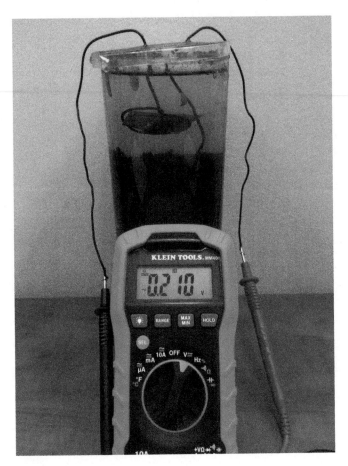

Figure 20.1   Sediment core with electrodes demonstrating the voltage potential created by microbial activity.
Andrew Laursen.

ever be a major component of a renewable energy strategy. However, large-scale fuel cells are being used to generate bioelectricity for local use from waste byproducts of some industries. Most commonly, we see them integrated into wastewater treatment facilities where there is always a steady source of rich organic fuel.

The microbial fuel cell is a microcosm of the processes we will talk about in this chapter. The flow of energy through a microbial ecosystem is coupled with the cycling of carbon, nitrogen, phosphorus, sulfur, and other elements. The voltage potential that allows us to extract energy from the fuel cell is a direct result of these biological processes. However, elemental cycles are important for far more than generation of a bit of power: indeed, they underpin the function of ecosystems.

The exchange of nutrients between organisms and their environment is an essential feature of an ecosystem. A diatom living in the surface waters of a lake absorbs a phosphate molecule from the surrounding water. It incorporates the phosphate into its DNA during cell division. A few hours later, one of the diatom's daughter cells is eaten by a cladoceran, an algae-feeding member of the zooplankton. The cladoceran incorporates the phosphate into a molecule of ATP. The cladoceran lives two days more and then is eaten by a planktivorous minnow. Within the minnow, the phosphate is combined with a lipid

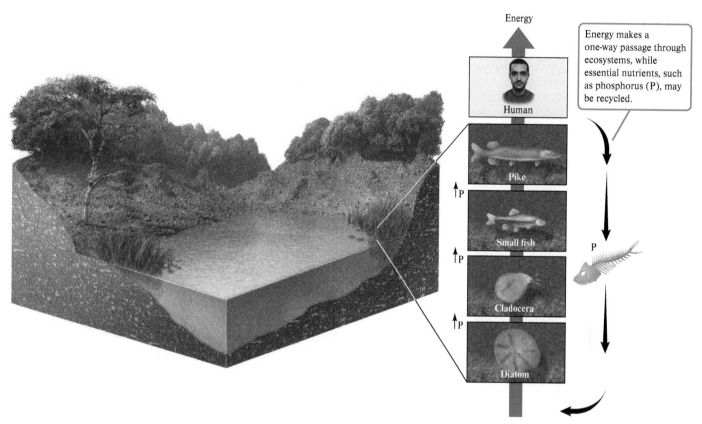

Figure 20.2   Phosphorus cycle in a lake ecosystem.

to form a phospholipid molecule in the cell membrane of one of the minnow's neural cells. A few weeks later, the minnow is eaten by a northern pike and the phosphate is incorporated into the pike's skeleton. During the following winter, the pike is caught by an intrepid person dropping a hook through the ice. The fish is filleted on site, with the fillets packed for home. The offal and skeleton are dropped back down the fishing hole, settling to the bottom of the lake. These tissues are attacked by bacteria and fungi that gradually decompose the remains of the pike. During decomposition, the phosphate in the skeleton is dissolved in the surrounding water. The following spring the very same phosphate molecule is taken up by another diatom, completing its cycle through the lake ecosystem (fig. 20.2).

The nutrient cycling processes that we will discuss shape the biological possibilities within an ecosystem. They constrain the flow of energy and the availability of macro and micro elements needed for building biomass. And by now it will probably not surprise you that biota, in their turn, shape the elemental cycles.

20.1   Nutrient Cycles

All common elements have global cycles that include biotic and abiotic pools. Ecological actions and chemical processes result in the movement of elements from one pool to another. Elements may reside in one pool for millennia or for minutes—depending upon a large number of biotic and abiotic processes.

Elements that are required for the development, maintenance, and reproduction of organisms are called **nutrients**, and ecologists refer to the use, transformation, movement, and reuse of nutrients within and among ecosystems as **nutrient cycling**. Because of the physiological importance of nutrients, their relative scarcity, and their influence on rates of primary production, nutrient cycling is one of the most significant ecosystem processes studied by ecologists. Elements in an ecosystem that are required by living organisms are labelled as *essential*. (In contrast, although uranium may be found in an organism, it is not an *essential* nutrient.) Essential nutrients can be further subdivided into **macronutrients** and **micronutrients**. Macronutrients are those essential elements required in large concentrations within an organism, while micronutrients are those required in only small concentrations. Carbon, hydrogen, oxygen, and phosphorus are macronutrients for all life on earth. However, the designation of other elements as macro or micro will depend upon the organism in question. For example, silica can be considered a macronutrient for diatoms but not for many other taxonomic groups. Because essential nutrients are typically actively taken up by organisms, they generally have a significant biotic component to their nutrient cycle.

All nutrients will cycle at several different scales of organization. For example, nitrogen taken up by a root in the soil will be translocated within a plant, perhaps into a growing leaf. As we discussed in chapter 7, that nitrogen is likely to be translocated to a new position within the plant prior to the leaf's falling from the plant. In other words, there is a nutrient cycle that occurs within an individual organism. That nitrogen will eventually leave that plant, where it may be used by other organisms or sit unused—with this process repeating through time. Thus, within an ecosystem is a second scale of nutrient cycling. A third scale exists when we realize that sometimes that nitrogen will leave the ecosystem through leaching, fire, or some other process. The nitrogen does not disappear; instead, it enters a new ecosystem (or resides in the atmosphere) where additional cycles may occur. Such nested scales of nutrient cycling occur for all nutrients used by living organisms, not just for nitrogen.

There are too many different elements in ecosystems for us to describe the cycles of each. Instead, we have chosen three nutrient cycles that play especially prominent roles in natural systems: the *phosphorus cycle*, the *nitrogen cycle*, and the *carbon cycle*. Nutrient cycles not described here, such as the sulfur cycle, are still important for the functioning of natural systems and, thus, to the quality of human life.

The Phosphorus Cycle

Phosphorus is essential to the energetics, genetics, and structure of living systems, forming part of ATP, RNA, DNA, and phospholipid molecules. While of great biological importance, phosphorus is not abundant in the biosphere. Increases in phosphorus in aquatic systems can cause large algal blooms (chapter 19), with cascading effects on fish and other aquatic species.

The global phosphorus cycle does not include a substantial atmospheric pool of phosphorus (fig. 20.3). Instead, the largest quantities of phosphorus occur in mineral deposits and marine sediments. Marine sediments will eventually be transformed into phosphate-bearing sedimentary rocks that through geological uplift can form new land. Phosphorus is slowly released to terrestrial and aquatic ecosystems through the weathering of this rock. As it is released, P is absorbed by plants and recycled within ecosystems. However, much of the phosphorus is washed into rivers and eventually finds its way to the oceans, where it passes though marine food webs. It will eventually find its way back to the ocean sediments when marine organisms die and sink. William Schlesinger (1991) points out that the phosphorus released by the weathering of sedimentary rocks has made at least one passage through the global phosphorus cycle.

Although phosphorus typically does not limit terrestrial plant growth, there are exceptions. In very old, weathered soils, such as those found in parts of the Canadian Shield and under wet tropical forests (chapter 2), plant growth may be limited by the availability of phosphorus. These soils may contain substantial quantities of phosphorus; however, much of this

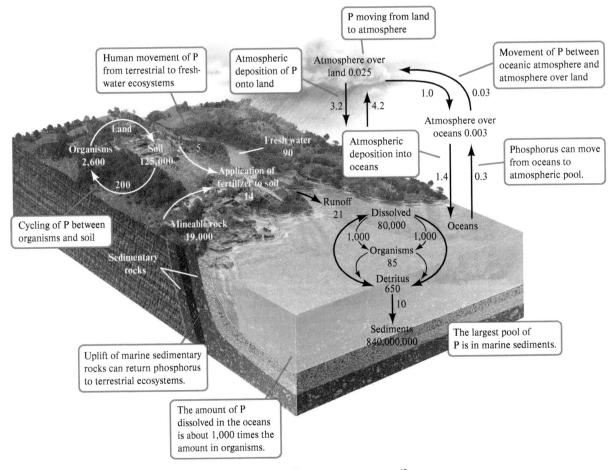

Figure 20.3 The global phosphorus cycle. Numbers are 10^{12} g P or fluxes as 10^{12} g P per year.
Data from Schlesinger 1991, after Richey 1983; Meybeck 1982; Graham and Duce 1979.

phosphorus occurs in chemical forms that are not directly available to plants. Phosphorus limitation can also occur in areas subjected to long-term agricultural production, where phosphorus has been absorbed from the soil by crops and removed with the harvest. Maintaining soil fertility in agricultural soils, then, often depends upon *phosphorus mining* of sedimentary rock, an inherently unsustainable system. There is currently substantial interest in and effort to reduce the loss of P from land to aquatic systems, driven both by a need to reduce eutrophication of lakes (chapter 19) and also to conserve P as a resource.

The Nitrogen Cycle

Nitrogen is important to the structure and functioning of organisms, forming part of key biomolecules, such as amino acids, nucleic acids, and the porphyrin rings of chlorophyll and hemoglobin. In addition, as we saw in chapter 19, nitrogen supplies may limit rates of primary production in marine and terrestrial environments. Much of modern agriculture attempts to overcome nitrogen limitation through fertilization. Nitrogen is also released into the atmosphere through the burning of coal (along with sulfur), where it hydrates and forms nitric

acid, contributing to acidification of many lakes in Canada and the United States. Later in this chapter we will discuss human impacts on the nitrogen cycle; here, we focus on an overview of the general cycle itself.

Two critical aspects of the nitrogen cycle are **mineralization** and **immobilization**. Mineralization is the conversion of organic forms of nitrogen (e.g., proteins) into mineral forms (e.g., ammonia and nitrate). Immobilization is the reverse process: the conversion of mineral forms of nitrogen into organic forms. Because mineral nitrogen often limits plant growth, the balance between these processes can greatly alter productivity. Microbes play a central role in nitrogen cycling.

The nitrogen cycle includes a major atmospheric pool in the form of molecular nitrogen, N_2 (fig. 20.4). However, only a few organisms, all prokaryotes, can use this form of nitrogen directly. These organisms, called nitrogen fixers, include (1) some cyanobacteria, or blue-green algae, of freshwater, marine, and soil environments; (2) free-living soil bacteria, such as *Azotobacter* and *Azospirillum*; (3) *Rhizobia* bacteria, associated with the roots of leguminous plants; and (4) *Frankia* bacteria, associated with the roots of alders and several other species of woody plants (fig. 20.5). Nitrogen

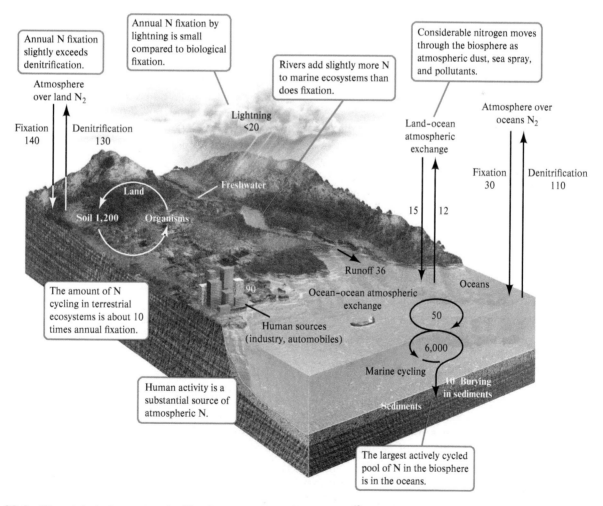

Figure 20.4 The global nitrogen cycle. Numbers represent fluxes as 10^{12} g N per year.
Data from Schlesinger 1991, after Söderlund and Rosswall 1982.

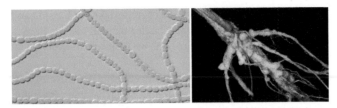

Figure 20.5 Some of the bacteria that can fix atmospheric nitrogen, converting it into a form usable by plants. Shown are cyanobacteria and root nodules containing *Rhizobia*.

Left: Courtesy of James W. Golden, Division of Biological Sciences, Molecular Biology section, University of California. Right: Worachat Tokaew/Shutterstock.com.

fixation is particularly important in supporting primary production in the oceans and in land plants—worth remembering when you consider the relative magnitudes of carbon flux to different pools in the next section. Because of the strong triple bonds between the two nitrogen atoms in the N_2 molecule, nitrogen fixation is a high energy-demanding process. During nitrogen fixation, N_2 is reduced to ammonia, NH_3. Nitrogen fixation takes place under aerobic conditions in terrestrial and aquatic environments, where nitrogen-fixing bacteria oxidize sugars to obtain the required energy. Nitrogen fixation also occurs as a physical process associated with the high pressures and energy generated by lightning; or through similar conditions through industrial production of nitrogen fertilizers. Pre-industrialization, the vast majority of the nitrogen cycling within ecosystems ultimately entered these cycles through nitrogen fixation by organisms or lightning. As we discuss later, humans now use large quantities of fossil fuels to generate the energy needed to break these triple bonds, creating mineral forms of nitrogen. Thus, we have been able to increase crop plant growth. In other words, humans are swapping the energy stored in fuels for the energy stored in plants by increasing the amount of N available to support plant growth. Of course, it is not a fully efficient system, and a consequence is the net dissipation of energy and increase in CO_2 in the atmosphere—a consequence we accept in order to eat.

Once nitrogen is fixed by nitrogen-fixing organisms (or lightning or burning of fossil fuels), it becomes available to other organisms within an ecosystem. Upon the death of an organism, the nitrogen in its tissues can be released by fungi and bacteria involved in the decomposition process. These fungi and bacteria release nitrogen as ammonium, NH_4^+, a process called **ammonification**. Ammonium may be converted to nitrate, NO_3^-, by other bacteria in a process called **nitrification**. Ammonium and nitrate can be used directly by some bacteria, fungi, or plants. The nitrogen in dead organic matter can also be used directly by some mycorrhizal fungi, which can be passed on to plants. The nitrogen in bacterial, fungal, and plant

biomass may pass on to populations of animal consumers or back to the pool of dead organic matter, where it will be recycled again.

Nitrogen may exit the organic matter pool of an ecosystem through denitrification. **Denitrification** is an energy-yielding process that occurs under anaerobic conditions and converts nitrate to molecular nitrogen, N_2. The molecular nitrogen produced by denitrifying bacteria moves into the atmosphere and can only re-enter the organic matter pool through nitrogen fixation. The mean residence time of fixed nitrogen in the biosphere is about 625 years. In contrast, the mean residence time of phosphorus in the biosphere is in the order of thousands of years.

The nitrogen cycle is unlike the phosphorus cycle in that not all processes are assimilatory or regenerative. The reason for this is that nitrogen, like sulfur and a number of other elements, may exist in a number of oxidation states (fig. 20.6). Because of this, nitrogen can be used in oxidation or reduction reactions coupled with other processes to generate cellular energy without nitrogen being incorporated into biomass. Nitrification results in a decrease in free energy, which can be used to fix carbon. Nitrate can be used as a terminal electron acceptor, reduced in a series of steps to N_2 (denitrification) or ammonium (dissimilatory nitrate reduction), and coupled with the oxidation of organic carbon to generate ATP. In some environments, reduction of nitrite, coupled with oxidation of ammonium, can provide bacteria with the energy to fix carbon, producing N_2 as a by-product (anammox). Availability of mineral forms of nitrogen (ammonium and nitrate), like availability of P, may limit primary production in an ecosystem. In addition, the relative availability of various nitrogen species can affect other processes related to the flow of energy through an ecosystem linked to nitrogen cycling processes.

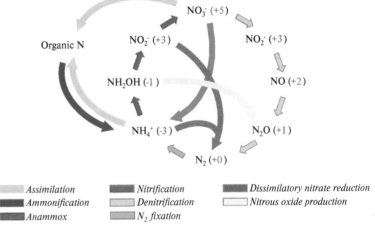

Figure 20.6 Nitrogen cycling processes, oxidation state of N provided in parentheses. Nitrogen participates in a variety of oxidation reactions (e.g., nitrification) and reduction reactions (e.g., denitrification, nitrogen fixation) that are linked to carbon cycling and energy flow.

The Carbon Cycle

Carbon is an essential part of all organic molecules. As constituents of the atmosphere, carbon compounds, such as carbon dioxide and methane (along with nitrous oxide), substantially influence global climate. This connection between atmospheric carbon and climate has drawn all nations of the planet into discussions of the ecology of carbon cycling and is discussed more fully in chapter 23.

Carbon moves between organisms and the atmosphere as a consequence of two reciprocal biological processes: photosynthesis and respiration (fig. 20.7), which are intimately linked to other elemental cycles. Photosynthesis removes CO_2 from the atmosphere, while respiration by primary producers and consumers, including decomposers, returns carbon to the atmosphere in the form of CO_2. In aquatic ecosystems, CO_2 must first dissolve in water before being used by aquatic primary producers. Once dissolved in water, CO_2 enters a chemical equilibrium with bicarbonate, HCO_3^-, and carbonate, CO_3^-. Carbonate may precipitate out of solution as calcium carbonate and may be buried in ocean sediments.

While some carbon cycles rapidly between organisms and the atmosphere, some remains sequestered in relatively unavailable forms for long periods of time. Carbon in soils, peat, fossil fuels, and carbonate rock would generally take a long time to return to the atmosphere. However, fossil fuels have become a major source of atmospheric CO_2 as humans have tapped into fossil fuel supplies to provide energy. We will discuss the effects of humans on the carbon cycle later in the chapter.

Ecosystem ecologists study the factors controlling the movement, storage, and conservation of nutrients within ecosystems. You can see broad outlines of these processes in figures 20.3, 20.4, and 20.7. However, much remains to be learned, especially concerning the factors controlling rates of nutrient exchange within and between ecosystems. Nutrient exchange is substantially affected by the process of decomposition, which we will discuss in the next section.

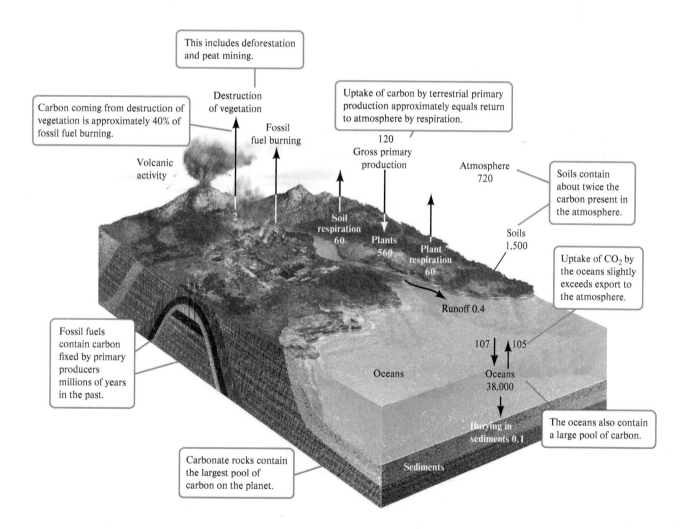

Figure 20.7 The global carbon cycle. Numbers are storage as 10^{15} g or fluxes as 10^{15} g per year.
Data from Schlesinger 1991.

CONCEPT 20.1 REVIEW

1. A critical aspect of nutrient cycles is the movement of elements from one pool into another. What are the largest pools for phosphorus, nitrogen, and carbon?

2. Apart from assimilation of N into biomass, how is the cycling of N connected to flow of energy through an ecosystem?

3. How does combustion of fossil fuels and destruction of vegetation compare with natural fluxes of CO_2 to the atmospheric pool of C?

4. The uptake of carbon by the oceans is slightly greater than release by respiration. What are some of the implications of this for the global C cycle?

20.2 Rates of Decomposition

Decomposition rate is influenced by temperature, moisture, and chemical composition of litter and the environment. The rate at which nutrients, such as nitrogen and phosphorus, are made available to the primary producers of terrestrial ecosystems is determined largely by the rate at which nutrient supplies are converted from organic to inorganic forms (mineralization). Mineralization takes place principally during **decomposition**, which is the breakdown of organic matter accompanied by the release of carbon dioxide.

Decomposition occurs partially through weathering but predominantly involves biotic interactions. Arthropods, fungi, and bacteria are common detritivores, using dead organic matter as their main energy source. As with all biological processes, decomposition rates are influenced by temperature and moisture, as well as the chemical composition of the dead material. Key chemical characteristics influencing decomposition rates include nitrogen concentration, phosphorus concentration, the carbon:nitrogen ratio, and lignin content. Ecologists have studied how several of these variables affect rates of leaf decomposition in Mediterranean ecosystems.

Decomposition in Two Mediterranean Woodland Ecosystems

Antonio Gallardo and José Merino (1993) studied how chemical and physical factors affect rates of decomposition of leaf litter in two Mediterranean woodland ecosystems in southwestern Spain (fig. 20.8). The mean annual temperature at the two sites differs by only 0.5° C and both sites experience Mediterranean climates with wet winters and dry summers. However, they differ significantly in annual rainfall. While Doñana Biological Reserve receives about 500 mm of rain annually, Monte La Sauceda receives about 1,600 mm, a difference driven by an elevational difference among sites. These two sites were ideally suited to study the effects of moisture on rates of decomposition.

Gallardo and Merino also explored the effects of litter chemistry on decomposition by using leaves from nine tree and shrub species that differed in concentrations of tannins, lignin, nitrogen, and phosphorus. You may remember from chapter 2 that many of the native plants from areas with a Mediterranean climate produce tough or sclerophyllous leaves. Gallardo and

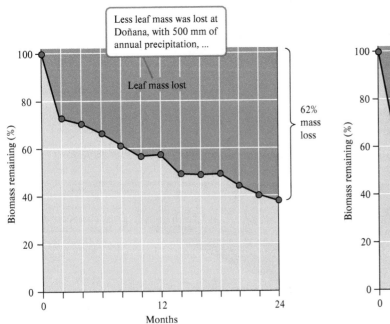
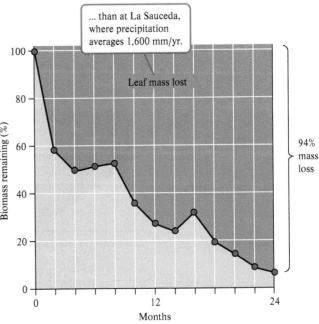

Figure 20.8   Decomposition of *Fraxinus angustifolia* leaves at wetter and drier sites.

Data from Gallardo and Merino 1993.

Merino also explored the influence of leaf toughness on decomposition rate.

The core research methodology in studies of decomposition is refreshingly straightforward. If you wanted to see how long dead material takes to disappear, what would you do? Here, approximately 2 g of air-dried leaves from each of the study species was put into several nylon mesh litter bags and placed at the Doñana Biological Reserve and at Monte La Sauceda. The litter bags had a mesh size of 1 mm—small enough to reduce the loss of small leaves, yet large enough to permit aerobic microbial activity and entry of small soil invertebrates. Every two months for two years Gallardo and Merino retrieved litter bags from each study site.

In the laboratory, the researchers measured the mass of leaf tissue remaining in replicate litter bags for each species. Figure 20.8 shows that the amount of leaf mass lost by ash leaves (*Fraxinus angustifolia*) was much higher at Monte La Sauceda. In fact, all species showed higher decomposition rates at Monte La Sauceda, supporting the idea that precipitation accelerates decomposition.

Differences in decomposition rates among species were similar at the two sites. For instance, the leaves of ash (*Fraxinus*) showed the greatest mass loss at both study sites, while the leaves of oak (*Quercus lusitanica*) showed the lowest mass loss at both study sites. Differences in mass loss by the nine species reflected differences in the physical and chemical characteristics of their leaves. In general, decomposition was fastest in species with high nitrogen and low leaf toughness (fig 20.9).

As we will see in the next example, the lignin—one aspect of leaf toughness—and nitrogen content also influence decomposition rates in temperate forest ecosystems.

Decomposition in Forest Ecosystems

Jerry Melillo, John Aber, and John Muratore (1982) used litter bags to study leaf decomposition in a temperate forest in New Hampshire. Their study species were beech (*Fagus grandifolia*), sugar maple (*Acer saccharum*), paper birch (*Betula papyrifera*), red maple (*Acer rubrum*), white ash (*Fraxinus americana*), and pin cherry (*Prunus pensylvanica*). They also compared their results with decomposition of leaves from white pine, chestnut oak, white oak, red maple, and flowering dogwood in a temperate forest in North Carolina.

In both the New Hampshire and North Carolina forests, the researchers found a negative correlation between the leaf mass remaining after one year of decomposition and the ratio of lignin to nitrogen concentrations in leaves. In other words, leaves with higher lignin:nitrogen lost less mass during the year-long study. As you can see in figure 20.10, the rate of loss was lower at the New Hampshire site than at the North Carolina site. What factors were responsible for these higher rates of decomposition at the North Carolina site? Melillo and his colleagues suggested that higher nitrogen availability in the soils at the North Carolina site may contribute to the higher rates of decomposition observed there. However, higher temperatures at the North Carolina site may also contribute to higher decomposition rates.

Studies in both temperate and Mediterranean regions suggest that rates of decomposition are positively correlated with

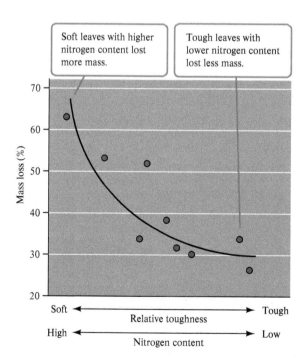

Figure 20.9 Influence of leaf toughness and nitrogen content on decomposition.

Data from Gallardo and Merino 1993.

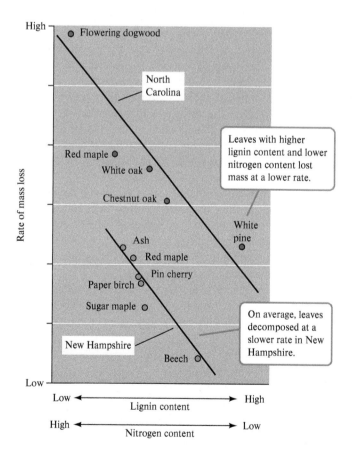

Figure 20.10 Influence of lignin and nitrogen content of leaves on decomposition.

Data from Melillo, Aber, and Muratore 1982.

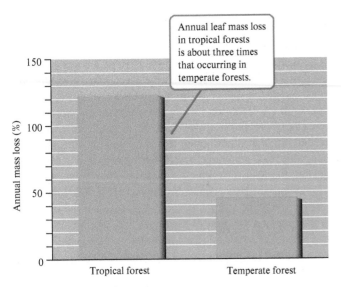

Figure 20.11 Decomposition in tropical and temperate forests.

Data from Anderson and Swift 1983.

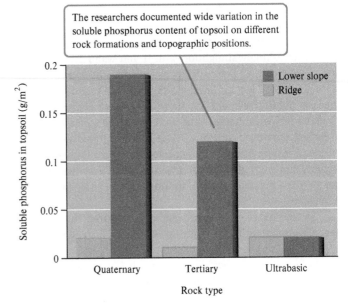

Figure 20.12 Concentrations of soluble phosphorus in topsoils formed on three rock types and at two topographic positions in Borneo.

Data from Takyu, Aiba, and Kitayama 2003.

temperature and moisture. Can we combine these two factors into one? In chapter 19, we reviewed how ecologists studying the effect of climate on terrestrial primary production combined temperature and precipitation into a single measure called actual evapotranspiration, or AET. Vernon Meentemeyer (1978) analyzed the relationship between AET and decomposition and found a significant positive relationship.

If decomposition rates increase with increased evapotranspiration, how would you expect rates of decomposition in tropical and temperate ecosystems to compare? As you probably predicted, rates of decomposition are generally higher in tropical ecosystems. The average annual mass loss in tropical forests shown in figure 20.11 is 120%, or three times the average rate measured in temperate forests. These higher rates probably reflect the effects of higher AET in tropical forests and indicate complete decomposition in less than a year.

Soil nutrient content has also been shown to have a strong positive effect on rates of nutrient cycling in tropical forests. Three forest ecologists, Masaaki Takyu, Shin-Ichiro Aiba, and Kanehiro Kitayama, took advantage of natural variation in nutrient content on different geologic formations and different topographic situations to explore the factors influencing tropical rain forest functioning in Borneo (Takyu et al. 2003). Within a geological formation, soil on ridges tended to have lower nutrient concentrations than soil on lower slopes. Nutrient concentrations

also varied among formations; soils overlying the younger Quaternary sedimentary rock were generally highest in nutrient content, followed by soils overlying Tertiary rock. Because all study sites were at approximately the same elevation and all were on south-facing aspects, the research team was able to isolate the influences of geologic conditions, especially soil characteristics. Takyu, Aiba, and Kitayama found higher rates of above-ground net primary production, higher rates of litter fall, and higher rates of decomposition on sites with higher concentrations of soluble phosphorus in topsoil (fig. 20.12). These results show that while climate may have primary influence on decomposition rates, within climatic regions soil fertility has an ecologically significant effect on decomposition and nutrient cycling rates.

In summary, decomposition in terrestrial ecosystems is influenced by moisture, temperature, soil fertility, and the chemical composition of litter, especially the relative concentrations of nitrogen and lignin. While decomposition was the focus of this section, it should not be lost on you that nutrient regeneration is linked with decomposition, and turnover of N and P (and other nutrients) should also be higher under conditions that favour decomposition. With the obvious exception of moisture, the same factors also influence decomposition rates in aquatic ecosystems, which we examine next.

 **ECOLOGY IN ACTION**

How Decomposition Can Change the World

In chapter 19 and in this chapter, we have provided a foundation for understanding the most basic ecosystem functions: primary production and nutrient cycling. We have

discussed how these ecological services can be altered by human activities, by the abiotic environment, and by interactions within the ecosystems themselves. The question

I am sure that many of you are asking is, so what? Although ecologists widely recognize that nutrient cycling is one of the most critical aspects of ecosystem ecology and that alteration of the rates of decomposition can have cascading effects, altering a variety of other ecological interactions and patterns of diversity, this message is not often clearly communicated to undergraduate students and the general population. Instead, decomposition is often viewed as among the dullest of subjects: studying things we can't see eating things that are dead. Why would anyone want to devote their life to the study of the rate at which dead leaves and roots turn into CO_2 and other molecules? The answer, quite simply, is that changes in decomposition will more directly and indirectly alter processes humans care about (such as climate change and biomass production) than nearly any other ecological process you will find in this book. Certainly, studying bear and elk in a national park is a great life, and understanding the ecology of these organisms is worthwhile. However, while a 10% increase or decrease in predation rates or population sizes of these charismatic creatures may alter their population sizes, it is not going to have much impact on global processes, climate, or how and where we live. But a 10% change in decomposition surely will.

Here we discuss one such example: the potential impact of altered rates of decomposition in the arctic and subarctic regions of the world. As we saw in chapters 2 and 3, northern regions are home to large expanses of peatlands and deep organic soils. These regions represent a large portion of the land mass on the planet, so we are talking about a lot of rich, organic soil. These areas are quite cold for much of the year, and in many areas deep layers of permafrost keep the layers of the ground frozen year round. What actually is frozen in the north? Is it simply clay, sand, and other layers of mineral soil? No. Although soil particles are frozen, much of the permafrost is organic matter—dead plants, animals, bacteria, and fungi. Put another way, the north is home to an enormous pool of frozen carbon, which could potentially be released into the atmosphere as CO_2 with a bit of liquid water and some warming. Let's try to put this into a larger perspective.

Between 20% to 60% of the carbon stored in the soil in the world is found in the northern regions, including the boreal forest and arctic tundra. This volume of C is roughly 10–100 times the amount of C released each year through deforestation and the burning of fossil fuels (Hobbie et al. 2000). Because of the magnitude of carbon stored in these soils, even a small change in decomposition rates has the potential to greatly increase the amount of carbon entering the atmosphere. As we discuss later in this chapter, increasing the amount of CO_2 in the atmosphere can further increase global temperatures. So, there is a strong possibility of a positive feedback cycle: increasing temperatures lead to higher decomposition rates in the Arctic, which, in turn, leads to more CO_2 entering the atmosphere, causing further increases in temperature and yet greater

decomposition rates. As you can see, the effects of rising temperatures in the Arctic on decomposition rates are of global importance. But, as you might imagine, the story is not quite this simple.

Although we often view the Arctic as a homogeneous expanse of land, it is not. There are many community types in the north, including salt marshes, dry grasslands, peatlands, and forested areas. The plants of different community types differ in tissue composition and, importantly, in the effects of increased temperature on decomposition rates (Shaver et al. 2006). In general, it is thought that the wetter areas will show the greatest increase in decomposition in response to increased temperatures (Shaver et al. 2006; Aerts 2006). In drier regions, it is thought that soil moisture, rather than soil temperature, limits decomposition rates. However, there is a lot of variation in the results of decomposition studies in the Arctic, in part due to different types of experimental treatments being imposed (Aerts 2006) (fig. 20.13). Some data even suggest that increased decomposition associated with warming may increase N mineralization, essentially fertilizing parts of the Arctic. This in turn may stimulate plant growth, resulting in increased, rather than decreased, storage of C in the soil! It is too early to say for certain what the direct effect of altered temperature will be on decomposition rates, though there is grave concern among many researchers.

A second complication is that even if increased temperature has a minimal effect on the rate of decomposition of the unfrozen parts of soil, it could greatly impact global carbon cycles if it causes a partial thawing of the permafrost. Substantial evidence already exists that this is

Figure 20.13 Open-top chambers, such as the one pictured here in a polar desert on Ellesmere Island, are commonly used to study the effects of warming on ecological processes.

OTC at Alexandra Fiord, Ellesmere Island by Cassandra Elphinstone, licensed under the Creative Commons Attribution-Share Alike 4.0 International license, https://creativecommons.org/licenses/by-sa/4.0/deed.en

occurring throughout much of the High Arctic (Serreze et al. 2000). A recent model based on observations of permafrost occurrence and mean annual air temperature predicts a global loss of permafrost of 4 million km^2 $°C^{-1}$ relative to baseline (1960–1990) (Chadburn et al. 2017). If global temperature rise is stabilized at 1.5°C—the current target of the Paris Accord—this would mean a loss of > 30% of the Arctic's permafrost. As a consequence of this thawing, more organic matter will be decomposed, even if the per area rate of decomposition is constant. Again, the impact on global carbon cycles will depend upon whether the increase in nitrogen that also occurs is enough to stimulate plant growth.

The effects of temperature on decomposition are not limited to direct impacts due to increased temperatures. Instead, decomposition rates can also be altered through changes in litter composition and changes in the soil fauna.

In particular, *Sphagnum* mosses have very low decomposition rates and may even reduce decomposition of the surrounding vegetation (Aerts 2006). Although long-term studies are few in number, those that have occurred suggest that moss abundances decrease under warming (Aerts 2006), supporting the idea that warming can enhance decomposition through a shift in plant composition and litter quality. As we discussed in chapter 2, the functional ecology and description of soil fauna communities is very poorly understood, and this lack of information is even more pronounced in northern systems.

As you can see here, the functional consequences of warming on soil communities are unknown, and major discoveries wait for the next generation of ecologists—that is, of course, if they are willing to take on the challenge of working (with organisms they can't see that eat dead things) on questions whose answers could change the world.

Decomposition in Aquatic and Wetland Ecosystems

Jack Webster and Fred Benfield (1986) reviewed what was known about the decomposition of plant tissues in freshwater ecosystems. Among the most important variables that emerged from their analysis were leaf species, temperature, and nutrient concentrations in the aquatic ecosystem.

Webster and Benfield summarized the rates of leaf breakdown for 596 types of woody and non-woody plants decaying in aquatic ecosystems and found that the average daily breakdown rate varied more than tenfold. As in terrestrial ecosystems, the chemical composition of litter significantly influences rates of decomposition in aquatic ecosystems.

The nutrient content of stream water can also influence rates of decomposition. Keller Suberkropp and Eric Chauvet (1995) studied how water chemistry affects rates of leaf decomposition, using the leaves of yellow poplar (*Liriodendron tulipifera*). They placed the leaves in several streams in the temperate zone that differed in water chemistry and were able to estimate the daily rate of mass loss.

Suberkropp and Chauvet found that leaves decayed faster in streams with higher concentrations of nitrates (fig. 20.14). This result is consistent with the suggestion by Melillo's research team that higher rates of decomposition at one of their study sites was due to higher availability of soil nitrogen. Similar results were found in streams draining a tropical forest. Amy Rosemond and colleagues (2002) found leaf decomposition rate increased markedly as phosphorus concentration increased to about 20 μg per litre, after which decomposition rate levelled off.

As in terrestrial ecosystems, litter chemistry and nutrient availability in the environment affect decomposition rates in aquatic ecosystems. These impacts of litter composition on water chemistry are found in all aquatic systems, including lakes and oceans, as well as in wetland systems, such as bogs and fens. The patterns discussed in this section emphasize the

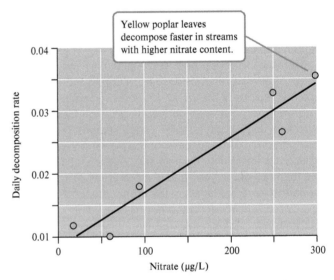

Figure 20.14 Stream nitrate and decomposition of *Liriodendron* leaves.
Data from Suberkropp and Chauvet 1995.

role played by the physical and chemical environment in the process of decomposition. As we shall see in the next section, animals and plants can also significantly affect the nutrient dynamics of ecosystems.

CONCEPT 20.2 REVIEW

1. During the past 30 years, thousands of papers have been published on decomposition within ecosystems. Why have ecologists spent so much time studying decomposition?

2. Why does litter chemistry alter decomposition rates?

20.3 Organisms and Nutrients

Plants and animals can modify the distribution and cycling of nutrients in ecosystems. In chapters 17 and 18, we discussed how interactions among organisms can cause changes to community structure, and in chapter 19 we discussed how these interactions influenced energy flow in ecosystems. These ecological interactions also impact nutrient cycling. One of the great realizations in ecosystem ecology over the last several decades has been that although the same ecological processes occur in terrestrial and aquatic habitats (e.g., decomposition, herbivory, predation), there are consistent differences in the patterns of nutrient cycling between these ecosystems. Jonathan Shurin, formerly of the University of British Columbia, has summarized many of the critical differences in nutrient cycling between aquatic and terrestrial habitats (fig. 20.15) (Shurin et al. 2006).

As we saw in chapter 19, there is strong evidence for top-down control of productivity in some aquatic systems, while terrestrial systems are generally thought to be controlled by bottom-up processes. However, Shurin describes a number of other differences in the trophic structure and distribution of nutrients among terrestrial and aquatic systems (fig. 20.15). For example, aquatic systems tend to have a greater proportion of autotrophs being consumed by herbivores than by detritivores when compared to terrestrial systems. A consequence of this is that these systems tend to have a lower proportion of carbon and nutrients stored in detritus and detritivores than in terrestrial systems.

Shurin and colleagues (2006) suggest that driving these differences are fundamental differences in life-history, morphology, and chemistry between phytoplankton and terrestrial plants. In general, phytoplankton appear less well-defended than terrestrial plants (chapter 15), resulting in higher consumption rates of phytoplankton by zooplankton than of terrestrial plants by herbivores. Additionally, growth rates of phytoplankton are generally much higher than terrestrial plants, facilitating rapid nutrient cycling.

Overall, species interactions, life-histories, and environmental chemistry can all interact to influence nutrient cycling within an ecosystem. This should serve as a reminder that although we have divided this book into different sections, this does not mean that ideas presented in the first few chapters are not relevant to our discussion here. (This is why professors often have cumulative final exams!) We now move away from general differences that occur among ecosystems and present a few specific examples of how organisms can influence the distribution and dynamics of nutrients within ecosystems.

Nutrient Cycling in Streams

Before we consider how stream animals influence the dynamics of nutrient turnover in streams, we have to consider some special features of this ecosystem. As we saw in chapter 3, the most distinctive feature of stream and river ecosystems is water flow. Jack Webster (1975) was the first to point out that because nutrients in streams are subject to downstream transport, there is little nutrient cycling in one place. Water currents move nutrients

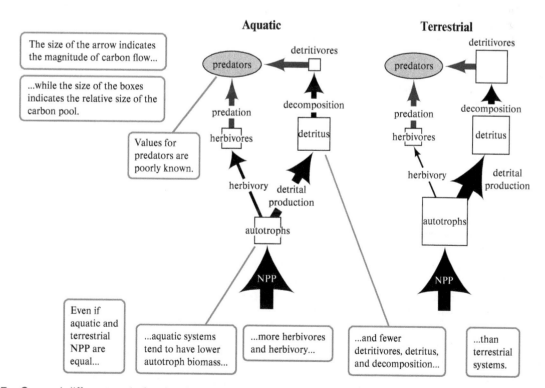

Figure 20.15 General differences in food webs and carbon flow among terrestrial and aquatic ecosystems.
Adapted from J. B. Shurin et al. 2006. All wet or dried up? Real differences between aquatic and terrestrial food webs. *Proceedings of the Royal Society B-Biological Sciences* 273:1–9.

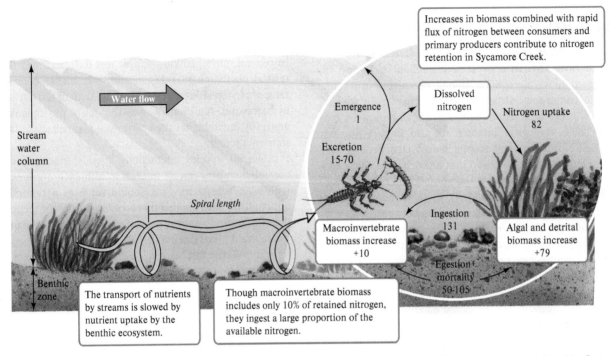

Figure 20.16 Nutrient spiralling in streams. Relative nitrogen fluxes are percentages of total nitrogen retained in Sycamore Creek, Arizona.
Data from Grimm 1988.

downstream. Webster suggested that rather than a stationary cycle, stream nutrient dynamics are better represented by a spiral. He coined the term **nutrient spiralling** to describe stream nutrient dynamics (fig. 20.16).

As an atom of a nutrient completes a cycle within a stream, it may pass through several ecosystem components, such as an algal cell, an invertebrate, a fish, or a detrital particle. Each of these ecosystem components may be displaced downstream by current and, therefore, contribute to nutrient spiralling. The length of stream required for a nutrient atom to complete a cycle is called the **spiralling length**. Spiralling length is related to the rate of nutrient cycling and average velocity of nutrient movement downstream. Denis Newbold and his colleagues (1983) represented spiralling length, S, as:

$$S = VT$$

where V is the average velocity at which a nutrient atom moves downstream and T is the average time for a nutrient atom to complete a cycle. If velocity, V, is low and the time to complete a nutrient cycle, T, is short, nutrient spiralling length is short. Where spiralling lengths are short, a particular nutrient atom may be used many times before it is washed out of a stream system.

The tendency of an ecosystem to retain nutrients is called **nutrient retentiveness**. In stream ecosystems, retentiveness is inversely related to spiralling length. Short spiralling lengths are equated with high retentiveness; and long spiralling lengths, with low retentiveness. Any factors that influence spiralling length affect nutrient retention by stream ecosystems. Why

does retentiveness matter? There are many possible answers, but most boil down to this: retentiveness affects how an ecosystem responds to nutrients. Phosphorus entering a stream with high retentiveness will have a greater impact than the same amount of P entering a stream with low retentiveness. It will be used more times, supporting higher rates of gross primary production and energy flow in a highly retentive stream. Nutrient retention in a stream can also be important in protecting downstream systems from excess nutrient loading. When nutrient loading to streams is excessive, and it often is in human-dominated ecosystems, retentive streams may store or remove some portion of this excess, reducing the impacts on lakes and coastal ecosystems downstream. We next look at some factors that affect spiralling length and, therefore, retentiveness.

Stream Invertebrates and Spiralling Length

Nancy Grimm (1988) showed that aquatic macroinvertebrates significantly increase the rate of nitrogen cycling in Sycamore Creek, Arizona. Streams in the arid American Southwest support high levels of macroinvertebrate biomass. Grimm estimated invertebrate population densities as high as 110,000 individuals per square metre and dry biomass as high as 9.62 g per square metre. More than 80% of macroinvertebrate biomass in Sycamore Creek was made up of species that feed on small organic particles, a feeding group that stream ecologists call *collector-gatherers*. The collector-gatherers of Sycamore Creek are dominated by two families of mayflies, Baetidae and Tricorythidae, and one family of Diptera, Chironomidae.

Grimm quantified the influence of macroinvertebrates on the nitrogen dynamics in the creek, where primary production is limited by nitrogen availability. She developed nitrogen budgets for stream invertebrates, mainly insect larvae and snails, by quantifying their rates of nitrogen ingestion, egestion (defecation), excretion, and accumulation during growth. By combining these rates with her estimates of macroinvertebrate biomass, Grimm was able to estimate the contribution of macroinvertebrates to the nutrient dynamics of the Sycamore Creek ecosystem.

Her measurements indicated that macroinvertebrates could play an important role in nutrient spiralling. To determine whether they play such a role, what information do we need? We need to know how much of the available nitrogen they ingest. If invertebrates ingest a large proportion of the nitrogen pool, then their influences on nitrogen spiralling may be substantial. Grimm measured the nutrient retention of Sycamore Creek as the daily difference between nitrogen inputs and outputs in her study area. She expressed this rate of retention as 100% and then expressed her estimates of flux rates among pools (e.g., excretion by invertebrates, ingestion by invertebrates, uptake by plants and algae) as percentages of this total (fig. 20.16). Nitrogen ingestion rates by macroinvertebrates averaged about 131%. How can ingestion rates be greater than 100%? What this means is that the collector-gatherers in the study stream re-ingest nitrogen in their feces. This is a well-known habit of detritivores, many of which gain more nutritional value from their food by processing it more than once.

Grimm suggests that this high rate of ingestion relative to the total N budget promotes rapid recycling of nitrogen. Macroinvertebrates excreted and recycled 15% to 70% of the nitrogen pool as ammonia. This recycling may increase primary production in Sycamore Creek. By their high rates of feeding on the particulate nitrogen pool and their high rates of excretion of ammonia, the macroinvertebrates of the creek reduce the T in the equation for spiral length, $S = VT$. The 10% of nitrogen tied up in macroinvertebrate biomass reduces V in the equation, as the macroinvertebrates are remaining in the stream, not being washed out. Collectively, these effects on V and T reduce the nitrogen spiral length, indicating a highly retentive stream ecosystem.

The Effect of Vertebrate Species on Nutrient Cycling in Aquatic Ecosystems

Vertebrate species, particularly fish, can move a surprising quantity of nutrients and carbon across ecosystem boundaries. We typically think about terrestrial, freshwater, and marine ecosystems as being connected by the downstream flow of nutrients and organic matter driven by gravity. The life cycle of anadromous Pacific salmon (*Oncorhynchus* spp.) is a dramatic example of how animals can affect nutrient cycling, reversing this flow by carrying marine-derived carbon and nutrients into freshwater streams. *Oncorhynchus* spp. spend most of their lives at sea before they return to spawn and die in the streams and lakes where they were born. Annual spawning of *Oncorhynchus* spp. provides an important seasonal food resource for mammals and birds. Stable isotope evidence demonstrates that marine-derived nutrients from salmon carcasses are used at multiple trophic levels in both freshwater and terrestrial ecosystems (fig. 20.17) (chapter 19, Ecology in Action) (Kline et al. 1993, Naiman et al. 2002).

Figure 20.17 Salmon transport nutrients from marine to freshwater and terrestrial ecosystems during and after spawning.
© Annie Reynolds/Photolink/Getty RF.

Each year over 100 million Pacific salmon make the journey from the ocean back to their natal streams in British Columbia and the U.S. Pacific northwest (Gresh et al. 2000). Nicole Mitchell and Gary Lamberti (2005) studied the response of dissolved nutrients and periphyton abundance (measured as chlorophyll a) to the run of spawning salmon in several Alaskan streams. The purpose was to learn if assimilation of marine nutrients into freshwater and terrestrial food webs could occur through bottom-up control. They studied one creek over two consecutive years and found that ammonium concentrations increased 20-fold during salmon runs in the two years, and phosphate concentrations increased 4- to 7-fold. In the first year, there was also a strong periphyton response to salmon, with chlorophyll a (per m^2) increasing 20-fold, although this was not evident the following year. Mitchell and Lamberti also measured response across six different streams during the second year of the study, and in a more controlled artificial stream mesocosm. The salmon greatly increased both ammonium and phosphate concentrations across all streams and within the mesocosm. Periphyton also increased in response to salmon carcasses within controlled conditions of the mesocosm. The response of periphyton to salmon-derived nutrients was variable across the natural streams, suggesting that other factors, such as light availability or disturbance, might constrain this response. Mitchell and Lamberti's study demonstrated that the return of salmon and decay of their carcasses can provide a large nutrient subsidy to the stream, affecting the function of these ecosystems. As we shall see in the next section, consumers can also substantially affect nutrient cycling in terrestrial ecosystems.

Animals and Nutrient Cycling in Terrestrial Ecosystems

Burrowing animals, such as ground squirrels and pocket gophers, can affect nutrient cycling processes. April Whicker and James Detling (1988) found that the feeding activities of prairie dogs also influence the distribution of nutrients within prairie ecosystems. This should not be surprising since these

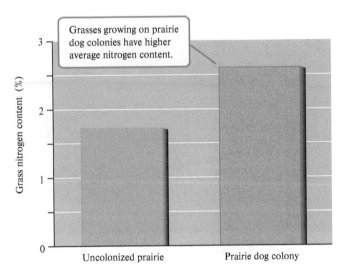

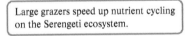

Figure 20.18 Early season nitrogen content of grasses growing on uncolonized prairie and on a young prairie dog colony.

Data from Whicker and Detling 1988.

researchers estimate that prairie dogs consume or waste 60% to 80% of the net annual production from the grass-dominated areas around their colonies. One result of this heavy grazing is that above-ground biomass is reduced by 33% to 67% and the young grass tissue that remains is higher in nitrogen content (fig. 20.18). This higher nitrogen content may influence the behaviour of bison, which spend a disproportionate amount of their time grazing near prairie dog colonies.

Bison and other large herbivorous mammals, such as moose and African buffalo, may also influence the cycling of nutrients within terrestrial ecosystems. Sam McNaughton and his colleagues (1988) report a positive relationship between grazing intensity and the rate of turnover of plant biomass in the Serengeti Plain of eastern Africa. Figure 20.19 suggests that increased grazing increases

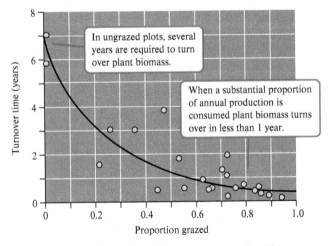

Figure 20.19 Effect of grazing on time required for turnover of plant biomass on the Serengeti ecosystem.

Data from McNaughton, Ruess, and Seagle 1988.

the rate of nutrient cycling. McNaughton et al. used these turnover time data, along with data on productivity and grazer population sizes and feeding rates, to construct a box model for N cycling. From their model, they concluded that nutrient cycling occurs more slowly in absence of the Serengeti's larger herbivores.

Steve Côte and colleagues at the Université Laval (Côte et al. 2004) suggest that deer may have similar effects in the forests of North America. Deer populations have increased rapidly for several decades throughout much of North America, reaching densities as high as 10/km² throughout the temperate forests (chapter 2). The causes of this population boom are numerous, ranging from reforestation on abandoned farmland, increased forage availability, and reduced predation by hunters and natural predators (Côte et al. 2004). Many forests are now experiencing an intensity of grazing that was not common in the evolutionary history of the species within these communities. As a result, many of the seedlings of the common canopy tree species, such as oak and maple, are poorly defended against high levels of herbivory. In areas of high deer density, prolonged browsing appears to be shifting the community toward species that are less palatable, such as conifers and ferns (Côte et al. 2004). This makes perfect sense given our understanding of natural selection, life histories, and the intermediate disturbance hypothesis. What is less obvious, but potentially of greater long-term effect, is what may be happening in the soil.

The changes in plant community composition reported by Côte and colleagues (2004) can, in turn, alter ecosystem processes. The research team found evidence that deer browsing can reduce the frequency of ectomycorrhizal infections among dominant trees, which could have negative implications for nutrient uptake. Additionally, intense grazing causes dominance of plant species that have substantial morphological and chemical defences. These species produce litter of lower quality than the former dominant plants, and thus rates of decomposition are reduced. As a result, some previously dominant plants seem hurt by a combination of browsing pressure, reduced nitrogen availability due to slower decomposition of leaf litter, and impaired foraging ability due to reduced mycorrhizal infection.

In the next section, we discuss how human activities and other disturbances alter nutrient cycling within ecosystems.

CONCEPT 20.3 REVIEW

1. The Great Plains of North America have experienced many changes over the past 200 years. Applying what you learned about grazing ungulates in the Serengeti, how has the extermination of wild bison likely influenced nutrient cycling?

2. How can differences in the intensity of herbivory cause differences in nutrient cycling between terrestrial and aquatic ecosystems?

3. How would you expect a high density of herbivores to affect nutrient retention in an ecosystem? Why? Although this is not restricted to stream systems, you might consider Nancy Grimm's study in answering.

20.4 Human Impacts on Elemental Cycles

Human activities and natural disturbance can dramatically impact nutrient cycling. Throughout the text we have emphasized how disturbances, both natural and anthropogenic, influence ecological and evolutionary processes. This remains true as we focus here on nutrients, rather than on communities and populations.

Industrial Activity and Nitrogen Enrichment

How has human activity altered the nitrogen cycle? To address this question, we need to review the sources and amounts of nitrogen fixed in the absence of human manipulation. Peter Vitousek (1994) summarized the natural background levels of nitrogen fixation as follows. The nitrogen fixed in terrestrial environments by free-living nitrogen-fixing bacteria and nitrogen-fixing plants totals approximately 100 terragrams (Tg) of nitrogen (N) per year (1 Tg = 10^{12} g). Nitrogen fixation in marine environments adds an additional 5 to 20 Tg N per year; fixation by lightning adds about 10 Tg N per year. These estimates of nonhuman sources of fixed nitrogen total approximately 130 Tg N per year.

Human activities also contribute to the total pool of fixed nitrogen. One of the traditional ways that humans have manipulated the nitrogen cycle is by planting agricultural land with nitrogen-fixing crops. At some point, agriculturists learned that rotating legumes such as alfalfa and soybeans with crops such as wheat and canola could increase crop yields. We now know that those increased yields are due mainly to nitrogen additions to the soil by the bacteria associated with legumes. Vitousek estimated that the plant–microbe mutualism that results in nitrogen-fixing crops fixes about 30 Tg N per year. As you know, farmers also apply nitrogen fertilizers produced through industrial processes. The nitrogen fixed by the fertilizer industry amounts to more than 80 Tg N per year. Finally, Vitousek estimated that the internal combustion engines in cars, trucks, and other conveyances emit about 25 Tg N per year as oxides of nitrogen. Smil (1990) estimated the total emission of nitrogen from all combustion of fossil fuels, including coal-fired electrical generation as well as internal combustion engines, at 35 Tg N per year. Vitousek's estimates of fixed nitrogen sources are now 25 years old (and Smil's are older still). Since then, the use of fertilizers has expanded, especially in tropical climates, and the use of fossil fuels has continued to grow. The main point here is that, on a global scale, human activities contribute as much, if not more, to the total pool of nitrogen than all nonhuman sources of fixed nitrogen combined (fig. 20.20).

The massive human contribution to the global nitrogen cycle is a recent phenomenon. For instance, the industrial production of fertilizers dates from the early twentieth century, and Vitousek estimated that 50% of all the commercial fertilizer produced prior to 1993 was applied to land between 1982 and 1993.

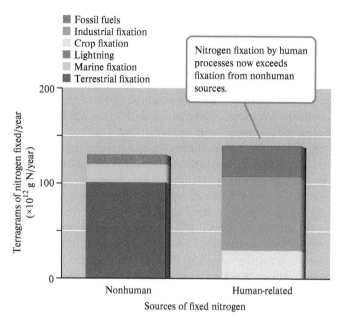

Figure 20.20   Human and nonhuman sources of fixed nitrogen.
Data from Vitousek 1994.

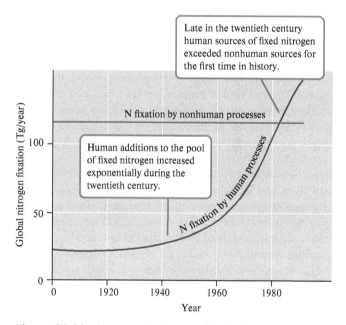

Figure 20.21   Increase in nitrogen fixation by human processes during the twentieth century.
Data from Vitousek 1994.

Figure 20.21 shows that human contributions to the global nitrogen cycle have increased exponentially, and by the late twentieth century human N fixation exceeded natural fixation.

What are some of the consequences of these human-induced alterations to the global nitrogen cycle? The near-shore marine environment, as discussed in chapter 3, is one of the most productive ecosystems on earth. It is also home to an incredible biological diversity. Most marine animals live or feed in shallow marine habitats, at least for some portion of their life cycles. In general, productivity is nitrogen limited, although there are some local and temporal variations on what limits primary production in the near shore marine environment. The export of nutrients from rivers to coastal marine systems stimulates the growth of algae. Algae may grow until they use up all available N or until some other nutrient becomes limiting to growth. Much of this biomass then sinks to the sediments of continental margins (shelf and slope). There it can be decomposed, the ammonium released is nitrified, and then the nitrate formed is denitrified, producing N_2, which leaves the system.

Nitrogen limitation in the modern ocean appears to be driven by this denitrification (McElroy 1983). Estimates of nitrogen loss by denitrification based on empirical modelling (Seitzinger and Giblin 1996) and direct measurements (e.g., Laursen and Seitzinger 2002) support the idea that denitrification on the continental shelf can contribute strongly to N removal. When we add in continental slope areas, denitrification in sediments of continental margins may remove nearly half of total nitrogen inputs to oceans (Christensen 1994). In fact, more recent data suggest that the ocean, including continental margins, may be an even greater sink for N than previously recognized (Codispoti 2007).

While the continental margins can be incredibly efficient at removing nitrogen and at preventing or limiting eutrophication of the open ocean, the near-shore ecosystems can pay a high cost. Increased productivity means more biomass sinking, more biomass decomposing, and more oxygen being consumed by bacteria. In the summer, water over the continental margins is usually stratified (chapter 3), and oxygen is consumed more rapidly than it is replenished by re-equilibration with the atmosphere. This can lead to areas of low (or no) dissolved oxygen in many marine coastal ecosystems, which are often referred to as dead zones due to the devastation that prolonged hypoxia has on ecosystem function and biological diversity (chapter 19). The number of marine dead zones has grown exponentially over the past several decades, with over 400 globally a decade ago (Diaz and Rosenberg 2008). Nancy Rabalais and her colleagues (2010) have suggested that stronger thermal stratification may increase the number of these areas. Most of the dead zones occur in areas predicted to experience at least a 2°C temperature increase by the end of the century, and climate change variables—such as temperature increases, ocean acidification, changing storm patterns, and rising sea levels—are predicted to act synergistically to increase the number and size of hypoxic zones globally (Altieri and Gedan 2015). Clearly, a comprehensive strategy beyond simply controlling nutrients is needed to protect the function of these important ecosystems.

In terrestrial systems, nitrogen addition can cause local reductions in plant and fungal diversity. Nitrogen enrichment appears to also alter the mutualistic relationship between plants and mycorrhizal fungi. Consequently, nitrogen enrichment over large regions threatens the health and survival of entire ecosystems as we know them. The health of forests near industrial areas has been in rapid decline. By creating environmental conditions favourable to some species and unfavourable to others, large-scale nitrogen enrichment threatens biological diversity. As we shall see in the Ecological Tools and Approaches section, nutrient enrichment of ecosystems by human activity is a worldwide problem.

One potential impact of nitrogen enrichment may be its contribution to forest encroachment on grasslands. When more nitrogen becomes available, for example by atmospheric deposition, trees tend to competitively exclude many grasses. The impacts of large-scale nitrogen deposition have been studied by Scott Wilson and his graduate student, Martin Köchy, of the University of Regina (Köchy and Wilson 2001). The northern region of the North American Great Plains is a sparsely populated area, much of which exists as a mosaic of grasslands and forests. Wilson and Köchy measured nitrogen dynamics and forest encroachment in six national parks in Manitoba, Saskatchewan, and Alberta. In each location, they measured nitrogen deposition, the amount of nitrogen available to plants in the soil, and the extent of forest invasion into land previously occupied by grasslands.

Nitrogen deposition varied among parks and was highest in parks surrounded by high human population densities (Elk Island, Prince Albert) and lowest in areas of low population densities (Jasper, Wood Buffalo). High rates of nitrogen deposition were positively associated with high levels of nitrogen availability in the soils. Through their studies of photographs, they found that in the last 50 to 60 years there has been an increase in forest cover in Elk Island, Prince Albert, and Riding Mountain national parks, but not in Jasper, Wood Buffalo, or Grasslands (fig. 20.22). Statistical analyses indicated these changes are positively correlated to both precipitation and nitrogen deposition rates, suggesting that both water and extra nitrogen lead to increased forest cover in the North American Great Plains. Additionally, in those parks with increased forest cover, the timing of change appears synchronized with the timing of human population growth in the prairies (fig. 20.22).

These results are just one of many examples suggesting that atmospheric nitrogen is causing shifts in the composition of natural plant communities. These changes have occurred over only the last several decades and likely will continue into the foreseeable future. As we show next, industrial activities have also greatly impacted the global carbon cycle.

Human Influence on Carbon Cycles

Globally, human activity has greatly increased the amount of carbon that occurs as atmospheric CO_2, leading to increased global temperatures. Industrial activity has increased steadily since about the year 1800. Over the same period, atmospheric CO_2 has increased steadily. The evidence discussed here shows that most of this atmospheric increase is due to the burning of fossil fuels. Changes in atmospheric composition that affect global climate will certainly affect the biota of terrestrial ecosystems. The effect of human activity on atmospheric CO_2 and other gases is one of the most thoroughly studied aspects of global ecology.

The concentration of CO_2 in the atmosphere has been dynamic over much of earth's history. Scientists have very carefully reconstructed atmospheric composition by studying air bubbles trapped in ice. As ice built up on glaciers in places such as Greenland and Antarctica, air spaces within the ice preserved a record of the ancient atmosphere. A record of atmospheric

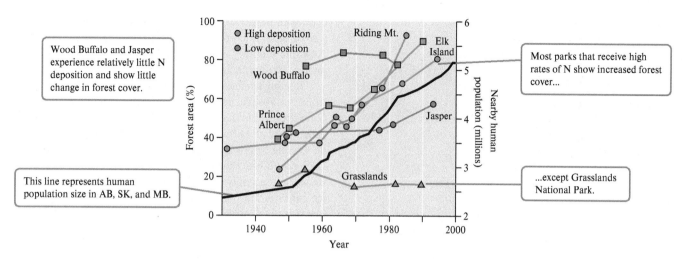

Figure 20.22 Changes in forest area and human population size throughout the prairie provinces of Canada.

M. Köchy and S. D. Wilson. 2001. Nitrogen deposition and forest expansion in the northern Great Plains. *Journal of Ecology* 89(5):807–17, Figure 5. Reprinted with permission of Blackwell Publishing.

composition during the last 160,000 years was extracted and analyzed by a joint team of scientists from France and the former Soviet Union (Lorius et al. 1985, Barnola et al. 1987). This international team studied a 2,083 m core of ice drilled by Soviet scientists and engineers near the Antarctic station of Vostok. Vostok, located in eastern Antarctica at a latitude of over 78° S, has a mean annual temperature of −55° C, ideal conditions for preserving samples of the atmosphere in ice. The Vostok research station sits on the high Antarctic plateau, where the ice is about 3,700 m thick. The amazing physical feat of extracting such a long ice core in such difficult physical circumstances is equalled by the dramatic climatic record contained within the Vostok ice core.

To extract air trapped within ice, scientists place sections of an ice core into a chamber and create a vacuum, removing traces of the current atmosphere in the process. The ice, still under vacuum, is then crushed and the air it contains is released into the chamber. Sampling devices then measure the CO_2 concentration of the air released from the ice. The Barnola team made 66 measurements along the length of the Vostok ice core. At each location they were also able to estimate the air temperature at the time the ice was formed. The scientists made measurements of CO_2 every 25 m along the length of the ice core from about 850 m depth to the bottom of the core. These lower sections of the core correspond to ages from 50,000 to 160,000 years. Because there were many fractures in the core above 850 m depth, the upper portion of the core was generally sampled at intervals greater than 25 m.

The core indicated two very large fluctuations in atmospheric CO_2 concentration (fig. 20.23). Overall, it shows that CO_2 concentrations have oscillated between low concentrations of approximately 190 to 200 parts per million (ppm) and high concentrations of 260 to 280 ppm. About 160,000 years ago, the atmospheric concentration of CO_2 was less than 200 ppm. This early period in the Vostok ice core corresponds to an ice age. Then, about 140,000 years ago, the atmospheric concentration of CO_2 began to rise abruptly, peaking at nearly 300 ppm. This rise

in CO_2 corresponds to a warmer interglacial period. High levels of CO_2 persisted until about 120,000 years ago. The concentration of CO_2 then declined and remained at relatively low concentrations until about 13,000 years ago, when atmospheric CO_2 again increased abruptly, marking the end of the last ice age.

Notice that the fluctuations in CO_2 within the Vostok ice core correspond to variation in temperature (fig. 20.23). The periods of low CO_2 correspond to the low temperatures experienced during ice ages, while the periods of high CO_2 correspond to warmer, interglacial periods.

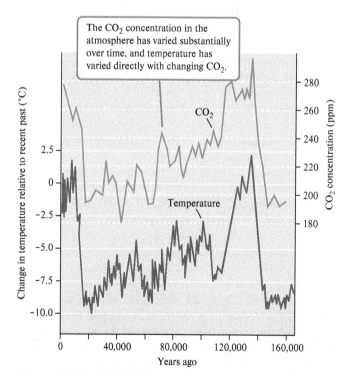

Figure 20.23 A 160,000-year record of atmospheric CO_2 concentrations and temperature change.

Data from Barnola et al. 1987.

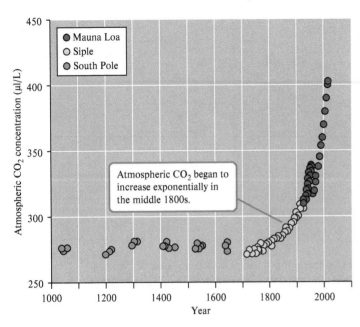

Figure 20.24 A 1,000-year atmospheric CO_2 record.
Data from Post et al. 1990.

The most recent measurements in the Vostok ice core are about 2,000 years old. How has atmospheric CO_2 varied since then? W. Post and colleagues (1990) assembled atmospheric CO_2 records from a number of sources to estimate atmospheric concentrations during the last 1,000 years (fig. 20.24). The first 1,000 years of the record come from the South Pole ice core, which was analyzed by Ulrich Siegenthaler and colleagues (1988) of the University of Bern, Switzerland. This record shows that the concentration of CO_2 remained relatively constant for approximately 800 years. Another study at the University of Bern provided a CO_2 record for the most recent 200 years (Friedli et al. 1986). This part of the CO_2 record comes from the Siple ice core, from Siple Station at about 75° S latitude. While the Siple ice core does not allow us to look as far back in time as the Vostok record, it provides a very detailed estimate of recent concentrations of atmospheric CO_2. H. Friedli and colleagues dated the beginning of the Siple record at about A.D. 1744. At that time, about two-and-a-half centuries ago, the atmospheric concentration of CO_2 was about 277 ppm. This estimated concentration is almost identical to those made by the Siegenthaler team for the same time period using the South Pole ice core. Therefore, both the South Pole and Siple ice cores indicate that the CO_2 concentration in the middle 1700s was approximately the same as at the end of the Vostok record, about 2,000 years earlier.

The Siple record showed that CO_2 increased exponentially from 1744 to 1953. The Friedli team estimated the 1953 concentration of CO_2 at 315 ppm. However, the trace in CO_2 concentrations shown in figure 20.24 extends beyond 1953 and above 315 ppm. Where do these later measurements come from? These later CO_2 concentrations are direct measurements made on Mauna Loa, Hawaii, by Charles Keeling and his associates over a period of about 40 years (Keeling and Whorf 1994). The U.S. National Oceanic and Atmospheric Administration (NOAA) Earth System Research Laboratory at Mauna Loa

continues to measure and publish CO_2 concentrations, which were used in extending Post's records through 2016. As of April 2019, the monthly average CO_2 concentration was 413 ppm, a nearly 100 ppm increase since 1953!

Keeling's measurements complement the ice core data from the Vostok, South Pole, and Siple stations in two ways. First, they extend the record into the present. Second, they help validate the measurements of CO_2 made from the ice cores. How do Keeling's measurements lend credence to the ice core data? Look carefully at the plot of CO_2 concentrations shown in figure 20.24. Notice that two of the measurements made from the Siple ice core overlap the period when Keeling and his team made measurements at Mauna Loa. Notice also that the two estimates made independently by Keeling at Mauna Loa and by Friedli and his colleagues from the Siple ice core are almost identical.

The data in figure 20.25 indicate that during the nineteenth and twentieth centuries the concentration of atmospheric CO_2 increased dramatically. This period of increase coincides with the Industrial Revolution. However, what evidence is there that human activity caused this observed increase? Vitousek provided evidence by pointing out that the annual increase in atmospheric carbon in the form of CO_2 is about 3,500 Tg (1 Tg = 10^{12} g), while the annual burning of fossil fuels releases about 5,600 Tg carbon as CO_2. So, fossil fuel burning alone produces more than enough CO_2 to account for recent increases in atmospheric concentrations.

If we look carefully at the pattern of CO_2 increase between 1860 and 1960 we find additional evidence for a human influence. Figure 20.25 shows three interruptions in the otherwise steady increase in the burning of fossil fuels. Those periods correspond to three major disruptions of global economic activity: World War I, the Great Depression, and World War II. At the end of each of these major global upheavals, the increase in atmospheric CO_2 resumed. These patterns provide circumstantial evidence that humans are responsible for the modern increase in atmospheric CO_2. However, there is also direct evidence.

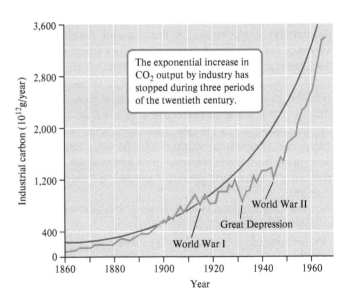

Figure 20.25 Deviations from recent exponential increases in fossil fuel burning.
Data from Bacastow and Keeling 1974.

Additional evidence that human industrial activity is at the heart of recent increases in atmospheric CO_2 comes from analyses of atmospheric concentrations of various carbon isotopes (see chapter 19). One of the most useful carbon isotopes for determining the contribution of fossil fuels to atmospheric CO_2 is radioactive ^{14}C. Because ^{14}C has a half-life of 5,730 years, fossil fuels, which have been buried for millions of years, contain very little of this carbon isotope. Consequently, burning fossil fuel adds CO_2 to an atmosphere that has little ^{14}C. If fossil fuel additions are a major source of increased atmospheric CO_2, then the relative concentration of ^{14}C in the atmosphere should be declining.

A recent decline in atmospheric ^{14}C was first described by Hans Suess (1955), a scientist with the U.S. Geological Survey. Suess made his discovery by analyzing the ^{14}C content of wood laid down by single trees at various times during their growth. He found that annual growth rings laid down in the late 1800s had significantly higher concentrations of ^{14}C than those laid down in the 1950s. Suess proposed that the ^{14}C content in wood was being progressively reduced because burning of fossil fuels was reducing the atmospheric concentration of ^{14}C. Because of his pioneering work, reduced atmospheric ^{14}C as a consequence of fossil fuel burning is called the **Suess effect**.

Robert Bacastow and Charles Keeling (1974) compiled ^{14}C data from several studies of ^{14}C in trees and plotted the date when the wood was formed against the relative ^{14}C content of the wood. As figure 20.26 shows, the concentration of ^{14}C was fairly stable from A.D. 1700 until about 1850. After 1850, ^{14}C concentrations in wood declined significantly. The curved line in figure 20.26 shows the predictions of ^{14}C concentrations based upon global patterns of fossil fuel burning and estimated rates of exchange of carbon between the ocean, the earth's biota, and the atmosphere.

What can we conclude from this evidence? Several things are clear. First, the concentration of CO_2 in the atmosphere has varied widely during the last 160,000 years and closely parallels variation in global temperatures. High levels of atmospheric CO_2 have corresponded to higher global temperatures. Second, the atmospheric concentration of CO_2 has increased substantially in the past two centuries. This modern increase has exceeded all levels reached during the past 160,000 years. Third, there is little doubt that the present levels of CO_2 in the atmosphere are strongly influenced by the burning of fossil fuels.

Deforestation and Nutrient Loss

As Gene Likens and Herbert Bormann watched, work crews felled the trees covering an entire stream basin in the Hubbard Brook Experimental Forest of New Hampshire. The felling of these trees was a key part of an experiment that Likens and Bormann had designed to study how forests affect the loss of nutrients, such as nitrogen, from forested lands (Bormann and Likens 1994; Likens and Bormann 1995). They had studied two small stream valleys for three years before cutting the trees in one of the valleys. The undisturbed stream valley would act as a control against which to compare the response of the deforested stream valley (fig. 20.27).

Before they deforested the experimental basin, Likens and Bormann inventoried the distribution of nutrients. Those measurements indicated that over 90% of the nutrients in the

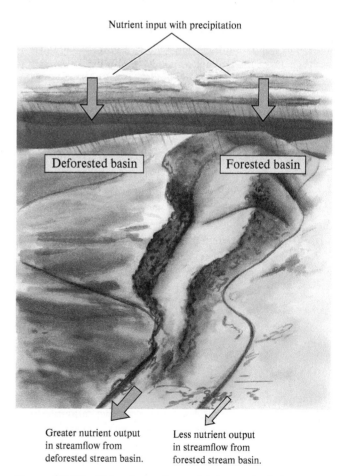

Nutrient input with precipitation

Deforested basin   Forested basin

Greater nutrient output in streamflow from deforested stream basin.

Less nutrient output in streamflow from forested stream basin.

Figure 20.27 This whole-stream-basin manipulation demonstrated the influence of forest trees on nutrient budgets of northeastern hardwood forests.

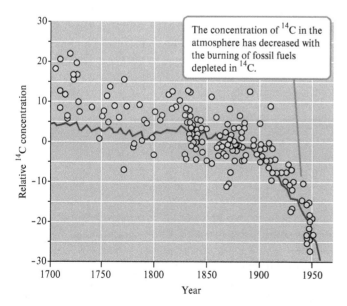

The concentration of ^{14}C in the atmosphere has decreased with the burning of fossil fuels depleted in ^{14}C.

Figure 20.26 The Suess effect.
Data from Bacastow and Keeling 1974.

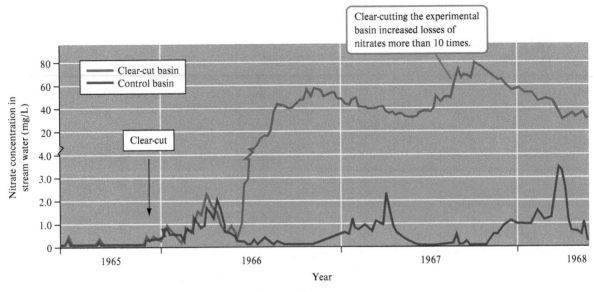

Figure 20.28   Deforestation and nitrate loss from a deciduous forest ecosystem.
Data from Likens et al. 1970.

ecosystem were tied up in soil organic matter. Most of the rest, 9.5%, was in vegetation. They estimated the rates at which some organisms fix atmospheric nitrogen and the rates at which weathering releases nutrients from the granite bedrock of the stream basins. They also measured the input of nutrients to the forest ecosystem from precipitation and nutrient outputs with stream water. The annual nutrient outputs in streamflow amounted to less than 1% of the amount contained within the forest ecosystems. After this preliminary work, Likens and Bormann cut the trees on their experimental stream basin. They then used herbicides to suppress regrowth of vegetation in their experimental basin and continued to apply herbicides for three years.

The increased rates of nutrient loss following forest cutting were dramatic. The connection between forest cutting and increased nutrient output is shown clearly by plotting nutrient concentrations in the streams draining experimental and control stream basins. Figure 20.28 shows the highly significant increases in nitrate losses following deforestation, which were 40 to 50 times higher than those in the deforested basin.

While removal of vegetation in Hubbard Brook and suppression of regrowth led to massive losses of nutrients from the

ecosystem, what might happen if plants were allowed to regrow? Monica Turner and her colleagues (2009) demonstrated biological influences on nutrient retention from forest ecosystems following the stand-replacing fires of 1988 in Yellowstone National Park, Wyoming. These forests are dominated by lodgepole pine (*Pinus contorta*) with a diverse understory plant community that quickly regenerated following the fire (Turner et al. 2003). The studies of the Yellowstone fires suggest that the young, rapidly growing *P. contorta* forest and understory vegetation was a nitrogen sink in the ecosystem. Turner's work also indicates that not all ecosystems lose nutrients following a disturbance and that many factors affect nutrient retention over time.

What do these results suggest about the role of vegetation in preventing losses of nitrogen from forest ecosystems? Over the short term, at least, uptake by vegetation in ecosystems with high rates of plant growth should be able to rapidly reduce nitrogen loss following disturbance, and this may extend to disturbances caused by humans, provided revegetation is not suppressed. This retains nutrients in the system, making them available to higher trophic levels and for recycling to support future plant growth.

ECOLOGICAL TOOLS AND APPROACHES

Altering Aquatic and Terrestrial Ecosystems

Human activity increasingly affects ecosystem nutrient cycles. Agriculture and forestry can remove nutrients from ecosystems. However, increasingly, human activity enriches ecosystems with nutrients, especially with nitrogen and phosphorus. Nitrogen enrichment comes from a variety of sources: combustion of fossil fuels, agricultural fertilizers, land clearing, forest burning, industry, and animal waste.

Nitrogen from anthropogenic sources enters the atmosphere as emissions or particulates, producing air pollution. Nitrogen fertilization occurs when biologically available forms of nitrogen fall from the atmosphere as either wet (precipitation) or dry (dry fall) deposition. In the temperate coastal forests of southern Chile, far from urban and industrial centres, inputs from nitrogen deposition amount to about 0.1 to 1.0 kg per hectare per year. In contrast, in the Netherlands, with its high population density and intense agriculture, the deposition of nitrogen to forest ecosystems adds up to about 60 kg of nitrogen per hectare per year.

Humans are also a major source of nutrient inputs to aquatic ecosystems. Nutrient enrichment of aquatic ecosystems can result in water quality problems and eutrophication, a process generally resulting in increased primary production, anoxic conditions, and reduced biodiversity. Benjamin Peierls and his colleagues (1991) examined the relationship of human population density within river basins and nitrate concentration and export by 42 major rivers. These rivers, which deliver approximately 37% of the total freshwater flow to the oceans, support human population densities ranging from 1 to 1,000 individuals per square kilometre.

Peierls noted that while the concentration and export of nitrate by rivers is affected by complex biotic, abiotic, and anthropogenic factors, a single variable—human population density—explains most of the variation in nitrate concentration and export (fig. 20.29). The most probable sources of nitrate enrichment of river ecosystems are sewage disposal, atmospheric deposition, agriculture, and deforestation, all of which generally increase with increased human population density. The broad range of sources of nitrate is one of the main reasons why it is difficult to control nitrogen pollution.

Cities are home to an increasing percentage of the human population. Worldwide, more people live in or near urban areas than in rural areas. The concentration of people in cities is also associated with the concentration and transformation of energy, materials, and waste in a small area, which can have disproportionate impacts on nutrient cycling. Prompted by a need for better understanding of urban areas, ecological studies of nutrient pools and fluxes within whole watersheds are being applied to these human-dominated ecosystems.

One of the first questions asked by ecologists is whether urban ecosystems within a watershed are a source or a sink for nutrients. Peter Groffman and his colleagues (2004) compared the nitrogen budgets of forested, agricultural, and urbanized watersheds as part of the Baltimore Ecosystem Study with surprising results. They constructed a budget by calculating inputs and outputs of nitrogen for each watershed type. Nitrate concentrations were measured as a major component of nitrogen outputs in streams draining each watershed. As expected, mean nitrate concentrations were very low in the forested watershed (fig. 20.30). However, nitrate levels in dense urban areas were lower than those in either the suburban or agricultural watersheds.

What caused higher nitrate concentrations in streams draining the agricultural and suburban watersheds? First, Groffman and his colleagues compared nitrogen inputs into the different watersheds. All of these watersheds receive similar amounts of atmospheric nitrogen deposition. The first major difference in inputs was in the application of fertilizers. Estimates of nitrogen inputs from fertilizers were highest for agricultural areas, but application of fertilizer to suburban lawns was also substantial. They also found that centralized urban sanitary systems can leak nitrogen but are controllable. In contrast, residential septic systems in suburban areas are designed to leak. Hence, they discharge nitrate and can contribute to nitrate concentrations in streams.

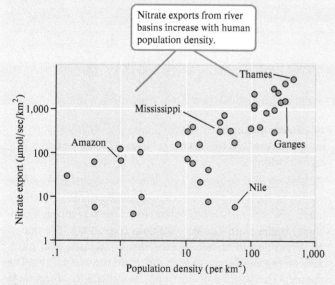

Figure 20.29   Human population density and nitrate export from river basins.

Data from Peierls et al. 1991.

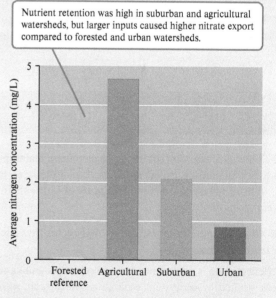

Figure 20.30   Nitrate export in streams draining watersheds with different land use in Baltimore County, Maryland.

Data from Pickett et al. 2008.

The difference in nitrogen outputs from these watersheds could not be explained by inputs alone. Another surprising result of Groffman's study was that the suburban watershed retained an estimated 75% of nitrogen inputs, approaching retention values of forested watersheds (95%). So even though the suburban areas had higher nitrogen inputs, only a quarter of this nitrogen was exported downstream. Groffman and his colleagues attribute this high capacity for nitrogen retention in suburban areas to actively growing lawns, woodlots, and riparian areas that serve as nitrogen sinks. These permeable areas within the watershed have the potential to decrease nitrogen export to surface water through biological uptake and denitrification of nitrate. These results call into question a common assumption that human alteration of the environment limits ecological processes in urbanized areas.

If urban areas can retain a large proportion of nitrogen inputs, why do we observe high nitrate export to rivers dominated by human activity worldwide? Studies of nitrogen budgets in cities are very limited and, to date, incomplete. For instance, the nitrogen budget for Baltimore did not include the large flux of food into and sewage out of the study watersheds. Wastewater is piped out for treatment on much larger streams or bays where wastewater effluent can be safely discharged. Most cities around the globe are facing the challenge of minimizing nitrogen pollution without proper infrastructure and planning. In a review of urban ecological studies, Emily Bernhardt and her colleagues (2008) suggest that cities need to integrate nitrogen reduction strategies into their management plans to minimize impacts on water quality. However, while scientists can make recommendations based on their research, they do not make or implement policy. Cities are dynamic, complex, socio-ecological systems that require close cooperation of scientists, managers, and citizens to minimize nutrient pollution.

In summary, we know that there is a direct connection between human activity and nutrient enrichment of ecosystems and that nutrient enrichment has a number of negative consequences. Application of an ecosystem approach to studies of nitrogen pools and fluxes within urban watersheds has advanced our understanding of nutrient cycling in urban systems, but much work remains at this frontier of ecology.

CONCEPT 20.4 REVIEW

1. How do human industrial activities impact nitrogen and carbon cycles?

2. Why did Suess look at the relative ^{14}C concentration wood as a function of age rather than the relative ^{13}C concentration?

3. Monica Turner found that a recently burned watershed was a net sink for nitrogen. This is in contrast to Likens and Bormann, who found the deforested Hubbard Brook watershed to be an exporter of N. Why did these two seemingly similar situations with recent forest lost have different outcomes in N retention?

SUMMARY

The elements organisms require for development, maintenance, and reproduction are called *nutrients*. Ecologists refer to the use, transformation, movement, and reuse of nutrients in ecosystems as *nutrient cycling*.

20.1 All common elements have global cycles that include biotic and abiotic pools.

Nutrient cycling is one of the most ecologically significant processes studied by ecosystem ecologists. The *carbon, nitrogen,* and *phosphorus cycles* have played especially prominent roles in studies of nutrient cycling. Chemical transformations move C, N, and P among different biotic and abiotic pools (fig. 20.31). Human actions and natural processes influence the rate of chemical flux and the size of each pool.

20.2 Decomposition rate is influenced by temperature, moisture, and chemical composition of litter and the environment.

The rate of decomposition affects the rate at which nutrients, such as nitrogen and phosphorus, are made available to primary producers. Rates of decomposition in terrestrial ecosystems are higher under warm, moist conditions (fig. 20.31). The rate of decomposition in terrestrial ecosystems increases with nitrogen content and decreases with the lignin content of litter. The chemical composition of litter and the availability of nutrients in the surrounding environment also influence rates of decomposition in aquatic ecosystems.

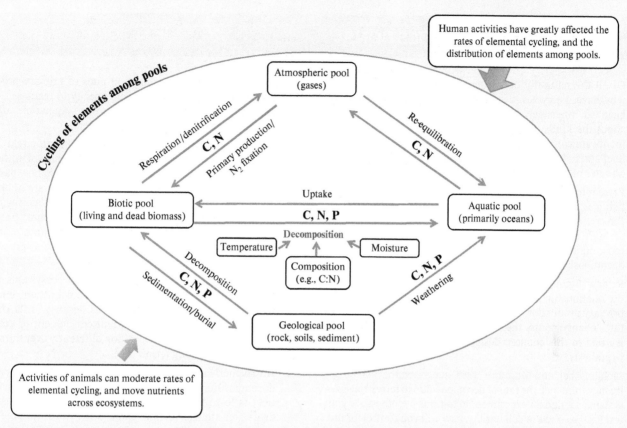

Figure 20.31   Concept map for chapter 20.

20.3 Plants and animals can modify the distribution and cycling of nutrients in ecosystems.

Aquatic and terrestrial systems have significant differences in their nutrient cycles. The dynamics of nutrients in streams are best represented by a spiral rather than a cycle. The length of stream required for an atom of a nutrient to complete a cycle is called the spiralling length. Stream macroinvertebrates can substantially reduce spiralling length of nutrients in stream ecosystems. Animals can also alter the distribution and rate of nutrient cycling in terrestrial ecosystems, accelerating turnover of plant matter.

20.4 Human activities and natural disturbance can dramatically impact nutrient cycling.

Analyses of air trapped in ice show that the concentration of CO_2 in the atmosphere has varied widely during the last 160,000 years and closely parallels variation in global temperatures. High levels of atmospheric CO_2 have corresponded to higher global temperatures. The buildup of atmospheric CO_2 during the past two centuries has reached levels of atmospheric CO_2 not equalled in the past 160,000 years. The present level of CO_2 in the atmosphere is strongly influenced by burning of fossil fuels. Increases in atmospheric CO_2 concentration are associated with increased global temperatures and a variety of environmental impacts. Human land use and pollution can also alter cycling of other elements in ecosystems and can affect plant communities; for example, nitrogen deposition can facilitate forest encroachment on grasslands. Vegetation exerts substantial control on nutrient retention by terrestrial ecosystems; and new, rapidly growing plants during a revegetation phase can allow a regenerating forest to be a net sink for N.

Nutrient enrichment by humans is altering aquatic and terrestrial ecosystems (fig 20.31). Nitrate concentration and export by the earth's major rivers correlate directly with human population density. A study of an urban watershed showed that cities can have higher nutrient retention than previously expected. Ecosystem-scale studies can be used as a tool to improve management of urban areas and to address challenging water-quality problems.

REVIEW QUESTIONS

1. Of all the naturally occurring elements in the biosphere, why have the cycles of carbon, nitrogen, and phosphorus been so intensively studied by ecologists? (Hint: Think about the kinds of organic molecules of which these elements are constituents. Also think back to our discussions, in chapter 19, of the influences of nitrogen and phosphorus on rates of primary production.)

2. Parmenter and Lamarra (1991) studied decomposition of fish and waterfowl carrion in a freshwater marsh. During the course of their studies they found that the soft tissues of both fish and waterfowl decomposed faster than the most rapidly decomposing plant tissues. Explain the rapid decomposition of these animal carcasses.

3. Review figure 19.7, in which Rosenzweig (1968) plotted the relationship between actual evapotranspiration and net primary production. How do you think that decomposition rates change across the same ecosystems? Using what you learned in this chapter, design an experiment to test your hypothesis.

4. Melillo, Aber, and Muratore (1982) suggested that soil fertility may influence the rate of decomposition in terrestrial ecosystems. Design an experiment to test this hypothesis. If you test for the effects of soil fertility, how will you control for the influences of temperature, moisture, and litter chemistry?

5. Many rivers around the world have been straightened and deepened to improve conditions for navigation. Side effects of these changes include increased average water velocity and decreased movement of water into shallow riverside environments, such as eddies and marginal wetlands. What are the probable influences of these changes on nutrient spiralling length?

6. Likens and Bormann (1995) found that vegetation substantially influences the rate of nutrient loss from small stream catchments in the northern hardwood forest ecosystem. How do vegetative biomass and rates of primary production in these forests affect their capacity to regulate nutrient loss? How much do you think vegetation affects nutrient movements in desert ecosystems?

7. McNaughton, Ruess, and Seagle (1988) proposed that grazing by large mammals increases the rate of nitrogen cycling on the savannas of East Africa. Explain how passing through a large mammal could increase the rate of breakdown of plant biomass. In chapter 19, we also saw how grazing mammals may increase the rate of primary production on the savanna. How might the disappearance of the large mammals of East Africa affect ecosystem processes on the savannas?

8. If rates of decomposition are higher in ecosystems with higher nutrient availability, how should nutrient enrichment affect rates of decomposition? Because of its effects on fungal diversity, could nutrient enrichment of ecosystems affect rates of decomposition differently over the short term versus the long term?

9. Atmospheric warming may cause increases or decreases in decomposition in the Arctic, particularly as more permafrost is lost. A shift toward either greater decomposition or greater storage in new plant growth has the potential to greatly alter the atmospheric concentration of CO_2, given the vast areas involved. These changes in CO_2 concentration can further alter global temperatures. What do you believe is the role of the scientist in public debate on this issue? More generally, should a scientist speak out on environmental issues? If so, when?

10. Atmospheric nitrogen deposition may contribute to forest encroachment on grasslands. What are the implications of this for gamma biological diversity in a mixed forest-grassland landscape? What are the implications in terms of carbon storage?

SECTION 6 LARGE-SCALE ECOLOGY

Many ecological processes occur at spatial scales much larger than individual ecosystems, and many patterns emerge only if we step back and look at natural systems from a great distance. We also gain a unique perspective on ecological understanding when we are able to see changes through time, recognizing that natural systems are dynamic. In this final section, we explore the mechanisms and consequences of interactions at scales much greater than individuals, populations, communities, or even ecosystems. Here we explore the ecology of landscapes (chapter 21), geographic regions (chapter 22), and changes through time (chapter 23).

Corbis/DAL.

CHAPTER 21   LANDSCAPE ECOLOGY

CHAPTER CONCEPTS

21.1 Landscapes are created and change in response to geological processes, climate, activities of organisms, and fire.
Concept 21.1 Review

21.2 Landscape structure includes the size, shape, composition, number, and position of patches, or landscape elements, in a landscape.
Concept 21.2 Review

21.3 Landscape structure influences processes such as the flow of energy, materials, and species distributions across a landscape.
Concept 21.3 Review
Ecology in Action: Linear Disturbances Across the Landscape
Ecological Tools and Approaches: Linking Population, Behavioural, and Landscape Ecology
Summary
Review Questions

A s you gaze across the landscape in this chapter's opening picture, you see it is a mosaic. A braided river passes through the valley, creating islands with young forests, probably recovering from the most recent flood. Small ponds and patches of wetland dot the floodplain. Shrubby plants grow on the sides of the hills, and more mature hardwood forests grow on the valley floor. Patches of forest have been cleared for farming on the floodplain to take advantage of its rich soil.

A **landscape** is heterogeneous. It is an area of distinctive patches—what landscape ecologists refer to as **landscape elements**. These elements include distinctive habitat types and geologic formations. In an urban landscape, they may include include parks, industrial districts, and residential areas. Many of the ecological processes and interactions in a landscape will be localized, occurring within habitat patches. However, as you again look at the opening picture, you will understand that the river shapes this valley and continues to influence the ecological processes throughout the landscape on a variety of spatial and temporal scales. Seasonal flooding will often reconnect it with ponds and wetlands. More extensive, less frequent flooding will reset the islands' plant communities, initiating secondary succession. Over a much longer time scale, the river carved the valley, creating the hillsides that are now suitable for shrubs. In turn, farming will affect nutrient cycling and primary production in the river, deer living in the forest patches will graze on the crops, and birds living on the margins of these patches will exploit different habitats for food and shelter. All of these landscape elements are ecologically interconnected.

Understanding of landscape structure and process has always been important to human survival. Hunters and gatherers are familiar with variation across the landscapes in which they live. This informs them where to find plants useful as food or medicines, where game animals hide and feed, and where game animals move with the seasons. Pastoralists understand how to locate forage for livestock, how the most productive pastures change with the seasons and between years, and where in the landscape predators and other dangers are likely to be encountered (fig. 21.1). Settled agriculturalists understand which areas are most suitable for planting crops and how to work and shape the land to guide the movement of water and avoid soil loss (fig. 21.2). Understanding landscape processes and the ecological consequences of landscape modification are no less critical today, as local human populations and the attendant development pressures grow.

Jianguo Wu and Richard Hobbs (2007) identify a thematic thread defining *landscape ecology* as the study of the relationship between spatial pattern and ecological processes over a range of scales. Though most landscape ecologists work at fairly large spatial scales (km, not cm), the concepts of landscape ecology can be applied to spatial patterns and ecological processes ranging from those relevant to ground beetles moving across a few metres of grassland (Wiens et al. 1997) to very large regional scales measured in thousands of square kilometres.

There are three key facets of landscape ecology to mention at the outset of the chapter. First of all, landscape ecology is generally highly interdisciplinary, even more so than most subdisciplines in ecology. It brings together biologists and

Figure 21.1 Managing large bands of grazing animals requires detailed knowledge of local landscapes, especially the locations of good forage, water, and shelter.
Salvator Barki/Getty Images.

Figure 21.2 Successful agriculturalists must have a basic understanding of landscape structure and process. These terraced rice fields in China are the result of human engineering of the landscape to retain water and prevent erosion.
© Visions of America, LLC/Alamy RF.

naturalists, physical geographers and geologists, to unfairly acknowledge but a few. Second, landscape ecology has included humans, and human influences on landscapes, since its beginnings. As a consequence, landscape ecology is often intertwined with conservation biology—though not all studies in landscape ecology necessarily have a conservation focus. Third, landscape ecology focuses on understanding the extent, origin, and ecological consequences of spatial heterogeneity across multiple spatial scales.

The full scope of landscape ecology cannot be covered in a single chapter. However, we will sample the discipline by reviewing some studies concerning core areas of landscape ecology. In earlier chapters, we discussed structure, process, and change within the context of populations, communities, and ecosystems. In this chapter, we revisit structure, process, and change within the context of landscapes. We begin by asking this: Where does a landscape come from?

21.1   Origins of Landscapes

Landscapes are created and change in response to geological processes, climate, activities of organisms, and fire. What creates the landscapes we see? Many forces combine in numerous ways to produce the diversity of landscape elements found in natural systems. In chapter 18, we saw how fire initiated succession in the boreal forest and other communities. We also discussed how Parks Canada was using fire and other disturbances to manage the biodiversity of the National Parks. In chapter 17, we discussed how the activity of ecosystem engineers could alter the landscape. For example, beaver dams increase riparian areas and have impacts on patterns of tree diversity. In this section, we discuss more explicitly how geological processes, climate, organisms, and fire contribute to the creation of landscapes.

Geological Processes, Climate, and the Landscape

Geological processes, such as volcanism, sedimentation, and erosion, interact with local climatic conditions to form many landscape elements. For instance, the alluvial deposits along a river valley provide growing conditions different from those on thin, well-drained soils on nearby hills. A volcanic cinder cone in the middle of a sandy plain offers different environmental conditions than the surrounding plain. Distinctive ecosystems may develop on each of these geological surfaces, creating patchiness in the landscape. In the following example, we shall see how glaciers have contributed to the vegetative patchiness found in much of Canada and other countries of mid-to-high latitudes.

Glaciations and Vegetation Mosaics in Northern North America

Earth's climate is subject to not only the immediate consequences of human activities but also a variety of naturally occurring cycles. Over the last many millions of years, we have had periods of **glacial ages**, which can last millions of years. Within these glacial ages are approximately 100,000-year cycles that include very cold periods lasting between 60,000 and 90,000 years (**glaciations**) and warmer periods lasting 10,000–40,000 years (**interglacial periods**). We are currently living within an interglacial period of a glacial age. The last glaciation was the Wisconsin, and it reached its peak 20,000 years ago. During the current interglacial period, only remnants of glaciers remain, and in their place is our current landscape, which was formed as plants and other species migrated out from areas not covered in ice.

The effects of glaciers on the physical structure of landscapes are dramatic and can been seen throughout Canada (fig. 21.3). Glaciers have an unrivalled ability to move soil and rock over great distances, literally reshaping the landscape. As a glacier moves forward, it carries with it large volumes of rock, scouring the landscape. More erosion occurs when rocks are ripped out of the earth and water enters cracks in the surrounding material and freezes, further widening the cracks and weakening the rock's structure. When alpine glaciers flow down valleys in mountains, they cause a U-shaped cross-section in the valley, in contrast to the familiar V-shape of valleys created by streams. Throughout a valley created by glaciers will be **talus**, great rock piles pushed aside and left behind by glaciers. Continental glaciers also leave a variety of signatures in the landscape. When the glaciers retreat, they leave behind large masses of **till**, unsorted material that includes clay, rocks, and boulders. When the till is piled up, either by being pushed to the side or left behind with glacial retreat, it forms **moraines**. Marking the furthest extent of glaciers are terminal moraines, formed by the materials that were pushed forward during the glacial advance. When a glacier passes over a moraine left by a prior glacier, it can be reshaped into **drumlins**, hills (or series of hills) drained by streams. When much debris flows out of streams fed by glaciers, long narrow ridges called **eskers** can be formed. When a block of ice becomes detached from the glacier, melting in place, a depression called a **kettle** is formed. As depressions generally fill with water, kettle lakes dot landscapes carved by glaciers.

These physical structures are common throughout Canada, and a close look while biking across the Canadian Shield will reveal the impacts of glaciers on the shape of a landscape. The story of the landscape, however, does not end with glacial melting; instead, for plants and animals, it just begins.

Glacial retreat reveals a bare, rocky substrate—no soil, no seedbank, no plants. Very quickly, however, seeds and spores arrive and new plants grow, initiating primary succession (chapter 18). We have seen evidence for these plant migrations throughout the text, such as in the work of Margaret Davis (chapter 1). But where, exactly, do these migrating plants come from? Some of these seeds come from **glacial refugia**, areas that through a variety of interactions between geology and climate were never glaciated, while others come from populations that were south of the terminal extent of the glaciers (fig. 21.4). A special type of refugia is the **nunatak**, mountain peaks that were surrounded, but not covered, by continental glaciers. Of course, not all mountains served as refugia, and instead many are (and were) home to a number of alpine glaciers that also carve a landscape into the rock.

What the colonizing plants encountered following the melt was a heterogeneous landscape. In some areas there was nothing but large rocks, a substrate nearly impossible to get roots into. Others areas had fine glacial till, facilitating root growth. These geological differences persist to this day, and a great variety of ecosystems can be found within a short distance along moraines, eskers, and kettles. The spatial arrangements of these different ecosystems are caused by interactions between species-specific traits of the colonizing plants and the changes to the landscape caused by the power of glaciers.

The effects of glaciers are most visibly obvious through their direct influence on the shape of the land on which they rested. However, their true impact can be global in scale. Global sea

Figure 21.3 Impacts of glaciers on landscapes can be seen as (*a*) a U-shaped valley in Labrador, (*b*) a drumlin field in Manitoba, (*c*) eskers in Québec, and (*d*) a till plain in the Northwest Territories.

(a) Photo 133517940 © Bobhilscher–Dreamstime.com. (b) Photo number 2001-067. Photographer: Lynda Dredge, Natural Resources Canada, 2001. Reproduced with the permission of the Department of Natural Resources, 2019. (c) Photo number 2004-093. Photographer: Jean Veillette, Natural Resources Canada, 2004. Reproduced with the permission of the Department of Natural Resources, 2019. (d) Photo number 2001-259. Photographer: Lynda Dredge, Natural Resources Canada, 2001. Reproduced with the permission of the Department of Natural Resources, 2019.

levels rise and fall with glaciers. As we saw in chapter 3, large volumes of water are stored in glaciers. When glaciers melt, much of that water ends up in the ocean, contributing to a rise in sea levels. The effects of rising sea levels are obvious and highlight the ephemeral (on a geological time scale) nature of mangrove forests and other coastal wetlands, and coral atolls (chapter 3). However, we can also imagine back to when much of the water currently found in the oceans was stored as ice across much of North America. During these periods of lower sea levels, many now isolated islands were connected by land bridges. These connections served as corridors for the movement of numerous species, allowing the colonization of new habitats.

Organisms and Landscape Structure

Organisms of all sorts, including people, influence the structure of landscapes. There is no shortage of examples of how humans have modified landscapes. We are sure that, through your own lived experience, you could name many examples that you observed while modifications were happening. Many studies of landscape change have focused on the conversion of forest to agricultural landscapes. In North America, an often-cited example of this sort of landscape change is that of Cadiz Township, Green County, Wisconsin (Curtis 1956). In 1831, approximately 93.5% of Cadiz Township was forested. By 1882, the percentage of forested land had decreased to 27%, and by 1902 forest cover had fallen to less than 9%. Between 1902 and 1950, the total area of forest decreased again to 3.4%. Similar changes in landscape structure have been observed throughout the Midwestern region of the United States, and in areas of Canada. However, in some other forested regions of North America and Europe, the pattern of recent landscape change has been different. For example, many abandoned farms in New England have reverted to forest, and in these landscapes forest cover has increased over the past century. In the Veluwe region of the central Netherlands, the abandonment of sheep grazing

Figure 21.4   The cypress hills in Alberta and Saskatchewan were the northernmost location that remained south of the glacial advance in North America. As a result, this area is home to unique vegetation and likely played a critical role in seed production and dispersal following the melt.
Darwin Wiggett/First Light/Getty Images.

and the deliberate planting of pine plantations have transformed the landscape over the past two centuries (fig. 21.5) (Hulshoff 1995).

The Cadiz Township and Veluwe district each provide an example of how human activities can change a landscape element—in both cases, forest cover. Although the direction of change in forest cover was different in these examples, the driving forces were the same: economics. A developing agricultural economy converted Cadiz Township from forest to farmland. The Veluwe landscape was converted from heathland to forest

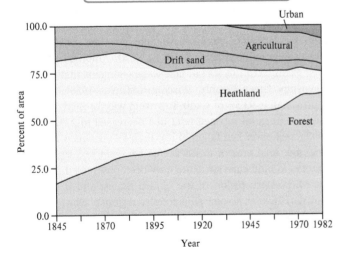

> The most substantial change in this landscape in the Netherlands was a shift from predominantly heathland to predominantly forest.

Figure 21.5   Change in a Dutch landscape.
Data from Hulshoff 1995.

as the local sheep-raising economy collapsed in response to inexpensive wool from Australia.

As we enter the twenty-first century, economically motivated human activity continues to change the structure of landscapes all over the globe. We examine current trends in land cover at the global scale in chapter 23. Before we do that, however, let's examine the effects of another species on landscape structure. There are many examples of non-human species that modify landscapes, such as the large herbivores of the North American grasslands and the Serengeti. However, we will let the beaver stand as one excellent example of how a species' ecology and behaviour can dramatically modify a landscape.

In chapters 17 and 18, we discussed keystone species and ecosystem engineers. As you may remember, beaver activity can change the course of streams, create ponds, and alter forest structure. Using the terms from this chapter, we now explore in more depth how beavers create and modify landscape structure.

The influences of beavers on landscape structure once shaped the face of entire continents. At one time, beavers modified nearly all the temperate stream valleys in the Northern Hemisphere. The range of beavers in North America extended from arctic tundra to the Chihuahuan and Sonoran Deserts of northern Mexico, a range of approximately 15 million km^2. Before European colonization, the North American beaver population numbered 60 to 400 million individuals. However, fur trappers eliminated beavers from much of their historical range and nearly drove them to extinction. With protection, North American beaver populations are recovering and large areas once again show the influence of beavers on landscape structure.

Carol Johnston, Robert Naiman, and their colleagues have carefully documented substantial effects of beavers on landscape structure (e.g., Naiman et al. 1994). Much of their work has focused on the effects of beavers on the 298 km^2 Kabetogama Peninsula in Voyageurs National Park, Minnesota. Following their near extermination, beavers reinvaded the Kabetogama Peninsula beginning about 1925. From 1927 to 1988, the number of beaver ponds on the peninsula increased from 64 to 834, a change in pond density from 0.2 to 3.0 per square kilometre. Over this 63-year period, the area of new ecosystems created by beavers, including beaver ponds, wet meadows, and moist meadows, increased from 200 ha (about 1% of the peninsula) to 2,661 ha (about 13% of the peninsula). Foraging by beavers altered another 12% to 15% of upland areas.

Beaver activity has changed the Kabetogama Peninsula from a landscape dominated by boreal forest to a complex mosaic of ecosystems. Figure 21.6 shows how beavers have changed a 45 km^2 catchment on the peninsula. Most of this change occurred between 1940 and 1986, during which time beavers increased landscape complexity within the catchment. Similar changes have occurred over nearly the entire peninsula.

Naiman and his colleagues quantified the effects of beaver over 214 km^2, or 72%, of the Kabetogama Peninsula. Within this area, there are about 2,763 ha of low-lying area that can be impounded by beavers. In 1927, the majority of the landscape, 2,563 ha, was dominated by forest. In 1927, moist meadow, wet meadow, and pond ecosystems covered only 200 ha. By 1988, moist meadows, wet meadows, and beaver ponds covered over

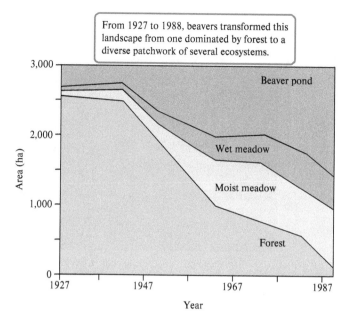

From 1927 to 1988, beavers transformed this landscape from one dominated by forest to a diverse patchwork of several ecosystems.

Figure 21.6   Beaver-caused landscape changes on the Kabetogama Peninsula, Minnesota.
Data from Naiman et al. 1994.

Figure 21.7   Areas of Mediterranean shrubland in southern California periodically burn over large areas, destroying human habitations in the process.
Kevin Galvin/Federal Emergency Management Agency.

2,600 ha and boreal forest was limited to 102 ha. Between 1927 and 1988, beavers transformed most of the landscape.

The changes in landscape structure induced by beavers substantially alter landscape processes, such as nutrient retention. Beaver activity between 1927 and 1988 increased the quantity of most major ions and nutrients in the areas affected by impoundments. The total quantity of nitrogen increased by 72%, while the amounts of phosphorus and potassium increased by 43% and 20%, respectively. The quantities of calcium, magnesium, iron, and sulfate stored in the landscape increased by even greater amounts.

Naiman and his colleagues offer three possible explanations for increased ion and nutrient storage in this landscape: (1) beaver ponds and their associated meadows may trap materials eroding from the surrounding landscape, (2) the rising waters of the beaver ponds may have captured nutrients formerly held in forest vegetation, and (3) the habitats created by beavers may have altered biogeochemical processes in a way that promotes nutrient retention. Whatever the precise mechanisms, beaver activity has substantially altered landscape structure and processes on the Kabetogama Peninsula.

Fire and the Structure of a Mediterranean Landscape

Fire contributes to the structure of landscapes ranging from tropical savanna to boreal forest. However, fire plays a particularly prominent role in regions with a Mediterranean climate. Terrestrial ecosystems in regions with Mediterranean climates, supporting woodlands and shrublands, are subject to frequent burning. Hot, dry summers combined with vegetation rich in essential oils create ideal conditions for fires, which can be easily ignited by lightning or by humans (fig. 21.7). In regions with

a Mediterranean climate, fire is responsible for a great deal of landscape structure and change.

Richard Minnich (1983) used satellite photos to reconstruct the fire history of southern California and northern Baja California, Mexico, from 1971 to 1980. He found that the landscapes of both areas consist of a patchwork of new and old burns. Though these regions experience similar Mediterranean climates and support similar natural vegetation, their fire histories diverged significantly in the early twentieth century. For centuries, lightning-caused fires burned, sometimes for months, until they burned out naturally. In addition, Spanish and Anglo-American residents would set fire to the land routinely to improve grazing for cattle and sheep. Then, early in the twentieth century, various government agencies in southern California began to suppress fires to protect property within an increasingly urbanized landscape.

Minnich proposed that the different fire histories of southern California and northern Baja California might produce landscapes of different structure. He suggested that fire suppression allowed more biomass to accumulate and set the stage for large, uncontrollable fires. His specific hypothesis was that the average area burned by wildfires would be greater in southern California.

Minnich tested his hypothesis using satellite images taken from 1972 to 1980. He found that between 1972 and 1980 the total area burned in the two regions was fairly similar (fig. 21.8). However, the size of burns differed significantly between the two regions. The frequency of small burns below 1,000 ha was higher in northern Baja California, while large burns above 3,000 ha were more frequent in southern California. Consequently, median burn size in southern California, 3,500 ha, was over twice that observed in Baja California, 1,600 ha (fig. 21.8).

These results are consistent with Minnich's hypothesis, but do they show conclusively that differences in fire management in southern California and Baja California have produced a difference in burn area? Other factors may contribute to the observed differences in the fire mosaic, including climatic differences, differences in age structure of vegetation, and

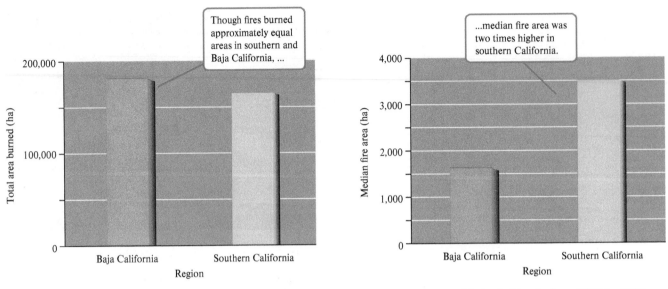

Figure 21.8   Characteristics of fires in the Mediterranean landscapes of southern and Baja California from 1972 to 1980. Data from Minnich 1983.

topographic differences. The exploration of fire's influence on the structure of Mediterranean landscapes continues.

Regardless of whether differences in median fire size between Baja California and southern California from 1972 to 1980 were related to management strategies, the pattern in California now is more but smaller fires. In 2018, the median size for wildfires in California was much less than 1,000 ha. This is not to say that fires are becoming less important in shaping landscapes. The 2018 California wildfire season was the most destructive on record, with the most area burned in a season. More than 8,500 fires burned a total of 766,00 ha, though much of this was in central California. The Mendocino Complex fire north of San Francisco alone burned 186,000 ha. This is roughly the same total area burned in Northern Baja California between 1972 and 1980! The trend in more total area burned during fire seasons means that much more of the landscape in southern California is shaped by recent wildfires.

Geological processes, fire, organisms, and climate lead to the development of the landscapes we see around the world. Knowing this, the next step for the ecologist is to understand how landscapes are organized and to determine whether such organization has biological consequences.

CONCEPT 21.1 REVIEW

1. What similarities are shared between beavers and glaciers in constructing the shape of a landscape?

2. Do the patterns described by Minnich (fig. 21.8) conclusively show that the differences in burn area in the two regions are the result of different fire management practices?

3. What are some common means by which humans modify landscape structure?

21.2 Landscape Structure

Landscape structure includes the size, shape, composition, number, and position of patches, or landscape elements, in a landscape. Much of ecology focuses on studies of structure and process; landscape ecology is no exception. What constitutes landscape structure? **Landscape structure** consists mainly of the size, shape, composition, number, and position of patches (landscape elements) within a landscape. As you look across a landscape, you can usually recognize its constituent ecosystems as distinctive patches. Landscape ecologists define a **patch** as a relatively homogeneous area that differs from its surroundings, for example, an area of forest surrounded by agricultural fields or an agricultural field surrounded by forest. The patches within a landscape form the mosaic that we call landscape structure. The background in this mosaic is called the **matrix**, which is the element within the landscape that is the most spatially continuous. Again, look at the opening picture of this chapter. What kinds of distinctive patches do you see? What is the matrix in the landscape?

Most questions in landscape ecology require that ecologists first quantify landscape structure. The following examples show how this has been done on some landscapes and how some aspects of landscape structure are not obvious without quantification.

The Structure of Six Landscapes in Ohio

In 1981, G. Bowen and R. Burgess published a quantitative analysis of several Ohio landscapes. These landscapes consisted of forest patches surrounded by other types of ecosystems. Six of the 10-by-10 km areas analyzed are shown in figure 21.9. If you look carefully at this figure you see that the landscapes, which are named after nearby towns, differ considerably in

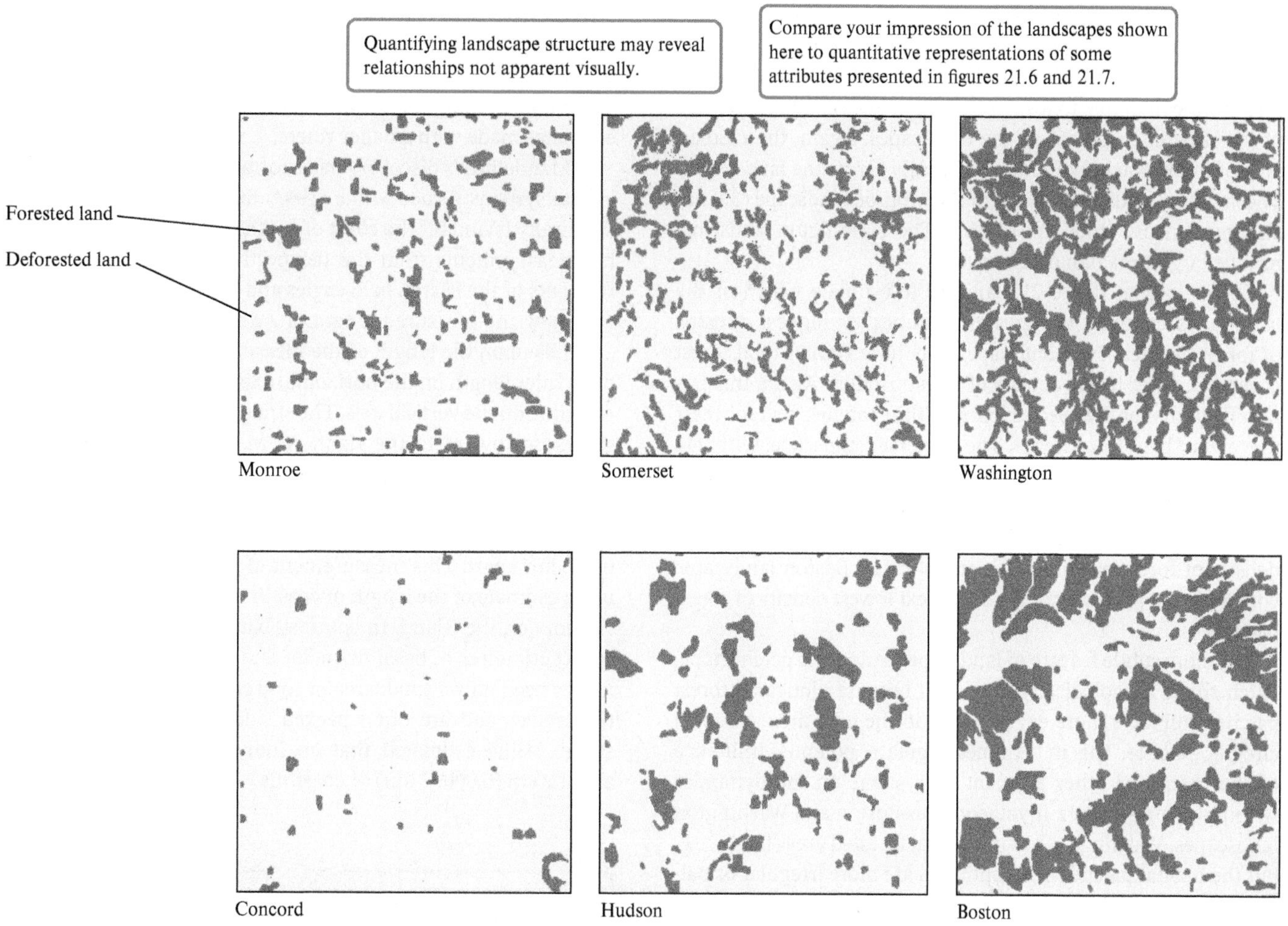

Quantifying landscape structure may reveal relationships not apparent visually.

Compare your impression of the landscapes shown here to quantitative representations of some attributes presented in figures 21.6 and 21.7.

Forested land

Deforested land

Monroe

Somerset

Washington

Concord

Hudson

Boston

Figure 21.9   Forest fragments, shown as dark green, in six landscapes in Ohio.
Data from Bowen and Burgess 1981.

total forest cover, the number of forest patches, the average area of patches, and the shapes of patches. Some of the landscapes are well forested, and others are not. Some contain only small patches of forest, while others include some large patches. In some landscapes, the forest patches are long and narrow, while in others they are much wider. These general differences are clear enough, but we would find it difficult to give more precise descriptions unless we quantified our impressions.

First, let's consider total forest cover, as this varies substantially among the six landscapes. The Concord landscape, with 2.7% forest cover, is the least forested. At the other extreme, forest patches cover 43.6% of the Washington landscape. Differences between these extremes are clear, but what about some of the less obvious differences? Compare the Monroe and Somerset landscapes (fig. 21.9), and try to estimate which is more forested and by how much. Somerset may appear to have greater forest cover, but how much more? You may be surprised to discover that Somerset, with 22.7% forest cover, has twice the forest cover of the Monroe landscape, which includes just 11.8% forest cover (fig. 21.10).

Apart from total forest cover, we might be interested in the characteristics of individual patches. The size of a patch may

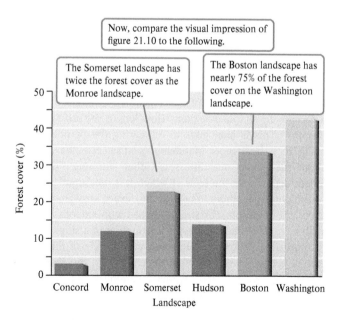

Now, compare the visual impression of figure 21.10 to the following.

The Somerset landscape has twice the forest cover as the Monroe landscape.

The Boston landscape has nearly 75% of the forest cover on the Washington landscape.

Figure 21.10   Percent forest cover in six landscapes in Ohio.
Data from Bowen and Burgess 1981.

be important to the community of organisms living within the patch. Populations that do not move freely between patches may be isolated. In small patches, these populations may be small and more vulnerable to local extirpation. Let's examine the size of forest patches in each of the landscapes. Again, the median area of forest patches differs significantly across the landscapes. The smallest median areas are in the Monroe landscape (3.6 ha) and the Concord landscape (4.1 ha). The Washington landscape has the largest median patch area.

Now look at figure 21.9 and try to estimate which of the landscapes contains the greatest number, or highest density, of forest patches. Two landscapes may have similar total forest cover, but differ in the density of forest patches. Again, this has ramifications for the species living within patches, and for their movement between patches. The Somerset landscape, with 244 forest patches, has the highest patch density, and the Monroe landscape, with 180 patches, has the next highest density of forest patches. Obviously, the Concord landscape has the lowest density of forest patches, with only 46. The Boston landscape, with 86 forest patches, contains the next lowest density of forest patches.

A more subtle feature of landscape structure is patch shape. Patch shape is ecologically important because elongated forest patches will have more edge relative to the total area than will circular patches. This in turn means greater potential influence of the matrix or other adjacent ecosystems on the dynamics within the forest patch. If you consider Boston and Washington landscapes, Washington has more total forested area (fig. 21.10), but the habitat patches in Washington are more irregular or palmate in shape, with more edge relative to patch area (fig. 21.9). Landscape ecologists have developed methods for representing landscape structure, including complex patch shape, using *fractal geometry*. Fractal geometry was developed by Benoit Mandelbrot (1982) to provide a method for describing the dimensions of natural objects as diverse as ferns, snowflakes, root systems, and patches in a landscape. Fractal geometry offers unique insights into the structure of nature.

The Fractal Geometry of Landscapes

During the development of fractal geometry, Mandelbrot asked a deceptively simple question: "How long is the coast of Great Britain?" This is analogous to estimating the perimeter of a patch in a landscape. Mandelbrot's answer to his question about the British coastline was rather stunning: "Coastline length depends on the scale at which it is measured"! At first, you might expect there to be only one, exact, answer, but think about the question. For simple shapes with smooth outlines, such as squares and circles, the assumption of a single answer is approximately correct. However, an estimate of the perimeter of a complex shape often depends upon the size of the measuring device. In other words, if you measure the coastline of Great Britain, you will find that your measurement depends upon the size of the ruler you use. If you were to step off the perimeter of Great Britain in 1 km lengths, which is like using a ruler 1 km long, you would get a smaller estimate than if you made your measurements with a 100 m ruler. If you measured

the coastline with a 10 cm ruler you would get an even larger estimate of the perimeter. The reason that a larger ruler gives a smaller estimate is that the large ruler misses many of the nooks and crannies along the coast. These smaller features show up in estimates made with smaller rulers.

Mandelbrot's discovery has enormous implications for ecological systems. Bruce Milne (1993) measured the coastline of Admiralty Island off the coast of southeastern Alaska. He made his measurements from the perspective of two very different residents of the island, bald eagles and barnacles. Milne considered how the measured length of Admiralty Island's coastline depends upon the length of the measuring device. Figure 21.11 plots ruler length on the horizontal axis and estimated length of coastline on the vertical axis. The straight line that joins the dots slopes downward to the right. As Mandelbrot suggested, the estimated coastline length decreases as ruler length increases.

Now, what "ruler" are bald eagles and barnacles using? The distribution of eagle nests around Admiralty Island are about 0.782 km apart. This measurement of inter-nest distance gives us an estimate of the length of coastline required by a bald eagle territory on the island. In contrast, barnacles range from 1 to a few centimetres in basal diameter and they are sedentary. Barnacles need only a small area of solid surface to which to attach themselves and are often packed side by side along a rocky shore. Milne estimated that an individual barnacle requires about 2 cm (0.00002 km) of coastline.

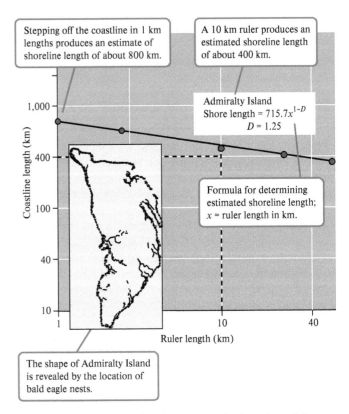

Figure 21.11 Relationship between ruler length and the measured length of the coastline of Admiralty Island, Alaska.

Data from Milne 1993.

Milne assumed that the eagles are, in effect, using a ruler 0.782 km long to step off the perimeter of the island and that barnacles use a ruler 0.00002 km long. Milne's analysis estimates that from the eagle's perspective, the perimeter of Admiralty Island is just a bit over 760 km. However, to a barnacle stepping off the coastline with its tiny ruler, the perimeter is over 11,000 km! Any of us would probably have assumed that the barnacle population "sees" a lot more of the spatial complexity around Admiralty Island. However, without Mandelbrot's fractal geometry, it would be difficult to predict that the difference in island perimeter for eagles and barnacles would be as great as 760 versus 11,000 km. Returning to the question of forest patch shapes, fractal geometry can allow us to express the total edge length of a patch to the patch area, and to do so at a scale that is relevant to any given species of interest resident in the patch.

As in other areas of science, describing aspects of landscape structure, such as the length of the coastline of Admiralty Island or the size, shape, and number of forest patches in Ohio landscapes, is not an end in itself. Landscape ecologists study landscape structure because it influences landscape processes and helps to benchmark changes that occur in these processes as a function of changes in structure. These are the next topics in the following section.

CONCEPT 21.2 REVIEW

1. In the landscapes shown in figure 21.9, what is patch and what is matrix?
2. Why can the length of an object, such as a coastline, depend upon the scale of measurement?

21.3 Landscape Processes

Landscape structure influences processes such as the flow of energy, materials, and species distributions across a landscape. Landscape ecologists study how the size, shape, composition, number, and position of ecosystems in the landscape affect landscape processes. Though less familiar than physiological and ecosystem processes, landscape processes are responsible for many important ecological phenomena.

Lenore Fahrig, of Carleton University, has written extensively on landscape ecology and what this subdiscipline of ecological study can provide that is unique from the other topics more traditionally associated with ecology (e.g., population growth, distributions, etc.). At the most basic level, if a goal of ecology is to understand where species are, and why, then it is important to understand all the mechanisms that govern these patterns. Fahrig (2005) developed a conceptual model that illustrates the central role of landscape structure on the outcomes of a number of other ecological patterns and processes. Landscape structure will influence how changes in abiotic factors impact biotic factors. This adds a level of complexity that was missing from our discussions of ecosystem ecology in chapters 19 and 20. As we will see in the following examples, landscape

structure affects ecologically important processes, such as the movement of organisms and the distribution of species on a landscape; local population density and extinction risk; and nutrient cycling and lake, river, and wetland chemistry.

Landscape Structure and the Movement of Animals

Landscape ecologists have proposed that landscape structure, especially the size, number, and isolation of habitat patches, can influence the movement of organisms between potentially suitable habitats.

Human activity often produces **habitat fragmentation**, which occurs where a road cuts through a forest, a housing development eliminates an area of shrubland, or tracts of forest are cut for timber. Habitat fragmentation is the division of a previously intact habitat into several isolated patches, typically due to human development and resource extraction. Because habitat fragmentation is increasing, ecologists commonly study how landscape structure affects the movements of organisms, movements that might mean the difference between population persistence and local extinction.

James Diffendorfer, Michael Gaines, and Robert Holt (1995) studied how patch size affects the movements of three small mammal species: cotton rats (*Sigmodon hispidus*), prairie voles (*Microtus ochrogaster*), and deer mice (*Peromyscus maniculatus*). They divided a 12 ha prairie landscape in Kansas into eight 5,000 m² areas. The prairie vegetation was mowed to maintain three patterns of fragmentation (fig. 21.12). The least fragmented areas consisted of large 50-by-100 m patches. The areas with medium fragmentation each contained 6 medium 12- by 24-m patches. The most fragmented landscapes contained 10 or 15 small 4- by 8-m patches.

The researchers predicted that animals would move farther in the more fragmented landscapes consisting of small

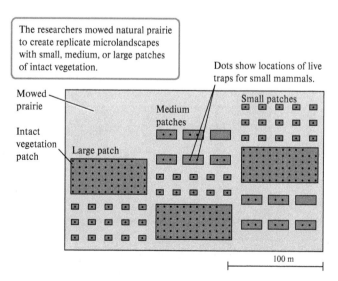

Figure 21.12 Experimental landscape for the study of small mammal movements.

Data from Diffendorfer, Gaines, and Holt 1995.

habitat patches. In fragmented landscapes, individuals must move farther to find mates, food, and cover. They also predicted that animals would stay longer in the more isolated patches within fragmented landscapes. Consequently, the proportion of animals moving would decrease with habitat fragmentation.

The rodent populations were monitored on the study site by trapping them with live traps twice each month from August 1984 to May 1992. When trapped for the first time, the sex of each individual was determined and the animal was fitted with an ear tag with a unique number. The researchers also weighed, recorded the location of, and checked the reproductive condition of each animal trapped. Over the course of their eight-year study, Diffendorfer, Gaines, and Holt amassed a data set consisting of 23,185 captures. They used these data to construct movement histories for individual animals to test their predictions. They expressed movements as *mean square distances*, a measurement that estimates the size of an individual's home range. A home range is the area that an animal occupies on a daily basis.

The behaviour of two of the three study species supports the hypothesis that small mammals move farther in more fragmented landscapes. As predicted, *Peromyscus* and *Microtus* living in small patches moved farther than individuals living in medium or large patches (fig. 21.14). The movements of *Sigmodon* in medium and large patches did not differ significantly. However, because few *Sigmodon* were captured within small patch areas, their movements within these areas could not be analyzed, and thus the overall comparisons for this species are of less value than for the other two species.

The proportion of *Sigmodon*, *Microtus*, and *Peromyscus* moving within the 5,000 m^2 experimental areas supported the hypothesis that animal movements decrease with habitat fragmentation (fig. 21.13). A larger proportion of *Sigmodon* moved

within large patch areas than moved within areas with medium patches. A larger proportion of *Microtus* and *Peromyscus* moved within large and medium patches than moved within small patches. To be clear, rodents in small patches, when they did move, generally moved a longer distance, from one patch to another. They likely were forced to do so in search of food, shelter, or mates. But once they arrived in a patch, they tended to stay there. Rodents in larger patches roamed locally within their patches but were less likely to move from one patch to another over long distances. These findings are important as they suggest that rodents in small patches may be relatively more isolated from the larger metapopulation than are rodents in larger patches.

In summary, this experiment shows a predictable relationship between landscape structure and the movement of organisms across landscapes. As the following example shows, these results are not necessarily universal.

The Relative Importance of Landscape Structure on Organisms

Charles Krebs (one of the population ecologists leading the Kluane Project described in chapter 14) has suggested that in comparison to disciplines such as behavioural ecology, population biology, and experimental biology, landscape ecology has not made great advances in the last 100 years (Krebs 2006). This point will raise the eyebrows of some researchers, but it is representative of a fairly common feeling that landscape ecology, much like the study of mutualism (chapter 15), has not become fully integrated into the broader ecological community. In this section we describe a few studies that have attempted to place the effects of landscape structure into the broader context of other ecological drivers. We begin with an experiment in the boreal forests of Alberta.

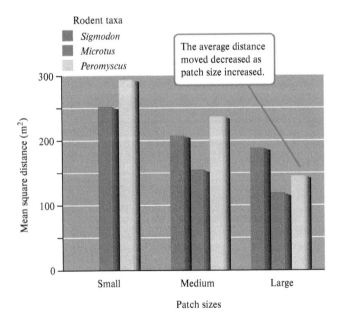
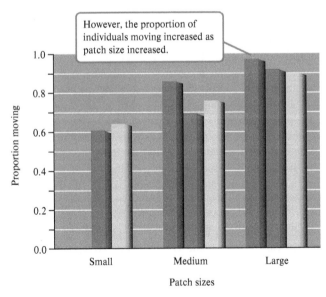

Figure 21.13 Influence of patch size on small mammal movements within experimental landscapes.
Data from Diffendorfer, Gaines, and Holt 1995.

Fragmentation Effects on Boreal Birds

In 1997, three researchers published a landmark study on the effect of habitat fragmentation on birds in the boreal forest (Schmiegelow et al. 1997). The team consisted of Fiona Schmiegelow, formerly of the University of British Columbia and now at the University of Alberta; Craig Machtans, now with the Canadian Wildlife Service; and Susan Hannon, a professor at the University of Alberta. The basic idea was similar to that of Diffendorfer and colleagues: they wanted to understand how landscape structure could alter the biology of a group of organisms. The central difference between these studies is that of scale. While Diffendorfer and colleagues created patches that ranged from 0.0032 to 0.50 ha in size, Schmiegelow and colleagues created patches that ranged from 1 to 100 ha in size. Additionally, Diffendorfer and colleagues focused on the response of three species, while Schmiegelow and her colleagues followed the responses of 59 species.

The study site was in the boreal mixedwood forest of northern Alberta. Dominant vegetation includes aspen, poplar, and spruce, and the forest is home to many resident and transient bird species. Forestry activity often results in a landscape of large and small forest patches separated by areas of clearcutting. Some of these patches will be isolated from intact forest, while others will be connected through thin belts of forest, often along the edges of rivers. A great strength of this study is that the authors set out to recreate the environment that organisms were likely to encounter in the real world due to human activities, and to test whether this scale of fragmentation and isolation influenced boreal bird species. Thus, their results are of great potential importance for understanding the ecological effects of logging on boreal birds and for developing possible strategies of mitigation.

The research team collaborated with the Alberta Forest Service and a number of forestry companies to create forest patches, varying in size from small (1 ha) to large (100 ha). Patches also varied by being connected to a forested riparian buffer or being isolated and surrounded on all sides by clearcutting. As an aside, a strength of this experiment is that it shows that industry and university biologists can work together to create science on a scale that is biologically meaningful to the organisms of interest.

So what did they find? In total, the research team collected 21,340 records of 59 bird species over three years in their study area. This is a remarkable sample size. As was expected, more species were found in larger patches, though the relationship between species richness and area was not influenced by whether patches were connected or isolated (fig. 21.14). Although species richness was not affected by whether patches were connected, the small isolated fragments changed in overall species composition during the experiment more than the larger and connected fragments. In other words, the bird communities were more dynamic in the small isolated patches. These patches tended to lose species that were resident species commonly found in older forests, and they accumulated more transient species. Immediately following fragmentation, isolated patches had increased numbers of birds relative to the connected

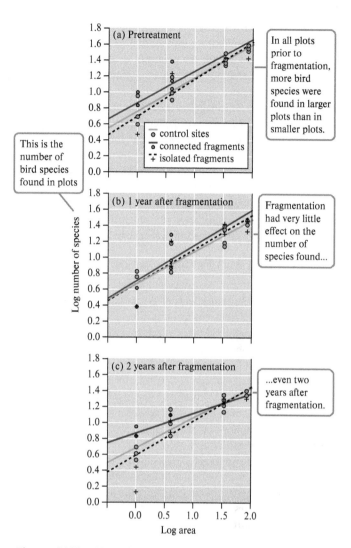

Figure 21.14 The relationship between bird community species richness and area in a large manipulative study in northern Alberta.

From F. K. A. Schmiegelow et al. 1997. Are boreal birds resilient to forest fragmentation? An experimental study of short-term community responses. *Ecology* 78:1914–32, Figure 3. Reprinted with permission.

fragments and controls of same patch size, though these effects largely disappeared by the second year of the experiment. After two years, there was some evidence that neotropical migrants and resident species were less abundant in fragmented forests than the controls, although this pattern was not found for short-distance migratory species. In general, species that prefer old forests decreased in abundance following fragmentation, and species that prefer younger forests increased in abundance.

Overall, Schmiegelow and her colleagues observed some significant effects of fragmentation and isolation on the bird community, primarily that smaller patches had fewer species. However, this pattern was likely a statistical sampling function. Intact forests had the same species of richness as a function of area as an isolated patch. The authors conclude that the breeding bird community in this boreal forest is relatively resilient to a severe disturbance causing habitat fragmentation, at least over the time scale of this study. The distance between patches, after all, was relatively small for a migratory bird. At the same time, they recognize that even if the community as a whole does not seem affected by changes in landscape structure, some groups of birds clearly are.

The work by Schmiegelow and her colleagues provides a strong contrast to the results of Diffendorfer and his colleagues. At a minimum, these results show that fragmentation is not necessarily a problem for all species. Instead, some groups of organisms with specific life-history traits will be strongly affected, while other organisms will not. By demonstrating this link between life-history and the impacts of fragmentation, this study provides a critical first step in integrating landscape ecology into the larger body of ecological theory.

Edge Effects and Fragmentation

The area of forest removed does not by itself give a complete picture of the ecological effects of deforestation. When a tract of forest is cut, the adjacent forest is affected by changes in the physical environment along its edges, by reduced habitat area, and by isolation. Let's look at the nature of these edge effects in Amazonian forest fragments.

In 1979, Brazil's National Institute for Research in Amazonia and the World Wildlife Fund began a long-term study of tropical forest fragmentation. This research project took advantage of a Brazilian law that requires that 50% of land developed in the Amazon Basin remain forested. The researchers worked with ranchers to leave forested tracts in particular areas to facilitate research on the ecological influences of forest fragment size and isolation. The fragments studied were 1, 10, 100, and 200 ha (fig. 21.15). These were compared to areas of 1, 10, 100, and 1,000 ha in undisturbed forest.

When a small fragment of forest is isolated by cutting the surrounding forest, its edge is exposed to greater amounts of

Figure 21.15   Forest fragments left by clear-cutting forest from the surrounding landscape have very different physical environments than intact forest.
© Richard O. Bierregaard, Jr.

solar radiation and wind. Wind and sun combine to change the physical environment within forest fragments. The physical environment along forest edges is hotter and drier; and the intensity of solar radiation, higher. These physical changes, in turn, affect the structure of the forest community. Tree mortality is higher along the edges of forest fragments, and the forest overstory decreases while the thickness of the understory vegetation increases. Fragmentation also decreases the diversity of many animal groups, including monkeys, birds, bees, and carrion and dung beetles. Some of these reductions in animal populations may have significant impacts on key ecological processes, such as pollination and decomposition.

Because edge effects, isolation, and reduced habitat area negatively affect biological diversity within tropical forest fragments, the spatial extent of deforestation and fragmentation will be greater than what one sees simply by recording the area logged for forestry. For example, David Skole and Compton Tucker (1993) conducted an analysis of edge effects associated with deforestation in the Amazon Basin. Between 1978 and 1988, they estimated 230,000 km^2 were cut down. (See chapter 23 for more detail.) However, when they assume that edge effects extend for 1 km from the forest edge, the estimate of impacted forest area increases to 588,000 km^2. In other words, depending upon the landscape pattern of patches, edge effects may greatly increase the negative effects associated with habitat loss that occur during fragmentation. Similar findings have been found for many other systems in many other locations. Reducing edge effects is now a central conservation goal that is considered in many development projects.

Fragmentation and Population Dynamics

Marc-André Villard, of the Université de Moncton, has also studied the role of landscape structure on the persistence of natural populations. Along with Marc Mazerolle, Villard conducted a review of the literature to determine whether including information about landscape structure improves one's ability to explain patterns of species abundances and distributions (Mazerolle and Villard 1999). They were able to find 61 studies, including papers on invertebrates, amphibians, reptiles, mammals, and birds. In fact, a full 36% of the studies that they found were focused on birds! Clearly, there has been a taxonomic bias in the study of fragmentation. Across all taxa, aspects of the local patch (size, age, plant community composition, etc.) influenced species presence and abundance in over 90% of the studies. In contrast, landscape variables (total cover and configuration) were significant in only 59% of the studies. Local factors were significant for all taxa, while the effects of landscape factors varied greatly. Only 20% of the studies on invertebrates showed an effect of landscape, in contrast to nearly 80% of the studies on vertebrates. Clearly, the effects of landscape will not be the same for all species that occupy that landscape.

In this section, we have shown how current research is moving beyond the stage of just documenting an effect of landscape on some biological process, and is now focused on understanding how these effects interact with other ecological processes. This is a major step in the development of this subdiscipline of ecology and is likely setting the stage for major breakthroughs over the next 100 years. Next we explore another topic of much interest: habitat corridors.

Habitat Corridors and Movement of Organisms

If fragmentation and isolation of patches can negatively impact the population dynamics of some species, a logical conservation goal would be to connect patches using **corridors**, thereby reducing patch isolation. Corridors are generally some sort of strip of habitat that connects patches across a landscape. This idea is so inherently attractive that it serves as a cornerstone in conservation biology and is widely promoted by environmental lobbying groups. However, the success of corridors has not matched the hope, despite their being extensively used throughout the world. Here we will discuss the science behind corridors.

The Trans-Canada Highway is a corridor that facilitates animal (human) movement. This strip of asphalt allows us to travel quickly between widely dispersed ecosystems. However, this corridor is also a barrier to the movement of many other species (see the Ecology in Action section in this chapter). The point here is that a corridor to one species may be a barrier to another, and this poses challenges to conservation biologists. Corridors may also facilitate the movement of parasites and diseases of the species of conservation interest, highlighting the point that corridors have the potential to affect the biology of more species than the target of any conservation program. Perhaps before worrying about barriers and disease, it is important to ask an even more basic question: Do animals actually use corridors?

As a sign of the importance of corridors to ecology and conservation biology, over 700 scientific papers discussing corridors have been published. However, very few of these demonstrate that corridors actually enhance animal movement, as opposed to just providing additional habitat. Cheryl-Lesley Chetkiewicz, Colleen St. Clair, and Mark Boyce at the University of Alberta argue that the lack of detailed information linking corridors to behavioural ecology and animal movement reduces the ability to design effective corridors, limiting their potential usefulness (Chetkiewicz et al. 2006). In other words, if some aspect of the landscape (e.g., predator densities) will prevent a target animal from entering a corridor in a certain location, then there is little economic or ecological value in putting a corridor in that location. Instead, it makes more sense to know what habitats an organism is likely to use, and then establish corridors in those areas. These ideas are very similar to what we found in the prior section, discussing the impacts of landscape structure on populations: the effects of the landscape (or corridors) will be dependent upon interactions between landscape structure, species-specific traits, and other ecological processes such as competition and predation. It is clear that much more research linking behavioural, population, and landscape ecology is needed.

Well, so what does determine where an animal moves? The tools that ecologists use to gain this information are discussed in the Ecological Tools and Approaches section of this chapter. But, first, we need to discuss the relationship between landscape structure and animal movement and the development of ecological patterns.

The Role of the Matrix in Influencing Animal Movement

In the context of landscape ecology, the matrix refers to the dominant, connected ecosystem on a landscape. For example, imagine a landscape that consists primarily of agricultural fields with an occasional patch of forest. In this example, the agricultural ecosystem will be the matrix. Now imagine a heavily forested area, with a single patch of agriculture on the landscape. Now it is the forest that is the matrix.

So far in this chapter we have shown that, sometimes, landscape structure can influence a variety of ecological processes, through fragmentation, isolation, and total habitat abundance. What is missing so far, and what helps differentiate landscape ecology from the study of metapopulations (chapter 10), is recognition that the nature of the matrix itself may alter biological processes, such as dispersal among patches. This can affect how organisms respond to the distribution of patches on the landscape. In some cases, the matrix may be completely inhospitable for a given species while other matrix ecosystems may be completely permeable. Consider Schmeigelow's study on fragmentation and boreal birds. For a bird, the matrix is deforested ground and air, not much of a barrier to dispersal. Now consider Diffendorfer's study on rodents and prairie patches. A dash across a matrix of open ground could be deadly with predators on watch. The nature of the matrix has the potential to enhance, or mitigate, the effects of isolation and fragmentation, and to do so differentially for different residents of a patch. To further explore this, we turn to an example of damselflies.

Philip Taylor, of Acadia University, and a former M.Sc. student, Ian Jonsen, were interested in understanding how movement of damselflies could be altered by changes in landscape structure (Jonsen and Taylor 2000). The researchers used two species, *Calopteryx aequabilis* and *Calopteryx maculata*, both of which are able to utilize both stream and forested habitats. The experiment was conducted in the Annapolis Valley of Nova Scotia. Six field sites were identified, all of which contained a stream running through surrounding matrix vegetation. What differed among sites, however, was the identity of the matrix vegetation. In forested landscapes, the stream flowed through continuous forest; in non-forested landscapes, the stream flowed through pastures with minimal forest; and in partially forested landscapes, the stream flowed through a mixture of pasture and forest—landscapes without a single clear matrix. Jonsen and Taylor captured a number of damselflies from each field site, moved them to streams in one of the six field sites, and measured animal movement and whether the animals left the stream habitat. A rather elegant aspect of this design is that they released all animals within the stream habitat in all landscapes. As a result, they can be certain that if an animal left the stream habitat, it was due to the surrounding vegetation (the matrix) and not due to any differences among the release sites themselves.

In total, they were able to release and follow 115 damselflies during their study. For both species, the probability of leaving the stream habitat was strongly influenced by the identity of the surrounding vegetation. Both species stayed on the stream when surrounded by a non-forested landscape, though they left the stream when forest was present. Interestingly, one species was most likely to leave when the landscape was completely forested, and the other was more likely to leave when the landscape was only partially forested. This is an important result, indicating how the matrix vegetation will have different effects on different species, even sympatric congeners!

Matrix effects have also been found in other species. For example, in the boreal mixedwoods, ovenbirds and the white-throated sparrow differ in their responses to different types of matrix vegetation (Gobeil and Villard 2002). In this study, the researchers translocated birds and measured the time it took them to return to their territories as a function of the landscape structure (agricultural, harvested forest, natural forest). For the sparrow, the natural forest landscape was the least penetrable, while that landscape was the most penetrable for the ovenbird. As in the prior study, the effects of matrix vegetation and landscape structure will differ among species.

Studies like those presented here are allowing landscape ecologists not only to describe the patterns they observe in a landscape but to also understand the ecological mechanisms that cause those patterns. This, in turn, is a critical step toward being able to use ecological knowledge to successfully manage conservation networks and design appropriate (and used) habitat corridors. We now turn our attention away from interactions between landscape structure and animal behaviour, and focus on how landscapes can alter a variety of characteristics of ecosystems themselves.

Landscape Position and Lake Chemistry

Katherine Webster and her colleagues (1996) at the Center for Limnology at the University of Wisconsin and the U.S. Geological Survey explored how the position of a lake in a landscape affects its chemical responses to drought. Drought can affect a wide range of lake ecosystem properties, including nutrient cycling and the concentrations of dissolved ions. However, all lakes do not respond in the same way to drought.

Webster and her colleagues set out to determine whether the contrasting chemical responses of lakes to drought can be explained by the position of the lake in the landscape. They worked in northern Wisconsin, where they defined the landscape position of a lake as its location within a hydrologic flow system, based on the proportion of total water inflow supplied by groundwater.

The sources of water for a lake are precipitation, surface water, and groundwater flow. Different lakes receive different proportions of their water from these sources, and these proportions depend upon a lake's position in the landscape. Figure 21.16 shows a series of lakes along a hydrologic flow system in northern Wisconsin. Morgan Lake, which receives the bulk of its water from precipitation, occupies the upper end of this continuum. Lakes such as this one occupy high points in the hydrologic flow system and are called hydrologically

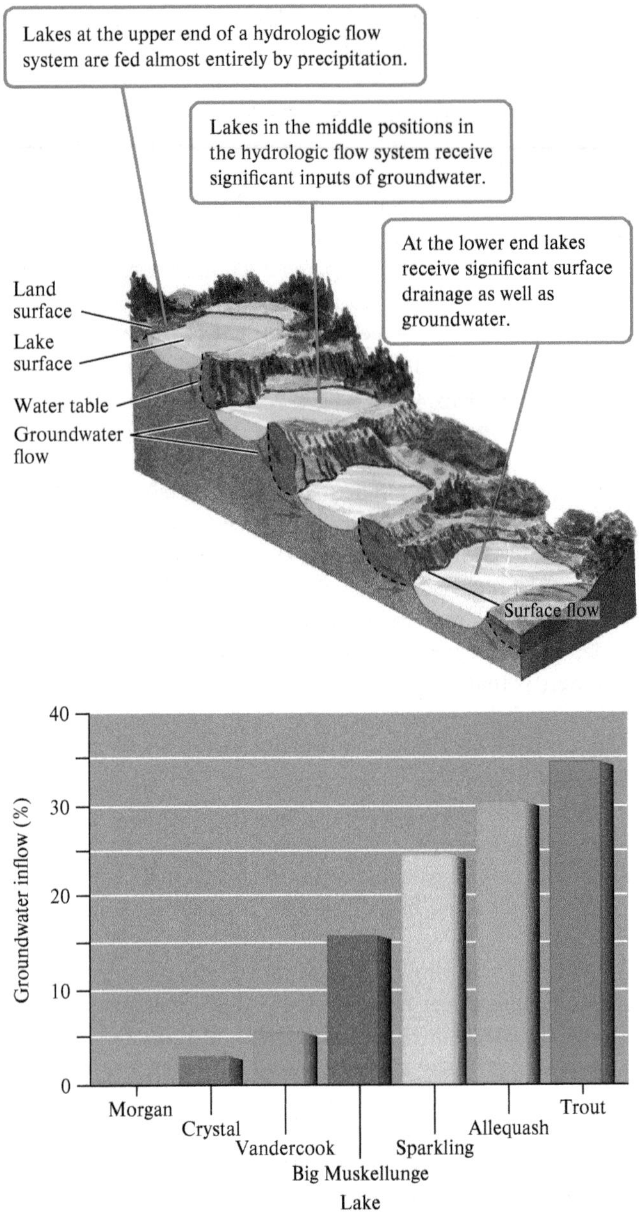

Lakes at the upper end of a hydrologic flow system are fed almost entirely by precipitation.

Lakes in the middle positions in the hydrologic flow system receive significant inputs of groundwater.

At the lower end lakes receive significant surface drainage as well as groundwater.

Land surface
Lake surface
Water table
Groundwater flow
Surface flow

Figure 21.16   Lake position in the landscape and proportion of water received as groundwater.
Data from Webster et al. 1996.

mounded lakes. These lakes are sources of water for the rest of the hydrologic flow system. Crystal Lake and Sparkling Lake, which occupy intermediate positions within the hydrologic flow system and receive significant inflows of groundwater, are considered groundwater flow-through lakes. Finally, at the lower end of the flow system are the drainage lakes that receive significant surface drainage as well as groundwater drainage.

The important point here is that the positions of these lakes in the landscape determine the proportion of water they receive as groundwater. Webster and her colleagues estimated that Morgan Lake receives no groundwater inflow, while Trout Lake, at the lower end of the hydrologic flow system, receives nearly 35% of its inflow as groundwater. The main source of water for a lake determines its response to drought.

The responses of these seven lakes to a drought were studied from 1986 to 1990. As you might expect, the levels of the lakes dropped during this four-year drought. However, the amount of drop in lake level was related to a lake's position in the landscape. The level of Morgan Lake, at the upper end of the hydrologic flow system, dropped 0.7 m, while the levels of Vandercook, Big Muskellunge, Crystal, and Sparkling lakes, in the middle of the hydrologic flow system, dropped 0.9 to 1.0 m. Meanwhile, the levels of Trout and Allequash Lakes, the two drainage lakes at the lower end of the hydrologic flow system, dropped very little.

Landscape position also significantly influenced a lake's chemical responses to the drought. The *concentrations* of dissolved ions such as calcium (Ca^{2+}) and magnesium (Mg^{2+}) increased in the majority of the lakes. However, the increase in ion concentration was highest at the upper and lower ends of the hydrologic flow system. Meanwhile, the combined *mass* of Ca^{2+} and Mg^{2+} increased in the three lakes at the lower end but did not change in Morgan Lake, at the upper end of the flow system, and either decreased or did not change in the lakes occupying the middle portions of the hydrologic flow system.

The researchers concluded that the increased mass of Ca^{2+} and Mg^{2+} seen at the lower end of the hydrologic flow system was due to an increased proportion of inflows from groundwater, rich in Ca^{2+} and Mg^{2+}. The declines in mass of Ca^{2+} and Mg^{2+} in Big Muskellunge Lake are likely due to reduced inflow of ion-rich groundwater. The stability of Ca^{2+} and Mg^{2+} mass in Morgan Lake was attributed to its isolation from the groundwater flow system. Morgan Lake receives almost no groundwater, even during wet periods. Regardless of the mechanisms, the chemical responses of these lakes to the drought were related to their positions in the landscape.

CONCEPT 21.3 REVIEW

1. Why might the two different species occupying the same patch habitat respond differently to fragmentation? Why might they differ in dispersion among patches?

2. What information is needed by ecologists to determine whether a corridor is effective at enhancing the movement and population sustainability of a particular species?

3. How can large-scale experiments be used to address questions in landscape ecology?

ECOLOGY IN ACTION

Linear Disturbances Across the Landscape

Viewed from above, it is clear that a variety of human activities have divided landscapes. Often the divisions are caused by sharp, linear disturbances. For example, the Trans-Canada Highway cuts a line through the centre of Banff National Park, and railroads, gas lines, and small access roads run throughout the Park. Forestry activity creates additional disturbances, from large clear-cut areas to the even more numerous roads used to move equipment and timber. Even recreational use by humans, through the creation of snowmobile, ATV, motorbike, bicycle, and hiking trails, creates linear disturbances. All of these disturbances become part of the landscape for the organisms that live within these ecosystems, and it is scientifically naive to imagine that they have no consequences for the species whose landscape has become subdivided. Conservation biologists are becoming increasingly interested in understanding what impacts the alteration of landscape structure, through the construction of linear disturbances, has on natural populations. Here we discuss one type of linear disturbance: roads.

Forman and Alexander (1998) estimate that over 1,000,000 vertebrates are killed per day on roads in the United States, a number much higher than mortality due to hunting. Of greater concern, however, is the effect roads may have on the rest of the animal populations, potentially serving as barriers to the movement of individuals, and their genes, as well as reducing the amount of suitable habitat in a landscape. For example, Simon Dyer and Stan Boutin from the University of Alberta, along with colleagues, found that threatened woodland caribou in western Canada crossed roads with moderate vehicle traffic six times less frequently than would be expected by chance (Dyer et al. 2002). Road avoidance behaviours effectively increase the isolation of patches, not due to distances but due to a behavioural shift in the animals. Such nondirect effects are similar to the nonconsumptive effects of predation (chapter 14). Once again, this issue emphasizes the need to link animal behaviour, landscape structure, and population biology in any successful conservation program.

One example of how these disciplines can be integrated to enhance conservation efforts comes from Anthony Clevenger from Parks Canada and Nigel Waltho from Carleton University (Clevenger and Waltho 2005). Clevenger and Waltho explored the effectiveness of different wildlife-crossing structures in Banff National Park (fig. 21.17). Crossing structures have been incorporated into road development across the world, with the hope that animals will use the structures, thereby reducing mortalities as

Figure 21.17 Structures built across the Trans-Canada Highway in Banff reduce road mortality of wildlife.
Adam T. Ford.

well as increasing permeability of the landscape. Clevenger and Waltho decided to test the effectiveness of different crossing designs along the Trans-Canada Highway in Banff, a road that carried an average of nearly 15,000 vehicles per day in 1999. The designs used included both under- and overpasses, with construction materials ranging from concrete to metal. Over the course of 34 months, they recorded 4,209 uses (by identifying tracks) by large mammals, including wolves, cougars, black bears, grizzly bears, deer, elk, and humans (8%). Not surprisingly, they found that use differed among species and that the species responded differently to different structures and location of the crossings in the landscape. Overall, the information provided by these researchers and others is of great value for future ecologists as they develop new crossings for the protection of these animals in Banff, and elsewhere.

Rebuilding Connectivity in Urban Natural Areas

Longitudinal barriers can fragment habitat, restricting migration and gene flow in an otherwise large, natural area. However, there are more intensive and pervasive agents of fragmentation that we have stopped seeing, as they are a normal part of our experience. Urbanization and development radically change the landscape, leaving behind highly fragmented and isolated natural areas. The natural areas that remain within an urban landscape have value for conservation. Despite efforts to conserve native species in these urban natural areas, small population sizes, edge effects associated with small, irregularly shaped patches, and other vulnerabilities conspire against conservation efforts in these urban natural areas, and even protected natural areas tend to lose native species over time.

Cootes Paradise Marsh is one of the largest remaining Great Lakes coastal wetlands. The marsh is on the west end of Lake Ontario, near the cities of Hamilton and Burlington in Ontario, Canada (fig. 21.18). The ecological significance of Cootes Paradise Marsh has been long recognized. The Province of Ontario designated the marsh a fish sanctuary in 1887 and a provincial wildlife sanctuary in 1927. Royal Botanical Gardens (RBG), which now owns most of the marsh, was created in part to protect Cootes Paradise and its surrounding habitat. Native plant species diversity in the nature sanctuaries of RBG is very high for any protected area in Canada (Galbraith et al. 2011), with over 1,150 species found within the ~900 ha owned by RBG (Smith 2003). Despite the relatively large size of Cootes, fragmentation, pollution, and invasive species have resulted in many changes.

The Niagara Escarpment, a UNESCO World Biosphere Reserve, is another ecologically important system, with high diversity and a number of endemic plant species. Historically, the Niagara Escarpment was connected to Great Lakes marsh ecosystems, with free movement of animals between habitats. Following decades of development in southern Ontario, the area north of Cootes Paradise Marsh is the only place along the Lake Ontario shoreline where two ecosystem types remain connected through an ecological corridor, albeit a vulnerable corridor largely following ravines. The land along the corridor was once almost entirely small farmsteads, but more recent housing development in some of these parcels has threatened the corridor's continuity. However, there is a growing awareness of the ecological significance of this corridor. In the early 1990s, a proposal for housing development on ~100 ha of land, critically positioned within the corridor, was opposed by local people and conservation groups. This led to a landmark decision by the Ontario Municipal Board that the land

Figure 21.18 Cootes Paradise Marsh near Hamilton, Ontario.
SF photo/Shutterstock.com.

remain open space, with any future development restricted to single detached dwellings on plots of 10 ha or greater.

Royal Botanical Gardens has been at the forefront of ecological restoration of Cootes Paradise and the surrounding landscape. These efforts include building effective buffers and corridors to reconnect the marsh with the Niagara Escarpment. David Galbraith, Head of Science at RBG, and Peter Kelly, Coordinator of the Cootes to Escarpment Eco-Park System, related a brief history of the EcoPark System. It is a remarkable example of building multilateral cooperation and collaboration among agencies and stakeholders to accomplish an ambitious ecological objective. For students, the story is a good lesson in how ecologists must work closely with urban planners, agency staff, and the public to implement policy or actions grounded in ecological science.

In 2006 a natural heritage planning group, including representatives of Royal Botanical Gardens, Hamilton Conservation Authority, Conservation Halton, the Hamilton Naturalists' Club, and the Hamilton Harbour Remedial Action Plan, met to consider an integrated conservation approach for Cootes Paradise Marsh and the corridor between the marsh and escarpment. The planning group, with funding support from Ontario's Friends of the Greenbelt Foundation, initiated research of the landscape, its natural and cultural heritage features, and recreational uses. The group engaged professional planners and assembled detailed reports on potential areas for further protection. After extensive consultation with key stakeholders, the public, and staff of participating agencies, a strategic plan was developed for creating the "Cootes to Escarpment EcoPark System." The proposed EcoPark System took the form of an alliance and collaboration among the nine different agencies and organizations that owned the existing natural protected areas. In 2013 these partners formally agreed to create the EcoPark System and support a central secretariat, at least for a start-up period spanning several years. A central tenet of the Cootes to Escarpment EcoPark System is that all participating public bodies and land-owning agencies have an equal voice in the development of programs related to the EcoPark System. The EcoPark System operates under a multi-year strategic plan first approved in 2010. Planned restoration projects, establishment of recreational linkages, and other work are then incorporated into the management plans and implemented by the relevant partner agencies.

Initial response to the Cootes to Escarpment EcoPark System has been very positive. Particularly encouraging have been donations of additional lands to one or more of the organizations in the park alliance, on the condition that the land remains undeveloped and is part of the larger EcoPark System. Approximately 220 acres of land have been protected since 2013 and restoration of these lands has begun with planting of native shrubs by volunteers. In the Cootes to Escarpment corridor itself, 100 acres of lands were purchased in 2015 and protected from development, creating for the first time a protected ecological connection between the escarpment and the wetland (apart from connections through ravines). Stewardship events and workshops began in 2014 and are organized on an ongoing basis throughout the EcoPark System. Personnel visit private landowners to provide them with advice on how they can properly steward their properties.

The partners are working together to realize the vision originally hatched in 2006. The Cootes to Escarpment EcoPark System may be in its infancy but the full potential of this unique partnership may only be realized in the years ahead.

ECOLOGICAL TOOLS AND APPROACHES

Linking Population, Behavioural, and Landscape Ecology

How much change to the landscape is too much to sustain natural populations of animals? What areas of the landscape are used by species of concern and thus are a high conservation priority? What areas on the landscape are rarely used, meaning that industrial development may have a less negative impact if located there? These are critical questions in ecology and conservation biology. In the last several years, there has been a growing appreciation that animal behaviour and landscapes are intimately tied. To begin to provide answers to the questions above, ecologists must work across disciplines and truly understand the systems in which they work. The rapid increase in available computing power has facilitated research, allowing the construction of detailed models predicting which ecological parameters are, or are not, likely to influence animal populations on the landscape. In this section, we will explore how ecologists are working at blending population, landscape, and behavioural ecology, with important consequences for management and conservation of natural resources.

Using Thresholds to Estimate Risk

There is significant societal pressure to develop natural areas. Development can take a variety of forms, including oil and gas exploration, construction of residential areas, forestry, agriculture, water extraction, dams, and road construction. As we have seen in this chapter, every activity that occurs changes the structure of the landscape. In some cases, these changes have no meaningful consequence for the long-term sustainability of natural populations. In other cases, these changes may cause the collapse of a population. Assuming politicians value land-use planning that protects both economic interests and ecological sustainability, it is critical that ecologists provide tools that help identify risk. The key question becomes this: How much habitat loss and change in landscape structure is too much?

The answer to this depends upon whether the effects of habitat loss and changes to landscape structure have proportional or disproportional effects on populations. Lenore Fahrig, whom we have highlighted before, has written a review exploring the impacts of fragmentation and habitat loss on populations (Fahrig 2003). She has found that the majority of theoretical studies suggest that the relationship between habitat amount and population sizes will be nonlinear. If this is true, it means that at some amount of habitat, well above zero, a population will go extinct. Fahrig suggests that habitat fragmentation can alter the exact location of this threshold, though empirical data is sparse. Regardless of the data available right now, thresholds are one tool that may allow a researcher to predict at what point development may switch a landscape from one that can support sustainable populations (or the organisms of interest) to one that cannot.

These ideas form the basis of **conservation thresholds**, points at which habitat loss and fragmentation cause populations to tip from sustainable to extinct. Ecologists are charged with finding those tipping points before they are reached. If these thresholds can be identified, then they can be incorporated into a regional land-use plan, ensuring adequate areas are left undeveloped while also allowing for development in areas that are redundant in terms of population sustainability. This approach recognizes that different citizens value different things (development, wilderness, sustainability), and the threshold approach holds promise by setting the point at which balanced land uses are no longer viable.

Using Resource Selection Functions to Link Movement to the Landscape

Thresholds can be a valuable tool in helping ecologists and land managers understand the point at which development is likely to cause collapse of natural populations. A complementary approach exists that is also proving to be critical to the development of scientifically sound management strategies. This approach—resource selection functions (RSF)—also blends measures of the local environment, landscape, and animal behaviour in models that allow researchers to describe (and predict) where animals will be found on the landscape. As we have discussed previously in the chapter, this information is critical to the development of corridors

that actually serve as corridors. Only by knowing which habitat animals will actually use can you hope to be successful in having functional links between isolated fragments.

Mark Boyce, of the University of Alberta, has been a leading advocate for greater use of RSFs in ecology. Boyce argues that the basis of RSFs is straightforward: if you want to know the distribution and abundance of species on a landscape, then it makes sense to know the distribution of resources on the landscape (Boyce and McDonald 1999). The mathematics behind RSF are beyond the scope of this textbook, but the output from the models they produce is very understandable. If a model determines that some

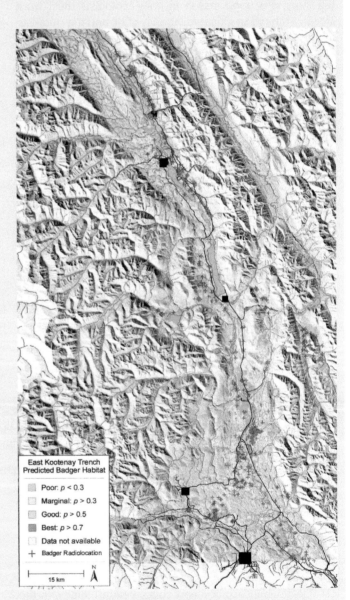

Figure 21.19   RSFs predict the preferred and avoided habitat for badgers in the east Kootenays of British Columbia.

C. D. Apps et al. 2002. Habitat associations of American badgers in southeastern British Columbia. *Canadian Journal of Zoology.* 80:1228–39, Figure 3. Reprinted with permission.

factor, such as elk density, is associated with the probability of some other factor, such as the presences of wolves, then the model will generate a probability function. In this case, the RSF would represent the probability of finding a wolf as a function of elk density. To develop this model requires locating large numbers of individuals of the species of concern through one of the methods previously discussed in chapter 11 (e.g., radiotelemetry, trapping, etc.). At the same time, the researchers would measure all aspects of their locations. Additional data would be collected about locations that the animals were not found in. The factors measured could include abiotic conditions, abundance of predators and prey, vegetation and habitat complexity, and any other factor thought to influence the ecology of that particular species.

A statistical model would then be constructed that relates the location of animals to these landscape and environmental measures. Those factors found to be of minimal explanatory power are usually discarded, resulting in a model that identifies what are likely the most important factors influencing the distribution of the animals on this particular landscape. Perhaps in this case that would include elk density, snow depth, and slope. What is particularly attractive about RSF is that these functions can all be combined on a map of the landscape, showing exactly where animals are most likely to occur (fig. 21.19). The maps that are developed are then very helpful guides for land managers, allowing them to visually understand which habitats on the landscape are preferred by the species of concern. This approach is rapidly spreading throughout western Canada, including the large national parks of Jasper and Banff.

RSFs, like thresholds, show that ecologists are developing the research tools that are critical to understanding the factors that drive species distributions and abundances. At the core of the models is the realization that there will not be a single factor that is most important but instead a suite of processes and conditions will influence the distribution of the species of concern.

SUMMARY

A landscape is a heterogeneous area composed of several ecosystems. The ecosystems making up a landscape generally form a mosaic of visually distinctive patches. These patches are called *landscape elements*. *Landscape ecology* is the study of landscape structure and processes.

21.1 Landscapes are created and change in response to geological processes, climate, activities of organisms, and fire.

Geological features produced by processes such as volcanism, sedimentation, and erosion interact with climate to provide a primary source of landscape structure (fig 21.20). Repeated glaciations in North America have created much of the landscape that is currently found in Canada. We are currently living in an interglacial period, with the last glaciation reaching a peak approximately 20,000 years ago. Glacial movement causes scouring and translocation of substantial amounts of soil, creating a topologically diverse landscape. The resulting variation in soil textures influences the distribution of plant species and ecosystems. While geological processes and climate set the basic template for landscape structure, the activities of organisms, including plants and animals, can be an additional source of landscape structure and change. Beavers, as one example, can quickly change landscape structure and processes over large

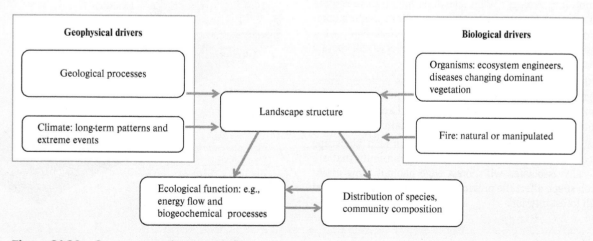

Figure 21.20 Concept map for chapter 21.

regions. Economically motivated human activity changes the structure of landscapes all over the globe. Fire contributes to the structure of landscapes ranging from tropical savanna to boreal forest. However, fire plays a particularly prominent role in regions with a Mediterranean climate.

21.2 Landscape structure includes the size, shape, composition, number, and position of patches, or landscape elements, in a landscape.

Most questions in landscape ecology require that ecologists quantify landscape structure. An area of mathematics called fractal geometry can be used to quantify the structure of complex natural shapes. One of the findings of fractal geometry is that the length of the perimeter of complex shapes, such as habitat patches, depends upon the size of the device used to measure the perimeter. One implication of this result is that organisms of different sizes may experience habitat fragmentation in very different ways and may exploit habitat patches in different ways.

21.3 Landscape structure influences processes such as the flow of energy, materials, and species distributions across a landscape.

Landscape ecologists have proposed that landscape structure, especially the size, number, and isolation of habitat patches, can interact with other ecological processes, such as competition, predation, and behaviour, to influence populations and communities (fig 21.20). Studies of the movements of small mammals in a prairie landscape show that a smaller proportion of individuals moves in more fragmented landscapes, but that the individuals that do move will move farther. Not all studies of landscape structure suggest biologically meaningful effects of fragmentation on natural populations. Fragmentation of the boreal forest appears to have only minor effects on the species composition of bird communities. Habitat loss and local factors, such as habitat quality, appear to have stronger impacts on most species than landscape structure. However, some species appear to be strongly affected by changes in landscape structure. Habitat corridors may reduce the negative effects of fragmentation and patch isolation for some species; however, there is little empirical data indicating that current practices in corridor design result in the desired conservation goals. Not all ecosystems on a landscape are equally permeable to animal movement; thus, the contrast between a patch and the surrounding matrix ecosystem can serve as another factor altering animal movement among patches. The source of water for lakes in a Wisconsin lake district is determined by their positions in the landscape, which in turn determine their hydrologic and chemical responses to drought.

Society requires scientific knowledge about the ecological impacts of landscape development. Providing answers requires a coordinated approach among landscape, population, and behavioural ecologists. Ecologists are currently using threshold models to understand the potential impacts of habitat loss on the distribution of species. Resource selection functions can be used to predict habitats of high and low value for focal species. These approaches are critical to the development of successful corridors and conservation programs, and to finding actual balances between development and species protection.

REVIEW QUESTIONS

1. How does landscape ecology differ from ecosystem and community ecology? What questions might an ecosystem ecologist ask about a forest? What questions might a community ecologist ask about the same forest? Now, what kinds of questions would a landscape ecologist ask about a forested landscape?

2. In the figure to the right, the green areas represent forest fragments surrounded by agriculture. Landscapes 1 and 2 contain the same total forest area. Will Landscape 1 or 2 contain more forest interior species? Explain.

3. How might the shapes of forest patches in a landscape affect the proportion of birds in the community that are typically associated with forest edge habitat? How might patch shape affect the presence of birds typically associated with forest interior?

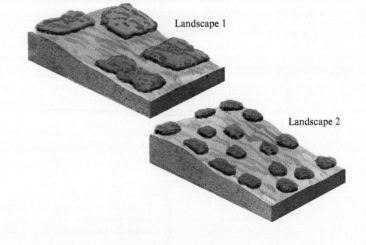

Landscape 1

Landscape 2

4. In this chapter, we have presented evidence that landscape structure can influence population growth. In section 3, we presented the idea that some populations exist as metapopulations. Describe the connections between our discussion of habitat patches in a landscape and metapopulations.

5. Do aspects of the landscape necessarily influence metapopulation dynamics? How do the characteristics of the species of interest and the nature of the matrix affect your response?

6. In the figure below, consider the options for preserving patches of riverside forest. Again, the two landscapes contain the same total area of forest, but the patches in the two landscapes differ in shape. Which of the two would be most dominated by forest edge species?

Landscape 1

Landscape 2

7. How do the positions of patches in a landscape affect the movement of individuals among habitat patches and among portions of a metapopulation? Again, consider the hypothetical landscapes shown in question 6. Which of the two landscapes would promote the highest rate of movement of individuals between forest patches? Can you think of any circumstances in which it might be desirable to reduce the movement of individuals across a landscape? (Hint: Think of the potential threat of pathogens that are spread mainly by direct contact between individuals within a population.)

8. Use fractal geometry and the niche concept to explain why the canopy of a forest should accommodate more species of predaceous insects than insectivorous birds. Assume that the numbers of bird and predaceous insect species are limited by competition.

9. Several of the studies we have discussed in this chapter find few effects of landscape structure on some natural populations. Other species, however, respond very strongly to changes in landscape structure. What aspects of an organism's life-history are likely to determine whether or not a species responds?

10. How do the activities of animals affect landscape heterogeneity? You might use either beaver or human activity as your model. What parallels can you think of between the influence of animal activity on landscape heterogeneity and the intermediate disturbance hypothesis? Which is concerned with the effect of disturbance on species diversity?

Steven dosRemedios/Getty Images.

CHAPTER 22   MACROECOLOGY

CHAPTER CONCEPTS

22.1 Information about a species' current distribution and niche requirements can be combined with spatial information to predict invasion and range expansion.
Concept 22.1 Review

22.2 On islands and habitat patches on continents, species richness increases with area and decreases with isolation.
Concept 22.2 Review

22.3 Species richness on islands can be modelled as a dynamic balance between immigration and extinction of species.
Concept 22.3 Review

22.4 Species richness generally increases from middle and high latitudes to the equator.
Concept 22.4 Review

22.5 Long-term historical and regional processes significantly influence the structure of biotas and ecosystems.
Ecology in Action: Biodiversity Hotspots
Ecological Tools and Approaches: Global Positioning Systems, Remote Sensing, and Geographic Information Systems
Concept 22.5 Review
Summary
Review Questions

On June 5, 1799, Alexander von Humboldt and Aimé Bonpland sailed out of the port of Coruña in northwest Spain. Their small Spanish ship managed to slip past a British naval blockade and sail on, first to the Canary Islands and then to South America. Humboldt was a Prussian engineer and scientist and Bonpland was a French botanist. Humboldt came equipped with the finest scientific instruments of the time and was prepared to systematically survey the lands that he and Bonpland would visit. He wrote a letter to his friend Karl Freiesleben a few hours before his ship left port outlining his purpose for the expedition: "I shall try to find out how the forces of nature interreact upon one another and how the geographic environment influences plant and animal life. In other words, I must find out about the unity of nature" (Botting 1973, p. 65).

Humboldt and Bonpland carried passports issued by the court of King Carlos IV of Spain, giving them permission to conduct scientific studies throughout the Spanish Empire, which then stretched from California to Texas in North America and south to the tip of South America. They had complete access to a vast area of the earth's surface that was essentially unexplored scientifically, and they put that access to productive use. Because their discoveries were so numerous and their explorations so thorough, Simón Bolívar, the liberator of most of Spanish America, referred to Humboldt as "the discoverer of the New World."

Humboldt's expedition was one of the most ambitious scientific explorations of the age. During the course of their expedition, Humboldt and Bonpland travelled nearly 10,000 km through South and North America. They travelled on foot, by canoe, or on horseback, visiting latitudes ranging between 12° S and 52° N. They also climbed to nearly 5,900 m on the slopes of Chimborazo—the highest recorded ascent by anyone in history up to that time (fig. 22.1).

The physical feats of their expedition, however, never took precedence over their scientific purpose. For instance, on their climb of Chimborazo, they faced the uncertain dangers of high altitude. Yet, as blood oozed from their lips and gums,

Figure 22.1 On the slopes of Chimborazo, a 6,310 m high volcanic peak in the Andes Mountains of Ecuador, Alexander von Humboldt and Aimé Bonpland meticulously recorded the altitudinal distributions of plants.
© Norman Owen Tomalin/Bruce Coleman/Avalon.

Humboldt and Bonpland recorded the altitudinal distributions of plants and animals. Later, Humboldt organized their observations of climate and plant distributions into ingenious visual representations of plant geography. What he did not accomplish, he inspired others to. One of those inspired to follow in Humboldt's footsteps was Charles Darwin. Darwin said that his reading of Humboldt's expedition to South America set the course of his whole life.

In the early decades of ecology, many ecologists continued in this tradition, studying broadscale patterns. For example, Robert H. MacArthur (1972) defined a subdiscipline of *geographic ecology* as the "search for patterns of plant and animal life that can be put on a map" (p. 1). As ecology matured in the 1970s and 1980s, there was increased emphasis placed on mechanism, and those decades saw the emergence of experimental ecology and decreased emphasis on broad pattern description. In 1989, James Brown and Brian Maurer published an influential paper in which they argued that, "Without a complementary emphasis on large-scale phenomena, there is little basis for determining which results simply reflect the idiosyncrasies of individual species and particular sites and which reflect the operation of more universal processes" (Brown and Maurer 1989, p. 1,145). In other words, Brown and Mauer argued that without *macroecology*, there is no context in which to place what we learn from *microecological* studies. This paper led to the widespread adoption of the term *macroecology* in reference to large-scale studies of species abundances and distribution, though it is itself conceptually linked to MacArthur's term of *geographic ecology*. Although the terminology is in debate, the underlying importance of studying ecological patterns over large spatial scales is not.

The development of macroecology continues as new generations of scientists equipped with a diversity of tools, both ancient and modern, search for the elusive patterns that can be put on maps. The breadth of macroecology is as vast as its subject. Consequently, we concentrate our discussions in this chapter on just a few aspects of the field: the distribution of species, island biogeography, latitudinal patterns of species diversity, and the influences of large-scale regional and historical processes on biological diversity.

22.1 Ecological Niche Modelling

Information about a species' current distribution and niche requirements can be combined with spatial information to predict invasion and range expansion. Ecologists have done a good job of explaining why many of the natural patterns we see have arisen. In other words, scientists are very good at describing the mechanisms that generate the natural history we can observe *now*. However, society needs us to predict the patterns we will see in the *future*. The field of population ecology has addressed this issue through its reliance on population growth models (chapter 12). However, these models rarely integrate information about both the species of interest and its niche requirements. Yes, it is helpful to describe why a novel disease or invasive species moved across a landscape, but it would be more helpful to be able to alert officials about the most at-risk locations for the spread of a disease (Mak et al. 2010) or an invasive species (Peterson and Vieglais 2001). It would also be helpful to be able to predict how climate change may alter species distributions before the changes occur (Peterson et al. 2004). Ecologists have begun to make great strides in this form of predictive ecology, and it only is possible through a mash-up of diverse data sets coupled with geographic information. This new approach goes by many names, including ecological niche modelling, species distribution modelling, and habitat modelling. Regardless of what it is called, the goal is to combine a species' niche requirements with the spatial distribution of environmental conditions on a landscape or across a region to identify specific locations where a species could occur.

In chapter 9, we first presented the concept of the niche, defining it as the combination of environmental factors that influence the growth, survival, and reproduction of a species. One of the critical aspects of this niche definition is that the niche is an abstract representation of the conditions a species needs, not an actual physical location on a map. However, to make specific predictions about how a species' range may change over time, we need to convert the abstract concept of the niche to specific locations across a landscape. How does one actually do this? In theory, it is pretty straightforward and requires three basic steps: (1) identify the niche of the species of concern, (2) determine the distribution of environmental conditions throughout the geographic area of concern, and (3) combine this information to produce a map of potential distributions of the species of concern. In chapter 15 we talked about the predicted range expansion of *Aedes* mosquito species that serve as vectors for dengue fever and the zika virus. This is an example of ecological niche modelling applied to better understand the future geography of disease. Similar exercises have been undertaken to predict the likely expansion of Asian carp species, guiding current preventive measures.

In reality, predicting a species of interest's potential distribution is a very difficult task requiring detailed field work coupled with complex statistical analyses. We must acknowledge that, in practice, the models generated tend to focus on the fundamental niche, the physical conditions under which an organism might live. Inclusion of biotic interactions based on principles of microecology is generally beyond the scope of these efforts. To demonstrate the complexity and potential benefits of this approach, we present two examples.

Predicting the Spread of an Invasive Crab Species Throughout North America

In chapter 14, we mentioned that a relaxation of exploitative relationships may lead to novel species rapidly increasing their range and invading throughout a landscape. Here, we show how ecological niche modelling can be used to identify the locations into which a species may invade, with the hope of preventative actions being taken to reduce or eliminate the environmental risk.

Figure 22.2 Chinese mitten crab (*Eriocheir sinensis*).
Photo 32863898 © Mikelane45–Dreamstime.com.

Hugh MacIsaac is a professor at the University of Windsor and a Canada Research Chair in aquatic invasive species. A study by MacIsaac and colleagues (Herborg et al. 2007) is a good illustration of niche modelling to predict the potential range of an invasive species, the Chinese mitten crab (*Eriocheir sinensis*). The mitten crab (fig. 22.2) is native to Asia, occurring throughout China, North Korea, and Hong Kong. The crab has spread throughout the planet by hitchhiking in ballast water of trade ships and through intentional introduction as seafood (Herborg et al. 2007). The crab is now widespread throughout Europe and has a very spotty distribution within North America. MacIsaac and colleagues recognized that a spotty distribution now does not mean there will be a spotty distribution in the future, and they wanted a way to predict the relative risk of invasion in the major ports throughout North America. To make such predictions realistic, the research team needed to understand the biology of the organism. Because this species is not yet widespread in North America, they needed to gather information from Europe and Asia.

Determining the fundamental niche of an organism is very difficult, and there are a number of methods that have been used over the years. The standard approach used in ecological niche modelling is to obtain (1) a list of locations where the study organism has been found (compiling new field data, museum records, etc.), (2) spatially explicit environmental information for the region in which the organism is found, and (3) similar environmental information for areas where the organism has not been found. Later in the chapter we will discuss how such spatially explicit data is collected (remote sensing). For now it is enough to know that just as molecular tools have revolutionized the field of evolutionary ecology, easy access to satellites has revolutionized large-scale ecological studies.

MacIsaac and colleagues had data on the distribution of *Eriocheir sinensis* in the crab's native range in Asia. They then chose 12 environmental parameters they thought might represent different niche axes (and for which they had spatially explicit data). These included parameters such as local topography, minimum and maximum temperatures, and precipitation. They then used a variety of statistical procedures (which are beyond the scope of this text) to relate these data sets, allowing them to generate an equation that described the multivariate environmental conditions under which the mitten crab had a high probability of occurring. This equation was a mathematical approximation of the species' niche, generated from data in locations where the crab currently exists. The research team then applied the niche equation to the environmental conditions found throughout North America. The resulting map indicates the strength of the match between niche requirements, as determined from its Asian distribution, and local environmental conditions in North America (fig. 22.3a).

Figure 22.3a looks quite troubling, as much of the United States (and pieces of Canada) have suitable environmental conditions for the growth and spread of this invasive species. However, MacIsaac and colleagues recognized that there is more to

this story that is critical for assessing invasion risk. First, there are issues related to the basic biology of this species. *Eriocheir sinensis* has a *catadromous* life cycle with planktonic larvae maturing in brackish-saline water, while the adult lives primarily in freshwater (essentially the opposite of the *anadromous* life cycle of salmon). As a result, when the researchers looked at existing distributions of this crab throughout Europe, they found that all reported occurrences were less than 1,261 km from the sea, and 90% of occurrences were less than 355 km from the sea (Herborg et al. 2007). This is critical information and suggests that locations in North America more than 355 km from the sea are unlikely to be invaded. When this niche axis (distance to ocean) is also applied to the data, we find a greatly reduced (though still troublesome!) potential range in North America (fig. 22.3b).

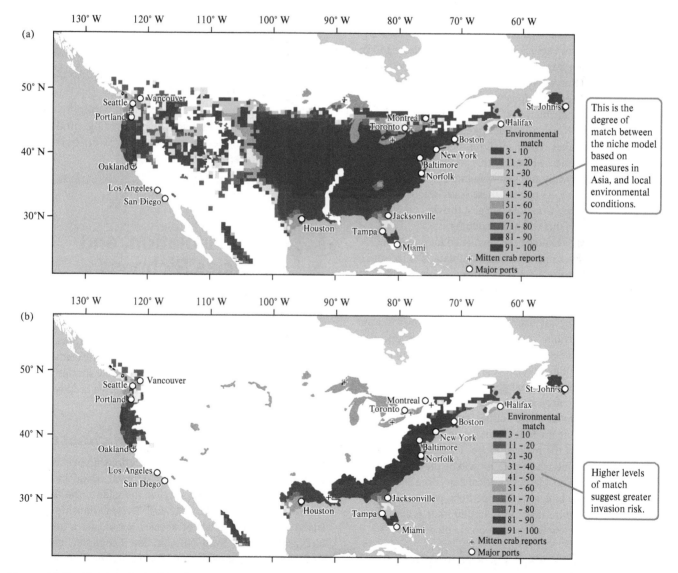

Figure 22.3 The predicted probabilities of Chinese mitten crabs occurring in different locations throughout North America. (a) This map assumes the crab can successfully maintain a population independent of distance from salt water. (b) A more biologically realistic model limits crab populations to <355 km away from a salt water source. Note that in both figures a "+" indicates mitten crabs were found, though this does not imply a population had successfully established.

L. M. Herborg, C. L. Jerde, D. M. Lodge, G. M. Ruiz, and H. J. MacIsaac. 2007. Predicting invasion risk using measures of introduction effort and environmental niche models. *Ecological Applications* 17:663–74, Figure 1.

A second issue that could influence invasion risk is the frequency with which this species is actually introduced at different locations. The dominant vectors for invasion are ships that pick up ballast water in Europe and Asia, and dump that water (and planktonic larvae) in foreign ports. MacIsaac and colleagues were able to estimate the frequency with which that happened in the major shipping ports in the United States. Using that information, coupled with the maps they generated describing environmental match (fig. 22.3b), they were able to identify specific ports as being most vulnerable due to a combination of environmental match and large ballast volumes. Such predictive ecology can help governmental officials focus their search efforts for this species in those locations, rather than spending limited dollars searching in areas unlikely to be invaded. This approach has the potential to greatly reduce the likelihood that this species will gain a foothold in North America.

As of 2019, sightings of the Chinese mitten crab have been primarily along the Atlantic coast between New York and Washington, along the Pacific coast near San Francisco, and in the St. Lawrence Seaway. These observations are reported by the U.S. Geological Survey Nonindigenous Aquatic Species Program. There have been occasional reports of the crab in Lakes Ontario and Erie, and, interestingly, several have been found as far inland as the North Shore of Lake Superior. If observations in the Great Lakes reflect small reproducing populations rather than simply released adults, this would suggest a shift in life history, specifically the requirements of brackish water for larval development. As most of these observations are more than a decade old, they would not suggest thriving populations of invaders. However, this will bear watching.

Similar studies have now been conducted for many species. There are readily available environmental data sets for much of the world, and geo-referenced occurrence data is found in most research museums and collections. Though the statistics involved are complicated, there are user-friendly interfaces that greatly facilitate ecological niche modelling. Heck, you can even predict where black rhinos could live if they were introduced to Canada! There are, however, some problems. First, though this is called niche modelling, this process focuses only on where a species is found in its native range, not where it could live. In other words, this is ecological *realized* niche modelling and does not use the *fundamental* niche. Rather, environmental parameters believed to define the fundamental niche are derived from what we know about the realized niche. These parameters are then exported to define what we think will be the fundamental niche in new areas. This may be a critical flaw if the factors that restrict a species are biological (competitors, predators, pathogens) rather than environmental. A second issue is even more basic. How do you know the species you are modelling?

Using Ecological Niche Modelling to Predict the Distribution of Rare Species

One use of ecological niche modelling is to identify the niche conditions for a rare or at-risk species, and then use that information to help identify potential locations on the landscape where that species may be found. Such efforts would provide scientists with more accurate information on the health of populations of at-risk species, leading to the development of more accurate conservation plans. For example, a team of researchers using niche modelling were able to find extant populations of a rare plant species, previously believed to be extinct, in a region of Brazil (de Siqueira et al. 2009). When done well, ecological niche modelling can highlight areas in which rare species are likely to occur and where they could move to under future environmental conditions. If the core data is accurate, this form of predictive ecology can be of great value to land managers and conservation biologists.

In the next section, we move away from describing the geographic distribution of a single species and focus on broader patterns of diversity. We start with one of the oldest ecological patterns ever described—the relationship between area and species diversity.

CONCEPT 22.1 REVIEW

1. What types of information are needed to conduct ecological niche modelling?
2. Why does the ability to accurately identify a species, or know that identifications by others are accurate, influence the validity of an ecological niche model?

22.2 Area, Isolation, and Species Richness

On islands and habitat patches on continents, species richness increases with area and decreases with isolation. Larger areas generally have more resources and can generally support larger populations, less vulnerable to extinction. They may also have greater niche diversity, supporting greater species richness. Isolation may be a barrier to a new species' reaching an island. Species that go extinct will not be readily replaced when isolation increases.

Island Area and Species Richness

Frank Preston (1962a) described a relationship between island area and the number of species on each island in the West Indies. He found that the smaller the island, the fewer bird species on the island (fig. 22.4a). The relationship between island area and number of species is not just a property of bird assemblages. Sven Nilsson, Jan Bengtsson, and Stefan Ås (1988) explored patterns of species richness among woody plants, carabid beetles, and land snails on 17 islands in Lake Mälaren, Sweden. The islands ranged in area from 0.6 to 75 ha and were all forested. The researchers were careful to choose islands that showed few or no signs of human disturbance. They found that island area was the best single predictor of species richness in all three groups of organisms (fig. 22.4b).

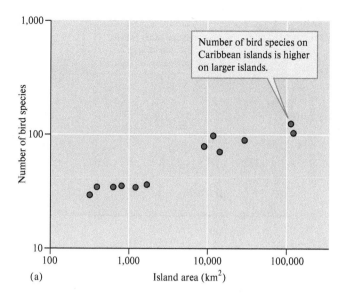

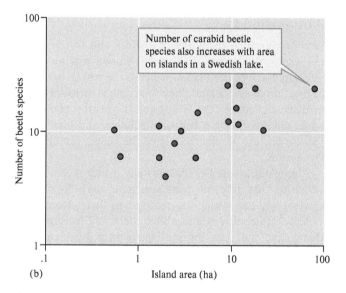

Figure 22.4 Relationship between island area and number of species.

Data from Preston 1962a; Nilsson, Bengtsson, and Ås 1988.

When most of us think of islands, the picture that generally comes to mind is a small bit of land in the middle of an ocean. However, many habitats on continents are so isolated that they can be considered as islands. Will these islands of isolation show similar patterns with respect to species richness?

Habitat Patches on Continents: Mountain Islands

The many isolated mountain ranges that extend across the Great Basin and southwestern regions of North America are now continental islands. During the late Pleistocene, 11,000 to 15,000 years ago, forest and woodland habitats extended unbroken from the Rocky Mountains to the Sierra Nevada in California. Then, as the Pleistocene ended and the climate warmed, forest and alpine habitats contracted to the tops of the high mountains scattered across the American Southwest. As montane habitats retreated to higher elevations, woodland, shrubland, grassland, or desert scrub vegetation invaded the lower elevations. As a consequence of these changes, once-continuous forest and alpine vegetation was converted to a series of island-like habitat patches associated with mountains and therefore called *montane*.

As montane vegetation contracted to mountaintops, montane animals followed. Mark Lomolino, James H. Brown, and Russell Davis (1989) studied the diversity of montane mammals on isolated mountains in the American Southwest. Similar to the studies of islands, the team found that montane mammal richness was positively correlated with habitat area. As figure 22.5 shows, the area of the 27 montane islands ranged from less than 7 km² to over 10,000 km², while the number of montane mammal species on them ranged from 1 to 16.

Lakes as Islands

Lakes can also be considered as habitat islands—aquatic environments isolated from other aquatic environments by land. However, lakes differ widely in their degree of isolation.

More recently, David Currie of the University of Ottawa and his graduate student Attila Kalmar compiled data on 346 marine islands scattered throughout the globe. Islands included in the database varied in size from 0.1 km² to 800,000 km² and were found in all major climatic regions on the planet. They then searched through field guides, checklists, and journals to compile lists of the breeding bird species found on each of the islands. Similar to Preston, they found a clear relationship between island area and the number of bird species (Kalmar and Currie 2006). The large data set also showed that some islands have substantially lower diversity for their size than would be expected. Kalmar and Currie suggested that island area results in an upper bound to diversity, while other factors, such as extreme temperatures and precipitation, can suppress diversity on the island.

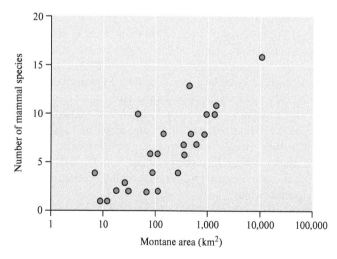

Figure 22.5 Area of montane habitat and number of montane mammal species on isolated mountain ranges in the American Southwest.

Data from Lomolino, Brown, and Davis 1989.

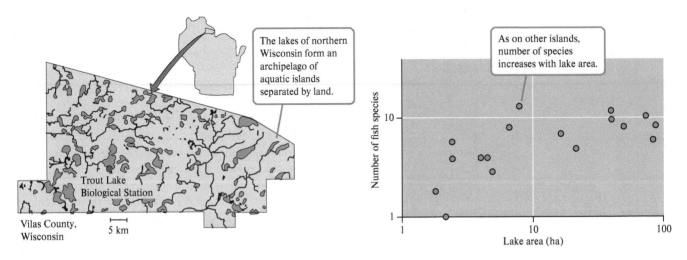

Figure 22.6 Lake area and number of fish species in lakes of northern Wisconsin.
Data from Tonn and Magnuson 1982.

Seepage lakes, which receive no surface drainage, are completely isolated, while drainage lakes, which have stream inlets and/or outlets, are less isolated (see chapter 21).

Bill Tonn, now of the University of Alberta, and John Magnuson, of the University of Wisconsin (1982), studied patterns of species composition and richness among fish inhabiting lakes in northern Wisconsin. They focused their research on 18 lakes in the Northern Highlands Lake District of Wisconsin and Michigan. The study was conducted in Vilas County, Wisconsin, which includes over 1,300 lakes (fig. 22.6). With so many lakes at their disposal, Tonn and Magnuson could match lakes carefully for a variety of characteristics. All 18 study lakes had similar bottom substrates and similar maximum depths. However, the lakes spanned a considerable range of surface area (2.4–89.8 ha).

Tonn and Magnuson collected a total of 23 species, 22 in summer and 18 in winter. If we combine their winter and summer collections on each lake and plot total species richness against area, there is a significant positive relationship (fig. 22.6). Once again, we see that the number of species increases with the area of an insular environment. However, these researchers worked with a single lake district. Is there a relationship between lake area and diversity when lakes from several regions are included in the analysis?

Clyde Barbour and James H. Brown (1974) studied patterns of species richness across a worldwide sample of 70 lakes. The lakes in their sample ranged in area from 0.8 to 436,000 km^2, while the number of fish species ranged from 5 to 245. Barbour and Brown also found a positive relationship between area and fish species richness.

Island Isolation and Species Richness

There is often a negative relationship between the isolation of an island and the number of species it supports. However, because organisms differ substantially in dispersal rates, an island that is very isolated for one group of organisms may be completely accessible to another group.

Marine Islands

We now return to the study of Kalmar and Currie (2006), who explored patterns of diversity among marine islands distributed across the planet. Because the researchers knew the location of each island, they were able to measure the linear distance between the island and the nearest continental shore. The relationship between isolation and bird species richness is clear: the more isolated the island, the fewer the bird species.

Comparative studies of diversity patterns on islands remind us that different organisms have markedly different dispersal abilities, which are reflected in their area-richness or isolation-richness relationships. Mark Williamson (1981) summarized the data for the relationship between island area and species richness for various groups of organisms inhabiting the Azore and Channel Islands. The Azore Islands lie approximately 1,600 km west of the Iberian Peninsula, while the Channel Islands are very near the coast of France. While vastly different in distance from mainland areas, both island groups experience moist temperate climates and have biotas that are of European origin. Consequently, a comparison of their biotas should reveal the potential influence of isolation on species richness.

Figure 22.7 shows Williamson's summary of species area relationships for ferns and fernlike plants (pteridophytes) and land- and water-breeding birds. Both groups of organisms show a positive relationship between island area and diversity on both the Channel and Azore Islands, similar to the patterns we saw in the last section. More relevant to the question of how isolation affects richness, Williamson found that species richness of birds was greater on the Channel Islands (which are relatively near Europe) than on the Azores (which are more distant), even controlling for differences in island area (fig. 22.7). However, pteridophyte richness was similar on islands of comparable size in the two island groups. The 1,600 km of ocean between the Azore Islands and the European mainland reduces the richness of

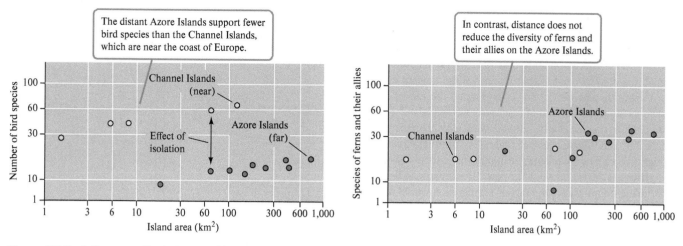

Figure 22.7   Influence of isolation on diversity of birds and ferns and their allies on the Channel and Azore Islands. Data from Williamson 1981.

birds but not pteridophytes. These differences in the effect of isolation reflect differences in the dispersal rates of these organisms. While land birds must fly across water barriers, pteridophytes produce large quantities of light spores that are easily dispersed by wind. One species of pteridophyte, bracken fern, has naturally established populations throughout the globe, including New Guinea, Britain, Hawaii, and New Mexico. When we consider the potential effects of isolation on diversity, we must also consider the dispersal capabilities of the study organisms.

So far, we have considered isolation as it relates to dispersal patterns. A great distance from a source of colonizing species is a barrier to dispersal, so it limits entry by new species and contributes to lower species richness. However, another effect of isolation may occur to you. As a barrier to dispersal, isolation restricts gene flow. Islands may be important sites of allopatric speciation (chapter 4).

In the next section, we take a dynamic, rather than static, view of island diversity. This will serve as the foundation for one of the most influential theories in ecology: the equilibrium model of island biogeography.

CONCEPT 22.2 REVIEW

1. In chapter 21, we discussed how species number decreases with habitat loss. Drawing from the information in this section, provide an explanation for that pattern.

2. Island size appears to set a maximal, rather than minimal, boundary for bird species richness. Why? What, apart from an island's size, will affect the species richness on the island?

3. Why can mountaintops also be considered *islands* in a biogeographic context?

22.3 The Equilibrium Model of Island Biogeography

Species richness on islands can be modelled as a dynamic balance between immigration and extinction of species. The examples we just reviewed show clear relationships between species richness and island area and isolation. When confronted with such a pattern, scientists look for explanatory mechanisms. What mechanisms might increase species richness on large islands and reduce richness on small and isolated islands? MacArthur and Wilson (1963, 1967) proposed a model that explained patterns of species richness on islands as the result of a balance between rates of immigration and extinction (fig. 22.8). This model is called the **equilibrium model of island biogeography**.

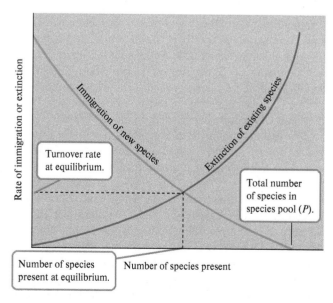

Figure 22.8   Equilibrium model of island biogeography. Data from MacArthur and Wilson 1963.

Figure 22.8 shows that the model presents rates of immigration and extinction as a function of numbers of species on islands. How might rates of immigration and extinction be influenced by the numbers of species on an island? To answer this question, we need to understand what MacArthur and Wilson meant by rates of immigration and extinction. They defined the *rate of immigration* as the rate of arrival of *new* species on an island. *Rate of extinction* was the rate at which species went extinct on the island. MacArthur and Wilson reasoned that rates of immigration would be highest on a new island with no organisms, since every species that arrived at the island would be new. Then, as species began to accumulate on an island, the rate of immigration would decline since fewer and fewer arrivals would be *new* species. They called the point at which the immigration line touches the horizontal axis *P* because it is the point representing the entire pool of species that might immigrate to the island.

How might numbers of species on an island affect the rate of extinction? MacArthur and Wilson predicted that the rate of extinction would rise with increasing numbers of species on an island for three reasons: (1) the presence of more species creates a larger pool of potential extinctions; (2) as the number of species on an island increases, the population size of each might diminish, increasing the risk of extinction; and (3) as the number of species on an island increases, the potential for competitive interactions between species, and hence competitive exclusion, will increase.

Since the immigration line falls and the extinction line rises as the number of species increases, the two lines must cross, as shown in figure 22.8. What is the significance of the point where the two lines cross? The point where the two lines cross predicts the number of species that will occur on an island. Thus, the equilibrium model represents the diversity of species on islands as the result of a dynamic balance between immigration and extinction.

MacArthur and Wilson used the equilibrium model to predict how island size and isolation should affect rates of immigration and extinction. They proposed that the rate of immigration is mainly determined by an island's distance from a source of immigrants, for example, the distance of an oceanic island from a mainland. They proposed that rates of extinction on islands would be determined mainly by island size. These predictions are represented in figure 22.9. Notice that the figure predicts that large, near islands will support the greatest number of species, while small, far islands will support the lowest number of species. The model predicts that small, near islands and large, far islands will support intermediate numbers of species.

The equilibrium model of island biogeography is a special type of ecological model, called a *neutral model*. In ecology, neutral models are ones that predict the outcome of ecological interactions independent of any differences among species. For example, the predictions of MacArthur and Wilson about the abundance of organisms on islands assumes that all species have the same probability of immigration and extinction. This is, of course, a biologically unjustifiable assumption. However, the critical issue here is whether making such a seemingly absurd assumption has any consequence for the accuracy of their patterns. Can one predict, to some rough approximation, the diversity of species on islands, assuming all species are functionally the same?

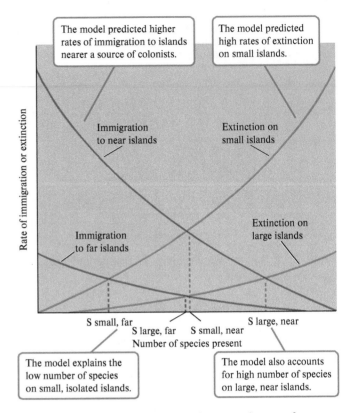

Figure 22.9   Island distance and area and rates of immigration and extinction.
Data from MacArthur and Wilson 1963.

The predictions of the equilibrium model of island biogeography are consistent with the patterns of island diversity reviewed in the previous section. Large islands hold more species than small islands, and islands near sources of immigrants hold more species than islands far from sources of immigrants. We should expect the equilibrium model to be consistent with known variation in species richness across islands since MacArthur and Wilson designed their model to explain the known patterns. Did the equilibrium model make any new predictions? The main new predictions were (1) that island diversity is the outcome of a highly dynamic balance between immigration and extinction, and (2) that the rates of immigration and extinction are determined mainly by the isolation and area of islands. In other words, the equilibrium model predicts that the species composition on islands is not static but changes over time. Ecologists call this change in species composition **species turnover**.

Species Turnover on Islands

In the equilibrium model of island biogeography, the equilibrium number of species predicted to be found on an island is determined by the value of species richness (x-axis) where immigration and extinction rates intersect (fig. 22.9). However, another critical prediction of this theory is that distance from mainland and island size will influence the rate of species turnover on the island. In other words, on some islands species will be predicted to persist for long periods, while the same species are predicted to persist only briefly on other islands. Using this model,

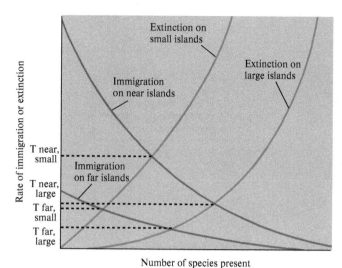

Figure 22.10 Island distance and size influence species turnover rates.

Data from MacArthur and Wilson 1963.

how can we predict which islands will have higher, or lower, turnover rates? The answer lies in taking a close look at the y-axis, the one that describes immigration and extinction rates. Just as the value of the x-axis at equilibrium indicates the equilibrium species richness, the value of the y-axis at equilibrium indicates the equilibrium turnover rate. You can see in figure 22.10 that turnover rates are predicted to be highest on small, near islands, and lowest on large, far islands. These conditions are different than those where we predict the highest, and lowest, number of species. It may seem paradoxical to talk about species turnover at equilibrium. However, it is important to remember that this model of biogeography predicts solely the number of species and rate of change, not the identity of the species on the island. Based upon this model, do you think that species composition is likely to be at equilibrium on any island? As you will see below, species turnover on islands is much more than a theoretical concept.

Turnover of bird species was demonstrated on the California Channel Islands by Jared Diamond (1969). Diamond surveyed the birds of the nine California Channel Islands in 1968, approximately 50 years after an earlier survey by A. B. Howell. The islands range in area from less than 3 to 249 km² and lie 12 to 61 km from the coast of southern California (fig. 22.11). Howell had thoroughly censused all of the islands except for San Miguel and Santa Rosa Islands, where he had difficulty getting permission to do bird surveys. In his later study, Diamond had full access to all the islands and was able to survey all land and water birds.

The results of Diamond's study support the equilibrium model of island biogeography. The number of bird species inhabiting the California Channel Islands remained almost constant over the 50 years between the two censuses. However, this stability in numbers of species was the result of an approximately equal number of immigrations and extinctions on each of the islands (fig. 22.11). The species turnover varied from 17% to 63% among the island communities, and turnover

was inversely related to island size, as predicted by the island biogeography model of MacArthur and Wilson, although there was no relationship between turnover and distance. This is not surprising as the islands are all within 100 km of the mainland, which may not be a substantial barrier for immigration by birds. Diamond's study is an excellent example of how theory can guide field ecology. He discovered the dynamics underlying the diversity of birds on the California Channel Islands because he went out to test the MacArthur-Wilson equilibrium model of island biogeography. Additional insights into this model have been provided by experiments.

Experimental Island Biogeography

As Diamond conducted his surveys of the California Channel Islands, Daniel Simberloff and Edward O. Wilson were engaged in experimental studies of mangrove islands in the Florida Keys (Wilson and Simberloff 1969, Simberloff and Wilson 1969). The Florida Keys support very large stands of mangroves, which are dominated by the red mangrove, *Rhizophora mangle.* Many of these stands occur as small islands that lie hundreds of metres from the nearest large patch of mangroves (fig. 22.12). Simberloff and Wilson chose eight of these small mangrove islands for their experimental study. Their study islands were roughly circular and varied from 11 to 18 m in diameter and 5 to 10 m in height. The distance of islands from large areas of mangroves that could act as a source of colonists varied from 2 to 1,188 m.

The main fauna inhabiting the small mangrove islands of the Florida Keys are arthropods, chiefly insects. Simberloff and Wilson estimated that of the approximately 4,000 species of insects in the Florida Keys, about 500 species inhabit mangroves. Of these 500 species, about 75 commonly live on small mangrove islands. In addition to insects, the mangroves supported 15 species of spiders and other arthropods. The number of insect species on the experimental islands averaged 20 to 40 and the number of spider species ranged from 2 to 10.

Simberloff and Wilson chose two of the islands to act as controls and designated the six others as experimental islands. They carefully surveyed all the islands prior to defaunating the experimental islands. The islands were defaunated by enclosing them with a tent and then fumigating with methyl bromide. Fumigating was done at night to avoid heat damage to the mangrove trees. Simberloff and Wilson examined the trees immediately after fumigating and found that, with the possible exception of some wood-boring insect larvae, all arthropods had been killed. They followed recolonization by periodically censusing the arthropods on each island for approximately one year.

The number of species recorded on the two control islands was virtually identical at the beginning and end of the experiment, although Simberloff and Wilson reported that species composition changed considerably during this time. In other words, there had been species turnover on the control islands, a result consistent with the equilibrium model of island biogeography.

The equilibrium model was also supported by the recolonization studies of the experimental islands. Following

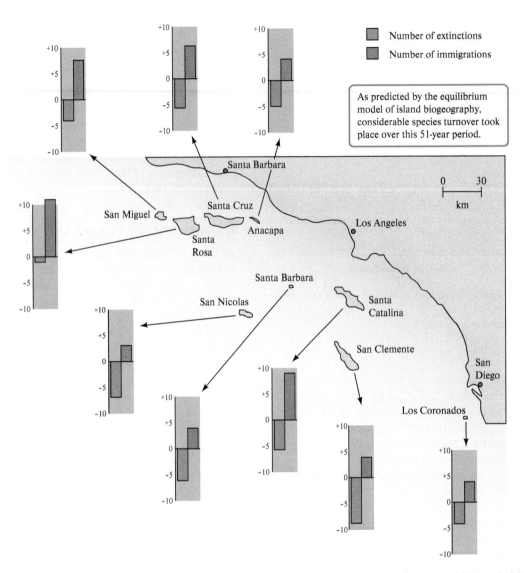

Figure 22.11   Extinction and immigration of bird species on the California Channel Islands between 1917 and 1968.
Data from Diamond 1969.

Figure 22.12   Some mangrove islands in the Florida Keys, which number in the thousands, are convenient places to test the equilibrium model of island biogeography.
©H.W. Kitchen/Science Source.

defaunation, the number of arthropod species increased on all of the islands. The distance of islands from large source areas of mangrove was related to immigration rates as predicted by the island biogeography model: more distant islands had slower rates of immigration. All of the islands, except the farthest island, eventually supported about the same number of species as they did prior to defaunation (fig. 22.13). Again, however, the composition of arthropods on the islands was substantially different than it had been prior to defaunation, indicating species turnover. Species turnover is also indicated by the colonization histories of individual islands, which include many examples of species appearing and then disappearing from the community.

The process of colonization of species onto islands can be studied either by removing organisms from existing islands, as Simberloff and Wilson did when they defaunated their mangrove islands, or by creating new islands. Creation of new islands is not always intentional. Many new islands formed in a large lake in southern Sweden when the level of the lake was

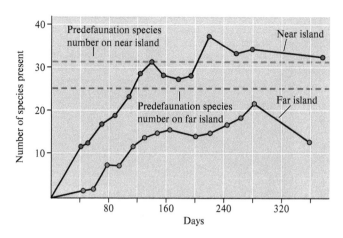

Figure 22.13 Colonization curves for two mangrove islands that were near and far from sources of potential colonists.
Data from Simberloff and Wilson 1969.

dropped at the end of the nineteenth century. Fortunately, some biologists recognized the rare opportunity offered by the new islands and studied their colonization by plants. These studies have continued for a century.

Colonization of New Islands by Plants

The site of this long-term study is Lake Hjälmaren, which covers about 478 km² in Sweden (fig. 22.14). The level of Lake Hjälmaren was lowered 1.3 m between 1882 and 1886, exposing many new islands. The first plant surveys of the new islands were conducted in 1886, and the islands were surveyed again in 1892, from 1903 to 1904, from 1927 to 1928, and from 1984 to 1985. Håkan Rydin and Sven-Olov Borgegård (1988) summarized the earlier surveys of these new islands and conducted their own surveys in 1985. The result was a unique long-term record of the colonization of 40 islands.

The study islands vary in area from 65 m² to over 25,000 m² and support a limited diversity of plants. Rydin and Borgegård estimated that approximately 700 species of plants occur around Lake Hjälmaren. Of these 700 plant species, the number recorded on individual islands during the first century of their existence varied from 0 to 127. As expected, this variation in species richness correlated positively with island area. Area alone accounted for 44% to 85% of the variation in species richness among islands. Island isolation had little effect on species richness, but, as with Diamond's studies on avian biogeography, the islands in Lake Hjälmaren were not greatly distant from source populations, at least not relative to the dispersal mechanisms available to many plant species.

Rydin and Borgegård used the censuses of 30 islands to estimate rates of plant immigration and extinction (fig. 22.14). There has been a slight excess of immigrations over extinctions on small- and medium-sized islands during the entire 100-year record, indicating that small and medium islands continue to accumulate species. In contrast, large islands attained approximately equal rates of immigration and extinction sometime between 1928 and 1985. Over this period, approximately

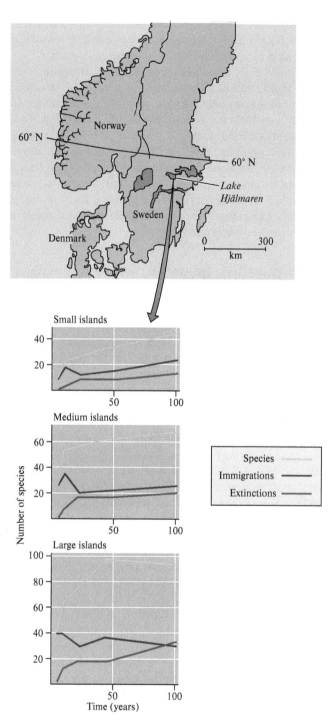

Figure 22.14 Species number, immigration, and extinction on 30 islands in Lake Hjälmaren, Sweden.
Data from Rydin and Borgegård 1988.

30 plants became extinct on each large island and another 30 new species arrived. In other words, it appears that the number of species may have reached equilibrium on large islands.

The observed patterns of colonization were consistent with the predictions of the equilibrium model of island biogeography. Plant species richness on the islands of Lake Hjälmaren, like arthropod richness on the mangrove islands studied by Simberloff and Wilson, appears to be maintained by a dynamic interplay between immigration and local extinction. Many studies support the basic predictions of the equilibrium model of island biogeography. However, many questions remain.

For instance, why do larger islands support more species? Is the greater species richness on large islands due to a direct effect of area, or do large islands support higher species richness because they include a greater diversity of habitats? Rydin and Borgegård found that measures of habitat diversity on the study islands accounted for only 1% to 2% of the variation in plant species richness. However, they point out that it is very difficult to separate the effects of habitat diversity from the effects of area. As we shall see in the next example, there is at least one experiment that came close to demonstrating that species richness on islands can be directly affected by area.

Manipulating Island Area

Daniel Simberloff (1976) tested the effect of island area on species richness experimentally. He surveyed the arthropods inhabiting nine mangrove islands that ranged in area from 262 to 1,263 m². The distance of these islands from large areas of mangrove forest ranged from 2 to 432 m. The islands were up to five times the size of the mangrove islands fumigated by Simberloff and Wilson in their earlier study of recolonization and so contained a larger number of arthropod species.

Simberloff kept one island as a control, while reducing the area of the eight other islands by 32% to 76%. Island area was reduced during low tide by removing whole sections of the islands. Workers cut mangroves off below the high tide level. Simberloff reduced the area of four experimental islands twice and the area of the other four experimental islands once only.

This is a novel approach to untangling the question of whether island area, *per se*, is important in determining species richness, or whether island area reflects habitat diversity, which then determines species richness. In Simberloff's experiment, a homogeneous habitat is systematically reduced in size. If species richness is reduced, this will be because of the change in island size, not because of a change in island habitat diversity.

The results of Simberloff's experiment show a positive relationship between area and species richness. In all cases where island area was reduced, species richness decreased (fig. 22.15). Meanwhile, species richness on the control island, which was not changed in area, increased slightly. Additional insights are offered by the contrasting histories of islands whose areas were reduced once and those whose areas were reduced twice. For instance, the area of Mud 2 island was reduced from 942 to 327 m² and the richness of its arthropod fauna fell from 79 to 62 species. The area of Mud 2 was not reduced further, and its arthropod richness remained almost constant. Meanwhile, the island whose area was reduced twice lost species with each reduction in area. Simberloff's results showed that area itself, without increased habitat heterogeneity, has a positive influence on species richness. Why? Perhaps a smaller area means a smaller population for individual species. For some rare species, this may increase the chances of local extinction, reducing the overall species richness on the island.

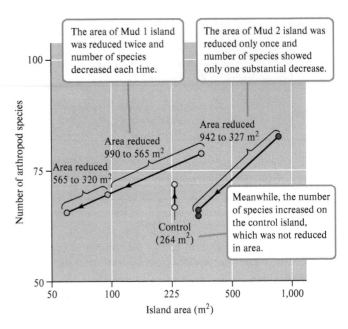

Figure 22.15   Effect of reducing mangrove island area on number of arthropod species.
Data from Simberloff 1976.

Island Biogeography Update

The equilibrium theory of island biogeography has had a major influence on the disciplines of biogeography and ecology. However, much has been discovered in the 50 years since MacArthur and Wilson proposed their theory. For instance, James Brown and Astrid Kodric-Brown (1977) showed how higher rates of immigration to near islands can reduce extinction rates. As a consequence, we now know that, contrary to the original MacArthur-Wilson model, island distance from sources of colonists also influences rates of extinction. Similarly, Mark Lomolino (1990) extended the original model when he proposed the *target hypothesis*, demonstrating that island area can alter rates of immigration to islands. Brown and Lomolino (2000) pointed out that we have also discovered that species richness is not in equilibrium on many islands. In addition, we now know that species richness on islands is affected by differences among species groups in their speciation, colonization, and extinction rates. And perhaps most significantly, area and isolation are only two of several environmental factors that affect species richness on islands. Brown and Lomolino suggest that we may be on the eve of another revolution in theories that will replace the MacArthur-Wilson model. If so, it will be the result of research largely inspired by their theory as well as by our fascination with the islands themselves.

Experiments on islands, such as those of Simberloff and Wilson, demonstrate the value of an experimental approach to answering ecological questions. However, there are important ecological patterns that occur over such large scales that experiments are virtually impossible. The ecologists who study these large-scale patterns must rely on other approaches. In the next section, we discuss one of these important large-scale patterns, latitudinal variation in species richness.

22.4 Latitudinal Gradients in Species Richness

Species richness generally increases from middle and high latitudes to the equator. Most groups of organisms are more species-rich in the tropics than they are at higher latitudes. This well-known increase in species richness toward the equator was apparent to scientists by the middle of the eighteenth century as taxonomists, led by Carolus Linnaeus, described tropical species sent back to Europe by explorers. Explorers and naturalists, such as Humboldt, Darwin, and Wallace, described overwhelming biological diversity in the tropics.

Figures 22.16 and 22.17 show examples of how plant species richness (Reid and Miller 1989) and bird species richness (Dobzhansky 1950) decrease as you move away from the equator and toward the poles. However, this pattern is not always

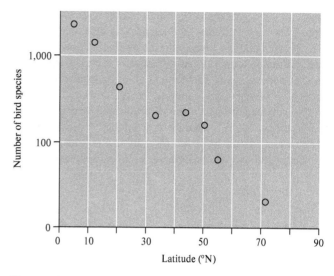

Figure 22.17 Latitudinal variation in number of bird species from Central to North America.
Data from Dobzhansky 1950.

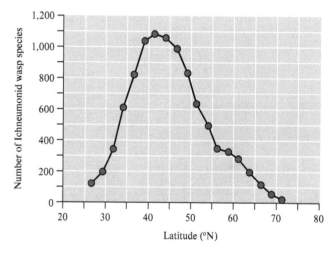

Figure 22.18 An exception to the general decline in species number with latitude:latitudinal variation in Ichneumonid wasp species richness.
Data from Janzen 1981c.

found, as shown in figure 22.18, leading some ecologists to question whether it was in fact a general phenomenon. In a meta-analysis, Helmut Hillebrand took on the daunting task of summarizing all of the published studies testing for latitudinal gradients in diversity (Hillebrand 2004). In total, he found 232 studies that described 581 gradients for different taxa. These studies included terrestrial, marine, and freshwater habitats; spanned between 10° and 90° latitude; sampled areas between 1 m² and 1,000,000 km²; and included taxa that ranged in body size across 12 orders of magnitude.

Across all of these studies, there was evidence for a clear and widespread pattern of increased diversity with decreasing latitudes (Hillebrand 2004). Even among the approximately one-third of studies that reported a lack of statistical support

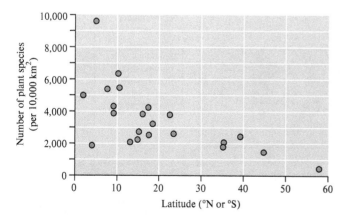

Figure 22.16 Variation in number of vascular plant species with latitude in the Western Hemisphere.
Data from Reid and Miller 1989.

for a latitudinal gradient, the overall trend was toward greater diversity at low latitudes. Hillebrand was also able to show that on average those nonsignificant studies had lower sample size and sampled a more narrow range of latitudes than studies that demonstrated a latitudinal gradient in diversity. This finding is an important reminder that a study's design and sample size can influence the direction and strength of the results (appendix A). Though most studies demonstrated at least a trend toward increased diversity in the tropics, a small number of studies (<5%) did demonstrate lower diversity in the

low latitudes. These are clearly exceptions belonging to a small number of taxa.

Underneath the general pattern of a latitudinal gradient of biodiversity, Hillebrand (2004) uncovered a number of ecological factors that influenced the strength of this relationship. The latitudinal gradient was quite strong for both marine and terrestrial taxa and, though significant, less strong for freshwater organisms (fig. 22.19a). The strength of the latitudinal gradient was greatest for higher trophic levels (fig. 22.19b) and for larger organisms (fig. 22.19c). The data set included both large

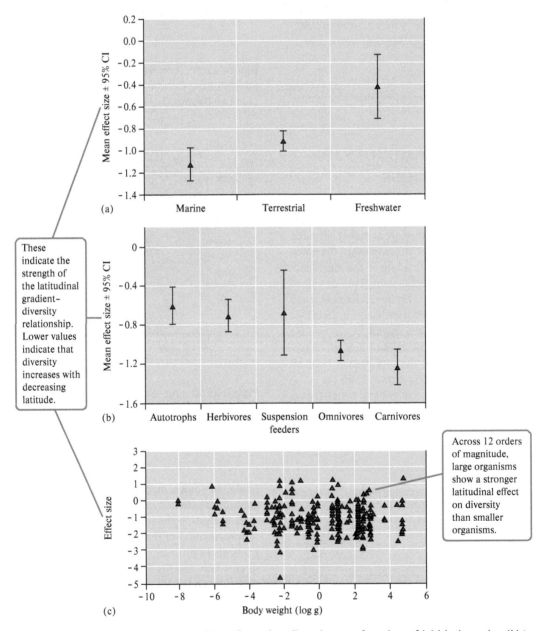

These indicate the strength of the latitudinal gradient–diversity relationship. Lower values indicate that diversity increases with decreasing latitude.

Across 12 orders of magnitude, large organisms show a stronger latitudinal effect on diversity than smaller organisms.

Figure 22.19 The strength of the latitudinal gradient of species diversity as a function of (*a*) biotic realm, (*b*) trophic position, and (*c*) organism body size. In all cases, negative values indicate increased diversity at lower latitudes, and more negative values indicate a stronger relationship.

H. Hillebrand. 2004. On the generality of the latitudinal diversity gradient. *American Naturalist* 163:192–211.

and small autotrophs (e.g., algae and trees) and large and small carnivores (e.g., Chaetognaths and cats), and so the findings of stronger latitudinal gradients for both larger organisms and predators likely reflect two separate mechanisms.

Overall, the pattern of increased numbers of species in the tropics is pervasive and dramatic. There are some variations due to biotic realm, size, and feeding biology, but in general this is a robust pattern. As this pattern is so well documented, and has been for nearly a century, it would stand to reason that ecologists know the underlying mechanisms. Unfortunately, proposed explanations are nearly as diverse as the taxa being studied, and there is no broad agreement among ecologists. One review suggests that 30 different mechanisms for the gradient have been proposed (Willig et al. 2003). But there is good news: a series of reviews by international teams of researchers have begun to provide clarity to one of ecology's most pervasive patterns (Mittelbach et al. 2007, Currie et al. 2004, and Schemske et al. 2009). Here, we describe just a few of the proposed mechanisms—ones that appear not to have been clearly refuted by data. That said, there is no promise these will still be the ones we talk about in the next edition of this text! Though there is no expectation that there is a single cause, the generality of the pattern does suggest the cause(s) should also be general, and not taxa specific.

Time and Area Effects

The latitudinal gradient is extremely old, found in fossils at least 250 million years old (Willig et al. 2003). Alfred Russel Wallace, the man who independently developed a theory of evolution by natural selection, was the first to propose a mechanism for the latitudinal diversity gradient (Wallace 1878). He suggested that there are more species in the tropics because the tropics are older and they are disturbed less frequently than other regions of the earth. More specifically, tropical regions have been less affected by glacial cycles (chapter 21), potentially allowing for more time for speciation to occur.

A related issue is that there is a greater area covered by tropical regions than other biomes, both currently and through much of geological history. As we have discussed previously in this chapter, species diversity tends to increase as area increases. It may not be immediately apparent from a map based on the *Mercator projection* that the tropics include a greater area of both land and water than do higher latitudes. Rosenzweig (1992) quantified the amount of land surface area in various latitudinal zones, divided into tropical (±26° of latitude), subtropical (26° to 36°), temperate (36° to 46°), boreal (46° to 56°), and tundra (>56°) zones. He then measured the area of land within these latitudinal zones and found that the area of land within the tropics far exceeds that of other areas (fig. 22.20).

Not only is there more land (and water) at tropical latitudes, but, in addition, temperatures are more uniform across this tropical belt. This pattern was put in the context of geographic ecology by Terborgh (1973), who plotted mean annual temperatures against latitude. As figure 22.21 shows, there is

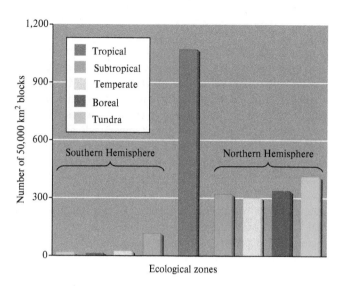

Figure 22.20 Land area in five latitudinal biomes. Data from Rosenzweig 1992.

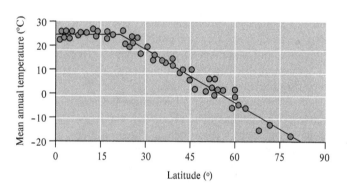

Figure 22.21 Mean annual temperature by latitude. Data from Rosenzweig, after Terborgh 1973.

little difference in mean annual temperatures between about 0° and 25° latitude. Because this temperature pattern occurs both north and south of the equator, mean annual temperature changes little over about 50° of latitude within the tropics. However, above 25° latitude, mean annual temperature declines linearly with latitude. What is the biological significance of this latitudinal pattern of temperature variation? One implication is that tropical organisms can disperse over large areas and not meet with significant changes in temperature.

How do patterns of temperature variation affect rates of speciation and extinction? Rosenzweig proposed that the larger area of tropical regions should reduce extinction rates in two ways. First, because tropical species can be distributed over a larger area, there should be more refuges in which to survive environmental disturbances. Second, because of their larger range, tropical species should also have greater total population sizes. Larger populations are less likely to become extinct.

Rate of Diversification

A second potential cause of the diversity gradient could be increased species diversification rates in the tropics, relative to low latitudes. In a synthesis of previous studies, Mittelbach et al. (2007) found that many clades of temperate species are actually nested within larger clades of tropical species. This suggests that the origin of much of the temperate diversity we see is rooted in older tropical species. This is supported by more recent phylogenetic and fossil studies of plants and animals across a breadth of phyla. Many of these studies were recently reviewed by P. V. A. Fine (2015). Collectively, they build support for the tropics as the source of most major plant and animal groups, with highest rates of diversification in tropical regions and dispersal of species to higher latitudes. The relative isolation of higher latitudes and niche requirements of novel species originating in the tropics may limit immigration of new species to higher latitudes, contributing to lower species richness.

What could cause increased speciation rates? One mechanism could be the interactions among species. Throughout much of this text, we have discussed the evolutionary implications of ecological interactions. These have included character displacement, host-race formation, changes in host–parasite dynamics, and a number of other responses. Over time, and under a number of conditions (chapter 4), these evolutionary responses could lead to speciation.

A number of ecologists have suggested that biotic interactions (e.g., competition, predation, herbivory, parasitism) are stronger in the tropics than at higher latitudes, leading to increased speciation and increased diversity. Schemske et al. 2009 compiled over 50 studies looking at predation, herbivory, parasitism, some mutualisms, and a variety of other interactions. Across all of these studies, not a single one reported greater intensities of interactions in high latitudes. Some reported no latitudinal gradient in species interactions; and most reported greater intensities of interactions at low latitudes. Although Schemske et al. strongly emphasize the need for more data on this question, it appears that there is a general pattern of more intense ecological interactions at low latitudes. This could contribute to more rapid specialization and diversification in the tropics.

Mittelbach et al. (2007) present a number of other mechanisms that could increase diversification rates in the tropics, some of which may increase speciation rates (as above), while others may reduce extinction rates. Many of these mechanisms will be tied to the age and area of the tropics, highlighting that no single mechanism is likely at play. For example, climatic variation at high latitudes may slow down speciation and increase extinction rates, while the larger areas of the tropics may increase the chance for parapatric and sympatric speciation (chapter 4), and increased productivity in the tropics may increase population sizes, reducing the probability of extinction.

The mammalian order Carnivora is an interesting exception to the latitudinal pattern of diversification. Rather than originating in the tropics and dispersing to higher latitudes, this order originated in temperate regions and dispersed to tropical regions and higher latitudes (Rolland et al. 2015). Unlike other mammalian orders, diversification rates are not higher in the tropics for Carnivora. Yet carnivores follow the typical latitudinal pattern of most other animal groups, with highest diversity in the tropics, most probably due to higher extinction rates at higher latitudes.

In summary, many factors may contribute to higher tropical species richness, including ecological, geological, geographical, and evolutionary hypotheses. The size of the tropical land mass allows large population sizes and dispersal over a large area with relatively stable climate conditions. A high rate of diversification in the tropics may make them a source of novel species, and dispersal to higher latitudes may be constrained by isolation and niche. In addition to higher rates of diversification, tropical areas may have lower rates of extinction. Hence even Carnivora, without a tropical origin or higher rates of diversification in the tropics, follows the general pattern of higher diversity in tropical areas. Despite being aware of this pattern for over a century, ecologists have yet to agree on the relative importance of these and a number of other potential mechanisms. Although we have no final answer to the causes of this pattern, we now turn to another example of geographic ecology: the relationship between local and regional diversity.

CONCEPT 22.4 REVIEW

1. Why is there no one factor that seems to explain latitudinal gradients in species diversity?
2. Why do ecologists use evolutionary biology when discussing the mechanisms of this ecological pattern?

22.5 Historical and Regional Influences

Long-term historical and regional processes significantly influence the structure of biotas and ecosystems. Macroecological patterns in diversity can be caused by local factors, such as area and ecological interactions. However, as we saw in the previous section, unique historical and geographic factors can also influence regional patterns in species richness. Here we will further explore how regional processes can influence local diversity.

Patterns of Local and Regional Diversity

What determines the number of species that are found in a given location? In this chapter, we have discussed how this

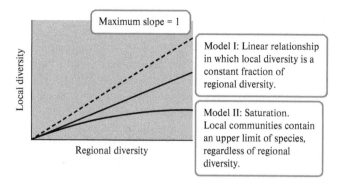

Figure 22.22 Hypothetical relationships between local and regional diversity.

Figure 22.23 A rich diversity of life lives in and among coral reefs.
Robert Semple.

could be influenced by area and isolation. In prior chapters, we have also described how competition, herbivory, and a variety of local processes can alter community structure. One factor we have not yet considered is the relatively straightforward idea that the number of species found in a community must be no greater than the regional species pool. Only species that are present somewhere in the region could possibly be found in any particular community, and thus the size of the species pool serves as an upper bound of local diversity. Therefore, as regional diversity increases, local diversity increases, too. Or does it? We have seen before that the presence of competitive dominant species may actually exclude other species from entering a community. Similarly, abiotic stress or herbivory could be so extreme in a given community that only a few, specially adapted species may persist, regardless of how many species are in the region. Similar statements could be made about all of the ecological processes we discussed in section 4 of the book. In short, even if there were an unlimited number of species in the regional pool, local processes might limit the number of species found in any particular community. These contrasting predictions can be summarized in a graph describing the hypothetical relationships between local and regional species richness (fig. 22.22). In both models, a line with a slope of 1 represents the theoretical maximum. In model I, there is a linear relationship between local and regional diversity. Such a relationship indicates that local diversity is a constant fraction of regional diversity. In model II, there is species saturation at high levels of regional diversity. This model predicts that there is only a set amount of niche space within a community, and thus species exclusion occurs through local processes. What do the data suggest?

Ronald Karlson, Howard Cornell, and Terence Hughes have provided one of the most comprehensive tests of this question (Karlson et al. 2004). They sampled the diversity of corals around 15 islands that were spread across five Indo-Pacific regions (fig. 22.23). In total, these locations represented a 10,000 km gradient—a truly ambitious research project. In each location, they measured coral diversity in three habitat types: (1) reef flats that were 5 to 10 m inshore of breaking waves; (2) reef crests that were seaward of breaking waves and

at a depth of 1 to 2 m; and (3) reef slopes, which were also seaward of breaking waves but at a depth of 6 to 7 m. In total, they sampled 41,710 coral colonies. There were clear differences in regional diversity among the five regions and local diversity among the three habitats they sampled, using species richness as a proxy. Reef flats consistently had the lowest diversity, and reef slopes, the highest, in nearly all regions. When they compared local and regional diversity, they found a clear linear relationship for all three habitats, supporting model I, although not necessarily precluding model II if local communities are not close to saturation.

Exceptional Patterns of Diversity

There are major differences in species richness that cannot be explained by differences in area. For instance, consider

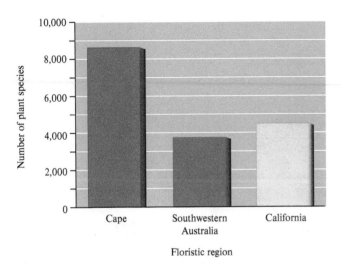

Figure 22.24   Number of plant species living in three regions with Mediterranean climates.
Data from Bond and Goldblatt 1984.

regions with Mediterranean climates that support Mediterranean woodlands and shrublands. Such regions include the Cape region of South Africa (90,000 km²), southwestern Australia (320,000 km²), and the California Floristic Province (324,000 km²). These regions have similar climates but differ significantly in area. How might we expect these regions to compare in species richness? The positive relationship between area and species richness that we have seen repeatedly would lead us to predict the lowest richness in the Cape region of South Africa. We would be wrong! Southwestern Australia and the California Floristic Province have the same area and approximately the same number of species. However, as figure 22.24 shows, the Cape region, the smallest area, contains more than twice the number of plant species as the other two regions.

The failure of area to explain a significant regional diversity pattern is not unique to this example. For instance, Roger Latham and Robert Ricklefs (1993) reported a striking contrast

ECOLOGY IN ACTION

Biodiversity Hotspots

Species are not distributed evenly across the globe; instead, biodiversity is concentrated into specific areas of the planet known as *biodiversity hotspots*. The realization that biodiversity is clustered into these hotspots across the planet is important for a variety of reasons. First, it is an intriguing ecological pattern that is certainly worthy of explanation. Second, the concentration of biodiversity across the planet suggests that loss of certain habitats and areas to development will result in a greater ecological cost than similar development in other areas. In other words, by identifying biodiversity hotspots, ecologists may provide ecological triage, identifying those areas that are most urgently in need of treatment and repair.

As we discussed in chapter 10, there are different types of rarity for species, with different consequences for conservation. Of particular concern are the species that have a narrow range and are endemic to a very small area. Even small amounts of development can threaten these species, if it were to occur in their relatively restricted habitat.

One concern about the hotspot approach to identifying areas of critical conservation need has been that high levels of species richness do not necessarily equate to high levels of rare and endemic species. Instead, it is possible that areas are particularly diverse due to large numbers of cosmopolitan species, ones not likely in need of protection. Jeremy Kerr, of York University, has analyzed this issue for several taxa. He has found that patterns of richness were generally correlated with patterns of endemism, supporting the hotspot approach (Kerr 1997). However, he

also found that the location of biodiversity hotspots varied among taxa, and protection of area for one group of species could not be assumed to provide an umbrella that would reach over and cover other taxa. Instead, each taxonomic group is likely going to have its own locations in most critical need of protection.

Norman Myers and colleagues have produced one of the more comprehensive studies identifying terrestrial biodiversity hotspots (Myers et al. 2000). They focused specifically on endemic plants, mammals, birds, reptiles, and amphibians. They state that because plants are "essential to virtually all forms of animal life" (p. 854), an area could only qualify as a hotspot if it contained a minimum of 0.5% of the world's plant species as endemics (this equates to 1,500 of the 300,000 known species). Only if a location met these criteria would information regarding endemic vertebrates be added for comparison. The research team did not include invertebrates in this analysis primarily because a large proportion of invertebrate diversity remains undescribed by science, and thus accurate information is lacking. An area only made the final cut for inclusion as a hotspot if it was under significant threat of development, with at least 70% or more of the vegetation lost. This criterion was added to allow this list to identify areas in need of urgent protection, rather than providing simply a map of diversity patterns.

In total, Myers et al. (2000) identified 25 hotspots around the globe (fig. 22.25). These areas represent only 1.4% of the planet's land base yet contain 44% of the known plant species. In total, 88% of the primary vegetation in

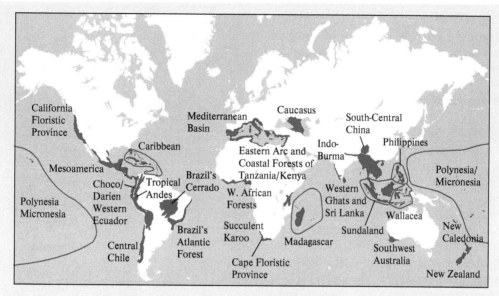

Figure 22.25 Identified terrestrial biodiversity hotspots around the planet.

these areas has already been lost to development. It should come as no surprise that a majority of these sites are in tropical areas, where diversity is high and pressure to develop the land is strong. Five of these hotspots alone contain 20% of all plant and 16% of all vertebrate species on earth, and yet occupy only 0.4% of the earth's surface. Clearly, not all areas on the planet are ecologically equivalent or of equal conservation priority.

The Critical Ecosystem Partnership Fund (CEPF) is a joint initiative of l'Agence Française de Développement, Conservation International, the European Union, the Global Environment Facility, the Government of Japan, and the World Bank. The CEPF has been active in funding conservation efforts in the 25 hotspots originally identified by Myers et al. and continues to assess new regions for listing. As of 2019, an additional 11 terrestrial biodiversity hotspots have been designated, including two in North America, three in Africa, one in Australia, and five in Asia.

Diversity hotspots can be identified in marine systems as well. By definition, these cannot be exactly the same place as the terrestrial hotspots. However, if these areas were in close proximity to one another, such as marine areas immediately offshore a terrestrial hotspot, that might facilitate conservation efforts. There have been numerous efforts to identify marine biodiversity hotspots. A group of researchers from Canada, the United States, and Australia investigated the location of marine

hotspots, focusing primarily on tropical reefs (Roberts et al. 2002). They found that the 10 richest hotspots contain only 16% of the world's reefs but 44% to 54% of the endemic reef species. In another example from marine systems, Boris Worm, Heike Lotze, and Ransom Myers of Dalhousie University have identified the majority of biodiversity hotspots for large ocean predators, such as tunas, sharks, and billfish, which occur at intermediate, rather than tropical, latitudes (Worm et al. 2003). These locations are generally at the intersection of the ranges of temperate and tropical prey species and are generally concentrated around variation in ocean bottom topography (e.g., reefs, shelf breaks, etc.).

Biodiversity is not spread evenly around the globe, and efforts such as these provide critical information for conservation programs. Though Canada is not home to the extreme concentrations of biodiversity found in countries at lower latitudes, there are pockets within Canada that are relatively high in biodiversity. For example, the Carolinian forests of southwestern Ontario have over 2,000 species of plants. This is a large number considering the entire country most likely has fewer than 5,000 species!

Understanding the distribution of diversity is a critical outcome of ecological research and an essential part of any conservation program. It is up to the next generation of ecologists to find ways to protect these areas.

in diversity of temperate zone trees that cannot be explained by an area effect. As we saw in chapter 2, the temperate forest biome covers approximately equal areas in Europe (1.2 million km²), eastern Asia (1.2 million km²), and eastern North America (1.8 million km²). The species–area relationship

would lead us to predict that these three regions would support approximately equal levels of biological diversity. However, eastern Asia contains nearly three times more tree species than eastern North America and nearly six times more species of trees than Europe.

Historical and Regional Explanations

How can we explain these exceptional patterns of biological diversity? What mechanisms produced these patterns, which are contrary to generalizations discussed in this chapter and in earlier chapters? In each case, it appears that geography and history offer convincing explanations.

The Cape Floristic Region of South Africa

Pauline Bond and Peter Goldblatt (1984) attributed the unusual species richness of the Cape floristic region to several historic and geographic factors. Selection for a distinctively Mediterranean flora in southern Africa began during the late Tertiary period, about 26 million years ago. At that time, the climate became progressively cooler and drier, conditions that selected for succulence; fire resistance; and smaller, sclerophyllous leaves. The initial sites for evolution of the Cape flora were likely in south-central Africa, not in the Cape region itself. At that time, Africa lay farther south and the Cape region had a cool, moist climate and supported an evergreen forest.

As Africa drifted northward, the climate of southern Africa became more arid, and the ancestors of today's Cape flora gradually migrated toward the Cape region. By the time Africa neared its present latitudinal position during the late Pliocene, about three million years ago, southern Africa was very arid and the Cape region had a Mediterranean climate. Bond and Goldblatt suggest that plant speciation within this region was promoted by the highly dissected landscape, the existence of a wide variety of soil types, and repeated expansion, contraction, and isolation of plant populations during the climatic fluctuations of the Pleistocene. They suggest that extinction rates were reduced by the existence of substantial refuge areas, even during times of peak aridity.

The Diversity of Temperate Trees

How did eastern Asia, eastern North America, and Europe, three temperate regions of approximately equal area and climate, end up with such different numbers of tree species? Latham and Ricklefs (1993) offer persuasive geographic and historical reasons. They propose that we need to consider what trees in the three regions faced during the last glacial period and how those conditions may have affected extinction rates.

Refer to chapter 2 and study the distributions of temperate forest in eastern Asia, eastern North America, and Europe. While there are no mountain barriers to north–south movements of organisms in eastern Asia and eastern North America, the mountains in Europe form barriers that are oriented east to west. Now imagine what happened to a tree species as glaciers began to advance during the last ice age and the climate of Europe became progressively colder. Temperate trees would have had their southward retreat largely cut off by mountain ranges running east to west.

This hypothesis proposes that the lower species richness of European trees has been at least partly a consequence of higher extinction rates during glacial periods. How would you test this hypothesis? Latham and Ricklefs searched the fossil record for extinctions in the three regions. They estimated the number of genera that have become extinct in the three regions during the

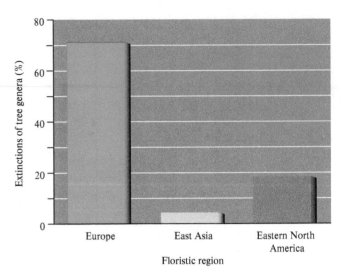

Figure 22.26   Extinctions of tree genera in Europe, East Asia, and eastern North America since the middle Tertiary period.

Data from Latham and Ricklefs 1993.

last 30 to 40 million years. Their analysis showed that most of the plant genera that once lived in Europe have become extinct. A larger proportion of genera has become extinct in Europe than in either eastern Asia or eastern North America (fig. 22.26).

Now consider eastern North America. The only mountain range, the Appalachians, runs north to south. Consequently, in eastern North America, temperate trees had an avenue of retreat in the face of advancing glaciers and cooling climate. The movement of temperate tree populations in the face of climate change has been well documented by paleontologists, such as Margaret Davis. There are also no mountain barriers in eastern Asia, where temperate trees can migrate even farther south than in eastern North America.

Higher rates of extinction during glacial periods can explain the lower diversity of trees in Europe. However, why does eastern North America include fewer tree species than eastern Asia? Latham and Ricklefs conclude that the fossil record and present-day distributions of temperate trees indicate that most temperate tree taxa originated in eastern Asia. These Asian taxa subsequently dispersed to Europe and North America. In addition, after the dispersal routes between eastern Asia and eastern North America were closed off, speciation continued in Asia, producing several endemic Asian genera. In other words, there are fewer tree species in eastern North America because most taxa originated in eastern Asia and never dispersed to North America.

Throughout this chapter we have shown how geographic factors can influence local species diversity. Many aspects of geographic variation in species richness can be explained by historical and regional processes, and do not necessarily rely on the processes described in section 5. The ecologist interested in understanding patterns of diversity at large spatial scales must consider processes occurring over similarly large scales and over long periods of time. As we shall see in chapter 23, a large-scale, long-term perspective is also essential for understanding global ecology.

ECOLOGICAL TOOLS AND APPROACHES

Global Positioning Systems, Remote Sensing, and Geographic Information Systems

Modern tools have revolutionized the field of macroecology. One of the reasons there is renewed interest among ecologists in studying the classic patterns of ecology is that the availability of inexpensive and highly accurate spatial data allows for improved analyses and understanding. Today, ecologists generally geo-reference their study location and often record their data on geographic information systems (GIS). GIS are computer-based systems that store, interpret, integrate, analyze, and display geographic information. In addition, the ecologists of today have access to more information of greater accuracy because of continued improvements in remote sensing and global positioning systems. Once again, we find that development of new and better methodologies is critical to advancement in ecology.

Global Positioning Systems

Where are you? This is one of the most basic questions the geographer can ask. Scientists, engineers, navigators, and explorers have spent centuries devising methods to measure elevation, latitude, and longitude. Recent technological advances have improved the accuracy of these measurements.

Alexander von Humboldt would appreciate these recent technological advances. As he explored South and North America, he carefully determined the latitude, longitude, and elevation of important geographic features. For instance, Humboldt was particularly interested in verifying the existence and location of a waterway called the Casiquiare Canal. The Casiquiare reportedly connected the Orinoco River with the Rio Negro, which flows into the Amazon. A connection between two major river systems would make the Casiquiare unique, but its existence was widely doubted.

Humboldt halted his expedition at the junction of the Casiquiare and the Rio Negro so that he could record the latitude and longitude. Biting insects tormented the explorers as they waited for nightfall. Luckily, that night the clouds parted and Humboldt could see the stars well enough to take sightings and determine their position. At other times, he was not so lucky. He once waited for nearly a month for the weather to clear sufficiently to make his sightings on the stars. Today, equipped with a global positioning system, Humboldt could have determined the latitude and longitude of the junction of the Casiquiare and the Rio Negro any time he wished, regardless of weather.

A **global positioning system (GPS)** determines locations on the earth's surface, including latitude, longitude, and altitude, using satellites as reference points. These satellites, which orbit the earth at a height of about 21,000 km, continuously transmit their position and the time. The satellites keep track of time with an extremely accurate atomic clock that loses or gains 1 second in about 30,000 years. A global positioning system receives the signals broadcast by these satellites. Because the system also includes an extremely accurate clock, the time required for the satellite signal to reach the receiver can be used as a measure of the distance between the two. With measurements of the distance to four satellites, a global positioning system can determine the latitude, longitude, and altitude of any point on earth with great accuracy (fig. 22.27). GPS units are now widely available, inexpensive, and embedded in many electronic devices and are remarkably easy to use (my seven-year-old showed me some of the basics). It is difficult to overstate the importance that access to accurate spatial data has for the ability to address many ecological questions. I suppose we all owe the U.S. military a thank-you, as it led the development of this technology (including paying those research bills) and, in the last decade, allowed civilians to have improved accuracy in their positioning records.

While navigation satellites and global positioning systems can accurately locate places on the ground, other satellites provide a wealth of other information about those localities. These remote sensing satellites transmit pictures of the earth that are extremely valuable to ecologists.

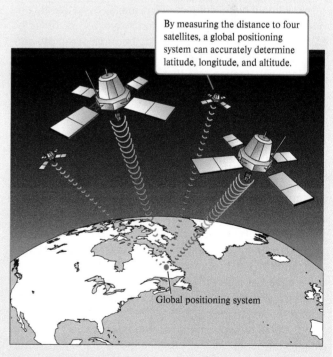

By measuring the distance to four satellites, a global positioning system can accurately determine latitude, longitude, and altitude.

Global positioning system

Figure 22.27 Global positioning systems determine latitude, longitude, and altitude by measuring the distance from several satellites.

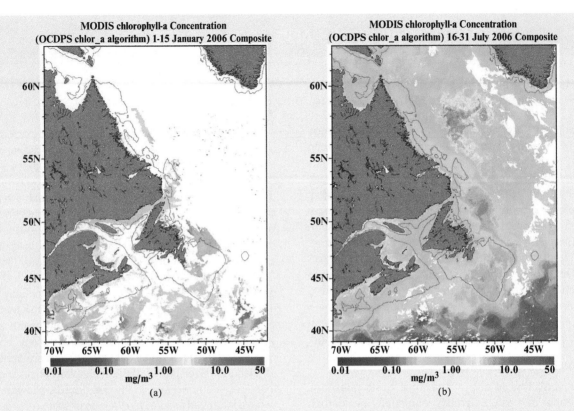

Figure 22.28 Measures of ocean chlorophyll-a concentrations from part of Atlantic Canada in (*a*) January 2006, and (*b*) July 2006.

MODIS data courtesy of NASA, image created by the Remote Sensing Unit at BIO, in collaboration with NASA GSFC.

Remote Sensing

Remote sensing refers to gathering information about an object without direct contact with it, mainly by gathering and processing electromagnetic radiation emitted or reflected by the object. Using this definition, the original remote sensor was the eye. However, we generally associate remote sensing with technology that extends the senses, technology ranging from binoculars and cameras to satellite-mounted sensors.

Remote-sensing satellites are generally fitted with electro-optical sensors that scan several bands of the electromagnetic spectrum. These sensors convert electromagnetic radiation into electrical signals that are in turn converted to digital values by a computer. These digital values can be used to construct an image. The earliest of the *Landsat* satellites monitored four bands of electromagnetic radiation, two bands of visible light (0.5 to 0.6 µm and 0.6 to 0.7 µm), and two bands in the near infrared (0.7 to 0.8 µm and 0.8 to 1.1 µm). From this beginning, satellite imaging systems have become progressively more sophisticated both in terms of the number of wavelengths scanned and the spatial resolution.

Satellite-based remote sensing has produced detailed images of essentially every square metre of the earth's surface. You may have already seen many of these through readily available services such as Google Earth. Ecologists use a diversity of satellite-based imaging processes to monitor a variety of ecological processes, including "greenness" and primary productivity. For example, the Department of Fisheries and Oceans uses remote sensing to monitor changes in ocean productivity, often measured as chlorophyll-a concentrations (fig. 22.28). When images are taken at different points in time, it is possible to measure changes. The most obvious changes would be seasonal shifts in productivity (fig. 22.28) but could also include other factors.

Incorporating satellite imaging with a variety of methods of analysis also allows scientists to categorize large geographic regions by the dominant vegetation. For example, using the Advanced Very High Resolution Radiometer satellite network, a team of researchers at the Canada Centre for Remote Sensing were able to develop a land cover map for all of Canada (fig. 22.29). It is important to recognize that a great diversity of satellites exist, satellites that are capable of conducting remote-sensing operations for ecological research. Some satellites, like those used to produce figure 22.29, are very good at imaging vast geographic regions (such as all of Canada!) but have relatively coarse resolution, such as 1 km². In contrast, other satellite systems can image the earth from space at a resolution of less than 1 m². Such detailed information is likely critical to assess change or characterize habitats within a local area (e.g., a single province) but would produce too great a volume of data to characterize larger areas (such as all of Canada).

Figure 22.29   Land cover map for all of Canada, based upon satellite imaging.

Source: Land Cover of Canada, Natural Resources Canada, 2010. Reproduced with the permission of the Department of Natural Resources, 2019.

Remote sensing allows ecologists to gather large volumes of data across a very large spatial scale—even more data than could be collected with an army of eager undergraduate assistants! However, these large quantities of data create another problem. Ecologists need a system for storing, sorting, analyzing, and displaying these large quantities of geographic information. This is the problem addressed by geographic information systems.

Geographic Information Systems

In the days of Humboldt, geographers often had too little data. Today, with new tools for gathering great quantities of information, geographers and geographic ecologists can be overwhelmed by data. **Geographic information systems (GIS)**, computer-based systems for storing, sorting, analyzing, and displaying geographic data, are designed to handle large quantities of data. Sometimes GIS are confused with computerized map-making. While these systems can produce maps, they do much more. Much of population ecology is concerned with understanding the factors controlling the distribution and abundance of organisms. However, the geographic context of populations has often been lost. Geographic information systems preserve this geographic information, thereby providing ecologists with a valuable tool for exploring large-scale population responses to climate change. GIS serves as a critical tool for many studies we have already discussed, including the ability to rapidly quantify landscape elements and conduct ecological niche modelling.

As we shall see in chapter 23, rapid global change challenges the field of ecology to continue to address large-scale environmental questions. As ecologists address these compelling questions, GIS, global positioning systems, and remote sensing will be increasingly valued parts of their tool kits.

CONCEPT 22.5 REVIEW

1. Why should evolutionary and geological history have such a strong influence on regional diversity patterns?

2. How does the combined evidence from studies of the flora of Mediterranean regions and the diversity of trees in temperate forest regions increase confidence that historical differences can outweigh the potential influence of area on diversity?

SUMMARY

Macroecology focuses on large-scale patterns of the distribution and diversity of organisms and ecological processes. Research areas include island biogeography, latitudinal patterns of species diversity, and the influences of regional and historical process on diversity and function.

22.1 Information about a species' current distribution and niche requirements can be combined with spatial information to predict invasion and range expansion.

Ecological niche modelling is a new approach designed to predict the potential distribution of a species across a broad geographic range. To create such models, an ecologist combines geo-referenced information about where a species is found with spatially explicit information about the environmental conditions that exist, resulting in statistical description of a species'

niche (fig. 22.30). This information can then be applied to new locations, predicting where one could find rare species, predict range shifts associated with climate change, and predict where an invasive species may spread. However, data quality is critical to accurate predictions, and pretty maps alone do not represent strong science.

22.2 On islands and habitat patches on continents, species richness increases with area and decreases with isolation.

Larger oceanic islands support more species of most groups of organisms than small islands. Isolated oceanic islands generally contain fewer species than islands near mainland areas (fig. 22.30). In addition to true islands, many habitats on continents (e.g., mountain tops, lakes) are so isolated that they can be considered as functional islands. However, because organisms

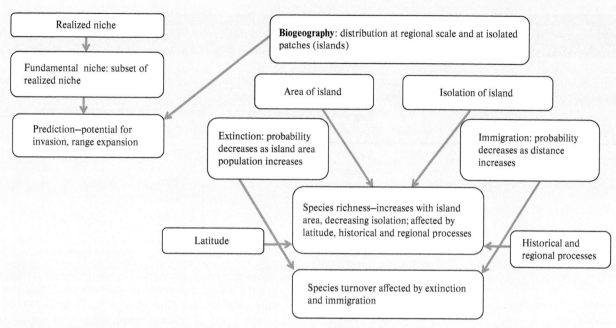

Figure 22.30 Concept map for chapter 22.

differ substantially in dispersal rates, an island that is very isolated for one group of organisms may be completely accessible to another group.

22.3 Species richness on islands can be modelled as a dynamic balance between immigration and extinction of species.

The equilibrium model of island biogeography proposes that the difference between rates of immigration and extinction determines the species richness on islands. The equilibrium model of island biogeography assumes that rates of species immigration to islands are mainly determined by distance from sources of immigrants. The model also assumes that rates of extinction on islands are determined mainly by island size. Species turnover is also predicted to vary as a function of isolation and island area (fig. 22.30). The predictions of the equilibrium model of island biogeography are supported by observations of species turnover on the islands and by colonization studies of mangrove islands in Florida and new islands in Lake Hjälmaren, Sweden.

22.4 Species richness generally increases from middle and high latitudes to the equator.

Most groups of organisms are more species-rich in the tropics. Many factors may contribute to higher tropical species richness, and these can be roughly categorized as (1) time and area effects, and (2) changes in the rate of diversification. Fully understanding the causes of this diversity gradient requires integration of information about phylogenetic patterns, geography, and local ecological interactions.

22.5 Long-term historical and regional processes significantly influence the structure of biotas and ecosystems.

Much geographic variation in species richness can be explained by historical and regional processes. Regional diversity can influence the diversity of local communities through a variety of mechanisms. Some exceptional situations that seem to have resulted from unique historical and regional processes include the exceptional species richness of the Cape floristic region of South Africa and the high species richness of temperate trees in East Asia. Dispersal among communities can result in meta-communities. These connections may buffer some effects of environmental change.

Global positioning systems, remote sensing, and geographic information systems are important tools for effective geographic ecology. A global positioning system determines locations on the earth's surface, including latitude, longitude, and altitude, using satellites as reference points. Remote-sensing satellites are generally fitted with electro-optical sensors that scan several bands of the electromagnetic spectrum. These sensors convert electromagnetic radiation into electrical signals that are in turn converted to digital values by a computer. These digital values can be used to construct an image. Geographic information systems are computer-based systems that store, analyze, and display geographic information. Global positioning systems, remote sensing, and geographic information systems are increasingly valuable parts of the ecologist's tool kit. Ecologists are using these new tools to study large-scale, dynamic ecological phenomena, such as interannual variation in primary production, land cover categorization, and potential responses to climate change.

REVIEW QUESTIONS

1. The following data (Preston 1962a) give the area and number of bird species on islands in the West Indies:

Island	Area	Log_{10} Area	# Species	Log # Species
Cuba	43,000	4.633	124	2.093
Isle of Pines	11,000	4.041	89	1.949
Hispaniola	47,000	4.672	106	2.021
Jamaica	4,470	3.650	99	1.996
Puerto Rico	3,435	3.536	79	1.898
Bahamas	5,450	3.736	74	1.869
Virgin Islands	465	2.667	35	1.544
Guadalupe	600	2.778	37	1.568
Dominica	304	2.483	36	1.556
St. Lucia	233	2.367	35	1.544
St. Vincent	150	2.176	35	1.544
Grenada	120	2.079	29	1.462

The numbers are expressed in two ways: as simple measurements and counts and as the logarithms of area and numbers of species. Use these data to plot your own species–area relationship. Plot area on the horizontal axis and number of species on the vertical axis. First plot the simple measurements of area and species number on one graph, and then plot the logarithms of area and species number on another graph. Which gives you the tightest relationship between area and species richness?

2. We discussed how Diamond (1969) documented immigrations and extinctions on the California Channel Islands by comparing his censuses of the birds of the islands with the birds recorded over 50 years earlier. Disregarding the numbers for San Miguel and Santa Rosa Islands, which were not well censused in 1917, Diamond showed that an average of approximately six bird species became extinct on California Channel Islands between 1917 and 1968. During the same period, an average of approximately five new bird species immigrated to the islands. Diamond suggested that his estimates of immigration and extinction were likely underestimates of the actual rates. Explain why his comparative study produced underestimates of rates of immigration and extinction.

3. Suppose you are about to study the bird communities on the islands shown below, which are identical in area but lie at different distances from the mainland. According to the equilibrium model of island biogeography, which of the islands should experience higher rates of immigration? What does the equilibrium model of island biogeography

predict concerning relative rates of extinction on the two islands?

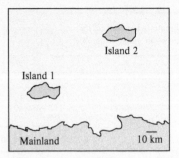

4. Now, suppose you are going to study the bird communities on the islands shown below, which lie equal distances from the mainland but differ in area. According to the equilibrium model of island biogeography, what should be the relative rates of immigration to the two islands? On which islands should rates of extinction be lowest? Explain.

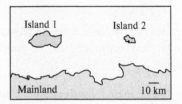

5. Review the major hypotheses proposed to explain the higher species richness of tropical regions compared to temperate and high-latitude regions. How are these hypotheses related to relative rates of speciation and extinction in tropical regions and temperate and high-latitude regions?

6. Carnivora are introduced in this chapter as an exceptional group that has evolved and diversified in temperate regions rather than in tropical regions. Yet, as a group, Carnivora is most species-rich in tropical areas and most species-poor in high latitudes. Site of origin and diversification are often posited as reasons for other groups of organisms being most diverse at low latitudes. Following this argument, why aren't carnivores most diverse at mid-latitude?

7. Ricklefs (1987) pointed out that many large-scale contrasts in species richness and composition cannot be explained by local processes, such as competition and predation. Ricklefs proposed that differences in history and geography can leave a unique stamp on regional biotas. The mammals of Australia, including kangaroos, koalas, and duck-billed platypuses, must be one of the best-known examples of a unique biota. How have history and geography, as opposed to local processes, combined to produce this unique assemblage of mammals?

8. Most examples of regional and latitudinal variation in species richness cited in this chapter have been terrestrial.

Consider regional variation in marine biotas. Like birds on land, fish are one of the best-studied groups of marine organisms. Moyle and Cech (1982) cite the following patterns of fish species richness:

Atlantic and Gulf Coasts of North America		Pacific Coast of North America	
Area	**Species**	**Area**	**Species**
Texas	400	Gulf of California	800
South Carolina	350	California	550
Cape Cod	250	Canada	325
Gulf of Maine	225		
Labrador	61		
Greenland	34		

As you can see, fish species richness decreases northward on both coasts. However, the Pacific coast generally supports a larger number of species. This contrast may be another situation requiring historical- and geographic-level explanations. Explore and explain this contrast in species richness using information from the fields of marine biology, oceanography, and ichthyology. Moyle and Cech (1982) and Briggs (1974) are good starting points.

9. The diversity of a local community is often linearly related to regional diversity. However, local diversity is lower than regional diversity. Why does local diversity not equal regional diversity? If the relationship between local and regional diversity does not saturate, does this mean that local processes, such as competition, are not important in structuring local communities?

10. How would you construct a map of the biodiversity hotspots for Canada? What information would you need for this to be accurate? How would you choose which taxa to include in constructing the map? Why does North America have very few biodiversity hotspots on global maps?

AGE Fotostock/Dal.

CHAPTER 23 GLOBAL ECOLOGY

CHAPTER CONCEPTS

23.1 The evolutionary history and distribution of species (past and present) are rooted in global-scale climate patterns and changes in the earth's land masses over a long geological time scale.

Concept 23.1 Review

23.2 Human activities have generated substantial threats to biological diversity.

Ecology in Action: Being an Ecologist

Concept 23.2 Review

23.3 Ecological information can be integrated with economic data to help meet conservation goals in a political landscape.

Ecological Tools and Approaches: Cooperative Research Networks and Distributed Ecology

Concept 23.3 Review

Summary

Review Questions

On October 4, 1957, the Soviet Union launched Sputnik, the first "artificial moon," into an Earth orbit. The space race was truly on. Soon after Sputnik, the United States launched the *Apollo 8* mission to the moon, which captured the indelible images of Earth rising above the moon's horizon (fig. 23.1). That image, of Earth as a shining blue ball against the blackness of space, instantaneously changed the perspective of Earth that most people held. Today, most people "know" what Earth looks like as a whole, not solely the boundaries of their village, city, or country.

Today, we are able to know the earth in ways never possible before the launch of satellites. The early exploration of near space enabled the communications infrastructure that most of us take for granted today. Thank Sputnik when a lecture gets dull and you are checking in on your social media. (Professors, meanwhile, will curse Sputnik like no one has since October 5, 1957.) The early exploration also enabled the development of tools used to study regional and global patterns of our dynamic planet. We can now see the entire planet and zoom in from space to virtually any place we wish. If you have never explored this with tools like Google Earth, try it. It blew my mind the first time I zoomed in to find an image from space of me changing a tire in my driveway (wish I had combed my hair that day). While that may not be the best example of value, we are now able to see ecological processes in near real time at spatial scales spanning orders of magnitude from metres to tens of thousands of kilometres. Meanwhile, advances in the tools of geology and geophysics allow us to explore ecological processes across vast stretches of time. While this was never the intention, the launch of Sputnik and the ensuing wave of interest in physics (largely driven by Cold War fear) ushered in the age of global ecology by providing a whole new set of tools.

As we move to address questions relevant to the planet as a whole, about processes spanning historical to geological time scales, we enter the realm of global ecology. Global ecology will include the science of how humans impact global processes, biological diversity, and the function of globally significant ecosystems. As the field of ecology has matured, its connections to other disciplines have become stronger. We now recognize that ecological function and ecological services are not simply ideas but have economic and societal value. We recognize that widespread loss of these functions and services has ramifications for the global village. In this final chapter, we will discuss the work of diverse groups of researchers, including geologists, biologists, physicists, chemists, sociologists, and economists. We begin by understanding that, in deep time, this planet has undergone substantial change.

23.1 Global-Scale Phenomena Drive Distribution of Species

The evolutionary history and distribution of species (past and present) are rooted in global-scale climate patterns and changes in the earth's land masses over a long geological time scale. In chapter 2, we discussed the influence of global climate patterns on the distribution of terrestrial biomes. We discussed how climate, particularly patterns in temperature and water availability, drive selection for vegetation adapted to different biomes. In chapter 3, we discussed global ocean circulation patterns. These patterns contribute to distribution of terrestrial biomes through their effects on climate but also differentiate the physical habitat in different areas of the ocean, influencing distribution of marine species. In the comparatively short time frame of human history (the past three centuries notwithstanding), global distribution of biomes and species diversity within these biomes have been fairly constant. We have noted that some grassland biomes have been maintained and expanded by human use of fire. Also, hunters in North America likely contributed to the extinction of many large animals, herbivores and predators, during the Pleistocene epoch, indirectly affecting plant communities and ecosystem function. Over a geologic time scale, the earth and its biological diversity exhibit a near-constant state of flux. Ecological communities, and the species that live within them, are ephemeral if we look through the lens of geological time. As has hopefully been evident throughout this book, abiotic conditions impose significant pressures on the organisms that live within a given location. These pressures can impact the fitness of an individual, the persistence of a population, and the structure and function of communities and ecosystems. Thus, it may come as no surprise that in the past as continents moved, oceans disappeared, and climatic patterns changed, the biological diversity of the planet and distributions of taxonomic groups also changed.

In this section, we'll discuss short-term oscillations in climate that are global in extent. These oscillations overlay the broader global climate patterns discussed in chapters 2 and 3. The oscillations affect distributions of species and population dynamics in a relatively short time scale (years), yet these short-term oscillations have occurred over a long period of time and

Figure 23.1　Oasis in space: earthrise over the moon's horizon.
© NASA.

impose oscillations in selective pressures. This can shape the evolution of species over a much longer time scale. We will also discuss plate tectonics, a decidedly long-term phenomenon that has played an important role in the global distribution of species. It may be a gross understatement, but the rending of a land mass creates a very effective barrier to gene flow and can set groups of taxonomically related species on very different evolutionary trajectories. The history of life on Earth is marked by several mass extinction events related to rapid climate change, extensive volcanic activity, changes in the atmospheric composition, and asteroid impacts. It is also marked by periods of rapid evolutionary diversification. In short, global-scale phenomena over a geological time scale have made Earth's biodiversity very dynamic.

In the second section, we will discuss changes in biological diversity, ecosystems, and processes that are caused by our own activity. In keeping with the theme of the chapter, we'll restrict this discussion to activities that have a global reach. The changes wrought by human activities may parallel those of natural phenomena described in the first section. However, the time scale at which human activities alter habitats, change biological diversity, alter ecosystem processes, and change climate are much more compressed, creating significant challenges for evolutionary adaptation.

Atmospheric Cycles: The Southern and North Atlantic Oscillations

At relatively short time scales, we find examples of earth-system processes that influence biological diversity. Two of the most relevant to us in Canada are the **Southern Oscillation** and the **North Atlantic Oscillation**. In 1904, a British mathematician named Gilbert Walker was appointed Director General of Observatories in India. Walker arrived in India shortly after a disastrous famine from 1899 to 1900 caused by crop failures during a drought. This tragic event led him to search for a way to predict the rainfall associated with the Asian monsoons. Walker (1924) eventually found a link between barometric pressure across the Pacific Ocean and the amount of rain falling during the monsoons. He found that reduced pressure in the eastern Pacific was accompanied by increased pressure in the western Pacific, and vice versa. Walker called this oscillation in barometric pressure the Southern Oscillation.

Today, meteorologists monitor the state of the Southern Oscillation with the Southern Oscillation Index. The value of the index is determined by the difference in barometric pressure between Tahiti and Darwin, Australia (fig. 23.2). Walker noticed that low values of the Southern Oscillation Index were associated with drought in Australia, Indonesia, India, and parts of Africa.

The connection between Walker's Southern Oscillation and patterns of ocean temperature during El Niños was eventually described by Jacob Bjerknes (1966, 1969). Bjerknes proposed that the gradient in sea surface temperature across the central Pacific Ocean produces a large-scale atmospheric circulation system that moves in the plane of the equator, as shown in figure 23.3. Air over the warmer western Pacific rises. This rising mass of air then divides, with part flowing westward (the western cell in fig. 23.3), and with part flowing eastward in

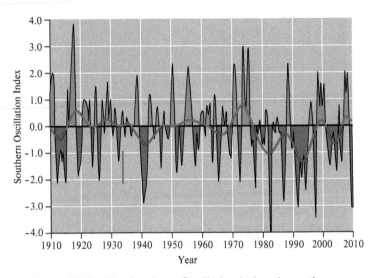

Figure 23.2   The Southern Oscillation Index shows the difference in barometric pressures between Tahiti and Darwin, Australia. Positive values indicate higher barometric pressure in the eastern Pacific Ocean.

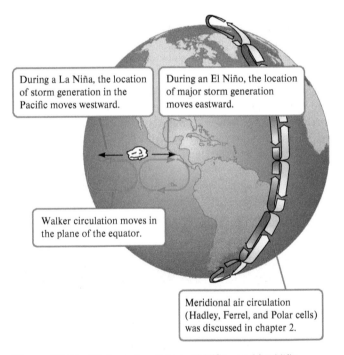

During a La Niña, the location of storm generation in the Pacific moves westward.

During an El Niño, the location of major storm generation moves eastward.

Walker circulation moves in the plane of the equator.

Meridional air circulation (Hadley, Ferrel, and Polar cells) was discussed in chapter 2.

Figure 23.3   Walker circulation, El Niño, and La Niña.

the upper atmosphere (the eastern cell in fig. 23.3). If we consider the eastern cell, the air mass flowing eastward in the upper atmosphere cools and sinks over the eastern Pacific. This air mass then flows westward along with the southeast trade winds, gradually warming and gathering moisture. This westward-flowing air eventually joins the rising air from the other cell in the western Pacific. As this warm and moist air rises, it forms rain clouds. Where these air masses converge and form rain clouds (i.e., how far west) is variable, occurring farther east in an El Niño period and farther west in a La Niña period (described below) (fig. 23.3). Bjerknes called this atmospheric system **Walker circulation** after Sir Gilbert Walker.

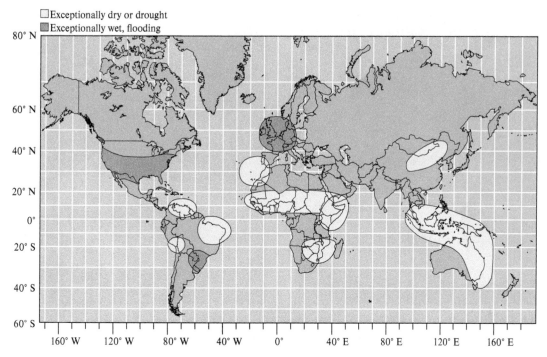

Figure 23.4 Effects of the exceptionally strong El Niño of 1982 to 1983 on patterns of global precipitation. Data from Diaz and Kiladis 1992.

The El Niño Southern Oscillation affects the climate of North America, South America, Australia, southern Asia, Africa, and parts of southern Europe (fig. 23.4).

During the mature phase of an **El Niño**, the sea surface in the eastern tropical Pacific Ocean is much warmer than average, and the barometric pressure over the eastern Pacific is lower than average. The combination of warm sea surface temperatures and low pressure promotes the formation of storms over the eastern Pacific Ocean. These storms bring increased precipitation to much of North and South America. Meanwhile, the sea surface in the western Pacific is cooler than average and the barometric pressure is higher. These conditions produce drought over much of the western Pacific region.

Periods of lower sea surface temperature and higher-than-average pressure in the eastern tropical Pacific have been named **La Niñas**. During a La Niña period, a pool of warm seawater moves far into the western Pacific. This warm water, combined with lower barometric pressures in the western Pacific Ocean, generates many storms. Consequently, La Niña brings higher-than-average precipitation to the western Pacific, and drought to much of North and South America. While often associated with the tropics, the influence of the El Niño Southern Oscillation extends well into temperate regions. During El Niños, much of the northern United States, Canada, and Alaska are much warmer than average. During La Niñas, these regions are colder than average.

El Niño and Marine Populations

As you might expect, this global climate system affects ecological systems around the globe. Some of the most dramatic ecological responses to El Niño occur in marine populations along the west coast of South America. Long before the recent discovery of the global extent of its effects, El Niño was known to produce declines in coastal populations of anchovies and sardines and the seabirds that feed upon them. How does El Niño induce these population declines? They are produced by changes in the pattern of sea surface temperatures and coastal circulation. Figure 23.5a shows sea surface temperatures off the west coast of South America during average conditions, when coastal waters are relatively cool along most of the west coast of South America. A tongue of cool water extends westward toward the open Pacific Ocean. This cool water is brought to the surface by upwelling. Upwelling along the coast is driven by the southeast trade winds, while the offshore upwelling is driven by the east winds of the Walker circulation.

With the onset of an El Niño, the easterly winds slacken and the pool of warm water in the western Pacific moves eastward, shutting off upwelling along the South American coast. Consequently, the supply of nutrients that upwelling usually delivers to surface waters is also shut off. A lower nutrient supply reduces primary production by phytoplankton. This decline in primary production reduces the supply of food available to consumers in the coastal food web and is followed by declines in populations of fish and their predators.

Remote sensing of phytoplankton pigments in surface waters around the Galápagos Islands shows that the 1982–83 El Niño reduced average primary production and dramatically changed the location of production hotspots. Changes in the rate and distribution of primary production induced reproductive failure, migration, and widespread death among seabird

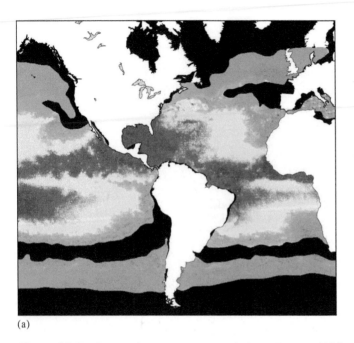

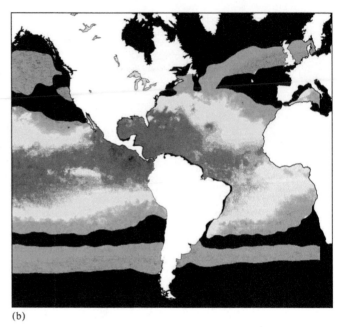

(a)

(b)

Figure 23.5   Sea surface temperature during (*a*) non–El Niño and (*b*) El Niño conditions.

populations in the Galápagos Islands and along the west coast of South America. The 1982–83 El Niño also had a major impact on fur seal and sea lion populations, mainly through reductions in food supply.

Though the Southern Oscillation is typically better known among the general public, the North Atlantic Oscillation generally has a stronger influence on the biological diversity of northern systems, including much of Canada. The North Atlantic Oscillation (NAO) is a fluctuation in atmospheric pressure between Iceland and the Azores off the coast of Portugal. Like El Niño, the NAO has been identified for over 200 years (Saabye 1776), though only recently has its importance in driving large-scale ecological patterns been realized (Ottersen et al. 2001). A major effect of changes in the NAO is a shift in the direction and speed of wind over the Atlantic Ocean between 40° and 60° latitude, particularly during winter months. When the NAO is in the positive phase, there are high atmospheric pressures below 55° and lower pressures toward the Arctic (Stenseth et al. 2003). This has the effect of moving the storms that travel across the Atlantic Ocean toward the north (the area of lower pressure), resulting in increased storm activity in southern Europe, higher temperatures over much of Europe and North America, reduced precipitation across much of the Canadian Arctic, and cool temperatures in eastern Canada. When the NAO is in the negative phase, these patterns are reversed, with the storm activity focused on southern Europe, cooler temperatures, and more precipitation in the Canadian Arctic. As a sign of the importance of the NAO on ecological communities, approximately 33% of the interannual variation in winter temperatures in the Northern Hemisphere is attributed to variation in the NAO (Hurrell 1996).

Eric Post and Nils Stenseth have explored the impacts of variation in the NAO on various populations of plants and animals (Post and Stenseth 1999). As we saw in chapter 9, plant phenology is responsive to changes in temperature and is already shifting in response to global warming. Can other large-scale phenomena, such as the NAO, also be important in determining the timing of flowering across large geographic regions? And how might this affect herbivores? Snow depth and the timing of snow can also impact large foragers (such as reindeer, moose, red deer, Soay sheep, feral goats, muskoxen, and caribou) with potential impacts on population growth. These large mammals are of great concern to Indigenous communities, conservation biologists, and the general public; thus, an understanding of whether large-scale climatic variation influences their populations is critically needed.

In general, plants flowered earlier in Norway following a positive NAO winter, which corresponds to a warmer, wetter year. There was evidence that the NAO influenced all ungulate species studied, explaining between 40% to 70% of the variation in body size and fecundity. The exact effects of positive NAO years varied among species and locations. In general, mainland populations had greater fecundity and smaller body size during positive NAO years, while maritime populations had increased body size and reduced fecundity during positive NAO winters. In total, this study provides clear evidence that the North Atlantic Oscillation can impact a diversity of populations across a broad geographic area.

Plate Tectonics

One of the most obvious features we use to describe a single location is whether it is predominantly terrestrial, aquatic, or a wetland. Though we recognize that disturbances, such as floods, beaver activity, and volcanoes, can submerge a forest or create land where there was once water, it is easy to view such changes as exceptions to the rule of geologic constancy. However, over deep geologic time, the movement of tectonic plates has created the landscapes we see now and destroyed many others that we never will.

Much as the atmosphere consists of many different layers, so too does the physical structure of the earth. A coarse description would list the solid inner and liquid outer cores, surrounded by a mantle, and then the outer layer called the crust (fig. 23.6). However, much as soil scientists define many horizons and sub-horizons in the soil (chapter 2), geologists use substantially more detail in their description of the earth's layers. Here, we are primarily concerned with the surface lithosphere, the hard crust that sits upon and drifts upon the slowly flowing asthenosphere. Where the lithosphere breaks, we observe faults. Currently, the lithosphere is arranged into 15 major tectonic plates, though this number and their sizes have changed over time (fig. 23.7).

Today, the idea that plates move over time, crashing into each other, separating, subsiding, and generally causing mayhem to the physical structure of the earth's surface is commonly understood; it is taught early and often in schools around the world. However, when Alfred Wegener first published the theory of continental drift (later subsumed by the theory of plate tectonics), the idea was revolutionary. Originally published in German (Wegener 1912), his work was only much later translated to English as *The Origin of Continents and Oceans* (Wegener 1966). The idea that the physical structure of the planet was dynamic rather than fixed challenged geological and religious doctrine. However, through decades of data collection, scientists have been able to support this revolutionary concept with solid evidence, among the most compelling of which is the ability to use satellite imagery to show plate movement over time (fig. 23.8). Rather than repeat a course in earth sciences in this ecology text, the question to ask here is this: Why should ecologists care?

Wegener supported his theory on continental drift based upon several lines of evidence, one line being fossil records that demonstrated the same (or morphologically indistinguishable) plant and animal species on two or more modern and unconnected land masses. Wegener inferred that these distributions of fossils would be explained only by migration among land masses (highly unlikely given the characteristics of some of these species); by independent origins on separate continents (in contradiction of Darwin's theory of evolution by natural selection); or by vicarance, where species with large geographical ranges were divided into separate populations with the breakup of continental land masses. The present-day diversity and distribution of species reflect, in part, the distributions of ancestral species and the rides they took on different bits of drifting rock.

Plate tectonics have, thus, contributed to the evolutionary history and biological diversity of terrestrial species by creating barriers to gene flow. But can continental drift also contribute to diversification of marine species? Tropical reefs are among the most biologically diverse ecosystems on earth. Fabien Leprieur and colleagues used fossil records that suggest marine biodiversity hotspots have migrated in geological time (Leprieur et al. 2016). The researchers coupled a mechanistic model of species diversification to a paleobathymetric model that defined positions of continents and shallow seas over the past 140 million years. Their model suggests that continental drift has created transient formation and closing of seas as well as connections and breakups of land masses, isolating populations and rejoining allopatric species. The model predicts the establishment and migration of diverse marine ecosystems as reflected in the fossil record.

Beyond its effects on genetic isolation, continental drift contributes to evolution and diversification through its effects on climate. Whereas the Southern Oscillation and North Atlantic Oscillation affect global climate at annual to decadal time scales, plate tectonics drive global climate change over geological time and affect climate in a number of different ways. Global circulation patterns dissipate energy from the equator toward the poles. This dissipation and the paths of oceanic and atmospheric currents are constrained by size and position of land masses. In chapters 2 and 3, we discussed these currents and how they affect the global distribution of biomes. The opening and closing of oceanic pathways with horizontal movement of plates changes circulation patterns and the pathways for energy dissipation, thereby changing terrestrial temperature regimes. Vertical uplift at subduction zones creates mountain ranges, which are barriers for atmospheric circulation and which contribute to west–east patterns of temperature and rainfall across mountain ranges. Subduction also increases volcanic activity, which recycles carbon stored in rock as $CaCO_3$ to the atmosphere as CO_2, contributing to the greenhouse effect. In contrast, the vertical upheaval of rock and weathering of silica minerals removes CO_2 through formation of $CaCO_3$. Over geological time scales, the effects of plate tectonics on weathering,

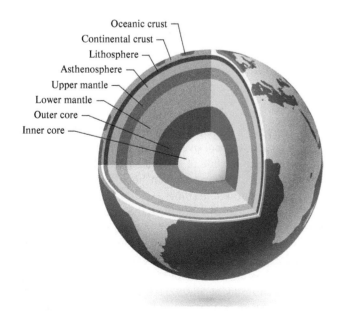

Oceanic crust
Continental crust
Lithosphere
Asthenosphere
Upper mantle
Lower mantle
Outer core
Inner core

Figure 23.6 The earth is made up of several layers.
Alhovik/Dreamstime.com.

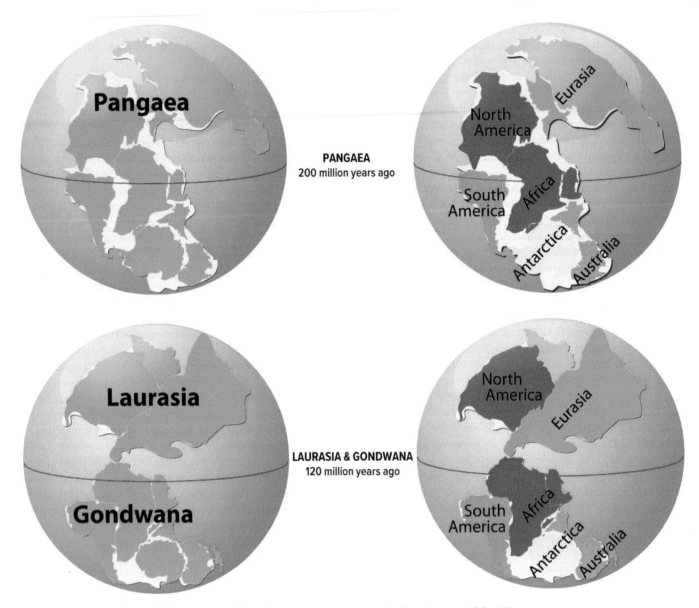

Figure 23.7   World map of Pangaea—200 million years ago; Laurasia, Gondwana—120 million years ago.
Illustration 25396938 © Designua–Dreamstime.com.

volcanism, and circulation patterns have created a dynamic global climate, driving novel evolutionary adaptations and biological diversification.

Extinction Events

Extinction is the expected fate of new taxa; some estimates suggest that only 1% of the species ever to occupy the earth are currently extant (Novacek 2001). However, given that ecologists cannot agree on how many species are currently extant (chapter 2), let alone how many were extant 100 million years ago, you should be a bit skeptical of this claim. Regardless of the true percentage, the concept it promotes emphasizes the importance of time in structuring natural systems,

as the diversity we find on the planet now is just a small sliver of the total species pool over the earth's history. As exciting as it might be to be able to swim alongside trilobites within Canada's oceans, the best we can hope for is to encounter them as fossils encased in stone.

Though extinction is expected, the rate of extinction has varied greatly over time (fig. 23.9). There is broad agreement that there have been five mass extinction events over the last 550 million years (Raup and Sepkoski 1982), each characterized by the loss of over 75% of the species estimated prior to the event (Barnosky et al. 2011). Some of these events may be familiar, such as the recent Cretaceous event (approximately 65 million years ago), the Permian event (approximately 250 million years ago), and the more distant Ordovician event

Figure 23.8 Using measurements from the global positioning system, researchers at NASA are able to visualize the movement of the earth's plates. Yellow arrows indicate direction and horizontal velocity of plate movement away from positions indicated by green circles.
Imagery © 2013 NASA, Terrametrics.

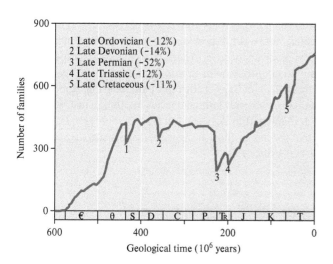

Figure 23.9 Estimated number of families of marine organisms over the last 600 million years, with five labelled mass extinction events. Estimates of the fraction of genera and species lost are substantially higher.

David M. Raup and J. John Sepkoski Jr. 1982, March 19. Mass extinctions in the marine fossil record. *Science* 215(4539):1501–03, Figure 2. Reprinted with permission from AAAS.

(approximately 443 million years ago) (Barnosky et al. 2011). The causes of these events are diverse and include periods of massive global warming or cooling, asteroid impacts, sea level changes, extensive volcanic activity, and changes in atmospheric composition. As you might expect, plate tectonic activity and solar periodicity can trigger or exaggerate some of these other more proximate causes of extinction. We have already mentioned the increased volcanic activity associated with

subduction zones. These causes of extinction events are not mutually exclusive, and multiple factors can lead to each mass extinction event.

Not included among these five events of the past 550 million years is the Great Oxygenation Event of the Precambrian (2.4 billion years ago), caused by photosynthetic oxygen production as a result of an evolutionary innovation, using water rather than H_2S as an electron donor. While undoubtedly devastating to life at the time, it opened the doors to subsequent innovations, such as aerobic respiration, without which we would not be around to ponder it.

Extinction events obviously have major impacts on biodiversity patterns through the loss of numerous genera and species. However, they can also impact biodiversity through periods of rapid speciation following the event (Erwin 2001). Why should extinction lead to high speciation? Though taxa die out during these events, this does not mean that all of the resources and habitats upon which they depended also disappear. Instead, adaptive radiation was often able to act on the few taxa remaining, as much of the niche space was no longer occupied by other species. Further, in many cases extinction events are associated with changes in the climate of the planet and chemistry of the oceans and atmosphere. Such changes would impose new opportunities and selective pressures for the species that remained, leading to further diversification. One of the most well-known examples is the rapid diversification of birds and mammals following the Cretaceous-Paleogene extinction event that killed all non-avian dinosaurs approximately 65 million years ago.

The first tetrapods (four-footed animals) to colonize land appeared during the mid-Devonian period, over 350 million years ago (if not earlier). Today, there are over 30,000 species of tetrapods living on Earth. The rise in diversity of tetrapods is linked to evolutionary innovation following a series of extinction events. One way of viewing the evolutionary innovation that can occur over time is to imagine the number of habitable ecological modes that are both possible and that are found in existing taxa. An ecological mode is analogous to an ecologist's description of an organism's niche, though the mode represents a potential way of existing (e.g., tree-nesting insectivore). This is in contrast with a formal statistical description of an organism's performance on multiple niche axes (chapter 9). Recently, a group of British and Canadian scientists have been able to show a tight linkage between the number of tetrapod families and the number of occupied modes over the last 350 Ma (fig. 23.10) (Sahney et al. 2010). Particularly noticeable is the rapid rise in occupied modes following the extinction of the dinosaurs during the Cretaceous event. In other words, it appears that when dinosaurs were no longer the dominant tetrapods, birds and mammals underwent substantial diversification both in terms of ecological modes and number of families. Sahney et al. (2010) suggest that only 36% of the potential ecological modes have so far been occupied by tetrapods, in contrast to 78% occupancy by marine animals. If true, this suggests there is substantial room for future innovation among tetrapods. It may also explain why, following mass extinctions, tetrapod families have not simply recovered to pre-event numbers but, rather, have continued to increase over time.

Room for future innovation may prove to be very important. There is substantial evidence that we are in the midst of a sixth mass extinction event (Barnosky et al. 2011). It may not be surprising that anthropogenic changes associated with land use, spread of invasive species, and changes to global climate have been identified as key drivers. We have already discussed several of these issues, and we will talk broadly about land use later in this chapter. Here, we present some context on the magnitude and rate of current biodiversity loss.

Using the definition of 75% species loss (as opposed to genera or families) as an indicator of a mass extinction event, the loss of species in the last 500 years would not qualify as a major extinction event; only a small percentage of each major taxonomic group are known to have gone extinct during that time period (Barnosky et al. 2011). However, a high percentage of these taxa are currently threatened, notably gastropods, cycads, bivalves, and amphibians. Importantly, the threatened taxa do not belong to a single clade but are instead widespread among many groups of organisms. Further, past mass extinction events did not occur on a time scale of 500 years; instead their durations were on the scale of millions of years. To account for the issue of time, Barnosky asks this question: How long would it take to reach 75% extinction if the extinction rates observed over the last 500 years continue? The answer ranges from hundreds of thousands to millions of years, timelines consistent with what occurred during the last five mass extinction events. The estimate of time to reach 75% extinction drops to less than 2,500 years if one assumes that species that are now critically endangered become extinct within 100 years; it drops to less than 600 years if you make the same assumption about currently threatened species.

A recent report from the Intergovernmental Science-Policy Platform on Biodiversity and Ecosystem Services (IPBES) (2019) created quite a stir. It provides the most complete picture of the global biodiversity crisis to date, compiled by 145 expert authors from 50 countries, with inputs from another 310 contributing authors. The findings of the report are sobering: approximately 1 million plant and animal species are threatened with extinction, many within decades. Further, the average abundance of native species in most terrestrial habitats has decreased by at least 20% since 1900.

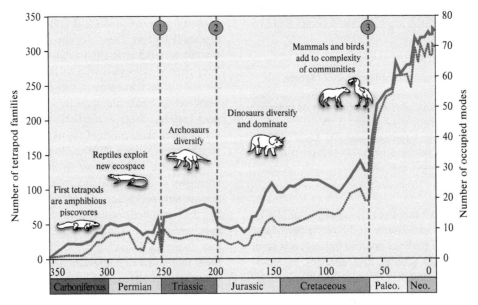

Figure 23.10   The estimated number of tetrapod families (red) and ecological modes used by tetrapods (blue) over the last 350 million years.

The challenge ahead is to change this future by rigorously applying ecological principles to conservation, and, just as important, by building the partnerships necessary for effective implementation. The IPBES report finds that transformative change is necessary and possible, but it also recognizes the challenges of such a fundamental change of technical, economic, and social systems that will be required. Later in this chapter, we will discuss some examples of novel ways that ecological information is being applied to lessen human impacts on the world around us.

CONCEPT 23.1 REVIEW

1. Why is it important for ecologists to understand phases of atmospheric cycles when studying long-term ecological processes?

2. Why do plate tectonics influence the diversity of life that ecologists find in different locations?

3. How common are mass extinction events, and what are some of their ecological consequences?

23.2 Human Activity Transforms the World

Human activities have generated substantial threats to biological diversity. In the previous section, we emphasized that the planet has always undergone periods of dramatic shifts, with pronounced consequences for the species that inhabit the land and sea. Even now, changes are occurring. Some are related to the same natural geological processes and atmospheric cycles described in the previous section. However, the rate of change has been accelerated due to the work of a truly effective ecosystem engineer: *Homo sapiens*. In chapter 20, we discussed the effects of industrialization on nutrient and carbon cycling. Here, we focus more generally on our seemingly inexhaustible consumption of the natural products produced through ecological processes. We will touch upon a number of the global impacts we have, but we admit up front that this coverage will of necessity be superficial and that there are many important topics we simply do not have space to cover.

Humans have changed the face of the earth. Human activities, mainly agriculture and urbanization, have significantly altered one-third to one-half of the ice-free land surface of the earth. Marshes have been drained and filled to build urban areas or airports. Tropical forests have been cut and converted to pasture. The courses of rivers have been changed. The Aral Sea in central Asia has been so starved for water that it is nearly dry. We will begin by taking a broad overview of some global patterns of land use. However, it is important to recognize that although the actions taken by individuals and governments in different countries can be summed to describe the global condition, not every country faces the same challenges. In a classic paper, Soulé (1991) suggests that the economic status of countries will strongly influence whether particular challenges to biodiversity are likely to be strong or weak. Habitat loss and fragmentation pose greater risks to conservation of genetic diversity, populations, and species diversity in poorer countries, as richer countries have largely already converted much of their lands. The greater challenges to rich countries for conservation of genetic and species diversity and for conservation of ecosystems come from pollution and climate change (fig. 23.11). Under this framework, Soulé provides an interesting analysis of various conservation approaches that may be best suited to contexts of population pressure and economic/political instability. This analysis suggests that tactics such as wilderness parks, biosphere reserves, and multiple-use wild lands may be suitable for wealthier countries with lower population pressures. However, tactics such as agroforestry may be more appropriate under high population pressure, and habitat restoration projects may be more suitable for poorer countries with relatively low population pressures.

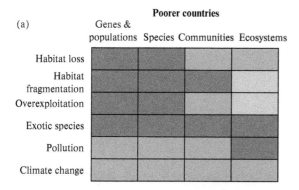

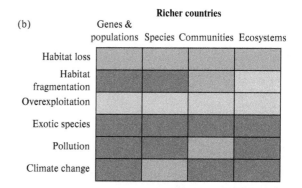

Figure 23.11   Human influences present different challenges to biodiversity as a function of ecological scale and economic status of a country. Lighter shading indicates lesser impact.

M. E. Soulé. 1991. Conservation—Tactics for a constant crisis. *Science* 253:744–50, Figure 2. Reprinted with permission from AAAS.

Human Appropriation of Net Primary Production

One of the best ways to understand the influence of humans on the planet is to ask a question right at the base of life: How much of the planet's net primary productivity (NPP) is used by humans? Though simple to ask, this question is hard to answer. One of the most thorough analyses comes from Helmut Haberl and colleagues in Europe (Haberl et al. 2007). Based upon global terrestrial data in 2000, the team estimates that humans appropriate nearly 24% of global NPP on land (HANPP = Human appropriation of net primary productivity). As can be seen in figure 23.12, the spatial distribution of HANPP is highly variable, with usage highest through much of Canada, the United States, Europe, and South and Southeast Asia. You will also note that HANPP is negative in some regions; these tend to be deserts or other very low productivity systems where human activities, such as irrigation, cause increased NPP.

Digging deeper into the data, Haberl and colleagues were able to isolate different human activities, identifying their individual contributions to HANPP. Direct harvest was the largest cause, accounting for over half of the measured HANPP. Perhaps not surprisingly, in areas occupied by cropland HANPP exceeded 80%. Though croplands and grazing areas account for only 12% of the non–ice covered regions of the planet, human activities in those regions account for over 75% of HANPP! Changes in land use, such as the construction of cities and industrial activities, are also responsible for a sizable fraction of the HANPP. More specifically, human land use has reduced global NPP by over 9% (Haberl et al. 2007).

Though humans are restricted to land as our primary habitat, we are increasingly exploiting the oceans for food. A global team of researchers, led by then–Ph.D. student Wilf Swartz from the University of British Columbia, has compiled the most complete understanding of the growth of fisheries (Swartz et al. 2010). One of the key differences in exploitation among terrestrial and aquatic systems is what humans tend to harvest. On land, it is predominantly plants; in water, it is predominately animals. Further, those harvested animals may themselves be herbivores, feeding upon algae, or carnivores. To allow comparison, a means of standardizing for this variation in trophic position is necessary. Swartz and his colleagues calculated the primary production required (PPR) to produce a given level of harvest by a fishery. For two catches of equal biomass, PPR will be higher for the harvested species that feeds at a higher trophic level, as more primary production is needed to produce equal amounts of carnivores than herbivores (chapter 19).

Swartz and his colleagues were able to calculate PPR throughout the world's oceans, historically (in 1950) and more recently (in 2005). The change is striking (fig. 23.13). There has been a substantial increase in areas heavily exploited since 1950. Interestingly, much of this growth has been in southern latitudes, as much of the northern latitudes were already heavily exploited in 1950. Swartz and colleagues contrast the intensity of PPR exploitation in the oceans versus agriculture. In marine systems, PPR exploitation increased 2.4-fold between 1961 and 1995, but the area of ocean exploited increased 4-fold over this period. In contrast, agricultural production and yield doubled between 1961 and 1995, despite only a 10% increase in the agricultural land base (Tilman 1999). Despite the relative efficiency suggested, agricultural expansion has changed the landscape of the world.

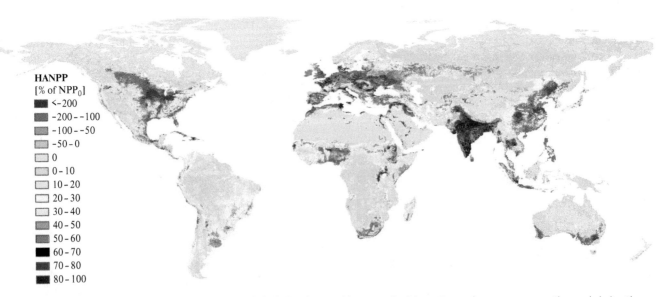

HANPP
[% of NPP_0]
- < -200
- $-200 - -100$
- $-100 - -50$
- $-50 - 0$
- 0
- $0 - 10$
- $10 - 20$
- $20 - 30$
- $30 - 40$
- $40 - 50$
- $50 - 60$
- $60 - 70$
- $70 - 80$
- $80 - 100$

Figure 23.12   A map showing the percentage of NPP that is used by people. Negative values can occur through irrigation and other agricultural activities.

Adapted from H. Haberl et al. 2007. Quantifying and mapping the human appropriation of net primary production in earth's terrestrial ecosystems. *Proceedings of the National Academy of Sciences Journal* 104:12942–7, Figure 1 (only lower panel). Copyright 2007 National Academy of Sciences, U.S.A.

1950

2005

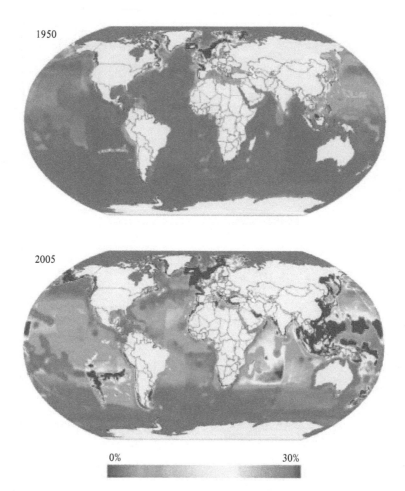

0%   30%

Figure 23.13 Maps showing what proportion of primary production is needed to maintain marine fisheries in 1950 and 2005.

Wilf Swartz, Enric Sala, Sean Tracey, Reg Watson, and Daniel Pauly. 2010. The spatial expansion and ecological footprint of fisheries (1950 to present). *PLoS ONE* 5(12):e15143. doi:10.1371/journal.pone.0015143. Reprinted with permission.

The Agricultural Footprint

The most dominant human land uses are cropland and pastures (fig. 23.14). Associated with conversion of native grasslands and forests to croplands and rangelands has been a 700% increase in fertilizer use, and a 70% increase in irrigated croplands in the last 40 years. These two activities associated with modern agricultural practices place enormous pressures on freshwater resources and the global nitrogen cycle. It is estimated that 85% of the freshwater used by humans goes to agriculture, representing 10% of the global reserves. In addition to more nitrogen being deposited from the atmosphere, fertilizers routinely leach into streams and groundwater, decreasing the quality of the water and changing aquatic ecosystems that surround agricultural fields.

In the last 300 years, between 7 to 11 million km² of forest have been cleared for timber and for conversion into agricultural land. Grasslands have not fared any better, with little native prairie remaining in many areas of the world, including North America (fig. 23.14). The rates of changes in land

use vary across the planet. Foley and colleagues suggest that as societies develop economically, so, too, does their impact on the surrounding land (fig. 23.15). Much of the land base in North America and Europe has already been altered; thus, most people do not recognize the extensive changes that these lands have already undergone. The large expanses of land that remain relatively intact, such as the boreal forest and arctic tundra, are regions that historically were not economically viable for development. However, continued changes to the world timber markets; new technologies for processing oil sands; discovery of extensive gas fields, diamonds, and other valuable minerals; and thinning ice and snow packs are placing significant pressures for development in formerly remote areas. In other parts of the world, such as the Amazon Basin and much of Africa, the rapid phase of development is just beginning.

Although this section is specifically discussing the agricultural footprint, there is a related broader discussion to be had on land pressure. The global human population is expected to grow to 9–10 billion by 2050 and to become more affluent,

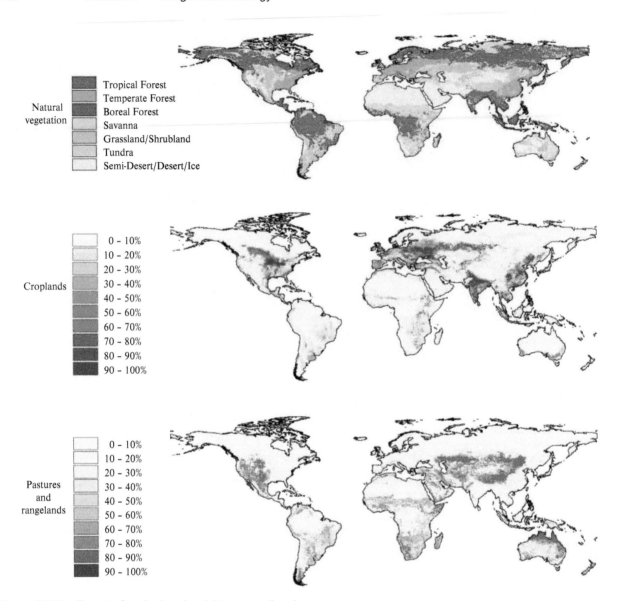

Figure 23.14   Extent of agricultural activity across the planet.

J. A. Foley et al. 2005. Global consequences of land use. *Science* 309:570–4, Figure 1. Reprinted with permission from AAAS.

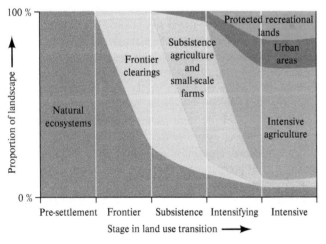

Figure 23.15   Changes in land use as societies develop.

J. A. Foley et al. 2005. Global consequences of land use. *Science* 309:570–4, Figure 2. Reprinted with permission from AAAS.

demanding an increase in agricultural products of 70–100% (Tilman et al. 2011), while biomass appropriation for bioenergy is projected to grow three- to six-fold by 2050 (Chum et al. 2012, Smith et al. 2014). There are competing demands for land for carbon sequestration to mitigate climate change, and for conservation. Competition for land as a resource may stimulate innovation and efficiency following economic theory. However, socio-economic and political context must be considered where there is a disparity of strength between competing actors or where socio-economic considerations compete with ecological considerations (Haberl 2015). Global changes in land use for agriculture and for other uses present some interesting moral questions: Do North American and European societies have the right to suggest that developing nations not develop their land, when these northern societies did exactly the same thing just a few centuries ago? Alternatively, do developed countries have a moral obligation to protect the world's biodiversity, as they may be the only countries that can afford to do so? Needless to say, there are no easy answers, even though the questions are of great importance.

In addition to direct impacts on vegetation cover (and thus habitat for animals and microbes), land-use changes have significant impact on global climate. For example, changes in the reflectance of land cover alter albedo (chapter 5) and, thus, temperatures. Burning large expanses of land to clear forest for agricultural or pastureland releases large reserves of CO_2 into the atmosphere. A major concern relating to land-use change is deforestation of tropical forests and the rate at which it is occurring. Tropical forests are home to high species diversity, including many of the most significant biodiversity hotspots (chapter 22), and loss of tropical forest has a disproportionate effect on global biodiversity.

Tropical Deforestation

Tropical forests support half or more of the earth's species. These forests occur in 73 countries and once covered 11,610,350 km². Three-fourths of the world's tropical forests occur in just 10 countries. The largest single tract of tropical forest, nearly one-third of the total, occurs in Brazil's Amazon Basin. In the late 1980s, Brazil was also understood to have the highest rates of deforestation of any nation; but in a poorly regulated industry where timber harvest occurred in remote locations, it was hard to know exactly how fast the Amazon Basin was losing its forest.

David Skole and Compton Tucker (1993) made use of a new tool, high-resolution photographs taken by *Landsat* satellites (fig. 23.16). They entered these images into another new tool, a geographic information system (see chapter 22). Using these tools, Skole and Tucker were able to estimate an annual loss of about 15,000 km² of tropical forest per year in the Amazon Basin between 1978 and 1988. They estimated that the total deforested area of the basin was 230,000 km² by 1988. Since then, expanded satellite coverage and more readily available data have allowed others to build upon the approach pioneered by Skole and Tucker. They have been able to address similar questions about deforestation, but now at a global scale.

A recent study by Matthew Hansen and colleagues used *Landsat* data with spatial resolution of 30 m to map global distributions of forests each year between 2000 and 2012 (Hansen et al. 2013). Net gain or loss of forest cover was quantified for each 0.05° × 0.05° grid and used to generate high-resolution digital maps (fig. 23.17) and to determine summary changes in various forest types and forest cover for individual countries.

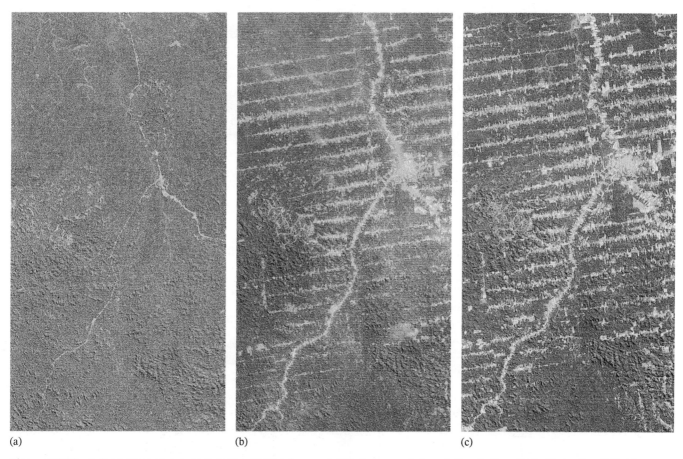

(a) (b) (c)

Figure 23.16 Information on tropical deforestation from satellite images: deforestation in Rondônia State, Brazil (light areas), in (*a*) 1975, (*b*) 1986, and (*c*) 1992.

(a), (b), (c): Landsat images courtesy of Eros Data Center/USGS.

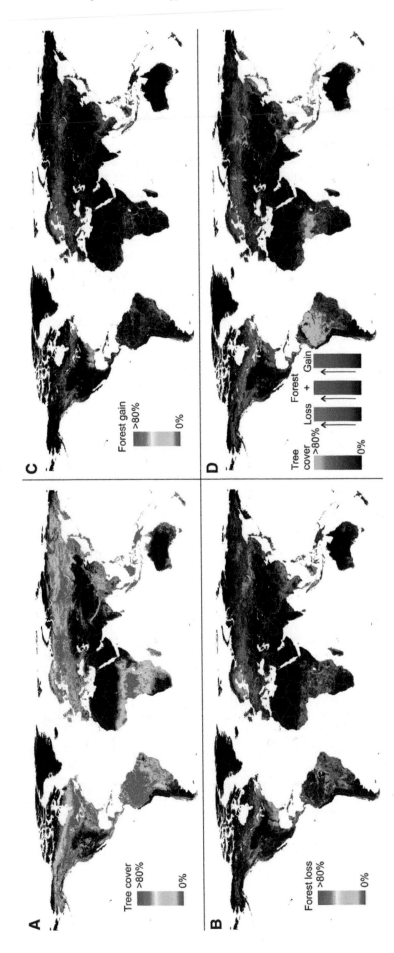

Figure 23.17 Global distributions of (*a*) tree cover, (*b*) forest loss, (c) forest gain, and (*d*) a composite of tree cover in green, forest loss in red, forest gain in blue, and forest loss and gain in magenta.

M. C. Hansen et al. 2013. High-resolution global maps of 21st century forest cover change. *Science* 342(6160):850–3, Figure 1. Reprinted with permission from AAAS.

Over this period of time, a global total 2.3 million km² of forest were lost, while 0.8 million km² were gained (net loss of 125,000 km² forest cover per year). Global net loss was dominated by deforestation in the tropics, with 858,000 km² lost over the study period, or 71,500 km² per year. Moreover, the rate of deforestation in the tropics increased over the study period by 2,101 km² per year.

What about Brazil? Deforestation in Brazil peaked in 2003–04 at 40,000 km² for the year. In 2004, the government introduced new policies to slow deforestation, and these have had some success. The rate of deforestation in Brazil decreased over the study period by 1,318 km² each year, and by 2011–12, the deforestation rate was down to 20,000 km² per year (this is still above Skole and Turner's estimate for the 1978–88 period). While this may sound like some good news, the slowdown in deforestation of the Amazon Basin is more than offset by increases elsewhere in the tropics. Indonesia, as one example, saw an increase in rates of deforestation by 1,021 km² per year. An important question is whether other countries will follow Brazil's path and make efforts to reduce deforestation rates. In 2011, Indonesia instituted a moratorium on new licensing of concessions in primary natural forests, and time will tell how effective that may be. Indonesia is an important player, as nearly half the increase in rates of tropical deforestation between 2000 and 2012 can be attributed to activities there. Interestingly, recent changes to the legal framework governing Brazil's forests may reverse that country's trend of decreasing deforestation rates. Gains realized by Indonesia's recent moratorium may be offset by a swing back to harvesting in Brazil.

Apart from loss of cover in tropical forests, there is also exploitation pressure on forests that may lead to partial or full conversion. This may run the gamut from extracting biomass without harvesting timber, to mixed use agroforestry systems, to wholesale replacement of natural vegetation with other tree species, such as oil palms. Forests represent a major biomass resource where NPP is nearly 50 Gt per year (Haberl 2015). The fraction of NPP that can be extracted is likely no more than 30% (Schulze et al. 2012); increasing extraction beyond this point would risk conversion to herbaceous vegetation and the release of carbon stored in soil and biota (Smith et al. 2014). Earlier, we discussed Soulé's assessment that conservation tactics such as agroforestry may be appropriate under socio-economic conditions with high population pressure and relatively stable economic and political regimes. This may involve planting crops interspersed with natural forest vegetation, maintaining much of the natural biological diversity. However, in large tracts of tropical forests, a more extreme form of agroforestry is common. The growth in global use of palm oil is a major driver in the conversion of natural tropical forests to oil palm plantations. This has been one of the principle causes of deforestation in Southeast Asia and, increasingly, in West Africa (Carrasco et al. 2014). Recent introduction of a new variety with increased yields could allow intensification, slowing the conversion of tropical forest and perhaps allowing reforestation;

or high-yield crops could lead to higher returns on investment for farmers and drive greater land conversion, threatening biodiversity of tropical forests. Time will tell.

How much land cover change is occurring outside the tropics? Though most people have focused on tropical deforestation, massive deforestation has occurred in temperate and boreal regions. As we saw in chapter 2, the temperate forest regions of Europe, eastern China, Japan, and North America support some of the densest human populations on earth. Large areas of Europe were deforested by the Middle Ages (Williams 1990), and much of the forest of eastern North America was cut by the middle 1800s. Moreover, the majority of old-growth temperate forests in northwestern North America have been cut (fig. 23.18), and the remaining old-growth forests are threatened by deforestation. In addition, vast areas of boreal forest are being cut in Russia and Canada. On net, nearly 400,000 km² of boreal forest, 112,000 km² of subtropical forest, and 117,000 km² of temperature forest were lost between 2000 and 2012 (Hansen et al. 2013). As you can see, deforestation is not limited to tropical regions.

Kates, Turner, and Clark (1990) estimated that human activity has transformed approximately half the ice-free land cover of the earth. In the process, many of the major terrestrial biomes of the earth (see chapter 2) have been highly fragmented. Others, such as tropical dry forest, have been nearly eliminated by conversion to agriculture. Because of the negative effect of reduced area on diversity (see chapter 22), these massive land conversions present a major threat to global diversity. However, land cover changes also have the potential to contribute, directly and indirectly, to other issues of concern, including the spread of invasive species.

Invasive Species

Throughout the text we have shown examples of how the introduction of a new species to a community can have

Figure 23.18   Deforestation in the forests of British Columbia.
Lynn A/Shutterstock.com.

dramatic consequences for community structure and nutrient cycling. Species introductions are happening across the planet at an ever-increasing pace, and, as Soulé suggests, these pose the most critical threat to ecological integrity and biodiversity of native communities, after only habitat loss. We begin with a definition of *biotic invaders* (fig. 23.19). According to Richard Mack and colleagues (Mack et al. 2000), these are defined as "species that establish a new range in which they proliferate, spread, and persist to the detriment of the environment" (p. 689). This generally accepted definition is critical because it differentiates invaders from alien or exotic species. The latter words describe species that historically were not found in a given location but, through some form of dispersal (human mediated or not), are now found in a novel area. For instance, in Canada there are about 4,200 species of vascular plants, and it is estimated that nearly one-third of these are exotic species. However, most exotic species are not invasive and instead represent a relatively small fraction of the biomass and drive only a small portion of the ecosystem function. What we are concerned about here are the few species able to establish, spread, and dominate an area: the biotic invaders.

Smallmouth and rock bass are two invaders of Canadian lakes. A collaboration between the Ontario Ministry of Natural Resources and researchers at McGill University has demonstrated how these fish cause significant changes to the trophic structure of the lakes they invade (Vander Zanden et al. 1999). These species are generally intentionally introduced to lakes well beyond their native range in an effort to increase fishing opportunities. By using stable isotopes to understand feeding relationships (chapter 19), the research team found that the introduced species caused a decline in the abundance of native prey-fish and caused the native lake trout to feed more on zooplankton. Such shifts in trophic structure are likely to have cascading effects on phytoplankton and nutrient cycles.

As in the example of sport-fish, humans often play an important role in transporting species from one location to another. This is not too surprising—humans are able to travel across the planet much more efficiently than the historical dispersal vectors of plants and animals. For some species, such as smallmouth bass, Pacific oysters, a variety of horticultural plants, and a diversity of bird species, the introductions are intentional. A person or governmental organization may, for example, decide to improve the use of land through new economic activities (e.g., fishing, oyster farms), or exercise aesthetic desires for non-native flora and fauna. It is estimated that 58% of Canada's exotic invasive plant species were intentionally introduced for agriculture, medicine, landscaping, and research. Many other introductions are unintentional, however, such as the zebra mussel and lamprey in the Great Lakes, a

(a)   (b)   (c)   (d)

Figure 23.19   Invasive species in Canada include (*a*) zebra mussels (*Dreissena polymorpha*), (*b*) sea lamprey (*Petromyzon marinus*), (*c*) Dutch elm disease (*Ophiostoma ulmi*), and (*d*) purple loosestrife (*Lythrum salicaria*).

(a) Randy Westbrooks, U.S. Geological Survey, Bugwood.org. (b) U.S. Fish and Wildlife Service Archive, U.S. Fish and Wildlife Service, Bugwood.org. (c) R. Scott Cameron, Advanced Forest Protection, Inc., Bugwood.org. (d) Randy Westbrooks, U.S. Geological Survey, Bugwood.org.

variety of insect pests, and numerous agricultural weeds. These species are often introduced when ships dump ballast water in foreign ports, as contaminants in food shipments, and through other forms of unintentional release. Regardless of the cause of introduction, species are quickly being introduced to novel locations across the world.

We have shown many of the ecological consequences of invasion throughout this book. David Pimentel and colleagues have conducted an assessment of some of the economic costs of invasive species within the United States, estimating the damages and loss due to these species to be nearly $120 billion ($US) per year (Pimentel et al. 2005). Although the data available for Canada are not as clear, Hugh MacIsaac and colleagues from the University of Windsor (chapter 22) suggest that costs associated with just 16 non-indigenous species can exceed $13 billion ($CAD) annually (Colautti et al. 2006). Why are these numbers so large? To begin with, there are a lot of alien species. Pimentel and colleagues report that there are an estimated 750,000 species in the United States; 50,000 of these are alien-invasive species. The economic costs associated with these species include attempted control programs as well as losses due to reduced agricultural production. For example, there are an estimated 25,000 alien species of plants alone in the United States. Of these, many are major weeds in crops, which Pimentel estimates cost $24 billion ($US) per year in reduced agricultural yield and an additional $3 billion ($US) per year in herbicides and other control programs. Another $14 billion and $21 billion ($US) per year are associated with introduced insect and microbial pests of crops, and $14 billion ($US) with introduced livestock diseases. In Canada, $320 million is spent each year just to protect one crop, canola, from one invasive species, Canada thistle.

The impact of invasive species on the functioning and biological integrity of natural areas is clear: the economic costs of these species are simply enormous. And due to continued movement by people, continued desires to improve native lands, and continued development, we are unlikely to see any reduction in these costs in the near future. It will be up to the current and next generations of ecologists to figure out how to reduce the negative effects of these species introductions and, perhaps, even how some of these species can be eliminated.

ECOLOGY IN ACTION

Being an Ecologist

> Unless someone like you cares a whole awful lot, Nothing is going to get better. It's not.
> — from *The Lorax* by Dr. Seuss

There are times when the challenges ahead seem daunting; and the world's problems, insurmountable. This section of the final chapter paints a bleak landscape, and I struggle to remain optimistic while I write it. I hope that you are able to while you read it. The bottom line is there are major challenges ahead, and not so very far. We need brilliant young people who are motivated to move the world in a better direction. We need ecologists who will bring understanding of living systems into the realm of decision making and public policy. We need ecologists to bring reason and evidence into public discourse. In short, we need you!

By now, you have been introduced to the work of ecologists, including a number of Canadian ecologists. Many of the examples we've provided come from work in university laboratories, but if you dig deep into some of the work we've cited, many of the examples, particularly recent examples, represent collaborations among universities, government agencies, NGOs, and industry. If you are asking yourself "Where do I practise ecology?" there are many directions you can take. The truth is that while we need the next generation of academic researchers, we also need some of you out there, directing change. So, I would like to use this final Ecology in Action to give you some ideas about how you might put "ecology in action."

One of the great joys in my professional life is working with talented students, undergraduate and graduate, to create new knowledge (fig. 23.20). To be involved in the creation and exchange of knowledge is a privilege, but academic researchers also have a social responsibility. The

Figure 23.20 Young ecologists in action.
Top centre photo courtesy of Mira Grkavac; all other photos courtesy of Andrew Laursen.

knowledge generated should be in the public interest, and much of our job is training the next generation of scientists to "move the ball forward." Sometimes we are exasperated, but more often we are energized by you, our students. You help keep us engaged and make the endeavour rewarding. I'll use this little platform as an opportunity to thank you all.

A professor is only one type of ecologist, one who combines research and teaching with service and public engagement. It is a great job, but there are many other rewarding careers in ecology.

A question I hear every year from students is this: What do ecologists do? The short answer is "everything." Similar to nearly all science degrees, engaged students with ecological training will have developed the capacity for analytical thought and the writing abilities that are valued by governments, NGOs, businesses, and industries. It is not always a satisfying answer, however, as it is not prescriptive. But think about how often you hear the word *ecosystem* used in fields other than ecology. Often the word is misapplied, but it reflects an incursion of ecology into those fields. It also reflects a recognized need to understand processes and patterns in those fields—in short, to apply some of the tools of ecology to non-ecological systems. However, many of you will want to be practising ecologists, not trained ecologists practising in another field. There are diverse career paths you might take. Some of the jobs described below can be stepped into right after convocation; others require more specialized training in graduate or professional schools.

Careers in Ecology

Government

All levels of government, from municipal to federal, hire substantial numbers of individuals with training in ecology. Why? There is abundant legislation on nearly all uses of land, sea, and air, and governments need help in updating the legislation, turning it into regulation, and monitoring activities. Governments not only regulate but have responsibility for stewardship of natural resources, including resources in the water, energy, forestry, and agricultural sectors. Governments also have responsibility for planning and in some cases for restoration. Additionally, governments own/run parks, and these need to be staffed and managed to achieve both recreational and conservation goals.

Governments employ many individuals to harvest and extract natural resources. Positions range from that of providing information to individual producers (e.g., range agrologist), to setting harvest quotas for fisheries and wild game, to those involved with developing policy, to those focused on monitoring environmental impacts. One specialized job is that of a wildlife forensic DNA specialist. In this position, individuals use techniques in molecular ecology to explore crimes involving wildlife (e.g., poaching, smuggling, etc.). Think *CSI* meets *The Nature of Things*.

Other jobs include the following:

Parks Scientist/Manager/Technician

Parks are bound by many regulations regarding the protection of wildlife and preservation of ecosystem integrity. Meeting these demands requires a diverse group of employees, from taxa-focused specialists through to ecosystem ecologists. Parks employees are also involved in mitigating human–wildlife conflict through trail and road design and through public awareness campaigns. Many are also hired to assist with weed/invasive species control, to implement fire/grazing as a conservation tool, to collect entrance fees, to assist/manage interpretive programs, and to assist with essentially any other task performed in a park.

Conservation Coordinator/Biodiversity Management

Many governments have specialized individuals who work directly with the public, offering guidance to individuals in terms of enhancing local conservation efforts. Duties may also include management of invasive species and/or recovery of species-at-risk.

Nongovernmental Organizations (NGOs)

There are many groups dedicated to specific issues related to the environment. These may be groups focused on the preservation and recovery of a single species or groups that focus on broader issues, such as climate change. NGOs may be political lobbying organizations, they may be focused on education, or they may be primarily action oriented (e.g., wildlife recovery). Such organizations are a common home to students of ecology, who often start out as interns or volunteers. (Someone needs to staff those fundraising campaigns!) A few examples of environmentally oriented NGOs include the Nature Conservancy; the Sierra Club; and many other local, national, or international organizations.

Outreach and Science Interpretation

Though most of us imagine that training in science leads to traditional careers as scientists, for many individuals their true passion lies in outreach and interpretation. The combination of skills that allows you to both understand scientific information and also have a sense of design, rhetoric, or strong writing is rare but critical to many careers. Examples include science writer and illustrator, editor/publisher, filmmaker and visual artist, tour guide/eco-adventure leader, and biological interpreter in parks and museums.

Education

A unique form of science interpretation is a career as a teacher in K–12 or post-secondary classrooms. In many parts of Canada, individuals who possess depth in scientific literacy combined with strong math skills are highly desired.

Personal experience in research, such as conducting an undergraduate project or assisting in a research lab, adds further depth of understanding that can be invaluable when helping the next generation of students develop to their full potential. Teaching science at the post-secondary level nearly always requires a Ph.D., or at least an M.Sc. Requirements for K–12 teaching vary among provinces.

Industry and Private Business

Companies associated with resource extraction and the harvest of natural products, housing and commercial development, and any number of other industries regularly hire ecology students to fill a diversity of positions. Many other students will find employment as consultants, either working for a firm or freelancing, with clients including government, industry, and NGOs. Combined, these industry-related positions are critical to conducting rare species surveys, making environmental impact assessments, developing plans to mitigate environmental risk, and implementing restoration and reclamation efforts.

Many science graduates develop their own businesses and, thus, create their own jobs. These may be related to their ecological training (e.g., integrated pest management) or their personal interests (e.g., beekeeper and honey maker), or may capture the benefits of sharp analytical thought (e.g., financial analyst).

Law, Medicine, Dentistry, Pharmacy, Architecture

Many undergraduates trained in ecology will move on to professional schools immediately following graduation. The idea that you must study biomedical health or be pre-med to pursue a medical degree is false. The idea that only undergraduate degrees in the humanities lead to law is also wrong. What professional schools are looking for are students who are highly capable, have applied themselves to difficult tasks, who write and speak well, and who demonstrate personal integrity and maturity. Though nontraditional paths to professional schools may require more work in terms of scheduling your classes to meet both degree and pre-req course requirements, it is often worth challenging untested assumptions about your future.

Researcher

Researchers find employment in industry, government, and academia. However, in all three cases, your level of responsibility is related (in part) to which degree you hold. In most organizations, only Ph.D.s will be given the flexibility to design and lead projects, while those with M.Sc. and B.Sc. degrees will (often) perform more of the technical work. Academia is a unique path, as it integrates teaching and research. The relative amount of time an individual spends teaching versus doing research varies highly among universities; though, not surprisingly, at research-intensive universities, the majority of a professor's time and effort will typically be devoted to research (and graduate teaching). An additional path for a researcher can be found in museums, both through curation of collections and interpretation of information. These may or may not be affiliated with universities, run by a nonprofit organization, or managed by government. The larger museums often serve not only as a location for science interpretation but also, through the work of researchers, as places of discovery.

Climate Change

Climate, as we have discussed many times, affects physiology of individuals, physical structure of the environment, biological diversity, and distribution of species. It affects interactions among species and ecosystem processes. Climate change, then, has vast implications for ecological function. It is the existential threat of our era, yet there are still climate change deniers. They walk among us. A common gambit among climate change deniers is to assert that natural cycles of climate change exist and that we cannot know that the current global warming is not simply a natural phenomenon. It has been an effective gambit for three reasons: (1) it provides alternate villains to explain climate change (the sun and the earth itself); (2) very few people, and very few politicians, will make the effort to unpack the argument; and (3) there are, in fact, natural patterns and variations in climate. In this section we will look at a few naturally occurring patterns that affect climate at global or regional scales. We will consider the temporal patterns at which they operate and where they fit into the current public conversation on climate change.

Several important recent studies have reconstructed climate on a geological time scale from Antarctic ice core data (fig 23.21) (Jouzel et al. 2007, Kawamura et al. 2007, Bereiter et al. 2015, Dome Fuji Project Members 2017, Brook and Buizert 2018). The ice that was cored accumulated over hundreds of thousands of years, capturing signatures of past climate. Scientists have been able to reconstruct climate over the past 800,000 years using the evidence in these cores. One important signature is that of ^{18}O in ice. Oxygen-18 is a stable isotope, much less abundant than another stable isotope, ^{16}O. Water containing the lighter isotope evaporates more readily. This discriminates against ^{18}O, and snowfall (which eventually becomes ice) will be isotopically lighter than the ocean. However, when climate is warmer, and the sea has more thermal energy, the discrimination is less. The snow that falls, and eventually becomes ice, will have a relatively higher abundance of ^{18}O during periods of higher global temperatures. The $\delta^{18}O$ in ice can then be used to reconstruct past global sea temperatures. Climate has varied greatly over the past 800,000 years. There have been several long periods of glaciation (ice ages), punctuated with brief interglacial periods, recurring about every 100,000 years. Figure 23.21, bottom panel,

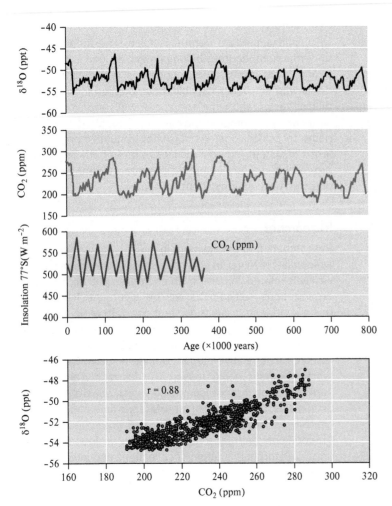

Figure 23.21 Paleoclimate data from Antarctic ice cores, top panel, $\delta^{18}O$ values from the Dome Fuji ice core ($^{18}O/^{16}O$ isotopic ratio of water) (Dome Fuji Project Members 2017); second panel, CO_2 concentration trapped in ice (EPICA Dome C/Vostok ice core) (Bereiter et al. 2015); third panel, summer solstice insolation at 77°S (Dome Fuji ice core data) (Kawamura et al. 2007); bottom panel, correlation between atmospheric CO_2 and $\delta^{18}O$ over 800,000 year record.

shows a strong relationship between between atmospheric CO_2 concentrations and global temperature extending back 800,000 years, through nine glacial-interglacial cycles.

Insolation is a measure of the amount of solar radiation reaching a surface. A number of radioisotopes are created by high-energy cosmic rays. The relative abundance of these different isotopes varies as a function of their different half-lives and the intensity of cosmic rays. The upshot is that these cosmogenic isotopes can be captured in ice as it forms and used to reconstruct patterns of insolation (fig. 23.22). Insolation has also varied greatly over time, although the periodicity between peaks in insolation (~25,000 years) is shorter than the periodicity of interglacials. Although you cannot see it in figure 23.22, a much smaller-scale variation in insolation also occurs but on a decadal scale (about 11 years peak to peak).

Okay, that may (or may not) be interesting to you, but so what? Let's pause for a couple of reflections. First, global climate

change is tightly coupled with global concentrations of CO_2, as demonstrated in the geological record for at least 800,000 years. Second, although correlation is not causation, we do understand the infrared absorption characteristics of CO_2, and we know that it acts as a greenhouse gas; a reasonable inference is that CO_2 drives temperature changes rather than the other way around (although rising temperatures could initiate positive feedback and release of stored carbon, as discussed in Chapter 22). Third, peaks in insolation do not invariably trigger interglacial periods of higher temperatures, although the initiation of at least the last four interglacial periods did coincide with peaks in insolation. While CO_2 accumulation appears to drive climate change, peaks in insolation are probably an important trigger in tipping global climate from ice age to interglacial.

Moving from geological time scales to historic time scales, let's ask what the evidence is for climate change. Climate change can be measured by looking at anomalies in global average temperature. An anomaly is the difference between the global average temperature in a given year and the global average temperature over a baseline period. Figure 23.22 shows temperature anomalies, using a baseline of 1901–2000. Measured against this 100-year climate baseline, there is a clear pattern of increasing temperature, decade over decade. In other words, no matter how much one might wish, or what someone with an agenda may say, climate is changing.

So, does the fact that climate is changing mean that humans are the cause of this change? We've previously discussed the rapid accumulation of CO_2 in the atmosphere over the past 200 years; CO_2 has increased by ~130 ppm since 1860. Current CO_2 concentrations exceed 410 ppm, ~25% higher than during any interglacial period in the past 800,000 years. And, we know that global temperature and atmospheric CO_2 are closely linked throughout an 800,000-year geological record. There is compelling evidence (the Suess effect) that the recent increase in CO_2 is driven by burning fossil fuels. The rise in CO_2 corresponds closely with the change in climate revealed by global temperature anomalies (fig 23.22). In other words, temperature and CO_2 are also closely linked on a historical time scale, just as they are on a geological time scale.

We are currently in an interglacial period, part of a natural cycle when CO_2 concentrations are naturally high. Could that explain the current pattern of climate change? The sharp, rapid rise in CO_2 that kicked off this interglacial started about 14,000 years ago. For the past 1,000 years, CO_2 has held steady at 270–280 ppm. It is really hard to argue that the current change is part of this natural cycle. The recent jump to > 410 ppm is exacerbating already high interglacial global temperatures; the natural increase in temperature characterizing the interglacial is not driving the recent jump in CO_2. What about natural cycles in insolation? Remember that insolation varies on two time scales: larger magnitude changes over a 25,000-year cycle and small magnitude changes over a decadal time scale. For the longer cycle, peak insolation is well in the rear view, by about

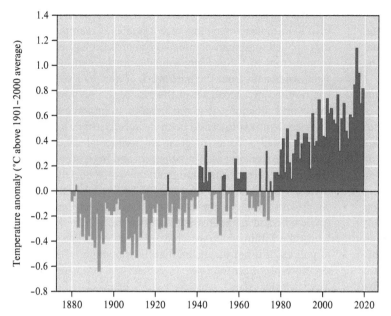

Figure 23.22 Land surface temperature anomalies, 1880–2018. Global mean average temperature from 1901–2000 is baseline; anomaly calculated as average annual global temperature minus baseline temperature.

10,000 years. We are actually much nearer the trough in this cycle, so this long cycle is not driving recent climate change. What about variation in the decadal cycle? First, global temperature has become progressively warmer decade by decade for over a century. It has not oscillated on a decadal scale that would correspond to this insolation cycle. Second, the magnitude of change in insolation on this short cycle is very small. The potential radiative forcing associated with this change is tiny compared with the potential radiative forcing associated with greenhouse gases. Recent climate change is not explained by higher solar radiation as part of a natural cycle.

The Intergovernmental Panel on Climate Change (IPCC) is the United Nations body for assessing the science of climate change. The IPCC brings together hundreds of experts in climate and other physical sciences from 195 countries. In its *Fifth Assessment Report* (IPCC 2014), the IPCC stated that warming of the global climate was unequivocal, with many of the changes unprecedented over decades to millennia. It further stated that "Human influence on the climate system is clear . . ." (p. 2). The IPCC is also clear that a projected increase of 1.5–2.0°C will place vulnerable ecosystems, such as tundra and coral reef systems, at high risk (IPCC 2018). For context, the Paris Agreement on Climate Change seeks to constrain warming to below 2.0°C. When you hear the tired idea that there is disagreement within the scientific community on the reality of climate change, remember two things: (1) The IPCC reports reflect the strong consensus of hundreds of leading researchers in the science of climate change. Consensus is that climate change is unequivocal, and that human influence is clear. There remains a very small number of scientists skeptical of the link to human activities, but it is certainly not a divided community, as often characterized. (2) Disagreement

largely lies in uncertainty: How much further change in climate are we likely to see? How is climate likely to change within regions? How much of the climate forcing is attributable to humans? The disagreement is not over whether climate is changing.

Hydrofracking and Air Pollution

Pollution is another major threat to biological diversity, particularly in nations with heavy industry. Covering the gamut of pollution would be a book in itself, so here we will provide a look at a couple different forms of pollution that are widespread, both in Canada and globally.

Hydraulic fracturing or "fracking" is injecting fluids under very high pressure to crack subsurface rock layers. This practice is common in extracting natural gas, which may be trapped in porous rock. The fracking fluid is mostly water but includes sand or other materials that help keep cracks open for better flow of gas. This is certainly not a new technology and has been practised in Canada since the 1950s. However, a boom in natural gas exploration has increased its use and brought it more into the public's awareness.

Natural gas generally burns cleaner and has a lower CO_2 footprint (per unit energy generated) than many other fossil fuels. However, extraction by fracking uses a lot of water. Between 2005 and 2014, extraction of shale gas by fracking used more than 700 billion litres of water, while extraction of oil by fracking used another 230 billion litres (Kondash and Vengosh 2015). This usage can stress limited water supplies. Moreover, some of the fluid pumped into rock layers at high pressure will inevitably flow back out of injection wells or follow fractures to groundwater, carrying with it oil and gas residues and other chemical additives of the fracking fluid. Containment, treatment, and disposal of this water are ongoing challenges for the industry.

Fracking has also been linked to increased seismic activity. A recent study by Amir Mansour Farahbod and colleagues delineated the spatial–temporal relationship between seismic activity and fracking operations in the Horn River Basin of northeast British Columbia between 2006 and 2011 (Farahbod et al. 2015). The number of tremors or earthquakes increased more than five-fold from 2002–2003, prior to fracking operations, to 2011 during the peak of operations. Further, the magnitude of the seismic events increased with the scale of the operation. However, the propensity toward seismic activities depends on local conditions. The majority of earthquakes thought to be triggered by fracking occurred along an area of high tectonic strain, a band to the east of the Canadian Rocky Mountains, near the Alberta–British Columbia border (Kao et al. 2018).

Fracking represents but one activity that contributes to groundwater pollution, but it is a widespread activity. Many other human activities contribute to air pollution. Generally, when we talk about air pollution, we are talking about particles and gases that enter the air from activities such as fossil fuel combustion (in vehicles or energy generation), burning of wood, construction, and agriculture. You may be familiar with the air quality index, or at least have heard of it. The index rates air quality according to ground level ozone, particulate matter and size distribution, and quantities of carbon monoxide and sulfur and nitrogen oxides.

A World Health Organization study in 2016 used satellite data to complement traditional ground-level measurements of air quality for ~3,000 locations globally. The study concluded that about 92% of people throughout the world live with high levels of air pollution, levels sufficient to cause or contribute to respiratory and cardiac disease. Air quality was poorest in southeast Asia and the western Pacific and in the eastern Mediterranean. Areas of Canada also suffer poor air quality. An International Institute for Sustainable Development study reported 7,700 deaths in Canada during 2015 attributed to air pollution. The study places the cost of air pollution at $36 billion for the same year. In Canada, as elsewhere, much of the air quality problem is caused by incomplete combustion of fossil fuels. The move to cleaner sources of energy, including the decommissioning of coal-fired power plants, has the potential to reduce particulate in the air and improve air quality.

CONCEPT 23.2 REVIEW

1. Why do patterns of human appropriation of ocean and terrestrial productivity differ spatially?

2. Why is reducing land cover through deforestation or agriculture a threat to biodiversity?

3. How do some alien species affect biodiversity of the communities they invade? What ecological interactions determine whether an alien species may be become invasive?

4. In what ways do human activities parallel the effects of natural geological processes and climate patterns on biodiversity?

23.3 Ecologically Informed Decision Making

Ecological information can be integrated with economic data to help meet conservation goals in a political landscape. There was a time when ecological research was focused nearly exclusively on wild areas; where researchers avoided field sites and study locations obviously impacted by humans. There were, of course, exceptions, such as Schindler's classic work on lake eutrophication due to phosphorus pollution (chapter 1). However, if you were transported back to even the 1970s, and you were to thumb through copies of *Ecology* or *The American Naturalist,* you would not have gained much appreciation for the extent of human impacts on the earth. You may have noticed that even within this book, where we reference foundational papers in ecological theory, the studies were in

relatively pristine systems. Times have changed, and we have tried to introduce some more recent studies as examples of ecology applied to human-dominated systems. Ecologists of today benefit from two things not available to the early ecologists. First, we benefit from the hard work of our predecessors that has resulted in a broad set of theories regarding how the natural world functions. It is much easier to improve ideas and theories than it is to create them *de novo*. Second, for the last several decades, issues of great environmental concern have been in the front pages of newspapers and have been lead stories on news broadcasts throughout the world. Society has said there are problems, and they need to be fixed. In this section, we present several examples of how ecologists have moved out of the wild and are addressing issues on the human-dominated landscape within which we all live. As this landscape is one full of politics, it is not surprising that the economics of ecological decisions play a central role.

Costs of Conservation

Globally, there is recognition that the protection of biological diversity is important, as evidenced by national laws (e.g., species-at-risk legislation) and international agreements (e.g., Convention of Biological Diversity). However, recovery programs for species that are threatened or endangered are not cheap, and it is typically difficult to convince the public to sign a blank cheque for such efforts. What are needed are robust cost estimates, and these can emerge when ecologists, economists, and political scientists work together.

Donal McCarthy and colleagues led a large international team in developing cost estimates for reducing the extinction risk for 211 of the 1,115 globally threatened bird species (McCarthy et al. 2012). In their economic model, they set the conservation goal of preventing species extinction as equivalent to downlisting a species one step in the International Union for Conservation of Nature (IUCN) listing categories (chapter 10). Birds were chosen in part because of the high quality of data available, allowing for more confidence in the resulting analyses. As you might imagine, measuring the costs of conservation—and the extinction risk—for a single species is difficult; doing so for over 200 species is impossible for a single person. Thus, the authors enlisted the help of experts. For each species, they contacted experts familiar with its ecology and recovery costs, and asked them to estimate both the current amount spent on conservation for that species as well as the total costs expected to successfully downlist the species within 10 years. They then combined this information with data related to the habitat needs of each species, the GDP of the nation or nations that contain the breeding range, and other factors. So, what is the bill?

Based upon 2012 dollar values, the estimated recovery costs ranged from $40,000 to $8.96 million per species (median = $848,000). After validating these estimates based upon the true costs of successful recovery of 25 species, they extrapolated their results to project the cost of recovering all 1,115 bird species. In total, McCarthy et al. (2012) estimate a price tag of $1.23 billion for each of the next 10 years. Interestingly, the price decreases as the degree of risk increases; they suggest that this is due to the most endangered species having the smallest distributions (thus land purchase costs are reduced). Recognizing that the ranges for some species overlap, such that land purchases may benefit multiple species, a more realistic estimate is a total cost of $880 million per year. Whether this is viewed as a very large cost or not is likely highly dependent upon one's country of origin.

Not surprisingly, the distribution of red-listed bird species is not uniform across the world; instead, most are concentrated near the equator (fig. 23.23a). Consequently, most of the costs associated with species recovery will be in countries considered low or lower middle income (McCarthy et al. 2012; fig. 23.23b). As these countries are poorly suited to pay for such conservation activities, large-scale political solutions will be needed. Making matters even more complicated is the recognition that birds are only one of many taxonomic groups that contain red-listed species. When McCarthy and colleagues (2012) extrapolate their costs to other species, they conservatively estimate global costs of $3.41 billion per year to downlist all listed species within 10 years. If the goal is moved away from simply delisting species to a broader goal of protecting areas of global biodiversity significance to reduce future listings (e.g., high diversity, endemic species, etc.), the costs rise to over $76 billion annually (McCarthy et al. 2012). For all countries, this is a large number.

Integrating Ecosystem Services into Decision Making

Clearly, conservation actions have real costs, and for many governments these cannot be incurred without assistance. However, equally important to knowing the costs of action are science-driven estimates of the costs of inaction. Throughout the book, we have discussed ecological services (chapter 16), such as nutrient cycling, water filtration, and biomass production. These services have economic value, and, as ecosystems deteriorate, their value also declines. Thus, conservation costs can result in economic gains and may be seen as an investment in natural capital. However, the framework for how to incorporate the value of natural capital into economic decisions has generally been lacking. Gretchen Daily and colleagues have developed a framework in which ecology and economics can be more formally integrated into decision-making processes (Daily et al. 2009), such as a more formal tool called InVEST (Integrated Valuation of Ecosystem Services and Tradeoffs) (http://www.naturalcapitalproject .org/). A key feature is that a number of costs and benefits of a given scenario (e.g., population growth, development) are explicitly discussed. This requires participants to understand tradeoffs rather than to focus solely on a single output (e.g., economic return on investment). The InVEST model is currently being applied to the future planning of the marine environment of the west coast of Vancouver Island (Guerry et al. 2012).

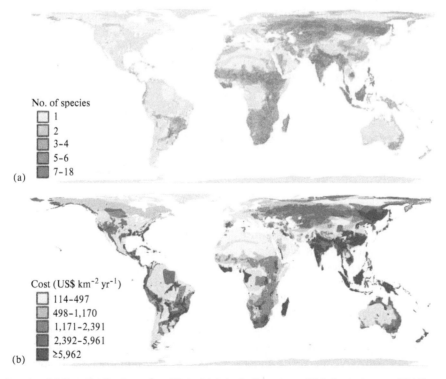

No. of species
- [ ] 1
- [ ] 2
- [ ] 3–4
- [ ] 5–6
- [ ] 7–18

(a)

Cost (US$ km⁻² yr⁻¹)
- [ ] 114–497
- [ ] 498–1,170
- [ ] 1,171–2,391
- [ ] 2,392–5,961
- [ ] ≥5,962

(b)

Figure 23.23   Maps showing (a) the distribution of red-listed (globally threatened) bird species, and (b) the estimated conservation costs of those species.

From D. P. McCarthy et al. 2012. Financial costs of meeting global biodiversity conservation targets: Current spending and unmet needs. *Science* 338:946. Reprinted with permission from AAAS.

The west coast of Vancouver Island is a base for commercial activities (fisheries, logging, etc.), a tourist destination, and a source of renewable energy, and it is also the object of deep beliefs among First Nations peoples and others regarding the natural landscape (Guerry et al. 2012). Consequently, any changes to the system, whether to increase conservation or to increase development, impact many stakeholders. Guerry and her team modified the InVEST model to address the specific issues relevant to this system; the outputs of the model are spatially explicit and relevant to stakeholders. For example, in a focal study of Lemmens Inlet, the research team was able to map the impacts of no policy change (= baseline), increased conservation, and industrial expansion on the quality of a number of factors. For more general discussions, these results can be visualized in a way that highlights tradeoffs. It is hoped that these more synthetic planning exercises will help governments better understand not simply the costs of conservation but also the value of protecting existing natural capital.

Using Ecological Understanding to Reduce Costs

As critical as it will be to show costs and benefits to conservation, it is also critical to use the dollars spent on conservation goals as efficiently as possible. Or, to use economic terms, there is a need to maximize the return on investment (ROI) on conservation efforts. In an ambitious study, John Withey and colleagues used an ROI approach to identify areas of priority for land conservation—over the entire 48 lower states in the U.S. mainland (Withey et al. 2013). Again, this was done through collaborations among ecological and social scientists and recognized existing political boundaries.

Within the United States, as in Canada, many land-use decisions are made at the county, rather than the state (or provincial), level. Consequently, that was the unit of measure used by Withey

and his colleagues. For nearly all of the 3,109 counties in the lower 48 states, the researchers collected several critical pieces of data.

Biodiversity

Though ideally this would be a measure of all species found within each county, such data do not exist. The authors chose to focus exclusively on the number of vertebrate species, as these are both a manageable (low) number and of relatively high data quality.

Risk and Gain

For each species, they calculated the percentage of its range that was currently under protection from development; those with high values would likely receive little value from increased land protection. For each county, they also estimated the threat of development both through the percent of area that exists as anthropogenic land cover (e.g., roads, cities, etc.), as well as the rate of change from natural to anthropogenic cover.

Costs

Using a number of economic assumptions and models, the authors estimated the cost of acquiring land for protection in each county. This estimate took into consideration the current land use and cover type (e.g., forest, grassland, cropland) as well as land values.

By combining these data into an ROI model, Withey et al. (2013) were able to show areas in which conservation efforts would be most, or least, effective. Conservation gain per dollar spent is highly variable, though typically highest in the central United States. Not surprisingly, general ROI is lowest on the coasts, where land prices tend to be very high. Tools such as those presented here are opening a new era for applying ecological knowledge to conservation. As we see next, this is not the only change happening in how ecologists conduct and use their research.

ECOLOGICAL TOOLS AND APPROACHES

Cooperative Research Networks and Distributed Ecology

How do you know if the ecological changes you observe are due to local processes or are instead part of a widespread phenomenon? For an individual researcher, it is not practical to set up experiments and studies throughout a single province, across a country, or around the world. Instead, the limited resources of time and money restrict most studies to a relatively small spatial scale over a very narrow window of time. As should be clear from this chapter, such approaches are not likely to allow scientists to observe—let alone understand—change. To overcome such limitations, researchers often form networks, casual or formal, working together to address specific issues in ecology. As global questions

become more pressing, and as scientists increasingly recognize the limitations of the traditional silo approach to ecological inquiry, the culture in which many ecologists conduct research is changing.

To effectively address the complex problems, scientists must appreciate a variety of scientific disciplines and be capable of working effectively within multidisciplinary teams. Such teams can conduct studies at spatial and temporal scales impossible for an individual researcher. As these networks develop, there have emerged two main approaches: (1) broad monitoring, and (2) coordinated distributed experiments (e.g., Fraser et al. 2013).

Broad Monitoring

A key to understanding whether patterns are regional or global in extent is to have a standardized monitoring program spread over a large geographical area. Some networks may be very focused in which data they collect, while others are quite broad. For example, FLUXNET is a network of towers established in a diversity of habitat types that measure micrometeorology, such as CO_2 concentrations. The goals of these measures include to provide a comprehensive understanding of the relationship between climate and ecosystem productivity and to understand long-term changes in microenvironment, including greenhouse gases. Towers are established in over 200 locations in 45 countries, including 22 sites in Canada. Hank Margolis of the Université Laval oversees the FLUXNET-Canada network, and has summarized some of the findings that are beginning to emerge (Margolis et al. 2006), including the following: (1) the forests of Canada are becoming a reduced carbon sink due to increased disturbances, such as insect outbreaks and fire; (2) changes in precipitation and evapotranspiration associated with climate change will have strong effects on the carbon balance of forests and peatlands throughout Canada; and (3) recent studies indicate that root production and soil respiration play a significant role in total ecosystem carbon fluxes, and thus more study is needed below ground.

The United States has long been a leader in large-scale ecological modelling. For the last several decades, the U.S. Long-Term Ecological Research (LTER) network has fostered cooperative, interdisciplinary research over large geographic areas. These sites include tropical forests, arctic tundra, temperate forests, grasslands, coastal ecosystems, deserts, and two cities. They extend from sea level to elevations over 4,000 m and from the Arctic to the Antarctic. The first International Long-Term Ecological Research (ILTER) workshop was held in 1993 (Nottrott et al. 1994). Scientists from around the world met to establish active interactions and collaboration between the LTER network and long-term ecological research programs from around the globe. Today, ILTER coordinates the efforts of 38 independent networks found in over 30 countries (including Canada) on five continents (fig. 23.24).

More recently, the United States has created NEON, the National Ecological Observatory Network. The goal of NEON is to understand continental-scale ecology, an unprecedented and ambitious project. To move toward this goal, NEON has divided the United States into 20 eco-climatic domains based upon the types of eco-climatic variables discussed throughout this book. Within each domain they have established one core site. In some domains they also have a paired aquatic site and additional sites focused on human impacts. In total, there are currently 106 sites within NEON. The intent is to have coordinated and detailed measures of the biotic and abiotic components of the United States for decades; what questions and solutions will emerge are not known, but they are likely to be significant.

Compared to the United States, Canada remains slow to recognize the need for ongoing federal support for long-term international research networks. Consequently, networks in Canada are typically focused on marshalling efforts of many individuals toward common goals rather than designating formal locations across Canada as priorities for in-depth research. Nonetheless, such networks can be extremely productive. For example, ArcticNet (http://www.arcticnet.ulaval.ca/) involves over 140 researchers throughout

Figure 23.24 The International Long-Term Ecological Research Network includes member networks located in over 30 countries.

Imagery © 2014 NASA, Terrametrics.

Canada and other Northern countries with a primary focus on climate change impacts. Critical to ArcticNet's mission is the involvement of local communities and cultures, along with social scientists, to help individuals understand and mitigate change.

Distributed Ecology

From observations will come hypotheses and models of ecological function. However, a critical aspect of scientific understanding is challenging hypotheses with data, and few tools are more powerful than the artfully designed experiment. However, individual ecological experiments suffer from the same limitation found within individual observations: an inability to know whether the measured response is general or idiosyncratic. A common approach for seeking synthesis is to combine the results of independent experiments in a meta-analysis. We present the results of many such efforts throughout the book. However, meta-analyses have substantial flaws and limitations of scale, potential bias, and sometimes a misunderstanding of the underlying natural history being studied (Whittaker 2010, Hillebrand and Cardinale 2010). However, more often than not, they are the best means available to try to draw a synthetic answer to a specific hypothesis.

Lauch Fraser from Thomson Rivers University and a number of colleagues have drawn attention to an alternative approach: coordinated distributed experiments (Fraser et al. 2013). The name is drawn from computing science, where complex problems can be solved by distributing the work among many individual computers. In this model, the costs to the individual (e.g., computer) are small, relative to the value of the solution to the computing problem. Fraser and colleagues suggest that such a model may be well suited to ecological research, where there is a need for replication over a large geographic scale, although individual budgets are typically tight. Two of the most successful examples of distributed ecological experiments involve substantial involvement by Canadian researchers: ITEX (International Tundra Experiment) and NutNet (Nutrient Network), focused on ecosystem responses to warming in the tundra (Henry and Molau 1997) and fertilization effects on biodiversity (Adler et al. 2011). Fraser suggests that what made these such strong efforts, and what is required in general for distributed ecological experiments to be successful, are a few key criteria. These include a clear hypothesis, standardized and inexpensive design, broad geographic replication, and clear rules for data sharing among team members. Many of these requirements swim against the current of academic independence. However, like the oceans, scientific tides change, and a growing number of ecologists are recognizing the scientific value of collaboration.

CONCEPT 23.3 REVIEW

1. Withey and colleagues assessed ROI for conservation and created a map (not shown in the text) describing which counties in the United States would show the greater return on conservation investment. What types of data are needed to generate such tools of conservation?

2. Why is it important to incorporate aspects of the natural environment into decision-making tools related to development?

3. In this section, nearly all papers were published by large research teams, as opposed to the work of a lonely genius. What aspects of the application of ecological knowledge require such collaborations?

SUMMARY

This chapter focuses on global-scale processes and phenomena, including the movement of tectonic plates, large-scale weather systems, and global change induced by humans. We also discuss novel approaches to conservation, integration, and ecological and economic information.

23.1 The evolutionary history and distribution of species (past and present) are rooted in global-scale climate patterns and changes in the earth's land masses over a long geological time scale.

The surface of the earth consists of numerous tectonic plates whose movement has changed the distribution of the planet's land and water. Through geographic isolation and through effects of plate tectonics on global climate, this geologic movement has influenced the distribution of species, including temperate tree species (fig. 23.25).

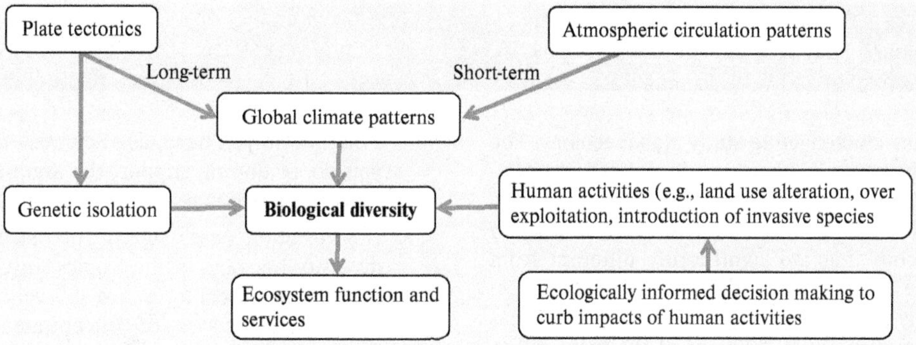

Figure 23.25 Concept map for chapter 23.

Over deep time, there have been substantial changes in the number and types of species found on the planet. Some estimates suggest that only 1% of all species that have ever existed are currently extant. There have been at least five mass extinction events over the last 500 million years, in which at least 75% of species present at the start of the event were extinct by the end of the event. The causes are varied and include climate change, tectonic activity, and chemical changes in the atmosphere. Current evidence suggests human activity is moving us into the sixth such extinction event. Although only a small percentage of species have gone extinct in the last 500 years, the large percentage of species that are currently at risk or threatened suggests that we may be on the point of a sixth mass extinction event.

In addition to changes on the earth's surface, the earth's atmosphere is very dynamic. The El Niño Southern Oscillation is a large-scale weather system that involves variation in sea surface temperature and barometric pressure across the Pacific and Indian Oceans. The mature phase of an El Niño brings increased precipitation to much of North America and parts of South America and drought to the western Pacific. La Niña brings drought to much of North America and South America and higher-than-average precipitation to the western Pacific. The North Atlantic Oscillation (NAO) influences the weather across more northern latitudes. In the positive phase there are cooler temperatures in eastern Canada, less precipitation in the Canadian Arctic, and wetter, warmer weather in northern Europe. The variation in weather caused by these oscillations has dramatic effects on marine and terrestrial populations around the world, shaping biological diversity (fig. 23.25).

23.2 Human activities have generated substantial threats to biological diversity.

Human activities, mainly agriculture and urbanization, have significantly altered one-third to one-half of the ice-free land surface of the earth. A striking example of these pressures is the appropriation of 24% of the terrestrial NPP by people. In the ocean, substantial amounts of primary productivity are used to support the world's fisheries. The conversion of land for agriculture is associated with applications of fertilizer and irrigation. These activities have placed significant pressures on aquatic systems. A widely cited example of land cover change is tropical deforestation. From 1978 to 1988, the rate of deforestation in the Amazon Basin of Brazil averaged about 15,000 km^2 per year. By 1988, the total area deforested within the Amazon Basin was 230,000 km^2. Rates of deforestation throughout the tropics continue to increase. Massive deforestation has also occurred outside the tropics. Because of the negative effect of reduced habitat area on diversity, these massive land conversions present a major threat to global biological diversity (fig. 23.25). An associated cost of human activities is the global spread of invasive species. Combined, these species are posing substantial harm to natural systems and result in massive economic costs to people. Human activities are unequivocally contributing to climate change that cannot be explained by natural cycles in insolation or CO_2. Pollution of water and air contribute to degradation of the environment, with negative effects on biological diversity and on public health.

23.3 Ecological information can be integrated with economic data to help meet conservation goals in a political landscape.

Ecology is no longer a new science, nor are many of its results of purely theoretical value. Increasingly, the science of ecology is being used to address the issue of conservation biology. This requires collaboration among scientists, economists, government, and other stakeholders. The costs of conservation are very high; however, the protection of natural capital is also of economic value. New frameworks have been developed that allow for more holistic conversations at the time of development planning, which incorporate economic and ecological costs and benefits. Ecologists are increasingly using the tools of economics to increase the ROI of conservation, allowing managers to prioritize land purchases. This represents a new phase to conservation, one where ecological issues are not viewed independently from societal values.

Cooperative research networks aid global ecology. Rapid climate change poses a substantial challenge to the scientific community. Studying ecology at a global scale requires that scientists develop new tools and approaches. New devices, often employing the most recent technological developments, are becoming more and more common in ecologists' tool kits. However, some of the most important developments required for global-scale research may involve changes in the culture of science. The complexity and large scale of global change requires that scientists work in multidisciplinary, national, and international teams. International networks of scientists now work on global-scale ecological problems in a research environment that emphasizes information sharing and a team approach to research.

REVIEW QUESTIONS

1. Ecologists are now challenged to study global ecology. The role played by humans in changing the global environment makes it imperative that we understand the workings of the earth as a global system. However, this study requires approaches that are significantly different from those that can be applied to traditional areas of ecological study. Historically, much of ecology focused on small areas and short-term studies. What are some of the main differences between global ecology and, for instance, the study of interspecific competition (see chapter 13) or forest succession (see chapter 18)? How will these differences affect the design of studies at the global scale?

2. Geologists, atmospheric scientists, and oceanographers have been conducting global-scale studies for some time. What role will information from these disciplines play in the study of global ecology? Why will global ecological studies generally be pursued by interdisciplinary teams? How can ecologists play a useful role in global studies?

3. What changes in sea surface temperatures and atmospheric pressures over the Pacific Ocean accompany El Niño? What physical changes accompany La Niña? How do El Niño and La Niña affect precipitation in North America, South America, and Australia?

4. Large-scale climatic processes, such as the North Atlantic Oscillation (NAO), are not amenable to experimental research. How would you design a study to determine whether the NAO impacts natural populations of plants and animals in different regions of Canada?

5. Our perception of the "normal" distributions of continents is strongly coloured by our living at only one small point in geological time. Why is it important that anyone interested in understanding the distribution of species also understand the past movement of tectonic plates?

6. There have been at least five mass extinction events, and we may be in a sixth. However, though current trends support this view, this sixth event has not yet happened. What evidence do you need, as a scientist, to determine whether you do, or do not, support the argument that humans are creating a sixth mass extinction event?

7. Deforestation poses significant risk to a number of biodiversity hotspots in the tropics. In Canada, deforestation rates of the boreal forest are also very high; however, there are few specific areas of concentrated biodiversity in these high-latitude forests. Does this mean that rates of deforestation are not of ecological concern in the boreal? How do you balance the need for economic development with a desire to preserve large areas of undisturbed forest?

8. Invasive species have been discussed throughout the text, in many different contexts. They are widely viewed as one of the greatest threats to biodiversity. Their spread is greatly facilitated by the increased pressures humans are putting on the planet. Why?

9. Humans have appropriated a large proportion of the terrestrial and marine NPP for our own use. Even then, fisheries more often collapse than remain stable. As the earth's population is projected to continue growing in the future, these pressures will likely increase. How can we determine at what point human appropriation of NPP is too high to allow for the delivery of critical ecological services?

10. The conservation costs of even a small group of taxa (birds) is extremely high. When we include other major taxonomic groups, it is likely enormous. How can ecologists use an ROI approach to optimize the protection of multiple types of species?

11. How does the geological record of CO_2 in ice cores support the tenet that climate change is driven by human activities? What data support the notion that recent increases in CO_2 have a human fingerprint and are not a natural phenomenon associated with the current interglacial? Assess the argument that the current pattern of climate change might be driven by natural variation in insolation. Is it a possible explanation?

Building a Statistical Toolbox

In chapter 1 we presented an overview of the scientific method, highlighting its importance to ecologists. A central component of the scientific method is the continual testing of theory and ideas with data. Throughout this text we have provided a broad overview of the types of data needed to answer questions at a variety of temporal and spatial scales. However, due to the complexity of nature, ecological data are often "messy," and in their raw form hard to interpret. Because of the importance of objective data in the scientific method, many statistical approaches have been developed to help discern patterns from seemingly incomprehensible pages of data. In this appendix, we provide a brief overview of the methods ecologists use to relate their collected data to their previously formed hypotheses and ideas. As a group, these critical ecological tools are referred to as statistical methods.

The idea of statistics will cause some students to panic, others to give up, and others to just want to go to sleep. Here's some advice to those dreading what comes next in this section: *Don't panic!* The key to understanding statistics is to realize that they sound intimidating to *everyone* at first. However, with practice and experience you will learn the needed vocabulary, and you will see both the utility and surprising simplicity of these approaches. As an aside, the basic statistics described here are used in nearly all scientific disciplines, not just in ecology.

Describing a Group

Imagine you are an ecologist in the Yukon, conducting a study on the size of male caribou in a population. After learning the procedures for handling large mammals in the wild, you and your field crew fly across the tundra in a helicopter catching animals and weighing them. In addition to an exhausted body, you bring back to your tent at base camp a rumpled notebook full of the weights of all the animals you have caught. Your professor is in camp with you and has asked you to give her an overview of the data collected. What do you do?

One of the most common and important steps in processing data is the production of summary statistics. In an ideal world, every caribou in a population could be measured easily and cheaply. In the real world, however, helicopter time is expensive, animals are evasive, and your classes start in September, which means that you have a limited summer field season. As a result, you are going to sample only a small proportion of the individuals that actually exist within the population, and you will only be able to *estimate* population measures. A *statistic* is a number that is used by scientists to estimate a measurable characteristic (e.g., weight) of an entire population.

Looking at your notebook, you see that you have measured 11 caribou. The average weight of these 11 animals is referred to as the **sample mean**, and this is one of the most common and useful of summary statistics. Because of its importance, it is worth describing how it is calculated. Consider the following sample of the weights of the 11 caribou measured:

Caribou Number	1	2	3	4	5	6	7	8	9	10	11
Weight (kg)	145	131	154	169	167	175	117	146	166	134	158

What is the average weight of caribou in this population? Since we did not capture all of the males, we cannot know the *true* population mean; however, our sample of 11 males does allow us to calculate a *sample* mean.

To calculate the sample mean, divide the sum of measurements by the number of animals measured:

$$\bar{X} = \frac{\Sigma X}{n}$$

Where,

Sample mean $= \bar{X}$

$n =$ sample size $= 11$

Sum of measurements $= \Sigma X$

$\Sigma X = 145 + 131 + 154 + 169 + 167 + 175 + 117$
$\qquad + 146 + 166 + 134 + 158 = 1{,}662$

$\bar{X} = 1662/11$

$\bar{X} = 151.1$ kg

So, your hard day's work is boiled down to a single number: 151.1 kg. This is the sample mean, your estimate of the true weight of the male caribou in the population at the time of this study. To be even more precise, we calculated the *arithmetic mean* in this example. Ecologists use other types of means, such as the *geometric mean* and the *harmonic mean*. However, a discussion of the uses of these other statistics is beyond the scope of this text.

While the sample mean is very useful, it is not the most appropriate statistic for some situations. One of the assumptions underlying the use of the sample mean is that the observations are drawn from a population with a normal, or bell-shaped, distribution (fig. A.1). This assumption was reasonable for the caribou example, but there will be many cases in which the distribution of values within a population will deviate substantially from a **normal distribution**. In those situations, it is generally better to use another estimator of the population average. One such statistic is the **sample median**. The sample median is simply the middle value when samples are ranked numerically. In our caribou example, there were 11 samples, with the middle caribou being the sixth largest (= sixth smallest), which

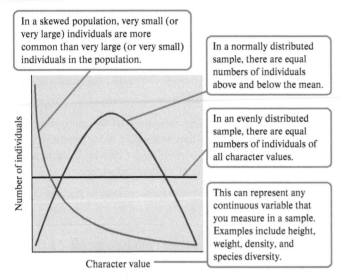

Figure A.1 Normal, skewed, and even distributions of values of a given character (e.g., weight) among individuals within a population.

was 154 kg. Notice that this value is very similar to the sample mean of 151.1 kg. This will be common in populations with normal distributions.

However, when the distribution of samples within a population is skewed, such that there are few very large or very small values, the sample median may give a better estimate of the typical individual within the population. Imagine you are once again back at base camp in the Yukon. Your professor wakes you up at 4:00 a.m., ready for a long day at work (it is light nearly 24 hours a day during the summer). Today you will be measuring the number of leaves found on individuals of *Dryas octopetala* (common name = avens). The area you will be sampling has been grazed heavily by caribou, and though not a preferred food source for these animals, many avens have been damaged by the animals' hooves. Back at camp, you are again asked to provide a summary of the day's data.

Avens Number	1	2	3	4	5	6	7	8	9	10	11	12	13	14
Number of leaves	1	6	2	4	12	15	1	3	9	1	18	2	1	3

In this example there are 14 samples. As this is an even number of samples, the median value will be the average of the seventh and eighth largest (and smallest) individuals:

$$\text{Sample median} = \frac{3+3}{2} = 3 \text{ leaves per plant}$$

$$\text{The sample mean} = \frac{\Sigma X}{n} = \frac{78}{14} = 5.6 \text{ leaves per plant}$$

The estimate of the population mean is nearly twice that of the population median. In this case it is clear that the sample median, which represents the middle value of observations, more closely estimates the number of leaves you are likely to encounter on an individual plant on this day.

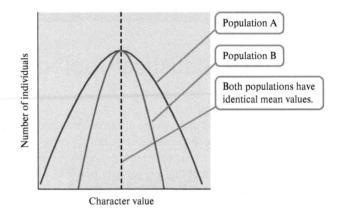

Figure A.2 Populations A and B have identical mean values for this character; however, the variation around the mean appears much greater in population A than in population B.

Being able to describe the typical individual in a population of samples using means and medians is a critical first step, but there is much more information left behind in your data books. A second important question we can ask is this: How much *variation* exists among individuals (fig. A.2)? This is important for several reasons. For example, two or more samples may have the same mean but quite different amounts of variation among the samples. That variation itself either may have an ecological cause or may influence some ecological process; thus, being able to describe variation is a critical tool for all ecologists.

Imagine now that it is the next field season and your hard work last summer resulted in a strong letter of recommendation from your supervisor. As a result, you were able to secure another field job, and you are now working on the east coast of Newfoundland, studying the diversity of invertebrate species in the rocky intertidal zones. Your basic research methods involve laying down a 50 × 50 cm quadrat (= 0.25 m²) and counting the different number of species of algae, barnacles, snails, and other macroscopic organisms you can find. You are able to finish 10 samples before lunch, and as you are eating your peanut butter and jelly sandwich (which tastes a bit salty), your professor requests a summary of the data.

Sample Number	1	2	3	4	5	6	7	8	9	10
Number of species per 0.25 m²	15	6	18	17	8	9	12	15	10	12

You quickly estimate the mean and median as 12.2 and 12 species per 0.25 m² plot. How do you quantify the variation around those numbers? The simplest index of variation is the **range**, which is the difference between the largest and smallest observations:

$$\text{Range} = 18 - 6 = 12$$

The range does not represent variation in samples very well since very different sets of observations can have the same range. A better representation of the variation in a sample is one that uses all the observations relative to the sample mean, not just the largest and smallest samples.

The underlying distribution of the population of samples influences nearly all choices about which statistics to use. For non-normally distributed data, one common method to represent variation is to divide the samples into four equal parts, called quartiles, and use the range of measurements between the upper bound of the lowest quartile and the lower bound of the highest quartile. This representation of variation in a sample is called the **interquartile range**. For illustration, imagine you have been asked to study the recovery of mayfly nymphs following a flash flood of Tesuque Creek, New Mexico, a high mountain stream in the southern Rocky Mountains. You took samples from two forks, one disturbed and one undisturbed by the flood. Median densities are 4.5 *Baetis bicaudatus* nymphs per 0.1 m² benthic sample from the disturbed fork and 40 nymphs per 0.1 m² benthic sample from the undisturbed fork. Interquartile ranges can be seen from the data (sorted from lowest density to highest):

Sample Number	1	2	3	4	5	6	7	8	9	10	11	12
Number of nymphs, disturbed fork	2	2	2	3	3	4	5	6	6	8	10	126
Number of nymphs, undisturbed fork	12	30	32	35	37	38	42	48	52	58	71	79
Quartiles	1st				2nd			3rd			4th	

Notice that the interquartile range for the undisturbed fork is from 32 to 58; for the disturbed fork, the interquartile range is 2 to 8. In both cases, 50% of the quadrat counts in each sample fall within the respective range.

For populations that follow a normal distribution, a variety of preferred methods exists for estimating the variation around the mean. One commonly used index is the sample **variance**. It is calculated by squaring the differences between the sample mean and each of the individual observations, adding them up to produce the "sum of squares." This value is then divided by the sample size minus one:

$$\text{Sum of squares} = \Sigma\,(X - \overline{X})^2$$

Using our measures of intertidal diversity, the sums of squares equals:

$$\begin{aligned}
\Sigma\,(X - \overline{X})^2 &= (15 - 12.2)^2 + (6 - 12.2)^2 + (18 - 12.2)^2 \\
&+ (17 - 12.2)^2 + (8 - 12.2)^2 + (9 - 12.2)^2 \\
&+ (12 - 12.2)^2 + (15 - 12.2)^2 \\
&+ (10 - 12.2)^2 + (12 - 12.2)^2 = 143.6
\end{aligned}$$

To calculate the sample variance, divide the sum of squares by the sample size minus 1. The sample size in this case is 10 measurements.

$$\begin{aligned}
\text{Sample variance} = S^2 = \frac{\Sigma\,(X - \overline{X})^2}{n-1} = \frac{143.6}{10-1} = 15.96 \text{ (Species per quadrat)}^2
\end{aligned}$$

Notice that the unit of the sample variance is the *square* of species number per quadrat, not species number itself. Because the sample variance is expressed in squares of the original units, we generally take the square root of the variance to calculate a measure of variation called the sample **standard deviation**.

$$\text{Standard deviation} = S = \sqrt{S^2} = \sqrt{15.96} = 3.99 \text{ species per quadrat}$$

While it took a little effort to calculate it, the standard deviation of 3.99 species per quadrat provides us with a standardized index of the variation in species number found in our intertidal study. This value, in addition to the mean of 12.2 species per quadrat, helps us understand patterns in complex ecological data sets. As you move forward in your scientific training, you will frequently use both mean and standard deviation, so you might as well take the time to truly understand them now!

As you may recall, our measures of sample mean and standard deviation are only *estimates* of the true values in the system. The only way we could ever know the true values themselves is to measure every nook and cranny of the intertidal zone, a feat that would be both extraordinarily difficult and unnecessary. It is instead much more cost effective to sample only enough to have a reliable estimate of the true values. How do you know how close a given sample mean is to the true population mean?

The answer to this question depends upon two factors: the variation within the population and the number of measurements in our sample of the population. Common sense suggests that we are more likely to estimate the true mean of a population that has low variability than one that has high variability. Similarly, more observations in our sample will bring us closer to the true value than few observations. Here we will build a way of representing the precision of a given estimate of a population means. Our first step will be to calculate a statistic called the **standard error** of the mean, $s_{\overline{X}}$:

$$s_{\overline{X}} = \sqrt{\frac{s^2}{n}} \text{ or } \frac{s}{\sqrt{n}}$$

where s^2 is the sample variance, s is the sample standard deviation, and n is the number of observations (sample size).

Applying this formula to our intertidal example, we find:

$$s_{\overline{X}} = \frac{s}{\sqrt{n}} = \frac{3.99}{\sqrt{10}} = 1.26 \text{ species per quadrat}$$

Now let us imagine we have sampled a second intertidal region, which surprisingly has given us the same sample mean (12.2) and the same standard deviation (3.99). However, because we were feeling refreshed after lunch, we were able to take 15, rather than 10, observations. The standard error calculated for this sample is:

$$s_{\overline{X}} = \frac{s}{\sqrt{n}} = \frac{3.99}{\sqrt{15}} = 1.03 \text{ species per quadrat}$$

Notice that because there were more quadrats in the second sample, the size of the standard error is reduced. In other words, due to increased sample size, our second sample mean is a more accurate estimate of the true population mean. We can further refine our estimate of the true population mean through the calculation of confidence intervals.

A **confidence interval** is a range of values within which the true population mean occurs with a particular probability. That probability is called the **level of confidence** and is calculated as 1 minus the significance level, α, which is generally 0.05 (see the next section for a discussion of what "significance" represents):

$$\text{Level of confidence} = 1 - \alpha = 1 - 0.05 = 0.95$$

Using this level confidence produces the 95% confidence interval:

$$\text{Confidence interval (CI) for } \mu = \bar{X} \pm s_{\bar{X}} t$$

where the true population mean, $\bar{X}$, is the sample mean; $s_{\bar{X}}$ is the standard error; and t is a value from the Student's t table.

The Student's t table is available in most statistics textbooks. The table summarizes the values of a statistical distribution known as the Student's t distribution, and these values are used in a variety of statistical tests. The exact value of t used for calculating a confidence interval is determined by the degrees of freedom of our sample (calculated as $n - 1$) and the significance level we want, which in this case is $\alpha = 0.05$.

Continuing the example of samples of diversity from two intertidal communities with identical means and standard deviations, but differing in sample size, we find that 2.26 and 2.14 are the t values for sample sizes of 10 and 15, respectively (at $\alpha = 0.05$). Using that information, we calculate:

Community 1: CI $= 12.2 \pm 1.26 \times 2.26 = 12.2 \pm 2.85$ species per quadrat

Community 2: CI $= 12.2 \pm 1.03 \times 2.14 = 12.2 \pm 2.20$ species per quadrat

With this confidence interval, we can say that there is a 95% probability that the true mean number of species per quadrat in community 1 is between 9.35 (12.2 − 2.85) and 15.05 (12.2 + 2.85). For community 2, the true mean number of species per quadrat is between 10 and 14.4. Put another way, the true population mean will fall within our confidence intervals 19 times out of 20. Although the mean and standard deviation are the same for the two communities, we have narrower confidence intervals for the community that we sampled more heavily.

Even though describing populations is important to many ecologists, this is only a very narrow component to the scientific method. Scientists use this information to formulate questions about the natural world and convert their questions into testable hypotheses. To evaluate the validity of a hypothesis, it is important to know whether an observed result is different from that predicted by the hypothesis. As you will see below, the most commonly used statistical methods do not allow scientists to prove anything to be true but instead are designed to test whether a hypothesis is false. A critical aspect of ecology is the construction of *falsifiable hypotheses*. Imagine the following two statements:

1. Blue flowers are pollinated by bumblebees.
2. Blue flowers are *not* pollinated by bumblebees.

The first assertion is very hard to test and essentially unfalsifiable. Why? Imagine you see a blue flower pollinated by a bumblebee. That would support #1 and reject #2. But now imagine you do *not* see a blue flower pollinated by a bumblebee. That supports #2, but you cannot reject #1, as the bees may have been sleeping, you may have been lazy, or you may just have had back luck in your sampling. In other words, #1 is a poor statistical hypothesis, as there is no data you can collect that would falsify it. In contrast, #2 is a good statistical hypothesis, as it can be falsified.

Because of the importance of falsifiable hypotheses, ecologists typically make a distinction between their working hypothesis and a statistical null hypothesis, with the latter being the one that is tested. For example, an ecologist may hypothesize that male elk are generally heavier than female elk. To test this, the ecologist will reword this as a *null hypothesis*, such as "There is no difference in mean weight between male and female elk." Data could be collected, at which point the ecologist needs to test whether the data support or reject the null hypothesis.

To determine this, we need to differentiate between the variation we find in our data that would be expected due to chance from the variation between our data and predictions that are unlikely to be caused by chance alone. When we find differences that are very unlikely to occur by chance, we refer to them as *significant* differences. The critical point here is in identifying when an observed measure, such as mean weight of elk, differs significantly from some theoretical explanation, such as that the mean values for males and females will be the same. That judgment is based upon the probability of being incorrect, and there are two ways we can be incorrect.

In one scenario, we could find a significant difference between our data and our predictions, when in fact no actual difference exists. Or, to put it a more formal way, we could reject our null hypothesis (that males and female elk are the same weight) when in fact our null hypothesis is true. This type of error is a *type I error* and should occur at the frequency of α, which ecologists generally set as $P = 0.05$. Type I error rates are also called false positives, and if $\alpha = 0.05$, they will occur 5% of the time. A second type of error is a *type II error*, or a false negative. In type II errors, the data fail to reject the null hypothesis when in fact it is false. The frequency of type II errors is determined by β, which is often set to $\beta = 0.20$. In other words, in a typical study, there is a 5% probability of being wrong due to a false positive, and a 20% probability of being wrong due to false negatives—not a particularly appealing reality! Why don't ecologists simply lower these values? α and β are related mathematically, such that decreasing one causes an increase in the other. As a result, ecologists must balance these two unavoidable risks and have historically felt that reducing false positive rates was more important than reducing false negative rates, although there has recently been disagreement with this historical decision. If ecologists cannot simply reduce both of these errors by decree, what can we do? As you might imagine, the risks of errors will be associated with the variation in the data we are collecting. The larger the variance in our populations, the larger the risk of type I and II errors. Therefore, increasing sample size can reduce error rates. A second factor, although outside our control, is **effect size**, the relative magnitude of difference between our two groups (i.e., are male elk 2% or 200% bigger than females?). The larger the effect size, the lower the risk of statistical errors. In other words, for the same amount of sampling effort, ecologists are more likely to detect big effects than small effects, even if both actually occur.

Type I and type II errors are hazards of all statistical tests and are not limited to ecology. As a result, all researchers place great importance on the quality of experimental designs and on the ability to replicate studies, as results repeated by others give more confidence than results found only once.

If the null hypothesis is true,
and if the statistical test suggests that the null
hypothesis is likely false,
this results in a Type I error.

If the null hypothesis is false,
and if the statistical test suggests that the null
hypothesis is likely true,
this results in a Type II error.

Common Statistical Tests

As we discussed before, some populations of samples will be normally distributed while others will be non-normally distributed. Different statistical tests make different assumptions about the underlying distribution of the data. In general, these can be divided into *parametric* and *nonparametric* procedures, with the former based upon normal distributions and the latter allowing for other distributions. In the remainder of this chapter we will discuss examples where a statistical test is needed, and we will provide solutions based upon parametric and nonparametric procedures. In general, we will not be providing the mathematical formulae for the procedures described, and instead we suggest that you to investigate statistics courses and books for more detailed information.

Relationships Among Variables

Ecologists are often interested in the relationship between two variables, which we might call X and Y. For example, an ecologist might be interested in seeing if there is a numerical response between predator and prey (chapter 14). One way of visualizing such relationships is with an X−Y scatterplot, with prey density on the *x*-axis and predator density on the *y*-axis. There are an infinite number of possible relationships between two variables, and we present a few in figure A.3. The most basic scatterplot is one in which there is no relationship between X and Y (fig. A.3*a*). In contrast, figure A.3*b* shows a negative relationship between the variables, in which larger values of X are associated with smaller values of Y. Figure A.3*c* shows a positive relationship, where larger values of X are associated with larger values of Y.

Scatterplots provide a visual overview of the relationships among variables in a study; however, it is equally important to perform statistical tests on the data to determine whether these relationships are likely to have arisen by chance. Two main

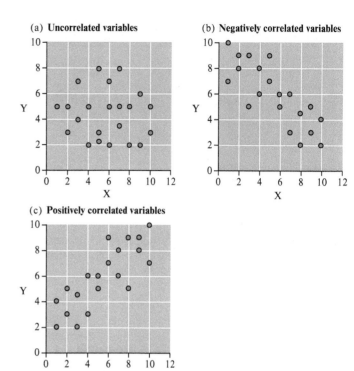

Figure A.3 A scatterplot is a useful tool for exploring relationships between any two variables, X and Y.

analyses can be used for this, **correlation** and **regression**. A simple test for correlation asks whether two continuous variables are related. A regression analysis requires a plausible causal link between the two variables. For example, if we measure soil N and P, we might ask whether these variables are correlated. There is no reason to think that high soil N will cause high (or low) soil P. Instead, it is likely that some other factor generates high soil fertility for all soil nutrients. Because there is no plausible causal relationship, we test for a correlation. For parametric data, a test for correlation is generally done using the *product-moment method*, which results in the index *r*. *r* can range from −1 to +1, with low negative values representing a strong negative correlation and high positive values representing a strong positive correlation. Correlations in nonparametric data can be tested using the *Spearman-Rank correlation*, which results in the index r_S. The main difference between the parametric and nonparametric tests is that the former uses the actual data in its calculations while the latter tests for correlations among ranks (smallest value = 1, second smallest = 2, etc.).

Regression analysis is more formal in its treatment of the two variables and is only conducted on normally distributed data. In this analysis, there is a plausible causal link between the two factors, such that you believe the level of factor X (**independent variable**) influences the level of factor Y (**dependent variable**). For example, in a study of predator–prey interactions, you may believe that predators will move toward areas of high prey density and that, thus, there would be a positive relationship between these variables. In regression analysis we construct X-Y plots as before; however, we now also determine the equation for a line called the **regression line**.

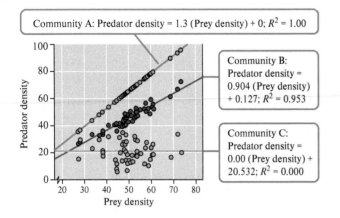

Community A: Predator density = 1.3 (Prey density) + 0; R^2 = 1.00

Community B: Predator density = 0.904 (Prey density) + 0.127; R^2 = 0.953

Community C: Predator density = 0.00 (Prey density) + 20.532; R^2 = 0.000

Figure A.4 Regression analysis indicates the strength and slope of the relationship between prey and predator densities in three hypothetical communities.

The regression line is the line that best fits the relationship between X and Y. When this line is linear, the regression equation takes the form:

$$Y = bX + a$$

where a is the Y-intercept and b is the slope of the line, also called the **regression coefficient**.

Figure A.4 shows different possible outcomes of a regression analysis between predator and prey densities in three different communities. You can see from the figures that the slope varies among communities, suggesting that different factors influence the relationship between prey and predator in these communities.

One statistic that can be derived from both correlation and regression analyses is the *coefficient of determination*, or R^2. This value can be calculated by squaring the r value from a correlation. There are additional methods for calculating this value in regression analysis, but the principle is the same. R^2 is a very commonly used value in ecology, and it tells us how much of the variation in Y is explained by variation in X (fig. A.4). High values represent "tighter fits" of the data to the regression line. As you can see in figure A.4, in addition to variations in slopes, the communities differ in R^2, suggesting a weaker relationship between predator–prey densities in some communities than in others.

Significance values (*P-values*) can be determined for both correlations and regression, again with the risks of type I and II errors. It is important to recognize that just because you believe there to be a causal relationship between two variables does not mean that there actually is a causal relationship between the variables, even if the statistical test is significant. The only clear way to demonstrate causality is with manipulative experiments, which is why experiments are given such prominence in science.

Differences Among Groups—Continuous Data

Correlations and regressions are useful tools for describing relationships between two variables. However, many ecological problems involve a single variable but multiple groups. For example, suppose you are concerned about the impacts of acid

rain on the diversity of plant species in the boreal forest. You have conducted an experiment in northern Québec in which you added low pH water to ten 2 × 2 m plots, and neutral pH water to an additional ten plots over the course of several growing seasons. At the end of the experiment you measure the number of vascular plant species found in each plot:

Measurement	1	2	3	4	5	6	7	8	9	10
Low pH—Species number	6	4	4	5	7	4	6	6	4	7
Neutral pH—Species number	12	8	10	8	13	10	16	9	6	5

You can use are a variety of parametric and nonparametric methods to determine whether the mean number of plants is significantly reduced through the addition of low pH water. The first would simply be to graph the mean values and calculate confidence intervals for each group, as we have done in figure A.5. As you can see in the figure, the average number of plant species is lower when acidified water is added to the forest. Recall from before that the true population means for each of the study populations has a 95% chance of falling somewhere within the 95% confidence intervals. Now notice that the 95% confidence intervals do not overlap. This indicates that there is less than a 5% chance that the two samples were drawn from a single larger statistical population with a common mean species density. In other words, we have a basis for saying that there is a statistically significant effect of adding low pH water on species diversity. There are, however, more direct ways of testing for such a difference.

As we saw in the analyses of correlation between two variables, parametric and nonparametric approaches differ in whether they use the raw data or the ranked data. We find the same difference in the analysis of groups. In our example of species diversity, we have two groups and we want to know whether the mean diversity differs between groups. The parametric procedure would be the *t*-test, and a nonparametric

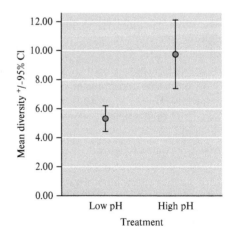

Figure A.5 Mean species diversity and 95% confidence limits for hypothetical plots treated with low and high pH water.

approach would use the *Mann-Whitney Test*. Because the *t*-test is so widely used, we present the formula here:

$$t = \frac{|\overline{X}_{acidified} - \overline{X}_{neutral}|}{s_{\overline{X}_{acidified} - \overline{X}_{neutral}}}$$

In this equation:

$\overline{X}_{acidified}$ = mean of sample from acidified water treatment = 5.3
$\overline{X}_{neutral}$ = mean of sample from neutral water control = 9.7

$s_{\overline{X}_{acidified} - \overline{X}_{neutral}}$ = the standard error of the difference between means, which is calculated as:

$$s_{\overline{X}_{acidified} - \overline{X}_{neutral}} = \sqrt{\frac{s_p^2}{n_{acidified}} + \frac{s_p^2}{n_{neutral}}}$$

where:

$n_{acidified}$ = number of acidified water addition plots = 10
$n_{neutral}$ = number of neutral water addition plots = 10
s_p^2 = pooled estimate of the variance, calculated as:

$$s_p^2 = \frac{SS_{acidified} + SS_{neutral}}{DF_{acidified} + DF_{neutral}}$$

In this equation:

$SS_{acidified}$ = sum of squares for the samples from the acidified water addition treatment = 14.1
$SS_{neutral}$ = sum of squares for the samples from the neutral water addition treatment = 98.1
$DF_{acidified}$ = degrees of freedom for the acidified water addition treatment = 9
$DF_{neutral}$ = degrees of freedom for the neutral water addition treatment = 9

Using this information, we calculate $s_p^2 = 6.23$ (species per plot)^2.

We can now calculate the standard error of the difference between means:

$$s_{\overline{X}_{acidified} - \overline{X}_{neutral}} = \sqrt{\frac{s_p^2}{n_{acidified}} + \frac{s_p^2}{n_{neutral}}}$$
$$= \sqrt{\frac{6.23}{10} + \frac{6.23}{10}} = 1.12 \text{ species per plot}$$

Now we have all the values we need to calculate *t*:

$$t = \frac{|\overline{X}_{acidified} - \overline{X}_{neutral}|}{s_{\overline{X}_{acidified} - \overline{X}_{neutral}}} = \frac{|5.3 - 9.7|}{1.12} = 3.93$$

At this point we need to compare the calculated *t* with the appropriate critical value. To do this, we need to know both the desired level of significance ($P < 0.05$ in this case) and the pooled degrees of freedom:

$$DF_{pooled} = DF_{acidified} + DF_{neutral} = 9 + 9 = 18$$

The Student's *t* for $P < 0.05$ and DF = 18 is 2.10. Since our calculated value of *t*, 3.93, is greater than this critical value, the probability that the population means are the same *is less than* 0.05. Therefore, we reject the null hypothesis that applying acidified and neutral water have equal effects on species diversity and instead accept the alternative hypothesis that acidification of water reduces diversity in this forest.

The *t*-test and Mann-Whitney tests are useful tools for comparing differences between two groups. However, there

are many ecological questions that require comparison among more than two groups, and different statistical tools are needed. For example, an ecologist may wish to know whether bluegill sunfish densities differ depending upon the species identity of the dominant predator found within the pond. To test this, one approach would be to create many artificial ponds (cattle watering tanks are often used), stocking each with a constant number of sunfish. To each pond you have added one predator species, such as large-mouth bass, northern pike, or grass pickerel. After adding the predators, you measure any changes in sunfish density. With enough replicate ponds, you can test the null hypothesis that "predator species identity has no impact on sunfish density." For parametric data, the standard statistical approach for comparing among multiple groups is *ANOVA*, or the *analysis of variance*. The most commonly used test for comparisons of more than two groups with nonparametric data is the *Kruskal-Wallis* test. As with the other nonparametric tests we have discussed, this test is based upon a rank-sum approach.

A detailed explanation of how an ANOVA is calculated is beyond the scope of this text, and thus we provide only an overview here. The most basic ANOVA is a *one-way* ANOVA, in which there is a single *factor*, such as predator species identity. In this example, we want to know whether bluegill sunfish densities are differentially affected by three predators (bass, pike, and pickerel). You choose an experimental approach, using cattle watering tanks as experimental lakes. In each tank you place a known density of bluegills and one of the three species of predators, and after several weeks you measure bluegill densities. In this study, we have a single factor (predator species identity) with three levels (bass, pike, and pickerel). It is important to note that this experiment does not have a **control**, such as tanks without any predators. Why? The answer is due to the specific research question that is being asked: "Does predator species identity impact sunfish densities?" This is different from the question of whether predators alter sunfish densities. In our example, we are not interested in the density of sunfish in the absence of predators, only if sunfish obtain different densities with different predators. The details of the research question being tested will determine the appropriate experimental treatments and controls for each research project.

In the ANOVA we derive a statistic and compare it to a critical value to determine whether the differences we observe among groups are likely to have occurred by chance. If not, then we reject our null hypothesis and accept the alternative hypothesis that predator identity significantly impacts bluegill densities. A critical underlying assumption of the ANOVA is that all samples taken come from a single statistical population. This assumption is the null hypothesis, and the goal of the statistical test is to determine the likelihood that it is true. Like all populations, variation will exist in the individual values of data around the mean. In ANOVA, significant effects of the factors are found if the amount of variation that can be attributed to the factor (between groups) is high relative to the amount of variation within a single level of a factor (within groups). In other words, if most of the overall variation in the data set is due to difference among groups, you likely will find a significant difference among groups. The test statistic used in ANOVA is the F-ratio, as it is a ratio of between-group variation to within-group variation.

ANOVAs are very flexible statistical tools and can be expanded to allow for more than a single factor in the experimental model. For example, suppose you believe that predator identity will only impact bluegill densities if the predators are at low abundance. At high abundance, you think all predators will be very efficient at reducing prey numbers. To test this, you again use experimental ponds in which you vary species identity (Factor A, 3 levels), but you also include a second factor of predator density by stocking predators at either high or low densities (Factor B, 2 levels). In a *factorial design*, you have treatment combinations such that every level of every factor is found in combination with each other. In this example, you would have a total of six treatment combinations: (1) predator A, low density; (2) predator A, high density; (3) predator B, low density; (4) predator B, high density; (5) predator C, low density; and (6) predator C, high density.

ANOVA partitions the total variation in the data set into groups, including predator identity (between groups), predator density (between groups), and the overall within group variation. In two-way ANOVAs (and other multi-way ANOVAs), an additional term may explain some of the variation in the data, and that is the interaction between the two factors (predator identity × predator density). Interaction terms are critical to many ecological studies, as some processes are likely to be important not by themselves but in combination with other factors. For example, in this case you have predicted that predator species identity will impact sunfish density only if predator density is low, which can be seen in figure A.6. In more general terms, this means that the effect of one factor is dependent upon the level of another factor. Such situations are common in ecology, and you encountered many throughout the text. It is the ability to extend beyond two levels and include more than one factor that makes ANOVAs a statistical workhorse in ecology.

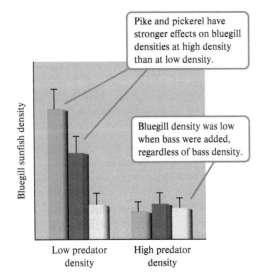

Figure A.6 Hypothetical interaction between predator species identity and predator density on bluegill sunfish densities.

Differences Among Groups—Categorical Data

So far we have discussed only ecological questions that generate continuous response variables, such as number of species or elk weight. However, many types of ecological data are categorical, such as flower colour or gender. If you were interested in whether some factor influenced flower colour, t-tests would clearly be inappropriate: What is the average of blue and red? (No, it is not purple!) Fortunately, there are statistical approaches that allow an ecologist to test whether the distributions of character states in a population differ from what would be expected by chance.

The simplest method to test hypotheses concerning the relationship between observed and hypothesized frequencies is the **chi-square (χ^2)** "goodness of fit" test. This test is used to judge how well an observed distribution of frequencies matches one expected from a particular hypothesis. Let's explore this test using the frequency of flower colours in a hypothetical population of *Claytonia virginica* (Virginia springbeauty). These plants are common in the forest understory throughout much of central and eastern North America, and different plants produce flowers that vary in colour from pure white to very dark pink. You explore a population in southern Ontario and are able to find 90 plants in flower, with individual plants displaying either white, light pink, or dark pink flowers. Let's consider this hypothetical data set and test the hypothesis that the three phenotypes are present in equal frequencies in the population.

Flower Colour	Observed Frequency (O)	Expected Frequency (E)
White	45	30
Light pink	30	30
Dark pink	15	30

Because our null hypothesis is that the phenotypes are present in equal proportions, and we have three possible phenotypes, our expected frequency for each phenotype is simply one-third the total number of samples (90) in our study population. The values of 45, 30, and 15 represent the number of individuals we encountered of each phenotype in this hypothetical population. The question then becomes: Is 45, 30, 15 significantly different from 30, 30, 30?

The value of χ^2 is calculated as:

$$\chi^2 = \Sigma \frac{(O - E)(O - E)^2}{E}$$

where O is the observed frequency of a particular group, and E is the expected frequency.

For this example:

$$\chi^2 = \Sigma \frac{(O - E)^2}{E} = \frac{(45 - 30)^2}{30} + \frac{(30 - 30)^2}{30} + \frac{(15 - 30)^2}{30} = 15$$

The next step is to determine whether this value of χ^2 is greater than that expected by chance, given this number of degrees of freedom. To do this, we again consult a list of critical χ^2 values, in this case for 2 degrees of freedom and $P < 0.05$. Our observed value of 15 is greater than the critical value of 5.991, and thus we can conclude that there is a significant difference in the frequencies of the three flower colour phenotypes in this population.

The χ^2 "goodness of fit" test is a powerful tool for identifying differences in frequencies among groups within a single population. However, how would you test whether some treatment (e.g., fertilization) had a significant impact on the frequency of flower colours? These questions are analogous to those we address using ANOVA and t-tests for continuous data, but the "goodness of fit" test is insufficient. Fortunately, several statistical approaches exist, such as the χ^2 "test for independence" and Fisher's exact test, that are well suited for this purpose.

More Complex Problems

Believe it or not, the statistics we have just described are only a basic introduction to what is a diverse and complex set of analytical tools. Like all tools, proficiency increases with use. Also like all tools, they are generally used for a reason. In ecology, we simply are unable to answer even the most basic questions without a means to synthesize extremely complex data sets. In other words, statistical methods are just as important to ecology as are sampling natural populations, coming up with good questions, or any other part of the scientific method.

As the complexity of the scientific question increases, so too does the statistical methodology. Many questions are centred on how whole communities, rather than individual species, respond to environmental changes. These questions are *multivariate* rather than *univariate* in nature, which means that each species of the community represents a different dimension in the analysis. In more practical terms, this means that you need a statistical method that allows for more than one *response variable*, not just more than one factor. Fortunately, a variety of methods have been developed, including MANOVA (multivariate analysis of variance), ordinations, and other classification methods. These latter approaches help reduce the complexity of data sets, allowing the ecologist to see underlying patterns. Although we will not discuss the details of these approaches here, results from such analyses were presented throughout the text.

Two factors that also greatly increase the complexity of ecological studies are variations in ecological patterns and processes in space and time. In other words, precipitation might strongly influence plant growth in some years but not in others. Similarly, elk may compete for forage in some locations but not in others. Understanding the contributions of spatial and temporal patterns can be critical to a holistic understanding of a natural system. Fortunately, there are advanced statistical methods to address these questions as well.

Glossary

A

A horizon a biologically active soil layer consisting of a mixture of mineral materials, such as clay, silt, and sand, as well as organic material, derived from the overlying O horizon; generally characterized by leaching.

absolute density See *density*.

abundance the total number of individuals, or the biomass, of a species present in a specified area.

abyssal zone a zone of the ocean depths between 4,000 and 6,000 m.

acclimation physiological adjustment to change in an environmental factor, such as temperature or salinity.

actual evapotranspiration (AET) the amount of water lost from an ecosystem to the atmosphere due to a combination of evaporation and transpiration by plants.

adaptation an evolutionary process that changes anatomy, physiology, or behaviour, resulting in a population's increased ability to live in a particular environment; the term is also applied to the anatomical, physiological, or behavioural characteristics produced by this process.

adhesion-adapted seeds with hooks, spines, or barbs that disperse by attaching to passing animals.

age distribution the distribution of individuals among age groups in a population; also called age structure.

albedo the proportion of incident radiation reflected by a surface.

allele one of the alternative forms of the same gene.

allochthonous inputs organic matter derived or created in a community external to the one in which they are eventually deposited.

allometry a study of scaling between body size and various biological functions, including shape, anatomy, physiology, and behaviour.

allopatric speciation speciation that occurs when isolating mechanisms evolve among geographically separated populations.

alluvial groundwater water that is derived from a surface stream in contrast to groundwater that is derived from underground streams and high water tables.

alternative states an ecological theory that suggests that a given location can persist as different community types depending upon disturbance regimes, nutrient inputs, and other external factors.

amensalism an ecological interaction in which one organism is harmed while other participants are neither harmed nor helped; a "–, 0" interaction.

ammonification the conversion of organic forms of nitrogen to ammonium, generally mediated by bacteria.

aposematic coloration bright and conspicuous coloration displayed by many toxic or distasteful potential prey species.

arbuscular mycorrhizal fungi (AMF) mycorrhizae in which the mycorrhizal fungus produces arbuscules (sites of exchange between plant and fungus), hyphae (fungal filaments), and vesicles (fungal energy storage organs within root conex cells).

arbuscule a bush-shaped organ on an endomycorrhizal fungus that acts as a site of material exchange between the fungus and its host plant.

archaea prokaryotes distinguished from bacteria on the basis of structural, physiological, and other biological features.

assortative mating mating among phenotypically similar (positive assortative mating) or dissimilar (negative assortative mating) individuals.

autoecology (or autecology) the ecological study of an individual organism or of an individual species, particularly its interactions with the environment.

autotroph an organism that can synthesize organic molecules using inorganic molecules and energy from either sunlight (photosynthetic autotrophs) or from inorganic molecules, such as hydrogen sulphide (chemosynthetic autotrophs).

B

B horizon a subsoil in which materials leached from above, generally from the A horizon, accumulate; may be rich in clay, organic matter, iron, and other materials.

Batesian mimicry evolution of a non-noxious species to resemble a poisonous or inedible species.

bathypelagic zone a zone within the deep ocean that extends from about 1,000 to 4,000 m.

behavioural ecology the study of the relationships between organisms and environment that are mediated by behaviour.

benthic refers to the bottom of bodies of waters, such as seas, lakes, or streams.

bioaccumulation the process by which toxic substances increase in concentration within a living organism due to intake rates greater than excretion and metabolism.

biological species concept where populations of organisms able to interbreed and produce viable, fertile offspring are classified as belonging to the same biological species.

biomagnification increase in toxin levels with increased trophic position within a food web, due to predators eating contaminated prey.

biomes large-scale classifications of terrestrial habitats, distinguished primarily by their predominant plants and associated with particular climates. They consist of distinctive plant formations, such as the tropical rain forest biome and the desert biome.

biosphere the portions of Earth that support life; also refers to the total global ecosystem.

bogs peat-forming wetlands with precipitation being the source of water entering the system.

boreal forest northern forests that occupy the area south of arctic tundra. Though dominated by coniferous trees, they also contain aspen and birch. Also called *taiga*.

bottom-up control control of a community or ecosystem by physical or chemical factors, such as temperature or nutrient availability.

brood parasite a species (generally birds) that lays its eggs in the nests of others, relying on the unrelated individuals to provide parental care

bundle sheath a structure, which surrounds the leaf veins of C_4 plants, made up of cells where four-carbon acids produced during carbon fixation are broken down to three-carbon acids and CO_2.

C

C horizon a soil layer composed of largely unaltered parent material, little affected by biological activity.

C_3 photosynthesis the photosynthetic pathway used by most plants and all algae, in which the product of the initial reaction is phosphoglyceric acid, or PGA, a three-carbon acid.

C_4 photosynthesis photosynthesis in which CO_2 is fixed in mesophyll cells by combining it with phosphoenolpyruvate, or PEP, to produce a four-carbon acid. Plants using C_4 photosynthesis are generally more drought tolerant than plants employing C_3 photosynthesis.

CAM (crassulacean acid metabolism) photosynthesis a photosynthetic pathway largely limited to succulent plants in arid and semiarid environments, in which carbon fixation takes place at night, when lower temperatures reduce the rate of water loss during CO_2 uptake. The resulting four-carbon acids are stored until daylight, when they are broken down into pyruvate and CO_2.

carnivores organisms that consume flesh; approximately synonymous with predator.

carrying capacity (K) the maximum population of a species that a particular ecosystem can sustain.

castes groups of individuals that are physically distinctive and that engage in specialized behaviour within a social unit, such as a colony.

cavitation rapid formation of air bubbles within the xylem of plants.

character displacement changes in the physical characteristics of a species' population as a consequence of natural selection for reduced interspecific competition.

chemosynthetic autotrophs that use inorganic molecules as a source of carbon and energy.

chi-square (χ^2) a statistic used to measure how much a sample distribution differs from a theoretical distribution.

chronosequence a series of communities or ecosystems representing a range of ages or times since disturbance.

climate diagram a standardized form of representing average patterns of variation in temperature and precipitation that identifies several ecologically important climatic factors, such as relatively moist periods and periods of drought.

climax community a community that occurs late in succession and whose populations remain stable until disrupted by disturbance.

cline See *ecocline*.

clumped distribution one in which individuals in a population have a much higher probability of being found in some areas than in others; individuals are aggregated rather than dispersed.

coefficient of relationship the probability that the alleles at a given locus will be identical by descent among two individuals in the population.

co-evolution a reciprocal evolutionary interaction between two or more species.

cohort a group of individuals of the same age.

cohort life table a life table based on individuals born (or beginning life in some other way) at the same time.

colonization cycle when stream populations are maintained through a dynamic interplay between downstream drift and upstream dispersal.

combined response the combined effect of functional and numerical responses by consumers on prey populations; determined by multiplying the number of prey eaten per predator times the number of predators per unit area, giving the number of prey eaten per unit area. Combined response is generally expressed as a percentage of the total number of prey.

commensalism an ecological interaction in which one organism receives a benefit while other participants are neither harmed nor helped; a "+, 0" interaction.

community an association of interacting species living in a particular area; also often defined as all of the organisms living in a particular area.

community assembly rules the processes that limit or promote coexistence.

community ecology the scientific study of interactions among species within a community.

community structure attributes of a community, such as the number of species or the distribution of individuals among species within the community.

competition coefficient expresses the magnitude of the negative effect of individuals of one species on individuals of a second species.

competitive exclusion principle that two species with identical niches cannot coexist indefinitely.

competitive hierarchies a nested ranking of species by competitive ability.

conduction the movement of heat between objects in direct physical contact.

confidence interval a range of values within which the true population mean occurs with a particular probability called the level of confidence.

conservation threshold a level of habitat loss and/or fragmentation below which a population is sustainable, and above which the population is likely to go extinct.

constitutive defences chemical or morphological defences that are produced continuously, regardless of whether the organism has been previously attacked. Contrast with *induced defences*.

consumptive effects of predation the direct effects of predators on prey populations through the capture and consumption of living prey.

control in an experiment, the individuals/plots/units to which the experimental treatment of interest is not applied.

convection the process of heat flow or transfer to a moving fluid, such as wind or flowing water.

cooperative breeding a social system in which adults help in the care of young that are not necessarily their own.

Coriolis effect a phenomenon caused by the rotation of the earth, which produces a deflection of winds and water currents to the right of their direction of travel in the Northern Hemisphere and to the left of their direction of travel in the Southern Hemisphere.

correlation a statistical test to determine whether two variables are related.

corridors regions of a landscape that provide connections among habitat fragments, potentially resulting in enhanced flow or movement of individuals or genes.

D

dead zones hypoxic areas (< 2mg/L oxygen) in aquatic systems, typically a consequence of pollution, eutrophication, and high rates of decomposition, that are essentially devoid of marine life.

decomposition the breakdown of organic matter accompanied by the release of carbon dioxide and other inorganic compounds; it is a key process in nutrient cycling.

deductive reasoning reasoning in which premises lead to a logically certain conclusion; the conclusion is reached reductively, as general rules or truths when applied allow only that conclusion(s).

denitrification the conversion of nitrate to gaseous nitrogen, generally mediated by bacteria.

density the number of individuals in a population per unit area.

density-dependent factors biotic factors in the environment, such as disease and competition, whose effects on populations may be related to, or depend upon, local population density.

density-independent factors abiotic factors in the environment, such as floods and extreme temperature, whose effects on populations may be independent of population density.

dependent variable the variable traditionally plotted on the vertical, or "Y," axis of a scatter plot.

detritivores organisms that feed on nonliving organic matter.

diffusion transport of material due to the random movement of particles; net movement is from areas of high concentration to areas of low concentration.

directional selection a form of natural selection that favours an extreme phenotype over other phenotypes.

disclimax community a community whose species composition is maintained through time by frequent disturbances, such as drought or grazing.

dispersal limitation the absence of a species from a community due to a lack of propagules entering the community.

disruptive selection a form of natural selection that favours two or more extreme phenotypes over the average phenotype in a population.

distribution the natural geographic range of an organism or the spatial arrangement of individuals in a local population.

disturbance White and Pickett (1985) define *disturbance* as any relatively discrete event that disrupts an ecosystem, community, or population structure and changes resources, substrate availability, or the physical environment.

DNA sequencing methods for determining the sequence of nucleic acids in DNA molecules.

dominance a species that is substantially more common than the other species in the community.

downwelling movement of surface ocean water toward the bottom; occurs most commonly along the east coasts of continents and in the Arctic.

drift the active or passive downstream movement of stream organisms.

drumlin a smooth hill, or series of hills, formed as a glacier cuts through a moraine.

dystrophic having brown, acidic water with low productivity and generally low oxygen.

E

ecocline   a gradual change in genotype and/or phenotype of a species over a large geographic area.

ecological density   the number of individuals of a species per unit area of suitable habitat.

ecological function   any of a number of biological, chemical, or physical processes that occur within an ecological system; typically with relevance to human needs or uses. Examples include biomass production, nutrient cycling, and provisioning of suitable habitat for wildlife.

ecological network   the interactions that occur among co-occurring species in a community.

ecological services   the processes and resources provided by ecological systems that are of value to humans.

ecological stoichiometry   the study of the balance of multiple chemical elements in ecological interactions, for example, in trophic interactions.

ecology   the study of the relationships between organisms and the environment.

ecosystem ecology   the subdiscipline of ecology that focuses on the flow of energy and nutrients among the biotic and abiotic components of an ecosystem.

ecosystem engineers   species whose activity creates, or fundamentally alters, habitats.

ecotones   spatial transitions from one type of ecosystem to another: for instance, the transition from a woodland to a grassland.

ecotype   a genetically identifiable subclass of a species that has evolved in response to local environmental conditions.

ectomycorrhizae (ECM)   an association between a fungus and plant roots in which the fungus forms a mantle around roots and a netlike structure around root cells.

ectotherm   an organism that relies mainly on external sources of energy for regulating body temperature.

effect size   statistical measurement of the magnitude of a treatment effect.

El Niño   a large-scale coupled oceanic-atmospheric system that has major effects on climate worldwide. During an El Niño, the sea surface temperature in the eastern Pacific Ocean is higher than average and barometric pressure is lower.

emigration   the movement of an organism out of a population.

endemic   naturally occurring in only a single geographic region.

endotherm   an organism that relies mainly on internal sources of energy for regulating body temperature.

epilimnion   the warm, well-lighted surface layer of lakes.

epipelagic zone   the warm, well-lighted surface layer of the oceans.

equilibrium   a state of balance in a system in which opposing factors cancel each other.

equilibrium model of island biogeography   a model developed by MacArthur and Wilson that predicts species diversity and rates of turnover on islands as a function of island sizes and location.

esker   a long and narrow ridge of glacial debris deposited by meltwater.

estivation   a dormant state that some animals enter during the summer; involves a reduction of metabolic rate.

estuary   the lowermost part of a river, which is under the influence of the tides and is a mixture of seawater and freshwater.

euphotic zone   the upper parts of aquatic environments that receive enough light to support photosynthesis.

eusociality   highly specialized sociality generally including (1) individuals of more than one generation living together, (2) cooperative care of young, and (3) division of individuals into sterile, or nonreproductive, and reproductive castes.

eutrophic   a term applied to lakes, and sometimes to other ecosystems, with high nutrient content and high biological production.

eutrophication   nutrient enrichment of a water body through natural processes or pollution, generally causing rapid algal growth and reduced dissolved oxygen levels.

evaporation   the process by which a liquid changes from liquid phase to a gas, as in the change from liquid water to water vapour.

evolution   a change in gene frequencies within a population over time.

evolutionary stable strategy   a behavioural strategy that is resistant to invasion and most likely to be maintained by natural selection.

exploitation   an interaction between species that enhances the fitness of the exploiting individual—the predator, the herbivore, etc.—while reducing the fitness of the exploited individual—the prey or host.

exploitative competition   use of a shared and limiting resource by two or more individuals.

exponential population growth   a J-shaped pattern of population increase where the change in numbers with time is the product of the per capita rate of increase, r, and population size, N.

F

facilitation model   a situation in which pioneer species modify the environment in such a way that it becomes less suitable for themselves and more suitable for species characteristic of later successional stages.

fecundity   the number of offspring produced by an organism.

fecundity schedule   a table of birth rates for females of different ages in a population.

female   the sex that produces larger, more energetically costly gametes (eggs or ova).

fens   peat-forming wetlands that obtain water both through precipitation and groundwater.

fitness   the number of offspring contributed by an individual relative to the number of offspring produced by other members of the population; ultimately defined as the relative genetic contribution of individuals to future generations.

flood pulse concept   a theory of river ecology identifying periodic flooding as an essential organizer of river ecosystem structure and functioning.

food web   a summary of the feeding relationships within an ecological community.

founder effect   a decrease in genetic diversity associated with the formation of a new, small population.

frequency-dependent selection   where the fitness of a genotype depends upon its relative abundance within a population.

functional group   a collection of organisms with similar ecological, morphological, physiological, behavioural features or trophic characteristics.

functional response   an increase in animal feeding rate, which eventually levels off, that occurs in response to an increase in food availability.

fundamental niche   the physical conditions under which a species might live, in the absence of interactions with other species.

G

generalist   a predator or herbivore that regularly includes a variety of prey species as part of its diet.

generation time, T   the average age within a population at which a female gives birth to her offspring. Note that this number is larger than the age of first reproduction if the female has multiple reproductive events.

geographic information system (GIS)   a computer-based system that stores, analyzes, and displays geographic information, generally in the form of maps.

geometric population growth   when generations do not overlap and successive generations differ in size by a constant ratio.

geometric rate of increase (λ)   the ratio of the population size at two points in time: $\lambda = N_{t+1}/N_t$ where N_{t+1} is the size of the population at some future time and N_t is the size of the population at some earlier time.

glacial age   a period of variably cool and warm global temperatures that can last for millions of years. Within a glacial age will be a number of glaciations and interglacial periods.

glacial refugia   areas that occur within the extent of a glacial landscape that remained uncovered by glaciers.

glaciation   a cold period generally lasting between 60,000 and 90,000 years within a glacial age. During glaciations, glaciers increase in size across the planet.

global ecology   the subdiscipline of ecology that focuses on the study of the biosphere.

global positioning system (GPS) a device that determines locations on the earth's surface, including latitude, longitude, and altitude, using radio signals from satellites as references.

gonadosomatic index (GSI) an index of reproductive effort calculated as ovary weight divided by body weight and adjusted for the number of batches of offspring produced per year.

granivore an animal that feeds chiefly on seeds.

gross primary production the total amount of energy fixed by all the autotrophs in an ecosystem.

group selection selection on traits benefiting a group, even if these traits are detrimental to the individual that possesses the trait.

guild a group of organisms that make their living in a similar way; for example, the seed-eating animals in a desert, the fruit-eating birds in a tropical rain forest, or the filter-feeding invertebrates in a stream.

gyre a large-scale, circular oceanic current that moves to the right (clockwise) in the Northern Hemisphere and to the left (counter-clockwise) in the Southern Hemisphere.

H

habitat fragmentation the division of a previously intact habitat into several isolated patches, typically due to human development and resource extraction.

hadal zone the deepest parts of the oceans, below about 6,000 m.

haplodiploidy sex inheritance in which males are haploid and females are diploid.

Hardy-Weinberg principle a principle that in a population mating at random in the absence of evolutionary forces, allele frequencies will remain constant.

herbivores organisms that eats plants.

herd immunity resistance of a population to the spread of a disease due to high rates of immunity among individuals within the population.

heritability the proportion of total phenotypic variation in a trait attributable to genetic variation; determines the potential for evolutionary change in a trait.

hermaphrodite an individual capable of producing both sperm or pollen and eggs or ova.

heterotroph an organism that uses organic molecules both as a source of carbon and as a source of energy.

hibernation a dormant state, involving reduced metabolic rate, that occurs in some animals during the winter.

homeotherm an organism that uses metabolic energy to maintain a relatively constant body temperature; such organisms are often called warm-blooded.

horizontal transmission the transfer of diseases among different individuals of the same generation.

humus partially decomposed organic matter, generally found in soil.

hydrologic cycle the sun-driven cycle of water through the biosphere through evaporation, transpiration, condensation, precipitation, and runoff.

hyperosmotic organisms with body fluids with a lower concentration of water and higher solute concentration than the external environment.

hypertonic pertaining to a solution that has higher osmotic pressure than another solution, e.g., the fluid surrounding a cell may have higher osmotic pressure than the intracellular fluid.

hyphae long, thin filaments that form the basic structural unit of fungi.

hypolimnion the deepest layer of a lake below the epilimnion and thermocline.

hypoosmotic organisms with body fluids with a higher concentration of water and lower solute concentration than the external environment.

hyporheic zone a zone below the benthic zone of a stream; a zone of transition between surface, streamwater flow, and groundwater.

hypotonic pertaining to a solution that has lower osmotic pressure than another solution, e.g., the fluid surrounding a cell may have lower osmotic pressure than the intracellular fluid.

I

immigration the movement of an organism into a population.

immobilization the conversion of inorganic ions, such as nitrate, into organic compounds, such as proteins.

inclusive fitness overall fitness determined by the survival and reproduction of an individual, plus the survival and reproduction of genetic relatives of the individual.

independent variable the variable traditionally plotted on the horizontal, or "X," axis of a scatter plot.

induced defences chemical or morphological defences that are produced or enhanced in response to an attack by a predator or herbivore.

inductive reasoning reasoning in which premises provide evidence for the truth of a conclusion; the conclusion is deemed probable based on the evidence available.

inhibition model a model of succession that proposes that early occupants of an area modify the environment in a way that makes the area less suitable for both early and late successional species.

initial floristics a model of succession in which most species are able to colonize a habitat soon after a disturbance. Species become more or less abundant over time due to shifts in limiting resources and environmental conditions.

insurance hypothesis the theory that increased diversity increases community stability due to an increased probability of there being some species present in the community able to cope with any particular disturbance.

interference competition form of competition involving direct antagonistic interactions between individuals.

interglacial periods relatively short warm periods (10,000–40,000 years) that occur between glaciations in a glacial age. During interglacials, glaciers retreat across the planet. Even without human-induced climate change, the planet is currently in an interglacial period.

interquartile range a range of measurements that includes the middle 50% of the measurements or observations in a sample, bounded by the lowest value of the highest 25% of measurements and the highest value of the lowest 25% of measurements.

intersexual selection sexual selection occurring when members of one sex choose mates from among the members of the opposite sex on the basis of some anatomical or behavioural trait, generally leading to the elaboration of that trait.

interspecific competition competition between individuals of different species.

intertidal zone See *littoral zone*.

intrasexual selection sexual selection in which individuals of one sex compete among themselves for mates.

intraspecific competition competition between individuals of the same species.

intrinsic rate of increase the maximum per capita rate of population increase; may be approached under ideal environmental conditions for a species.

introgression the transfer of genetic information among species caused by hybridization and repeated back-crossing.

invasive species a species that is able to rapidly increase its population size and species range, often to the detriment of the surrounding species; both native and introduced species have the potential to be invasive species.

irradiance the level of light intensity, often measured as photon flux density.

I_{sat} the irradiance required to saturate the photosynthetic capacity of a photosynthetic organism.

isoclines of zero population growth lines, in the graphical representation of the Lotka–Volterra competition model, where population growth of the species in competition is zero.

isolating mechanisms some process that prevents the production of a viable offspring between two individuals. Isolating mechanisms are critical to species integrity and can occur pre- or postzygote formation.

isosmotic organisms with body fluids containing the same concentration of water and solutes as the external environment.

isotonic pertaining to a solution that has the same osmotic pressure as another solution, e.g., the fluid surrounding a cell may have the same osmotic pressure as the intracellular fluid.

iteroparity reproduction that involves production of an organism's offspring in two or more events, generally spaced out over the lifetime of the organism.

K

kettle a small depression on the landscape formed by a block of glacial ice melting in place.

keystone species species that, despite low biomass, exert strong effects on the structure of the communities they inhabit.

kin selection selection in which individuals increase their inclusive fitness by helping increase the survival and reproduction of relatives (kin) that are not offspring.

L

La Niña the opposite of an El Niño, where the sea surface temperature in the eastern Pacific Ocean is lower than average and barometric pressure is higher.

landscape an area of land containing a patchwork of ecosystems.

landscape ecology the study of landscape structure and processes.

landscape elements the ecosystems in a landscape, which generally form a mosaic of visually distinctive patches.

landscape structure the size, shape, composition, number, and position of ecosystems within a landscape.

large-scale phenomena phenomena of a geographic scale rather than a local scale.

law of toleration the abundance and distribution of an animal can be determined by the deviation between the local conditions and the optimum set of conditions for a species.

level of confidence 1 minus the significance level, α, which is generally 0.05; for example, level of confidence $= 1 - 0.05 = 0.95$.

LFH horizon the L, F, and H layers, known collectively as the LFH horizon, consist of leaves, twigs, and other organic materials. LFH horizons are found primarily in upland habitats, such as forests.

life history the adaptations of an organism that influence aspects of its biology, such as the number of offspring it produces, its survival, and its size and age at reproductive maturity.

life table age-specific survival and death, or mortality, rates in a population.

life-form body pattern or growth form characterizing a kind of organism (such as emergent macrophytes, or algae).

light compensation point (LCP) that amount of light necessary for a plant's respiration rate to equal its photosynthetic rate.

limnetic zone the open lake beyond the littoral zone.

littoral zone the shallowest waters along a lake or ocean shore; where rooted aquatic plants may grow in lakes.

logistic equation $dN/dt = r_{max} N(K - N/K)$. This equation can be rearranged and presented as $dN/dt = r_{max} N(1 - N/K)$.

logistic population growth a pattern of growth that produces a sigmoidal, or S-shaped, population growth curve; population size levels off at carrying capacity (K).

M

Müllerian mimicry co-mimicry among several species of noxious organisms.

macroclimate the prevailing climate for a region.

macroecology a subdiscipline of ecology that focuses on the study of ecological patterns and processes that occur over a large geographic area.

macronutrient an essential element required in large concentrations within an organism.

male sex that produces smaller, less costly gametes (sperm or pollen).

mangrove forest a forest of subtropical and tropical marine shores dominated by salt-tolerant woody plants, such as *Rhizophora* and *Avicennia*.

marginal value theorem developed by Eric Charnov, a theory based on optimality, which describes the "optimal" time for a forager to move from one food patch to another.

mating system the social structure of a population in relation to sexual interactions and offspring rearing. Examples include monogamy and polygynandry.

matric pressure the pressure resulting from water's tendency to adhere to the walls of containers, such as cell walls, or the soil particles lining a soil pore, often referred to as pore water pressure.

matrix the landscape element within a landscape mosaic that is the most continuous spatially, for example, the forest that surrounds small isolated patches of meadow.

Mediterranean woodland and shrubland a biome associated with mild, moist winter conditions and usually dry summers. Vegetation is characterized by small, tough (sclerophyllous) leaves and adaptations to fire. This biome is found around the Mediterranean Sea and in western North America, Chile, southern Australia, and southern Africa. Also known as *chaparral, garrigue, maquis,* and *fynbos*.

mesocosm an experimental system that is intermediate between field and laboratory conditions.

mesopelagic zone a middle depth zone of the oceans, extending from about 200 to 1,000 m.

meta-analysis a statistical technique that combines the results of several studies on a single topic to test specific hypotheses.

metabolic heat energy released within an organism during the process of cellular respiration.

metabolic water water released during oxidation of organic molecules.

metalimnion a depth zone between the epilimnion and hypolimnion characterized by rapid decreases in temperature and increases in water density with depth; often used synonymously with the term *thermocline*.

metapopulation a group of subpopulations living in separate locations with active exchange of individuals among subpopulations.

microclimate a small-scale variation in climate caused by a distinctive substrate, location, or aspect.

micronutrient an essential element required in only small concentrations.

microsatellite sequence of randomly repetitive DNA, 10 to 100 base pairs long.

mineralization the breakdown of organic matter from organic to inorganic form during decomposition.

mixotrophy the ability to gain energy both from photosynthesis and from consuming organic or inorganic compounds.

monogamy a mating system in which one male and one female have an exclusive relationship, at least for some duration of time.

moraine a large pile of glacial till, typically formed along the edges of a glacier.

morphological species concept a classification of organisms belonging to the same species based on conserved morphological (anatomical) features; this concept may be useful when organisms do not reproduce sexually or are extinct and known only through fossils.

N

natural selection differential reproduction and survival of individuals in a population due to environmental influences on the population; proposed by Charles Darwin as the primary mechanism driving evolution.

nectar robbers animals that visit flowers and remove nectar without providing pollination services.

neritic zone a coastal zone of the oceans, extending to the margin of a continental shelf, where the ocean is about 200 m deep.

net primary production (NPP) the amount of energy left over after autotrophs have met their own energetic needs (gross primary production minus respiration by primary producers); the amount of energy available to the consumers in an ecosystem.

net reproductive rate (R_0) the average number of offspring produced by an individual in a population.

neutralism an ecological interaction in which all participants are neither harmed nor helped; a "0, 0" interaction.

niche the set of biotic and abiotic conditions in which an organism is able to survive and reproduce. See also *fundamental niche* and *realized niche*.

nitrification the conversion of ammonia to nitrate, generally mediated by bacteria.

nitrogen use efficiency (NUE)   the magnitude of plant growth per unit nitrogen.

nonconsumptive effects of predation   changes to prey that result as a consequence of predators being present, including shifts in morphological traits, stress-physiology, and altered behaviour.

nonequilibrial theory   theories of ecological systems that do not assume equilibrial conditions.

normal distribution   a bell-shaped distribution, proportioned so that predictable proportions of observations or measurements fall within one, two, or three standard deviations of the mean.

North Atlantic Oscillation (NAO)   an interannual fluctuation in atmospheric pressure between Iceland and the Azores off the coast of Portugal. Changes in the NAO are associated with altered climate and can have impacts on numerous plant and animal species.

numerical responses   changes in the density of a predator population in response to increased prey density.

nunatak   a unique form of glacial refugia in which a mountain peak was surrounded, but not covered by, continental glaciers.

nutrient   a chemical substance required for the development, maintenance, and reproduction of organisms.

nutrient cycling   the use, transformation, movement, and reuse of nutrients in ecosystems.

nutrient retentiveness   the tendency of an ecosystem to retain nutrients.

nutrient spiralling   a representation of nutrient dynamics in streams, which, because of downstream displacement of organisms and materials, are better represented by a spiral than a cycle.

O

O (organic) horizon   the most superficial soil layer containing substantial amounts of organic matter, including whole leaves, twigs, other plant parts, and highly fragmented organic matter.

oceanic zone   the open ocean beyond the continental shelf with water depths generally greater than 200 m.

oligotrophic   refers to lakes of low nutrient content, abundant oxygen, and low primary production.

omnivores   heterotrophic organisms that eat a wide range of food items, usually including both animal and plant matter.

optimal foraging theory   attempts to model how organisms feed as an optimizing process, a process that maximizes or minimizes some quantity, such as energy intake or predation risk.

optimization   a process that maximizes or minimizes some quantity.

osmosis   diffusion of water down its concentration gradient.

overcompensation   increased plant growth following herbivory, compared to growth of plants that did not experience herbivory.

P

paleoecology   the study of ecological interactions among organisms and their environment over geological time scales.

parallel evolution   the independent evolution of similar traits in geographically separated species.

parapatric speciation   speciation that occurs when a population expands into a new habitat-type within the pre-existing range of the parent species.

parthenogenesis   the production of offspring by a female without fertilization of the egg.

patch   a relatively homogeneous area in a landscape that differs from its surroundings, for example, an area of forest surrounded by agricultural fields.

peat   partially decomposed organic matter that builds up in certain poorly drained wetland habitats.

pelagic   a term referring to marine life zones or organisms above the bottom; for instance, tuna are pelagic fish that live in the epipelagic zone of the oceans.

per capita rate   the rate of some ecological process (e.g., births) divided by the number of individuals in a population.

per capita rate of increase   usually symbolized as r, equals per capita birth rate minus per capita death rate: $r = b - d$.

permafrost   a permanently frozen layer of soil that remains frozen even during the summer months.

phenology   the study of the relationship between climate and the timing of ecological events, such as the date of arrival of migratory birds on their wintering grounds, the timing of spring plankton blooms, or the onset and ending of leaf fall in a deciduous forest.

phenotypic plasticity   the ability to produce different phenotypes from a single genotype as a function of local conditions.

photic zone   the upper layers of an ocean or lake in which there is enough light to support photosynthesis.

photon flux density (PFD)   the number of photons of light striking a square metre surface each second.

photorespiration   an energetically wasteful process in plants that occurs when O_2 binds to RUBISCO, leading to the release of CO_2 from the plant.

photosynthesis   process in which the photosynthetic pigments of plants, algae, or bacteria absorb light and transfer their energy to electrons; the energy carried by these electrons is used to synthesize ATP and NADPH, which in turn serve as donors of electrons and energy for the synthesis of sugars.

photosynthetic   describes organisms capable of photosynthesis.

photosynthetically active radiation (PAR)   wavelengths of light between 400 and 700 nm that photosynthetic organisms use as a source of energy.

phreatic zone   the region below the hyporheic zone of a stream; contains groundwater.

physiological ecology   the scientific study of how physiological limitations and adaptation influence the ability of organisms to cope with biotic and abiotic stress.

phytoplankton   microscopic photosynthetic organisms that drift with the currents in the open sea or in lakes.

pioneer community   the first community, in a successional sequence of communities, to be established following a disturbance.

pistil   female organ of a flower.

plant growth form   a combination of a plant's structure and its growth dynamics; includes trees, vines, annual plants, sclerophyllous vegetation, grasses, and forbs.

P_{max}   the maximum rate of photosynthesis for a particular species of plant growing under ideal physical conditions.

poikilotherm   an organism whose body temperature varies directly with environmental temperatures; commonly called cold-blooded.

pollen vector   biotic or abiotic agents, such as wind and bees, that move pollen from an anther to a stigma.

polyandry   a mating system in which one female mates with multiple males while each male mates with just one female.

polygynandry   a mating system in which groups of multiple males and multiple females mate with each other.

polygyny   a mating system in which one male mates with multiple females while each female mates with just one male.

population   a group of potentially interbreeding individuals of a single species inhabiting a specific area.

population ecology   the scientific study of the structure and dynamics of populations.

population structure   patterns of mortality, age distributions, sex ratios, and dispersal within a population.

predator   a heterotrophic organism that kills and eats other organisms for food; usually an animal that hunts and kills other animals for food.

predator satiation   a defensive tactic in which prey reduce their individual probability of being eaten by occurring at very high densities; predators can only capture and eat so many prey and so become satiated when prey are at very high densities.

primary production   the fixation of energy by autotrophs in an ecosystem.

primary succession   succession on newly exposed geological substrates, not significantly modified by organisms; for instance, on newly formed volcanic lava or on substrate exposed during the retreat of a glacier.

prokaryotes   organisms with cells that have no membrane-bound nucleus or organelles; includes the bacteria and the archaea.

promiscuity   a mating system where individuals may have multiple sexual partners.

Q

quantum yield   in photosynthesis, the number of molecules of carbon dioxide fixed per photon absorbed.

R

radiation   the transfer of heat through electromagnetic radiation, mainly infrared light.

random distribution   one in which individuals within a population have an equal chance of living anywhere within an area.

range   the difference between the largest and smallest values in a set of measurements or observations.

range of tolerance   the entire set of conditions, such as air temperature or soil moisture, under which an organism is potentially able to survive; levels outside this range will be lethal.

rank-abundance curve   portrays the number of species in a community and their relative abundance; constructed by plotting the relative abundance of species against their rank in abundance.

rate of primary production   the amount of energy fixed by the autotrophs in an ecosystem over some interval of time.

realized niche   the actual niche of a species whose distribution is restricted by biotic interactions, such as competition, predation, disease, and parasitism.

reciprocal altruism   a mutually beneficial behaviour in which one individual helps another in expectation of a reciprocal behaviour.

recruitment   the addition of new individuals to a population, either through survival of juveniles to a critical life stage or through immigration.

regression   a statistical procedure to determine whether a dependent variable is related to an independent variable.

regression coefficient   the slope of a regression line.

regression line   the line that best fits the relationship between two variables, X and Y.

regular distribution   one in which individuals in a population are uniformly spaced.

relative humidity   a measure of the water content of air relative to its content at saturation; relative humidity = water vapour density/saturation water vapour density × 100.

relay floristics   a model of succession in which species colonize a habitat in sequential waves. The first wave of colonizers is replaced by the second wave, and so on, until a climax community is established.

remote sensing   gathering information about an object without direct contact with it, mainly by gathering and processing electromagnetic radiation emitted or reflected by the object; such measurements are typically made from remote sensing satellites.

reproductive effort   the allocation of energy, time, and other resources to the production and care of offspring, generally involving reduced allocation to other needs, such as maintenance and growth.

resilience   the capacity to recover structure and function after disturbance; a highly resilient community or ecosystem may be completely disrupted by disturbance but quickly return to its former state.

resistance   the capacity of a community or ecosystem to maintain structure and/or function in the face of potential disturbance.

resource limitation   limitation of population growth by resource availability.

restriction enzymes   the enzymes produced by bacteria to cut up foreign DNA; used in DNA studies to cut DNA molecules at particular places called restriction sites.

restriction sites   the particular locations where a restriction enzyme cuts a DNA molecule.

riparian vegetation   vegetation growth along rivers or streams.

riparian zone   the transition between the aquatic environment of a river or stream and the upland terrestrial environment, generally subject to periodic flooding and elevated groundwater table.

river continuum concept   a model that predicts change in physical structure, dominant organisms, and ecosystem processes along the length of temperate rivers.

root exudates   organic compounds, such as amino acids, enzymes, and carbohydrates, that are secreted by plant roots into the surrounding soil.

ruderals   plants or animals that live in highly disturbed habitats and that may depend on disturbance to persist in the face of potential competition from other species.

S

salt marsh   a marine shore ecosystem dominated by herbaceous vegetation, found mainly along sandy shores from temperate to high latitudes.

sample mean   the average of a sample of measurements or observations; an estimate of the true population mean.

sample median   the middle value in a series of measurements or observations, chosen so that there are equal numbers of measurements in the series that are larger than the median and smaller than the median.

saturation water vapour pressure   the pressure exerted by the water vapour in air that is saturated with water vapour.

secondary production   the assimilation of organic matter by heterotrophs to produce biomass.

secondary succession   succession where disturbance has destroyed a community without destroying the soil; for instance, forest succession following a forest fire or logging.

sedimentation   the deposition of suspended matter onto a surface, such as a lake bottom.

selection coefficient (s)   the relative selection costs or benefits (decreased or increased fitness) associated with a particular biological trait.

self-incompatibility   incapacity of a plant to fertilize itself; such plants must receive pollen from another plant to develop seeds.

self-thinning   reduction in population density as a stand of plants increase in biomass, due to intraspecific competition.

self-thinning rule   a rule resulting from the observation that plotting the average weight of individual plants in a stand against density often produces a line with an average slope of approximately -3/2, or that plotting the logarithm of total plant biomass against the logarithm of plant density results in a line with an average slope of approximately -1/2.

semelparity   reproduction that involves production of all of an organism's offspring in one event, generally over a short period of time.

sex ratio   the relative frequency of each sex type in a population.

sex types   the distribution of male and female fertility among individuals of a species. For example, males, females, and hermaphrodites would be three possible sex types.

sexual selection   results from differences in reproductive rates among individuals as a result of differences in mating success due to *intrasexual selection*, *intersexual selection*, or a mixture of the two forms of sexual selection.

sigmoidal population growth curve   an S-shaped pattern of population growth, with population size levelling off at the carrying capacity of the environment.

size-selective predation   prey selection by predators based on prey size.

small-scale phenomena   takes place on a local scale.

sociality   group living generally involving some degree of cooperation between individuals.

soil   the upper layer of the earth's land surface, consisting of organic matter and minerals.

Southern Oscillation   an oscillation in atmospheric pressure that extends across the Pacific Ocean.

spate   sudden flooding in a stream.

species composition   the species that occur in a given community.

species diversity   a measure of diversity that increases with species evenness and species richness.

species evenness   the relative abundance of species in a community or collection.

species richness   the number of species in a community or collection.

species turnover   changes in species composition on islands resulting from some species becoming extinct and others immigrating.

spiralling length   the length of stream required for an atom of a nutrient to complete a cycle from release into the water column to re-entry into the benthic ecosystem.

stability　a community's ability to withstand or recover from disturbance.

stabilizing selection　a form of natural selection that acts against extreme phenotypes; can act to impede changes in populations.

stable age distribution　a population in which the proportion of individuals in each age class is constant.

stable isotope analysis　analysis of the relative concentrations of stable isotopes, such as ^{13}C and ^{12}C, in materials; used in ecology to study the flow of energy and materials through ecosystems.

stamen　male organ of a flower.

standard deviation　the square root of the variance.

standard error　an estimate of variation among means of samples drawn from a population.

standing biomass　the amount of plant biomass found at a given location at a single point in time. This is in contrast to primary productivity.

static life table　a life table constructed by recording the age at death of a large number of individuals; involves a snapshot of survival within a population during a short interval of time.

stress　any strong negative environmental condition that induces physiological responses in an organism or alters the structure of functioning of an ecosystem.

succession　the gradual change in plant and animal communities in an area following disturbance or the creation of new substrate.

Suess effect　reduced concentration of ^{14}C in the atmosphere as a consequence of fossil fuel burning.

survivorship curve　a graphical summary of patterns of survival in a population.

symbionts　organisms in a symbiotic relationship (a close and typically interdependent relationship between two or more species). The outcome of the relationship may or may not be mutually beneficial.

sympatric speciation　speciation that occurs when isolation mechanisms evolve among populations with overlapping geographic ranges.

T

taiga　northern forests that occupy the area south of arctic tundra. Though dominated by coniferous trees, they also contain aspen and birch. Also called *boreal forest*.

talus　rock piles pushed aside and left behind by glaciers.

temperate forest　deciduous or coniferous forests generally found between 40° and 50° of latitude, where annual precipitation averages anywhere from about 650 mm to over 3,000 mm; this biome receives more winter precipitation than temperate grasslands.

temperate grasslands　grasslands growing in middle latitudes that receive between 300 and 1,000 mm of annual precipitation, with maximum precipitation usually falling during the summer months.

thermal neutral zone　the range of environmental temperatures over which the metabolic rate of a homeothermic animal does not change.

thermocline　a depth zone in a lake or ocean through which temperature changes rapidly with depth, generally about 1°C per metre of depth.

thermophilic　a term applied to organisms that tolerate or require high-temperature environments.

till　unsorted materials, such as clay, rocks, and boulders, left behind by glaciers.

tolerance model　a model of succession in which initial stages of colonization are not limited to a few pioneer species; juveniles of species dominating at climax can be present from the earliest stages of succession, and species colonizing early in succession do not facilitate colonization by species characteristic of later successional stages. Later successional species are simply those tolerant of environmental conditions early in succession.

top-down control　the control or influence of consumers on ecosystem processes.

torpor　a state of low metabolic rate and lowered body temperature.

trophic (feeding) biology　the study of the feeding biology of organisms.

trophic dynamics　the transfer of energy from one part of an ecosystem to another.

trophic level　trophic position in an ecosystem; for instance primary producer, primary consumer, secondary consumer, tertiary consumer, and so forth.

trophic pyramid　a graphical representation of the amount of energy contained in different trophic levels within an ecosystem. Traditionally, primary producers appear at the bottom; top consumers, at the top. Due to losses of energy between levels, the resulting graph is pyramid shaped.

tundra　a northern biome dominated by mosses, lichens, and dwarf willows, receiving low to moderate precipitation and having a very short growing season.

type I survivorship curve　a pattern of survivorship with high rates of survival among young and middle-aged individuals, followed by high rates of mortality among the aged.

type II survivorship curve　a pattern of survivorship with constant rates of survival throughout life.

type III survivorship curve　a pattern of survivorship with a period of extremely high rates of mortality among the young, followed by a relatively high rate of survival.

U

upwelling　movement of deeper ocean water to the surface; occurs most commonly along the west coasts of continents and around Antarctica.

V

vapour pressure deficit (VPD)　the difference between the actual water vapour pressure and the saturation water vapour pressure at a particular temperature.

variance　a measure of variation in a population or a sample from a population.

vertical transmission　the transfer of a disease from parent to offspring.

vesicle　storage organ in vesicular-arbuscular mycorrhizal fungi.

viviparous　a reproductive system in which females bear live young rather than eggs, with some degree of embryonic development occurring within the body.

W

Walker circulation　a large-scale atmospheric circulation system that moves in the plane of the equator.

water potential　the capacity of water to do work, which is determined by its free energy content; water flows from positions of higher to lower free energy. Increasing solute concentration decreases water potential.

water vapour pressure　the atmospheric pressure exerted by the water vapour in air; increases as the water vapour in air increases.

weed　a species that a person does not want in a certain location at a certain point in time.

Z

zooplankton　animals that drift in the surface waters of the oceans or lakes; most zooplankton are microscopic.

References

Adams, S. M., B. L. Kimmel, and G. R. Ploskey. 1983. Sources of organic matter for reservoir fish production: A trophic dynamics analysis. *Canadian Journal of Fisheries and Aquatic Sciences* 40:1480–95.

Addicott, J. F. 1986. Variation in the costs and benefits of mutualism: The interaction between yuccas and yucca moths. *Oecologia* 70:486–94.

Addicott, J. F. 1996. Cheaters in yucca/moth mutualism. *Nature* 380(6570):114–15.

Adler, P. B., E. W. Seabloom, E. T. Borer, H. Hillebarnd, Y. Hautier, A. Hector, W. S. Harpole, L. R. O'Halloran, J. B. Grace, T. M. Anderson, J. D. Bakker, L. A. Biederman, C. S. Brown, Y. M. Buckley, L. B. Calabrese, C.-J. Chu, E. E. Cleland, S. L. Collins, K. L. Cottingham, M. J. Crawley, E. I. Damschen, K. F. Davies, N. M. DeCrappeo, P. A. Fay, J. Firn, P. Frater, E. I. Gasarch, D. S. Gruner, N. Hagenah, J. H. R. Lambers, H. Humphries, V. L. Jin, A. D. Kay, K. P. Kirkman, J. A. Klein, J. M. H. Knops, K. J. La Pierre, J. G. Lambrinos, W. Li, A. S. MacDougall, R. L. McCulley, B. A. Melbourne, C. E. Mitchell, J. L. Moore, J. W. Morgan, B. Mortensen, J. L. Orrock, S. M. Prober, D. A. Pyke, A. C. Risch, M. Schuetz, M. D. Smith, C. J. Stevens, L. L. Sullivan, G. Wang, P. D. Wragg, J. P. Wright, L. H. Yang. 2011. Productivity is a poor predictor of plan species richness. *Science* 333(6050):1750–53.

Aerts, R. 2006. The freezer defrosting: Global warming and litter decomposition rates in cold biomes. *Journal of Ecology* 94:713–24.

Agrawal, A. A., and P. M. Kotanen. 2003. Herbivores and the success of exotic plants: A phylogenetically controlled experiment. *Ecology Letters* 6(8):712–15.

Alberta Environment and Parks. 2015. *Total Area of the Oil Sands Tailing Ponds over Time*. http://osip.alberta.ca/library/Dataset/Details/542. Accessed November 13, 2016.

Allen, E. B., and M. F. Allen. 1986. Water relations of xeric grasses in the field: Interactions of mycorrhizae and competition. *New Phytologist* 104:559–71.

Altieri, A. H., and K. B. Gedan. 2015. Climate change and dead zones. *Global Change Biology* 21:1395–406.

Anderson, J. M., and M. J. Swift. 1983. Decomposition in tropical forests. In S. L. Sutton, T. C. Whitmore, and A. C. Chadwick. eds. *Tropical Rain Forest: Ecology and Management*. Oxford: Blackwell Scientific Publications.

Anderson, M. J., T. O. Crist, J. M. Chase, M. Vellend, B. D. Inouye, A. L. Freestone, N. J. Sanders, H. V.

Cornell, L. S. Comita, K. F. Davies, S. P. Harrison, N. J. B. Kraft, J. C. Stegen, and N. G. Swenson. 2011. Navigating the multiple meanings of β diversity: A roadmap for the practicing ecologist. *Ecology Letters* 14:19–28.

Anderson, R. M., and R. M. May. 1979. Population biology of infectious-diseases. *Nature* 280(5721):361–67.

Anderson, J. J. 2018. The relationship of mammal survivorship and body mass modeled by metabolic and vitality theories. *Population Ecology* 60:111–125.

Andersson, L.C., and J.D. Reynolds. 2017. Effects of habitat features on size-biased predation on salmon by bears. *Oecologia* 184:101–114.

Apps, C. D., N. J. Newhouse, and T. A. Kinley. 2002. Habitat associations of American badgers in southeastern British Columbia. *Canadian Journal of Zoology-Revue/Canadienne de Zoologie* 80(7):1228–39.

Arcese, P. 1987. Age, intrusion pressure and defence against floaters by territorial male song sparrows. *Animal Behaviour* 35:773–84.

Arditi, R., and L. R. Ginzburg. 1989. Coupling in predator–prey dynamics: Ratio-dependence. *Journal of Theoretical Biology* 139:311–26.

Arnqvist, G., and L. Rowe. 2002. Antagonistic coevolution between the sexes in a group of insects. *Nature* 415(6873):787–89.

Ashman, T. L., and D. J. Schoen. 1994. How long should flowers live? *Nature* 371(6500):788–91.

Ashman, T. L., and D. J. Schoen. 1997. The cost of floral longevity in *Clarkia tembloriensis*: An experimental investigation. *Evolutionary Ecology* 11(3):289–300.

Atwood, M. 2005. *The Penelopiad*. Toronto, ON: Knopf, Canada.

Bacastow, R., and C. D. Keeling. 1974. Atmospheric carbon dioxide and radiocarbon in the natural carbon cycle: II. Changes from AD 1700 to 2070 as deduced from a geochemical model. In G. M. Woodwell and E. V. Pecan. eds. *Carbon and the Biosphere*. BHNL/CONF 720510. Springfield, VA: National Technical Information Service.

Bailey, N. T. J. 1951. On estimating the size of mobile populations from recapture data. *Biometrika* 38:293–306.

Bailey, N. T. J. 1952. Improvements in the interpretation of recapture data. *Journal of Animal Ecology* 21:120–27.

Baillie, J. E. M., C. Hilton-Taylor, and S. N. Stuart. ed. 2004. *2004 IUCN Red List of Threatened Species. A Global Species Assessment*. Gland, Switzerland, and Cambridge, UK: IUCN.

Baker, M. C., L. R. Mewaldt, and R. M. Stewart. 1981. Demography of

white-crowned sparrows (*Zonotrichia leucophrys nuttalli*). *Ecology* 62:636–44.

Baldwin, J., and P. W. Hochachka. 1970. Functional significance of isoenzymes in thermal acclimation: Acetylcholinesterase from trout brain. *Biochemical Journal* 116:883–87.

Balvanera P., A. B. Pfisterer, N. Buchmann, J. S. He, T. Nakashizuka, D. Raffaelli, and B. Schmid. 2006. Quantifying the evidence for biodiversity effects on ecosystem functioning and services. *Ecology Letters* 9:1146–56.

Barbour, C. D., and J. H. Brown. 1974. Fish species diversity in lakes. *American Naturalist* 108:473–89.

Barnola, J. M., D. Raynaud, Y. S. Korotkevich, and C. Lorius. 1987. Vostok ice core provides 160,000-year record of atmospheric CO_2. *Nature* 329:408–14.

Barnosky, A. D., N. Matzke, S. Tomiya, G. Wogan, B. Swartz, T. Quental, C. Marshall, J. L. McGuire, E. L. Lindsey, K. C. Maguire, B. Mersey, and E. A. Ferrer. 2011. Has the earth's sixth mass extinction already arrived? *Nature* 471:51–57.

Barrie, L. A., and 24 others. 1997. *Canadian Arctic Contaminant Assessment Report*. Ottawa, Canada: Department of Indian and Northern Affairs.

Baur, B., and A. Baur. 1993. Climatic warming due to thermal radiation from an urban area as possible cause for the local extinction of a land snail. *Journal of Applied Ecology* 30:333–40.

Bell, G., M. J. Lechowicz, and M. J. Waterway. 2000. Environmental heterogeneity and species diversity of forest sedges. *Journal of Ecology* 88(1):67–87.

Bennett, A. F., and R. E. Lenski. 2007. An experimental test of evolutionary trade-offs during temperature adaptation. *Proceedings of the National Academy of Sciences of the United States of America*, 104 supplement 1:8649–54.

Bennett, K. D. 1983. Postglacial population expansion of forest trees in Norfolk, UK. *Nature* 303:164–67.

Ben-Shahar, Y., A. Robichon, M. B. Sokolowski, and G. E. Robinson. 2002. Influence of gene action across different time scales on behavior. *Science* 296(5568):741–44.

Bereiter, B., S. Eggleston, J. Schmitt, C. Nehrbass-Ahles, T. F. Stocker, H. Fischer, S. Kipfstuhl, J. Chappellaz. 2015. Revision of the EPICA Dome C CO_2 record from 800 to 600 kyr before present. *Geophysical Research Letters*. doi:10.1002/2014GL061957

Bergeron, P., D. Reale, M. M. Humphries, and D. Garant. 2011. Anticipation and tracking of pulsed resources drive population dynamics

in eastern chipmunks. *Ecology* 92(11):2027–34.

Bergeron, Y. 2000. Species and stand dynamics in the mixed woods of Quebec's southern boreal forest. *Ecology* 81(6):1500–16.

Bernhardt, E. S., L. E. Band, C. J. Walsh, and P. E. Berke. 2008. Understanding, managing, and minimizing urban impacts on surface water nitrogen loading. *Annals of the New York Academy of Sciences* 1134:61–96.

Bernhardt, T. 2010. The Canadian Biodiversity website. http://canadianbiodiversity.mcgill.ca/english/index.htm

Berry, J., and O. Björkman. 1980. Photosynthetic response and adaptation to temperature in higher plants. *Annual Review of Plant Physiology* 31:491–543.

Berteaux, D., D. Reale, A. G. McAdam, and S. Boutin. 2004. Keeping pace with fast climate change: Can arctic life count on evolution? *Integrative and Comparative Biology* 44(2):140–51.

Bertschy, K. A., and M. G. Fox. 1999. The influence of age-specific survivorship on pumpkinseed sunfish life histories. *Ecology* 80:2299–313.

Bird, D. F., and J. Kalff. 1986. Bacterial grazing by planktonic lake algae. *Science* 4737:493–95.

Bird R. D. 1930. Biotic communities of the Aspen parkland of central Canada. *Ecology* 11:356–442.

Bjerknes, J. 1966. A possible response of the atmospheric Hadley circulation to equatorial anomalies of ocean temperature. *Tellus* 18:820–29.

Bjerknes, J. 1969. Atmospheric teleconnections from the equatorial Pacific. *Monthly Weather Review* 97:163–72.

Blais, J. M., D. W. Schindler, D. C. G. Muir, L. E. Kimpe, D. B. Donald, and B. Rosenberg. 1998. Accumulation of persistent organochlorine compounds in mountains of western Canada. *Nature* 395:685–88.

Bloom, A. J., F. S. Chapin III, and H. A. Mooney. 1985. Resource limitation in plants—an economic analogy. *Annual Review of Ecology and Systematics* 16:363–92.

Boag, D. A., and J. O. Murie. 1981. Population ecology of Columbian ground-squirrels in southwestern Alberta. *Canadian Journal of Zoology* 59:2230–40.

Boag, P. T., and P. R. Grant. 1978. Heritability of external morphology in Darwin's finches. *Nature* 274:793–94.

Boag, P. T., and P. R. Grant. 1984. Darwin's finches on Isla Daphne Major, Galápagos: Breeding and feeding ecology in a climatically variable environment. *Ecological Monographs* 54:463–89.

Bolduc, E., C. M. Buddle, N. J. Bostanian, and C. Vincent. 2005. Ground-dwelling spider fauna (Araneae) of two vineyards in southern Quebec. *Environmental Entomology* 34(3):635–45.

Bollinger, G. 1909. *Zur Gastropodenfauna von Basel und Umgebung.* Ph.D. dissertation. University of Basel, Switzerland.

Bond, P., and P. Goldblatt. 1984. Plants of the Cape Flora. *Journal of South African Botany. Supplementary Volume No. 13.*

Bongaarts, J. 2013. The implementation of preferences for male offspring. *Population and Development Review* 39(2):185–208.

Bonner, J. T. 1965. *Size and Cycle: An Essay on the Structure of Biology.* Princeton, NJ: Princeton University Press.

Boonstra, R., D. Hik, G. R. Singleton, and A. Tinnikov. 1998. The Impact of Predator-Induced Stress on the Snowshoe Hare Cycle. *Ecological Monographs* 68(3):371–94.

Booth, R. E., and J. P. Grime. 2003. Effects of genetic impoverishment on plant community diversity. *Journal of Ecology* 91(5):721–30.

Bormann, F. H., and G. E. Likens. 1981. *Pattern and Process in a Forested Ecosystem.* New York: Springer-Verlag.

Bormann, F. H., and G. E. Likens. 1994. *Pattern and Process in a Forested Ecosystem.* New York: Springer-Verlag.

Botting, D. 1973. *Humboldt and the Cosmos.* New York: Harper and Row.

Bowen, G. W., and R. L. Burgess. 1981. A quantitative analysis of forest island pattern in selected Ohio landscapes. ORNL/TM 7759. Oak Ridge, TN: Oak Ridge National Laboratory.

Boyce, M. S., and L. L. McDonald. 1999. Relating populations to habitats using resource selection functions. *Trends in Ecology & Evolution* 14(7):268–72.

Braune, B. M., P. M. Outridge, A. T. Fisk, D. C. G. Muir, P. A. Helm, K. Hobbs, P. F. Hoekstra, Z. A. Kuzyk, M. Kwan, R. J. Letcher, W. L. Lockhart, R. J. Norstrom, G. A. Stern, and I. Stirling. 2005. Persistent organic pollutants and mercury in marine biota of the Canadian Arctic: An overview of spatial and temporal trends. *Science of the Total Environment* 351:4–56.

Briggs, J. C. 1974. *Marine Zoogeography.* New York: McGraw-Hill.

Brock, T. D. 1978. *Thermophilic Microorganisms and Life at High Temperatures.* New York: Springer-Verlag.

Broders, H. G., S. P. Mahoney, W. A. Montevecchi, and W. S. Davidson. 1999. Population genetic structure and the effect of founder events on the genetic variability of moose, *Alces alces*, in Canada. *Molecular Ecology* 8:1309–15.

Brook, E.J., C. Buizert. 2018. Antarctic and global climate history viewed from ice cores. *Nature* 558: 200–08.

Brooker, R.M., P.L. Munday , D.P. Chivers, and G.P. Jones. 2015. You are what you eat: Diet-induced chemical crypsis in a coral-feeding reef fish. *Proceedings of the Royal Society B, Biological Sciences* 282:20141887. doi.org/10.1098/rspb.2014.1887

Brown, G. P., and P. J. Weatherhead. 1999. Demography and sexual size dimorphism in northern water snakes, *Nerodia sipedon. Canadian Journal of Zoology* 77:1358–66.

Brown, J. H., and A. Kodric-Brown. 1977. Turnover rates in insular biogeography: Effects of immigration on extinction. *Ecology* 58:445–49.

Brown, J. H., and M. V. Lomolino. 2000. Concluding remarks: Historical perspective and the future of island biogeography theory. *Global Ecology and Biogeography* 9:87–92.

Brown, J. H., and B. A. Maurer. 1989. Macroecology: The division of food and space among species on continents. *Science* 243:1145–50.

Brown, J. H., D. W. Mehlman, and G. C. Stevens. 1995. Spatial variation in abundance. *Ecology* 76:2028–43.

Brown, J. H., and J. C. Munger. 1985. Experimental manipulation of a desert rodent community: Food addition and species removal. *Ecology* 66:1545–63.

Brown, J. S., and B. P. Kotler. 2004. Hazardous duty pay and the foraging cost of predation. *Ecology Letters* 7:999–1014.

Brown J. S., J. W. Laundre, and M. Gurung. 1999. The ecology of fear: Optimal foraging, game theory, and trophic interactions. *Journal of Mammalogy* 80(2):385–99.

Brown, W. L., and E. O. Wilson. 1956. Character displacement. *Systematic Zoology* 5:49–64.

Bshary, R. 2003. The cleaner wrasse, *Labroides dimidiatus*, is a key organism for reef fish diversity at Ras Mohammed National Park, Egypt. *Journal of Animal Ecology* 72:169–72.

Caddy, J. F. 1999. Fisheries management in the twenty-first century: Will new paradigms apply? *Reviews in Fish Biology and Fisheries* 9(1):1–43.

Canada. Environment Canada. Canadian Wildlife Service. Minister's Round Table under the Species At Risk Act. 2006. *Conserving Wildlife Species and Recovering Species at Risk in Canada.*

Canada. Natural Resources Canada. 2010. www.nrcan.gc.ca/forests.

Canada. Species At Risk Act Public Registry. 2007. www.registrelep-sararegistry.gc.ca/default.asp?lang=en&n=24F7211B-1. Accessed November 15, 2016.

Cardillo, M., A. Purvis, W. Sechrest, J. L. Gittleman, J. Bielby, and G. M. Mace. 2004. Human population density and extinction risk in the world's carnivores. *Plos Biology* 2(7):909–14.

Cardinale, B. J., M. A. Palmer, and S. L. Collins. 2002. Species diversity enhances ecosystem functioning through interspecific facilitation. *Nature* 415:426–29.

Cargill, S. M., and R. L. Jefferies. 1984. The effects of grazing by lesser snow geese on the vegetation of a sub-arctic salt-marsh. *Journal of Applied Ecology* 21(2):669–86.

Carignan, V., and M.-A. Villard. 2002. Selecting indicator species to monitor ecological integrity: A review. *Environmental Monitoring and Assessment* 78:45–46.

Carpenter, F. L., M. A. Hixon, C. A. Beuchat, R. W. Russell, and D. C. Patton. 1993. Biphasic mass gain in migrant hummingbirds: Body composition changes, torpor, and ecological significance. *Ecology* 74:1173–82.

Carpenter, S. R., and J. F. Kitchell. 1988. Consumer control of lake productivity. *BioScience* 38:764–69.

Carpenter, S. R., and J. F. Kitchell. 1993. *The Trophic Cascade in Lakes.* Cambridge, UK: Cambridge University Press.

Carpenter, S. R., J. F. Kitchell, and J. R. Hodgson. 1985. Cascading trophic interactions and lake productivity. *BioScience* 35:634–39.

Carpenter, S. R., T. M. Frost, J. F. Kitchell, T. K. Kratz, D. W. Schindler, J. Shearer, W. G. Sprules, M. J. Vanni, and A. P. Zimmerman. 1991. Patterns of primary production and herbivory in 25 North American lake ecosystems. In J. Cole, G. Lovett, and S. F. Findlay. eds. *Comparative Analyses of Ecosystems: Patterns, Mechanisms, and Theories.* New York: Springer-Verlag.

Carrasco, L. R., C. Larrosa, E. J. Milner-Gulland, and D. P. Edwards. 2014. A double-edged sword for tropical forests. *Science* 346(6205):38–40.

Carruthers, R. I., T. S. Larkin, H. Firstencel, and Z. Feng. 1992. Influence of thermal ecology on the mycosis of a rangeland grasshopper. *Ecology* 73:190–204.

Caughley, G. 1977. *Analysis of Vertebrate Populations.* New York: John Wiley & Sons.

Caughley, G., J. Short, G. C. Grigg, and H. Nix. 1987. Kangaroos and climate: An analysis of distribution. *Journal of Animal Ecology* 56:751–61.

Central Intelligence Agency. 2007. *The World Factbook.* https://www.cia.gov/library/publications/the-world-factbook/index.html

Chadburn, S.E., E.J. Burker, P.M. Cox, P. Friedlingstein, G. Hugelius, and S. Westermann. 2017. An observation-based constraint on permafrost loss as a function of global warming, *Nature Climate Change* 7:340–344.

Chapin, F. S. III, L. R. Walker, C. L. Fastie, and L. C. Sharman. 1994. Mechanisms of primary succession following deglaciation at Glacier Bay, Alaska. *Ecological Monographs* 64:149–75.

Charnov, E. L. 1973. *Optimal Foraging: Some Theoretical Explorations.* Ph.D. Dissertation. Seattle, WA: University of Washington.

Charnov, E. L. 1976. Optimal foraging: The marginal value theorem. *Theoretical Population Biology* 9:129–36.

Charnov, E. L., J. Maynard Smith, and J. J. Bull. 1976. Why be a hermaphrodite? *Nature* 263:125–26.

Chetkiewicz, C. L. B., C. C. S. Clair, and M. S. Boyce. 2006. Corridors for conservation: Integrating pattern and process. *Annual Review of Ecology Evolution and Systematics* 37:317–42.

Chiariello, N. R., C. B. Field, and H.A. Mooney. 1987. Midday wilting in a tropical pioneer tree. *Functional Ecology* 1:3–11.

Christensen, J. P. 1994. Carbon export from continental shelves, denitrification, and atmospheric carbon dioxide. *Continental Shelf Research* 14:547–76.

Christian, C. E. 2001. Consequences of a biological invasion reveal the importance of mutualism for plant communities. *Nature* 413:635–39.

Chum, H., A. Faaij, J. Moreira, G. Berndes, P. Dhamija, B. Gabrielle, A. G. Eng, W. Lucht, M. Makapo, O. Masera Cerruti, T. McIntyre, T. Minowa, and K. Pingoud. 2012. Bioenergy. In O. Edenhofer, R. Pichs-Madruga, Y. Sokona, K. Seyboth, P. Matschoss, S. Kadner, T. Zwickel, P. Eickemeier, G. Hansen, S. Schlömer, and C. von Stechow. eds. *IPCC Special Report on Renewable Energy Sources and Climate Change Mitigation* (pp. 209–332). Cambridge, UK: Cambridge University Press.

Clausen, J., D. D. Keck, and W. M. Hiesey. 1940. *Experimental Studies on the Nature of Species. I. The Effect of Varied Environments on Western North American Plants.* Washington, DC: Carnegie Institution of Washington, Publication no. 520.

Clements, F. E. 1916. *Plant Succession: An Analysis of the Development of Vegetation.* Washington, DC: Carnegie Institution of Washington, Publication 242.

Clements, F. E. 1936. Nature and structure of the climax. *Journal of Ecology* 24:252–84.

Clevenger, A. P., and N. Waltho. 2005. Performance indices to identify attributes of highway crossing structures facilitating movement of large mammals. *Biological Conservation* 121(3):453–64.

Codispoti, L. A. 2007. An oceanic fixed nitrogen sink exceeding 400 Tg N a-1 vs the concept of homeostasis in the fixed-nitrogen inventory. *Biogeosciences* 4:233–53.

Cody, M. L., and J. M. Diamond. 1975. *Ecology and Evolution of Communities.* Cambridge, Mass.: Harvard University Press.

Coffey, H. M. P., and L. Farrig. 2012. Relative effects of vehicle pollution, moisture and colonization sources on urban lichens. *Journal of Applied Ecology* 49:1467–74.

Colautti, R. I., S. A. Bailey, C. D. A. van Overdijk, K. Amundsen, and H. J. MacIsaac. 2006. Characterised and projected costs of nonindigenous species in Canada. *Biological Invasions* 8(1):45–59.

Coltman, D. W., P. O'Donoghue, J. T. Jorgenson, J. T. Hogg, C. Strobeck, and M. Festa-Bianchet. 2003. Undesirable evolutionary consequences of trophy hunting. *Nature* 426:655–58.

Combalbert, S., G. Hernandez-Raquet. 2010. Occurrence, fate, and degradation of estrogens in sewage and manure, *Applied Microbiology and Biotechnology* 86:1671–1692.

Connell, J. H. 1961a. The effects of competition: Predation by *Thais lapillus* and other factors on natural populations of the barnacle, *Balanus balanoides. Ecological Monographs* 31:61–104.

Connell, J. H. 1961b. The influence of interspecific competition and other factors on the distribution of the barnacle *Chthamalus stellatus. Ecology* 42:710–23.

Connell, J. H. 1975. Some mechanisms producing structure in natural communities: A model and evidence from field experiments. In M. L. Cody and J. Diamond. eds. *Ecology and Evolution of Communities.* Cambridge, Mass.: Harvard University Press.

Connell, J. H. 1978. Diversity in tropical rain forests and coral reefs. *Science* 199:1302–10.

Connell, J. H. 1980. Diversity and the coevolution of competitors, or the ghost of competition past. *Oikos* 35:131–38.

Connell, J. H., and R. O. Slatyer. 1977. Mechanisms of succession in natural communities and their role in community stability and organization. *The American Naturalist* 111:1119–44.

Conti, M. E., and G. Cecchetti. 2001. Biological monitoring: Lichens as bioindicators of air pollution assessment—a review. *Environmental Pollution* 114:471–92.

Cooper, P. D. 1982. Water balance and osmoregulation in a free-ranging tenebrionid beetle, *Onymacris unguicularis*, of the Namib Desert. *Journal of Insect Physiology* 28:737–42.

Coppock, D. L., J. K. Delling, J. E. Ellis, and M. I. Dyer. 1983. Plant herbivore interactions in a North American mixed-grass prairie: Effects of black-tailed prairie dogs on intraseasonal aboveground plant biomass and nutrient dynamics and plant species diversity. *Oecologia* 56:1–9.

COSEWIC. 2006. *Canadian Species at Risk.* Committee on the Status of Endangered Wildlife in Canada.

Côte, S. D., T. P. Rooney, J. P. Tremblay, C. Dussault, and D. M. Waller. 2004. Ecological impacts of deer overabundance. *Annual Review of Ecology Evolution and Systematics* 35:113–47.

Coupland, R. T., and R. E. Johnson. 1965. Rooting characteristics of native grassland species in Saskatchewan. *Journal of Ecology* 53:475–507.

Crutsinger, G. M., M. D. Collins, J. A. Fordyce, Z. Gompert, C. C. Nice, and N. J. Sanders. 2006. Plant genotypic diversity predicts community structure and governs an ecosystem process. *Science* 313(5789): 966–68.

Culp, J. M., and G. J. Scrimgeour. 1993. Size dependent diel foraging periodicity of a mayfly grazer in streams with and without fish. *Oikos* 68:242–50.

Currie, D.J., G. G. Mittelbach, H. V. Cornell, R. Field, J. F. Guegan, B. A. Hawkins, D. M. Kaufman, J. T. Kerr, T. Oberdorff, E. O'Brien, and J. R. G. Turner. 2004. Predictions and tests of climate-based hypotheses of broad-scale

variation in taxonomic richness. *Ecology Letters* 7(12):1121–34.

Curtis, J. T. 1956. The modification of mid-latitude grasslands and forests by man. In W. L. Thomas Jr. ed. *Man's Role in Changing the Face of the Earth.* Chicago: University of Chicago Press.

Daily, G. C., S. Polasky, J. Goldstein, P. M. Kareiva, H. A. Monney, L. Pejchar, T. H. Ricketts, J. Salzman, and R. Shallenberger. 2009. Ecosystem services in decision-making: Time to deliver. *Frontiers in Ecology and the Environment* 7(1):21–28.

Damuth, J. 1981. Population density and body size in mammals. *Nature* 290:699–700.

Darimont, C. T., S. M. Carlson, M. T. Kinnison, P. C. Paquet, T. E. Reimchen, and C. C. Wilmers. 2009. Human predators outpace other agents of trait change in the wild. *PNAS* 106:952–54.

Darwin, C. 1839. *Journal of Researches into the Geology and Natural History of the Various Countries Visited During the Voyage of H.M.S. 'Beagle' Under the Command of Captain FitzRoy, R.N., From 1832–1836.* London: Henry Colborn.

Darwin, C. 1842. *Journal of Researches into the Geology and Natural History of the Various Countries Visited During the Voyage of H.M.S. 'Beagle' Under the Command of Captain FitzRoy, R.N., From 1832–1836.* London: Henry Colborn.

Darwin, C. 1859. *The Origin of Species by Means of Natural Selection, or the Preservation of Favored Races in the Struggle for Life.* New York: Modern Library.

Darwin, C. 1871. *The Descent of Man, and Selection in Relation to Sex.* London: John Murray.

Davis, M. B. 1981. Quaternary history and the stability of forest communities. In D. C. West, H. H. Shugart, and D. B. Botkin. eds. *Forest Succession: Concepts and Application.* New York: Springer-Verlag.

Davis, M. B. 1983. Quaternary history of deciduous forests of eastern North America and Europe. *Annals of the Missouri Botanical Garden* 70:550–63.

Davis, M. B. 1989. Retrospective studies. In G. E. Likens. ed. *Long-Term Studies in Ecology.* New York: Springer-Verlag.

Davison, P.J., and J. Field. 2018. Environmental barriers to sociality in an obligate eusocial sweat bee. *Insectes Sociaux* 65:549–559.

Dawson, T. E., S. Mambelli, A. H. Plamboeck, P. H. Templer, and K. P. Tu. 2002. Stable isotopes in plant ecology. *Annual Review of Ecology and Systematics* 33:507–99.

Deevey, E. S. 1947. Life tables for natural populations of animals. *Quarterly Review of Biology* 22:283–314.

De La Torre, A. R., D. R. Roberts, and S. N. Aitken. 2014. Genome-wide admixture and ecological niche modelling reveal the maintenance of species boundaries despite long history of interspecific gene flow. *Molecular Ecology* 23:2046–59.

de Leon, L. F., E. Bermingham, J. Podos, and A. P. Hendry. 2010. Divergence with gene flow as

facilitated by ecological differences: Within-island variation in Darwin's finches. *Philosophical transactions of the Royal Society B-Biological Sciences* 365:1041–52.

Demeester, L. 1993. Genotype, fish-mediated chemicals, and phototactic behavior in daphnia-magna. *Ecology* 74(5):1467–74.

Dempson, J. B., M. F. O'Connell, and N. M. Cochrane. 2001. Potential impact of climate warming on recreational fishing opportunities for Atlantic salmon, *Salmo salar L.*, in Newfoundland, Canada. *Fisheries Management and Ecology* 8:69–82.

DeNiro, M. J., and S. Epstein. 1981. Influence of diet on the distribution of nitrogen isotopes in animals. *Geochimica et Cosmochimica Acta* 45:495–506.

Denno, R. F., and G. K. Roderick. 1992. Density-related dispersal in planthoppers: Effects of interspecific crowding. *Ecology* 73:1323–34.

Derocher, A. E., I. Stirling, and W. Calvert. 1997. Male-biased harvesting of polar bears in western Hudson Bay. *Journal of Wildlife Management* 61:1075–82.

Derocher, A. E., H. Wolkers, T. Colborn, M. Schlabach, T. S. Larsen, and O. Wiig. 2003. Contaminants in Svalbard polar bear samples archived since 1967 and possible population level effects. *Science of the Total Environment* 301(1–3):163–74.

de Siqueira, M. F., G. Durigan, P. de Marco Jr, and A. T. Peterson. 2009. Something from nothing: Using landscape similarity and ecological niche modeling to find rare plant species. *Journal for Nature Conservation* 17:25–32.

Dewailly, E. A., J. P. Nantel, J. P. Weber, and F. Meyer. 1989. High levels of PCBs in breast milk of Inuit women from Arctic Quebec. *Bulletin of Environmental Contamination and Toxicology* 43:641–46.

Diamond, J. M. 1969. Avifaunal equilibria and species turnover rates on the Channel Islands of California. *Proceedings of the National Academy of Sciences of the United States of America* 64:57–63.

Diamond, J. M. 1984. "Normal" extinctions of isolated populations. In N.H. Nitecki. ed. *Extinctions.* Chicago: Chicago University Press.

Diaz, H. F., and G. N. Kiladis. 1992. Atmospheric teleconnections associated with the extreme phases of the Southern Oscillation. In H. F. Diaz and V. Markgraf. eds. *El Niño Historical and Paleoclimatic Aspects of the Southern Oscillation.* Cambridge, UK: Cambridge University Press.

Diaz, R. J., and R. Rosenberg. 2008. Spreading dead zones and consequences for marine ecosystems. *Science* 321(5891):926–29.

Diffendorfer, J. E., M. S. Gaines, and R. D. Holt. 1995. Habitat fragmentation and movements of three small mammals (*Sigmodon, Microtus,* and *Peromyscus*). *Ecology* 76:827–39.

Dillon, P. J., and F. H. Rigler. 1974. The phosphorus–chlorophyll relationship

in lakes. *Limnology and Oceanography* 19:767–73.

Dirzo, R., and A. Miranda. 1990. Contemporary neotropical defaunation and forest structure, function, and diversity—a sequel to John Terborgh. *Conservation Biology* 4:444–47.

Dobzhansky, T. 1950. Evolution in the tropics. *American Scientist* 38:209–21.

Dodd, M., J. Silvertown, K. McConway, J. Potts, and M. Crawley. 1995. Community stability: A 60-year record of trends and outbreaks in the occurrence of species in the Park Grass Experiment. *Journal of Ecology* 83:277–85.

Dome Fuji Project Members. 2017. State dependence of climatic instability over the past 720,000 years from Antarctic ice cores and climate modeling. *Sci. Adv. 3*, e1600446.

Donkor, N. T., and J. M. Fryxell. 1999. Impact of beaver foraging on structure of lowland boreal forests of Algonquin Provincial Park, Ontario. *Forest Ecology and Management,* 118:83–92.

Donlan, J., H. W. Greene, J. Berger, C. E. Bock, J. H. Bock, D. A. Burney, J. A. Estes, D. Foreman, P. S. Martin, G. W. Roemer, F. A. Smith, and M. E. Soulé. 2005. Re-wilding North America. *Nature* 436(7053):913–14.

Downing, J. A., Y. T. Prairie, J. J. Cole, C. M. Duarte, L. J. Tranvik, R. G. Striegl, W. H. McDowell, P. Kortelainen, N. F. Caraco, J. M. Melack, and J. J. Middelburg. 2006. The global abundance and size distribution of lakes, ponds, and impoundments. *Limnology and Oceanography* 51:2388–97.

Drew, M. C. 1975. Comparison of effects of a localized supply of phosphate, nitrate, ammonium and potassium on growth of seminal root system, and shoot, in barley. *New Phytologist* 75(3):479–90.

Dubois, F. D., and L. A. Giraldeau. 2005. Fighting for resources: The economics of defense and appropriation. *Ecology* 86(1):3–11.

Dulvy, N. K., and R. E. Forrest. 2010. Life histories, population dynamics, and extinction risks in Chondrichthyans. In J. C. Carrier, J. A. Musick, and M. R. Heithaus, eds. *Sharks and Their Relatives II: Biodiversity, Adaptive Physiology, and Conservation.* Boca Raton, FL: CRC Press.

Dyer, S. J., J. P. O'Neill, S. M. Wasel, and S. Boutin. 2002. Quantifying barrier effects of roads and seismic lines on movements of female woodland caribou in northeastern Alberta. *Canadian Journal of Zoology-Revue Canadienne De Zoologie* 80(5):839–45.

Ecological Stratification Working Group. 1996. *A National Ecological Framework for Canada.* Ottawa/Hull: Agriculture and Agri-Food Canada, Research Branch, Centre for Land and Biological Resources Research and Environment Canada, State of Environment Directorate.

Edney, E. B. 1953. The temperature of woodlice in the sun. *Journal of Experimental Biology* 30:331–49.

Egler, F. E. 1954. Vegetation science concepts I. Initial floristic composition. A factor in old-field vegetation development. *Vegetatio* 4:412–17.

Ehleringer, J., and O. Björkman. 1977. Quantum yields for CO_2 uptake in C3 and C4 plants. *Plant Physiology* 59(1):86–90.

Ehleringer, J. R., J. Roden, and T. E. Dawson. 2000. Assessing ecosystem-level water relations through stable isotope ratio analyses. In O. E. Sala, R. B. Jackson, H. A. Mooney, and R. W. Howarth. eds. *Methods in Ecosystem Science*. New York: Springer.

Ehleringer, J. R., S. L. Phillips, W. S. F. Schuster, and D. R. Sandquist. 1991. Differential utilization of summer rains by desert plants. *Oecologia* 88:430–34.

El-Sabaawi, R. W., M. C. Marshall, R. D. Bassar, A. López-Sepulcre, E. P. Palkovacs, and C. Dalton. 2015. Assessing the effects of guppy life history evolution on nutrient recycling: From experiments to the field. *Freshwater Biology* 60: 590–601.

Eliason, E. J., T. D. Clark, M. J. Hague, L. M. Hanson, Zoe S. Gallagher, K. M. Jeffries, M. K. Gale, D. A. Patterson, S. G. Hinch, and A. P. Farrell. 2011. Differences in thermal tolerance among sockeye salmon populations. *Science* 332:109–12.

Ellis, R. J., M. R. van den Heuvel, E. Bandelj, M. A. Smith, L. H. McCarthy, T. R. Stuthridge, and D. R. Dietrich. 2003. In vivo and in vitro assessment of the androgenic potential of a pulp and paper mill effluent. *Environmental Toxicology and Chemistry* 22(7):1448–56.

Elser, J. J. 1999. The pathway to noxious cyanobacterial blooms in lakes: The food web as the final turn. *Freshwater Biology* 42(3):537–43.

Elton, C. 1924. Periodic fluctuations in the numbers of animals: Their causes and effects. *British Journal of Experimental Biology* 2:119–63.

Elton, C. 1927. *Animal Ecology*. London: Sidgewick & Jackson.

Elton, C. A. 1958. *The Ecology of Invasions by Animals and Plants*. London: Methuen.

Endler, J. A. 1980. Natural selection on color patterns in *Poecilia reticulata*. *Evolution* 34:76–91.

Endler, J. A. 1995. Multiple-trait coevolution and environmental gradients in guppies. *Trends in Ecology & Evolution* 10:22–9.

Erickson, G. M., P. J. Currie, B. D. Inouye, and A. A. Winn. 2006. Tyrannosaur Life Tables: An Example of Nonavian Dinosaur Population Biology. *Science* 313:213.

Erwin, D. H. 2001. Lessons from the past: Biotic recoveries from mass extinctions. *Proceedings of the National Academy of Sciences of the United States of America* 98:5399–403.

Evans, M. S., D. Muir, W. L. Lockhart, G. Stern, M. Ryan, and P. Roach. 2005. Persistent organic pollutants and metals in the freshwater biota of the Canadian Subarctic and Arctic: An overview. *Science of the Total Environment* 351:94–147.

FAO. 1972. *Atlas of the Living Resources of the Sea*. 3d ed. Rome: FAO.

Fahrig, L. 2003. Effects of habitat fragmentation on biodiversity. *Annual Review of Ecology Evolution and Systematics* 34:487–515.

Fahrig, L. 2005. When is a landscape perspective important? In J. A. Wiens and M. R. Moss, eds. *Issues and Perspective in Landscape Ecology*. Cambridge, England: Cambridge University Press.

Fallon, R. D., S. Harrits, R. S. Hanson, and T. D. Brock. 1980. The role of methane in internal carbon cycling in Lake Mendota during summer stratification. *Limnology and Oceanography* 25:357–60.

Findlay, D. L., and S. E. M. Kasian. 1987. Phytoplankton community responses to nutrient addition in Lake 226, Experimental Lakes Area, northwestern Ontario. *Canadian Journal of Fisheries and Aquatic Sciences* 44(Suppl. 1):35–46.

Fine, P. V. A. 2015. Ecological and evolutionary drivers of geographic variation in species diversity. *Annual Reviews of Ecology, Evolution, and Systematics* 46:369–92.

Fisher, R. A. 1930. *The genetical theory of natural selection*. Oxford, UK: Clarendon Press.

Fisher, S. G., L. J. Gray, N. B. Grimm, and D. E. Busch. 1982. Temporal succession in a desert stream ecosystem following flash flooding. *Ecological Monographs* 52:93–110.

Foley, J. A., R. DeFries, G. P. Asner, C. Barford, G. Bonan, S. R. Carpenter, F. S. Chapin, M. T. Coe, G. C. Daily, H. K. Gibbs, J. H. Helkowski, T. Holloway, E. A. Howard, C. J. Kucharik, C. Monfreda, J. A. Patz, I. C. Prentice, N. Ramankutty, and P. K. Snyder. 2005. Global consequences of land use. *Science* 309(5734):570–74.

Folmar, L.C., N. D. Denslow, V. Rao, M. Chow, D. A. Crain, J. Enblom, J. Marcino, and L. J. Guillette Jr. 1996. Vitellogenin induction and reduced serum testosterone concentrations in feral male carp (*Cyprinus carpio*) captured near a major metropolitan sewage treatment plant. *Environmental Health Perspectives* 104:1096–1100.

Forel, F. A. 1892. *Le Léman: Monograhie limnologique*. Tome I, Géographie, Hydrographie, Géologie, Climatologie, Hydrologie. Lausanne, F. Rouge. Reprinted Genève, Slatkine Reprints, 1969.

Forman, R. T. T., and L. E. Alexander. 1998. Roads and their major ecological effects. *Annual Review of Ecology and Systematics* 29:207–31.

Fortin, M. J., R. J. Olson, S. Ferson, L. Iverson, C. Hunsaker, G. Edwards, D. Levine, K. Butera, and V. Klemas. 2000. Issues related to the detection of boundaries. *Landscape Ecology* 15:453–66.

Fortin, M. J., T. H. Keitt, B. A. Maurer, M. L. Taper, D. M. Kaufmann, and T. M. Blackburn. 2005. Species' geographic ranges and distributional limits: Pattern analysis and statistical issues. *Oikos* 108:7–17.

Fox, J. W. 2013. The intermediate disturbance hypothesis should be abandoned. *Trends in Ecology & Evolution* 28(2):86–92.

Frahbod, A.M., H. Kao, D.M. Walker, and J.F. Cassidy. 2015. Investigation of regional seismicity before and after hydraulic fracturing in the Horn River Basin, northeastern British Columbia. *Canadian Journal of Earth Sciences* 52(2): 112–122.

Frank, P. W., C. D. Boll, and R. W. Kelly. 1957. Vital statistics of laboratory cultures of *Daphnia pulex* De Geer as related to density. *Physiological Zoology* 30:287–305.

Fraser, L. H., H. A. L. Henry, C. N. Carlyle, S. R. White, C. Beierkuhnlein, J. F. Cahill, B. B. Casper, E. Cleland, S. L. Collins, J. S. Dukes, A. K. Knapp, E. Lind, R. Long, Y. Luo, P. B. Reich, M. D. Smith, M. Sternberg, and R. Turkington. 2013. Coordinated distributed experiments: An emerging tool for testing global hypotheses in ecology and environmental science. *Frontiers in Ecology and the Environment* 11(3):147–55.

Friedli, H., H. Lotscher, H. Oeschger, U. Siegenthaler, and B. Stauffer. 1986. Ice core record of the $^{13}C/^{12}C$ ratio of atmospheric CO_2 in the past two centuries. *Nature* 324:237–38.

Friedmann, H. 1955. The honey-guides. *Bulletin of the United States National Museum* 208:1–292.

Fryxell, J. M., A. Mosser, A. R. E. Sinclair, and C. Packer. 2007. Group formation stabilizes predator–prey dynamics. *Nature* 449:1041–43.

Fu, C. H., R. Mohn, and L. P. Fanning. 2001. Why the Atlantic cod (*Gadus morhua*) stock off eastern Nova Scotia has not recovered. *Canadian Journal of Fisheries and Aquatic Sciences* 58(8):1613–23.

Funk, D. J., P. Nosil, and W. J. Etges. 2006. Ecological divergence exhibits consistently positive associations with reproductive isolation across disparate taxa. *Proceedings of the National Academy of Sciences of the United States of America* 103(9):3209–13.

Galbraith, D. A., N. E. Iwanycki, B. V. McGoey, and J. McGregor. 2011. The evolving role of botanical gardens and natural areas: A floristic case study from Royal Botanical Gardens, Canada. *Plant Diversity and Resources* 33:123–31.

Gallardo, A., and J. Merino. 1993. Leaf decomposition in two Mediterranean ecosystems of southwest Spain: Influence of substrate quality. *Ecology* 74:152–61.

Gamberg, M., B. Braune, E. Davey, B. Elkin, P. F. Hoekstra, D. Kennedy, C. Macdonald, D. Muir, A. Nirwal, M. Wayland, and B. Zeeb. 2005. Spatial and temporal trends of contaminants in terrestrial biota from the Canadian Arctic. *Science of the Total Environment* 351:148–64.

Gaudet, C. L., and P. A. Keddy. 1988. A comparative approach to predicted competitive ability from plant traits. *Nature* 334:242–43.

Gause, G. F. 1934. *The Struggle for Existence*. Baltimore: Williams & Wilkins. Reprinted by Hafner Publishing Company. New York. 1969.

Gallardo, A., and J. Merino. 1993. Leaf decomposition in two Mediterranean ecosystems of southwest Spain: Influence of substrate quality. *Ecology* 74:152–61.

Gersani, M., J. S. Brown, E. E. O'Brien, G. M. Maina, and Z. Abramsky. 2001. Tragedy of the commons as a result of root competition. *Journal of Ecology* 89(4):660–69.

Getzin, S., C. Dean, F. L. He, J. A. Trofymow, K. Wiegand, and T. Wiegand. 2006. Spatial patterns and competition of tree species in a Douglas-fir chronosequence on Vancouver Island. *Ecography* 29(5):671–82.

Gibbs, H. L., and P. R. Grant. 1987. Ecological consequences of an exceptionally strong El Niño event on Darwin's finches. *Ecology* 68:1735–46.

Gillson, L., and K. J. Willis. 2004. As Earth's testimonies tell: Wilderness conservation in a changing world. *Ecology Letters* 7(10):990–98.

Gleason, H. A. 1926. The individualistic concept of the plant association. *Torrey Botanical Club Bulletin* 53:7–26.

Gleason, H. A. 1939. The individualistic concept of the plant association. *American Midland Naturalist* 21:92–110.

Gobeil, J. F., and M. A. Villard. 2002. Permeability of three boreal forest landscape types to bird movements as determined from experimental translocations. *Oikos* 98(3):447–58.

Goodman, D. 1975. The theory of diversity-stability relationships in ecology. *The Quarterly Review of Biology* 50(3):237–66.

Gorrell, J. C., A. G. McAdam, D. W. Coltman, M. M. Humphries, and S. Boutin. 2010. Adopting kin enhances inclusive fitness in asocial red squirrels. *Nature Communications* 1:22. doi:10.1038/ncomms1022

Gosz, J. R., R. T. Holmes, G. E. Likens, and F. H. Bormann. 1978. The flow of energy in a forest ecosystem. *Scientific American* 238(3):92–102.

Graham, W. F., and R. A. Duce. 1979. Atmospheric pathways of the phosphorus cycle. *Geochimica et Cosmochimica Acta* 43:1195–208.

Granéli, E., K. Wallström, U. Larsson, W. Granéli, and R. Elmgren. 1990. Nutrient limitation of primary production in the Baltic Sea area. *Ambio* 19:142–51.

Grant, B. R., and P. R. Grant. 1989. *Evolutionary Dynamics of a Natural Population*. Chicago: University of Chicago Press.

Grant, P. R. 1986. *Ecology and Evolution of Darwin's Finches*. Princeton, N.J.: Princeton University Press.

Grassle, J. F. 1973. Variety in coral reef communities. In O. A. Jones and R. Endean. eds. *Biology and Geology of Coral Reefs*. Vol. 2. New York: Academic Press.

Grassle, J. F. 1991. Deep-sea benthic biodiversity. *BioScience* 41(7):464–69.

Gresh, T., J. Lichatowich, and P. Schoonmaker. 2000. An estimation of historic and current levels of salmon production in the Northeast Pacific ecosystem: Evidence of a nutrient deficit in the freshwater systems of the Pacific Northwest. *Fisheries* 25:15–21.

Griffith, S. C., I. P. F. Owens, and K. A. Thuman. 2002. Extra pair paternity in birds: A review of interspecific variation and adaptive function. *Molecular Ecology* 11:2195–212.

Grime, J. P. 1973. Competition and diversity in herbaceous vegetation. *Nature* 244:311.

Grime, J. P. 1977. Evidence for the existence of three primary strategies in plants and its relevance to ecological and evolutionary theory. *American Naturalist* 111:1169–94.

Grime, J. P. 1979. *Plant Strategies and Vegetation Processes*. New York: John Wiley & Sons.

Grimm, N. B. 1987. Nitrogen dynamics during succession in a desert stream. *Ecology* 68:1157–70.

Grimm, N. B. 1988. Role of macroinvertebrates in nitrogen dynamics of a desert stream. *Ecology* 69:1884–93.

Grinnell, J. 1917. The niche-relationships of the California Thrasher. *Auk* 34:427–33.

Grinnell, J. 1924. Geography and evolution. *Ecology* 5:225–29.

Groffman, P. M., N. L. Law, K. T. Belt, L. E. Band, and G. T. Fisher. 2004. Nitrogen fluxes and retention in urban watershed ecosystems. *Ecosystems* 7:393–403.

Gross, M. R. 1985. Disruptive selection for alternative life histories in salmon. *Nature* 313:47–8.

Gross, M. R. 1991. Salmon breeding behavior and life history evolution in changing environments. *Ecology* 72:1180–6.

Gross, J. E., L. A. Shipley, N. T. Hobbs, D. E. Spalinger, and B. A. Wunder. 1993. Functional response of herbivores in food-concentrated patches: Tests of a mechanistic model. *Ecology* 74:778–91.

Grutter, A. S. 1999. Cleaner fish really do clean. *Nature* 398:672–73.

Guerry, A. D., M. H. Ruckelshaus, K. K. Arkema, J. R. Bernhardt, G. Guannel, C.-K Kim, M. Marsik, M. Papenfus, J. E. Toft, G. Verutes, S. A. Wood, M. Beck, F. Chan, K. M. A. Chan, G. Gelfenbaum, B. D. Gold, B. S. Halpern, W. B. Labiosa, S. E. Lester, P. S. Levin, M. McField, M. L. Pinsky, M. Plummer, S. Polasky, P. Ruggiero, D. A. Sutherland, H. Tallis, A. Day, and J. Spencer. 2012. Modeling benefits from nature: Using ecosystem services to inform coastal and marine spatial planning. *International Journal of Biodiversity Science, Ecosystem Services & Management* 8(1–2):107–21.

Guiguer, K. R. R. A., and D. R. Barton. 2002. The trophic role of *Diporeia* (Amphipoda) in Colypoys Bay (Georgian Bay) benthic food web: A stable isotope approach. *Journal of Great Lakes Research* 28(2):228–39.

Gunderson, D. R. 1997. Trade-off between reproductive effort and adult survival in oviparous and viviparous fishes. *Canadian Journal of Fisheries and Aquatic Sciences* 54:990–98.

Haberl, H. 2015. Competition for land: A sociometabolic perspective. *Ecological Economics* 119:424–31.

Haberl, H., K. H. Erb, F. Krausmann, V. Gaube, A. Bondau, C. Pluzar, S. Gingrich, W. Lucht, and M. Fischer-Kowalski. 2007. Quantifying and mapping the human appropriation of net primary production in Earth's terrestrial ecosystems. *Proceedings of the National Academy of Sciences Journal* 104(31):12942–47.

Hadley, N. F., and T. D. Schultz. 1987. Water loss in three species of tiger beetles (*Cicindela*): Correlations with epicuticular hydrocarbons. *Journal of Insect Physiology* 33:677–82.

Hamilton, W. D. 1964. The genetical evolution of social behaviour, I and II. *Journal of Theoretical Biology* 7:1–52.

Hansen, M. C., P. V. Potapov, R. Moore, M. Hancher, S. A. Turubanova, A. Tyukavina, D. Thau, S. V. Stehman, S. J. Goetz, T. R. Loveland, A. Kommareddy, A. Egorov, L. Chini, C. O. Justice, and J. R. G. Townshend. 2013. High-resolution global maps of 21st century forest cover change. *Science* 342(6160):850–53.

Hansen, P.-D., H. Dizer, B. Hock, A. Marx, J. Sherry, M. McMaster, and C. Blaise. 1998. Vitellogenin—a biomarker for endocrine disruptors. *Trends in Analytical Chemistry* 17(7):448–51.

Hardie, K. 1985. The effect of removal of extraradical hyphae on water uptake by vesicular-arbuscular mycorrhizal plants. *New Phytologist* 101:677–84.

Hardin, G. 1960. The competitive exclusion principle. *Science* 131:1292–97.

Haukioja, E., K. Kapiainen, P. Niemelä, and J. Tuomi. 1983. Plant availability hypothesis and other explanations of herbivore cycles: Complementary or exclusive alternatives? *Oikos* 40:419–32.

Hawkes, C. V., and J. J. Sullivan. 2001. The impact of herbivory on plants in different resource conditions: A meta-analysis. *Ecology* 82(7):2045–58.

Heard, S.B. 2012. Use of host-plant trait space by Phytophagous insects during host-associated differentiation: The gape-and-pinch model. *International Journal of Ecology* 2012:192345. doi:10.1155/2012/192345

Hebert, P. D. N., A. Cywinska, S. L. Ball, and J. R. DeWaard. 2003. Biological identifications through DNA barcodes. *Proceedings of the Royal Society of London Series B-Biological Sciences* 270(1512):313–21.

Hedin, L. O., P. M. Vitousek, and P. A. Matson. 2003. Nutrient losses over four million years of tropical forest development. *Ecology* 84:2231–55.

Hegazy, A. K. 1990. Population ecology and implications for conservation of *Cleome droserifolia*: A threatened xerophyte. *Journal of Arid Environments* 19:269–82.

Hendry, A. P., S. K. Huber, L. F. de Leon, A. Herrel, and J. Podos. 2009. Disruptive selection in a bimodal population of Darwin's finches. *Philosophical Transactions of the Royal Society B-Biological Sciences* 276:753–59.

Henry, G. H. R., and U. Molau. 1997. Tundra plants and climate change: The International Tundra Experiment (ITEX). *Global Change Biology* 3(S1):1–9.

Herborg, L. M., C. L. Jerde, D. M. Lodge, G. M. Ruiz, and H. J. MacIsaac. 2007. Predicting invasion risk using measures of introduction effort and environmental niche models. *Ecological Applications* 17:663–74.

Heske, E. J., J. H. Brown, and S. Mistry. 1994. Long-term experimental study of a Chihuahuan Desert rodent community: 13 years of competition. *Ecology* 75:438–45.

Hik, D. S., and R. L. Jefferies. 1990. Increases in the net aboveground primary production of a salt-marsh forage grass—a test of the predictions of the herbivore-optimization model. *Journal of Ecology* 78(1):180–95.

Hillebrand, H. 2004. On the generality of the latitudinal diversity gradient. *American Naturalist* 163:192–211.

Hillebrand, H., and B. J. Cardinale. 2010. A critique for meta-analyses and the productivity–diversity relationship. *Ecology* 91(9):2545–9.

Hillis, D. M., B. K. Mable, A. Larson, S. K. Davis, and E. A. Zimmer. 1996. Nucleic acids IV: Sequencing and cloning. In D. M. Hillis, C. Moritz, and B. K. Mable. eds. *Molecular Systematics*. Sunderland, Mass.: Sinauer Associates, Inc.

Hobbie, S. E., J. P. Schimel, S. E. Trumbore, and J. R. Randerson. 2000. Controls over carbon storage and turnover in high-latitude soils. *Global Change Biology* 6:196–210.

Hobbs, R. J., and L. F. Huenneke. 1992. Disturbance, diversity, and invasion—implications for conservations. *Conservation Biology* 6(3):324–37.

Hobson, K. A. 1999. Tracing origins and migration of wildlife using stable isotopes: A review. *Oecologia* 120:314–26.

Hodkinson, I. D., and S. J. Coulson. 2004. Are high Arctic terrestrial food chains really that simple? The Bear Island food web revisited. *Oikos* 106:427–31.

Hoegh-Guldberg, O., P. J. Mumby, A. J. Hooten, R. S. Steneck, P. Greenfield, E. Gomez, C. D. Harvell, P. F. Sale, A. J. Edwards, K. Caldeira, N. Knowlton, C. M. Eakin, R. Inglesias-Prieto, N. Muthiga, R. H. Bradbury, A. Dubi, and M. E. Hatziolos. 2007. Coral reefs under rapid climate change and ocean acidification. *Science* 318(5857):1737–42.

Hogetsu, K., and S. Ichimura. 1954. Studies on the biological production of Lake Suwa. 6. The ecological studies in the production of phytoplankton. *Japanese Journal of Botany* 14:280–303.

Hölldobler, B., and E. O. Wilson. 1990. *The Ants*. Cambridge, Mass.: The Belknap Press of Harvard University Press.

Holling, C. S. 1959. The components of predation as revealed by a study of small mammal predation of the European pine sawfly. *The Canadian Entomologist* 91:293–320.

Honn Kao, H., R. Hyndman, Y. Jiang, R. Visser, B. Smith, A. Babaie Mahani, L. Leonard, H. Ghofrani, and J. He. 2018. Induced seismicity in Western Canada linked to tectonic strain rate: Implications for regional seismic hazard. *Geophysical Research Letters* 45(20):11104–11115.

Hooper, D. U., F. S. Chapin III, J. J. Ewel, A. Hector, P. Inchausti, S. Lavorel, J. H. Lawton, D. Lodge, M. Loreau, S. Naeem, B. Schmid, H. Setälä, A. J. Symstad, J. Vandermeer, and D. A. Wardle. 2005. Effects of biodiversity on ecosystem functioning: A consensus of current knowledge. *Ecological Monographs* 75:3–35.

Houde, A. E. 1997. *Sex, Color, and Mate Choice in Guppies*. Princeton, N.J.: Princeton University Press.

Howe, W. H., and F. L. Knopf. 1991. On the imminent decline of the Rio Grande cottonwoods in central New Mexico. *Southwestern Naturalist* 36:218–24.

Hudson, P. J., A. P. Dobson, and D. Newborn. 1992. Do parasites make prey vulnerable to predation? *Journal of Animal Ecology* 61:681–92.

Huffaker, C. B. 1958. Experimental studies on predation: Dispersion factors and predator-prey oscillations. *Hilgardia* 27:343–83.

Hulshoff, R. M. 1995. Landscape indices describing a Dutch landscape. *Landscape Ecology* 10:101–11.

Hurrell, J. W. 1996. Influence of variations in extratropical wintertime teleconnections on Northern Hemisphere temperature. *Geophysical Research Letters* 23(6):665–68.

Huston, M. 1994. *Biological Diversity*. New York: Cambridge University Press.

Hutchings, J. A. 1996. Spatial and temporal variation in the density of northern cod and a review of hypotheses for the stock's collapse. *Canadian Journal of Fisheries and Aquatic Sciences* 53(5):943–62.

Hutchinson, G. E. 1957. Concluding remarks. *Cold Spring Symposia on Quantitative Biology* 22:415–27.

Hutchinson, G. E. 1959. Homage to Santa Rosalia or why are there so many kinds of animals? *American Naturalist* 93:145–59.

Hutchinson, G. E. 1961. The paradox of the plankton. *American Naturalist* 95:137–45.

Hutchinson, G. E. 1978. *An Introduction to Population Ecology*. New Haven, Conn.: Yale University Press.

Ichimura, S. 1956. On the standing crop and productive structure of phytoplankton community in some lakes of central Japan. *Japanese Botany Magazine Tokyo* 69:7–16.

Innes, D. J., and P. D. N. Hebert. 1988. The origin and genetic-basis of obligate parthenogenesis in daphnia-pulex. *Evolution* 42(5):1024–35.

Insel, T. R., and L. E. Shapiro. 1992. Oxytocin receptor distribution reflects social organization in monogamous and polygamous voles. *Proceedings of the National Academy of Sciences of the United States of America* 89:5981–85.

IPBES. 2019. Global assessment report on biodiversity and ecosystem services of the Intergovernmental Science-Policy Platform on Biodiversity and Ecosystem Services.

IPCC. 2001. *Climate Change 2001: The Scientific Basis. Contribution of Working Group I to the Third Assessment Report of the Intergovernmental Panel on Climate Change* [Houghton, J.T., Y. Ding, D.J. Griggs, M. Noguer, P.J. van der Linden, X. Dai, K. Maskell, and C.A. Johnson (eds.)]. Cambridge, UK, and New York, NY: Cambridge University Press.

IPCC. 2014. Climate Change 2014: Synthesis Report. Contribution of Working Groups I, II and III to the Fifth Assessment Report of the Intergovernmental Panel on Climate Change [Core Writing Team, R.K. Pachauri and L.A. Meyer (eds.)]. IPCC, Geneva, Switzerland, 151 pp.

IPCC. 2018. Global Warming of 1.5°C. An IPCC Special Report on the impacts of global warming of 1.5°C above pre-industrial levels and related global greenhouse gas emission pathways, in the context of strengthening the global response to the threat of climate change, sustainable development, and efforts to eradicate poverty [Masson-Delmotte, V., P. Zhai, H.-O. Pörtner, D. Roberts, J. Skea, P.R. Shukla, A. Pirani, W. Moufouma-Okia, C. Péan, R. Pidcock, S. Connors, J.B.R. Matthews, Y. Chen, X. Zhou, M.I. Gomis, E. Lonnoy, Maycock, M. Tignor, and T. Waterfield (eds.)]. World Meteorological Organization, Geneva, Switzerland, 32 pp.

Iriarte, J. A., W. L. Franklin, W. E. Johnson, and K. H. Redford. 1990. Biogeographic variation of food habits and body size of the American puma. *Oecologia* 85:185–90.

Isack, H. A., and H.-V. Reyer. 1989. Honeyguides and honey gatherers: Interspecific communication in a symbiotic relationship. *Science* 243:1343–46.

Isbell, F. V. Calcagno, A. Hector, J. Conolly, W. S. Harpole, P. B. Reich, M. Scherer-Lorenzen, B. Schmid, D. Tilman, J. van Ruijven, A. Weigelt, B.J Wilsey, E. S. Zavaleta, and M. Loreau. 2011. High plant diversity is needed to maintain ecosystem services. *Nature* 477:199–202.

Jakobsson, A., and O. Eriksson. 2000. A comparative study of seed number, seed size, seedling size and recruitment in grassland plants. *Oikos* 88:494–502.

Janzen, D. H. 1966. Coevolution of mutualism between ants and acacias in Central America. *Evolution* 20:249–75.

Janzen, D. H. 1967a. Fire, vegetation structure, and the ant x acacia interaction in Central America. *Ecology* 48:26–35.

Janzen, D. H. 1967b. Interaction of the bull's-horn acacia (*Acacia cornigera* L.) with an ant inhabitant (*Pseudomyrmex ferruginea* F. Smith) in eastern Mexico. *The University of Kansas Science Bulletin* 47:315–558.

Janzen, D. H. 1981a. Guanacaste tree seed-swallowing by Costa Rican range horses. *Ecology* 62:587–92.

Janzen, D. H. 1981b. Enterolohium cyclocarpum seed passage rate and survival in horses, Costa Rican Pleistocene seed dispersal agents. *Ecology* 62:593–601.

Janzen, D. H. 1981c. The peak in North American Ichneumonid species richness lies between 38 degrees and 42 degrees N. *Ecology* 62(1):532–37.

Janzen, D. H. 1985. Natural history of mutualisms. In D. H. Boucher. ed. *The Biology of Mutualism: Ecology and Evolution.* London: Croom Helm.

Jarvis, J. U. M. 1981. Eusociality in a mammal: Cooperative breeding in naked mole-rat colonies. *Science* 212:571–73.

Jenny, H. 1980. *The Soil Resource.* New York: Springer Verlag.

Jensen, M.P. , C.D. Allen, T. Eguchi, I.P. Bell, E.L. LaCasella, W.A. Hilton, C.A.M. Hof, and P.H. Dutton. 2018. Environmental warming and feminization of one of the largest sea turtle populations in the world. *Curr. Biol.* 28:154–9.

Johnson, N. C. 1993. Can fertilization of soil select less mutualistic mycorrhizae? *Ecological Applications* 3:749–57.

Jones, C. G., J. H. Lawton, and M. Shachak. 1994. Organisms as ecosystem engineers. *Oikos* 69:373–86.

Jonsen, I. D., and P. D. Taylor. 2000. Fine-scale movement behaviors of caloptergyid damselflies are influenced by landscape structure: An experimental manipulation. *Oikos* 88(3):553–62.

Jouzel, J., V. Masson-Delmotte, O. Cattani, G. Dreyfus, S. Falourd, G. Hoffmann, et al. 2007. Orbital and millennial Antarctic climate variability over the past 800,000 years. *Science* 317: 793–796.

Junk, W.J., P.B. Bayley, R.E. Sparks. 1989. The flood pulse concept in river-floodplain systems. In D.P. Dodge (ed.) Proceedings of the International Large River Symposium, *Ca. Spec. Publ. Fish. Aquat. Sci.* 106: 111–127.

Kairiukstis, L. A. 1967. In J. L. Tselniker. ed. *Svetovoi rezhim fotosintez i produktiwnost lesa* (*Light Regime, Photosynthesis and Forest Productivity*). Moscow: Nauka.

Kallio, P., and L. Kärenlampi. 1975. Photosynthesis in mosses and lichens. In J. P. Cooper. ed. *Photosynthesis and Productivity in Different Environments.* Cambridge, England: Cambridge University Press.

Kalmar, A., and D. J. Currie. 2006. A global model of island biogeography. *Global Ecology and Biogeography* 15(1):72–81.

Karlson, R. H., H. V. Cornell, and T. P. Hughes. 2004. Coral communities are regionally enriched along an oceanic biodiversity gradient. *Nature* 429(6994):867–70.

Kates, R. W., B. L. Turner II, and W. C. Clark. 1990. The great transformation. In B. L. Turner II, W. C. Clark, R. W. Kates, J. F. Richards, J. T. Mathews, and W. B. Meyer, eds. *The Earth as Transformed by Human Action.* Cambridge, England: Cambridge University Press.

Katona, S. K. 1989. Getting to know you. *Oceanus* 32:37–44.

Kawamura, K., Parrenin, F., Lisiecki, L., Uemura, R., Vimeux, F., Severinghaus, J.P., et al. 2007. Northern Hemisphere forcing of climatic cycles in Antarctica over the past 360,000 years. *Nature* 448: 912–916.

Keddy, P. A., and B. Shipley. 1989. Competitive Hierarchies in Herbaceous Plant-Communities. *Oikos* 54:234–41.

Keeler, K. H. 1981. A model of selection for facultative nonsymbiotic mutualism. *American Naturalist* 118:488–98.

Keeler, K. H. 1985. Benefit models of mutualism. In D. H. Boucher. ed. *The Biology of Mutualism: Ecology and Evolution.* London: Croom Helm.

Keeling, C. D., and T. P. Whorf. 1994. Atmospheric CO_2 records from sites in the SIO air sampling network. In T. A. Boden, D. P. Kaiser, R. J. Sepanski, and F. W. Stoss. eds. *Trends '93: A Compendium of Data on Global Change.* ORNL/CDIAC-65, Oak Ridge, Tenn.: Carbon Dioxide Information Analysis Center, Oak Ridge National Laboratory.

Keith, L. B. 1963. *Wildlife's Ten-Year Cycle.* Madison, Wis.: University of Wisconsin Press.

Keith, L. B. 1983. Role of food in hare population cycles. *Oikos* 40:385–95.

Keith, L. B., J. R. Cary, O. J. Rongstad, and M. C. Brittingham. 1984. Demography and ecology of a declining snowshoe hare population. *Wildlife Monographs* 90:1–43.

Kembel, S. K., and J. F. Cahill Jr. 2005. Plant phenotypic plasticity belowground: A phylogenetic perspective on root foraging tradeoffs. *American Naturalist* 166:216–30.

Kendall, K. C. 2010. Noninvasive methods for monitoring bear population trends: U.S. Geological Survey Fact Sheet, 2010–3054, 2 p.

Kerr, J. T. 1997. Species richness, endemism, and the choice of areas for conservation. *Conservation Biology* 11(5):1094–100.

Kevan, P. G. 1975. Sun-tracking solar furnaces in high arctic flowers: Significance for pollination and insects. *Science* 189:723–26.

Killingbeck, K. T., and W. G. Whitford. 1996. High foliar nitrogen in desert shrubs: An important ecosystem trait or defective desert doctrine? *Ecology* 77:1728–37.

Kleiber, M. 1947. Body size and metabolic rate. *Physiological Reviews* 27:511–541.

Klemmedson, J. O. 1975. Nitrogen and carbon regimes in an ecosystem of young dense ponderosa pine in Arizona. *Forest Science* 21:163–68.

Kline, T. C. J., J. J. Goering, O. A. Mathisen, and P. H. Poe. 1993. Recycling of elements transported upstream by runs of Pacific salmon: II. $d^{15}N$ and $d^{13}C$ evidence in the Kvichak River watershed, Bristol Bay, southwestern Alaska. *Canadian Journal of Fisheries and Aquatic Sciences* 50:2350–65.

Klinka, D. R., and T. E. Reimchen. 2009. Adaptive coat colour polymorphism in the Kermode bear of coastal British Columbia. *Biological Journal of the Linnean Society* 98:479–88.

Klironomos, J. N. 2003. Variation in plant response to native and exotic arbuscular mycorrhizal fungi. *Ecology* 84(9):2292–301.

Kloppers, E. L., C. C. St. Clair, and T. E. Hurd. 2005. Predator-resembling aversive conditioning for managing habituated wildlife. *Ecology and Society* 10(1):31. www.ecologyandsociety.org /vol10/iss1/art31/

Köchy, M., and S. D. Wilson. 2001. Nitrogen deposition and forest expansion in the northern Great Plains. *Journal of Ecology* 89(5):807–17.

Kodric-Brown, A. 1993. Female choice of multiple male criteria in guppies: Interacting effects of dominance, coloration and courtship. *Behavioral Ecology and Sociobiology* 32:415–20.

Koh, L. P., R. R. Dunn, N. S. Sodhi, R. K. Colwell, H. C. Proctor, and V. S. Smith. 2004. Species coextinctions and the biodiversity crisis. *Science* 305(5690):1632–34.

Kohl, M. T., D.R. Stahler, M.C. Metz, J.D. Forester, M.J. Kauffman, N. Varley, P.J. White, D.W. Smith, and D.R. MacNulty. 2018. Diel predator activity drives a dynamic landscape of fear. *Ecological Monographs* 88(4):638–652.

Kondash, A.J., and A.Vengosh. 2015. Water footprint of hydraulic fracturing. *Environmental Science and Technology Letters* 2(10):276–280.

Kontiainen, P., J. E. Brommer, P. Karell, and H. Pietiäinen. 2008. Heritability, plasticity and canalization of Ural owl egg size in a cyclic environment. *Journal of Evolutionary Biology* 21:88–96.

Korpimäki, E. 1988. Factors promoting polygyny in European birds of prey—a hypothesis. *Oecologia* 77:278–85.

Korpimäki, E., and K. Norrdahl. 1991. Numerical and functional responses of kestrels, short-eared owls, and long-eared owls to vole densities. *Ecology* 72:814–26.

Kotanen, P. M., and R. L. Jefferies. 1997. Long-term destruction of sub-arctic wetland vegetation by lesser snow geese. *Ecoscience* 4(2):179–82.

Krawchuk, M. A., S. G. Cumming, M. D. Flannigan, and R. W. Wein. 2006. Biotic and abiotic regulation of lightning fire initiation in the mixedwood boreal forest. *Ecology* 87(2):458–68.

Krebs, C. J. 2006. Ecology after 100 years: Progress and pseudo-progress. *New Zealand Journal of Ecology* 30(1):3–11.

Krebs, C. J., R. Boonstra, S. Boutin, and A. R. E. Sinclair. 2001. What drives the 10-year cycle of snowshoe hares? *BioScience* 51:25–36.

Krebs, C. J., S. Boutin, R. Boonstra, A. R. E. Sinclair, J. N. M. Smith, M. R. T. Dale, K. Martin, and R. Turkington. 1995. Impact of food and predation on the snowshoe hare cycle. *Science* 269:1112–15.

Krebs, C.J., S. Boutin, and R. Boonstra (eds.). 2001. *Ecosystem Dynamics of the Boreal Forest: The Kluane Project.* Oxford: Oxford University Press.

Kubien, D. S., S. von Cammerer, R. T. Furbank, and R. F. Sage. 2003. C-4 photosynthesis at low temperature. A study using transgenic plants with reduced amounts of Rubisco. *Plant Physiology* 132(3):1577–85.

Lack, D. 1968. *Ecological Adaptations for Breeding in Birds*. London: Methuen Ltd.

Lacy, R. C. 1997. Importance of genetic variation to the viability of mammalian populations. *Journal of Mammalogy* 78:320–35.

Laird, R. A., and B. S. Schamp. 2006. Competitive intransitivity promotes species coexistence. *American Naturalist* 168:182–93.

Laloe, J.-O., N. Esteban, J. Berkel, and G. C. Hays. 2016. Sand temperatures for nesting sea turtles in the Caribbean: Implications for hatchling sex ratios in the face of climate change. *Journal of Experimental Marine Biology and Ecology* 474:92–99.

Lamb, E. G., A. U. Mallik, and R. W. Mackereth. 2003. The early impact of adjacent clearcutting and forest fire on riparian zone vegetation in northwestern Ontario. *Forest Ecology and Management* 177(1–3):529–38.

Lamberti, G. A., and V. H. Resh. 1983. Stream periphyton and insect herbivores: An experimental study of grazing by a caddisfly population. *Ecology* 64:1124–35.

Lamichhane, K., and R. Babcock, Jr. 2012. An economic appraisal of using source separation of human urine to contain and treat endocrine disruptors in the USA. *Journal of Environmental Monitoring* 14:2557–2565.

Lampert, W., E. McCauley, and B. F. J. Manly. 2003. Trade-offs in the vertical distribution of zooplankton: Ideal free distribution with costs? *Proceedings of the Royal Society, B: Biological Sciences* 270(1516):765–73.

Landhausser, S. M., and V. J. Lieffers. 2001. Photosynthesis and carbon allocation of six boreal tree species grown in understory and open conditions. *Tree Physiology* 21(4):243–50.

Larcher, W. 1995. *Physiological Plant Ecology*. 3d ed. Berlin: Springer.

Larsson, D. G. J., H. Hällman, and L. Förlin. 2000. More male fish embryos near a pulp mill. *Environmental Toxicology and Chemistry* 19(12):2911–17.

Latham, R. E., and R. E. Ricklefs. 1993. Continental comparisons of temperate-zone tree species diversity. In R. E. Ricklefs and D. Schluter. eds. *Species Diversity in Ecological Communities*. Chicago: University of Chicago Press.

Laursen, A. E., and S. P. Seitzinger. 2002. The role of denitrification in nitrogen removal and carbon mineralization in Mid-Atlantic Bight sediments. *Continental Shelf Research* 22:1397–1416.

Lechowicz, M. J., and G. Bell. 1991. The ecology and genetics of fitness in forest plants: Microspatial heterogeneity of the edaphic environment. *Journal of Ecology* 79(3):687–96.

Ledig, F. T., V. Jacob-Cervantes, P. D. Hodgskiss, and T. Eguiluz-Piedra.

1997. Recent evolution and divergence among populations of a rare Mexican endemic, Chihuahua spruce, following Holocene climatic warming. *Evolution* 51:1815–27.

Leibold, M. A. 1991. Trophic interactions and habitat segregation between competing Daphnia species. *Oecologia* 86(4):510–20.

Lemon, W. C. 1993. Heritability of selectively advantageous foraging behavior in a small passerine. *Evolutionary Ecology* 7(4):421–28.

Leprieur, F., P. Descombes, T. Gaboriau, P. F. Cowman, V. Parravicini, M. Kulbicki, C. J. Melián, C. N. de Santana, C. Heine, D. Mouillot, D. R. Bellwood, and L. Pellissier. 2016. Plate tectonics drive tropical reef biodiversity dynamics. *Nature Communications* 7:11461. doi:10.1038/ncomms11461

Levang-Brilz, N., and M. E. Biondini. 2002. Growth rate, root development and nutrient uptake of 55 plant species from the Great Plains Grasslands, USA. *Plant Ecology* 165:117–44.

Leverich, W. J., and D.A. Levin. 1979. Age-specific survivorship and reproduction in *Phlox drummondii*. *American Naturalist* 113:881–903.

Levins, R. 1968. *Evolution in Changing Environments*. Princeton, N.J.: Princeton University Press.

Levin, S. 1992. The problem of pattern and scale in ecology: The Robert H. MacArthur Award lecture. *Ecology* 73:1943–67.

Lie, E., H. J. S. Larsen, S. Larsen, G. M. Johnsen, A. E. Derocher, N. J. Lunn, R. J. Norstrom, O. Wiig, and J. U. Skaare. 2004. Does high organochlorine (OC) exposure impair the resistance to infection in polar bears (*Ursus maritimus*)? Part I: Effect of OCs on the humoral immunity. *Journal of Toxicology and Environmental Health—Part a—Current Issues* 67(7):555–82.

Lie, E., H. J. S. Larsen, S. Larsen, G. M. Johansen, A. E. Derocher, N. J. Lunn, R. J. Norstrom, O. Wiig, and J. U. Skaare. 2005. Does high organochlorine (OC) exposure impair the resistance to infection in polar bears (*Ursus maritimus*)? Part II: Possible effect of OCs on mitogen- and antigen-induced lymphocyte proliferation. *Journal of Toxicology and Environmental Health-Part a-Current Issues* 68(6):457–84.

Liebig, J. 1840. *Chemistry in its Application to Agriculture and Physiology*. London: Taylor and Walton.

Likens, G. E., and F. H. Bormann. 1995. *Biogeochemistry of a Forested Ecosystem*. 2d ed. New York: Springer-Verlag.

Likens, G. E., F. H. Bormann, N. M. Johnson, D. W. Fisher, and R. S. Pierce. 1970. Effects of forest cutting and herbicide treatment on nutrient budgets in the Hubbard Brook watershed-ecosystem. *Ecological Monographs* 40:23–47.

Likens, G. E., F. H. Bormann, R. S. Pierce, and W. A. Reiners. 1978. Recovery of a deforested ecosystem. *Science* 199:492–96.

Lim, M. M., Z. Wang, D. E. Olazábal, X. Ren, E. F. Terwilliger, and L. J.

Young. 2004. Enhanced partner preference in a promiscuous species by manipulating the expression of a single gene. *Nature* 429:754–57.

Lindeman, R. L. 1942. The trophic-dynamic aspect of ecology. *Ecology* 23:399–418.

Liu J., J. M. Chen, J. Cihlar, and W. Chen. 2002. Net primary productivity mapped for Canada at 1-km resolution. *Global Ecology and Biogeography* 11:115–29.

Lomolino, M. V. 1990. The target hypothesis—the influence of island area on immigration rates of non-volant mammals. *Oikos* 57:297–300.

Lomolino, M. V., J. H. Brown, and R. Davis. 1989. Island biogeography of montane forest mammals in the American Southwest. *Ecology* 70:180–94.

Lorius, C., J. Jouzel, C. Ritz, L. Merlivat, N. I. Barkov, Y. S. Korotkevich, and V. M. Kotlyakov. 1985. A 150,000-year climatic record from Antarctic ice. *Nature* 316:591–96.

Lotka, A. J. 1925. *Elements of Physical Biology*. Baltimore, Md.: Williams and Wilkins.

Lotka, A. J. 1932a. The growth of mixed populations: Two species competing for a common food supply. *Journal of the Washington Academy of Sciences* 22:461–69.

Lotka, A. J. 1932b. Contribution to the mathematical theory of capture. I. Conditions for capture. *Proceedings of the National Academy of Sciences of the United States of America* 18:172–200.

Louda, S. M., R. W. Pemberton, M. T. Johnson, and P. A. Follett. 2003. Nontarget effects—the Achilles' Heel of biological control? Retrospective analyses to reduce risk associated with biocontrol introductions. *Annual Review of Entomology* 48:365–96.

MacArthur, R. H. 1955. Fluctuations of animal populations and a measure of community stability. *Ecology* 36:533–36.

MacArthur, R. H. 1958. Population ecology of some warblers of northeastern coniferous forests. *Ecology* 39:599–619.

MacArthur, R. H. 1972. *Geographical Ecology*. New York: Harper & Row.

MacArthur, R. H., and J. W. MacArthur. 1961. On bird species diversity. *Ecology* 42:594–98.

MacArthur, R. H., and E. R. Pianka. 1966. On optimal use of a patchy environment. *American Naturalist* 100:603–9.

MacArthur, R. H., and E. O. Wilson. 1963. An equilibrium theory of insular zoogeography. *Evolution* 17:373–87.

MacArthur, R. H., and E. O. Wilson. 1967. *The Theory of Island Biogeography*. Princeton, N.J.: Princeton University Press.

MacDonald, J. S., E. A. MacIsaac, and H. E. Herunter. 2003. The effect of variable-retention riparian buffer zones on water temperatures in small headwater streams in sub-boreal forest ecosystems of British Columbia. *Canadian Journal of Forest Research* 33:1371–82.

Mack, R. N., D. Simberloff, W. M. Lonsdale, H. Evans, M. Clout, and F. A. Bazzaz. 2000. Biotic invasions: Causes, epidemiology, global consequences, and control. *Ecological Applications* 10(3):689–710.

Mackey, R. L., and D. J. Currie. 2001. The diversity-disturbance relationship: Is it generally strong and peaked? *Ecology* 82:3479–92.

MacLulich, D. A. 1937. Fluctuation in the numbers of the varying hare (*Lepus americanus*). University of Toronto Studies in Biology Series No. 43.

Mak, S., M. Morshed, and B. Henry. 2010. Ecological Niche Modelling of Lyme Disease in British Columbia, Canada. *Journal of Medical Entomology* 47:99–105.

Mallet, J. 2008. Hybridization, ecological races and the nature of species: Empirical evidence for the ease of speciation. *Philosophical Transactions of the Royal Society B*. 363:2971–86.

Mandelbrot, B. 1982. *The Fractal Geometry of Nature*. New York: W. H. Freeman.

Mao, J. S., M. S. Boyce, D. W. Smith, F. J. Singer, D. J. Vales, J. M. Vore, and E. H. Merrill. 2005. Habitat selection by elk before and after wolf reintroduction in Yellowstone National Park. *Journal of Wildlife Management* 69:1691–1707.

Marchand, P. J. 1996. *Life in the Cold*. Hanover, N.H.: University Press of New England.

Margolis, H. A., L. B. Flanagan, and B. D. Amiro. 2006. The Fluxnet-Canada Research Network: Influence of climate and disturbance on carbon cycling in forests and peatlands. *Agricultural and Forest Meteorology* 140(1–4):1–5.

Maron, J. L., and E. Crone. 2006. Herbivory: Effects on plant abundance, distribution and population growth. *Proceedings of the Royal Society B-Biological Sciences* 273(1601):2575–84.

Marshall, D. L. 1990. Non-random mating in a wild radish, *Raphanus sativus*. *Plant Species Biology* 5:143–56.

Marshall, D. L., and M. W. Folsom. 1991. Mate choice in plants: An anatomical to population perspective. *Annual Review of Ecology and Systematics* 22:37–63.

Marshall, D. L., and O. S. Fuller. 1994. Does nonrandom mating among wild radish plants occur in the field as well as in the greenhouse? *American Journal of Botany* 81:439–45.

Marshall, D. L., M. W. Folsom, C. Hatfield, and T. Bennett. 1996. Does interference competition among pollen grains occur in wild radish? *Evolution* 50:1842–48.

Mathewson, D. D., M. D. Hocking, and T. E. Reimchen. 2003. Nitrogen uptake in riparian plant communities across a sharp ecological boundary of salmon density. *BMC Ecology* 3:4.

May, R. M. 1975. Patterns of species abundance and diversity. In M. L. Cody and J. M. Diamond. eds. *Ecology and Evolution of Communities*. Cambridge, Mass.: Harvard University Press.

Maynard Smith, J. 1982. *Evolution and the Theory of Games*. Cambridge, England: Cambridge University Press.

Mayor, S.J., RP. Guralnick, M.W. Tingley, J. Otegui, J.C. Withey, S.C. Elmendorf, M.E. Andrew, S. Leyk, I.S. Pearse, and D.C. Schneider. 2017. Increasing phenological asynchrony between spring green-up and arrival of migratory birds. *Scientific Reports* 7:1902.

Mayr, E. 1942. *Systematics and the Origin of Species.* New York: Columbia University Press.

Mayr, E. 2001. *What Evolution Is.* New York: Basic Books.

Mazerolle, M. J., and M. A. Villard. 1999. Patch characteristics and landscape context as predictors of species presence and abundance: A review. *Ecoscience* 6(1):117–24.

McCarthy, D. P., P. F. Donald, J. P. W. Scharlemann, G. M. Buchanan, A. Balmford, J. M. H. Green, L. A. Bennun, N. D. Burgess, L. D. C. Fishpool, S. T. Garnett, D. L. Leonard, R. F. Malony, P. Morling, H. M. Schaefer, A. Symes, D. A. Wiedenfeld, and S. H. M. Butchart. 2012. Financial costs of meeting global biodiversity conservation targets: Current spending and unmet needs. *Science* 338(6109):946–49.

McCarthy, M. J., P. J. Lavrentyev, L. Yang, L. Zhang, Y. Chen, B. Qin, and W. S. Gardner. 2007. Nitrogen dynamics and microbial food web structure during a summer cyanobacterial bloom in a subtropical, shallow, well-mixed, eutrophic lake (Lake Taihu, China). *Hydrobiologia* 581(1):195–207.

McCormick, S. D. 2001. Endocrine control of osmoregulation in teleost fish. *American Zoologist* 41:781–94.

McElroy, M. B. 1983. Marine biological controls on atmospheric CO_2 and climate. *Nature* 302:328–29.

McKinnon, J. S., S. Mori, B. K. Blackman, L. David, D. M. Kingsley, L. Jamieson, J. Chou, and D. Schluter. 2004. Evidence for ecology's role in speciation. *Nature* 429(6989):294–98.

McLean, M. A., and D. Parkinson. 2000. Field evidence of the effects of the epigeic earthworm *Dendrobaena octaedra* on the microfungal community in pine forest floor. *Soil Biology & Biochemistry* 32(3):351–60.

McNaughton, S. J. 1976. Serengeti migratory wildebeest: Facilitation of energy flow by grazing. *Science* 191:92–94.

McNaughton, S. J. 1985. Ecology of a grazing ecosystem: The Serengeti. *Ecological Monographs* 55:259–94.

McNaughton, S. J., R. W. Ruess, and S. W. Seagle. 1988. Large mammals and process dynamics in African ecosystems. *BioScience* 38:794–800.

Meentemeyer, V. 1978. An approach to the biometeorology of decomposer organisms. *International Journal of Biometeorology* 22:94–102.

Melillo, J. M., J. D. Aber, and J. F. Muratore. 1982. Nitrogen and lignin control of hardwood leaf litter decomposition dynamics. *Ecology* 63:621–26.

Meybeck, M. 1982. Carbon, nitrogen, and phosphorus transport by world rivers. *American Journal of Science* 282:401–50.

Miller, A.K., B. Maritz, S. McKay, X. Glaudas, and G.J. Alexander. 2015. An ambusher's arsenal: Chemical crypsis in the puff adder (*Bitis arietans*). *Proceedings of the Royal Society B, Biological Sciences* 282:20152182. doi.org/10.1098/rspb.2015.2182

Miller, R. B. 1923. First report on a forestry survey of Illinois. *Illinois Natural History Bulletin* 14:291–377.

Mills, K. H., and D. W. Schindler. 1987. Preface. *Canadian Journal of Fisheries and Aquatic Sciences* 44(Suppl. 1):3–5.

Millward, A., M. Torchia, A. Laursen, and L. Rothman. 2014. Vegetation placement for summer built surface temperature moderation in an urban microclimate. *Environmental Management* 53(6):1043–57.

Milne, B. T. 1993. Pattern analysis for landscape evaluation and characterization. In M. E. Jensen and P. S. Bourgeron. eds. *Ecosystem Management: Principles and Applications.* Gen. Tech. Report PNW-GTR-318. Portland, Ore.: U.S. Department of Agriculture Forest Service, Pacific Northwest Research Station.

Minnich, R. A. 1983. Fire mosaics in southern California and northern Baja California. *Science* 219:1287–94.

Miranda, A. C., H. Schielzeth, T. Sonntag, and J. Partecke. 2013. Urbanization and its effects on personality traits: A result of microevolution or phenotypic plasticity? *Global Change Biology* 19(9):2634–44.

Mitchell, N. L., and G. A. Lamberti. 2005. Responses in dissolved nutrients and epilithon abundance to spawning salmon in southeast Alaska streams. *Limnology and Oceanography* 50:217–27.

Mittelbach, G. G., D. W. Schemske, H. V. Cornell, A. P. Allen, J. M. Brown, M. B. Bush, S. P. Harrison, A. H. Hurlbert, N. Knowlton, H. A. Lessios, C. M. McCain, A. R. McCune, L. A. McDade, M. A. McPeek, T. J. Near, T. D. Price, R. E. Ricklefs, K. Roy, D. F. Sax, F. Dov, D. Schluter, J. M. Sobel, and M. Turelli. 2007. Evolution and the latitudinal diversity gradient: Speciation, extinction and biogeography. *Ecology Letters* 10(4):315–31.

Molles, M. C. Jr. 1978. Fish species diversity on model and natural reef patches: Experimental insular biogeography. *Ecological Monographs* 48:289–305.

Mooers, A. O., L. R. Prugh, M. Festa-Bianchet, and J. A. Hutchings. 2007. Biases in legal listings under Canadian endangered species legislation. *Conservation Biology* 21:572–75.

Moore, D. R. J., P. A. Keddy, C. L. Gaudet, and I. C. Wisheu. 1989. Conservation of wetlands—do infertile wetlands deserve a higher priority? *Biological Conservation* 47:203–17.

Moore, J. 1983. Responses of an avian predator and its isopod prey to an acanthocephalan parasite. *Ecology* 64:1000–15.

Moore, J. 1984a. Altered behavioral responses in intermediate hosts—an acanthocephalan parasite strategy. *American Naturalist* 123:572–77.

Moore, J. 1984b. Parasites that change the behavior of their host. *Scientific American* 250:108–15.

Moore, J. A. H., and T. J. Roper. 2003. Temperature and humidity in badger *Meles meles* setts. *Mammal Review* 33:308–13.

Moore, J. K., S. C. Doney, and K. Kindsay. 2004. Upper ocean ecosystem dynamics and iron cycling in a global three-dimensional model. *Annual Review of Ecology and Systematics* 33:235–63.

Mooring, M. S., and W. M. Samuel. 1999. Premature loss of winter hair in free-ranging moose (*Alces alces*) infested with winter ticks (*Dermacentor albipictus*) is correlated with grooming rate. *Canadian Journal of Zoology-Revue Canadienne De Zoologie* 77(1):148–56.

Moran, P. A. P. 1949. The statistical analysis of the sunspot and lynx cycles. *Journal of Animal Ecology* 18:115–16.

Moritz, R. E., C. M. Bitz, and E. J. Steig. 2002. Dynamics of recent climate change in the Arctic. *Science* 297:1497–502.

Mosser, J. L., A. G. Mosser, and T. D. Brock. 1974. Population ecology of *Sulfolobus acidocaldarius.* I. Temperature strains. *Archives for Microbiology* 97:169–79.

Moyle, P. B., and J. J. Cech Jr. 1982. *Fishes and Introduction to Ichthyology.* Englewood Cliffs, N.J.: Prentice Hall.

Muir, J. 1915. *Travels in Alaska.* Boston: Houghton Mifflin.

Müller, K. 1954. Investigations on the organic drift in north Swedish streams. *Reports of the Institute of Freshwater Research of Drottningholm* 35:133–48.

Müller, K. 1974. Stream drift as a chronobiological phenomenon in running water ecosystems. *Annual Review of Ecology and Systematics* 5:309–3.

Mullon, C., P. Freon, and P. Cury. 2005. The dynamics of collapse in world fisheries. *Fish and Fisheries* 6(2):111–20.

Munger, J. C., and J. H. Brown. 1981. Competition in desert rodents: An experiment with semipermeable exclosures. *Science* 211:510–12.

Murie, A. 1944. The wolves of Mount McKinley. *Fauna of the National Parks of the U.S.. Fauna Series No.5.* Washington, D.C.: U.S. Department of the Interior, National Park Service.

Murie, A. 1961. *A Naturalist in Alaska.* New York: Devin-Adair Company.

Murie, J. O. 1985. A comparison of life history traits in two populations of Columbian ground squirrels in Alberta, Canada. *Acta Zool. Fennica* 173:43–45.

Murphy, P. G., and A. E. Lugo. 1986. Ecology of tropical dry forest. *Annual Review of Ecology and Systematics* 17:67–88.

Murphy-Klassen, H. M., T. J. Underwood, S. G. Sealy, and A. A. Czyrnyj. 2005. Long-term trends in spring arrival dates of migrant birds at Delta Marsh, Manitoba, in relation to climate change. *Auk* 122(4):1130–48.

Muscatine, L., and C. F. D'Elia. 1978. The uptake, retention, and release of ammonium by reef corals. *Limnology and Oceanography* 23:725–34.

Muyzer, G., E.C. de Waal, and A.G. Uitterlinden. 1993. Profiling of complex microbial populations by denaturing gradient gel electrophoresis analysis of polymerase chain reaction-amplified genes coding for 16S rRNA. *Applied and Environmental Microbiology* 59:695–700.

Myers, N., R. A. Mittermeier, C. G. Mittermeier, G. A. B. da Fonseca, and J. Kent. 2000. Biodiversity hotspots for conservation priorities. *Nature* 403(6772):853–58.

Nagelkerken, I., and S. D. Connell. 2015. Global alteration of ocean ecosystem functioning due to increasing human CO_2 emissions. *Proceedings of the National Academy of Sciences of the United States of America* 112:13272–77.

Naiman, R. J., G. Pinay, C. A. Johnston, and J. Pastor. 1994. Beaver influences on the long-term biogeochemical characteristics of boreal forest drainage networks. *Ecology* 75:905–21.

Naiman, R. J., R. E. Bilby, D. E. Schindler, and J. M. Helfield. 2002. Pacific salmon, nutrients, and the dynamics of freshwater and riparian ecosystems. *Ecosystems* 5:399–417.

Newbold, J. D., J. W. Elwood, R. V. O'Neill, and A. L. Sheldon. 1983. Phosphorus dynamics in a woodland stream ecosystem: A study of nutrient spiraling. *Ecology* 64:1249–65.

Newbold, T., L. N. Hudson, S. L. L. Hill, S. Contu, I. Lysenko, R. A. Senior, L. Börger, D. J. Bennett, A. Choimes, B. Collen et al. 2015. Global effects of land use on local terrestrial biodiversity. *Nature* 520:45–50.

Newman, E. I. 1973. Competition and diversity in herbaceous vegetation. *Nature* 244:310–11.

NIH. 2016. National Human Genome Research Institute. www.genome.gov/. Accessed November 13, 2016.

Nilsson, S. G., J. Bengtsson, and S. Ås. 1988. Habitat diversity or area per se? Species richness of woody plants, carabid beetles and land snails on islands. *Journal of Animal Ecology* 57:685–704.

Norris, R. D., P P. Marra, T. K. Kyser, and L. M. Ratcliffe. 2005. Tracking habitat use of a long-distance migratory bird, the American redstart *Setaphaga ruticilla,* using stable-carbon isotopes in cellular blood. *Journal of Avian Biology* 36164–70.

Nottrott, R. W., J. F. Franklin, and J. R. Vande Castle. 1994. *International Networking in Long-Term Ecological Research.* Seattle: U.S. LTER Network Office, University of Washington.

Novacek, M. G. 2001. *The Biodiversity Crisis: Losing What Counts.* New York: New Press.

Ødegaard, F. 2000. How many species of arthropods? Erwin's estimate revised. *Biological Journal of the Linnean Society* 71(4):583–97.

O'Donoghue, M., S. Boutin, C. J. Krebs, and E. J. Hofer. 1997. Numerical responses of coyotes and lynx to the snowshoe hare cycle. *Oikos* 80:150–62.

O'Donoghue, M., S. Boutin, C. J. Krebs, G. Zuleta, D. L. Murray, and E. J. Hofer. 1998. Functional responses of coyotes and lynx to the snowshoe hare cycle. *Ecology* 79:1193–208.

Odum, E. P. 1953. *Fundamentals of Ecology*. Philadelphia: Saunders,

Ohman, M.D. 1990. The demographic benefits of diel vertical migration by zooplankton. *Ecological Monographs* 60(3):257–81.

Olff, H., and M. E. Ritchie. 1998. Effects of herbivores on grassland plant diversity. *Trends in Ecology & Evolution* 13(7):261–65.

Olsen, G. H., M. Mauritzen, A. E. Derocher, E. G. Sormo, J. U. Skaare, O. Wiig, and B. M. Jenssen. 2003. Space-use strategy is an important determinant of PCB concentrations in female polar bears in the Barents sea. *Environmental Science & Technology* 37(21):4919–24.

Ostfeld, R. S., C. G. Jones, and J. O. Wolff. 1996. Of mice and mast. *Bioscience* 46:323–30.

Ottersen, G., B. Planque, A. Belgrano, E. Post, P. C. Reid, and N. C. Stenseth. 2001. Ecological effects of the North Atlantic Oscillation. *Oecologia* 128(1):1–14.

Packer, C., and A. E. Pusey. 1982. Cooperation and competition within coalitions of male lions: Kin selection or game-theory? *Nature* 296:740–42.

Packer, C., and A. E. Pusey. 1983. Cooperation and competition in lions: Reply. *Nature* 302:356.

Packer, C., and A. E. Pusey. 1997. Divided we fall: Cooperation among lions. *Scientific American* 276(5):52–59.

Packer, C., D. A. Gilbert, A. E. Pusey, and S. J. O'Brien. 1991. A molecular genetic analysis of kinship and cooperation in African lions. *Nature* 351:562–65.

Packer, L. 1991. The evolution of social-behavior and nest architecture in sweat bees of the subgenus evylaeus (Hymenoptera, halictidae)—a phylogenetic approach. *Behavioral Ecology and Sociobiology* 29(3):153–60.

Paine, R. T. 1966. Food web complexity and species diversity. *American Naturalist* 100:65–75.

Paine, R. T. 1969. A note on trophic complexity and community stability. *American Naturalist* 103:91–93.

Paine, R. T. 1976. Size-limited predation: An observational and experimental approach with the *Mytilus-Pisaster* interaction. *Ecology* 57:858–73.

Palumbi, S. R. 2001. Humans as the world's greatest evolutionary force. *Science* 293:1786–90.

Papke, R. T., N. B. Ramsing, M. M. Bateson, and D. M. Ward. 2003. Geographical isolation in hot spring cyanobacteria. *Environmental Microbiology* 5(8):650–59.

Park, T. 1948. Experimental studies of interspecific competition. I. Competition between populations of flour beetles *Tribolium confusum* Duval and *Tribolium castaneum* Herbst. *Ecological Monographs* 18:267–307.

Park, T. 1954. Experimental studies of interspecific competition. II. Temperature, humidity and competition in two species of *Tribolium*. *Physiological Zoology* 27:177–238.

Park, T., D. B. Mertz, W. Grodzinski, and T. Prus. 1965. Cannibalistic predation in populations of flour beetles. *Physiological Zoology* 38:289–321.

Parmenter, R. R., and V.A. Lamarra. 1991. Nutrient cycling in a freshwater marsh: The decomposition of fish and waterfowl carrion. *Limnology and Oceanography* 36:976–87.

Parmenter, R. R., C. A. Parmenter, and C. D. Cheney. 1989. Factors influencing microhabitat partitioning among coexisting species of arid-land darkling beetles (Tenebrionidae): Behavioural responses to vegetation architecture. *The Southwestern Naturalist* 34:319–29.

Parmesan, C., and G. Yohe. 2003. A globally coherent fingerprint of climate change impacts across natural systems. *Nature* 421(6918):37–42.

Partel, M., and S. D. Wilson. 2002. Root dynamics and spatial pattern in prairie and forest. *Ecology* 83(5):1199–203.

Pauly, D., V. Christensen, J. Dalsgaard, R. Froese, and F. Torres. 1998. Fishing down marine food webs. *Science* 279(5352):860–63.

Pearcy, R. W. 1977. Acclimation of photosynthetic and respiratory carbon dioxide exchange to growth temperature in *Atriplex lentiformis* (Torr.) Wats. *Plant Physiology* 59:795–99.

Pearcy, R. W., and A. T. Harrison. 1974. Comparative photosynthetic and respiratory gas exchange characteristics of *Atriplex lentiformis* (Torr.) Wats. in coastal and desert habitats. *Ecology* 55:1104–11.

Peckarsky, B. L. 1980. Behavioural interactions between stoneflies and mayflies: Behavioural observations. *Ecology* 61:932–43.

Peckarsky, B. L. 1982. Aquatic insect predator-prey relations. *BioScience* 32:261–66.

Peierls, B. L., N. F. Caraco, M. L. Pace, and J. J. Cole. 1991. Human influence on river nitrogen. *Nature* 350:386–87.

Peters, R. H., and K. Wassenberg. 1983. The effect of body size on animal abundance. *Oecologia* 60:89–96.

Peters, V. S., S. E. Macdonald, and M. R. T. Dale. 2006. Patterns of initial versus delayed regeneration of white spruce in boreal mixedwood succession. *Canadian Journal of Forest Research-Revue Canadienne de Recherche Forestière* 36(6):1597–609.

Peterson, A. T., and D. A. Vieglais. 2001. Predicting species invasions using ecological niche modelling: New approaches from bioinformatics attack a pressing problem. *Bioscience* 51:363–71.

Peterson, A. T., E. Martínez-Meyer, C. González-Salazar, and P. W. Hall. 2004. Modeled climate change effects on distributions of Canadian butterfly species. *Canadian Journal of Zoology* 82(6):851–58.

Peterson, B. J., R. W. Howarth, and R. H. Garritt. 1985. Multiple stable isotopes used to trace the flow of organic matter in estuarine food webs. *Science* 227:1361–63.

Pianka, E. R. 1970. On r and K selection. *American Naturalist* 102:592–97.

Pianka, E. R. 1972. r and K selection or b and d selection. *American Naturalist* 106:581–88.

Pickett, S. T. A., M. L. Cadenasso, J. M. Grove, P. M. Groffman, L. E. Band, C. G. Boone, W. R. Burgch Jr., C. S. B. Grimmond, J. Hom, J. C. Jenkins, N. L. Law, C. H. Nilon, R. V. Pouyat, K. Szlavec, P. S. Warren, and M. A. Wilson. 2008. Beyond urban legends: An emerging framework of urban ecology, as illustrated by the Baltimore Ecosystem Study. *BioScience* 58:139–50.

Pielou, E. C. 1966. Measurement of diversity in different types of biological collections. *Journal of Theoretical Biology* 13:131–44.

Pielou, E. C. 1977. *Mathematical Ecology*. New York: Wiley.

Pielou, E. C. 1991. *After the ice age: The Return of Life to Glaciated North America*. Chicago: University of Chicago Press.

Pimentel, D., R. Zuniga, and D. Morrison. 2005. Update on the environmental and economic costs associated with alien-invasive species in the United States. *Ecological Economics* 52(3):273–88.

Pimlott, D. H. 1953. Newfoundland moose. *Transactions of the North American Wildlife Conference* 18:563–81.

Pimm, S. L. 1982. *Food Webs*. London: Chapman and Hall.

Platt, T. 1975. Spectral Analysis in Ecology. *Annual Review of Ecology and Systematics* 6:189–210.

Platt, T., and A. D. Jassby. 1976. Relationship between photosynthesis and light for natural assemblages of coastal marine phytoplankton. *Journal of Phycology* 12:421–30.

Podos, J. 2010. Acoustic discrimination of sympatric morphs in Darwin's finches: A behavioural mechanism for assortative mating? *Philosophical Transactions of the Royal Society B-Biological Sciences* 365:1031–39.

Polischuk, S. C., R. J. Norstrom, and M. A. Ramsay. 2002. Body burdens and tissue concentrations of organochlorines in polar bears (*Ursus maritimus*) vary during seasonal fasts. *Environmental Pollution* 118(1):29–39.

Post, D. M. 2002. Using stable isotopes to estimate trophic position: Models, methods and assumptions. *Ecology* 83:703–18.

Post, E., and N. C. Stenseth. 1999. Climatic variability, plant phenology, and northern ungulates. *Ecology* 80(4):1322–39.

Post, W. M., T.-H. Peng, W. R. Emanuel, A. W. King, V. H. Dale, and D. L. DeAngelis. 1990. The global carbon cycle. *American Scientist* 78:310–26.

Poulin, R., and W. L. Vickery. 1995. Cleaning symbiosis as an evolutionary game—to cheat or not to cheat. *Journal of Theoretical Biology* 175(1):63–70.

Power, M. E. 1990. Effects of fish on river food webs. *Science* 250:811–14.

Preisser, E. L., D. I. Bolnick, and M. F. Benard. 2005. Scared to death? The effects of intimidation and consumption in predator-prey interactions. *Ecology* 86(2):501–9.

Preston, F. W. 1948. The commonness, and rarity, of species. *Ecology* 29:254–83.

Preston, F. W. 1962a. The canonical distribution of commonness and rarity: Part I. *Ecology* 43:185–215.

Preston, F. W. 1962b. The canonical distribution of commonness and rarity: Part II. *Ecology* 43:410–32.

Purvis, A., J. L. Gittleman, G. Cowlishaw, and G. M. Mace. 2000. Predicting extinction risk in declining species. *Proceedings of the Royal Society of London Series B-Biological Sciences* 267(1456):1947–52.

Rabalais, N. N., R. E. Turner, and W. J. Wiseman. 2002. Gulf of Mexy hypoxia, aka "The dead zone." *Annual Review of Ecology and Systematics*. 33:235–63.

Rabalais, N. N., R. J. Diaz, L. A. Levin, R. E. Turner, D. Gilbert, and J. Zhang. 2010. Dynamics and distribution of natural and human-caused hypoxia. *Biogeosciences* 7: 585–619.

Rabinowitz, D. 1981. Seven forms of rarity. In H. Synge. ed. *The Biological Aspects of Rare Plant Conservation*. New York: John Wiley & Sons.

Ralph, C. J. 1985. Habitat association patterns of forest and steppe birds of northern Patagonia, Argentina. *The Condor* 87:471–83.

Raup, D. M., and J. J. Sepkoski. 1982. Mass extinctions in the marine fossil record. *Science, New Series* 215(4539):1501–3.

Rawson, T. 2001. *Changing Tracks— Predators and Politics in Mt. McKinley National Park*. Fairbanks: University of Alaska Press.

Reader, R. J., S. D. Wilson, J. W. Belcher, I. Wisheu, P. A. Keddy, D. Tilman, E. C. Morris, J. B. Grace, J. B. McGraw, H. Olff, R. Turkington, Y. Klein, B. Leung, B. Shipley, R. Van Hulst, E. Johansson, C. Nilsson, J. Gurevitch, K. Grigulis, and B. E. Beisner. 1994. Plant competition in relation to neighbor biomass: An intercontinental study with *Poa pratensis*. *Ecology* 75(6):1753–60.

Réale, D., A. G. McAdam, S. Boutin, and D. Berteaux. 2003. Genetic and plastic responses of a northern mammal to climate change. *Proceedings of the Royal Society of London Series B-Biological Sciences* 270(1515):591–96.

Redfield, A. C. 1934. On the proportions of organic derivatives in sea water and their relation to the composition of plankton. In R. J. Daniel. ed. *James Johnstone Memorial Volume*, pp. 176–92. Liverpool: Liverpool University Press.

Redfield, A. C. 1958. The biological control of chemical factors in the environment. *American Scientist* 46:205–21.

Redford, K. H. 1992. The empty forest. *BioScience* 42:412–22.

Refsnider, J.M., and F.J. Janzen. 2016. Temperature-dependent sex determination under rapid anthropogenic environmental change: Evolution at a turtle's pace? *Journal of Heredity* 107:61–70.

Reich, P. B., D. Tilman, F. Isbell, K. Mueller, S. E. Hobbie, D. F. B. Flynn, and N. Eisenhauer. 2012. Impacts of biodiversity loss escalate through time as redundance fades. *Science* 336(6081):589–92.

Reid, W. V., and K. R. Miller. 1989. *Keeping Options Alive: The Scientific Basis for Conserving Biodiversity.* Washington, D.C.: World Resources Institute.

Reiners, W. A., I. A. Worley, and D. B. Lawrence. 1971. Plant diversity in a chronosequence at Glacier Bay, Alaska. *Ecology* 52:55–69.

Reznick, D. A., H. Bryga, and J. A. Endler. 1990. Experimentally induced life-history evolution in a natural population. *Nature* 346:357–59.

Reynolds, H. L., and C. D'Antonio. 1996. The ecological significance of plasticity in root weight ratio in response to nitrogen: Opinion. *Plant and Soil* 185:75–97.

Reynolds, J. D. 2003. Life histories and extinction risk. In T. M. Blackburn and K. J. Gaston. eds. *Macroecology.* Oxford: Blackwell Publishing.

Richey, J. E. 1983. The phosphorus cycle. In B. Bolin and R. B. Cook. eds. *The Major Biogeochemical Cycles and Their Interaction.* New York: John Wiley & Sons.

Ricklefs, R. E. 1987. Community diversity: Relative roles of local and regional processes. *Science* 235:167–71.

Ripple, W. J., and R. L. Beschta. 2006. Linking wolves to willows via risk-sensitive foraging by ungulates in the northern Yellowstone ecosystem. *Forest Ecology and Management* 230:96–106.

Roberts, C. M., C. J. McClean, J. E. N. Veron, J. P. Hawkins, G. R. Allen, D. E. McAllister, C. G. Mittermeier, F. W. Schueler, M. Spalding, F. Wells, C. Vynne, and T. B. Werner. 2002. Marine biodiversity hotspots and conservation priorities for tropical reefs. *Science* 295(5558):1280–84.

Robertson, G. P., M. A. Huston, F. C. Evans, and J. M. Tiedje. 1988. Spatial variability in a successional plant community: Patterns of nitrogen availability. *Ecology* 69:1517–24.

Rodríguez-Verdugo, A., D. Carillo-Cisneros, A. González- González, B. S. Gaut, and A. F. Bennett. 2014. Different fitness tradeoffs result from alternate genetic adaptations to a common environment. *Proceedings of the National Academy of Sciences of the United States of America* 111(33):12121–26.

Roland, J., N. Keyghobadi, and S. Fownes. 2000. Alpine Parnassius butterfly dispersal: Effects of landscape and population size. *Ecology* 81:1642–53.

Rolland, J., F. L. Condamine, C. R. Beeravolu, F. Jiguet, and H. Morlon. 2015. Dispersal is a major driver of the latitudinal diversity gradient of Carnivora. *Global Ecology and Biogeography* 24(9):1059–71.

Rood, S. B., S. G. Bigelow, and A. A. Hall. 2011. Root architecture of riparian trees: River cut-banks provide natural hydraulic excavation, revealing that cottonwoods are facultative phreatophytes. *Trees* 25:907–17.

Rood, S. B., J. H. Braatne, and F. M. R. Hughes. 2003. Ecophysiology of riparian cottonwoods: Stream flow dependency, water relations and restoration. *Tree Physiology* 23(16):1113–24.

Rood, S. B., G. M. Samuelson, J. H. Braatne, C. R. Gourley, F. M. R. Hughes, and J. M. Mahoney. 2005. Managing river flows to restore floodplain forests. *Frontiers in Ecology and the Environment* 3(4):193–201.

Rooney, R. C., and S. E. Bayley. 2011. Setting appropriate reclamation targets and evaluating success: Aquatic vegetation in natural and post-oil-sands mining wetlands in Alberta, Canada. *Ecological Engineering* 37:569–79.

Root, T. 1988. *Atlas of Wintering North American Birds.* Chicago: University of Chicago Press.

Root, T. L., J. T. Price, K. R. Hall, S. H. Schneider, C. Rosenzweig, and J. A. Pounds. 2003. Fingerprints of global warming on wild animals and plants. *Nature* 421(6918):57–60.

Rosell, F., O. Bozser, P. Collen, and H. Parker. 2005. Ecological impact of beavers *Castor fiber* and *Castor canadensis* and their ability to modify ecosystems. *Mammal Review* 35: 248–76.

Rosemond, A. D., C. M. Pringle, A. Ramirez, M. J. Paul, and J. L. Meyer. 2002. Landscape variation in phosphorus concentration and effects on detritus-based tropical streams. *Limnology and Oceanography* 47: 278–89.

Rosenzweig, M. L. 1968. Net primary productivity of terrestrial environments: Predictions from climatological data. *American Naturalist* 102:67–84.

Rosenzweig, M. L. 1992. Species diversity gradients: We know more and less than we thought. *Journal of Mammalogy* 73:715–30.

Rosenzweig, M. L., and R. MacArthur. 1963. Graphical representation and stability conditions of predator–prey interaction. *American Naturalist* 97:209–23.

Roth J. D. 2002. Temporal variability in arctic fox diet as reflected in stable-carbon isotopes; the importance of sea ice. *Oecologia* 133:70–77.

Rowe, L., G. Arnqvist, A. Sih, and J. Krupa. 1994. Sexual conflict and the evolutionary ecology of mating patterns—water striders as a model system. *Trends in Ecology & Evolution* 9(8):289–93.

Rydin, H., and S-O. Borgegård. 1988. Plant species richness on islands over a century of primary succession: Lake Hjälmaren. *Ecology* 69:916–27.

Ryther, J. H. 1969. Photosynthesis and fish production in the sea. *Science* 166:72–76.

Saabye, H. E. 1776. Fragments of a diary kept in Greenland during the years 1770–1779. In H. Ostermann. ed. 1942. *Reports from Greenland.* Copenhagen: GED Gad Commission.

Saccheri, I., M. Kuussaari, M. Kankare, P. Vikman, W. Fortelius, and I. Hanski. 1998. Inbreeding and extinction in a butterfly metapopulation. *Nature* 392:491–94.

Sagan, L. 1967. On the origin of mitosing cells. *Journal of Theoretical Biology* 14(3):225–74.

Sage, R. F. 1999. Why C4 photosynthesis? In R. F. Sage and R. K. Monson. eds. *C4 Plant Biology.* San Diego, CA: Academic Press.

Sage, R. F. 2004. The evolution of C-4 photosynthesis. *New Phytologist* 161(2):341–70.

Sage, R. F., and D. S. Kubien. 2003. *Quo vadis* C_4? An ecophysiological perspective on global change and the future of C_4 plants. *Photosynthesis Research* 77:209–25.

Sahney, S. M. J. Benton, and P. A. Ferry. 2010. Links between global taxonomic diversity, ecological diversity and the expansion of vertebrates on land. *Biology Letters* 6:544–47.

Sakai, A., and C. J. Weiser. 1973. Freezing resistance of trees in North America with reference to tree regions. *Ecology* 54(1):118–26.

Sakamoto, M. 1966. Primary production by phytoplankton community in some Japanese lakes and its dependence on lake depth. *Archive für Hydrobiologie* 62:1–28.

Sala, O. E., W. J. Parton, L. A. Joyce, and W. K. Laurenroth. 1988. Primary production of the central grassland regions of the United States. *Ecology* 69:40–45.

Samuel, B. 2004. *White as a Ghost: Winter Ticks and Moose.* Edmonton, AB: Federation of Alberta Naturalists.

Sanderson, E. W., M. Jaiteh, M. A. Levy, K. H. Redford, A. V. Wannebo, and G. Woolmer. 2002. The human footprint and the last of the wild. *Bioscience* 52(10):891–904.

Scheu S., and D. Parkinson. 1994. Effects of Invasion of an Aspen Forest (Canada) by *Dendrobaena-Octaedra* (Lumbricidae) on Plant-Growth. *Ecology* 75(8):2348–61.

Schemske, D.W., G. G. Mittelbach, H. V. Cornell, J. M. Sobel, and K. Roy. 2009. Is there a latitudinal gradient in the importance of biotic interactions? *Annual Review of Ecology Evolution and Systematics* 40:245–69.

Schenk, H. J. 2006. Root competition: Beyond resource depletion. *Journal of Ecology* 94(4):725–39.

Schenk, H. J., and R. B. Jackson. 2002. The global biogeography of roots. *Ecological Monographs* 72:311–28.

Schielzeth, H., E. Bolund, B. Kempenaers, and W. Forstmeier. 2011. Quantitative genetics and fitness consequences of neophilia in zebra finches. *Behavioral Ecology* 22(1):126–34.

Schimel, D. S. 1995. Terrestrial ecosystems and the carbon cycle. *Global Change Biology* 1:77–91.

Schindler, D. W. 1974. Eutrophication and recovery in experimental lakes: Implications for lake management. *Science,* 184:897–99.

Schindler, D. W. 1977. Evolution of phosphorus limitation in lakes. *Science,* 195:260–62.

Schlesinger, W. H. 1991. *Biogeochemistry: An Analysis of Global Change.* New York: Academic Press.

Schulze, E., C. Körner, B. E. Law, H. Haberl, and S. Luyssaert. 2012. Large-scale bioenergy from additional harvest of forest biomass is neither sustainable nor greenhouse gas neutral. *Global Change Biology Bioenergy* 4:611–16.

Schluter, D. 1994. Experimental evidence that competition promotes divergence in adaptive radiation. *Science* 266:798–800.

Schluter, D., and J. D. McPhail. 1992. Ecological character displacement and speciation in sticklebacks. *The American Naturalist* 140:85–108.

Schmidt-Nielsen, K. 1964. *Desert Animals: Physiological Problems of Heat and Water.* Oxford: Clarendon Press.

Schmidt-Nielsen, K. 1983. *Animal Physiology: Adaptation and Environment.* 3d ed. Cambridge, England: Cambridge University Press.

Schmiegelow, F. K. A., C. S. Machtans, and S. J. Hannon. 1997. Are boreal birds resilient to forest fragmentation? An experimental study of short-term community responses. *Ecology* 78(6):1914–32.

Schmitt, J., A. C. McCormac, and H. Smith. 1995. A test of the adaptive plasticity hypothesis using transgenic and mutant plants disabled in phytochrome-mediated elongation responses to neighbors. *American Naturalist* 146(6):937–53.

Scholander, P. F., R. Hock, V. Walters, F. Johnson, and L. Irving. 1950. Heat regulation in some arctic and tropical mammals and birds. *Biological Bulletin* 99:237–58.

Schultz, T. D., M. C. Quinlan, and N. F. Hadley. 1992. Preferred body temperature, metabolic physiology, and water balance of adult *Cicindela longilabris*: A comparison of populations from boreal habitats and climatic refugia. *Physiological Zoology* 65:226–42.

Seitzinger, S. P., and A. E. Giblin. 1996. Estimating denitrification in North Altantic continental shelf sediments. *Biogeochemistry* 35:235–60.

Serreze, M. C., J. E. Walsh, F. S. Chapin, T. Osterkamp, M. Dyurgerov, V. Romanovsky, W. C. Oechel, J. Morison, T. Zhang, and R. G. Barry. 2000. Observational evidence of recent change in the northern high-latitude environment. *Climatic Change* 46:159–207.

Shannon, C.E. 1948. A mathematical theory of communication. *Bell System Technical Journal* 27:379–423.

Shaver, G. R., and F. S. Chapin III. 1986. Effect of fertilizer on production and biomass of tussock tundra, Alaska, U.S.A. *Arctic and Alpine Research* 18:261–66.

Shaver, G. R., A. E. Giblin, K. J. Nadelhoffer, K. K. Thieler, M. R.

Downs, J. A. Laundre, and E. B. Rastetter. 2006. Carbon turnover in Alaskan tundra soils: Effects of organic matter quality, temperature, moisture and fertilizer. *Journal of Ecology* 94:740–53.

Shelford, V. E. 1911. Physiological animal geography. *Journal of Morphology* 22:551–618.

Sherman, P.W., J. U. M. Jarvis, and S. H. Braude. 1992. Naked mole rats. *Scientific American* 257(8):72–78.

Shine, R., and E. L. Charnov. 1992. Patterns of survival, growth, and maturation in snakes and lizards. *American Naturalist* 139:1257–69.

Shipley B. 1993. A Null Model for Competitive Hierarchies In Competition Matrices. *Ecology* 74:1693–99.

Shurin, J. B., D. S. Gruner, and H. Hillebrand. 2006. All wet or dried up? Real differences between aquatic and terrestrial food webs. *Proceedings of the Royal Society B-Biological Sciences* 273:1–9.

Siegenthaler, U., H. Friedli, H. Loetscher, E. Moor, A. Neftel, H. Oeschger, and B. Stauffer. 1988. Stable-isotope ratios and concentrations of CO_2 in air from polar ice cores. *Annals of Glaciology* 10:151–56.

Silvertown, J. 1987. Ecological stability: A test case. *American Naturalist* 130:807–10.

Simard, S. W., D. A. Perry, M. D. Jones, D. D. Myrold, D. M. Durall, and R. Molina. 1997. Net transfer of carbon between ectomycorrhizal tree species in the field. *Nature* 388(6642):579–82.

Simberloff, D. S. 1976. Experimental zoogeography of islands: Effects of island size. *Ecology* 57:629–48.

Simberloff, D. S. 1998. Flagships, umbrellas, and keystones: Is single-species management passe in the landscape era? *Biological Conservation* 83:247–57.

Simberloff, D. S., and E. O. Wilson. 1969. Experimental zoogeography of islands: The colonization of empty islands. *Ecology* 50:278–96.

Sinclair, A. R. E. 1977. *The African Buffalo*. Chicago: University of Chicago Press.

Sinclair, A. R. E. 2003. Mammal population regulation, keystone processes and ecosystem dynamics. *Philosophical Transactions of the Royal Society of London Series B-Biological Sciences* 358:1729–40.

Skole, D., and C. Tucker. 1993. Tropical deforestation and habitat fragmentation in the Amazon: Satellite data from 1978 to 1988. *Science* 260:1905–10.

Smil, V. 1990. Nitrogen and phosphorus. In B. L. Turner II, W. C. Clark, R. W. Kates, J. F. Richards, J. T. Mathews, and W. B. Meyer. eds. *The Earth as Transformed by Human Action*. Cambridge, England: Cambridge University Press.

Smith, C. L., and J. C. Tyler. 1972. Space resource sharing in a coral reef fish community. Natural History Museum of Los Angeles County. *Science Bulletin* 14:125–70.

Smith J. M. 1964. Group selection and kin selection. *Nature* 201:1145–47. doi:10.1038/2011145a0

Smith, J. N. M., and P. Arcese. 1994. Brown-headed cowbirds and an island population of song sparrows—a 16-year study. *Condor* 96(4):916–34.

Smith, P., M. Bustamante, H. Ahammad, H. Clark, H. Dong, E. A. Elsiddig, H. Haberl, R. Harper, J. House, M. Jafari, O. Masera, C. Mbow, N. H. Ravindranath, C. Rice, C. Robledo Abad, A. Romanovskaya, F. Sperling, and F.N. Tubiello. 2014. Agriculture, Forestry and Other Land Use (AFOLU). In O. Edenhofer, R. Pichs-Madruga, and Y. Sokona. eds. *Climate Change 2014: Contributions of Working Group III to the 5th Assessment Report of the IPCC* (Chapter 11). Cambridge, England: Intergovernmental Panel on Climate Change, Cambridge University Press.

Smith, T. W. 2003. Checklist of the spontaneous flora of Royal Botanical Gardens' nature sanctuaries. Contribution no. 113.

Smith, V. H. 1979. Nutrient dependence of primary productivity in lakes. *Limnology and Oceanography* 24:1051–64.

Smol, J. P., A. P. Wolfe, H. J. B. Birks, M. S. V. Douglas, V. J. Jones, A. Korhola, R. Pienitz, K. Ruhland, S. Sorvari, D. Antoniades, S. J. Brooks, M. A. Fallu, M. Hughes, B. E. Keatley, T. E. Laing, N. Michelutti, L. Nazarova, M. Nyman, A. M. Paterson, B. Perren, R. Quinlan, M. Rautio, E. Saulnier-Talbot, S. Siitonen, N. Solovieva, and J. Weckstrom. 2005. Climate-driven regime shifts in the biological communities of arctic lakes. *Proceedings of the National Academy of Sciences of the United States of America* 102:4397–402.

Snelgrove, P. V. R. 1999. Getting to the bottom of marine biodiversity: Sedimentary habitats. *Bioscience* 49:129–38.

Snelgrove, P. V. R. 2000. Linking biodiversity above and below the marine sediment-water interface. *Bioscience* 50:1076–88.

Snelgrove, P. V. R., P. Archambault, S. K. Juniper, P. Lawton, A. Metaxas, P. Pepin, J. C. Rice, and V. Tunnicliffe. 2012. Canadian healthy oceans network (CHONe): An academic-government partnership to develop scientific guidelines for conservation and sustainable usage of marine biodiversity. *Fisheries* 37:296–304.

Söderlund, R., and T. Rosswall. 1982. The nitrogen cycles. In O. Hutzinger. ed. *The Handbook of Environmental Chemistry, vol. I, part B. The Natural Environment and the Biogeochemical Cycles*. New York: Springer-Verlag.

Soulé, M. E. 1991. Conservation—Tactics for a Constant Crisis. *Science* 253(5021):744–50.

Sousa, W. P. 1979a. Disturbance in marine intertidal boulder fields: The nonequilibrium maintenance of species diversity. *Ecology* 60:1225–39.

Sousa, W. P. 1979b. Experimental investigations of disturbance and ecological succession in a rocky intertidal algal community. *Ecological Monographs* 49:227–54.

Sousa, W. P. 1984. The role of disturbance in natural communities. *Annual Review of Ecology and Systematics* 15:353–91.

Spector, W. S. 1956. *Handbook of Biological Data*. Philadelphia: W. B. Saunders.

Stastny, M., U. Schaffner, and E. Elle. 2005. Do vigour of introduced populations and escape from specialist herbivores contribute to invasiveness? *Journal of Ecology* 93(1):27–37.

Stearns, S. C. 1976. Life-history tactics: A review of the ideas. *Quarterly Review of Biology* 51(1):3–47.

Stenseth, N. C., G. Ottersen, J. W. Hurrell, A. Mysterud, M. Lima, K. S. Chan, N. G. Yoccoz, and B. Adlandsvik. 2003. Studying climate effects on ecology through the use of climate indices: The North Atlantic Oscillation, El Niño, Southern Oscillation and beyond. *Proceedings of the Royal Society of London Series B-Biological Sciences* 270(1529):2087–96.

Stevens, O. A. 1932. The number and weight of seeds produced by weeds. *American Journal of Botany* 19:784–94.

Stireman, J. O., J. D. Nason, and S. B. Heard. 2005. Host-associated genetic differentiation in phytophagous insects: General phenomenon or isolated exceptions? Evidence from a goldenrod-insect community. *Evolution* 59(12):2573–87.

Stireman, J. O., J. D. Nason, S. B. Heard, and J. M. Seehawer. 2006. Cascading host-associated genetic differentiation in parasitoids of phytophagous insects. *Proceedings of the Royal Society B-Biological Sciences* 273(1586):523–30.

Storey, K. B., and J. M. Storey. 1992. Natural freeze tolerance in ectothermic vertebrates. *Annual Review of Physiology* 54:619–37.

Strasburg, J. L., N. A. Sherman, K. M. Wright, L. C. Moyle, J. H. Willis, and L. H. Rieseberg. 2012. What can patterns of differentiation across plant genomes tell us about adaptation and speciation? *Philosophical Transactions of the Royal Society B*, 367:364–73.

Strong, D. R. 1992. Are trophic cascades all wet? Differentiation and donor-control in speciose ecosystems. *Ecology* 73:747–54.

Suberkropp, K., and E. Chauvet. 1995. Regulation of leaf breakdown by fungi in streams: Influences of water chemistry. *Ecology* 76:1433–45.

Suess, H. E. 1955. Radiocarbon concentration in modern wood. *Science* 122:415–17.

Sugihara, G. 1980. Minimal community structure: An explanation of species abundance patterns. *American Naturalist* 116:770–87.

Summerhayes, V. S., and C. S. Elton. 1923. Contribution to the ecology of Spitsbergen and Bear Island. *Journal of Ecology* 11:214–86.

Swartz, W., E. Sala, S. Tracey, R. Watson, and D. Pauly. 2010. The spatial expansion and ecological footprint of fisheries (1950 to present). *PLoS ONE* 5(12):e15143.

Swift, J. 1726. *Travels into Several Remote Nations of the World, in Four Parts. By Lemuel Gulliver, First a Surgeon, and then a Captain of Several Ships*. London: Benjamin Motte.

Swift, M., O. Heal, and J. Anderson. 1979. *Decomposition in Terrestrial Ecosystems*. Oxford: Blackwell Scientific Publications.

Takyu, M., S.-I. Aiba, and K. Kitayama. 2003. Changes in biomass, productivity and decomposition along topographical gradients under different geological conditions in tropical lower montane forests on Mount Kinabalu, Borneo. *Oecologia* 134:397–404.

Tamschick, S., B. Rozenblut-Kościsty, M. Ogielska, A. Lehmann, P. Lymberakis, F. Hoffmann, I. Lutz, W. Kloas, and M. Stöck. 2016. Sex reversal assessments reveal different vulnerability to endocrine disruption between deeply diverged anuran lineages. *Nature Scientific Reports*6:23825.

Tansley, A. G. 1917. On competition between *Galium saxatile* L. (*G. hercynicum* Weig.) and *Galium sylvestre* Poll. (*G. asperum* Schreb.) on different types of soil. *Journal of Ecology* 5:173–79.

Tennyson, A. 1849. *In Memoriam A. H. H.* http://en.wikisource.org/wiki/In_Memoriam_A._H._H.#LVI

Terborgh, J. 1973. On the notion of favorableness in plant ecology. *American Naturalist* 107:481–501.

Terborgh, J. 1988. The big things that run the world: A sequel to E. O. Wilson. *Conservation Biology* 2:402–3.

Thomson, D. A., and C. E. Lehner. 1976. Resilience of a rocky intertidal fish community in a physically unstable environment. *Journal of Experimental Marine Biology and Ecology* 22:1–29.

Thoreau, H. D. 1854. *Walden*. G. S. Haight ed. Reprinted 1942. New York: W. J. Black.

Tilley, D., S.Ball, J. Ellick, B.J. Godley, N. Weber, S.B. Weber, and A.C. Broderick. 2019. No evidence of fine scale thermal adaptation in green turtles. *Journal of Experimental Marine Biology and Ecology* 514–515:110–117.

Tilman, D. 1977. Resource competition between planktonic algae: An experimental and theoretical approach. *Ecology* 58:338–48.

Tilman, D. 1982. *Resource Competition and Community Structure*. Princeton, N.J.: Princeton University Press.

Tilman, D. 1987. The importance of the mechanisms of interspecific competition. *The American Naturalist* 129(5):767–74.

Tilman, D. 1999. Global environmental impacts of agricultural expansion: The need for sustainable and efficient practices. *Proceedings of the National Academy of Sciences Journal* 96(11):5995–6000.

Todd, A. W., and L. B. Keith. 1983. Coyote demography during a snowshoe hare decline in Alberta. *Journal of Wildlife Management* 47:394–404.

Tonn, W. M., and J. J. Magnuson. 1982. Patterns in the species composition and richness of fish assemblages in northern Wisconsin lakes. *Ecology* 63:1149–66.

Toolson, E. C. 1987. Water profligacy as an adaptation to hot deserts: Water loss rates and evaporative cooling in the Sonoran Desert cicada, *Diceroprocta apache* (Homoptera, Cicadidae). *Physiological Zoology* 60:379–85.

Toolson, E. C., and N. F. Hadley. 1987. Energy-dependent facilitation of transcuticular water flux contributes to evaporative cooling in the Sonoran Desert cicada. *Diceroprocta apache* (Homoptera, Cicadidae). *Journal of Experimental Biology* 131:439–44.

Tracy, R. L., and G. E. Walsberg. 2000. Prevalence of cutaneous evaporation in Merriam's kangaroo rat and its adaptive variation at the subspecific level. *Journal of Experimental Biology* 203:773–81.

Tracy, R. L., and G. E. Walsberg. 2001. Intraspecific variation in water loss in a desert rodent, *Dipodomys merriami*. *Ecology* 82:1130–37.

Tracy, R. L., and G. E. Walsberg. 2002. Kangaroo rats revisited: Re-evaluating a classic case of desert survival. *Oecologia* 133:449–57.

Trivers, R.L., and D.E. Willard. 1973. Natural selection of parental ability to vary the sex ratio of offspring. *Science* 179:90–2.

Turkington R., E. John, C. J. Krebs, M. R. T. Dale, V. O. Nams, R. Boonstra, S. Boutin, K. Martin, A. R. E. Sinclair, and J. N. M. Smith. 1998. The effects of NPK fertilization for nine years on boreal forest vegetation in northwestern Canada. *Journal of Vegetation Science* 9:333–46.

Turner, M. G., E. A. H. Smithwick, D. B. Tinker, and W. H. Romme. 2009. Variation in foliar nitrogen and aboveground net primary production in young postfire lodgepole pine. *Canadian Journal of Forest Research* 39:1024–35.

Turner, M. G., W. H. Romme, and D. B. Tinker. 2003. Surprises and lessons from the 1988 Yellowstone fires. *Frontiers in Ecology and the Environment* 1:351–58.

Turner, R. M. 1990. Long-term vegetation change at a fully protected Sonoran Desert site. *Ecology* 71:464–77.

Turner, T. 1983. Facilitation as a successional mechanism in a rocky intertidal community. *The American Naturalist* 121:729–38.

Turner, T. F., and J. C. Trexler. 1998. Ecological and historical associations of gene flow in darters (Teleostei: Percidae). *Evolution* 52:1781–801.

U.S. Bureau of the Census, International Data Base. 2006. www.census.gov/pub/ipc/www/idbnew.html

Underwood, T. J., and S. G. Sealy. 2006. Influence of shape on egg discrimination in American robins and gray catbirds. *Ethology* 112(2):164–73.

United Nations Population Information Network. 2006. www.un.org/popin/.

Urton, E. J. M., and K. A. Hobson. 2005. Intrapopulation variation in gray wolf isotope (delta N-15 and delta C-13) profiles: Implications for the ecology of individuals. *Oecologia* 145(2):317–26.

USDA Agricultural Research Service. 2011. http://ars.usda.gov/Research/docs.htm?docid=11059&page=6.

USFWS. 2010. Species profile: Whooping crane (*Grus americana*). http://ecos.fws.gov/speciesProfile/profile/speciesProfile.action?spcode=B003.

Usher, M. B., P. Davis, J. Harris, and B. Longstaff. 1979. A profusion of species? Approaches towards understanding the dynamics of the population of microarthropods in decomposer communities. In R. M. Anderson, B. D. Turner, and L. R. Taylor. eds. *Population Dynamics*, pp. 359–84. Oxford: Blackwell Scientific Publications.

Valenzuela, N., R. Literman, J.L. Neuwald, B. Mizoguchi, J.B. Iverson, J.L. Riley, and J.D. Litzgus. 2019. Extreme thermal fluctuations from climate change unexpectedly accelerate demographic collapse of vertebrates with temperature-dependent sex determination. *Scientific Reports* 9:4254.

Vancouver, G. 1801. *A Voyage of Discovery to the North Pacific Ocean and Round the World*. London: J Stockdale, Piccadilly.

Vander Zanden, M. J., J. M. Casselman, and J. B. Rasmussen. 1999. Stable isotope evidence for the food web consequences of species invasions in lakes. *Nature* 401(6752):464–67.

Vannote, R. L., G. W. Minshall, K. W. Cummins, J. R. Sedell, and C. E. Cushing. 1980. The river continuum. *Canadian Journal of Fisheries and Aquatic Sciences* 37:130–37.

Van Oers, K., P. J. Drent, P. de Goede, and A. J. van Noordwijk. 2004. Realized heritability and repeatability of risk-taking behaviour in relation to avian personalities. *Proceedings of the Royal Society B: Biological Sciences* 271:65–73.

Van Ruijven, J., and F. Berendse. 2005. Diversity-productivity relationships: Initial effects, long-term patterns, and underlying mechanisms. *Proceedings of the National Academy of Sciences of the United States of America* 102(3):695–700.

Verhulst, P. F., and A. Quetelet. 1838. Notice sur la loi que la population suit dans son accroissement. *Correspance in Mathematics and Physics* 10:113–21.

Verreault, J., D. C. G. Muir, R. J. Norstrom, I. Stirling, A. T. Fisk, G. W. Gabrielsen, A. E. Derocher, T. J. Evans, R. Dietz, C. Sonne, G. M. Sandala, W. Gebbink, F. F. Riget, E. W. Born, M. K. Taylor, J. Nagy, and R. J. Letcher. 2005. Chlorinated hydrocarbon contaminants and metabolites in polar bears (*Ursus maritimus*) from Alaska, Canada, East Greenland, and Svalbard: 1996–2002. *Science of the Total Environment* 351:369–90.

Vitousek, P. M. 1994. Beyond global warming: Ecology and global change. *Ecology* 75:1861–76.

Volterra, V. 1926. Variations and fluctuations of the number of individuals in animal species living together. Reprinted 1931. In R. Chapman. ed. *Animal Ecology*. New York: McGraw-Hill.

Wade, M. J. 1977. Experimental-study of group selection. *Evolution* 31(1):134–53.

Wagner, R. G., K. M. Little, B. Richardson, and K. McNabb. 2006. The role of vegetation management for enhancing productivity of the world's forests. *Forestry* 79:57–79.

Walker, G. T. 1924. Correlation in seasonal variations of weather. no. 9: A further study of world weather. *Memoirs of the Indian Meteorology Society* 24:275–332.

Wall, D. H., A. H. Fitter, and E. A. Paul. 2005. Developing new perspectives from advances in soil biodiversity research. In R. D. Bardgett, M. B. Usher, and D. W. Hopkins. eds. *Biological Diversity and Function in Soils*. Cambridge, England: Cambridge University Press.

Wallace, A. E. 1878. *Tropical Nature and Other Essays*. New York: Macmillan.

Walter, H. 1985. *Vegetation of the Earth*. 3d ed. New York: Springer-Verlag.

Wan, C. S. M., and R. F. Sage. 2001. Climate and the distribution of C-4 grasses along the Atlantic and Pacific coasts of North America. *Canadian Journal of Botany-Revue Canadienne de Botanique* 79(4):474–86.

Wang, L., F. Tian, Y. Wang, Z. Wu, G. Schurgers, and R. Fensholt. 2018. Acceleration of global vegetation greenup from combined effects of climate change and human land management. *Global Change Biology* 24:5484–99.

Ward, J. V. 1985. Thermal characteristics of running waters. *Hydrobiologia* 125:31–46.

Warwick, S. I. , A. Légère, M.-J. Simard, and T. James. 2008. Do escaped transgenes persist in nature? The case of an herbicide resistance transgene in a weedy *Brassica rapa* population. *Molecular Ecology* 17(5):1387–95.

Watwood, M. E., and C. N. Dahm. 1992. Effects of aquifer environmental factors on biodegradation of organic contaminants. In *Proceedings of the International Topical Meeting on Nuclear and Hazardous Waste Management Spectrum '92*. La Grange Park, Ill.: American Nuclear Society.

Webster, J. R. 1975. Analysis of potassium and calcium dynamics in stream ecosystems on three southern Appalachian watersheds of contrasting vegetation. Ph.D. thesis, University of Georgia. Athens.

Webster, J. R., and E. F. Benfield. 1986. Vascular plant breakdown in freshwater ecosystems. *Annual Review of Ecology and Systematics* 17:567–94.

Webster, K. E., T. K. Kratz, C. J. Bowser, J. J. Magnuson, and W. J. Rose. 1996. The influence of landscape position on lake chemical responses to drought in northern Wisconsin. *Limnology and Oceanography* 41:977–84.

Wegener, A. 1912. Die Herausbildung der Grossformen der Erdrinde (Kontinente und Ozeane), auf geophysikalischer Grundlage. *Petermanns Geographische Mitteilungen* [in German] 63:185–95, 253–6, 305–09. Presented at the annual meeting of the German Geological Society, Frankfurt am Main (January 6, 1912).

Wegener, A. 1966. *The Origin of Continents and Oceans*. New York: Dover. Translated from the fourth revised German edition by John Biram; British edition: Methuen, London (1968).

Wegner, N. C., O. E. Snodgrass, H. Dewar, and J. H. Hyde. 2015. Whole-body endothermy in a mesopelagic fish, the opah, *Lampris guttatus*. *Science* 348(6236):786–89.

Weiher E., and P. A. Keddy. 1999. *Ecological Assembly Rules: Perspectives, Advances, Retreats*. Cambridge, England: Cambridge University Press.

Weiser, C. J. 1970. Cold resistance and injury in woody plants. *Science* 169(3952):1269–78.

Werner, E. E., and G. G. Mittelbach. 1981. Optimal foraging: Field tests of diet choice and habitat switching. *American Zoologist* 21:813–29.

Westoby, M. 1984. The self-thinning rule. *Advances in Ecological Research* 14:167–255.

Westoby, M., M. Leishman, and J. Lord. 1996. Comparative ecology of seed size and dispersal. *Philosophical Transactions of the Royal Society of London Series B* 351:1309–18.

Wetzel, R.G. 1975. *Limnology*. Philadelphia: W. B. Saunders.

Whicker, A. D., and J. K. Detling. 1988. Ecological consequences of prairie dog disturbances. *BioScience* 38:778–85.

White, C. S., and J. T. Markwiese. 1994. Assessment of the potential for *in sutu* bioremediation of cyanide and nitrate contamination at a heap leach mine in central New Mexico. *Journal of Soil Contamination* 3:271–83.

White, J. 1985. The thinning rule and its application to mixtures of plant populations. In J. White. ed. *Studies in Plant Demography*. New York: Academic Press.

White, P. S., and S. T. A. Pickett. 1985. Natural disturbance and patch dynamics: An introduction. In S. T. A. Pickett and P. S. White. eds. *The Ecology of Natural Disturbance and Patch Dynamics*. New York: Academic Press.

White, T. C. R. 2008. The role of food, weather and climate in limiting the abundance of animals. *Biological Reviews* 83:227–48.

Whittaker, R. H. 1965. Dominance and diversity in land plant communities. *Science* 147:250–60.

Whittaker, R. H. 1972. Evolution and measurement of species diversity. *Taxon* 21(2/3):213–51.

Whittaker, R. A. 2010. Meta-analysis and mega-mistakes: Calling time on meta-analysis of the species richness–productivity relationship. *Ecology* 91(9):2522–33.

Whittaker, R. H., and G. E. Likens. 1973. The primary production of the biosphere. *Human Ecology* 1:299–369.

Whittaker, R. H., and G. E. Likens. 1975. The biosphere and man. In *Primary Productivity of the Biosphere*. New York: Springer-Verlag.

Whittaker, W. H. 1975. *Communities and Ecosystems*. New York: Macmillan Publishing Co.

Wiebe, H. H., R. W. Brown, T. W. Daniel, and E. Campbell. 1970. Water potential measurement in trees. *BioScience* 20:225–26.

Wiens, J. A., R. L. Schooley, and R. D. Weeks. 1997. Patchy landscapes and animal movements: Do beetles percolate? *Oikos* 78:257–64.

Williams, G. C. 1966. *Adaptation and Natural Selection*. Princeton, N.J.: Princeton University Press.

Williams, G. C., and R. M. Nesse. 1991. The dawn of Darwinian medicine. *Quarterly Review of Biology* 66(1):1–22.

Williams, K. S., K. G. Smith, and F. M. Stephen. 1993. Emergence of 13-year periodical cicadas (Cicadidae, *Magicicada*): Phenology, mortality, and predator satiation. *Ecology* 74:1143–52.

Williams, M. 1990. Forests. In B. L. Turner II, W. C. Clark, R. W. Kates, J. F. Richards, J. T. Mathews, and W. B. Meyer. eds. *The Earth as Transformed by Human Action*. Cambridge, England: Cambridge University Press.

Williamson, M. 1981. *Island Populations*. Oxford: Oxford University Press.

Willig, M. R., D. M. Kaufman, and R. D. Stevens. 2003. Latitudinal gradients of biodiversity: Pattern, process, scale, and synthesis. *AREES* 34:273–309.

Wilmers, C. C., and W. M. Getz. 2005. Gray wolves as climate change buffers in Yellowstone. *Plos Biology* 3:571–76.

Wilmers, C. C., R. L. Crabtree, D. W. Smith, K. M. Murphy, and W. M. Getz. 2003. Trophic facilitation by introduced top predators: Grey wolf subsidies to scavengers in Yellowstone National Park. *Journal of Animal Ecology* 72:909–16.

Wilson, D. R., and J. F. Hare. 2004. Ground squirrel uses ultrasonic alarms. *Nature* 430(6999):523.

Wilson, E. O. 1980. Caste and division of labor in leafcutter ants (Hymenoptera: Formicidae: *Atta*), I: The overall pattern in *A. sexdens. Behavioral Ecology and Sociobiology* 7:143–56.

Wilson, E. O., and D. S. Simberloff. 1969. Experimental zoogeography of islands: Defaunation and monitoring techniques. *Ecology* 50:267–78.

Winemiller, K. O. 1990. Spatial and temporal variation in tropical fish trophic networks. *Ecological Monographs* 60:331–67.

Winemiller, K. O. 1995. Fish ecology. In *Encyclopedia of Environmental Biology, Vol. 2*, pp. 49–65. New York: Academic Press, Inc.

Winemiller, K. O., and K. A. Rose. 1992. Patterns of life-history diversification in North American fishes: Implications for population regulation. *Canadian Journal of Fisheries and Aquatic Sciences* 49:2196–218.

Winston, M. L. 1992. Biology and management of Africanized bees. *Annual Review of Entomology* 37:173–93.

Wirsing, A. J., M. R. Heithaus, and L. M. Dill. 2007. Fear factor: Do Dugongs (*Dugong dugon*) trade food for safety from tiger sharks (*Galeocerdo cuvier*)? *Oecologia* 153:1031–40.

Wirta, H. K., P. D. N. Hebert, R. Kaartinen, S. W. Prosser, G. Várkonyi, and T. Roslin. 2014. Complementary molecular information changes our perception of food web structure. *Proceedings of the National Academy of Sciences of the United States of America* 111(5):1885–90.

Wisheu, I. C., and P. A. Keddy. 1992. Competition and Centrifugal Organization of Plant-Communities—Theory and Tests. *Journal of Vegetation Science* 3:147–56.

Withey, J. C., J. J. Lawler, S. Polasky, A. J. Plantinga, E. J. Nelson, P. Kareiva, C. B. Wilsey, C. A. Schloss, T. M. Nogeire, A. Ruesch, J. Ramos Jr., and W. Reid. 2013. Maximising return on conservation investment in the conterminous USA. *Ecology Letters* 15:1249–56.

World Health Organization. 2016 (October 6). *Situation Report: Zika virus, microcephaly, Guillain-Barre syndrome.*

Worm, B., H. K. Lotze, and R. A. Myers. 2003. Predator diversity hotspots in the blue ocean. *Proceedings of the National Academy of Sciences of the United States of America* 100(17):9884–88.

Worm, B., E. B. Barbier, N. Beaumont, J. E. Duffy, C. Folke, B. S. Halpern, J. B. C. Jackson, H. K. Lotze, F. Micheli, S. R. Palumbi, E. Sala, K. A. Selkoe, J. J. Stachowicz, and R. Watson. 2006. Impacts of biodiversity loss on ocean ecosystem services. *Science* 314(5800): 787–90.

Wright, L.P., L. Zhang, I. Cheng, J. Aherne, and G.R. Wentworth. 2018. Impacts and effects indicators of atmospheric deposition of major pollutants to various ecosystems—a review. *Aerosol and Air Quality Research* 18:1953–1992.

Wu, C. I. 2001. The genic view of the process of speciation. *Journal of Evolutionary Biology* 14:851–65.

Wu, J., and R. Hobbs. 2007. Landscape ecology: The state of the science. In J. Wu and R. Hobbs. eds. *Key Topics in Landscape Ecology*, Topic 15, pp. 271–87. Cambridge, England: Cambridge University Press.

WWF. 2006. *Living Planet Report 2006*. Gland, Switzerland: WWF—World Wildlife Fund for Nature.

Wynne-Edwards, V. C. 1962. *Animal Dispersion in Relation to Social Behavior*. London: Oliver & Boyd.

Zhu, Y., H. Chen, J. Fan, Y. Wang, Y. Li, J. Chen, J. Fan, S. Yang, L. Hu, H. Leung, T. W. Mew, P. S. Teng, Z. Wang, and C. C. Mundt. 2000. Genetic diversity and disease control in rice. *Nature*. 406:718–22.

Sources

Chapter 2

Figure 2.7*(c)*: Modified from Whittaker 1975.

Chapter 3

Figure 3.2: Data from William H. Schlesinger. 1991. *Biogeochemistry: An Analysis of Global Change.* San Diego: Academic Press.
Figure 3.9: Data from Grassle 1991.
Figure 3.19: Data from Wetzel 1975.
Figure 3.21: Adapted from Figure 3.1 from W. J. Mitsch, and Gosselink, J. G. 2000. *Wetlands,* 3rd ed. © John Wiley and Sons.

Chapter 4

Figure 4.3: Data from Clausen, Keck, and Hiesey 1940.
Figure 4.6: Data from Kontiainen et al. 2008.
Figure 4.9: Data from Hendry et al. 2009.
Figure 4.17: From J. Mallet. 2008. Hybridization, ecological races and the nature of species: Empirical evidence for the ease of speciation. *Philosophical Translations of the Royal Society B* 363:2971–86, Table 2.

Chapter 7

Figure 7.7: Data from Ehleringer and Björkman 1977.
Figure 7.8: Data from Spector 1956.
Figure 7.19, 20: Data from Landhausser and Lieffers 2001.

Chapter 8

Figure 8.20: Data from Marshall et al. 1996.

Chapter 11

Figure 11.5: Data from Leverich and Levin 1979, *top,* and Deevey 1947, *bottom.*
Figure 11.6: Deevey 1947, Baker, Mewaldt, and Stewart 1981 (*top*); Brown and Weatherhead 1999 (*bottom*).
Figure 11.10: Data from Larsson et al. 2000.

Chapter 12

Figure 12.10: Table based on G. P. Brown and Weatherhead, P. J. 1999. Demography and sexual size dimorphism in northern water snakes, *Nerodia sipedon. Canadian Journal of Zoology* 77:1358–66 (Survival of northern water snakes).
Figure 12.22: Data from Sinclair 1977.

Chapter 13

Figure 13.18: Data from T. Park 1954. Experimental studies of interspecific competition. II. Temperature, humidity and competition in two species of Tribolium. Physiological Zoology 27:177–238.
Figure 13.25: Data from Gaudet, Connie L., and Paul A. Keddy. 1988. A comparative approach to predicting competitive ability from plant traits. *Nature,* 334(6179):242–243. Copyright 1988.

Chapter 15

Figure 15.12: Adapted from Ashman and Schoen 1994.

Chapter 17

Figure 17.17: Modified from Guiguer and Barton 2002.
Figure 17.18: Adapted as a subset of the interaction network presented in Wirta et al. 2014.

Chapter 18

Figure 18.30: Data from Turner 1990.

Chapter 22

Figure 22.25: Data from Myers et al. 2000.

Chapter 23

Figure 23.21: Dome Fuji Project Members (2017). State dependence of climatic instability over the past 720,000 years from Antarctic ice cores and climate modeling. *Sci. Adv.* 3:e1600446.
Bereiter, B., Eggleston, S., Schmitt, J., Nehrbass-Ahles, C., Stocker, T.F., Fischer, H., Kipfstuhl, S. Chappellaz, J. (2015). Revision of the EPICA Dome C CO_2 record from 800 to 600 kyr before present. *Geophysical Research Letters.* doi:10.1002/2014GL061957
Kawamura, K., Parrenin, F., Lisiecki, L., Uemura, R., Vimeux, F., Severinghaus, J.P., et al. (2007). Northern Hemisphere forcing of climatic cycles in Antarctica over the past 360,000 years. *Nature* 448:912–916.
Figure 23.22: National Oceanic and Atmospheric Administration, National Centers for Environmental Information, https://www.ncdc.noaa.gov/cag/global/time-series

Index

A

A horizon, 19
Aber, John, 467
abiotic factors, 259, 389
absolute density, 215
abundance, 2, 231–233
   estimating abundance, 233–235
   human population, 275
   log scale, 364
   patterns of species' abundances,
     364–365
   rank-abundance curve, 367–368,
     367f, 368f
   resources, and population growth, 264
   snowshoe hares and their predators,
     316–318
   species abundances, and diversity,
     363–368
   and temperature, 157f
abyssal zone, 45
Acari, 21f
acclimation, 97, 106
acetylcholinesterase, 96
acidification, 60
actual evapotranspiration (AET),
   439–440, 468
Adams, S. M., 400
adaptationist, 165
adaptations, 67, 97
   and competition, 304–305
   and fitness, 93
   water regulation. See water regulation
adhesion-adapted, 191
adjacency, 331
adjacent errors hypothesis, 331
adjacent oligophagy hypothesis, 331
Admiralty Island, Alaska, 494–495, 494f
adult survival, and reproductive allocation,
   192–195
aerobic respiration, 437–438
AET. See actual evapotranspiration (AET)
Africa, 275
African buffalo (Syncerus caffer), 242, 269,
   270f, 452, 474
African clawed frog (Xenopus laevis), 246
African elephant, 200f, 328–329, 328f
African lions, 167–170, 328–329, 328f
African savanna, 328
Africanized honeybees, 218–219

age, and sediment cores, 61
age distribution, 241, 247–249, 262
agricultural development, 34
agricultural footprint, 547–549
agriculture, 487f
agriculture ecosystems, 30, 32–33
Aiba, Shin-Ichiro, 468
air pollution, 557–558
Aitken, Sally, 8
albedo, 91, 91f
alder (Alnus), 415
alfalfa (Medicago sativa), 151
algae, 92f
   see also specific algae species
   densities, 392
   diversity of, 370–372
   niche, 370
   and nitrogen, 476
Algonquin Provincial Park, Ontario,
   394–397
alleles, 67
allocation, 93–94, 388
allochthonous inputs, 441
allometric scaling, 189
allometry, 189
allopatric speciation, 80, 81
alluvial groundwater, 124
alpha diversity, 363
alpine plants, 99–100
alternative states, 407
altruism, 165–167
Alvin, 146
Amazon Basin, 498, 549
Amazon River, 52
amensalism, 283
American crow (Corvus brachyrhynchos),
   225, 226f
American redstart (Setophaga ruticilla),
   5, 5f, 6f
American robin (Turdus migratorius), 243
ammonification, 464
anadromous fish, 82
Anderson, James, 244–245
Anderson, Luke, 146
Andes Mountain, Ecuador, 509f
androgens, 247
animal burrows, 91
animal display, 324
Animal Ecology (Elton), 400
animals

   see also specific animals
   aerobic respiration, 437–438
   ectothermic animals, 100–102
   endothermic animals, 102–103
   functional response, and food density,
     150–151
   grazing. See grazing
   human-wildlife conflict, 168–170
   and landscape structure, 489–491
   landscape structure, relative importance
     of, 496–499
   law of toleration, 94, 94f
   movement. See movement of organisms
   nutrient cycling, in terrestrial
     ecosystems, 473–474
   and nutrients, 471–474
   "problem wildlife," 168
   range of tolerance, 94–95
   size, 229–230
   small animal movements, 495–496, 495f
   temperature, and animal performance,
     95–96
   temperature regulation, 100–103
   water acquisition, 120
   water conservation, 122–124
Annapolis Valley, Nova Scotia, 499
Antarctica, 275, 444
antibiotic resistance, 74
Anticosti Island, QC, 22f
ants
   Argentine ant (Linepithema humile),
     398, 398f
   seed-dispersing ants, 398
Apollo 8, 537
aposematic coloration, 324
apple maggot (Rhagoletis pomonella), 330
aquatic animals, 543f
   see also fish
   El Niño, and marine populations,
     539–540
   endothermic, 103
   temperature regulation, 102–103
aquatic environments
   see also water
   alteration of, 480–482
   aquatic animals. See aquatic animals
   benthic, 45
   biodiversity of, 47–48
   biological properties, 42f
   bogs, 42f, 53–57